Principles
Engineering Economics

Wiley Custom Learning Solutions

To order books or for customer service, please call 1(800)-CALL-WILEY (225-5945).

Printed in the United States of America.

ISBN 978-1-118-79311-4
Printed and bound by Strategic Content Imaging.

10 9 8 7 6 5 4 3

Brief Contents

	Use of Tables, Formulas, and Excel® Functions		
	A	B	
1	P=	$1,000.00	
2	i=	10%	
3	n=	5	
4	F=	$1,610.51	

(F|P i%,n) - Single Sum, Future Worth Factor			
Table	F = P(F|P i%,n)	F = B1*(F|P 10%,5) = B1*1.61051 =	$1,610.51
Formula	F = P(1+i)^n	F = B1*(1+B2)^B3 =	$1,610.51
Excel®	F =FV(i%,n,,-P)	F =FV(B2,B3,,-B1) =	$1,610.51

(P|F i%,n) - Single Sum, Present Worth Factor			
Table	P = F(P|F i%,n)	P = B4*(P|F 10%,5) = B4*0.62092 =	$1,000.00
Formula	P = F(1+i)$^{-n}$	P = B4*(1+B2)^-B3 =	$1,000.00
Excel®	P =PV(i%,n,,-F)	P =PV(B2,B3,,-B4) =	$1,000.00

	A	B	
1	A=	$263.80	
2	i=	10%	
3	n=	5	
4	P=	$1,000.00	

(P|A i%,n) - Uniform Series, Present Worth Factor			
Table	P = A(P|A i%,n)	P = B1*(P|A 10%,5) = B1*3.79079 =	$1,000.01
Formula	P = A(((1+i)^n-1)/(i(1+i)^n))	P = B1*(((1+B2)^B3-1)/(B2*(1+B2)^B3)) =	$1,000.00
Excel®	P =PV(i%,n,-A)	P =PV(B2,B3,-B1) =	$1,000.00

(A|P i%,n) - Capital Recovery Factor			
Table	A = P(A|P i%,n)	A = B4*(A|P 10%,5) = B4*0.26380 =	$263.80
Formula	A = P(i(1+i)^n/((1+i)^n-1))	A = B4*(B2*(1+B2)^B3/((1+B2)^B3-1)) =	$263.80
Excel®	A =PMT(i%,n,-P)	A =PMT(B2,B3,-B4) =	$263.80

	A	B	
1	A=	$263.80	
2	i=	10%	
3	n=	5	
4	F=	$1,610.51	

(F|A i%,n) - Uniform Series, Future Worth Factor			
Table	F = A(F|A i%,n)	F = B1*(F|A 10%,5) = B1*6.10510 =	$1,610.53
Formula	F = A(((1+i)^n-1)/i)	F = B1*(((1+B2)^B3-1)/B2) =	$1,610.51
Excel®	F =FV(i%,n,-A)	F =FV(B2,B3,-B1) =	$1,610.51

(A|F i%,n) - Sinking Fund Factor			
Table	A = F(A|F i%,n)	A = B4*(A|F 10%,5) = B4*0.16380 =	$263.80
Formula	A = F(i/((1+i)^n-1))	A = B4*(B2/((1+B2)^B3-1)) =	$263.80
Excel®	A =PMT(i%,n,,-F)	A =PMT(B2,B3,,-B4) =	$263.80

Use of Tables, Formulas, and Excel® Functions, Continued

	A	B
1	G=	$145.73
2	i=	10%
3	n=	5
4	P=	$1,000.00
5	A=	$263.80

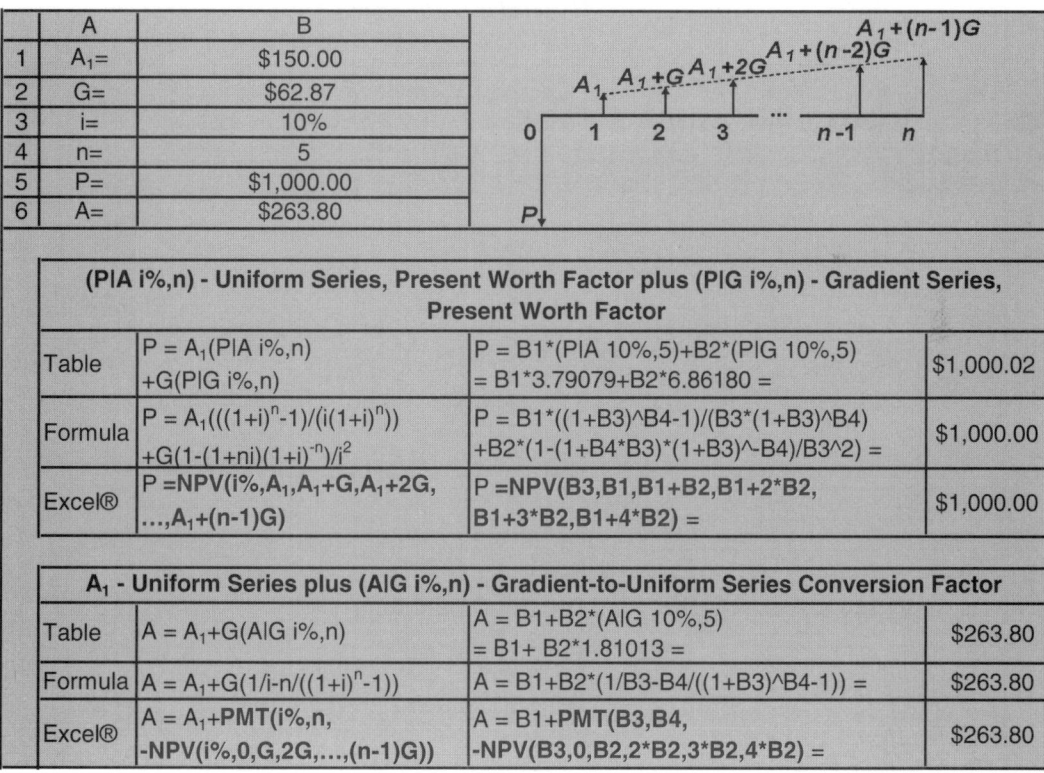

(P|G i%,n) - Gradient Series, Present Worth Factor

Table	$P = G(P\|G\ i\%,n)$	$P = B1*(P\|G\ 10\%,5) = B1*6.86180 =$	$999.97
Formula	$P = G(1-(1+ni)(1+i)^{-n})/i^2$	$P = B1*(1-(1+B3*B2)*(1+B2)\wedge-B3)/B2\wedge2 =$	$1,000.00
Excel®	$P =NPV(i\%,0,G,2G,...,(n-1)G)$	$P =NPV(B2,0,B1,2*B1,3*B1,4*B1) =$	$1,000.00

(A|G i%,n) - Gradient-to-Uniform Series Conversion Factor

Table	$A = G(A\|G\ i\%,n)$	$A = B1*(A\|G\ 10\%,5) = B1*1.81013 =$	$263.79
Formula	$A = G(1/i-n/((1+i)^n-1))$	$A = B1*(1/B2-B3/((1+B2)\wedge B3-1)) =$	$263.80
Excel®	$A =PMT(i\%,n,$ $-NPV(i\%,0,G,2G,...,(n-1)G))$	$A =PMT(B2,B3,$ $-NPV(B2,0,B1,2*B1,3*B1,4*B1)) =$	$263.80

	A	B
1	A_1=	$150.00
2	G=	$62.87
3	i=	10%
4	n=	5
5	P=	$1,000.00
6	A=	$263.80

(P|A i%,n) - Uniform Series, Present Worth Factor plus (P|G i%,n) - Gradient Series, Present Worth Factor

Table	$P = A_1(P\|A\ i\%,n)$ $+G(P\|G\ i\%,n)$	$P = B1*(P\|A\ 10\%,5)+B2*(P\|G\ 10\%,5)$ $= B1*3.79079+B2*6.86180 =$	$1,000.02
Formula	$P = A_1(((1+i)^n-1)/(i(1+i)^n))$ $+G(1-(1+ni)(1+i)^{-n})/i^2$	$P = B1*((1+B3)\wedge B4-1)/(B3*(1+B3)\wedge B4)$ $+B2*(1-(1+B4*B3)*(1+B3)\wedge-B4)/B3\wedge2) =$	$1,000.00
Excel®	$P =NPV(i\%,A_1,A_1+G,A_1+2G,$ $...,A_1+(n-1)G)$	$P =NPV(B3,B1,B1+B2,B1+2*B2,$ $B1+3*B2,B1+4*B2) =$	$1,000.00

A₁ - Uniform Series plus (A|G i%,n) - Gradient-to-Uniform Series Conversion Factor

Table	$A = A_1+G(A\|G\ i\%,n)$	$A = B1+B2*(A\|G\ 10\%,5)$ $= B1+ B2*1.81013 =$	$263.80
Formula	$A = A_1+G(1/i-n/((1+i)^n-1))$	$A = B1+B2*(1/B3-B4/((1+B3)\wedge B4-1)) =$	$263.80
Excel®	$A = A_1+PMT(i\%,n,$ $-NPV(i\%,0,G,2G,...,(n-1)G))$	$A = B1+PMT(B3,B4,$ $-NPV(B3,0,B2,2*B2,3*B2,4*B2)) =$	$263.80

Use of Tables, Formulas, and Excel® Functions, Continued

	A	B
1	$A_1=$	\$236.59
2	$i=$	10%
3	$j=$	6%
4	$n=$	5
5	$P=$	\$1,000.00
6	$F=$	\$1,610.51

$(P|A_1\ i\%,j\%,n)$ - Geometric Series, Present Worth Factor

Table	$P = A_1(P|A_1\ i\%,j\%,n)$	$P = B1*(P|A_1\ 10\%,6\%,5) = B1*4.22668 =$	\$999.99
Formula	$P = A_1(1-(1+j)^n(1+i)^{-n})/(i-j)\quad i \neq j$ $P = nA_1/(1+i)\quad i=j$	$P =IF(B2=B3,B4*B1/(1+B2),B1*(1-(1+B3)^\wedge B4*(1+B2)^\wedge -B4)/(B2-B3)) =$	\$1,000.00
Excel®	$P =NPV(i\%,A_1,(1+j)A_1,$ $(1+j)^2A_1,...,(1+j)^{n-1}A_1)$	$P =NPV(B2,B1,(1+B3)*B1,(1+B3)^\wedge 2$ $*B1,(1+B3)^\wedge 3*B1,(1+B3)^\wedge 4*B1) =$	\$1,000.00

$(F|A_1\ i\%,j\%,n)$ - Geometric Series, Future Worth Factor

Table	$F = A_1(F|A_1\ i\%,j\%,n)$	$F = B1*(F|A_1\ 10\%,6\%,5) = B1*6.80711 =$	\$1,610.49
Formula	$F = A_1((1+i)^n-(1+j)^n)/(i-j)\quad i\neq j$ $F = nA_1(1+i)^{n-1}\quad i=j$	$F =IF(B2=B3,B4*B1*(1+B2)^\wedge(B4-1),B1*((1+B2)^\wedge B4-(1+B3)^\wedge B4)/(B2-B3)) =$	\$1,610.51
Excel®	$F =FV(i\%,n,,-NPV(i\%,A_1,$ $(1+j)A_1,(1+j)^2A_1,...,(1+j)^{n-1}A_1)$	$F =FV(B2,B4,,-NPV(B2,B1,(1+B3)*B1,(1+B3)^\wedge 2*B1,(1+B3)^\wedge 3*B1,(1+B3)^\wedge 4*B1)) =$	\$1,610.51

Use of RATE, IRR, and NPER Excel® Functions

	A	B		C
1	$P=$	\$1,000.00		-\$1,000.00
2	$A=$	\$263.80		\$263.80
3	$i=$	10.00%		\$263.80
4	$n=$	5		\$263.80
5	$IRR=$	10.00%		\$263.80
6	$MARR=$	10.00%		\$263.80
7	$F=$	\$1,610.51		

IRR=	IRR =RATE(n,A,-P)	IRR =RATE(B4,B2,-B1) =	10.00%
IRR=	IRR =RATE(n,,-P,F)	IRR =RATE(B4,,-B1,B7) =	10.00%
IRR=	IRR =RATE(n,-A,,F)	IRR =RATE(B4,-B2,,B7) =	10.00%
IRR=	IRR =IRR(value1:valueN)	IRR =IRR(C1:C6) =	10.00%
n=	n =NPER(i%,A,-P)	n =NPER(B3,B2,-B1) =	5.00
n=	n =NPER(i%,,-P,F)	n =NPER(B3,,-B1,B7) =	5.00
n=	n =NPER(i%,-A,,F)	n =NPER(B3,,-B2,B7) =	5.00

Use of EFFECT Excel® Function

	A	B
1	$P=$	\$1,000.00
2	$r=$	10.00%
3	$m=$	4
4	$n=$	5
5	$i_{eff}=$	10.3813%
6	$A=$	\$266.37

Formula	$i_{eff} = (1+r/m)^m-1$	$i_{eff} = (1+B2/B3)^\wedge B3-1 =$	10.3813%
Excel®	$i_{eff} =EFFECT(r,m)$	$i_{eff} =EFFECT(B2,B3) =$	10.3813%
Excel®	$A =PMT(i_{eff},n,-P)$	$A =PMT(B5,B4,-B1) =$	\$266.37

Sixth Edition

PRINCIPLES OF ENGINEERING ECONOMIC ANALYSIS

John A. White
University of Arkansas

Kenneth E. Case
Oklahoma State University

David B. Pratt
Oklahoma State University

WILEY

John Wiley & Sons. Inc.

VP & EXECUTIVE PUBLISHER	Don Fowley
ACQUISITIONS EDITOR	Jennifer Welter
SENIOR PRODUCTION EDITOR	
MARKETING MANAGER	Christopher Ruel
SENIOR DESIGNER	
PRODUCTION MANAGEMENT SERVICES	Thomson Digital Limited
ASSISTANT EDITOR	Samanth Mandel
CONTENT EDITOR	Wendy Ashenberg
DIGITAL PRODCTION MANAGER	Soraya Torres
MANAGER OF CONTENT TECHNOLOGY	Kevin Holm
PRODUCT DESIGNER	Tom Kulesa
MEDIA SPECIALIST	Lisa Sabatini
COVER PHOTOS (clockwise)	David Dear/Getty Images, Inc. Orlando Rosu/iStockphoto iStockphoto Alex Loban/iStockphoto Imad Birkholz/iStockphoto © kali9/iStockphoto © David Jones/iStockphoto © Tomislav Zivkovic/iStockphoto

Microsoft product screen shots are reprinted with permission from Microsoft Corporation.

This book was set in Times Roman by Thomson Digital and printed and bound by R.R. Donnelley/Willard. The cover was printed by R.R. Donnelley/Willard.

This book is printed on acid free paper. ⊗

To order books or for customer service please, call 1-800-CALL WILEY (225-5945).

Library of Congress Cataloging-in-Publication Data

Principles of engineering economic analysis / John A. White. . .[et al.]. – 6th ed.
    p.   cm.
   Includes index.
   ISBN 978-1-118-16383-2 (cloth)
1. Engineering economy. I. White, John A., 1939–
   TA177.4.W48 2009
   658.15'5–dc22   2008020136

Printed in the United States of America

10 9 8 7 6 5 4 3 2

CONTENTS

PREFACE

INTRODUCTION

Welcome to the 6th edition of *Principles of Engineering Economic Analysis*!

Times have changed since our book debuted in 1977. Technology has been the most visible change, with the vast majority of college students never knowing life without access to a computer and the Internet. Fluidity and immediacy of information flow, ease of doing research from home or office, worldwide competition, global buying and selling, and – well, you get the picture – are all changes enabled through technology. Isn't it time that the teaching and learning of "engineering economy" integrate the power of these changes right into the text and the course? We think so, and have staked our 6th edition on this belief. In short, we are taking advantage of positive change, while retaining the basic tenets of proper engineering economic analysis.

One of the things that has *not* changed, except in its increased importance, is the need to "sell" engineering projects and products to managers, executives, and customers *economically*, as well as technologically, environmentally, aesthetically, and so on. Face it, only those projects and products that are considered satisfactory or better on an *economic* basis will even be given a chance to show their other well-designed attributes. Engineering work perceived as an economic loser, all things considered, is perceived as a loser, period.

One of our aims in this revision is to help engineers properly and methodically evaluate their work on an economic basis, and be able to *convey* it to those who have the power to say "yea" or "nay." Usually, some of those involved in making decisions will come at economic analysis from a "finance" or an "accounting" point of view. They will be familiar with financial packages and spreadsheet functions. They will likely *not* be familiar with the engineering economy factors that have been taught and used for at least six decades. So, what's the message here? Engineers will do well to learn some of the language of finance, including the financial analysis functions readily available in Excel®, Calc®, and Lotus 1-2-3, some of the topic-specific "calculators" available on the Web, and even balance sheets, profit and loss statements, and financial reports from accounting. We want engineers to be well-prepared and confident!

Oh, and when engineers are on the other side of the fence making management decisions, it will be helpful to know what constitutes a proper economic analysis, to be financially multi-lingual, and be able to ferret out errors in methodology and logic – these are not uncommon, and yet may be impossible to spot without a solid background. Go to the bank on it – some economic justifications are just plain wrong and we want engineers, including those who are also managers, to be able to ask the right questions and know when they are hearing the right answers.

Are you still with us? We know that reading a preface is not high on your list of fun activities. So, let us focus you, section-by-section, on some important points regarding this 6th edition. We'll try to keep it useful and short, in that order.

WHAT'S OUR MOTIVATION?

First and foremost, John, Ken, and David are interested in providing faculty members and students an exceptional "leapfrog" text for teaching, learning, and especially *using* engineering economic analysis in the competitive world of business. We will be highly rewarded if we help you in teaching, learning, and/or applying the material in this book.

Collectively, we have more than 100 years of classroom teaching as tenure-track professors, with many of those, even today, involving engineering economic analysis at both the undergraduate and graduate levels. Our experience includes an industry and consulting side, where we have worked with about 85 companies. Universities make economic decisions, too, and we have also experienced a great deal of public sector decision-making within the academic environment. In case you are interested, there are brief bio-sketches of us on page xvii. Why do we mention these things? So you know we have "been there, done that." And, we are still "going there, doing that."

We have been involved in hundreds of presentations, from the engineering level, through the management level, and into the C-level (CEO, COO, CFO, CTO, CIO) and the Board Room. We have stood before the customer, or even been the customer. We have seen many things that work well and many that do not work at all; we have seen presenters well prepared and those who weren't; we have seen engineers glide through presentations and hard questions because they were solidly grounded, and we have seen the opposite. We prefer the "former" in each case! We do not claim to have all the answers, and yet we hope our experience, conveyed through this book, will be of immense help to you.

New to This Edition

The 6th Edition provides students and instructors with the latest tax information, as well as up-to-date company and industry information in the chapter opening stories, reflecting changes resulting from the recent tumult in the economy, so that students can work with the most current and relevant information.

The 6th Edition also highlights opportunities for instructors and students to benefit from the teaching and learning resources available in the *WileyPLUS* course (instructors may choose to adopt this text with *WileyPLUS*), including:

- **Algorithmic homework problems** that provide instant feedback to students, link-to-text where students may review if they're having trouble, and Tutorial and Video Solution help. All Tutorial help is available at the instructor's discretion.

- **Worked Problem Videos** that demonstrate how to solve problems, both algebraically and with Excel.

- **Excel data files** for the homework problems.
- **TVM Factor Calculators** pre-built in Excel.

Icons in this 6th Edition identify:

- **25 Video Lessons for key topics**, available in *WileyPLUS*.
  Brief lectures prepared by Kellie Grasman at Missouri S&T, explaining concepts from the text, so that students may have multiple means of better understanding the content.

- **Exercises available for instructors to assign in *WileyPLUS***, including:
  ○ Algorithmic problems
  ○ GO Tutorial problems

- **96 Problems with Video Solutions** (including 45 new Video Solutions prepared by Kellie Grasman and Sean Schmidt of Missouri S&T)

IMPORTANT FEATURES

Following are some important design features of this book:

1. An integrated approach is used to the subject:
   a. Chapters are in a logical and built-up order.
   b. Ten Principles of Engineering Economic Analysis are presented and revisited throughout the text.
   c. A seven-step Systematic Evaluation and Analysis Technique (SEAT) is emphasized throughout the book to provide direction and maintain consistency.
   d. Three typical engineering situations are revisited using linked examples throughout the book. Each stands alone, and yet also permits comparison of results under different situations (e.g., no tax vs. tax; equity funding vs. partial loan, etc.).
2. A cash flow approach is taken throughout. To the extent that the amount and timing of cash flows are right, a proper engineering economic analysis will be right.
3. The text is multi-colored with icons to better delineate text, examples, important points, and the use of computers.
4. The number of chapters has been increased from 8 to 16, helping to ensure that some important topics are not "buried" within related chapters, and to provide more flexibility in using the book.
5. Appropriate emphasis and attention are given to external sources available on the Internet, including loan and mortgage calculators, retirement calculators, corporate financial statements, depreciation and tax documents, public sector documents, and more.
6. "Boxes" are used in the text of each chapter to emphasize key points.
7. "Summary" sections are provided at the end of each chapter, reiterating key takeaways in the text.
8. "Pit Stops," consisting of true/false questions, appear at the end of each chapter, testing comprehension and understanding of major concepts presented.
9. There are over 280 examples, 250 figures, 140 tables, and 130 boxes in the chapters.
10. A mix of business/industry and personal finance examples and homework problems are provided.

11. There are over 950 end-of-chapter problems, each with the relevant text section identified to facilitate self-study as well as assignment of homework. Answers to even-numbered problems are provided at the end of the book.

12. Over 180 Fundamentals of Engineering (FE) – type questions are provided, covering all chapters, even those that are not currently included on the FE exam.

13. Coverage is comprehensive and appropriate for those who will be performing engineering economic analyses, with topics including:

   a. Principles and methodology for engineering economic analyses with or without considering the time value of money.

   b. Time value of money including all commonly used cash flow profiles.

   c. Borrowing, lending, and investing with business and personal applications.

   d. Planning horizon and cost of capital determination, including a hurdle rate calculator used by a multinational corporation.

   e. Measures of economic worth including present worth, capitalized worth, future worth, annual worth, internal rate of return, external rate of return, benefit-cost, cost-effectiveness, and revenue requirements.

   f. Depreciation including MACRS and its foundation methods – double declining balance and straight line, plus several heritage approaches.

   g. After-tax economic analyses with and without borrowing, plus the investment tax credit and Section 179 deduction.

   h. Before- and after-tax replacement analysis, optimal replacement interval, and Section 1031 like-kind property exchanges.

   i. Inflation including before- and after-tax analyses.

   j. Supplementary analyses including breakeven, sensitivity analysis, and risk analysis, as well as use of @RISK simulation software.

   k. Public sector applications using benefit-cost approaches, and evaluation in utilities using the revenue requirements method.

   l. Capital budgeting to make sound overall investments under monetary constraints.

   m. Costs, estimation, accounting, and Economic Value Added concepts.

14. Discrete factor tables to 5 places after the decimal are provided in the book for 25 common interest rates, covering single sums, uniform series, and gradient series; 25 pairs of rates for geometric series factors are provided; and smaller tables exist for continuous compounding with both discrete and continuous flows. In their electronic form, the tables are programmable to cover other rates.

15. A detailed Instructor's Solutions Manual has been prepared and is available electronically; it includes solutions in Excel® spreadsheet form to make it easy to see the solutions, to select particular cells to see the formula used, or to convert the entire worksheet to see the formulas used in all cells. Visit the instructor section of the book website at **www.wiley.com/college/white** to register for a password to access the Instructor's Manual.

16. PowerPoint® slides for each chapter are available electronically.

COVERAGE IN THE COURSE

Coverage of material in any class is a constrained optimization problem. There is so much good material available, so many points to be made, so much excitement in seeing light bulbs turn on, the thrill of watching students be fascinated by the time value of money – and yet *so few hours to get it all done*! We cannot plan your course for you, and yet we can give you our biases, including some alternative approaches to teaching a course from this book.

Our perspective is a traditional 3-credit hour semester course taught in a traditional classroom, via distance learning, or online to undergraduates at the sophomore or junior level. Students at this level may not be ready for everything in this text, and yet an exceptional course can be developed. Some of this material can easily form the basis for an advanced undergraduate level course or a graduate level course. Those teaching a single course in 1- or 2-credit hours will need to focus on only the most essential material.

We have specifically attempted to build the text as an "integrated" set of material, presented in a logical and "built-up" order. For this reason, we think the order of chapters is most effective as presented and would caution against "skipping around" much in the text. There is, however, one exception to be mentioned later. The table below presents the chapters, in order, with chapter number and title, plus our thoughts as to which of the following 5 terms is most appropriate:

- C-E: Core material – Essential
- C-R: Core material – Recommended
- C-O: Core material – Optional
- N-R: Non-core material – Recommended
- N-O: Non-core material – Optional

Chapter	Chapter Title	C-E Sections	C-R Sections	C-O Sections	N-R Sections	N-O Sections
1	Engineering Economic Analysis	1.1-1.4; 1.6	1.5			
2	Time Value of Money	2.1-2.6; 2.8			2.A.1	2.7; 2.A.2
3	Borrowing, Lending, and Investing	3.1-3.3; 3.5; 3.7; 3.9-3.10	3.4; 3.6; 3.8			
4	Establishing the Planning Horizon and the Minimum Attractive Rate of Return	4.1-4.4				
5	Present Worth Analysis	5.1-5.7; 5.10	5.8; 5.9			
6	Future Worth Analysis			6.1-6.6		
7	Annual Worth Analysis	7.1-7.7				
8	Rate of Return Analysis	8.1-8.7				8.A.1-8.A.2
9	Depreciation Methods	9.1-9.8				9.A-9.C
10	After-Tax Economic Analysis	10.1-10.6; 10.11	10.7-10.8	10.9-10.10		
11	Replacement Analysis	11.1-11.2	11.4; 11.6	11.5		11.3
12	Inflation Effects	12.1-12.6				
13	Supplementary Analysis		13.1-13.3; 13.5			13.4; 13.A
14	Economic Analysis in the Public and Regulated Sectors		14.1; 14.7; 14.13	14.2-14.6; 14.8		14.9-14.12; 14.A
15	Capital Budgeting		15.1-15.2; 15.6-15.7	15.3-15.5		
16	Obtaining and Estimating Cash Flows			16.1-16.6		

The one exception to chapter order mentioned in the previous paragraph is Chapter 16. It includes material on costs, estimation, accounting, and Economic Value Added. Some faculty will wish to introduce that material early in the course, using it to launch the rest of the material to be covered. Others may wish to cover it somewhere else in the course, perhaps last. Others may not cover it at all; if that is the case, we recommend that you read the chapter in advance when preparing to make a presentation to an audience that includes attendees with finance and accounting backgrounds.

ACCURACY AND PRECISION

It is important for us to "pick our battles well." One battle that often engages us is what constitutes a "correct answer" in engineering economic analysis. We need to remember that every time value of money (TVOM) problem has literally an infinite number of correct approaches. For example, to calculate a simple present worth of a single amount one year hence, we can simply find its worth at year 0. Or, we can move it to year 2 and then to year 0; or, to year 3 and then to year 0; and so on. That's not all. Even when we use the same approach, we may get different answers when carried to the penny. Differences in solution results can depend on whether we use tabulated interest factors with differing numbers of places after the decimal in the tables, formulas in an engineering calculator or a spreadsheet, a hand-held financial calculator, spreadsheet financial functions, various truncation or rounding policies, Web-based specialty calculators, or many other factors. Add to all of this the fact that not everyone sees solutions the same way; what is simple for one may be difficult for another. We try to be guided by two thoughts: (1) as long as we are correctly applying TVOM factors and methods, we will get a "correct" result, and (2) we encourage everyone to "solve what they see" and not try to guess how somebody else may set up a problem.

In the text and the solutions to problems, there are cases where we have deliberately solved the same problem in multiple ways, often getting different (but close) answers. There is a dual purpose for this. The most important purpose is to help convey the use of the traditional interest tables and formulas, both of which are allowed on the Fundamentals of Engineering (FE) exam, followed by the transition to Excel® spreadsheet financial functions, which we highly recommend. The other important purpose is to illustrate the point above about getting different (but close) answers. Our factors are generally set to provide five places after the decimal – a nice improvement from the traditional four places. Still, however, they are technically only close – and one must use the Excel® financial functions, the interest formulas, or a financial calculator to get an "exact" answer. Keep in mind, however, that even with our attempts at precision of calculation, we are still at the mercy of the usually much larger inaccuracies of our estimated cash flows and their timing. These can easily be off by 5, 10, 20% and more! Many persons and companies advocate rounding off to about three significant digits for presentation and comparison purposes. In this book, we have not rounded. Rather, we usually carry solutions to either the dollar or to the penny for comparative purposes – not to imply that we can get it right to the last decimal place!

WRITING STYLE

We have tried to use a friendly tone throughout the book. We have included numerous reminders to things already covered, to help both you and us. The writing might be described as conversational, and yet precise. We think the style used here is highly appropriate for use in a textbook of this nature, even though we would not use it in an engineering technical report or a project proposal. We hope you appreciate the conversational tone and realize we are doing our best to help propel your career by ensuring that you get the most from the book and the course.

CLOSING THOUGHTS

The manuscript has been tested in the classroom. The orientation of the material and its organization has been influenced by the recommendations of numerous colleagues and undergraduate and graduate students.

All 16 chapters have been developed from our collective experience inside and outside the classroom. Although elementary calculus is a sufficient prerequisite for the majority of the text, an introductory course in probability theory is suggested as a prerequisite for the risk analysis material in Section 13.4.

Of course, we strongly encourage faculty and students to master the use of the basic formulas and interest factors for single sums, uniform series, gradient series, and geometric series. These have formed the heart of time value of money evaluations by engineers over the past 60 years. We would be remiss, however, if we did not also strongly encourage faculty and students to become fluent with the Excel® financial factors. We have provided many examples to facilitate this. One of our authors has been out in front, using the Excel® financial factors for several years. Another of us had never used them; he quickly (and mistakenly) decided they were not intuitive and awkward. As the authors jointly made the decision to strongly move the book to explicitly include the Excel® factors, the one naysayer had to drag himself, kicking and screaming, to use them. Fluency took a half-dozen hours spread over a few days. He now finds them intuitive, and even more convenient than either formulas or factors on problems of any size that require a spreadsheet.

WEB SITE

The Web site for this text is **www.wiley.com/college/white.** It is a repository for:

* useful **Excel® utilities** such as spreadsheets that assist in performing specific engineering economy analyses
* **PowerPoint® lecture slides** for each chapter facilitate teaching and learning from the book; these may be used for lecture and presentation purposes, or they may serve as templates from which your own slides may be developed.

- The **Instructor's Solutions Manual** includes solutions in Excel® spreadsheet form to make it easy to see the solutions, to select particular cells to see the formula used, or to convert the entire worksheet to see the formulas used in all cells. The Instructor's Manual is password-proteced, and accessible only to instructors adopting this text. Please visit the instructor section of the website at **www.wiley .com/college/white** to register for a password.

WILEYPLUS

WileyPLUS combines the complete, dynamic online text with all of the teaching and learning resources you need, in one easy-to-use system. You assign *WileyPLUS*, but students decide how to buy it: they can buy the new, printed text packaged with a *Wiley-PLUS* registration code or choose digital delivery of *WileyPLUS*, use the online text and integrated read, study, and practice tools, and save off the cost of the new book.

WileyPLUS offers today's engineering students the interactive and visual learning materials they need to help them grasp difficult concepts—and apply what they've learned to solve problems in a dynamic environment. A robust variety of examples and exercises enable students to work problems, see their results, and obtain instant feedback including hints and reading references linked directly to the online text.

Contact your local Wiley representative, or visit **www.wileyplus.com** for more information about using *WileyPLUS* in your course.

ACKNOWLEDGEMENTS

Many people influenced the development of this textbook. In particular, we have benefited from either taking coursework from or teaching with John R. Canada, Wolter J. Fabrycky, Richard S. Leavenworth, William T. Morris, G.T. Stevens, Jr., and Gerald J. Thuesen, who have authored or coauthored one or more texts on the subject. Our approach to the subject has been influenced by our associations with Ronald G. Askin, Richard H. Bernhard, William E. Biles, Leland T. Blank, James A. Bontadelli, James R. Buck, Lynn E. Bussey, Claus Christiansen, Thomas P. Cullinane, Camille F. DeYong, Stuart E. Dreyfus, Carl B. Estes, Gerald A. Fleischer, David R. Freeman, Jorge Haddock, Joseph C. Hartman, Lynwood A. Johnson, Marilyn S. Jones, Robert S. Kaplan, W.J. Kennedy, Jr., William J. Kolarik, Dennis Kulonda, Jerome P. Lavelle, Jack R. Lohmann, Raymond P. Lutz, Edward L. McCombs, Leon F. McGinnis, Heather Nachtmann, Kim LaScola Needy, Chan S. Park, Mukul S. Patki, Paul A. Nelson, M. Wayne Parker, James L. Riggs, Gunter P. Sharp, Donald R. Smith, William G. Sullivan, J.M.A. Tanchoco, Suleyman Tufekci, Thomas M. West, Eric A. Woodruff, and Donovan B. Young. In addition, we recognize and appreciate the many undergraduate and graduate students, including numerous "honors contract" students, who have offered problems, as well as constructive criticism – albeit sometimes humbling. We also acknowledge and appreciate the efforts of 10 students (freshmen, sophomores, and juniors) who used the manuscript in an honors section of the engineering economic analysis course taught by one of the authors.

We would like to thank the following instructors who reviewed the manuscript at various stages, or reviewed and contributed to the WileyPLUS course:

Jerome N. Borowick, California Polytechnic State University - Pomona
Karen M. Bursic, University of Pittsburgh
John Callister, Cornell University
Viviana I. Cesani, University of Puerto Rico
Qingbin Cui, University of Alabama
Julie Fortune, University of Alabama
Kellie Grasman, Missouri S&T
Gene McGinnis, Christian Brothers University
Krishna K. Krishnan, Wichita State University
Alberto Marquez, Lamar University
R. Eugene McGinnis, Christian Brothers University
William C. Moor, Arizona State University
Thomas L. Morin, Purdue University
Heather Nachtmann, University of Arkansas
Michael L. Nobs, Washington University
Irmak Renda-Tanali, George Washington University
Surendra Singh, University of Tulsa
Sean Schmidt, Missouri S&T
Bob White, Western Michigan University
Tao Yang, California Polytechnic State University - San Luis Obispo

Obtaining input, counsel, examples, corporate analysis tools, data, and pictures has been made much easier through the exceptional cooperation of the following individuals and others in their organizations (listed alphabetically by company):

- Abbott Laboratories: Miles D. White, Chairman and Chief Executive Officer.
- Arvest Bank Group: Jim C. Walton, Chairman of the Board, Jennie Hill, Mortgage Loan Manager, and Lindsay Reeves, Private Banking Officer.
- Charter I Realty & Marketing: Dennis Puckey, Realtor.
- Clyde Light & Power: Kevin Wright, Superintendent
- Eastman Chemical Company: J. Brian Ferguson, Chairman and Chief Executive Officer (retired), and William Fortenberry, Jr., Corporate Development Director.
- Ernst & Young: Kevin White and Donald Zimmerman, partners in the assurance and advisory business services practice.
- Intel: Craig R. Barrett, Chairman of the Board.
- J.B. Hunt Transport Services, Inc.: Jerry W. Walton, Executive Vice President and Chief Financial Officer, Donald G. Cope, Sr. Vice President, Controller, and Chief Accounting Officer, and David G. Mee, Sr. Vice President, Tax and Risk Management.
- KPMG: Mary Pat McCarthy, Vice Chair, and Billy Parker and Dennis Parrott, audit partners.
- Motorola: Dr. Thomas F. Davis, Corporate Vice President and Chief Economist.
- Novit & Scarminach, P.A.: Herbert L. Novit, of Counsel.

- Schneider National, Inc.: Dr. Christopher B. Lofgren, President and Chief Executive Officer.
- Wal-Mart Stores, Inc.: Michael T. Duke, President and Chief Executive Officer.
- Webco Industries, Inc.: Dana S. Weber, Vice Chairman, President and Chief Operating Officer, and Michael P. Howard, Chief Financial Officer and Senior Vice President – Finance and Administration.

Our respective staff members have been most helpful, particularly Leanne Bowles, Tarri Fennel, and Marcia Overby at the University of Arkansas, and Patsy Coleman, Paulette Lauer, and Janice Walter at Oklahoma State University. We would like to acknowledge their assistance in preparing the manuscript and helping in myriad ways.

Choosing to perform radical surgery to the 4th edition of the book was not an easy decision. It is always risky to strike out in a radically different direction, especially after more than 30 years of success. However, we felt that it was needed-that students would benefit and that the connections between the engineering economy field and engineering practice needed to be tightened. With the encouragement and support of Jennifer Welter, Acquisitions Editor at John Wiley & Sons, we embarked on a multi-year effort to transform *Principles of Engineering Economic Analysis*. She deserves enormous credit for encouraging, advising, and assisting us throughout the publication process. Quite frankly, were it not for her patience, persistence, and professionalism, this version of the text would not exist. Thank you, Jenny.

We would like to remember the late Dr. Marvin H. Agee, a man of the highest integrity, a great friend, a wonderful "boss," and a co-author on the first three editions. Marvin's many enduring contributions to this book are recognized and appreciated.

Finally, we thank our wives Mary Lib, Lynn, and Jan for their patience and understanding while we have disappeared during this project. They continue to demonstrate considerable insight on the subject by the gentle reminder, "If you know so much about investments, why aren't we rich?"

John A White
Kenneth E. Case
David B. Pratt

ABOUT THE AUTHORS

John A. White, Ph.D., P.E., is Chancellor Emeritus and Distinguished Professor of Industrial Engineering at the University of Arkansas. From 1997 to 2008, he served as chancellor of the University of Arkansas. He has served on the industrial engineering faculties of Georgia Tech (22 years) and Virginia Tech (8 years). From 1988 to 1991, he served as Assistant Director for Engineering at the National Science Foundation. His corporate board experience includes service on the boards of directors of Eastman Chemical Company; J.B. Hunt Transport Services, Inc.; Logility, Inc.; Motorola, Inc.; and Russell Corporation. He founded and served as chairman of SysteCon, a logistics consulting firm, until its acquisition by Coopers & Lybrand in 1984. He has served as a consultant to a wide variety of organizations, including AT&T, Briggs & Stratton, Burlington, Coca-Cola, Corning, DuPont, Federal Reserve Bank, Ford, IBM, L.L. Bean, Tektronix, Texas Instruments, U.S. Navy, Westinghouse, and Xerox. A member of the National Academy of Engineering, he received his BSIE degree from the University of Arkansas, his MSIE degree from Virginia Tech, and his PhD degree from The Ohio State University. He served two 6-year terms on the National Science Board. Also, he has served as President of the Institute of Industrial Engineers, the Foundation for the Malcolm Baldrige National Quality Award, and the National Consortium for Graduate Degrees for Minorities in Engineering and Science, and Chairman of both the American Association of Engineering Societies and the Arkansas Science and Technology Authority. He is a recipient of the AAES Kenneth Andrew Roe Award, the IIE Frank and Lillian Gilbreth Outstanding Industrial Engineer Award, the IIE Albert G. Holzman Distinguished Educator Award, the IIE David F. Baker Distinguished Research Award, the IIE Book of the Year Award (twice), the ASEE Donald E. Marlowe Distinguished Education Administration Award, the ASEE John L. Imhoff Global Excellence Award, and the SME Educator of the Year Award, among others.

Kenneth E. Case, Ph.D., P.E. is Regents Professor Emeritus at Oklahoma State University. He served on the industrial engineering faculty at OSU for 30 years, at Virginia Tech for 5 years, and was a management scientist for GTE Data Services. He serves on the Board of Webco Industries, Inc., and has been a consultant to a wide variety of organizations including Abbott, AT&T, Boeing, Dayton Tire, ExxonMobil, FDA, Ford, MerCruiser, Rockwell, Rubbermaid, Sprague, U.S. PTO, and Zebco. A member of the National Academy of Engineering, he received his BSEE, MSIE, and

Ph.D. degrees from Oklahoma State University. He served as President of both the Institute of Industrial Engineers and the American Society for Quality. He also served as a Senior Examiner (1987-90) and a Judge (1991-3) for the Malcolm Baldrige National Quality Award. He is an Academician in the International Academy for Quality. He has been named Outstanding Engineer in Oklahoma, received the Oklahoma Foundation for Excellence Outstanding Educator Award (1st and only engineer), and is a recipient of the IIE Frank and Lillian Gilbreth Outstanding Industrial Engineer award. Active in scouting, he has received the Distinguished Eagle Scout and Silver Beaver medals. He is an avid ham radio operator with the call K5KC.

David B. Pratt, Ph.D., P.E., is an Associate Professor and the Undergraduate Program Director in the School of Industrial Engineering and Management at Oklahoma State University. He holds B.S., M.S., and Ph.D. degrees in Industrial Engineering. Prior to joining academia, he held technical and managerial positions in the petroleum, aerospace, and pulp & paper industries for over 12 years. He has served on the industrial engineering faculty at his alma mater, Oklahoma State University, since 1992. His research, teaching, and consulting interests include production planning and control, economic analysis, and manufacturing systems design. He is a registered Professional Engineer, an APICS Certified Fellow in Production and Inventory Management, and an ASQ Certified Quality Engineer. He is a member of IIE, NSPE, APICS, INFORMS, and ASQ.

Chapter 1

ENGINEERING ECONOMIC ANALYSIS

A high speed sortation conveyor system in one of Wal-Mart's distribution centers. (Courtesy of Wal-Mart Stores, Inc.)

Walmart

In fiscal year (FY) 2011, Wal-Mart, Inc. (WMT) employed more than 2.1 million people worldwide, including 1.4 million in the U.S. Its annual sales increased 3.47% from the previous year to a record $419 billion; income increased 6.3% to a record $15.4 billion. As of January 31, 2011, Walmart had a total of 8,907 retail outlets worldwide, including 3,804 Supercenters, discount stores, and Neighborhood Markets as well as 609 SAM'S CLUBs in the U. S. and 4,557 retail outlets in stores in 14 countries outside the U.S. Walmart imports billions of dollars of products from 70 countries. Its imports are greater than that of most countries in the world. In a 15-year period (from 1990 to 2005) the number of Walmart stores in the U.S. increased by more than 2,000; in the next 6-year period (from 2005 to 2011), the number of stores increased by 3,800.

   A major factor in Walmart's success has been the efficiency of its supply chain. It was among the first to adopt electronic data interchange (EDI), allowing it to pay vendors for products purchased by Walmart's customers in its stores. The real-time management of money across its thousands of stores has contributed significantly to Walmart's economic performance.

An international leader in logistics, Walmart's logistics operations employ more than 85,000 associates. Its distribution network includes approximately 150 distribution centers and 50 transportation offices. A major user of transportation services from external sources, Walmart has the fourth-largest private fleet of trucks in the U.S., including 7,200 tractors, 53,000 trailers, and 8,000 drivers. Highly regarded for its rapid response to the September 11, 2001 attacks on the World Trade Center, to Hurricane Katrina in 2005, and to the 2010 oil spill in the Gulf of Mexico, Walmart has 9 disaster distribution centers, strategically located across the U.S. and stocked with relief supplies to assist communities in distress.

Walmart was a pioneer in the use of radio frequency identification (RFID) to do real-time tracking of products throughout the supply chain. Recently, Walmart targeted sustainability and worked with its vendor community to allow itself to dramatically reduce the amount of waste arriving at and leaving from its stores in the form of packing and packaging materials. Its engineers work with vendors' engineers to significantly reduce energy consumption in distributing the products it sells, and to increase energy efficiency in its stores. Walmart gives priority attention to reducing life-cycle costs, resulting in a 19.2 percent return on investment (ROI) in FY2011.

*   *   *

Robert Thompson is a recent engineering graduate who desires to invest a portion of his annual income each year. He is unsure about the kind of investments he should make—stocks, bonds, mutual funds, U.S. Treasury notes, certificates of deposit, rental property, land, and so on. Also, he is undecided about how much of his annual income he should set aside for investment. Further, he does not know what annual return he should expect to earn on his investments. Finally, he wonders how long it will take for him to achieve his financial goals.

What do the preceding examples have in common? Whether a single person or one of the largest employers in the world, each is faced with a wide range of investment opportunities. Each has a finite amount of capital to invest and has a financial goal to be met, whether it is providing adequate income for retirement or paying for a child's college education or providing an adequate return to shareholders. Each can apply the material and tools provided in this text to make wise investment decisions. Each will take advantage of the *time value of money*!

1-1 INTRODUCTION

The subject matter discussed in this book is variously referred to as *economic analysis*, *engineering economy*, *economic justification*, *capital investment analysis*, and *economic decision analysis*, among other names. Traditionally, the application of economic analysis techniques in the comparison of engineering design alternatives has been referred to as *engineering economy*. However, the emergence of a widespread interest in economic analysis in public-sector decision making has brought about greater use of the more general term *economic analysis*. We define *engineering economic analysis* as using a combination of quantitative and qualitative techniques to analyze *economic differences* among engineering design alternatives in selecting the preferred design.

We will use a *cash flow approach* to the subject. A cash flow occurs when money actually changes hands from one individual to another or from one organization .to another. Thus, money received and money dispersed (spent or paid) constitutes a cash flow. We also emphasize the fundamentals of economic analysis.

In this chapter, you will learn a number of very important things. While it's always tempting to skip the first chapter of an engineering textbook, it would be a big mistake to do so here. For example, in the chapter, you will learn about the time value of money—what it means and how it is used in making economic decisions. You will also learn the four discounted cash flow rules. In addition, you will learn 10 principles of engineering economic analysis. Finally, you will learn a seven-step process used to perform engineering economic analyses.

1-2 TIME VALUE OF MONEY (*TVOM*)

This fundamental concept underlies much of the material covered in the text: *money has a time value*. By this, we mean that the *value* of a given sum of money depends on both the amount of money and the point in time when the money is received or paid. Just as the placement of forces along a beam matters in designing structures, so does the placement in time matter of money received or money paid when evaluating the economic worth of an investment.

EXAMPLE 1.1   The Time Value of Money Illustrated

To illustrate the time value of money (*TVOM*) concept, suppose a wealthy individual approaches you and says, ''Because of your outstanding ability to manage money, I am prepared to present you with a tax-free gift of $1,000. However, if you prefer, I will postpone the presentation for a year, at which time I will guarantee that you will receive a tax-free gift of $X.'' (For purposes of this example, assume that the guarantee is risk-free.) In other words, you can choose to receive $1,000 today or receive $X 1 year from today. Which would you choose if X equals (1) $1,000, (2) $1,050, (3) $1,100, (4) $1,500, (5) $2,000, (6) $5,000, (7) $10,000, (8) $100,000?

In presenting this situation to students in our classes, none preferred to receive $1,000 a year from now instead of receiving $1,000 today. Also, none preferred to receive $1,050 a year from now instead of $1,000 today. Gradually, as the value of X increased, more and more students switched from preferring $1,000 today to preferring $X a year from now. Not surprisingly, every student preferred to receive $100,000 a year from now to receiving $1,000 today. Also, it was no surprise that all students preferred to receive $10,000 a year from now to receiving $1,000 today. The greatest debate and uncertainty among the students as to which to choose occurred between X equaling $1,100 and $2,000.

For each student, some value (or range of values) of $X exists for which he or she is indifferent (i.e., has no preference) between receiving $1,000 today versus receiving $X a year from today. If a student is indifferent when X equals $1,200, then we would conclude that $1,200 occurring 1 year from now has a *present value* or *present worth* of $1,000 for that particular student in his or her current circumstances. For this student, we would conclude that his or her *TVOM* is 20 percent.

From past experiences in asking students to respond to the questions posed in the example, we have noted patterns in the choices made. Several indicate a very strong need for money now, not later. Their personal circumstances are such that they do not believe they can wait a year to receive the money, even if significantly more will come to them at that time. Others are skeptical regarding the guarantee of the money being available a year later—they resort to the ''bird in the hand, versus many birds in the bush'' philosophy.

Such responses occur in industry as well. We have observed corporate executives exhibiting similar tendencies when faced with current versus deferred choices. Likewise, there is no value of X large enough to cause some people to defer receiving $1,000 today. In their case, they might know that they will not be alive to receive the money a year later. Or they might have a child or loved one who desperately needs medicine that can be purchased for $1,000. Personal and corporate circumstances can be such that the *TVOM* can be quite large, much larger than we normally consider in this book.

Occasionally, students will claim that *inflation* will make the future amount of money worth less to them. While it is certainly true that inflation, which represents a decrease in the purchasing power of money, will diminish the *present worth* of a future sum of money, *money has time value in the absence of inflation.* (In Chapter 12, we examine the effects of inflation on engineering economic decisions.)

Why do we claim that money has time value in the absence of inflation? Because of the ''earning power'' of money. Suppose, for example, you arrive in a city by airplane and need local transportation. Depending on the city, you could choose to use public transportation (train or bus), hire a taxi or a limousine, or rent or buy a car. Buying a car would not normally make sense, but if you are going to be in the city for an extended period of time, it might be a viable option. Excluding the purchase option, the amount charged for using someone else's vehicle will be greater than the operating cost, since the owner will need to make a profit in the transaction.

To continue the example, when you arrive in the city, you will need a place to stay. As with transportation, several alternatives exist: you can rent a hotel room, apartment, or house; or you can buy a house or a condominium. As before, purchasing a home is unlikely to be the most economic choice, depending on the duration of the time spent in the city. And, as before, excluding the purchase option, the rental charge for housing will be greater than the construction and operating cost for the hotel room, apartment, or house, because the owner will need to make a profit on the transaction.

To complete the example, after you arrive in the city, suppose you need money. Again, many options are available, two of which are you can go to a bank or ATM, or you can rent (or borrow) money from a business or person and pay interest. If you rent (or borrow) money, you normally repay the owner more than what you borrow, since the money's owner needs to make a profit in the transaction. Borrowing and repaying money illustrates the earning power of money.

If you own money and someone else temporarily needs it, you can rent it to them and charge them a rental fee. Of course, different terminology is used in the case of money—you can loan it to them and charge them interest on the loan. The interest rate you charge should be based on your *TVOM*. After all, if you loan it to someone, then you can no longer invest it; hence, you forego the opportunity to earn a return on your money. The lost opportunity should factor into how much you charge someone for using your money. Because of this, the *TVOM* is sometimes referred to as the *opportunity cost* of money.

Other terms used to express the *TVOM* are *interest rate*, *discount rate*, *hurdle rate*, *minimum attractive rate of return*, and *cost of capital*. We will use these terms somewhat interchangeably throughout the text. However, in the first few chapters, we tend to use *interest rate* and *discount rate* most frequently.

Another term used in financial circles and throughout the text is *discounted cash flows*, often referred to as *DCF*. Originally, *DCF* referred to the process of using the *TVOM* or discount rate to convert all future cash flows to a *today* or *present single sum equivalent*. Today, *DCF* tends to refer to any movement of money backward or forward in time.

Although we are getting ahead of ourselves, we cannot resist pointing out that money having a time value changes how mathematical operations involving money should be performed. Simply stated: because money has a time value, one should not add or subtract money unless it occurs at the same point in time.

Having introduced the notion of new rules when dealing with money, we might as well share with you the *four DCF rules*:

1. Money has a time value.
2. Money cannot be added or subtracted unless it occurs at the same point(s) in time.
3. To move money forward one time unit, multiply by 1 plus the discount or interest rate.
4. To move money backward one time unit, divide by 1 plus the discount or interest rate.

Four Discounted Cash Flow Rules

1. Money has a time value;
2. Money cannot be added or subtracted unless it occurs at the same point(s) in time;
3. To move money forward one time unit, multiply by one plus the discount or interest rate;
4. To move money backward one time unit, divide by one plus the discount or interest rate.

EXAMPLE 1.2   Applying the *Four DCF Rules*

Recall the previous example, where the student's *TVOM* was 20 percent. Suppose the student is guaranteed to receive $1,100 one year from today, and nothing thereafter, if $1,000 is invested today in a particular venture. It would be a mistake for the student to subtract the $1,000 investment from the $1,100 return and conclude that the investment yielded a net positive return of $100. Why? Rule 1 established that money has a time value; for this student, it can be represented by a 20 percent annual rate. Rule 2 established that the $1,000 cannot be subtracted from the $1,100, since they occur at different points in time.

So, what should the student do? Apply either Rule 3 or Rule 4! Using Rule 3, the student would conclude that the *future value* or *future worth* of the $1,000 investment, based on a 20 percent *TVOM*, equals $1,000(1.20) or $1,200 one year later. Since the $1,000 was an expenditure or investment, it is a negative cash flow, whereas the $1,100 return on the investment was a positive cash flow. Hence, the net future worth of the investment is –$1,200 + $1,100, or –$100. Since the future worth is negative, it would not be considered a good investment by the student.

Using Rule 4, the student would conclude that the *present value* or *present worth* of $1,100 a year from now equals $1,100/1.20, or $916.67. Therefore, the $1,000 investment yields a negative net present value of $83.33. Again, the student should conclude that it was not a good investment. (Notice, different conclusions would have occurred if the student's *TVOM* had been 8 percent, instead of 20 percent. By the way, if you did not follow the mathematics used, don't worry. The mathematics of *TVOM* operations are the subject of Chapters 2 and 3. If you don't understand them after covering the material in Chapters 2 and 3, then you should be *very* worried!)

1-3 TEN PRINCIPLES OF ENGINEERING ECONOMIC ANALYSIS

The subject of this text is principles of engineering economic analysis. Consequently, throughout the text, we present basic principles that can be used by *all* engineers in analyzing the economic performance of the products, processes, and systems they design. No matter how impressive or how sophisticated an engineering design might be, if it fails to "measure up" economically, it will usually be doomed to failure.

The following 10 principles of engineering economic analysis provide a foundation for this text:

1. *Money has a time value.* This principle underlies almost everything we cover in the text. Due to the *TVOM*, we prefer to receive a fixed sum of money sooner rather than later; likewise, we prefer to pay a fixed sum of money later, rather than sooner. (Notice how many of the following principles are corollaries of the *TVOM* principle.)

2. *Make investments that are economically justified.* The second principle is captured in a succinct statement attributed to Henry Ford in the early 1900s: "If you need a new machine and don't buy it, you pay for it without ever getting it." Ford understood a fundamental principle of economic justification—make investments that yield positive economic returns. The key to his quote is the word *need*; need indicates justification. The need can manifest itself in terms of cost reductions that will occur if a new machine is purchased, or the need can reflect the added business that will result from adding new manufacturing capacity or capability. Hence, if savings or revenues that will easily offset the purchase price of a new machine are foregone, then the new machine's price is paid by continuing to incur higher costs than will occur with the new machine or by passing up the profits that will result from increased capacity or added capability.

3. *Choose the mutually exclusive investment alternative that maximizes economic worth.* The third principle considers only monetary aspects of the

alternatives. We recognize that there might be nonmonetary considerations that will cause an alternative to be chosen that does not maximize economic worth. The third principle addresses the situation when multiple investment alternatives exist and only one can be chosen. We refer to such investments as *mutually exclusive.* In such cases, the third principle, which is a corollary of the first and second principles, holds. (The third principle underlies Chapters 5, 6, 7, and 8.)

4. *Two investment alternatives are equivalent if they have the same economic worth.* The fourth principle is an extension of the third, which states that for well-behaved cash flow profiles, the equivalence only holds for the *TVOM* that equates their economic worths. (Chapters 2, 3 and 8 examine this principle more closely.)

5. *Marginal revenue must exceed marginal cost.* The fifth principle comes from a first course in economics. Based on the principle, one should not make an investment unless the added revenues are greater than the added costs. Based on the first principle, the *TVOM* must be used in comparing marginal revenues and marginal costs if they occur at different points in time. (Although the principle is applied in several chapters, it is addressed explicitly in Chapter 16.)

6. *Continue to invest as long as each additional increment of investment yields a return that is greater than the investor's TVOM.* The sixth principle, a corollary of the fifth principle, was verbalized in a statement made in 1924 by General Motors' chief financial officer, Donald Brown: "The object of management is not necessarily the highest rate of return on capital, but ... to assure profit with each increment of volume that will at least equal the economic cost of additional capital required." The sixth principle can also be stated as follows: *Use someone else's money if you can earn more by investing it than you have to pay to obtain it.* Of course, one must consider the risks involved in borrowing money in order to make investments. (We have more to say about this principle in Chapters 3, 8, 10, 12, and 15.)

7. *Consider only differences in cash flows among investment alternatives.* In performing engineering economic analyses, decisions are between alternatives; hence, costs and revenues that are common to all investment alternatives can be ignored in choosing the preferred investment. (The seventh principle, which is also a corollary of the fifth principle, is at the heart of Chapters 5 through 14.)

8. *Compare investment alternatives over a common period of time.* The eighth principle is often violated. When alternatives have useful lives that differ in duration, there is a temptation to compare a life cycle of one investment with an unequal life cycle of another. As you will learn, it is important to compare the alternatives over the same length of time. (We address this principle in Chapters 4 through 7, and in Chapter 15.)

9. *Risks and returns tend to be positively correlated.* The higher the risks associated with an investment, the greater the anticipated returns must be to justify the investment. We do not include gambling in this principle! The greater some risks, the more negative the returns! (The ninth principle will be explored in more depth in Chapters 4 and 13.)

10. *Past costs are irrelevant in engineering economic analyses, unless they impact future costs.* The tenth principle relates to past costs or investments made previously. Past costs, also called *sunk costs,* must be ignored except, as indicated, when they have a carryover effect in the future. (Applications of this principle will occur throughout the text.)

Principles of Engineering Economic Analysis

1. Money has a time value;
2. Make investments that are economically justified;
3. Choose the mutually exclusive investment alternative that maximizes economic worth;
4. Two investment alternatives are equivalent if they have the same economic worth;
5. Marginal revenue must exceed marginal cost;
6. Money should continue to be invested as long as each additional increment of investment yields a return that is greater than the investor's time value of money;
7. Consider only differences in cash flows among investment alternatives;
8. Compare investment alternatives over a common period of time;
9. Risks and returns tend to be positively correlated; and
10. Past costs are irrelevant in engineering economic analyses, unless they impact future costs.

EXAMPLE 1.3 The Tenth Principle of Engineering Economic Analysis

To illustrate the tenth principle, suppose you paid $2,800 for an old BMW that was in very poor condition. As a hobby, you planned to spend $7,200 overhauling it and restoring it to ''like new'' condition and then selling it for $15,000. Since you will be doing the work yourself during your spare time, you do not charge anything for the time you will spend on the project.

After spending $6,000 on repairing and restoring the car, you learn that the computer system and the transmission have to be replaced. You have located a computer system and transmission that were in a wrecked BMW, same model and year. However, you estimate it will cost $9,000 to purchase the needed replacement parts and complete the reconditioning. To date, you have spent $8,800 on the car. If you spend the additional $9,000, you will have spent more than you hope to receive when you sell the reconditioned car. What should you do?

Based on the tenth principle, the $8,800 you have already spent is a sunk cost and should not be considered in your decision. Essentially, you have two choices: stop work on the car and try to sell it as is (you estimate it will sell for no more than $4,000) or spend the $9,000 in order to receive $15,000. On this basis, if you are very confident the cost of completing the project will not continue to increase and will not, ultimately, cost more than $11,000, then you are better off finishing the job. Why is $11,000 the maximum? Because your choices are to receive $4,000 now or to receive $15,000 less what you have yet to spend in reconditioning the car. If it will cost more than the $11,000 difference in what you hope to receive and what you can get now, then you are better off stopping work and selling the car for $4,000.

Was it correct to assign zero cost to the work done by the car's owner? If, truly, the time spent working on the car would not have otherwise been used to generate income, then it was a correct approach. However, if, by working on the car, the owner passed up the *opportunity* to earn money then it is not correct to conclude that the ''spare time'' is worth nothing! (Recall the previous brief discussion on the opportunity cost of money.)

This text emphasizes principles used in choosing the best investment to make and addresses specific kinds of investment. The text's intended audience is engineers and engineering students. This is not an economics text; it is an engineering economics text. As such, it addresses investments resulting from engineering designs and analyses.

What kind of investments do we consider? When an existing production machine or process must be replaced, many alternatives are usually available as replacement candidates, but which one is best? Alternative candidates for replacement also exist when faced with replacing bridges, transformers, telecommunications base stations, computers, road surfaces, sewers, chemical mixers, furnaces, and so forth. Likewise, investments in existing equipment—such as overhauling the equipment or adding new features to extend its useful life or to add new production capability—are included in the text.

In designing a new product, many design decisions involve choosing from among alternatives. Some examples of choices include using standardized parts that can be purchased or using specially designed parts that must be produced; enclosing the product in a molded plastic case or a formed metal case; using standard, replaceable batteries or a specially designed rechargeable battery; performing the manufacturing and assembly in-house versus outsourcing the manufacturing and assembly. Decisions must also be made regarding materials to use in construction and repair activities, as well as transportation alternatives to be used in moving people and materials. Discounted cash flow methods also play a critical role in decisions regarding mergers, acquisitions, and disposition of manufacturing plants. Regardless of the branch of engineering involved, numerous choices occur in designing and improving products, processes, and systems.

Finally, the text includes a wide range of analysis techniques that can be used to assist the engineer in reaching a decision regarding the particular product, process, or system recommended to management. And, while the book emphasizes engineering applications, the material presented in the text can be of great personal value. The principles provided can be used to identify the "best" engineering design, product, process, or system, and to assist in personal investing. This is particularly true for material presented in Chapters 2 and 3.

1-4 SYSTEMATIC ECONOMIC ANALYSIS TECHNIQUE (SEAT)

In performing engineering economic analyses, we recommend the following seven questions be answered:

1. What investment alternatives are available?
2. What is the length of time over which the decision is to be made?
3. What *TVOM* will be used to move monies forward or backward in time?
4. What are the best estimates of the cash flows for each of the alternatives?
5. Which investment seems best, based on the economic criterion chosen?
6. How sensitive is the economic preference to changes in or errors in the estimates used in the analysis?
7. Which investment is recommended?

Helping you answer these seven questions is this book's principal objective. (Notice, we introduced several terms in the seven questions without having defined them. We'll endeavor to limit such practices in the future; we did so here to motivate the balance of the discussion in this chapter.)

Based on the seven questions, the following seven-step *systematic economic analysis technique* is recommended:

1. Identify the investment alternatives
2. Define the planning horizon
3. Specify the discount rate
4. Estimate the cash flows
5. Compare the alternatives
6. Perform supplementary analyses
7. Select the preferred investment

Systematic Economic Analysis Technique

1. Identify the investment alternatives
2. Define the planning horizon
3. Specify the discount rate
4. Estimate the cash flows
5. Compare the alternatives
6. Perform supplementary analyses
7. Select the preferred investment

1.4.1 Identify the Investment Alternatives

Generally, we are interested in selecting the best investment from a *feasible set* of *mutually exclusive* and *collectively exhaustive* investment alternatives. By *mutually exclusive,* we mean "either/or but not both." By *collectively exhaustive,* we mean no other investment alternatives are available—all possible investments are considered.

The collectively exhaustive assumption is critical. After all, to choose the best investment, it must be included in the set of alternatives being considered. Hence, care must be taken when forming the set of alternatives to ensure that all available alternatives are being considered.

To facilitate our consideration of a process for forming mutually exclusive investment alternatives, it is useful to distinguish between *investment proposals* and *investment alternatives.* An investment alternative can consist of multiple investment proposals. These are distinguished from investment alternatives, which are decision options; investment proposals are single projects or opportunities that are being considered as investment possibilities.

EXAMPLE 1.4   Distinguishing Investment Proposals from Investment Alternatives

---

To illustrate the distinction between investment proposals and investment alternatives, consider a distribution center that receives pallet loads of product, stores the product, and ships pallet loads of product to various customer locations. A new distribution center is to be constructed, and the following proposals have been made:

1. Proposed methods of moving materials from receiving to storage and from storage to shipping include
   a. conventional lift trucks for operating in 12-foot aisles.
   b. narrow-aisle lift trucks for operating in 8-foot aisles.
   c. automated guided vehicles.
   d. towline conveyor.
   e. pallet conveyor.

2. Proposed methods of placing materials in and removing materials from storage include
   a. conventional lift trucks for operating in 12-foot aisles.
   b. narrow-aisle lift trucks for operating in 8-foot aisles.
   c. very-narrow-aisle lift trucks for operating in 5-foot aisles.
   d. very-narrow-aisle, operator-driven, rail-guided storage/retrieval vehicles.
   e. very-narrow-aisle, automated, rail-guided storage/retrieval vehicles.

3. Proposed methods of storing materials include
   a. block stacking pallet loads of material (8 feet high, 12-foot aisles).
   b. conventional pallet rack (20 feet high, 12-foot aisles).
   c. conventional pallet rack (30 feet high, 8-foot aisles).
   d. conventional pallet rack (40 feet high, 5-foot aisles).
   e. pallet flow rack (20 feet high, 12-foot aisles).
   f. pallet flow rack (30 feet high, 8-foot aisles).
   g. pallet flow rack (40 feet high, 5-foot aisles).
   h. very-narrow-aisle, high-rise, pallet rack (70 feet high, 5-foot aisles).

Given the set of proposals, alternative designs for the material handling system can be obtained by combining a proposed method of moving pallet loads of material from receiving to storage, a proposed method of placing pallet loads of material in storage, a proposed method of storage, a proposed method of removing pallet loads of material from storage, and a proposed method of transporting pallet loads of material from storage to shipping. Some of the combinations of proposals will be eliminated because of their incompatibility and practicality. For example, lift trucks requiring 12-foot aisles cannot be used to place pallet loads in and remove pallet loads from storage where 5-foot aisles are used. Likewise, it would not be practical to use a very-narrow-aisle, automated, rail-guided storage/retrieval vehicle to perform block stacking. Other combinations might be eliminated due to budget limitations; a desire to minimize the variation in types of equipment due to maintainability, availability, reliability, flexibility, and operability considerations; ceiling-height limitations; physical characteristics of the product (crushable products might require the use of storage racks); and a host of other considerations. Characteristically, experience and judgment are used to trim the list of possible combinations to a manageable number.

EXAMPLE 1.5   Forming Mutually Exclusive Investment Alternatives from Investment Proposals

To illustrate the formation of investment alternatives from a set of investment proposals, consider a situation involving m investment proposals. Let x_j be defined to be 0 if proposal j is not included in an alternative, and let x_j be defined to be 1 if proposal j is included in an alternative. Using the binary variable x_j, we can form 2^m alternatives. Thus, if there are three investment proposals, we can form eight investment alternatives, as depicted in Table 1.1.

TABLE 1.1
Developing Investment Alternatives from Investment Proposals.

Alternative	x_A	x_B	x_C	Explanation
1	0	0	0	Do nothing (proposals A, B, and C are not included)
2	0	0	1	Accept proposal C only
3	0	1	0	Accept proposal B only
4	0	1	1	Accept proposals B and C only
5	1	0	0	Accept proposal A only
6	1	0	1	Accept proposals A and C only
7	1	1	0	Accept proposals A and B only
8	1	1	1	Accept all three proposals

Among the eight alternatives formed, some might be infeasible, depending on the restrictions or constraints placed on the problem. For instance, there might be a budget limitation that precludes the possibility of combining all three proposals; thus, Alternative 8 would be eliminated. Additionally, some of the proposals might be *mutually exclusive*: if Proposals A and B are alternative computer designs and at most one can be selected, then Alternative 7 would be eliminated from consideration. Other proposals might be *contingent,* so one proposal cannot be selected unless another proposal is selected: if Proposal C involves the procurement of computer terminals based on the computer design associated with Proposal B, then Alternatives 2 and 6 would be infeasible. In many cases, the "do nothing" alternative is not feasible, due to health, safety, environmental, or other considerations; if that was the case here, Alternative 1 would be eliminated. Thus, depending on the restrictions present, the number of feasible alternatives that result can be considerably less than 2^m.

In many organizations, a rather formalized hierarchy exists for determining how the organization will invest its funds. Typically, the entry point in this hierarchy involves an individual analyst or engineer who is given an assignment to solve a problem; the problem may be one requiring the design of a new product, the improvement of an existing construction or manufacturing process, or the development of an improved system for performing a service. The individual performs the steps involved in the systematic economic analysis technique procedure and recommends the preferred solution to the problem. In arriving at the preferred solution, a number of alternative solutions are normally compared.

The preferred solution is usually forwarded to the next level of the hierarchy for approval. In fact, one would expect many preferred solutions to various problems to be forwarded to the second level of the hierarchy for approval. Each preferred solution becomes an investment *proposal,* the resulting set of mutually exclusive investment *alternatives* are formed, and the process of comparing economic investment alternatives is repeated. This sequence of operations is usually performed in various forms at each level of the hierarchy until, ultimately, the preferred solution by the individual analyst or engineer is accepted or rejected. In this textbook, we concentrate on the process of comparing investment alternatives at the first level of the hierarchy; however, keep in mind the need for such comparisons at many levels of the organization.

One danger inherent in the hierarchical approval approach is the use of *size gates.* In particular, companies often delegate approval authority over investment alternatives based on the level of funding required. Depending on the investment's size, a different *approval gate* might be required. For example, a plant manager might have the authority to make decisions on investments involving less than $100,000 in capital; for those investments requiring from $100,000 to $500,000 in capital, division-level approval might be required; for those requiring in excess of $500,000 but less than $1 million in capital, corporate-level approval might be required; and for those requiring $1 million or more, board-of-directors approval might be required. (We return to this subject in Chapter 15.)

Due to the use of size gates, piecemeal investment strategies are often used. Namely, major investments are subdivided into smaller pieces in order to obtain approval at lower levels of the hierarchy. Rather than seek approval to undertake the entire project in 1 year, a multiyear strategy is developed—simply because of "gamesmanship" in coping with size gates! The adage of "eating the elephant one bite at a time" becomes the strategy for obtaining approval for major system changes—again, because of size gates.

Unfortunately, the benefits of an integrated system could be postponed for years, due to the incremental approach. Further, one of the "bites" might not be approved, simply because of the number of competing proposals that year or because of the difficulty of quantifying the benefits of some critical element of the overall system. As a result, small incremental changes would be made, rather than major system-wide improvements.

Before concluding our consideration of the generation of engineering investment alternatives, a further word is required concerning the use of the "do nothing" alternative. The "do nothing" alternative will frequently be included in the set of feasible investment alternatives to be compared. Such an alternative is intended to represent "business as usual" or "maintain the status quo." However, it is rarely the case that business conditions stand still. Doing nothing does not mean that nothing will be done; rather, it might mean that management has opted to pass up the opportunity to influence future events. The "do nothing" alternative is often used as a baseline against which other investment alternatives are compared.

In this text, as a matter of convenience, we often associate zero incremental costs to doing nothing. In practice, when the "do nothing" alternative is feasible, extreme care must be taken *not* to underestimate the cost of doing nothing. For many firms, business as usual is their most expensive alternative; "standing pat" for too long can prove to be a disastrous course, because *while the firm is doing nothing, its competitors are generally doing something.*

Over a period of time, a series of decisions to not make capital investments or to do nothing can result in a firm's losing market share due to obsolete products and/or processes. Considered individually, each decision to do nothing might seem the most economic at the time. However, collectively, the decisions might prove to be disastrous to the firm's long-term well-being, due to their being based on too narrow a perspective. In defense of do-nothing decisions, they are made in the absence of perfect knowledge of the future (and the competition).

Ironically, it is because management cannot accurately predict the economic outcome of change that changes do not occur. Yet, there is also uncertainty concerning the economic impact of doing nothing—of failing to change. One must guard against taking too narrow a view of the economic impact of choosing to follow the do-nothing path.

In the case of manufacturing and distribution modernizations, a common reason engineers fail to view the do-nothing alternative from a broad perspective is the propensity to restrict their thinking to the costs that arise *inside* the manufacturing plant or distribution facility. An engineer seldom looks beyond the facility's walls and assesses the impact of a do-nothing decision on, say, the marketplace. However, when the engineer enlists the assistance of persons from the marketing organization in analyzing the impact of doing nothing, automated manufacturing and distribution systems are frequently justified and installed successfully.

1.4.2 Define the Planning Horizon

As noted in the eighth principle of engineering economic analysis, it is important to compare investment alternatives over a common period of time. In this text, we call that period of time the *planning horizon*. In the case of investments in, say, equipment to perform a required service, the period of time over which the service is required might be used as the planning horizon. Likewise, with one-shot investment alternatives, the period of time over which receipts continue to occur might define the planning horizon.

In a sense, the planning horizon defines the width of the "window" through which the economic performance of each investment alternative will be viewed. Obviously, using a planning horizon that is too short can preclude selecting an investment that will yield very sizeable returns in the long run. Likewise, using a planning horizon that is too long can result in the firm going out of business before realizing the promised long-term benefits.

Although we address the selection of the planning horizon in Chapter 4, we return to this topic throughout the text. Hopefully it will be obvious what the planning horizon's duration should be. However, occasions will arise in which it is not immediately obvious what the planning horizon should be.

EXAMPLE 1.6 Choosing a Planning Horizon for "One-Shot" Investments

Suppose you are presented with an opportunity to invest $10,000 in one of three investment alternatives. Alternative 1 will return $6,100 a year for 3 years, Alternative 2 will return $4,050 a year for 5 years, and Alternative 3 will return $2,500 a year for 10 years. The investments are "one-shot" opportunities; in other words, they are not repeatable. What planning horizon should be used?

Here, it is obvious that a 10-year planning horizon is appropriate. Why? Because it is the longest time period involved.

EXAMPLE 1.7   Choosing a Planning Horizon for Investments with Unequal Lives

A small manufacturing company is faced with selecting one machine from among three equipment alternatives. Alternative 1 has the smallest initial investment but will last only 3 years. Alternative 2 is more expensive to purchase but will last 5 years. Alternative 3 requires the largest initial investment but will last 10 years. What planning horizon should be used? Here the answer is not so obvious.

If a 10-year planning horizon is chosen, what assumptions must be made regarding Alternative 1? After 3 years, will it be replaced with an identical piece of equipment, or will new technology be available that will last longer without a significantly greater initial investment? What about Alternative 2? After 5 years, will it be replaced with an identical piece of equipment that will last 5 years, or will a less expensive alternative be available to replace it?

As we will note in Chapter 4, when investment alternatives have unequal lives, a popular approach is to set the planning horizon equal to the *least common multiple of lives*. For Example 1.7, such an approach would produce a 30-year planning horizon, which is the least common multiple of 3, 5, and 10. Using a 30-year planning horizon is unlikely to be a good decision due to the technological changes that will occur over that time period.

Numerous approaches can be used to deal with investment alternatives having unequal lives. However, standard planning horizons will generally be used by a particular company, with the length of the planning horizon being influenced by the type of investment being considered. Planning horizons of 10 years are quite popular, but occasionally 5-year planning horizons are used. (As noted previously, we will return to this subject in Chapter 4, as well as in later chapters.)

1.4.3   Specify the Discount Rate

Because the *TVOM* is of critical importance in evaluating investment alternatives, its choice merits special attention. For that reason, the choice of the discount rate is addressed in Chapter 4. Two principal determinants of the *TVOM* are the cost of investment capital and the opportunity cost of money.

1.4.4   Estimate the Cash Flows

Once the planning horizon is determined, cash flow estimates are needed for each investment alternative for each year of the planning horizon. If the planning horizon is greater than the lives of equipment and/or facilities included in the alternatives, cash flow estimates will be needed for the remaining years in the planning horizon. Identical replacements or replacement with improved technologies should be considered. If replacements occur and the planning horizon ends before the useful lives of the equipment or facilities, then estimates will be needed for the economic values of the assets in question.

Because investments are made in anticipation of future benefits, it is important that the cash flow estimates be more than simple extrapolations of past costs. Obtaining and estimating cash flows is the subject of Chapter 16.

1.4.5 Compare the Alternatives

Having identified the investment alternatives, defined the planning horizon, specified the discount rate, and estimated the cash flows, we are ready to evaluate the alternatives in terms of their economic performances. When doing the comparison, it is necessary to select a criterion to use. Many options exist. In fact, we have already presented two. In Example 1.2, we evaluated the investment on the basis of its *present value* or *present worth*, as well as its *future value* or *future worth.* In addition to present worth analysis (covered in Chapter 5, along with payback period, discounted payback period, and capitalized worth analyses) and future worth analysis (addressed in Chapter 6), we will also describe, annual worth analysis (the subject of Chapter 7), rate of return analysis (see Chapter 8), and benefit-cost analysis (presented in Chapter 14).

Depending on the particular type of investment, as well as the country in which the investment is made, consideration of depreciation (see Chapter 9), income taxes (see Chapter 10), replacement (see Chapter 11), inflation (see Chapter 12), and public-sector investments (see Chapter 14) will be required in comparing the alternatives.

1.4.6 Perform Supplementary Analyses

The sixth step in comparing investment alternatives is performing supplementary analyses. The intent of this step is to answer as many "what if" questions as possible. Up to this point, it has been assumed that the cash flow estimates, the length of the planning horizon, and the *TVOM* used were error free. Obviously, that is not always going to be the case. Conditions change, errors are made, risks and uncertainties exist. In this step, explicit consideration of risk and uncertainty occurs. Chapter 13 presents a number of approaches that can be used in performing supplementary analyses.

1.4.7 Select the Preferred Investment

The final step in comparing investment alternatives is selecting the preferred alternative. Because many factors must be considered in making the selection, the preferred investment may not be the one that performs best using the various economic criteria addressed in Step 5.

Multiple criteria typically exist, rather than a single criterion of maximizing, say, present worth. The presence of multiple criteria, coupled with the risks and uncertainties associated with estimating future outcomes, makes the selection process quite complicated. To make the process easier, the engineer is encouraged to address as many of management's concerns as possible in comparing the investment alternatives. To the extent that management's concerns have been addressed, the selection decision will agree with the engineer's recommendations.

Throughout the text, we concentrate on economic factors. However, keep in mind that management's ultimate choice may be based on a host of criteria, rather than a single monetary criterion. Despite attempts to quantify all benefits in economic terms, some intangible factors or attributes will probably not be reduced to dollars. Consider, for example, such factors as improved safety, reduced cycle times, improved quality, increased flexibility, increased customer service, improved employee morale, being the first in the industry to use a particular technology, and increased market visibility. Clearly, some of these factors are more readily measured in economic terms than others.

An impressive body of knowledge has been developed treating the subject of multiple-criteria decision making. However, we can introduce the subject by using the weighted factor comparison technique to cope with multiple criteria. To perform a weighted factor comparison, numerical values or weights are assigned proportionally to each factor reflecting the degrees of importance for the factors. A numerical score is then assigned to each alternative based on its performance against a particular factor. The scores are then multiplied by the weights, and the products are summed over all factors to obtain a total weighted score. The investment alternative with the highest score is deemed the preferred choice. Although there are obvious scaling difficulties associated with the technique, it is quite popular.

In an attempt to ensure consistency and to minimize the chances of a *halo effect,* a paired comparison is recommended. The halo effect is a phenomenon that occurs when a high or low ranking on one factor carries over and influences the ranking on other factors. In essence, the halo effect causes objectivity to be lost in making qualitative judgments.

To illustrate the paired comparison approach, suppose there are five investment alternatives (A, B, C, D, and E). Further, suppose the following preferences are obtained by comparing the alternative two at a time: A < B, A < C, A > D, A < E, B > C, B > D, B > E, C > D, C > E, and E > D, where A < B means that A ranks lower than B, and A > D means A ranks higher than D. Combining the paired comparisons yields the following ranking: B > C > E > A > D. Next, numerical values are assigned to each alternative in direct proportion to the alternative's performance for the factor in question. Clearly, this is the most difficult and most subjective aspect of the process.

Figure 1.1 provides a weighted factor comparison form for evaluating up to 5 investment alternatives and 10 factors. In some applications of weighted factor comparison, pairwise comparisons are performed of the factors to facilitate the assignment of weights (Wt). In Figure 1.1, weights summing to 100 are assigned to the factors. For each factor, the alternatives are rated and numerical values are

Company: Prepared by: Date:

Description of investment:

Factor	Wt	A		B		C		D		E	
		Rt	Sc	Rt	Sc	Rt	Sc	Rt	Sc	Rt	Sc
1.											
2.											
3.											
4.											
5.											
6.											
7.											
8.											
9.											
10.											
Totals	100										

FIGURE 1.1
Weighted Factor Comparison Form.

assigned (Rt), ranging from 0 to 10. The weight of the factor is multiplied by the numerical rating to obtain a score (Sc) for each alternative.

EXAMPLE 1.8   Applying the Weighted Factor Comparison Method

Three alternatives (A, B, and C) are being considered by the Ajax Manufacturing Company. The present worths (PW) are $25,000, $20,000, and $18,000, respectively. The three alternatives perform quite differently in terms of product quality (Q), time required to fill a customer's order (T), and the reputation of the supplier of the technology (R).

A ranking of the factors (PW, Q, T, and R) yields the following weights being assigned: PW (30), Q (40), T (20), and R (10). In rating the three alternatives against the three factors and assigning rating values, the following resulted:

	A	B	C
Present worth (PW)*	10	8	7.2
Product quality (Q)	8	10	5
Fill time (T)	3	10	7
Supplier reputation (R)	8	5	10

*Rt $= 10(PW)/\$25,000$

The weighted factor comparison for the three investment alternatives is summarized in Figure 1.2. From the results of the analysis, Alternative B has the highest score. If the weights and ratings truly reflect management's feelings, then B would be recommended. From the analysis, we can conclude that the improved performance of B over A in product quality and time to fill a customer's order is worth at least $5,000, based on the difference in present worths.

Company: Ajax Manufacturing Company			Prepared by: JAW					Date: 4/1/09			
Description of investment: order picking equipment for Chicago distribution center											

Factor	Wt	A		B		C		D		E	
		Rt	Sc	Rt	Sc	Rt	Sc	Rt	Sc	Rt	Sc
1. Present worth	30	10	300	8	240	7.2	216				
2. Product quality	40	8	320	10	400	5	200				
3. Fill time, customer order	20	3	60	10	200	7	140				
4. Supplier reputation	10	8	80	5	50	10	100				
5.											
6.											
7.											
8.											
9.											
10.											
Totals	100		760		890		656				

FIGURE 1.2

Completed Weighted Factor Comparison Form for Example 1.8.

With the exception of Chapter 15, as noted previously, the text's focus is on choosing the ''best'' investment from among a set of mutually exclusive engineering investment alternatives. When enough capital is available to allow more than one investment to be made, but there is not enough capital to allow all economically attractive investments to be made, capital budgeting or capital rationing will be required. Selecting the optimum investment portfolio is addressed in Chapter 15.

Having been involved in performing numerous engineering economic analyses, we provide the following advice when presenting to management the recommended investment alternative(s) to be pursued:

1. Obtain the support of the users of the recommended system before presenting it to management. Although the operators and users of the system are not the decision makers, they can be the decision wreckers. If they are opposed to or have doubts about the recommendation, then you should try to win them over.

   We are reminded of the distribution center manager who decided to replace conventional counterbalanced lift trucks with narrow-aisle lift trucks to increase substantially space utilization and throughput in the distribution center. The lift-truck operators opposed the change, so the manager obtained films of the narrow-aisle trucks being used in other distribution centers and showed them to the operators. Next, the lead drivers were taken on a tour of an installation where the narrow-aisle trucks were used. There, the lead drivers talked with operators of the equipment and drove the trucks. The operators were won over! The manager's next challenge was assuring the lead drivers they would get the first narrow-aisle trucks that arrived.

2. Pre-sell the recommendation and eliminate surprises. Typically, managers do not like surprises. Therefore, it is imperative that communication lines be two-way and open throughout the economic justification process. Performing an engineering economic analysis is not like writing a mystery. Management should not have to wait until the end to learn ''who done it.'' Throughout the process, information should be shared with management to ensure that reservations are surfaced and concerns are addressed.

3. Don't fall in love with the technical aspects of the recommended investment. As engineers, we typically become enamored with the technical details of the preferred alternative. However, management will not be won over by technical details.

4. Remember, managers tend to have very broad perspectives. Therefore, it is important to know management's priorities and to tailor the economic justification package to address those priorities. Consequently, make every effort to relate the recommended investment to the firm's well-being and to show how the investment relates to the firm's strategic plan and stated corporate objectives.

5. Remember, your proposal will be only one of many that will be submitted, and very few will be funded. Just as failure to fund your proposal does not mean management is stupid, neither does a decision to fund it mean management is brilliant. Don't confuse unfavorable results with destiny. Timing is everything! If your recommendation is not approved this budget cycle, it does not mean it should be abandoned. It could be that an unusually strong set of investment alternatives were available this budget cycle or that investment funds were more limited than usual. Remember, a firm's ability to finance the recommended investment is as important as its economic merit. Too many great designs have been abandoned because of timing. If you really believe it is a great investment, don't give up on it too quickly.

6. Remember, profit maximization is not always "the name of the game," but "selling" is! Ultimately, it comes down to how persuasive you are when you present your recommended investment. That, more than any other reason, is why we emphasize supplementary analysis; we want to make sure to address any "what if" questions management might ask. The firm's economic justification process might not require supplementary analysis, but we do it to enhance our confidence that all bases have been touched. Going the extra mile and doing supplementary analyses can pay huge dividends during the selection step.

7. Remember these three things: (1) think big—you get what you pay for, so don't be "penny-wise and dollar-foolish''; (2) the Golden Rule—those with the gold make the rules; and (3) the less you bet, the more you stand to lose if you win.

1-5   WHEN THE TIME VALUE OF MONEY NEED NOT BE CONSIDERED

Even though we have emphasized the need to incorporate the *TVOM* in choosing from among engineering investment alternatives, there are situations where time is not a significant factor, so the *TVOM* does not have to be considered. For example, discounted cash flow calculations are not helpful when (1) no investment of capital is required, and all cash flows occur within a limited time period, such as 1 year, (2) no investment of capital is required and annual cash flows for the various alternatives are roughly proportional to their cash flows the first year, (3) the alternatives require the same capital investment but differ in equal-annual operating costs and/or revenues, and (4) there are no essential differences in the cash flows among the alternatives after the first year. We present four examples to illustrate the kind of economic decisions that do not require explicit consideration of the *TVOM*.

EXAMPLE 1.9   Traveling to and from Spring Break

Six college students are planning a 1,200-mile trip for spring break. The transportation options available to them are to travel by bus, train, or plane; to rent two cars; or to rent a van. After checking bus and train schedules, they eliminated those two alternatives because of the travel times required. If they drive, they will share driving responsibilities and essentially travel nonstop (except for gas, food, and restroom stops). They checked with a wide range of rental car companies and arrived at the lowest rates for renting two cars and renting a van. They also checked with all the airlines that served their departure and arrival points and arrived at the lowest airfare available if they purchase their nonrefundable tickets several months in advance of spring break. They also contacted numerous hotels and motels at their destination to find the most economical housing available for a 7-day stay. Since the housing choice is not impacted by their transportation choice, they did not include it in their analysis. Similarly, they did not include food and beverage costs, because they concluded those costs were not dependent on the transportation choice. Finally, they concluded they would not need a rental car during spring break. So, they had to decide whether to rent two cars or a van and incur drop charges or park the vehicle(s) during the 7-day stay.

The final data used in their analysis of transportation options are as follows: round-trip airfare per person ($300); daily rental rate for each car, all charges except fuel ($50); rental car gas mileage (20 miles/gallon); drop charge for each car ($150); daily rental rate for a van, all charges except fuel ($80); rental van gas mileage (12 miles/gallon); drop charge for the van ($225); cost to travel to or from the airport at the spring break destination ($50 per cab, two cabs required); and average price of gasoline ($4.00/gallon). If they keep the rental vehicle, the charges will be for 7 days; if they drop the rental vehicle, the charges will be for 2 days. Friends will drop them off and pick them up at their ''home airport'' at no incremental cost if they decide to travel by plane.

Alternatives

1. Fly to/from spring break
2. Use two rental cars and incur drop charges
3. Use two rental cars and do not incur drop charges
4. Use a rental van and incur drop charges
5. Use a rental van and do not incur drop charges.

Economic Analysis

1. Total cost = 6 passengers ($300/passenger) + 2 taxis ($50/taxi)(2 trips) = $2,000
2. Total cost = 2 rental cars ($50/day)(2 days) + 4 drops ($150/drop) + 2,400 miles/car (2 cars)($4.00/gallon)/(20 miles/gallon) = $1,760
3. Total cost = 2 rental cars ($50/day)(7 days) + 2,400 miles/car (2 cars)($4.00/gallon)/(20 miles/gallon) = $1,660
4. Total cost = 1 rental van ($80/day)(2 days) + 2 drops ($225/drop) + 2,400 miles/van (1 van)($4.00/gallon)/(12 miles/ gallon) = $1,410
5. Total cost = 1 rental van ($80/day)(7 days) + 2,400 miles/van (1 van)($4.00/gallon)/(12 miles/gallon) = $1,360

Based on their analysis, the students decided to rent a van for their trip and park it once they arrived at their spring break destination. Notice, making the maximum use of incremental analysis, the decision could have been structured as follows:

Alternatives

1. Fly to/from spring break
2. Use two rental cars
   a. Incur drop charges
   b. Do not incur drop charges
3. Use a rental van
   a. Incur drop charges
   b. Do not incur drop charges

Economic Analysis

1. Total cost = 6 passengers ($300/passenger) + 2 taxis($50/taxi)(2 trips) = $2,000
2. Driving cost = 2,400 miles/car (2 cars)($4.00/gallon)/(20 miles/gallon)+ 2 rental cars ($50/day)(2 days) = $1,160
   a. Cost = 4 drops ($150/drop) = $600
   b. Cost = 2 rental cars ($50/day)(5 days) = $500
   Lowest cost = $1,660
3. Driving cost = 2,400 miles/van (1 van)($4.00/gallon)/(12 miles/gallon)+ 1 rental van ($80/day)(2 days) = $960
   a. Cost = 2 drops ($225/drop) = $450
   b. Cost = 1 rental van ($80/day)(5 days) = $400
   Lowest cost = $1,360

EXAMPLE 1.10 Evaluating Two Leasing Alternatives

A building contractor is considering leasing earthmoving equipment for a year. After that time, the contractor will decide whether to continue leasing or to purchase the equipment. Two alternatives have been identified; they have the same earthmoving capacity, but they have very different monthly lease and operating costs. The operating costs include fuel and maintenance. Diesel fuel costs $4.85 per gallon. The contractor estimates the equipment will be used 6 hours a day, 5 days a week, and 50 weeks a year. The following additional data are available:

Cost Parameters	Alternative 1	Alternative 2
Monthly lease cost	$1,000	$1,350
Fuel consumption (gallons/hour)	6.1	4.6
Hourly maintenance cost ($/hour)	$2.75	$5.85

Annual Cost Analysis

Alternative 1 = 12 months/year ($1,000/month) + 6.1 gallons/hour (1,500 hours/year) ($4.85/gallon) + $2.75/hour (1,500 hours/year) = $60,502.50/year

Alternative 2 = 12 months/year ($1,350/month) + 4.6 gallons/hour (1,500 hours/year) ($4.85/gallon) + $5.85/hour (1,500 hours/year) = $58,440.00/year

Based on the values of the parameters provided, Alternative 2 is the least cost alternative.

Recalling Step 6 of the systematic economic analysis technique, let's consider the following question before leaving the example: How sensitive is the choice of earthmoving equipment to changes in fuel cost and operating hours per year? For our purposes, we will examine two questions: (1) What fuel cost per gallon would result in the two alternatives having the same annual cost? and (2) For the stated fuel cost, for what number of operating hours per year would the two alternatives have the same annual cost?

Fuel cost analysis: Setting the two annual costs equal, with fuel cost as the unknown, yields

$12,000/year + 9,150 gallons($X/gallon) + $4,125/year = $16,200 + $6,900 gallons ($X/gallon) + $8,775/year.

Solving for X gives, X = $3.93/gallon.

Fuel cost would have to decrease 18.97 percent for Alternative 1 to be preferred. This is unlikely, but possible given the recent history of diesel fuel prices.

Annual operating hours analysis: Setting the two annual costs equal, with the number of hours operated annually as the unknown, yields

$12,000/year + $29.585/hour(Y hours/year) + $2.75/hour(Y hours/year) = $16,200/year + $22.32/hour (Y hours/year) + $5.85/hour (Y hours/year)

Solving for Y gives Y = ($4,200/year)/(4.175 hours/year) = 1,005.988 hours/year

During a 50-week year and 5-day operating weeks, the equipment would have to be used only 4.02 hours daily for Alternative 1 to be preferred. Hence, it is unlikely that Alternative 1 would ever be preferred over Alternative 2 based on the number of hours the equipment is operated annually.

EXAMPLE 1.11   Choosing Manufacturing Equipment

A particular metal component part can be machined on either an engine lathe or a turret lathe. In either case, the machines are not used exclusively for this particular part. Rather, parts are produced in batches according to a customer's order. If the part is produced on the turret lathe, a setup of the machine is required each time a customer's order is processed. The setup is required only once per order if the order size is less than or equal to 300 units. If the order size is greater than 300 units, then a setup is required every 300 units. The material cost per unit is the same regardless of the machine used. Relevant time and cost data for the engine lathe and the turret lathe are given below. Which machine should be used for order sizes of 25, 100, and 500 units?

Parameter	Engine Lathe	Turret Lathe
Setup time	Negligible	2 hours/order
Direct labor and machine time	10 minutes/part	5 minutes/part
Direct labor rate	$15/hr	$24/hr
Machine rate	$24/hr	$36/hr
Cutting tool cost	$0.50/part	$0.25/part

For the engine lathe, the cost for an order of size Q parts is obtained as follows:

Direct labor cost/minute = $15/60 = $0.25/min
Direct labor cost/part = $0.25/min(10 min/part) = $2.50/part
Machine cost/minute = $24/60 = $0.40/min
Machine cost/part = $0.40/min(10 min/part) = $4/part
Cutting tool cost/part = $0.50/part
Total cost/part = $2.50 + $4.00 + $0.50 = $7.00/part
Total cost for Q units = $7.00Q

For the turret lathe, to obtain the cost of an order of size Q parts, we first let N equal the number of setups required for an order of Q parts. The total cost is obtained as follows:

Set-up cost/order = N setups/order(2 hr/setup)($24/hr + $36/hr) = $120N/order
Direct labor cost/minute = $24/60 = $0.40/min
Direct labor cost/part = $0.40/min(5 min/part) = $2/part
Machine cost/minute = $36/60 = $0.60/min
Machine cost/part = $0.60/min(5 min/part) = $3/part
Cutting tool cost/part = $0.25/part
Total cost/order = $120N + ($2.00 + $3.00 + $0.25)Q = $120N + $5.25Q

For Q = 25, N = 1; for Q = 100, N = 1; for Q = 500, N = 2. Therefore, the total costs are

Order Size (Q)	Total Cost (Engine Lathe)	Total Cost (Turret Lathe)
25	$7(25) = $175	$120(1) + $5.25(25) = $251.25
100	$7(100) = $700	$120(1) + $5.25(100) = $645
500	$7(500) = $3,500	$120(2) + $5.25(500) = $2,865

Based on the analysis, the engine lathe should be used to produce the smallest sized order, and the turret lathe should be used to produce the 100-unit and 500-unit orders. (An obvious question is, For what order size would you be indifferent between using the engine lathe and turret lathe? Since the choice switched between a 25-unit order and the 100-unit order, the ''indifference point'' is somewhere between those two values. A calculation establishes that an order of 120/1.75, or 68.57 units will have the same total cost, regardless of the machine used.

EXAMPLE 1.12   Which Lightbulb Is Least Costly?

Hugh Kinney, who owns a small business, recently rented an office building that is equipped with ceiling-mounted light fixtures. The office did not come equipped with bulbs, so Hugh had to purchase them. When he went to the local Wal-Mart, he found several alternatives available. To simplify the analysis, we will restrict the choices he considered to GE Soft White 100 incandescent bulbs and GE Soft White 100 helical fluorescent bulbs. The cost per bulb equaled $0.26 and $3.22, respectively. The light output per bulb, measured in lumens, is 1,690 lumens and 1,700 lumens, respectively. The energy used per bulb, measured in watts, is 100 watts and 26 watts, respectively. The rated life of each bulb is 750 hours and 12,000 hours, respectively. The actual wattage the bulb draws and the light output it emits depends on the bulb's efficiency and the voltage of the power source used. However, for his purposes, Hugh assumed the advertised values were accurate.

Hugh expects the lights to be turned on an average of 2,500 hours per year (10 hours per day, 5 days per week, and 50 weeks per year). If electrical energy costs $0.10 per kilowatt-hour (kWh), then he determined the energy cost per bulb will be as follows:

GE Soft White 100 incandescent $(2,500/1,000)(100)($0.10) = $25/yr$
GE Soft White 100 helical fluorescent $(2,500/1,000)(26)($0.10) = $6.25/yr$

Since labor must be expended to remove burned-out bulbs and replace them with new bulbs, Hugh decided to incorporate in his analysis the cost of replacement. He assumed it would cost at least $2 to obtain a new bulb from storage, secure a ladder, replace the bulb, store the ladder, and dispose of the burned-out bulb.

The acquisition plus installation/removal of bulbs, expressed on an annual basis, were determined to be as follows:

GE Soft White 100 incandescent $(2,500/750)($2.00 + $0.26) = $7.53/yr$
GE Soft White 100 helical fluorescent $(2,500/12,000)($2.00 + $3.22) = $1.09/yr$

Hence, the total annual cost for each alternative was found to be

GE Soft White 100 incandescent $25/yr + $7.53/yr = $32.53/yr$
GE Soft White 100 helical fluorescent $6.25/yr + $1.09/yr = $7.34/yr$

Hugh concluded the GE Soft White 100 helical fluorescent bulb was the least cost alternative.

(Note: Hugh's analysis violated the first *DCF* rule: What about the *TVOM*? The GE Soft White 100 incandescent bulb is expected to last less than 4 months before replacement occurs. However, the GE Soft White 100 helical fluorescent bulb is expected to last 4.8 years. In Chapter 2, we will show that incorporating the *TVOM* in the calculation will increase the annual cost of the fluorescent bulb. However, the increase will not offset the differences in the annual costs of the two alternatives. In general, one should consider the *TVOM* when investments last more than 1 year.)

Principle #7

Consider only differences in cash flows among investment alternatives.

EXAMPLE 1.13   Shedding More Light on the Example

When Hugh Kinney described to his daughter, Stacey, how he performed his analysis, she asked him several questions. Based on his answers, she pointed out several errors he made. Stacey, an engineering graduate, remembered from her engineering economic analysis course the importance of incremental analysis and Principle 7.

Stacey asked how her father determined the electrical energy cost per kilowatt-hour. He said he divided his monthly cost of electricity by the number of kilowatt-hours used that month. Stacey told him his monthly bill includes a fixed cost of $7.10 per meter, which would not be affected by his choice of bulb. She also told him the rate for electrical energy was 8.803¢ per kWh for the first 2,000 kWh and 8.087¢ per kWh greater than 2,000 per month. The heating and air-conditioning power consumption, plus the energy costs for computers, printers, and other business equipment, will exceed 2,000 kWh per month. Therefore, Stacey said the incremental cost of electrical power would be 8.087¢ per kWh, not the 10¢ per kWh Hugh used in his calculations.

Next, she asked how he determined the labor cost to replace the bulbs. Hugh said he estimated how long it would take and used the average hourly wage of the person who would replace the bulbs. Stacey asked if replacing the bulb would increase the amount of money actually paid to the person who replaced them. Hugh said the person was paid a monthly salary, and since he would replace the bulbs during regular business hours, he would not be paid overtime for doing so. As he answered Stacey's question, Hugh realized there would not be an incremental cost to replace the bulbs.

Stacey performed the following analysis:

Energy cost

GE Soft White 100 incandescent $(2,500/1,000)(100)(\$0.08087) = \$20.2175/\text{yr}$

GE Soft White 100 helical fluorescent $(2,500/1,000)(26)(\$0.08087) = \$5.2566/\text{yr}$

Bulb cost

GE Soft White 100 incandescent $(2,500/750)(\$0.26) = \$0.8667$

GE Soft White 100 helical fluorescent $(2,500/12,000)(\$3.22) = \$0.6708/\text{yr}$ (ignoring the *TVOM*)

GE Soft White 100 helical fluorescent = \$0.9883/yr (using Excel®'s **PMT** financial worksheet function, described in Chapter 2, with a 15 percent annual *TVOM*)[1]

Annual cost

GE Soft White 100 incandescent \$20.2175/yr + \$0.8667/yr = \$21.0842/yr

GE Soft White 100 helical fluorescent \$5.2566/yr + \$0.6708/yr = \$5.9274/yr (ignoring the *TVOM*)

GE Soft White 100 helical fluorescent \$5.2566/yr + \$0.9883/yr = \$6.2449/yr (including a 15 percent annual compound interest rate, as will be demonstrated in Chapter 2)

1-6 SUMMARY

In this chapter, you learned several things that will be of critical importance as we move through the text. In the order of occurrence, here's what you learned:

1. Money has a time value.

2. Four rules to follow when dealing with cash flows that occur at different points in time

3. Ten principles of engineering economic analysis that underlie the material presented in the text

4. A seven-step systematic economic analysis technique to use when performing engineering economic analyses

5. A weighted factor comparison method to use in deciding which engineering economic investment to make when multiple criteria exist

6. Not all economic decisions require explicit consideration of the *TVOM*.

In comparison with subsequent chapters, the content of this chapter is much more qualitative. As a result, once we begin solving the problems presented in the coming chapters, students tend to forget many of the points made in this chapter. For that reason, we strongly encourage students to periodically review the material presented here, particularly that which is found in Section 1.4.

Pit Stop #1—Checking Your Pulse!

1. True or False: If someone offers you the choice of receiving \$1,000 today versus receiving \$1,000 a year from today, you should take the money today if your time value of money is greater than zero.

2. **True of False:** A strength of the weighted factor comparison technique is its scientific foundation and its elimination of subjectivity from decision making.

---

[1]Stacey pointed out that even though in this instance the same recommendation resulted, it would not always be the case when you focus on total costs instead of incremental costs and when you ignore the *TVOM*. Her advice was most appropriate and timely, since *TVOM* calculations are the subject of the next chapter!

3. True or False: If your time value of money is 10% annually, then you will be indifferent between receiving $1000 today and receiving $1100 one year from today.

4. True or False: Based on the principles of engineering economic analysis, you should bet on the horse with the lowest odds to win, because risk and returns tend to be positively correlated.

5. True or False: Every economic decision should be based on the time value of money.

Tutoring problem available (at instructor's discretion) in *WileyPLUS*.

Problem available (at instructor's discretion) in *WileyPLUS*.

Worked Problem Video available in *WileyPLUS*.

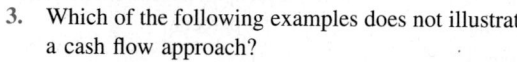

FE-LIKE PROBLEMS

1. The fact that one should not add or subtract money unless it occurs at the same point in time is an illustration of what concept?
   a. Time value of money
   b. Marginal return
   c. Economy of scale
   d. Pareto principle

2. If a set of investment alternatives contains all possible choices that can be made, then the set is said to be which of the following?
   a. Coherent
   b. Collectively exhaustive
   c. Independent
   d. Mutually exclusive

3. Which of the following examples does not illustrate a cash flow approach?
   a. A payroll manager writes a check to pay a shop worker.
   b. A neighbor pays $0.25 to buy a glass of lemonade at a lemonade stand.
   c. A hungry teenager pays for snacks with a debit card.
   d. A building contractor buys lumber on account at a local lumberyard.

4. The "discounting" in a discounted cash flow approach requires the use of which of the following?
   a. An interest rate
   b. The economic value added
   c. The gross margin
   d. The incremental cost

5. Risks and returns are generally ___ correlated.
   a. inversely
   b. negatively
   c. not
   d. positively

6. Assuming zero incremental costs for the do-nothing alternative is generally
   a. appropriate.
   b. risky.
   c. optimistic.
   d. realistic.

7. Answering "what if" questions with respect to an economic analysis is an example of which step in the systematic economic analysis technique?
   a. Identifying the investment alternatives
   b. Defining the planning horizon
   c. Comparing the alternatives
   d. Performing supplementary analysis

8. Which of the following is useful in making a final selection when multiple criteria exist?
   a. Four discounted cash flow rules
   b. Seven-step systematic analysis technique
   c. Ten principles of engineering economic analysis
   d. Weighted factor comparison method

9. Time value of money calculations may not be required in an economic evaluation for all of the following reasons except
   a. annual cash flows are proportional to the first year cash flow.

   b.   inflation is absent.

   c.   no investment of capital is required.

   d.   there are no differences in the cash flows of the alternatives after the first year.

10.   If a student's time value of money rate is 30 percent, then the student would be indifferent between $100 today and how much in 1 year?

   a. $30

   b. $100

   c. $103

   d. $130

11.   A bottled mango juice drink must contain at least 17 percent mango juice for proper taste. The drink is created by blending unprocessed juice from two orchards. RightRipe Orchard sells unprocessed juice that is 12.5 percent mango juice and 87.5 percent base liquids. PureBlend Orchard sells unprocessed juice that is 20 percent mango juice and 80 percent base. What percentage of unprocessed juice from each orchard is required to exactly meet the 17 percent specification?

   a.   40 percent RightRipe; 60 percent PureBlend

   b.   50 percent RightRipe; 50 percent PureBlend

   c.   60 percent RightRipe; 40 percent PureBlend

   d.   Cannot be determined from the information given

12.   A printed circuit board is produced by passing through a sequence of three steps. The scrap rates for steps one through three are 5 percent, 3 percent, and 3 percent, respectively. If 10,000 good parts are needed, the number that should be started at step one is closest to which of the following?

   a.   11,100

   b.   11,140

   c.   11,190

   d.   11,240

13.   Reconsider the preceding problem assuming that the sequence can be rearranged such that the processing step with the 5 percent scrap rate occurs last rather than first. Using this redesigned sequence, the number of parts that should be started will

   a.   increase.

   b.   decrease.

   c.   be unchanged.

   d.   Cannot be determined from the information given

PROBLEMS

Section 1.2

1.   Wylie has been offered the choice of receiving $5,000 today or an agreed-upon amount in 1 year. While negotiating the future amount, Wylie notes that he would be willing to take no less than $5,700 if he has to wait a year. What is his *TVOM* in percent?

2.   RT is about to loan his granddaughter Cynthia $20,000 for 1 year. RT's *TVOM*, based upon his current investment earnings, is 8 percent. Cynthia's *TVOM*, based upon earnings on investments, is 12 percent.

   a.   Should they be able to successfully negotiate the terms of this loan?

   b.   If so, what range of paybacks would be mutually satisfactory? If not, how far off is each person from an agreement?

3.   RT is about to loan his granddaughter Cynthia $20,000 for 1 year. RT's *TVOM*, based upon his current investment earnings, is 12 percent, and he has no desire to loan money for a lower rate. Cynthia is currently earning 8 percent on her investments, but they are not easily available to her, and she is willing to pay up to $2,000 interest for the 1-year loan.

   a.   Should they be able to successfully negotiate the terms of this loan?

   b.   If so, what range of paybacks would be mutually satisfactory? If not, how many dollars off is each person from reaching an agreement?

4.   If your *TVOM* is 15 percent and your friend's is 20 percent, can the two of you work out mutually satisfactory terms for a 1-year $3,000 loan? Assume the lender has the money available and neither person wants to go outside their acceptable *TVOM* range. Be explicit about who is lending and what is the acceptable range of money paid back on the loan.

Sections 1.3 and 1.4

5.   The following stages of a project are each contingent upon the preceding stage. If the preceding stage is not performed (accepted), then none of the subsequent stages may be performed.

Stage	Investment	Cost in Today's $	Revenues in Today's $
1	A small FCC-licensed commercial radio station	$180,000	$270,000
2	New antenna and hard-line from transmitter	$30,000	$50,000
3	New amplifier to boost from 5,000 watts to 30,000 watts	$40,000	$30,000
4	New lightning-protection equipment	$30,000	$60,000
5	New control console	$15,000	$5,000

a. Remembering that no stages can be skipped, which set of the five stages do you recommend be purchased?

b. Of the ten principles, which one(s) is well illustrated by this problem?

c. Of the systematic economic analysis technique's seven steps, which one(s) is well illustrated by this problem?

6. Barbara and Fred have decided to put in an automatic sprinkler system at their cabin. They have requested bids, and the lowest price received is $5,500 from Water Systems Inc (WSI). They decide to do the job themselves and obtain a set of materials (plastic pipe, nozzles, fittings, and regulators) from an all-sales-are-final discount house for $1,100. They begin the installation and rent a trencher at $80 per day. Unfortunately, they quickly hit sandstone in many places of the yard and require a jackhammer and air compressor at another $80 per day. They keep all the rental equipment for 5 days. By this time, Fred has hurt his knee, and Barbara is sick of the project. They again contact WSI, who tells them that they can use only some of the materials, reducing the cost by $500, and only some of the trenching, reducing the cost by another $500, bringing the total to $4,500, finished and ready to go.

a. How much have they already spent?

b. How much will they have spent when the project is over if they accept the new offer from WSI?

c. A different contractor, Sprinkler Systems (SS), who heard of their situation approaches Barbara and Fred and recommends a design for a sprinkler system that would require a different set of materials and a new routing of the trenches. They offer to (1) backfill all existing trenches, (2) cut new trenches with their rock-impervious Ditch Witch, and (3) install the system. Their charge is $6,000, for a finished-and-ready-to-go project, and they correctly note that this is less than the total that will have been spent if Barbara and Fred go with WSI. Should Barbara and Fred go with WSI or SS? Why?

d. Of the ten principles, which one(s) is well illustrated by this problem?

e. Of the systematic economic analysis technique's seven steps, which one(s) is well illustrated by this problem?

7. List some nonmonetary factors in the alternative decision process that you should be prepared to address when presenting a proposal to management. Let your mind run free and think this out on your own, rather than trying to find words that fit from the text.

a. Come up with 10 or more items.

b. Of the ten principles, which one(s) is well illustrated by this problem?

c. Of the systematic economic analysis technique's seven steps, which one(s) is well illustrated by this problem?

8. Four proposals (A, B, C, and D) are available for investment. Proposals A and C cannot both be accepted; Proposal B is contingent upon the acceptance of either Proposal C or D; and Proposal A is contingent on D.

a. List all possible combinations of proposals and clearly show which are feasible.

b. Of the ten principles, which one(s) is well illustrated by this problem?

c. Of the systematic economic analysis technique's seven steps, which one(s) is well illustrated by this problem?

9. Five proposals (V, W, X, Y, and Z) are available for investment. At least two and no more than four must be chosen. Proposals X and Y are mutually exclusive. Proposal Z is contingent on either Proposal X or Y being funded. Proposal V cannot be pursued if either W, X, Y, or any combination of the three are pursued.

a. List all feasible mutually exclusive investment alternatives.

b. Of the ten principles, which one(s) is well illustrated by this problem?

c. Of the systematic economic analysis technique's seven steps, which one(s) is well illustrated by this problem?

10. Three proposals (P, Q, and R) are available for investment. Exactly one or two proposals must be chosen; Proposals P and Q are mutually exclusive. Proposal R is contingent on Proposal P being funded. List all feasible mutually exclusive investment alternatives.

11. You have been out of school and gainfully employed for 5 years. You have three alternatives available for investment with your own money. Each has some element of risk, although some are safer than others. Following is a summary of the alternatives, the risks, and the returns:

Alternative	You Invest, $	Chance of Success	Returned to You If Success, $	Chance of Failure	Returned to You If Failure, $
A	$100	95%	$110.79	5%	$95.00
B	$100	60%	$150.00	40%	$50.00
C	$100	20%	$510.00	80%	$10.00

   a. Which would you select?

   b. Why would you make this selection?

   c. Of the ten principles, which one(s) is well illustrated by this problem?

   d. Of the systematic economic analysis technique's seven steps, which one(s) is well illustrated by this problem?

12. Suppose you have been out of school and gainfully employed for 5 years. You have three alternatives available for investment with your own money. Each has some element of risk, although some are safer than others. Following is a summary of the alternatives, the risks, and the returns:

Alternative	You Invest, $	Chance of Success	Returned to You If Success, $	Chance of Failure	Returned to You If Failure, $
A	$100,000	95%	$110,789.47	5%	$95,000
B	$100,000	60%	$150,000.00	40%	$50,000
C	$100,000	20%	$510,000.01	80%	$10,000

   a. Which would you select?

   b. Why would you make this selection?

   c. Of the ten principles, which one(s) is well illustrated by this problem?

   d. Of the systematic economic analysis technique's seven steps, which one(s) is well illustrated by this problem?

13. AutoFoundry has contacted Centrifugal Casting Company about the purchase of machines for the production of (1) Babbitt bearings, and (2) diesel cylinder liners (engine sleeves). The cost of the machines prohibits AutoFoundry from purchasing both, so they decide to base their selection on which machine will provide the greatest net income on a "today" basis (also known later as a *present worth basis*). The bearing machine has a life of 5 years, after which it is expected to be replaced. It has "today" costs (considering first cost and 5 years of operating cost, maintenance, etc.) of $460,000 and provides new revenues over the 5 years of $730,000 in today's dollars. The cylinder liner machine has a life of 9 years, with "today" costs and new revenues over the 9-year life of $650,000 and $990,000, respectively.

   a. What would you recommend that AutoFoundry do?

   b. Of the ten principles, which one(s) is well illustrated by this problem?

   c. Of the systematic economic analysis technique's seven steps, which one(s) is well illustrated by this problem?

14. A Payne County commissioner has $20,000 remaining in the budget to spend on one of three worthy projects. Each is a one-time investment, and there would be no follow-on investment, regardless of which project is chosen. Project

A involves the placement of gravel on a rough and often muddy road leading to a public observatory, providing net benefits (consider this as net revenue-in-kind) of $8,000 per year for 4 years at which time the road will again be in disrepair. Project B involves the building of a water-retention dam to hold water during big rains, thereby lessening damage due to flash flooding; the benefits are expected to be worth $6,000 for each of 6 years, after which silt will have made the pond ineffective. Project C is to provide water, sewer, and electrical hookups for recreational vehicles at the fairgrounds; net benefits of $4,000 per year would be realized for 10 years, after which the system would need to be replaced. No matter which alternative is selected, once its useful life is over, there will be no renewal.

    a. What planning horizon should be used in evaluating these three projects?

    b. Of the ten principles, which one(s) is well illustrated by this problem?

    c. Of the systematic economic analysis technique's seven steps, which one(s) is well illustrated by this problem?

15. Reconsider the county commissioner's evaluation of three projects in Problem 14. Take the facts as given, except now suppose the commissioner can commit the county to renewing these investments, even if a different commissioner is elected. So, after 4 years in project A, the road would be renewed with gravel or perhaps even paved. After 6 years, the water-retention dam could be dredged and renewed, or a new dam could be built. After 10 years, the RV hookups could be modernized and replaced.

    a. What are the considerations in selecting the appropriate planning horizon in this case?

    b. Of the ten principles, which one(s) is well illustrated by this problem?

    c. Of the systematic economic analysis technique's seven steps, which one(s) is well illustrated by this problem?

16. Modern Designs is seeking a supplier of copper wire for artistic and cosmetic effects on high-end decorative consumer products. Considerable research into suppliers has been conducted, and all except four suppliers have been eliminated from consideration. These include Beauty Copper (BC), Copper Inventions (CI), Specialty Wire (SW), and Wire Cosmetics (WC). Based upon the best quote from each for the identical quantity and performance requirements, the prices were, respectively, $85,000, $79,000, $105,000, and $93,000. Recognizing that "lowest first cost" is not always the best alternative, Modern Designs has identified other factors, in addition to price, that are desired to retain their leadership position in the international marketplace. Each of the factors has been weighted in terms of its importance. Factors and weights include Price (P)—20%; Quality (Q) of metallurgical properties and consistency of color—30%; Delivery (D) reliability for lean production—25%; Return policy (R)—15%; and Ease (E) of working with the supplier—10%. The Materials Procurement group has researched and provided ratings on a 10-point maximum scale for each factor. These are given in the following table:

Supplier	Factor P	Factor Q	Factor D	Factor R	Factor E
BC	9.2	10	9	6	8
CI	10.0	7	7	5	9
SW	6.7	8	10	7	6
WC	8.2	6	7	10	10

Where Factor $P = 10*(1 - (\text{Price} - \text{Min Price})/\text{Min Price}) = 10*(1 - (\text{Price} - \$79,000)/\$79,000)$

    a. Using the weighted factor comparison method, determine the score for each of the potential suppliers.

    b. What is the imputed value, in dollars, for the differences in quality, delivery, and reliability between Suppliers BC and CI?

    c. Of the ten principles, which one(s) is well illustrated by this problem?

    d. Of the systematic economic analysis technique's seven steps, which one(s) is well illustrated by this problem?

17. Four investment alternatives (A, B, C, and D) are under consideration. The present worth (PW) for each alternative is $187,500, $300,000, $225,000, and $262,500. The payback periods (PP) for the alternatives were 2, 3, 1, and 4 years. The risk levels (RL) associated with each alternative are quite different, with A being most risky, D being least risky, and B and C being equally risky. The weights for PW, PP, and RL have been assigned as 35, 40, and 25. The following ratings have been assigned to each alternative for each factor:

	Alternative A	Alternative B	Alternative C	Alternative D
PW	6.3	10.0	7.5	8.8
PP	9.1	7.7	10.0	5.8
RL	7.5	9.0	9.0	10.0

    a. Using the weighted factor comparison method, which alternative would be recommended?

    b. What is the imputed value, in terms of present worth, for the difference in payback period for Alternatives B and C?

    c. Of the ten principles, which one(s) is well illustrated by this problem?

    d. Of the systematic economic analysis technique's seven steps, which one(s) is well illustrated by this problem?

Section 1.5

18. The Go-Fast Car Company (GFCC) has a large excess inventory of two paint colors (G1 and G2). The first color (G1) has 11 percent blue paint and 89 percent green paint. The second color (G2) has 22 percent blue paint and 78 percent green paint. Marketing has suggested that customers are satisfied when there is at least 18 percent blue paint in the mixture. If the cost of G1 is $7.50/gallon and the cost of G2 is $13.50/gallon

    a. what percentage of G1 can be mixed with G2 and still satisfy the customers?

    b. what is the resulting paint cost per gallon?

19. Vector Manufacturing (VM) makes replacement parts for the automotive industry. One particular part can be manufactured at a unit cost of $0.75 for material and $0.25 for direct labor. Nonfactory costs are estimated to be twice the direct labor costs. An order for 500,000 units is currently being processed. Halfway through the current order, a new manufacturing process becomes available that will reduce unit costs to $0.52 for material and $0.16 for direct labor. Under the new method, nonfactory costs are still estimated at twice the direct labor cost but must be updated to reflect the new direct labor unit cost. If implemented, the new process will require the purchase of $90,000 in additional tooling just to complete this single order.

    a. What is the cost for the second half of the order if VM completes the order using the original method?

    b. What is the cost for the second half of the order if VM switches to the new manufacturing method?

    c. Based on cost, which method should be selected?

20. A cranberry juice drink mix must contain at least 15.5 percent cranberry juice by volume for proper taste. Juice Company A sells an unprocessed juice that is 12.5 percent cranberry juice and 87.5 percent other constituents for $1.00/gallon. Juice Company B sells an unprocessed juice that is 20 percent cranberry juice and 80 percent other constituents for $2.50/gallon.

    a. What percentage of unprocessed juice should be bought from each source?

    b. What is the resulting material cost per gallon of the drink?

21. A food processing company is considering developing a new line of product. Depending on the quality of raw material, different yields and different quality of the final products can be expected. The product development department has identified three alternatives and produced them on a pilot test. The marketing department has used this pilot test to estimate potential sales and pricing strategies. The three alternatives would use existing equipment but different process conditions and specifications. These are summarized in the following table. If the objective is to maximize total profit per year, indicate which alternative seems to be the best according to the estimated data.

	Alt. 1	Alt. 2	Alt. 3
lb. of raw material A per unit product (at $5.18/lb)	0.05	0.07	0.075
lb. of raw material B per unit product (at $1.61/lb)	0.19	0.18	0.260
lb. of raw material C per unit product (at $2.82/lb)	0.14	0.12	0.170
Other processing costs ($/unit product)	$0.24	$0.36	$0.34
Expected wholesale price ($/unit product)	$1.43	$1.58	$1.88
Project sales volume (units of product)	1,000,000	1,250,000	800,000

22. A study made in the assembly department of a small electronics manufacturing firm revealed that workers typically produce 100 to 150 assemblies in an 8-hour workday. For simplicity, assume the production rates are 100, 125, or 150 units per day. If 100 units are produced, an average of 3 percent are rejected. When 125 units are produced, an average of 8 percent are rejected. At the 150 units/day rate, 20 percent are rejected. The total material costs per unit are $5.50, and rejected units are worthless scrap. Workers are paid $1.40 per acceptable assembly.

   a. What is the preferred production rate from the worker's point of view?

   b. Which production rate results in the lowest unit cost per acceptable unit for the company?

23. CustomMetalworks in Oregon produces guy wire attachments for towers (cell, broadcasting, etc.) according to customer order. The company has determined that guy attachments can be produced on three different machine tools: M1, M2, or M3. An analysis of production cost reveals the following data, where "fixed cost" is a one-time setup cost at an order's beginning, and "variable cost" is simply a cost per unit produced:

Machine Tool	Fixed Cost/Order	Variable Cost/Unit
M1	$300	$9
M2	$750	$3
M3	$500	$5

   a. Determine the most economical machine tool to use for *all* order sizes between 1 and 200 units. Hint: Determine the subranges within the overall range of 1 to 200 for which each machine tool is preferred.

   b. For an order of size 75, which machine tool should be used to produce the order, and what is the total production cost?

   c. For an order of size 160, assume that the preferred (most economical) machine is unavailable. What penalty (expressed in dollars of *additional* production cost) must be paid if the second most economical machine is used? The third?

24. A new engineering building is to contain 400,000 square feet. The total cost of the building (TC) is given by

$$TC = (200 + 80X + 2X^2)A$$

where

   $X =$ number of floors

   $A =$ floor area in ft^2/floor

   a. Create a table that shows the total building cost, average cost per floor, and cost reduction from successive numbers of floors (1 to 2, 2 to 3, 3 to 4, and so on).

   b. Based on your table, what is the optimal number of floors for the building? Justify your answer based on the "total building cost" column.

   c. Using differential calculus, demonstrate that your answer matches that in Part c. Note: For this part, assume that X is a continuous variable.

WILEY ⊙ **25.** In Example 1.11, it is noted that an order of 68.57 units will have the same total cost, regardless of machine used.

   a. Show the complete calculation to determine this breakeven value of 68.57 units.

   b. For 68 units or less, per order, which machine is more economical?

   c. For an order of 400 units, how much will be saved by using the more economically attractive lathe?

26. A subsidiary of a major furniture company manufactures wooden pallets. The plant has the capacity to produce 300,000 pallets per year. Presently, the plant is operating at 70 percent of capacity. The pallets' selling price is $18.25 per pallet, and the variable cost per pallet is $15.75. At zero output, the subsidiary plant's annual fixed costs are $550,000. This amount remains constant for any production rate between zero and plant capacity.

   a. With the present 70 percent of capacity production, what is the expected annual profit or loss for the subsidiary plant?

   b. What annual volume of sales (units) is required in order for the plant to break even?

   c. What would be the annual profit or loss if the plant is operating at 90 percent of capacity?

   d. If fixed costs could be reduced by 40 percent, what would be the new breakeven sales volume?

WILEY ⊙ **27.** An antenna analyzer for checking resonant frequency, impedance, and even feed line characteristics over 1 MHz to 170 MHz can be produced by either of two processing sequences, S_1 or S_2. Sequence S_1 consists of processing through five workstations: W1, W2, W3, W4, and W5. For sequence S_2, there are workstations WA, WB, and WC. The scrap rate for each of these workstations is as follows: W1 = 3 percent, W2 = 5 percent, W3 = 5 percent, W4 = 4 percent, W5 = 4 percent, WA = 5 percent, WB = 3 percent, and WC = 3 percent. Assume a lot size of 1,000 antenna analyzers is to be processed through each sequence. The raw material cost is $30 per unit. The processing cost through sequence S_1 is $180 and through sequence S_2 is $210, not including raw material cost. Which sequence of processing results in the lowest cost of good final product? Scrap materials have no value.

28. Brenda Johnson is considering purchasing a new car for business purposes. She has narrowed her choice to three cars; the cost details are given below:

Car Type	Car A	Car B	Car C
Fixed cost/month (depreciation, insurance, etc.)	$550	$400	$800
Miles per gallon of fuel	25	19	33
Estimated cost of maintenance ($/mile)	$0.20	$0.25	$0.15

Brenda estimates she will travel about 4,000 miles/month. The cost of fuel is $3.25/gallon.

   a. Based on a total cost/month comparison, determine the most economical car to purchase.

   b. If Car C is purchased, what will be the average cost per mile of travel?

WILEY ⊙ **29.** The relationship between cutting tool life (T) in minutes and cutting speed (V) in feet/minute is expressed by Taylor's equation: $VT^n = K$, where K is a constant. From this equation, it is possible to mathematically derive an equation to find the total tool life resulting in minimum unit cost. The equation is:

$$T_c = \left(t_c + \frac{c_c}{c_o}\right)\left(\frac{1}{n} - 1\right)$$

where

$\quad T_c =$ tool life for minimum unit cost, minutes

$\quad t_c =$ tool change time, minutes

$\quad c_c =$ cost per cutting edge, $/edge

c_o = cost of labor and overhead, \$/minute

n = Taylor's tool life exponent

A metal machining company is evaluating three different types of cutting tool inserts for one of their high-volume NC turning operations. The specifications and cost information available for the inserts are as follows:

	Tungsten Carbide Insert	Coated Carbide Insert	Ceramic Insert
n	0.22	0.27	0.38
t_c	2	2	2
c_c	\$0.40	\$1.80	\$3.00
c_o	\$1.00	\$1.00	\$1.00
K	150	250	550

a. For each insert type, determine the tool life for minimum unit cost and the corresponding cutting speed.

b. Which insert type is preferred to maximize the metal removal rate (proportional to cutting speed), and hence the production rate?

30. The process engineer at Strowbridge Metal Works has the choice of machining a particular part on either of two machines. Orders for this part are received regularly, but the order size varies. When the order is processed on Machine A, four sequential setup operations of 1 hour each are required. Once set up, the machining time is 0.50 hours per unit. When the order is processed on Machine B, eight sequential setup operations of 0.75 hours each are required. Once set up, the machining time per unit is 0.55 hours. The hourly wage rates for the operators are \$20 and \$18 for Machine A and Machine B, respectively. The hourly overhead rates, including setup time, are \$30 and \$27 for Machine A and Machine B, respectively.

a. Which machine is preferred if the order size is 100 units?

b. Which machine is preferred if the order size is 500 units?

c. What is the breakeven order size?

Chapter 2

TIME VALUE OF MONEY

Investment decisions will be faced by all engineering majors, including these civil engineering students who are covering a canoe mold evenly with batches of freshly mixed concrete as they prepare their annual entry into the American Society of Civil Engineers Concrete Canoe Competition. (Copyright Georgia Institute of Technology/Rob Felt)

Kellie Schneider

Immediately after receiving her engineering degree, Kellie Schneider began employment with a multinational company. Her initial salary was $60,000 per year. Kellie decided she would invest 10 percent of her gross salary each month. Also, based on discussions with the company's personnel and with a person in human resources, she believed her salary would increase annually at a rate ranging from 3 percent to 15 percent, depending on her performance. Likewise, after analyzing various investment opportunities, she anticipated she would be able to earn between 5 percent and 10 percent annually on her investment portfolio of mutual funds, stocks, bonds, U.S. Treasury notes, and certificates of deposit. Finally, Kellie believed annual inflation would vary from 2 percent to 5 percent over her professional career. With this information in hand, she calculated the range of possible values for her net worth, first after 30 years of employment, and second after 40 years of employment. She was amazed and pleased at what she learned.

In this chapter, you will learn how to do nearly all the things Kellie Schneider did in analyzing what her net worth would be several years in the future. The only thing we will not cover in this chapter is how to incorporate the effects of inflation on her net worth; we save that for Chapter 12. Also, you will learn how to determine the present worth and the future worth for three particular types of cash flow series.

2-1 INTRODUCTION

In the previous chapter, we identified 10 principles of engineering economic analysis:

1. Money has a time value.
2. Make investments that are economically justified.
3. Choose the mutually exclusive investment alternative that maximizes present worth.
4. Two investment alternatives are equivalent if their present worths are equal.
5. Marginal revenue must exceed marginal cost.
6. Continue to invest as long as each additional increment of investment yields a return that is greater than the investor's *TVOM*.
7. Consider only differences in cash flows among investment alternatives.
8. Compare investment alternatives over a common period of time.
9. Risks and returns tend to be positively correlated.
10. Past costs are irrelevant in engineering economic analyses, unless they impact future costs.

Principle #1 is the subject of this chapter. As noted in Chapter 1, *TVOM* considerations apply when moving money forward or backward in time. Recall, we referred to the movement of money forward or backward in time as *discounted cash flow* or *DCF*. Also, recall the following *four DCF* rules:

1. Money has a time value.
2. Money cannot be added or subtracted unless it occurs at the same point(s) in time.
3. To move money forward one time unit, multiply by 1 plus the discount or interest rate.
4. To move money backward one time unit, divide by 1 plus the discount or interest rate.

In this chapter, we present the mathematics and basic operations needed to perform engineering economic analyses incorporating the *DCF* rules. The material in this chapter serves as a foundation for the remainder of the text. Hence, a solid understanding of the mathematics and concepts contained in this chapter is essential: They can be applied in professional engineering practice, and they can be used in personal investment planning.

2-2 CASH FLOW DIAGRAMS

Just as it is helpful to use force diagrams when analyzing physical forces along a beam, it is helpful to use cash flow diagrams (*CFDs*) when analyzing cash flows that occur over several time periods. As shown in Figure 2.1, a *CFD* is constructed using a segmented horizontal line as a time scale, with vertical arrows indicating cash flows. An upward arrow indicates a cash inflow or positive-valued cash flow, and a downward arrow indicates a cash outflow, or negative-valued cash flow. The arrows are placed along the time scale to correspond with the timing of the cash flows. The lengths of the arrows can be used to suggest the magnitudes of the corresponding cash flows, but

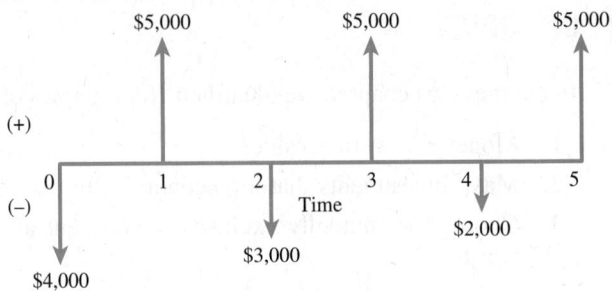

FIGURE 2.1

A Cash Flow Diagram (CFD).

in most cases, little is gained by precise scaling of the arrows. Depending on the application, the *TVOM* or interest rate can be shown at the end of the time scale to indicate the rate that is applicable to the analysis.

The *CFD* in Figure 2.1 depicts an expenditure of $4,000, followed by the receipt of $5,000, followed by an expenditure of $3,000, followed by a second receipt of $5,000, followed by a final expenditure of $2,000, followed by a final receipt of $5,000. The *CFD* is drawn from the investor's perspective: downward arrows denote expenditures, and upward arrows denote receipts.

EXAMPLE 2.1 Cash Flow Diagrams for Two *TVOM* Alternatives

Julian Stewart, a consulting engineer, is considering two investment alternatives (A and B) having the cash flow profiles shown in Table 2.1. Both alternatives involve $100,000 investments that last 5 years. Alternative A is an investment in a land-development venture located near Dallas, Texas. Julian and several other limited partners are considering purchasing land, subdividing it, and selling land parcels over a 5-year period. The land is anticipated to increase in value. There will be differences in the sizes of the parcels sold. Consequently, an increasing revenue profile is anticipated.

Investment B is for a computer and the software required to provide specialized computer-design capabilities for clients. Since Julian anticipates that competition will develop quickly if his plan proves successful, a declining revenue profile is anticipated.

Julian has funds available for only one investment. The cash flows shown are after applicable taxes and other expenses have been deducted. Both investments result in $150,000 being received over the 5-year period; hence, a net cash flow of $50,000 occurs in both cases, ignoring the *TVOM*.

TABLE 2.1

Cash Flow Profiles for Two Investment Alternatives.

End of Year (EOY)	A	B	B−A
0	−$100,000	−$100,000	$0
1	$10,000	$50,000	$40,000
2	$20,000	$40,000	$20,000
3	$30,000	$30,000	$0
4	$40,000	$20,000	−$20,000
5	$50,000	$10,000	−$40,000

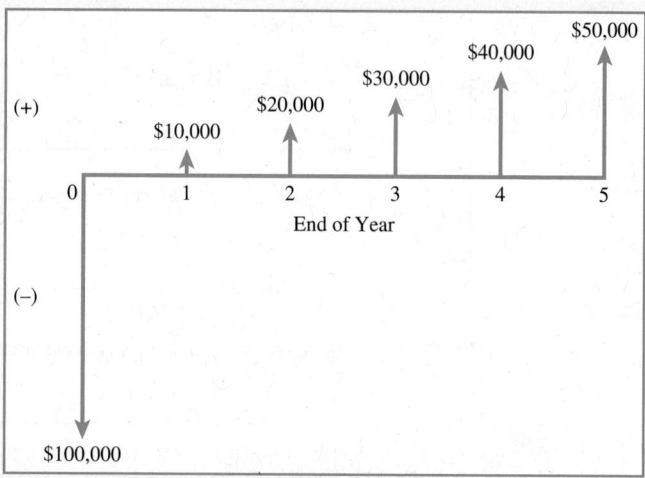

FIGURE 2.2

CFD **for Investment A.**

Figure 2.2 provides a *CFD* for Alternative A, with the $100,000 investment shown at a point in time defined as 0 (the present); $10,000 is received 1 year later; $20,000 is received 2 years after the investment; $30,000 is received 3 years after the investment; $40,000 is received 4 years after the investment; and $50,000 is received 5 years after the investment. As shown in Figure 2.3, Investment B consists of the same investment and same receipts, but their time sequence is reversed. Assuming Julian will make one of the investments, which is best?

Based on the *TVOM* discussion in Chapter 1, we know Alternative B is preferred. Why? Given the reverse images of the positive-valued cash flows, we prefer to receive the $50,000 sooner rather than later. If we apply Principle #7 and examine the difference in cash flows for the two investment alternatives, it is easy to see why Alternative B is preferred. As shown in Figure 2.4, by choosing Alternative B, money is received quicker than it is with Alternative A.

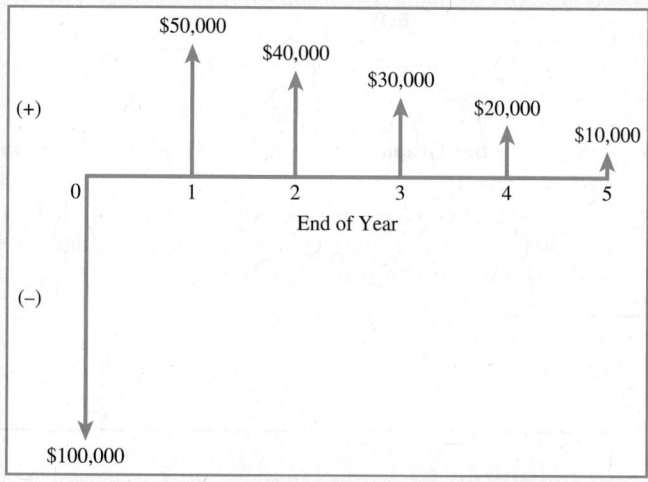

FIGURE 2.3

CFD **for Investment B.**

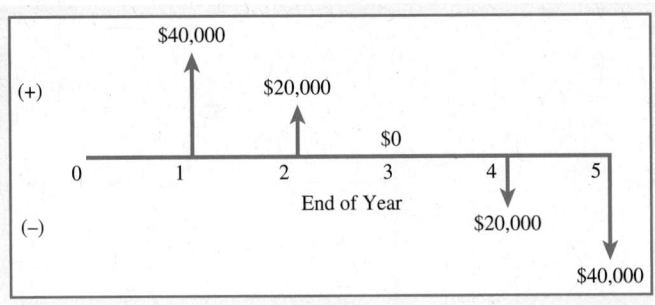

FIGURE 2.4

CFD **for the Difference in Cash Flows (Investment B – Investment A).**

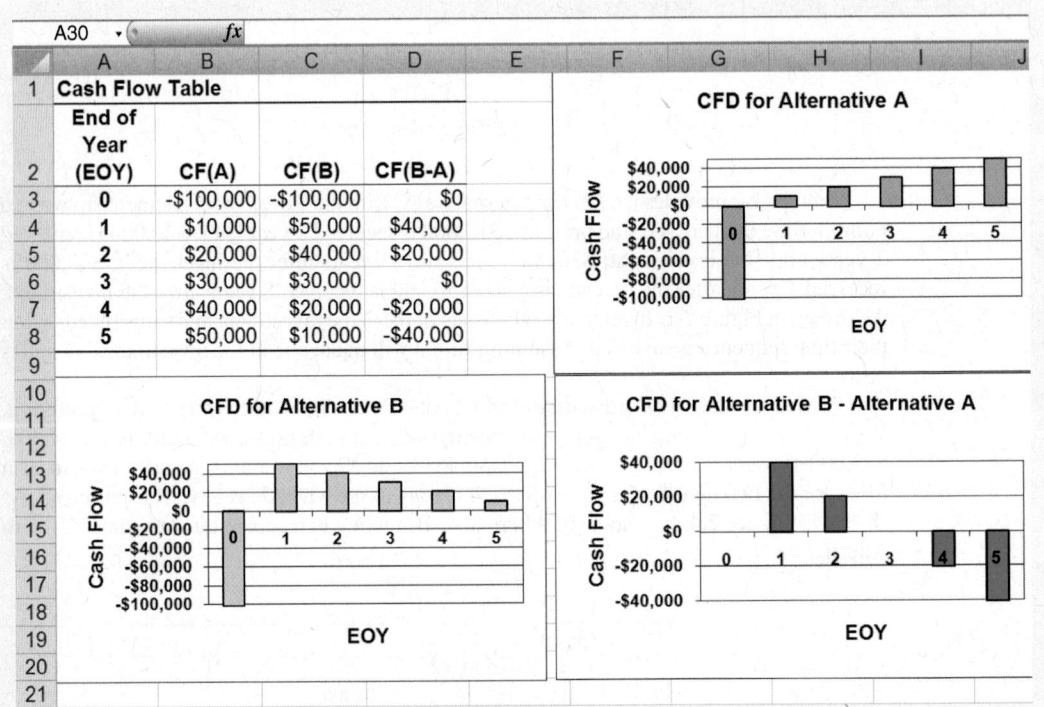

FIGURE 2.5

Bar Graph Representation of Cash Flow Diagrams.

Instead of using arrows to represent cash flows, bars can be used, as shown in Figure 2.5. Using Excel®, the bar graphs were produced directly from the table of cash flow profiles for the alternatives.

Principle #7

Consider only differences in cash flows among investment alternatives.

EXAMPLE 2.2 A Simple Illustration of the Time Value of Money

As another illustration of how *TVOM* can impact the preference between investment alternatives, consider investment Alternatives C and D, having the cash flow profiles depicted in Figure 2.6. The *CFDs* indicate that the positive cash flows for Alternative C are identical to those for Alternative D, except that the former occurs 1 year sooner; both alternatives require an investment of $6,000. *If exactly one of the alternatives must be selected*, then Alternative C would be preferred to Alternative D, based on the time value of money.

When faced with cash flows of equal magnitude occurring at different points in time, a corollary to the four *DCF* rules in Chapter 1 is *when receiving a given sum of money, we prefer to receive it sooner rather than later, and when paying a given sum of money, we prefer to pay it later rather than sooner.* Since we prefer to receive the $3,000 sooner, Alternative C is preferred to Alternative D.

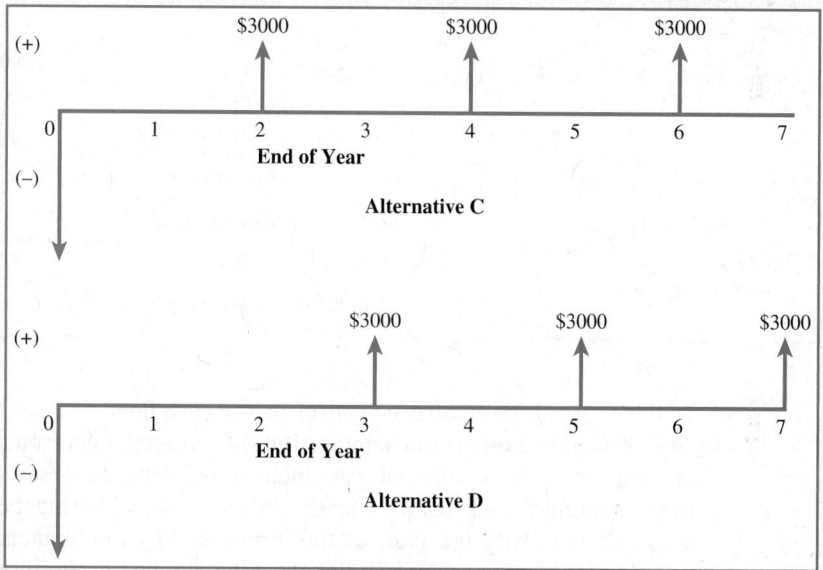

FIGURE 2.6
CFDs **for Alternatives C and D.**

EXAMPLE 2.3 A Consistency Check on One's Time Value of Money

A third illustration of *TVOM's* effect on selecting the preferred investment alternative is presented in Figure 2.7. Either Alternative E or Alternative F must be selected; the only differences in the performance characteristics of the two alternatives are economic. As shown in Figure 2.7, the economic differences reduce to a situation in which the receipt of $1,000 is delayed in order to receive $2,000 a year later. For this illustration, we would conclude that most of the students described in Example 1.1 would prefer Alternative E to Alternative F, since most of the students preferred $X when it equaled $2,000.

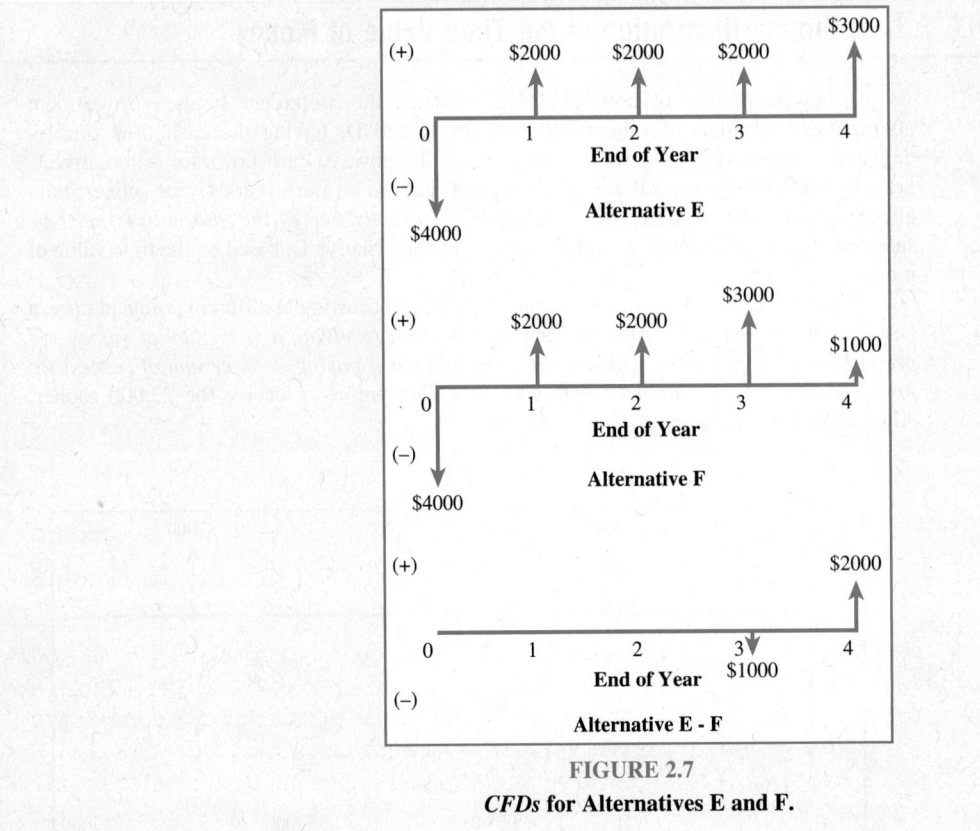

FIGURE 2.7

CFDs for Alternatives E and F.

In this chapter, we emphasize end-of-period cash flows and end-of-period compounding.[1] Depending on the financial institution involved, in personal finance transactions, savings accounts might not pay interest on deposits made in "the middle of a compounding period." Consequently, answers obtained using the methods we describe may not be exactly the same as those provided by the financial institution.

Beginning-of-period cash flows can be handled easily by noting that the end of period t is the beginning of period $t + 1$. To illustrate, rental payments might be made at the beginning of each month. However, one can think of the payment made at the beginning of, say, March as having been made at the end of February.

In this and subsequent chapters, end-of-year cash flows are assumed unless otherwise noted. It is realized that in many cases, monetary transactions take place during a calendar year, but it is often convenient to ignore any compounding effects within a year and deal directly with end-of-year cash flows.

EXAMPLE 2.4   Developing a Cash Flow Diagram (*CFD*) for an Investment

Figure 2.8 illustrates a loan transaction: $1,000 is borrowed at $t = 0$ (today) and repaid with five equal annual payments of $231, with the first payment occurring 1 year after receipt of the $1,000. An annual compound interest rate of 5 percent applies to the loan.

---

[1]The exception to this is the treatment of continuous cash flows, discussed in Appendix 2.A.

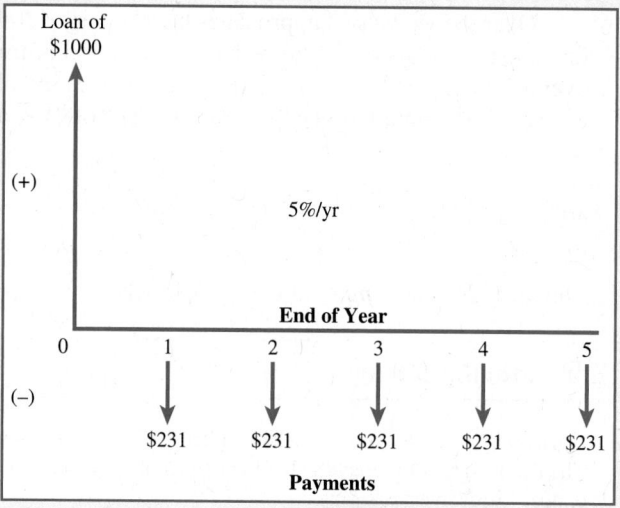

FIGURE 2.8
CFD **for a Uniform Series of Loan Payments.**

The *CFD* in Figure 2.8 is drawn from the borrower's perspective, since the $1,000 is shown as an inflow, and the $231 payments are shown as outflows. A *CFD* from the lender's perspective is easily drawn by reversing the directions of the arrows, since a cash inflow to the borrower is a cash outflow to the lender and vice versa.

Drawing *CFDs* for economic transactions is important for at least two reasons. First and foremost, *CFDs* are powerful communication tools. A *CFD* presents a clear, concise, and unambiguous description of the amount and timing of all cash flows associated with an economic analysis. Usually, a well-drawn *CFD* can be readily understood by all parties of an economic transaction regardless of whether they have had any formal training in economic analysis.

A second important reason for drawing *CFDs* is that they frequently aid in the identification of significant cash flow patterns that might exist within an economic transaction. One such pattern, illustrated in Figure 2.8, is a *uniform series*. The loan payments in Figure 2.8 represent a uniform series of length, 5 years, and magnitude, $231. In later sections of this chapter, the significance and usefulness of recognizing this and other patterns will become more apparent.

2-3 SIMPLE INTEREST CALCULATIONS

In considering the time value of money, it is convenient to represent mathematically the relationship between the current or *present* value of a single sum of money and its *future* value. Letting time be measured in years, if a single sum of money has a current or *present* value of P, its value in n years would be equal to

$$F_n = P + I_n \qquad (2.1)$$

where F_n is the accumulated value of P over n years, or the *future* value of P, and I_n is the increase in the value of P over n years. I_n is referred to as the accumulated *interest* in borrowing and lending transactions and is a function of P, n, and the *annual interest rate*, i. The annual interest rate is defined as the change in the value for $1 over a 1-year period.

Over the years, two approaches have emerged for computing the value of I_n. The first approach considers I_n to be a linear function of time. Since i is the rate of change over a 1-year period, it is argued that P changes in value by an amount Pi each year. Hence, it is concluded that I_n is the product of P, i, and n, or,

$$I_n = Pin \tag{2.2}$$

and

$$F_n = P(1 + in) \tag{2.3}$$

This is called the *simple interest* approach.

EXAMPLE 2.5   Loaning Money

A friend approaches you and asks to borrow $6,000 at 0.5 percent simple interest per month. The friend agrees to repay the loan with a single payment after 1 year. How much should you expect to receive?

Based on Equation 2.3, $F_{12} = \$6,000[1 + 0.005(12)] = \$6,360$. You should expect to receive $6,360 after 1 year.

EXAMPLE 2.6   An Alternative Repayment Plan

In the previous example, what monthly payments should you expect to receive if your friend agrees to repay the loan in the following way: $500 monthly payments against the principal amount borrowed, plus 0.5 percent on the unpaid balance of the loan?

As shown in Table 2.2, the monthly payments range from $530 to $502.50 over the 12-month period.

TABLE 2.2
Tabular Solution to Example 2.6.

Month	Unpaid Balance at the Beginning of the Month	Monthly Interest	Payment	Unpaid Balance at the End of the Month
1	$6,000.00	$30.00	$530.00	$5,500.00
2	$5,500.00	$27.50	$527.50	$5,000.00
3	$5,000.00	$25.00	$525.00	$4,500.00
4	$4,500.00	$22.50	$522.50	$4,000.00
5	$4,000.00	$20.00	$520.00	$3,500.00
6	$3,500.00	$17.50	$517.50	$3,000.00
7	$3,000.00	$15.00	$515.00	$2,500.00
8	$2,500.00	$12.50	$512.50	$2,000.00
9	$2,000.00	$10.00	$510.00	$1,500.00
10	$1,500.00	$7.50	$507.50	$1,000.00
11	$1,000.00	$5.00	$505.00	$500.00
12	$500.00	$2.50	$502.50	$0.00

EXAMPLE 2.7   Another Simple Interest Transaction

Mattie borrows $4,000 from Becca and agrees to pay $1,000 plus accrued interest at the end of the first year and $3,000 plus the accrued interest at the end of the fourth year. What are the amounts for the two payments if 8 percent annual simple interest applies?

For the first year, the payment equals $1,000 + 0.08($4,000) = $1,320. For the fourth year, the payment equals $3,000 + 0.08($4,000 − $1,000)(3) = $3,720.

2-4   COMPOUND INTEREST CALCULATIONS

Lending agencies seldom use simple interest calculations. Furthermore, the concept of simple interest ignores an important opportunity cost. To illustrate what we mean, suppose someone asks you to loan them $1,000 for 1 month at 0.5 percent monthly interest. After 1 month, the person returns and says, "I want to delay repaying you anything for one more month." If you agree to extend the loan period, then you should respond, "That is fine; however, you now have $1,005 of my money—the $1,000 you borrowed plus the $5 interest you owe me. If you want to keep my money for another month, I will have to charge you 0.5 percent on $1,005." If the person keeps the principal amount ($1,000) and the interest owed ($5) for another month, you have lost the opportunity to invest the $1,005 and earn a return on it. For that reason, interest should be charged against the principal and accumulated interest to date. Such a process is called *compounding*. It is at the heart of everything else we do in the text.

When compound interest is used, the interest rate (i) is interpreted as *the rate of change in the accumulated value of money*, and the value of I_n in Equation 2.2 is given by

$$I_n = \sum_{t=1}^{n} iF_{t-1} \tag{2.4}$$

where t increments the years from 1 to n and $F_0 = P$ and

$$F_n = F_{n-1}(1 + i) \tag{2.5}$$

EXAMPLE 2.8   Compounding Interest for 5 Years

Suppose you loan $10,000 for 1 year to an individual who agrees to pay you interest at a compound rate of 10 percent/year. At the end of 1 year, the individual asks to extend the loan period an additional year. The borrower repeats the process several more times. Five years after loaning the person the $10,000, how much would the individual owe you?

As shown in Table 2.3, the $10,000 owed, compounded over a 5-year period at 10 percent annual compound interest, totals $16,105.10. (Had simple interest been used, the amount owed would have been $15,000. The $1,105.10 difference is due to the effect of compounding.)

TABLE 2.3
Tabular Solution to Example 2.8.

Year	Unpaid Balance at the Beginning of the Year	Annual Interest	Payment	Unpaid Balance at the End of the Year
1	$10,000.00	$1,000.00	$0.00	$11,000.00
2	$11,000.00	$1,100.00	$0.00	$12,100.00
3	$12,100.00	$1,210.00	$0.00	$13,310.00
4	$13,310.00	$1,331.00	$0.00	$14,641.00
5	$14,641.00	$1,464.10	$16,105.10	$0.00

2.4.1 Single Cash Flows

The previous example involved two cash flows: an amount borrowed and an amount repaid. We can generalize the loan example and develop an equation to determine the amount owed after n periods, based on a compound interest rate of $i\%$/period, if P is borrowed. As shown in Table 2.4, the future amount, F, owed is related to P, i, and n as follows:

$$F = P(1 + i)^n \qquad (2.6)$$

where i is expressed as a decimal amount or as an equivalent percentage. As a convenience in computing values of F (the future worth) when given values of P (the present worth), the quantity $(1 + i)^n$ is tabulated in Appendix A for various values of i and n. The quantity $(1 + i)^n$ is referred to as the *single sum, future worth factor*. It is denoted $(F|P\ i\%,n)$ and reads "the F, given P factor at $i\%$ for n periods." The above discussion is summarized as follows.

Let P = the equivalent value of an amount of money at time zero, or present worth.

     F = the equivalent value of an amount of money at time n, or future worth.

TABLE 2.4
Derivation of Equation 2.6.

End of Period	(A) Amount Owed	(B) Interest for Next Period	(C) = (A) + (B) Amount Owed for Next Period*
0	P	Pi	$P + Pi = P(1 + i)$
1	$P(1 + i)$	$P(1 + i)i$	$P(1 + i) + P(1 + i)i = P(1 + i)^2$
2	$P(1 + i)^2$	$P(1 + i)^2 i$	$P(1 + i)^2 + P(1 + i)^2 i = P(1 + i)^3$
3	$P(1 + i)^3$	$P(1 + i)^3 i$	$P(1 + i)^3 + P(1 + i)^3 i = P(1 + i)^4$
$\vdots$	$\vdots$	$\vdots$	$\vdots$
$n - 1$	$P(1 + i)^{n-1}$	$P(1 + i)^{n-1}i$	$P(1 + i)^{n-1} + P(1 + i)^{n-1}i = P(1 + i)^n$
n	$P(1 + i)^n$		

*Notice, the value in column (C) for the end of period $(n - 1)$ provides the value in column (A) for the end of period n.

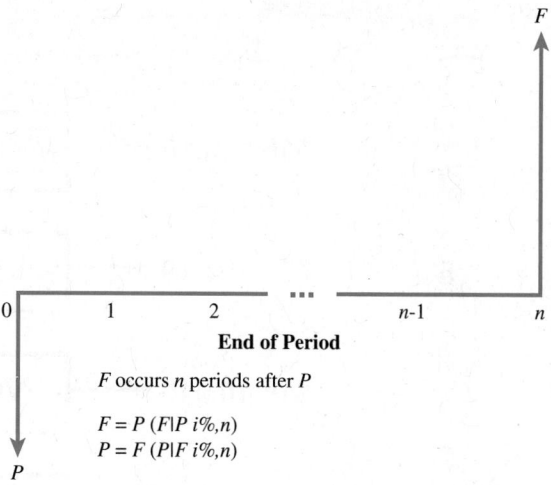

FIGURE 2.9

CFD **of the Time Relationship Between *P* and *F* in a Savings Account.**

$i = $ the interest rate per interest period.

$n = $ the number of interest periods.

Thus, the mathematical relationship between the future and present worths is given by Equation 2.6; the pneumonic representation is given by[2]

$$F = P(F|P\,i\%,n)$$ (2.7)

A *CFD* depicting the relationship between *F* and *P* for the savings account example is given in Figure 2.9. Remember, *F* occurs *n* periods after *P*.

In addition to solving numerically for the value of $(1 + i)^n$ and using tabulated values in Appendix A of the single sum, future worth factor, $(F|P\,i\%,n)$, an Excel® financial function[3] can be used to solve for the future worth. Specifically, the **FV**, or future value, function can be used. The parameters for the **FV** function are, in order of appearance, interest rate (i), number of periods (n), equal-sized cash flow per period (A), present amount (P), and *type*, which denotes either end-of-period cash flows (0 or omitted) or beginning-of-period cash flows (1).[4]

To solve for *F* when given *i*, *n*, and *P*, the answer can be obtained by entering the following in any cell in an Excel® spreadsheet: **=FV($i, n,,-P$)**. Notice there are no spaces between the equal sign and the closing parenthesis; also, two commas are placed between *n* and *P* in the function, since no equal cash flow per period applies, and type is not included, since end-of-period cash flows apply. Finally, notice that a negative value is entered for *P*, since the sign of the value obtained for *F* by using the **FV** function will be opposite the sign used for *P*. The reason for the sign change in

---

[2]A comma may be placed between the factor identifier and the interest rate. Thus, $(F|P,i\%,n)$ and $(F|P\,i\%,n)$ are equivalent representations of $(1 + i)^n$.

[3]Microsoft's Excel® software is used throughout the text. Where a computer is used to generate a solution, a computer icon appears in the margin and software functions are shown in blue boldface type in the text.

[4]Since we tend to assume end-of-period cash flows, we seldom have need for the parameter that indicates whether the cash flows are end-of-period or beginning-of-period. If no value is given for the parameter, end-of-period is the default.

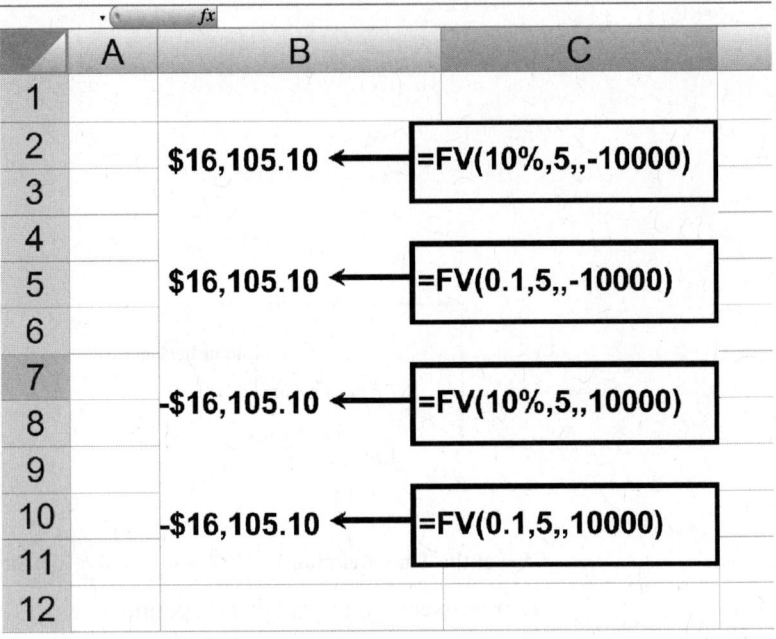

FIGURE 2.10

The Excel® FV Financial Function Used with a Single Sum of Money.

Excel® is simple: the **FV** function was developed for a loan situation where $P are loaned (negative cash flow) in order to receive $F (positive cash flow) n periods in the future when the money is loaned at $i\%$ interest per period.

Recall Example 2.8, in which $10,000 was loaned for 5 years at 10 percent annual compound interest. An Excel® solution to the example is shown in Figure 2.10. As indicated, the value of i can be entered as a decimal or as a percentage, and the value of P can be entered as either a positive or a negative amount, since the sign for the future value obtained will be opposite that used for P. Finally, notice that dollar signs and commas are not used in denoting the value of P.

EXAMPLE 2.9 Repaying a 5-Year Loan with a Single Payment

Dia St. John borrows $1,000 at 12 percent compounded annually. The loan is to be paid back after 5 years. How much should she repay?

Using the compound interest tables in Appendix A for 12 percent and 5 periods, the value of the single sum, future worth factor $(F|P\,12\%,5)$ is shown to be 1.76234. Thus,

$$F = P(F|P\,12\%,5)$$
$$= \$1000(1.76234)$$
$$= \$1762.34$$

Using the Excel® **FV** worksheet function,

$$F = \text{FV}(12\%,5,,-1000) = \$1762.34$$

How would you determine the length of time required for money to double in value if invested at $i\%$ compounded per period? The following example illustrates six approaches to answering this question:

1. Obtain an approximation by using the *Rule of 72*.

2. Consult the tables in Appendix A for the stated interest rate and find the value of n that makes the $(F|P\,i\%,n)$ factor equal 2, then interpolate as necessary.

3. Solve mathematically for the value of n that makes $(1+i)^n$ equal 2.

4. Use the Excel® **NPER** worksheet function.

5. Use the Excel® **GOAL SEEK** tool.

6. Use the Excel® **SOLVER** tool.

EXAMPLE 2.10   Doubling Your Money

How long does it take for an investment to double in value if it earns (a) 2 percent, (b) 3 percent, (c) 4 percent, (d) 6 percent, (e) 8 percent, or (f) 12 percent annual compound interest?

The first approach is to apply a rule of thumb called the *Rule of 72*. Specifically, the quotient of 72 and the interest rate provides a reasonably good approximation of the number of interest periods required to double the value of an investment:

a. 72/2 = 36 yrs

b. 72/3 = 24 yrs

c. 72/4 = 18 yrs

d. 72/6 = 12 yrs

e. 72/8 = 9 yrs

f. 72/12 = 6 yrs

The second approach is to consult Appendix A and, for each value of i, determine the value of n for which $(F|P\,i\%,n) = 2$.

a. For $i = 2\%$, n is between 30 and 36; interpolating gives $n \approx 30 + 6(2.0000 - 1.81136)/(2.03989 - 1.81136) = 34.953$ yrs

Similarly, for the remaining interest rates, the following approximations are obtained:

b. $n \approx 23 + (2.0000 - 1.97359)/(2.03279 - 1.97359) = 23.446$ yrs

c. $n \approx 17 + (2.0000 - 1.94790)/(2.02582 - 1.94790) = 17.669$ yrs

d. $n \approx 11 + (2.0000 - 1.89830)/(2.01220 - 1.89830) = 11.893$ yrs

e. $n \approx 9 + (2.0000 - 1.99900)/(2.15892 - 1.99900) = 9.006$ yrs

f. $n \approx 6 + (2.0000 - 1.97382)/(2.21068 - 1.97382) = 6.111$ yrs

With the third approach, we solve mathematically. Solving for n such that $(1+i)^n = 2$ gives $n = \log2/\log(1+i)$. Therefore, the correct values of n (to 3 decimal places) are

a. $n = \log2/\log1.02 = 35.003$ yrs;

b. $n = \log2/\log1.03 = 23.450$ yrs;

c. $n = \log2/\log1.04 = 17.673$ yrs;

d. $n = \log2/\log1.06 = 11.896$ yrs;

e. $n = \log2/\log1.08 = 9.006$ yrs; and

f. $n = \log2/\log1.12 = 6.116$ yrs.

The parameters of the Excel® **NPER** worksheet function are, in order of placement, interest rate, equal-sized cash flow per period, present amount, future amount, and *type*. As before, *type* refers to end-of-period (0 or omitted) versus beginning-of-period (1) cash flows. Letting F equal 2 and P equal -1, the **NPER** function *yields identical results to those obtained mathematically*:

a. =NPER(2%,,-1,2) =35.003 yrs

b. =NPER(3%,,-1,2)=23.450 yrs

c. =NPER(4%,,-1,2)=17.673 yrs

d. =NPER(6%,,-1,2)=11.896 yrs

e. =NPER(8%,,-1,2)=9.006 yrs

f. =NPER(12%,,-1,2)=6.116 yrs

To use the Excel® **GOAL SEEK** tool requires a spreadsheet, as shown in Figure 2.11. Letting x denote the row number in the spreadsheet, the parameters for **GOAL SEEK** are the following:

Set cell: Cx

To value: 2

By changing cell: Bx

Any number is entered in cell Bx, and the future value of \$1, invested at interest rate Ax for Bx years, is calculated using the Excel® **FV** worksheet function. Then, the Excel® **GOAL SEEK** tool is used to determine the value of Bx that makes C$x = 2$. The results obtained by **GOAL SEEK** are shown in Figure 2.11. Namely,

a. $n = 34.999$ yrs;

b. $n = 23.448$ yrs;

c. $n = 17.672$ yrs;

	A	B	C	D
C7			fx =FV(A7,B7,,-1)	
1	*i%*	*n*	*(F|P i%,n)*	**Excel's FV Function**
2	2%	34.99911185231	1.99985437960	**=FV(A2,B2,,-1)**
3	3%	23.44819333654	1.99990666057	**=FV(A3,B3,,-1)**
4	4%	17.67238866717	1.99995301273	**=FV(A4,B4,,-1)**
5	6%	11.89466421507	1.99988383488	**=FV(A5,B5,,-1)**
6	8%	9.00760138602	2.00017440810	**=FV(A6,B6,,-1)**
7	12%	6.11628834874	2.00000747394	**=FV(A7,B7,,-1)**
8				

Goal Seek [?][X]

Set cell: C7

To value: 2

By changing cell: B7

[OK] [Cancel]

FIGURE 2.11

The Excel® GOAL SEEK Tool Used to Solve Example 2.10.

d. $n = 11.895$ yrs;

e. $n = 9.008$ yrs; and

f. $n = 6.116$ yrs.

Notice, the values obtained using **GOAL SEEK** are not identical to those obtained mathematically or with the Excel® **NPER** worksheet function. **GOAL SEEK** uses a search procedure that can end prematurely (i.e., before obtaining an exact solution).

The same spreadsheet used with **GOAL SEEK** can be used with the Excel® **SOLVER** tool, as shown in Figure 2.12. The **SOLVER** parameters are the following:

Set Target Cell: C*x*

Equal To: ○ Max ○ Min ● Value of: 2

By Changing Cells:

B*x*

As with **GOAL SEEK**, any number is entered in cell B*x*, and the future value of $1, invested at interest rate A*x* for B*x* years, is calculated using the Excel® **FV** worksheet function. Then, the Excel® **SOLVER** tool is used to determine the value of B*x* that makes C*x* = 2, where *x* denotes the row number in the spreadsheet. The results obtained by **SOLVER** are shown in Figure 2.12. Namely,

a. $n = 35.003$ yrs;

b. $n = 23.450$ yrs;

c. $n = 17.673$ yrs;

d. $n = 11.896$ yrs;

e. $n = 9.006$ yrs; and

f. $n = 6.116$ yrs.

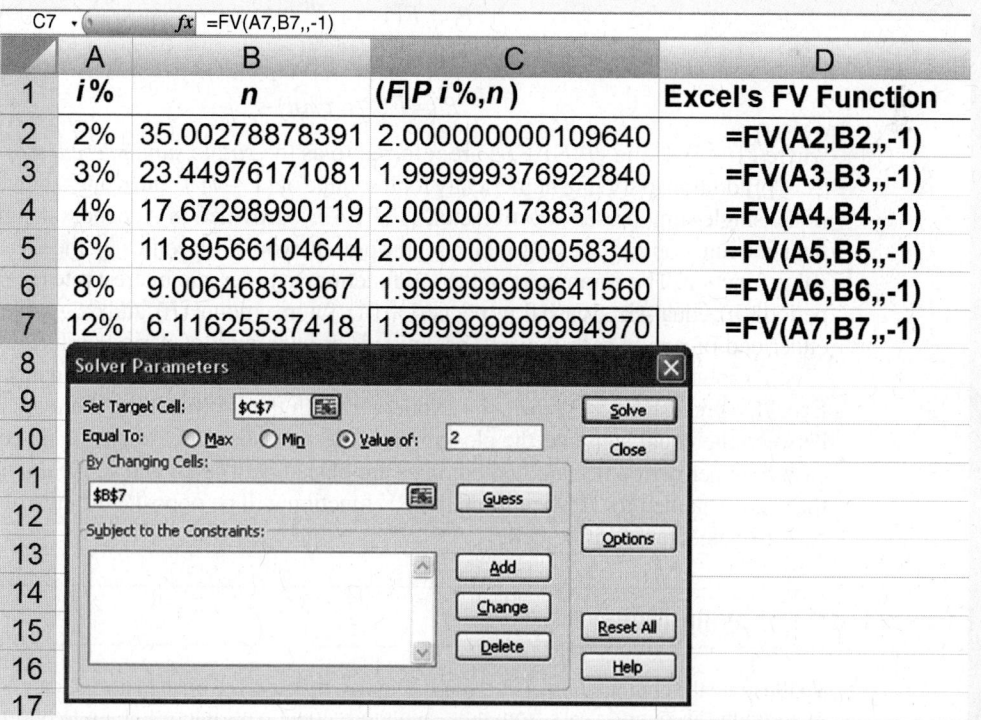

FIGURE 2.12
The Excel® SOLVER Tool Used to Solve Example 2.10.

The answers obtained using **SOLVER** differ from those obtained using the Excel® **GOAL SEEK** tool and **NPER** worksheet function, especially if the calculation is carried out to 8 or 10 decimal places. As with **GOAL SEEK**, **SOLVER** uses a search procedure to obtain a solution; it, too, can end prematurely, resulting in different values than obtained mathematically and with the Excel® **NPER** worksheet function. Of the six approaches to solving this example, only the mathematical one, using logarithms, and the Excel® **NPER** function yielded exact solutions.

Unfortunately, no rule of thumb exists for determining how long it takes to triple or quadruple an investment. However, the interest tables in Appendix A, a mathematical approach, and the Excel® **NPER** worksheet function can be used. (Again, the Excel® **GOAL SEEK** and **SOLVER** tools can be used, but they are not guaranteed to yield as accurate a solution as a mathematical approach or as accurate as can be obtained using the Excel® **NPER** worksheet function.) If one wants to know, for example, how long it will take for money to triple in value, then, mathematically, $n = \log(3)/\log(1 + i)$; or, in any cell of an Excel® spreadsheet, one can enter =NPER(i%,,-1,3) to determine the value of n that will triple the value of money.

Since we can determine values of F when given values of P, i, and n, it is a simple matter to determine the values of P when given values of F, i, and n. In particular, from Equation 2.6,

$$F = P(1 + i)^n \tag{2.8}$$

When dividing both sides of Equation 2.8 by $(1 + i)^n$, we find that the present worth and future worth have the relation,

$$P = F(1 + i)^{-n} \tag{2.9}$$

or

$$P = F(P|F\ i\%,n) \tag{2.10}$$

where $(1 + i)^{-n}$ and $(P|F\ i\%,n)$ are referred to as the *single sum, present worth factor*.

In addition to solving numerically for the value of $(1 + i)^{-n}$ and using tabulated values of the single sum, present worth factor, $(P|F\ i\%,n)$, provided in Appendix A, an Excel® financial function can be used to solve for the present worth—specifically, the **PV**, or present value function. The parameters of the **PV** function, in order, are interest rate (i), number of periods (n), equal-sized cash flow per period (A), future amount (F), and *type*, which denotes either end-of-period cash flows (0 or omitted) or beginning-of-period cash flows (1).

To solve for P when given i, n, and F, the following can be entered in any cell in an Excel® spreadsheet: =PV(i,n,,-F). Notice, as with the **FV** function, there are no spaces between the equal sign and the closing parenthesis; also, as before, since no equal-sized cash flow per period occurs, two commas are placed between n and F. Again, the sign of the value obtained for P when using the **PV** function will be opposite the sign of the value of F that is entered in the cell.

EXAMPLE 2.11 Saving Money

To illustrate the computation of P given F, i, and n, suppose you wish to accumulate $10,000 in a savings account 4 years from now, and the account pays interest at a rate of 5 percent compounded annually. How much must be deposited today?

	A	B	C	D
1				
2				
3				
4		$8,227.02 ←	=PV(5%,4,,-10000)	
5				
6		$8,227.02 ←	=PV(0.05,4,,-10000)	
7				
8		-$8,227.02 ←	=PV(5%,4,,10000)	
9				
10		-$8,227.02 ←	=PV(0.05,4,,10000)	
11				
12				
13				

FIGURE 2.13

The Excel® PV Financial Function Used with a Single Sum of Money.

Using the compound interest tables in Appendix A for 5 percent and 4 periods, the value of the single sum, present worth factor, $(P|F\,5\%,4)$, is shown to be 0.82270. Thus,

$$P = F(P|F\,5\%,4)$$
$$= \$10,000(0.82270)$$
$$= \$8,227.00$$

As shown in Figure 2.13, using the Excel® **PV** worksheet function,

$$P = PV(5\%,4,,-10000) = \$8227.02$$

(The 2¢ difference in the answers is due to round-off error in the tables in Appendix A.)

$$\left.\begin{array}{l} F = P(1+i)^{n} \\[4pt] F = P(F|P\,i\%,n) \\[4pt] F = FV(i\%,n,,-P) \end{array}\right\} \text{single sum, future worth factor}$$

$$\left.\begin{array}{l} P = F(1+i)^{-n} \\[4pt] P = F(P|F\,i\%,n) \\[4pt] P = PV(i\%,n,,-F) \end{array}\right\} \text{single sum, present worth factor}$$

2.4.2 Multiple Cash Flows

Most engineering economic analyses involve more than a single return occurring after an investment is made. In such cases, the present worth equivalent of the future cash flows can be determined by adding the present worths of the individual cash flows. Similarly, the future worth of multiple cash flows can be determined by adding the future worths of the individual cash flows. (Recall Rules 2, 3, and 4: money cannot be added or subtracted unless it occurs at the same point(s) in time; to move money forward one time unit, multiply by 1 plus the discount or interest rate; and to move money backward one time unit, divide by 1 plus the discount or interest rate.)

EXAMPLE 2.12   Determining the Economic Worths of Multiple Cash Flows

To illustrate how *DCF* methods can be applied to multiple cash flows, consider the *CFD* in Figure 2.14. A $100,000 investment produces returns of $50,000, $40,000, $30,000, $40,000, and $50,000 at the end of years (EOY) 1 through 5, respectively. Based on a 10 percent annual compound interest rate, what are the present worth and future worth equivalents for the multiple cash flows shown?

As shown in Table 2.5, using the tabulated values in Appendix A, the present worth equals $59,418.20, and the future worth equals $95,694. Using Excel®, the present worth

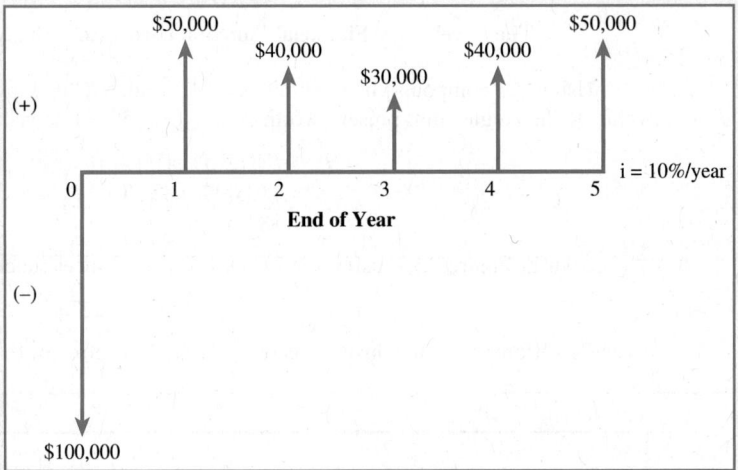

FIGURE 2.14
***CFD* for Example 2.12.**

TABLE 2.5
Present Worth and Future Worth Calculations for Example 2.12.

EOY (n)	Cash Flow (CF)	(P|F 10%,n)	Present Worth	PV (10%,n,,−CF)	(F|P 10%, 5−n)	Future Worth	FV(10%, 5−n,,−CF)
0	−$100,000	1.00000	−$100,000.00	−$100,000.00	1.61051	−$161,051.00	−$161,051.00
1	$50,000	0.90909	$45,454.50	$45,454.55	1.46410	$73,205.00	$73,205.00
2	$40,000	0.82645	$33,058.00	$33,057.85	1.33100	$53,240.00	$53,240.00
3	$30,000	0.75131	$22,539.30	$22,539.44	1.21000	$36,300.00	$36,300.00
4	$40,000	0.68301	$27,320.40	$27,320.54	1.10000	$44,000.00	$44,000.00
5	$50,000	0.62092	$31,046.00	$31,046.07	1.00000	$50,000.00	$50,000.00
SUM			$59,418.20	$59,418.45		$95,694.00	$95,694.00

equals \$59,418.45, and the future worth equals \$95,694. (The 25¢ difference in present worths is due to round-off error in the interest tables.)

Notice, the future value of the cash flow that occurs at the end of year 5 is the value of the cash flow, since the future value of the entire series of cash flows {−\$100,000, \$50,0000, \$40,000, \$30,000, \$40,000, \$50,000} occurs at the end of year 5.

Based on the results for Example 2.12, it is obvious how the present worth of a cash flow series can be obtained. In particular, if we let A_t denote the magnitude of a cash flow (receipt or disbursement) at the end of time period t, then

$$P = A_1(1+i)^{-1} + A_2(1+i)^{-2} + A_3(1+i)^{-3} + \cdots$$
$$+ A_{n-1}(1+i)^{-(n-1)} + A_n(1+i)^{-n} \tag{2.11}$$

or, using summation notation,

$$P = \sum_{t=1}^{n} A_t(1+i)^{-t} \tag{2.12}$$

or, equivalently,

$$P = \sum_{t=1}^{n} A_t(P|F\ i\%,t) \tag{2.13}$$

EXAMPLE 2.13 Computing the Present Worth of a Series of Cash Flows

Consider the series of cash flows depicted by the *CFD* given in Figure 2.15. Using an interest rate of 6 percent per interest period, the present worth equivalent is given by

$$P = \$300(P|F\ 6\%,1) - \$300(P|F\ 6\%,3) + \$200(P|F\ 6\%,4) + \$400(P|F\ 6\%,6)$$
$$+ \$200(P|F\ 6\%,8)$$
$$= \$300(0.94340) - \$300(0.83962) + \$200(0.79209) + \$400(0.70496)$$
$$+ \$200(0.62741)$$
$$= \$597.02$$

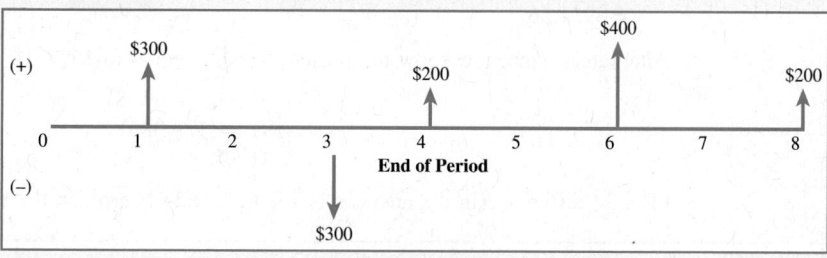

FIGURE 2.15
***CFD* of Multiple Cash Flows.**

The future worth equivalent of a cash flow series is equal to the sum of the future worth equivalents for the individual cash flows. Thus,

$$F = A_1(1+i)^{n-1} + A_2(1+i)^{n-2} + A_3(1+i)^{n-3} + \cdots$$
$$+ A_{n-2}(1+i)^2 + A_{n-1}(1+i) + A_n \tag{2.14}$$

or, using summation notation,

$$F = \sum_{t=1}^{n} A_t (1+i)^{n-t} \tag{2.15}$$

or, equivalently,

$$F = \sum_{t=1}^{n} A_t (F|P\,i\%,n-t) \tag{2.16}$$

Notice, in Equations 2.14 and 2.15, the exponent of the interest factor counts the number of periods between the cash flow and the time period where F is located. By convention, the future worth coincides in time with the nth or last cash flow; as such, it does not draw interest, as shown by A_n in Equation 2.14.

Alternately, since we know the value of future worth is given by

$$F = P(1+i)^n \tag{2.17}$$

substituting Equation 2.12 into Equation 2.17 yields

$$F = (1+i)^n \sum_{t=1}^{n} A_t (1+i)^{-t}$$

Hence,

$$F = \sum_{t=1}^{n} A_t (F|P\,i\%,n-t) \tag{2.18}$$

EXAMPLE 2.14   Determining the Future Worth of a Series of Cash Flows

Given the series of cash flows in Figure 2.15, determine the future worth at the end of the eighth period using an interest rate of 6 percent per interest period.

$$F = \$300(F|P\,6\%,7) - \$300(F|P\,6\%,5) + \$200(F|P\,6\%,4) + \$400(F|P\,6\%,2) + \$200$$
$$= \$300(1.50363) - \$300(1.33823) + \$200(1.26248) + \$400(1.12360) + \$200$$
$$= \$951.56$$

Alternately, since we know the present worth is equal to $597.04,

$$F = \$597.02(F|P\,6\%,8)$$
$$= \$597.04(1.59385)$$
$$= \$951.59$$

(The 3¢ difference in the answers is due to round-off error in the tables in Appendix A.)

Although we said it before, it bears repeating: Notice that in computing the future worth of a cash flow series, *the future worth amount obtained occurs at the end of time period n.* Thus, if a cash flow occurs at the end of the time period, it earns no interest in computing the future worth amount at the end of the nth period.

Obtaining the present worth and future worth equivalents of a cash flow series by summing the individual present worths and future worths, respectively, can be time-consuming if many cash flows are included in the series. However, the Excel® **NPV** financial function is well suited for determining the present worth of a series of cash flows. This function computes the net present value or net present worth of a specified range of cash flows. Importantly, *the value obtained occurs one time period prior to the first cash flow in the range given*. Its parameters, in order, are interest rate (*i*), followed by the individual cash flows.

EXAMPLE 2.15   Using Excel® to Compute the Present Worth of Multiple Cash Flows

Recall Example 2.12 in which $100,000 was invested and produced returns of $50,000, $40,000, $30,000, $40,000, and $50,000 over a 5-year period. The cash flow profile is provided in the spreadsheet shown in Figure 2.16. Based on a 10 percent interest rate, the following can be entered in any cell in the Excel® spreadsheet: =NPV(10%,C5: C9)+C4.

The range of cash flows to be included is denoted by **C5:C9**. Notice, because the **NPV** function provides the present worth one time period before the beginning point of the range of cash flows, C5 through C9, it coincides with C4. However, since the present worth does not include C4, its value must be added to the **NPV** calculation. As anticipated, the answer obtained, $59,418.45, is identical to that obtained using the **PV** function in Table 2.5.

However, the **NPV** function can be applied without creating a spreadsheet. For the example, the present worth can be obtained by making the following entry in any cell in an Excel® spreadsheet:

=NPV(10%,50000,40000,30000,40000,50000)-100000

The result, $59,418.45, is identical to that obtained using the approach depicted in Figure 2.16. Notice, as shown in the figure, we can determine the future worth of a cash flow series by embedding in the Excel® **FV** function the value obtained from the Excel® **NPV** function.

C10	▾	*fx* =NPV(10%,C5:C9)+C4			
	A	B	C	D	E	F
1						
2						
3		**End of Year (n)**	**Cash Flow (CF)**			
4		0	-$100,000			
5		1	$50,000			
6		2	$40,000			
7		3	$30,000			
8		4	$40,000			
9		5	$50,000			
10		P =	$59,418.45	●—●=NPV(10%,C5:C9)+C4		
11		F =	$95,694.00	●—●=FV(10%,5,,-C10)		
12						

FIGURE 2.16
The Excel® NPV and FV Financial Functions Used to Solve Example 2.15.

EXAMPLE 2.16   Using the Excel® NPV Function

Recall Example 2.13, depicted in Figure 2.15. The Excel® NPV worksheet function is well suited for such a problem. However, as shown in Figure 2.17, no blank cells can be included in the range of cash flows, and every time period must be accounted for. Finally, since the cash flow at time zero is, in fact, zero, there is no need to add the value of C3 to the NPV calculation. As before, the future worth can be obtained by using the NPV value. Notice, the value obtained for the present worth, $597.02, is within 2¢ of the value obtained in Example 2.13 using the interest tables in Appendix A, and the value obtained for the future worth, $951.56, is identical to the value obtained in Example 2.14 using the interest tables in Appendix A.

C12		fx	=NPV(6%,C4:C11)				
	A	B	C	D	E	F	G
1							
2		**End of Year (n)**	**Cash Flow (CF)**				
3		0	$0				
4		1	$300				
5		2	$0				
6		3	-$300				
7		4	$200				
8		5	$0				
9		6	$400				
10		7	$0				
11		8	$200				
12		P =	$597.02	=NPV(6%,C4:C11)			
13		F =	$951.56	=FV(6%,8,,-C12)			

FIGURE 2.17

The Excel® NPV and FV Financial Functions Used to Solve Example 2.13.

When there are many cash flows involved, solving for the present worth or future worth equivalent by treating each cash flow individually can be time consuming, particularly if a computer is not available. Fortunately, many cash flow series are "well behaved," allowing the use of shortcuts in determining the present worth and future worth. Three particular series come to mind: the uniform series, the gradient series, and the geometric series. They are defined mathematically as follows:

Uniform Series of Cash Flows

$$A_t = A \qquad t = 1, \ldots, n$$

Gradient Series of Cash Flows

$$A_t = (t - 1)G \qquad t = 1, \ldots, n$$

where G is defined as the magnitude of the gradient "step."

Geometric Series of Cash Flows

$$A_t = A_1(1+j)^{t-1} \quad t = 1,\ldots,n$$

where j is the percent change in the size of a cash flow from one time period to the next.

2.4.2.1 Uniform Series of Cash Flows

A uniform series of cash flows exists when all cash flows in a series are equally sized and spaced. In the case of a uniform series the present worth equivalent is given by

$$P = \sum_{t=1}^{n} A(1+i)^{-t} \tag{2.19}$$

where A is the magnitude of an individual cash flow in the series.

Letting $X = (1+i)^{-1}$ and bringing A outside the summation yields

$$P = A\sum_{t=1}^{n} X^t$$

$$= AX\sum_{t=1}^{n} X^{t-1}$$

Letting $h = t - 1$ gives the geometric series

$$P = AX\sum_{h=0}^{n-1} X^h \tag{2.20}$$

Since the summation in Equation 2.20 represents the first n terms of a geometric series, the closed-form value for the summation is given by

$$\sum_{h=0}^{n-1} X^h = \frac{1 - X^n}{1 - X} \tag{2.21}$$

Replacing X with $(1+i)^{-1}$ yields the following relationship between P and A:

$$P = A\frac{(1+i)^n - 1}{i(1+i)^n} \tag{2.22}$$

more commonly expressed as

$$P = A(P|A\,i\%,n) \tag{2.23}$$

where $(P|A\,i\%,n)$ is referred to as the *uniform series, present worth factor* and is tabulated in Appendix A for various values of i and n.

EXAMPLE 2.17   Computing the Present Worth of a Uniform Series of Cash Flows

Troy Long wishes to deposit a single sum of money in a savings account so that five equal annual withdrawals of $2,000 can be made before depleting the fund. If the first withdrawal is to occur 1 year after the deposit and the fund pays interest at a rate of 5 percent compounded annually, how much should he deposit?

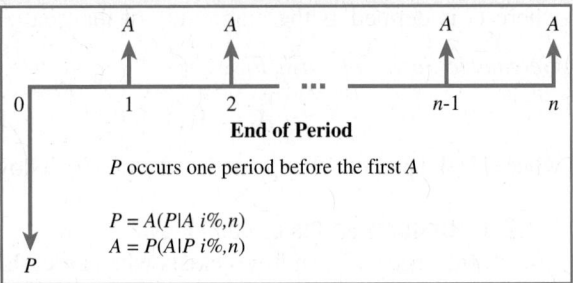

FIGURE 2.18

CFD **of the Relationship Between P and A in a Loan Transaction.**

Because of the relationship of *P* and *A*, as depicted in Figure 2.18, in which *P* occurs one period before the first *A*, we see that

$$P = \$2,000(P|A\,5\%,5)$$
$$= \$2,000(4.32948)$$
$$= \$8,658.96$$

Thus, if $8,658.96 is deposited in a fund paying 5 percent compounded annually, then five equal annual withdrawals of $2,000 can be made. After the fifth withdrawal, the fund will be depleted.

The Excel® **PV** function can be used to determine the present worth of a uniform series. Recall, when we used the **PV** function previously, we included two commas in consecutive order because equal-sized cash flows per period were not present for the application. Now, with a uniform series of cash flows being present, an entry is required for the third parameter (*A*). Therefore, when the present worth of a uniform series is desired, given *i*, *n*, and *A*, the following can be entered in any cell in an Excel® spreadsheet: $=$**PV**$(i,n, -A)$. As before, a negative sign is used for *A* because the **PV** function reverses the sign of *A* when calculating the value of *P*.

Using the Excel® **PV** worksheet function,

$$P = \textbf{PV}(5\%,5,\text{-}2000) = \$8,658.95$$

(The 1¢ difference in the answers is due to round-off error in the tables in Appendix A.)

EXAMPLE 2.18 Computing the Present Worth of a Delayed Uniform Series of Cash Flows

In Example 2.17, suppose the first withdrawal does not occur until 3 years after the deposit. How much should be deposited?

As depicted in Figure 2.19, the value of *P* to be determined occurs at $t = 0$, whereas a straightforward application of the $(P|A\,5\%,5)$ factor will yield a single sum equivalent at $t = 2$, one period before the first *A*. Hence, to determine the present worth, the value obtained after using the $(P|A\,5\%,5)$ factor must be moved backward in time 2 years. The latter operation is performed using the $(P|F\,5\%,2)$ factor. Therefore,

$$P = \$2,000(P|A\,5\%,5)(P|F\,5\%,2)$$
$$= \$2,000(4.32948)(0.90703)$$
$$= \$7,853.94$$

Delaying the first withdrawal for 2 years reduces the amount of the deposit by $8,658.96 − $7,853.94 = $805.02.

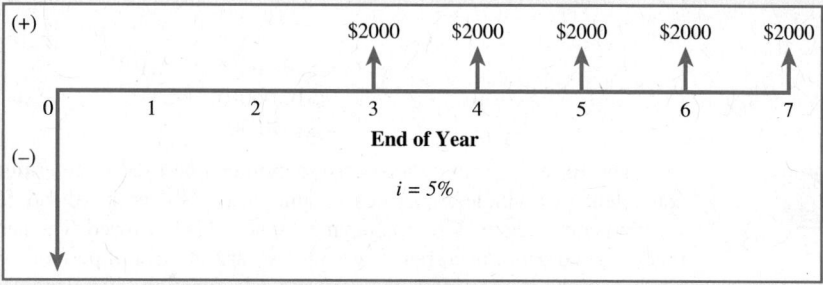

FIGURE 2.19
CFD **for Example 2.18.**

 Again, the Excel® **PV** function can be used to determine the present worth for this example. The example also provides an opportunity to show how an Excel® worksheet function can be embedded in another Excel® worksheet function. Specifically, for this example, the following can be entered in any cell in an Excel® spreadsheet:

$$P = PV(5\%,2,,-PV(5\%,5,-2000)) = \$7853.93$$

(The 1¢ difference in the answers is due to round-off error in the tables in Appendix A.)

Notice, two **PV** function calculations are performed; we will refer to them as the "outside" **PV** function and the "inside," or embedded, **PV** function. By entering two commas in the outside **PV** function, the next entry is a single sum, future worth amount. (Notice, as before, the use of a negative sign.) Instead of entering a dollar amount for the single sum, future worth amount, we entered the inside **PV** function to calculate the present worth of the uniform series over time periods 3 through 7. Since the value obtained by the inside **PV** function occurred at the end of the second time period, a value of 2 was entered for n in the outside **PV** function.

The reciprocal relationship between P and A can be expressed as

$$A = P\frac{i(1+i)^n}{(1+i)^n - 1} \tag{2.24}$$

or as

$$A = P(A|P\,i\%,n) \tag{2.25}$$

The expression $(A|P\,i\%,n)$ is called the *capital recovery factor,* since it provides the annual savings or recovery of funds (A) required to justify the capital investment (P). The $(A|P\,i\%,n)$ factor is used frequently in both personal financing and in comparing economic investment alternatives.

EXAMPLE 2.19 What Size Uniform Withdrawals Can Occur?

Suppose Rachel Townsley deposits $10,000 into an account that pays 8 percent interest compounded annually. If she withdraws 10 equal annual amounts from the account, with the first withdrawal occurring 1 year after the deposit, how much can she withdraw each year in order to deplete the fund with the last withdrawal?

Since we know that A and P are related by

$$A = P(A|P\,i\%,n)$$

then

$$A = \$10,000(A|P\ 8\%,10)$$
$$= \$10,000(0.14903)$$
$$= \$1490.30$$

The Excel® **PMT** worksheet function can be used to determine the uniform series equivalent to a single sum, present amount. (**PMT** is shorthand for "payment.") This function computes the size of a payment when P is borrowed. The parameters of the **PMT** function, in order of occurrence, are interest rate, number of periods, present amount, future amount, and *type*. As with the **PV** and **FV** functions, *type* indicates end-of-period or beginning-of-period. To obtain the uniform series equivalent of a single sum, present amount, the latter two parameters are omitted.

Using the Excel® **PMT** worksheet function,

$$A = \text{PMT}(8\%,10,-10000) = \$1490.29$$

(The 1¢ difference in the answers is due to round-off error in the tables in Appendix A.)

EXAMPLE 2.20 Repaying a Loan with Equal Annual Payments

A firm borrows $2,000,000 at 12 percent annual interest and pays it back with 10 equal annual payments. What will be the size of its annual payments?

To answer the question, we apply Equation 2.25,

$$A = \$2,000,000(A|P\ 12\%,10)$$
$$= \$2,000,000(0.17698)$$
$$= \$353,960$$

Using the Excel® **PMT** worksheet function,

$$A = \text{PMT}(12\%,10,-2000000) = \$353,968.33$$

(The $8.33 difference in the answers is due to round-off error in the tables in Appendix A.)

EXAMPLE 2.21 Lowering the Interest Rate by Extending the Loan Period

Continuing with the loan described in Example 2.20, suppose the firm decides to extend the payment period in order to obtain a lower interest rate. Specifically, suppose it agrees to pay back the loan over 15 years in order to obtain a 10 percent interest rate. What would be the size of the annual payment?

As before, we apply Equation 2.25:

$$A = \$2,000,000(A|P\ 10\%,15)$$
$$= \$2,000,000(0.13147)$$
$$= \$262,940$$

Using the Excel® **PMT** worksheet function,

$$A = \text{PMT}(10\%,15,-2000000) = \$262,947.55$$

Based on the Excel® results, extending the loan period 5 years reduced the size of the annual payment by $91,020 or, using Excel®, **$91,020.78**.

EXAMPLE 2.22   Determining the Size of Delayed Uniform Withdrawals

Suppose, in Example 2.19, the first withdrawal is delayed for 2 years, as depicted in Figure 2.20. How much can be withdrawn each of the 10 years?

The amount in the fund at $t = 2$ equals

$$
\begin{aligned}
V_2 &= \$10{,}000(F|P\,8\%,2) \\
&= \$10{,}000(1.16640) \\
&= \$11{,}664
\end{aligned}
$$

Therefore, the size of the equal annual withdrawal will be

$$
\begin{aligned}
A &= \$11{,}664.00(A|P\,8\%,10) \\
&= \$11{,}664.00(0.14903) \\
&= \$1{,}738.29
\end{aligned}
$$

Thus, delaying the first withdrawal for 2 years increases the size of each withdrawal by $247.99.

The Excel® **FV** worksheet function can be used to determine the future worth of a uniform series. To solve the example problem, one Excel® worksheet function will be embedded in another. Specifically, the following can be entered in any cell in an Excel® spreadsheet:

$$A = \text{PMT}(8\%,10,\text{-FV}(8\%,2,,\text{-}10000)) = \$1{,}738.28$$

(The 1¢ difference in the answers is due to round-off error in the tables in Appendix A.)

Notice, in this case, the **FV** function was embedded in the **PMT** function. The "inside" financial function calculated the future value of $10,000 moved forward 2 years at 8 percent annual compound interest.

Instead of using the embedded approach, separate Excel® calculations could be performed, as shown below:

$$V_2 = \text{FV}(8\%,2,,\text{-}10000) = \$11{,}664.00$$

$$A = \text{PMT}(8\%,10,\text{-}11664) = \$1{,}738.28$$

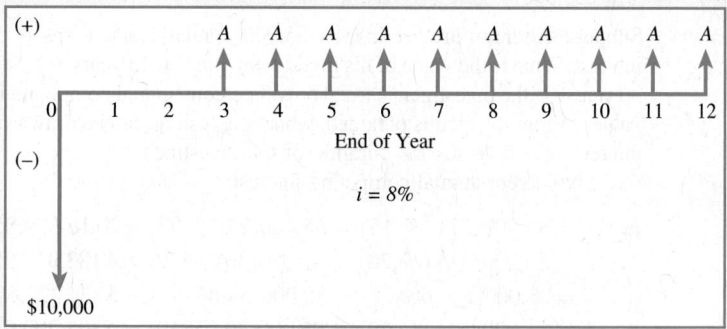

FIGURE 2.20

CFD **for the Deferred Payment Example.**

Relationships among *P*, *F*, and *A*

- *P* occurs at the same time as A_0, i.e., at $t = 0$
- *F* occurs at the same time as A_n, i.e., at $t = n$

The future worth of a uniform series is obtained by recalling that

$$F = P(1 + i)^n \qquad (2.26)$$

Substituting Equation 2.22 into Equation 2.26 for P and reducing yields

$$F = A\frac{(1 + i)^n - 1}{i} \qquad (2.27)$$

or, equivalently,

$$F = A(F|A\ i\%,n) \qquad (2.28)$$

where $(F|A\ i\%,n)$ is referred to as the *uniform series, future worth factor.*

EXAMPLE 2.23 Determining the Future Worth of a Uniform Series of Cash Flows

If Luis Jimenez makes annual deposits of $1,000 into a savings account for 30 years, how much will be in the fund immediately after his last deposit if the fund pays 6 percent interest compounded annually?

$$F = \$1,000(F|A\ 6\%,30)$$
$$= \$1,000(79.05819)$$
$$= \$79,058.19$$

 The Excel® **FV** worksheet function can be used to determine the future worth of a uniform series. Using the Excel® **FV** worksheet function,

$$F = \mathbf{FV(6\%,30,\text{-}1000) = \$79,058.19}$$

EXAMPLE 2.24 What a Difference 5 Years Make!

Suppose Andrew Brewer invests $5,000 annually and earns 6 percent annual compound interest. What is the value of his investment after (a) 15 years, (b) 20 years, (c) 25 years, and (d) 30 years? If the investment earned only 3 percent annual compound interest, what would be the values? From the results obtained, what conclusions can be drawn regarding the impact of the interest earned versus the duration of the investment?

Six percent annual compound interest:

a. $F = \$5,000(F|A\ 6\%,15) = \$5,000(23.27597) = \$116,379.85$
b. $F = \$5,000(F|A\ 6\%,20) = \$5,000(36.78559) = \$183,927.95$
c. $F = \$5,000(F|A\ 6\%,25) = \$5,000(54.86451) = \$274,322.55$
d. $F = \$5,000(F|A\ 6\%,30) = \$5,000(79.05819) = \$395,290.95$

Three percent annual compound interest:

a. $F = \$5,000(F|A\ 3\%,15) = \$5,000(18.59891) = \$92,994.55$
b. $F = \$5,000(F|A\ 3\%,20) = \$5,000(26.87037) = \$134,351.85$
c. $F = \$5,000(F|A\ 3\%,25) = \$5,000(36.45926) = \$182,296.30$
d. $F = \$5,000(F|A\ 3\%,30) = \$5,000(47.57542) = \$237,877.10$

The single sum, compound amount factor, $(1 + i)^n$, answers the question regarding the impact of the interest earned versus the investment's duration. Because the duration (n) is in the exponent, time is far more critical than the interest rate earned on investments. For that reason, it is essential that an individual begin investing sooner rather than later.

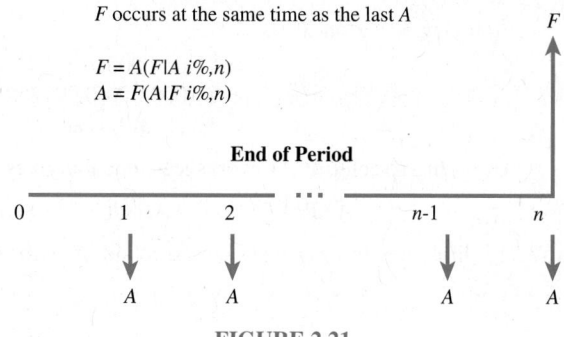

F occurs at the same time as the last A

$F = A(F|A\ i\%,n)$

$A = F(A|F\ i\%,n)$

End of Period

FIGURE 2.21

CFD of the Relationship Between A and F in an Investment Scenario.

The reciprocal relationship between A and F is easily obtained from Equation 2.27. Specifically, we find that

$$A = F\frac{i}{(1 + i)^n - 1} \tag{2.29}$$

or, equivalently,

$$A = F(A|F\ i\%,n) \tag{2.30}$$

The expression $(A|F\ i\%,n)$ is referred to as the *sinking fund factor*, since it is used to determine the size of a deposit to place (sink) in a fund in order to accumulate a desired future amount. As depicted in Figure 2.21, F *occurs at the same time as the last* A. Thus, the last A or deposit earns no interest.

EXAMPLE 2.25   **Determining Annual Investment Requirements to Achieve an Investment Goal**

If Coby Durham wishes to accumulate $1,500,000 in 25 years, how much must he deposit annually in a fund paying 7 percent interest compounded annually in order to accumulate the desired amount immediately after making the last deposit?

$$A = \$1,500,000(A|F\ 7\%,25) = \$1,500,000(0.01581) = \$23,715$$

The Excel® **PMT** worksheet function can be used to determine the uniform series equivalent to a single sum, future amount. The following can be entered in any cell in an Excel® spreadsheet:

$$A = \text{PMT}(7\%,25,,-1500000) = \$23,715.78$$

(The 78¢ difference in answers is due to round-off error in the tables in Appendix A.)

EXAMPLE 2.26   **Who Wants to Be a Millionaire?**

Suppose Crystal Wilson wants to accumulate $1,000,000 by the time she retires in 40 years. If she earns 10 percent on her investments, how much must she invest each year in order to realize her goal?

Applying Equation 2.30,

$$A = \$1,000,000(A|F,10\%,40)$$
$$= \$1,000,000(0.0022594)$$
$$= \$2,259.40/\text{year}$$

Using the Excel® **PMT** worksheet function gives

$$A = \text{PMT}(10\%,40,,-1000000) = \$2,259.41/\text{year}$$

(The 1¢ difference in answers is due to round-off error in the tables in Appendix A.)

Thus far, we have solved for F when given P; solved for P when given F; solved for P when given A; solved for A when given P; solved for F when given A; and solved for A when given F. We did so by using compound interest factors and tabulated values in Appendix A, as well as by using the Excel® **PV**, **FV**, and **PMT** functions. What about solving for, say, A when given P and F? The following example illustrates how the Excel® worksheet functions can be applied when two of the three cash flows (P, A, and F) are given.

EXAMPLE 2.27 Applying the Excel® PV, FV, and PMT Functions

An electronics manufacturing company acquired a surface mount placement (SMP) machine in order to increase productivity, reduce annual operating costs, and improve quality of the printed circuit board assemblies it produced. The $500,000 investment produced annual savings of $92,500. At the end of the 10-year planning horizon, the SMP machine was sold for $50,000. Based on a 10 percent *TVOM*, what single sum of money at time zero (P) is equivalent to the cash flows that occurred with the investment? What single sum of money at the end of the planning horizon (F) is equivalent to the cash flows? What uniform annual series (A) is equivalent to the cash flows?

Solving for P when given i, n, A, and F, with Excel®:

$$P = \text{PV}(10\%,10,-92500,-50000)-500000 = \$87,649.62$$

Solving for F when given i, n, P, and A, with Excel®:

$$F = \text{FV}(10\%,10,-92500,500000)+50000 = \$227,340.55$$

Solving for A when given i, n, P, and F, with Excel®:

$$A = \text{PMT}(10\%,10,500000,-50000)+92500 = \$14,264.57$$

We return to this example in Chapters 5 through 13.

$P = A\left[\dfrac{(1+i)^n - 1}{i(1+i)^n}\right]$	uniform series, present worth factor $= A(P|A\ i\%,n) = \text{PV}(i\%,n,\text{-A})$
$A = P\left[\dfrac{i(1+i)^n}{(1+i)^n - 1}\right]$	uniform series, capital recovery factor $= P(A|P\ i\%,n) = \text{PMT}(i\%,n,\text{-P})$
$F = A\left[\dfrac{(1+i)^n - 1}{i}\right]$	uniform series, future worth factor $= A(F|A\ i\%,n) = \text{FV}(i\%,n,\text{-A})$
$A = F\left[\dfrac{i}{(1+i)^n - 1}\right]$	uniform series, sinking fund factor $= F(A|F\ i\%,n) = \text{PMT}(i\%,n,,\text{-F})$

2.4.2.2 Gradient Series of Cash Flows

A gradient series of cash flows occurs when the value of a given cash flow is greater than the value of the previous cash flow by a constant amount, G, *the gradient step*. Consider the series of cash flows depicted in Figure 2.22. The series can be represented by the sum of a uniform series and a gradient series. By convention, *the gradient series is defined to have the first positive cash flow occur at the end of the second time period*. The size of the cash flow in the gradient series occurring at the end of period t is given by

$$A_t = (t-1)G \quad t = 1, \ldots, n \tag{2.31}$$

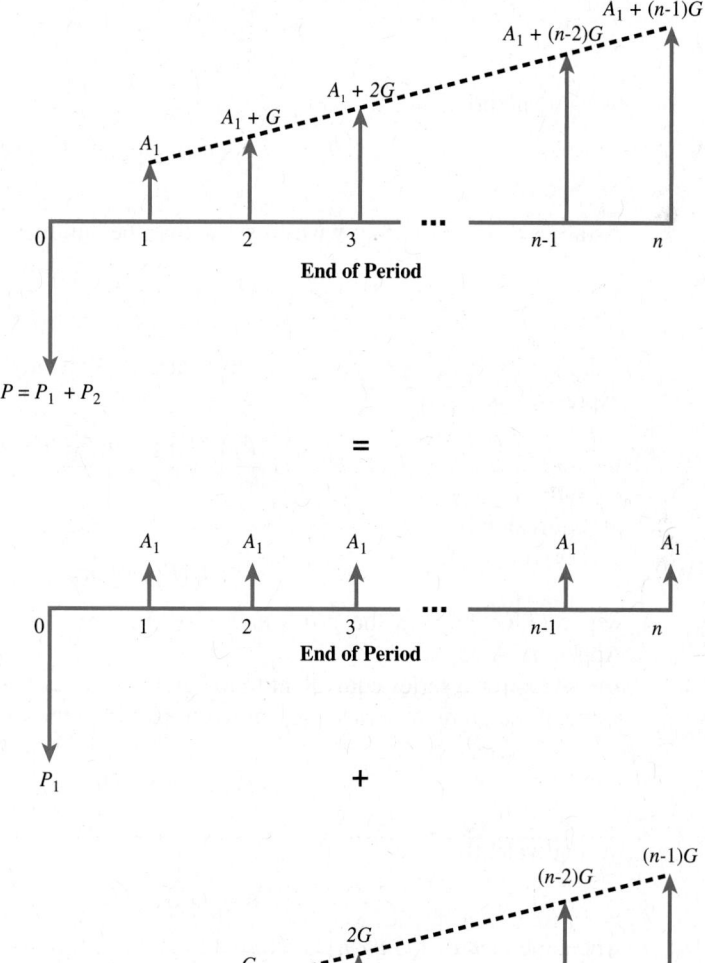

FIGURE 2.22

***CFD* of a Combination of Uniform and Gradient Series in an Investment Scenario.**

The gradient series arises when the value of an individual cash flow differs from the preceding cash flow by a constant, G. As an illustration, if an individual receives an annual bonus and the size of the bonus increases by \$100 each year, then the series is gradient. Also, operating and maintenance costs tend to increase over time because of inflation effects and a gradual deterioration of equipment; such costs are often approximated by a gradient series.

The present worth equivalent of a gradient series is obtained by recalling

$$P = \sum_{t=1}^{n} A_t(1+i)^{-t} \tag{2.32}$$

Substituting Equation 2.31 into Equation 2.32 gives

$$P = \sum_{t=1}^{n} (t-1)G(1+i)^{-t} \tag{2.33}$$

or, equivalently,

$$P = G \sum_{t=1}^{n} (t-1)(1+i)^{-t} \tag{2.34}$$

As an exercise, you may wish to show that the summation reduces to

$$P = G\left[\frac{1 - (1+ni)(1+i)^{-n}}{i^2}\right] \tag{2.35}$$

Taking advantage of interest factors already developed, Equation 2.36 can be expressed as

$$P = G\frac{(P|A\ i\%,n) - n(P|F\ i\%,n)}{i} \tag{2.36}$$

or, equivalently,

$$P = G(P|G\,i\%,n) \tag{2.37}$$

where $(P|G\ i\%,n)$ is the *gradient series, present worth factor* and is tabulated in Appendix A.

A uniform series equivalent to the gradient series is obtained by multiplying the value of the gradient series, present worth factor by the value of the $(A|P\ i\%,n)$ factor:

$$A = G\left[\frac{1}{i} - \frac{n}{i}(A|F\ i\%,n)\right]$$

or, equivalently,

$$A = G(A|G\,i\%,n) \tag{2.38}$$

where the factor $(A|G\ i\%,n)$ is referred to as the *gradient-to-uniform series conversion factor* and is tabulated in Appendix A.

To obtain the future worth equivalent of a gradient series at time n, multiply the value of the $(A|G\ i\%,n)$ factor by the value of the $(F|A\ i\%,n)$ factor to obtain the $(F|G\ i\%,n)$ factor:

$$F = G\left[\frac{(1+i)^n - (1+ni)}{i^2}\right] \tag{2.39}$$

(The $(F|G\ i\%,n)$ *gradient series, future worth* factor is *not* tabulated in Appendix A.)

Often a cash flow series is the sum or difference of a uniform series and a gradient series. To determine the present and future worth equivalents of such a composite, one can deal with each special type of series separately.

EXAMPLE 2.28   Determining the Present Worth of a Gradient Series (Sitting on Top of a Uniform Series)

Maintenance costs for a particular production machine increase by $1,000/year over the 5-year life of the equipment. The initial maintenance cost is $3,000. Using an interest rate of 8 percent compounded annually, determine the present worth equivalent for the maintenance costs.

As shown in Figure 2.23, the cash flow series consists of the sum of a $3,000 uniform series and a $1,000 gradient series. Converting the gradient series to an equivalent uniform series gives

$$A_G = \$1,000(A|G\,8\%,5)$$
$$= \$1,000(1.84647)$$
$$= \$1,846.47$$

(*Notice that* n *equals 5 even though only four positive cash flows are present in the gradient series.*)

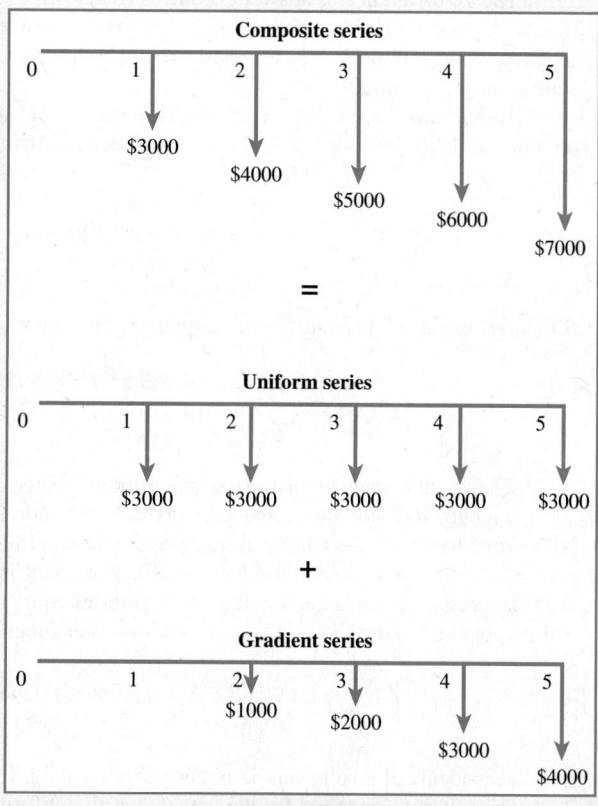

FIGURE 2.23
***CFD* for Example 2.28.**

Adding the "converted" uniform series to the "base" uniform series gives $A = \$1,846.47 +$ \$3,000, or \$4,846.47. Therefore, converting the uniform series to its present worth equivalent,

$$
\begin{aligned}
P &= \$4,846.47(P|A\ 8\%,5) \\
&= \$4,846.47(3.99271) \\
&= \$19,350.55
\end{aligned}
$$

Alternately, the "base" uniform series can be converted to a present worth equivalent:

$$
\begin{aligned}
P_U &= \$3,000(P|A\ 8\%,5) \\
&= \$3,000(3.99271) \\
&= \$11,978.13
\end{aligned}
$$

Next, the gradient series can be converted to its present worth equivalent:

$$
\begin{aligned}
P_G &= \$1,000(P|G\ 8\%,5) \\
&= \$1,000(7.37243) \\
&= \$7,372.43
\end{aligned}
$$

Hence, the present worth equivalent of the maintenance costs will be

$$
\begin{aligned}
P &= P_U + P_G \\
&= \$11,978.13 + \$7,372.43 \\
&= \$19,350.56
\end{aligned}
$$

(The 1¢ difference in answers is due to round-off error in the tables in Appendix A.) Notice, the first approach to determining the present worth equivalent produced the uniform series equivalent of the cash flow series given in Figure 2.23. In particular, the uniform series equivalent is \$4,846.50.

To determine the future worth equivalent, we can use either the uniform series or present worth equivalent. Using the uniform series equivalent gives

$$
\begin{aligned}
F &= \$4,846.47(F|A\ 8\%,5) \\
&= \$4,846.47(5.86660) \\
&= \$28,432.30
\end{aligned}
$$

Similarly, using the present worth equivalent, the future worth equivalent is

$$
\begin{aligned}
F &= \$19,350.55(F|P\ 8\%,5) \\
&= \$19,350.55(1.46933) \\
&= \$28,432.34
\end{aligned}
$$

(The 4¢ difference in answers is due to round-off error in the tables in Appendix A.) Excel® does not have a special worksheet function for gradient series. However, the NPV worksheet function can be used. Specifically, the following entry can be made in any cell: =NPV(8%,3000,4000,5000,6000,7000). The result is a present worth of \$19,350.56; once the present worth is known, the uniform series equivalent and future worth equivalent can be obtained using the PMT and FV worksheet functions:

$$
P = \text{PMT}(8\%,5,-19350.56) = \$4846.47
$$
$$
F = \text{FV}(8\%,5,-19350.56) = \$28,432.32
$$

Near-identical results can be obtained by creating a spreadsheet, as shown in Figure 2.24. The solutions obtained for the present worth, uniform series, and future worth values for the gradient series are, respectively, \$19,350.56, \$4,846.47, and \$28,432.31. (The future worths differ by 1¢ due to round-off errors.)

| C11 ▾ | *fx* =FV(8%,5,-C10) | | | |

	A	B	C	D	E
1					
2		**End of Year (n)**	**Cash Flow (CF)**		
3		0	$0		
4		1	$3,000		
5		2	$4,000		
6		3	$5,000		
7		4	$6,000		
8		5	$7,000		
9		**P =**	$19,350.56	●—●**=NPV(8%,C4:C8)**	
10		**A =**	$4,846.47	●—●**=PMT(8%,5,-C9)**	
11		**F =**	$28,432.31	●—●**=FV(8%,5,-C10)**	
12					

FIGURE 2.24
Excel® Solution to Example 2.28.

EXAMPLE 2.29 Determining the Future Worth of a Decreasing Gradient Series

Amanda Dearman makes five annual deposits into a fund that pays 8 percent interest compounded annually. Her first deposit equals $800; her second deposit equals $700; her third deposit equals $600; her fourth deposit equals $500; and her fifth deposit equals $400. Determine the amount in the fund immediately after the fifth deposit.

As depicted by the *CFDs* in Figure 2.25, the cash flow series can be represented by the difference in a uniform series of $800 and a gradient series of $100. The uniform series equivalent of the gradient series is given by

$$A = \$100(A|G\,8\%,5)$$
$$= \$100(1.84647)$$
$$= \$184.65$$

Therefore, a uniform series having cash flows equal to $800 − $184.65, or $615.35, is equivalent to the original cash flow series. The future worth equivalent is found to be

$$F = \$615.35(F|A\,8\%,5)$$
$$= \$615.35(5.86660)$$
$$= \$3,610.01$$

Using a combination of the **FV** and **NPV** worksheet functions, the future worth for the decreasing gradient series can be determined by entering the following in any cell:

=FV(8%,5,,-NPV(8%,800,700,600,500,400))

The future worth obtained, $3,610.03, is identical to that which resulted from using the spreadsheet approach depicted in Figure 2.26.

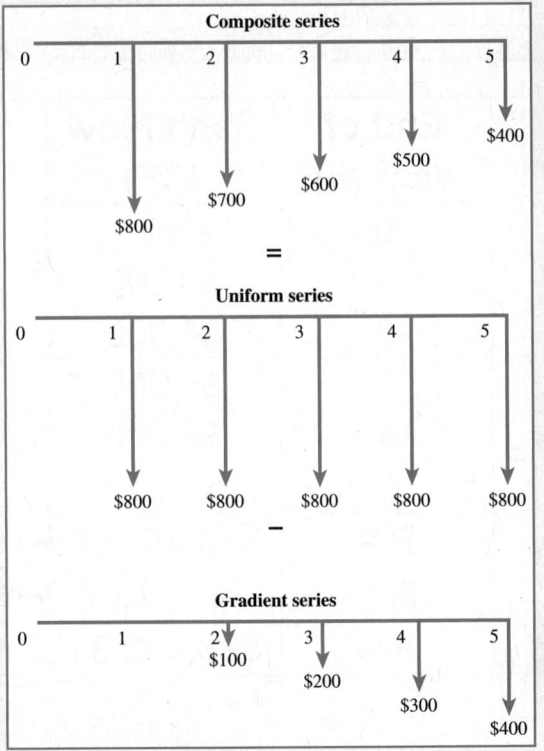

FIGURE 2.25

***CFD* for the decreasing gradient series in Example 2.29.**

	A	B	C	D	E	F	G
			fx =NPV(8%,C4:C8)				
1							
2		**End of Year (n)**	**Cash Flow (CF)**				
3		0	$0				
4		1	$800				
5		2	$700				
6		3	$600				
7		4	$500				
8		5	$400				
9		P =	$2,456.93	=NPV(8%,C4:C8)			
10		F =	$3,610.03	=FV(8%,5,,-C9)			

FIGURE 2.26

Excel® Solution to Example 2.29.

Question: What if the five cash flows occurred in reverse order (i.e., what if the cash flow series were {$400, $500, $600, $700, $800})? Would the future worth be greater than, less than, or equal to the future worth of the series {$800, $700, $600, $500, $400}? What does your intuition suggest?

Answer: The future worth of the increasing gradient series will be less than that for the decreasing gradient series. Why? The annual worth equivalent for the increasing gradient series equals the sum of $400 and $184.65, or $584.65, which is less than the uniform series equivalent for the decreasing gradient series ($615.35). Therefore, the future worth equivalent will also be less.

$$P = G\left[\frac{1 - (1 + ni)(1 + i)^{-n}}{i^2}\right]$$ gradient series, present worth factor
$$= G(P|G\,i\%,n)$$

$$A = G\left[\frac{(1 + i)^n - (1 + ni)}{i[(1 + i)^n - 1]}\right]$$ gradient-to-uniform series conversion factor
$$= G(A|G\,i\%,n)$$

$$F = G\left[\frac{(1 + i)^n - (1 + ni)}{i^2}\right]$$ gradient series, future worth factor
$$= A(F|G\,i\%,n)$$

2.4.2.3 Geometric Series of Cash Flows

The geometric cash flow series, as depicted in Figure 2.27, occurs when the size of a cash flow increases (decreases) by a fixed percent from one time period to the next. If j denotes the percent change in a cash flow's size from one period to the next, the size of the tth cash flow can be given by

$$A_t = A_{t-1}(1 + j) \quad t = 2, \ldots, n$$

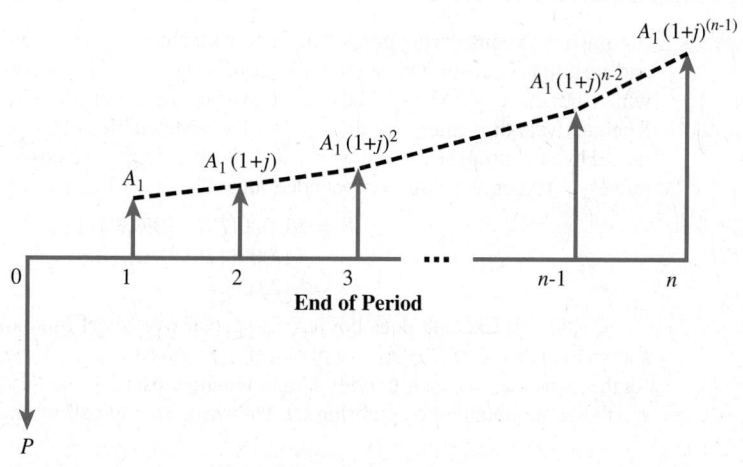

FIGURE 2.27

***CFD* for a Geometric Series.**

or, more conveniently,

$$A_t = A_1(1 + j)^{t-1} \quad t = 1, \ldots, n \tag{2.40}$$

The geometric series is used to represent the growth (positive j) or decay (negative j) of costs and revenues undergoing annual percentage changes. As an illustration, if labor costs increase by 10 percent a year, then the resulting series representation of labor costs will be geometric.

The present worth equivalent of the cash flow series is obtained by substituting Equation 2.39 into Equation 2.12 to obtain

$$P = \sum_{t=1}^{n} A_1(1 + j)^{t-1}(1 + i)^{-t}$$

or

$$P = A_1(1 + j)^{-1}\sum_{t=1}^{n}(1 + j)^{t}(1 + i)^{-t} \tag{2.41}$$

As an exercise, you may wish to show that the following relationship results:

$$P = \begin{cases} A_1 \dfrac{1 - (1 + j)^{n}(1 + i)^{-n}}{i - j} & i \neq j \\ nA_1/(1 + i) & i = j \end{cases} \tag{2.42}$$

or

$$P = A_1(P|A_1\ i\%,j\%,n) \tag{2.43}$$

where $(P|A_1 i\%,j\%,n)$ is the *geometric series, present worth factor* and is tabulated in Appendix A for various values of i, j, and n.

For the case of $j \geq 0$ and $i \neq j$, the relationship between P and A can be conveniently expressed in terms of compound interest factors previously considered.

$$P = A_1\left[\frac{1 - (F|P\ j\%,n)(P|F\ i\%,n)}{i - j}\right] \quad i \neq j,\ j \geq 0 \tag{2.44}$$

EXAMPLE 2.30 Determining the Present Worth of a Geometric Series

A company is considering purchasing a new machine tool. In addition to the initial purchase and installation costs, management is concerned about the machine's maintenance costs, which are expected to be $1,000 at the end of the first year of the machine's life and increase 8 percent/year thereafter. The machine tool's expected life is 15 years. Company management would like to know the present worth equivalent for expected costs. If the firm's time value of money is 10 percent/year compounded annually, what is the present worth equivalent?

$$\begin{aligned} P &= \$1,000(P|A_1\ 10\%,8\%,15) \\ &= \$1,000(12.03040) \\ &= \$12,030.40 \end{aligned}$$

 Although Excel® does not have a special worksheet function for geometric series, as shown in Figure 2.28, the **NPV** worksheet function can be used to compute the present worth for the increasing geometric series of maintenance costs, **$12,030.40**. Alternatively, the present worth can be obtained by entering the following in any cell of an Excel® spreadsheet:

=1000*NPV(10%,1,1.08,1.08^2,1.08^3,1.08^4,1.08^5,1.08^6,1.08^7,1.08^
8,1.08^9,1.08^10,1.08^11,1.08^12,1.08^13,1.08^14).

| | C19 | ▾ | fx | =NPV(10%,C4:C18) | | | | | | |

	A	B	C	D	E	F	G	H	I	J
1										
2		**End of Year (n)**	**Cash Flow (CF)**							
3		0	$0							
4		1	$1,000							
5		2	$1,080							
6		3	$1,166							
7		4	$1,260							
8		5	$1,360							
9		6	$1,469							
10		7	$1,587							
11		8	$1,714							
12		9	$1,851							
13		10	$1,999							
14		11	$2,159							
15		12	$2,332	●———	=C14*1.08					
16		13	$2,518							
17		14	$2,720							
18		15	$2,937							
19		**P =**	$12,030.40	●——●	=NPV(10%,C4:C18)					

FIGURE 2.28
Excel® Solution to Example 2.30.

The resulting present worth, **$12,030.40**, is identical to that obtained using the spreadsheet approach in Figure 2.28. (When more than 10 values are included in the range of cash flows, the spreadsheet approach is much preferred to entering the individual cash flow values in the **NPV** worksheet function.)

The future worth equivalent of the geometric series is obtained by multiplying the value of the geometric series, present worth factor by the $(F|P\ i\%,n)$ factor to obtain

$$F = \begin{cases} A_1\left[\dfrac{(1+i)^n - (1+j)^n}{i-j}\right] & i \neq j \\ nA_1(1+i)^{n-1} & i = j \end{cases} \qquad (2.45)$$

or

$$F = A_1(F|A_1\ i\%,j\%,n)$$

where $(F|A_1\ i\%,j\%,n)$ is the *geometric series, future worth factor* and is tabulated in Appendix A. From Equation 2.45, notice that $(F|A_1\ i\%,j\%,n) = (F|A_1\ j\%,i\%,n)$.

EXAMPLE 2.31   Determining the Future Worth of a Geometric Series

Mattie Bookhout receives an annual bonus and deposits it in a savings account that pays 8 percent compounded annually. The size of her bonus increases by 10 percent each year; her initial deposit is $500. Determine how much will be in the fund immediately after her tenth deposit.

	C14	▾	fx =NPV(8%,C4:C13)					
	A	B	C	D	E	F	G	H
1								
2		**End of Year (n)**	**Cash Flow (CF)**					
3		0	$0					
4		1	$500					
5		2	$550					
6		3	$605					
7		4	$666	●———	=C6*1.1			
8		5	$732					
9		6	$805					
10		7	$886					
11		8	$974					
12		9	$1,072					
13		10	$1,179					
14		**P =**	$5,035.12	●———	=NPV(8%,C4:C13)			
15		**F =**	$10,870.44	●———	=FV(8%,10,,-C14)			

FIGURE 2.29

Excel® Solution to Example 2.31.

In this case, $A_1 = \$500$, $i = 8\%$, $j = 10\%$, and $n = 10$. Thus, the value of F is given by

$$F = \$500(F|A_1\ 8\%,10\%,10)$$
$$= \$500(21.74087)$$
$$= \$10,870.44$$

Excel® does not have a worksheet function for geometric series. However, as with gradient series, the **NPV** worksheet function can be used to determine the present worth, uniform series, and future worth equivalents to a geometric series. For the example, the future worth for the geometric series is $10,870.44, as shown in Figure 2.29.

EXAMPLE 2.32   A Decreasing Geometric Series

An investment of $100,000 is made in a limited partnership in a natural-gas drilling project. The first year of the investment produced net revenue of $25,000. Over a 20-year period, the net revenue received from the investment decreased by 10 percent each year. Based on a *TVOM* of 12 percent, what is the present worth for the investment?

For the example, $A_1 = \$25,000$, $i = 12\%$, $j = -10\%$, and $n = 20$. Therefore, the present worth equals $-\$100,000 + \$25,000(P|A_1\ 12\%,-10\%,20)$, or

$$P = -\$100,000 + \$25,000\left[\frac{1 - (0.90)^{20}(1.12)^{-20}}{0.12 - (-0.10)}\right]$$

$$= \$12,204.15$$

The same result is obtained by using the **NPV** worksheet function, as shown in Figure 2.30.

| C15 | ▾ | fx =C14*0.9 |

	A	B	C	D	E	F	G	H	I	J
2		End of Year (n)	Cash Flow (CF)							
3		0	-$100,000							
4		1	$25,000							
5		2	$22,500							
6		3	$20,250							
7		4	$18,225							
8		5	$16,403							
9		6	$14,762							
10		7	$13,286							
11		8	$11,957							
12		9	$10,762							
13		10	$9,686							
14		11	$8,717							
15		12	$7,845	●——●=C14*0.9						
16		13	$7,061							
17		14	$6,355							
18		15	$5,719							
19		16	$5,147							
20		17	$4,633							
21		18	$4,169							
22		19	$3,752							
23		20	$3,377							
24		P =	$12,204.15	●——●=NPV(12%,C4:C23)+C3						
25										

FIGURE 2.30
Excel® Solution to Example 2.32.

EXAMPLE 2.33   An Increasing Geometric Series

Upon graduating with your engineering degree, suppose you accept employment at an annual salary of $60,000. If you invest 10 percent of your annual income, receive 8 percent annual increases in your salary, and earn (a) 6 percent and (b) 8 percent on your investments, what will be the size of your investment portfolio after 40 years?

Solving for (a):

$$A_1 = \$6,000, \ i = 6\%, \ j = 8\%, \ n = 40, \ F = ?$$

$$F = \$6,000(F|A_1 \ 6\%, 8\%, 40)$$

$$= \$6,000(571.94018)$$

$$= \$3,431,641.08$$

Solving for (b):

$$A_1 = \$6,000, \ i = 8\%, \ j = 8\%, \ n = 40, \ F = ?$$

$$F = \$6,000(F|A_1 \ 8\%, 8\%, 40)$$

$$= \$6,000(804.61191)$$

$$= \$4,827,671.46$$

EXAMPLE 2.34 The Penalty of Starting Late in Investing

In the previous example, suppose you delay beginning your investment for 10 years, invest only 5 percent of your annual income, and earn 6 percent on your investments. How much will you have after 30 years of investing?

$$A_1 = \$3,000(1.08)^{10}, \; i = 6\%, \; j = 8\%, \; n = 30, \; F = ?$$

$$F = \$3,000(F|P\, 8\%,10)(F|A_1\, 6\%,8\%,30)$$

$$= \$3,000(2.15892)(215.95829)$$

$$= \$1,398,710.01$$

$$P = A_1\left[\frac{1 - (1+j)^n(1+i)^{-n}}{i-j}\right] \qquad \text{geometric series, present worth factor} \; i \neq j$$

$$P = nA_1/(1+i) \qquad\qquad\qquad\qquad\quad i = j$$

$$P = A_1(P|A_1\, i\%,j\%,n)$$

$$F = A_1\left[\frac{(1+i)^n - (1+j)^n}{i-j}\right] \qquad \text{geometric series, future worth factor} \; i \neq j$$

$$F = nA_1(1+i)^{n-1} \qquad\qquad\qquad\qquad i = j$$

$$F = A_1(F|A_1\, i\%,j\%,n)$$

The interest factors we've covered are summarized in Table 2.6; values of the factors are given in Appendix A.

2-5 MULTIPLE COMPOUNDING PERIODS IN A YEAR

WILEY
VIDEO LESSON

Thus far, when referring to an interest rate, we said that it was $x\%$ compounded annually or $x\%$ annual compound interest. While it is true that practically all engineering economic analyses incorporate annual compounding, in personal financing, compounding typically occurs more frequently than once a year. For example, credit cards charge interest of, say, 1½ percent on the unpaid balance of the account *each month*. As a result, if you owe $1,000 and do not pay it by the monthly payment deadline, your balance owed increases to $1,015. If you do not make any payments, the interest owed the next month will be 1½ percent of $1,015. Hence, monthly compounding is at work. This also occurs with a number of other financial instruments. (In addition, with many credit cards, penalties are added for lack of payment and they, too, draw interest. Credit card debt can be a very expensive form of debt.)

DCF(x=)

TABLE 2.6
Summary of Discrete Compounding Interest Factors.

To Find	Given	Factor	Symbol	Name
P	F	$(1+i)^{-n}$	$(P\|F\,i\%,n)$	Single sum, present worth factor
F	P	$(1+i)^{n}$	$(F\|P\,i\%,n)$	Single sum, compound amount factor
P	A	$\dfrac{(1+i)^{n}-1}{i(1+i)^{n}}$	$(P\|A\,i\%,n)$	Uniform series, present worth factor
A	P	$\dfrac{i(1+i)^{n}}{(1+i)^{n}-1}$	$(A\|P\,i\%,n)$	Uniform series, capital recovery factor
F	A	$\dfrac{(1+i)^{n}-1}{i}$	$(F\|A\,i\%,n)$	Uniform series, compound amount factor
A	F	$\dfrac{i}{(1+i)^{n}-1}$	$(A\|F\,i\%,n)$	Uniform series, sinking fund factor
P	G	$\dfrac{[1-(1+ni)(1+i)^{-n}]}{i^{2}}$	$(P\|G\,i\%,n)$	Gradient series, present worth factor
A	G	$\dfrac{(1+i)^{n}-(1+ni)}{i[(1+i)^{n}-1]}$	$(A\|G\,i\%,n)$	Gradient to uniform series conversion factor
P	A_{1},j	$\dfrac{1-(1+j)^{n}(1+i)^{-n}}{i-j}$ for $i\neq j$	$(P\|A_{1}\,i\%,j\%,n)$	Geometric series, present worth factor
F	A_{1},j	$\dfrac{(1+i)^{n}-(1+j)^{n}}{i-j}$ for $i\neq j$	$(F\|A_{1}\,i\%,j\%,n)$	Geometric series, future worth factor

In the case of 1½ percent per month, an alternate way of expressing the interest rate is 18 percent per annum compounded monthly, or 18 percent per year per month. When expressed in this form, 18 percent is known as the *nominal annual interest rate*. We designate the nominal rate[5] as r.

In the examples presented thus far, cash flows occurred on an annual basis and money was compounded annually. When cash flow frequency and compounding frequency are not the same, one of two approaches must be employed: the period interest rate approach or the effective interest rate approach.

To utilize the period interest rate approach, we must define a new term—the *period* interest rate:

$$\text{Period interest rate} = \frac{\text{Nominal annual interest rate}}{\text{Number of interest periods per year}}$$

When the interest period and the compounding period are the same (monthly), the factors in Appendix A can be applied directly. *Note*, however, the number of interest periods (n) must be adjusted to match the new frequency.

[5]In the text, we will consider nominal interest rates that are annual and compounding periods that are either annual or more frequent than annual. The approach presented in this section can easily be generalized to other cases.

EXAMPLE 2.35 Determining Future Worth with Multiple Compounding Periods per Year

Two thousand dollars is invested in an account that pays 12 percent per year compounded monthly. What is the account balance after 3 years?

Nominal annual interest rate $= 12\%/\text{year}$

Number of interest periods/year $= 12$ months/year

Period interest rate $= \frac{12\%/\text{year}}{12\,\text{months/year}} = 1\%/\text{month}$

Number of interest periods $= 3$ years (12 months/year) $= 36$ months

$$F = \$2,000(F|P\,1\%,36)$$
$$= \$2,000(1.43077)$$
$$= \$2,861.54$$

Now, consider 12 percent per year compounded semiannually:

Nominal annual interest rate $= 12\%/\text{year}$

Number of interest periods/year $= 2$ semiannual periods/year

Period interest rate $= \frac{12\%/\text{year}}{2\,\text{semiannual periods/year}} = 6\%/\text{semiannual period}$

Number of interest periods $= 3$ years (2 semiannual periods/year) $= 6$ semiannual periods

$$F = \$2,000(F|P\,6\%,6)$$
$$= \$2,000(1.41852)$$
$$= \$2,837.04$$

Next, consider 12 percent per year compounded quarterly:

Nominal annual interest rate $= 12\%/\text{year}$

Number of interest periods/year $= 4$ quarters/year

Period interest rate $= \frac{12\%/\text{year}}{4\,\text{quarters/year}} = 3\%/\text{quarter}$

Number of interest periods $= 3$ years (4 quarters/year) $= 12$ quarters

$$F = \$2,000(F|P\,3\%,12)$$
$$= \$2,000(1.42576)$$
$$= \$2,851.54$$

Finally, consider 12 percent per year compounded daily:

Nominal annual interest rate $= 12\%/\text{year}$

Number of interest periods/year $= 365$ days/year

Period interest rate $= \frac{12\%/\text{year}}{365\,\text{days/year}} = 0.0329\%/\text{day}$

Number of interest periods $= 3$ years (365 days/year) $= 1,095$ days

$$F = \$2,000(F|P\,0.0329\%,1095)$$
$$= \$2,000(1.000329)^{1,095}$$
$$= \$2,867.22$$

EXAMPLE 2.36 Determining Car Payments

Rebecca Carlson purchases a car for $25,000 and finances her purchase by borrowing the money at 8 percent per year compounded monthly; she pays off the loan with equal monthly payments for 5 years. What will be the size of her monthly loan payment?

Nominal annual interest rate $= 8\%/\text{year}$

Number of interest periods/year $= 12$ months/year

Period interest rate $= \dfrac{8\%/\text{year}}{12\,\text{months/year}} = 0.66667\%/\text{month}$

Number of interest periods $= 5$ years (12 months/year) $= 60$ months

$$A = \$25,000(A|P\,0.66667\%,60) = \frac{0.0066667(1.0066667)^{60}}{(1.0066667)^{60} - 1} = \$506.91/\text{month}$$

Using the Excel® **PMT** worksheet function,

$$A = \text{PMT}(0.08/12,60,-25000) = \$506.91$$

The second approach to solving problems when compounding is not annual is the effective interest rate approach. The *effective annual interest rate* is the annual interest rate that is equivalent to the period interest rate as previously calculated.

For example, if the interest rate is 12 percent per year compounded quarterly, then the nominal annual interest rate is 12 percent, and there are four interest periods per year. Thus, the period interest rate is 3 percent per quarter. Hence, $1 invested for 1 year at 3 percent per quarter has a future worth of

$$\begin{aligned}
F &= \$1(F|P\,3\%,4)\\
&= \$1(1.12551)\\
&= \$1.12551
\end{aligned}$$

To obtain the same value in 1 year requires an annual compound interest rate of 12.551 percent. This value is called the *effective annual interest rate* and is given by $(1.03)^4 - 1 = 0.12551$, or 12.551 percent.

The Excel® **EFFECT** worksheet function can be used to determine the effective annual interest rate. This function has the following parameters: r (nominal rate) and m (number of compounding periods in a year).

The general equation for the effective annual interest rate, i_{eff}, is

$$i_{eff} = (1 + r/m)^m - 1 = \text{EFFECT}(r,m) \tag{2.46}$$

where r is the nominal annual interest rate and m is the number of interest periods per year.

EXAMPLE 2.37 Calculating the Effective Annual Interest Rate

Calculate the effective annual interest rate for each of the following cases: (a) 12 percent per year compounded semiannually; (b) 12 percent per year compounded quarterly; (c) 12 percent per year compounded monthly; (d) 12 percent per year compounded weekly; (e) 12 percent per year compounded daily; (f) 12 percent per year compounded hourly; (g) 12 percent per year compounded every minute; and (h) 12 percent per year compounded every second.

a. Twelve percent per year compounded semiannually: $r = 12\%$; $m = 2$

From Equation 2.46

$$i_{eff} = (1.06)^2 - 1$$
$$= 0.1236 = 12.36\%$$

Using the Excel® EFFECT worksheet function gives the same result:

$$i_{eff} = \text{EFFECT}(12\%,2) = 12.36\%$$

b. Twelve percent per year compounded quarterly: $r = 12\%$; $m = 4$

From Equation 2.46,

$$i_{eff} = (1.03)^4 - 1$$
$$= 0.12551 = 12.551\%$$

Using the Excel® EFFECT worksheet function gives the same result:

$$i_{eff} = \text{EFFECT}(12\%,4) = 12.551\%$$

c. Twelve percent per year compounded monthly: $r = 12\%$; $m = 12$

From Equation 2.46,

$$i_{eff} = (1.01)^{12} - 1$$
$$= 0.12683 = 12.683\%$$

Using the Excel® EFFECT worksheet function gives the same result:

$$i_{eff} = \text{EFFECT}(12\%,12) = 12.683\%$$

d. Twelve percent per year compounded weekly: $r = 12\%$; $m = 52$

From Equation 2.46, to eight decimal places,

$$i_{eff} = (1 + 0.12/52)^{52} - 1$$
$$= 0.12734099 = 12.734099\%$$

Using the Excel® EFFECT worksheet function gives the same result:

$$i_{eff} = \text{EFFECT}(12\%,52) = 12.734099\%$$

e. Twelve percent per year compounded daily: $r = 12\%$; $m = 365$

From Equation 2.46, to eight decimal places,

$$i_{eff} = (1 + 0.12/365)^{365} - 1$$
$$= 0.12747462 = 12.747462\%$$

Using the Excel® EFFECT worksheet function gives the same result:

$$i_{eff} = \text{EFFECT}(12\%,365) = 12.747462\%$$

f. Twelve percent per year compounded every hour: $r = 12\%$; $m = 8,760$

From Equation 2.46, to eight decimal places,

$$i_{eff} = (1 + 0.12/8760)^{8,760} - 1$$
$$= 0.12749592 = 12.749592\%$$

Using the Excel® EFFECT worksheet function gives

$$i_{eff} = \text{EFFECT}(12\%,8760) = 12.749592\%$$

g. Twelve percent per year compounded every minute: $r = 12\%$; $m = 525{,}600$

From Equation 2.46, to eight decimal places,

$$i_{eff} = (1 + 0.12/525{,}600)^{525{,}600} - 1$$
$$= 0.12749684 = 12.749684\%$$

Using the Excel® **EFFECT** worksheet function gives

$$i_{eff} = \mathbf{EFFECT}(12\%,525600) = 12.749684\%$$

h. Twelve percent per year compounded every second: $r = 12\%$; $m = 31{,}536{,}000$

From Equation 2.46, to eight decimal places,

$$i_{eff} = (1 + 0.12/31{,}536{,}000)^{31{,}536{,}000} - 1$$
$$= 0.12749685 = 12.749685\%$$

Using the Excel® **EFFECT** worksheet function gives[6]

$$i_{eff} = \mathbf{EFFECT}(12\%,4) = 12.749685\%$$

EXAMPLE 2.38   Determining the Effective Annual Interest Rate for a Loan Transaction

Wenfeng Li borrowed $1,000 and paid off the loan with interest after 4.5 years. The amount paid was $1,500. What was the effective annual interest rate for the transaction? Letting the interest period be 6 months, it is seen that the payment of $1,500 and the debt of $1,000 are related by the expression

$$F = P(F|P\,i\%,n)$$

Thus, since $F = \$1{,}500$, $P = \$1{,}000$, and $n = 9$,

$$\$1{,}500 = \$1{,}000(F|P\,i\%,9)$$

or

$$\$1{,}500 = \$1{,}000(1 + i)^9$$

Dividing both sides by $1,000 gives

$$1.5 = (1 + i)^9$$

Taking the logarithm of both sides yields

$$\log 1.50 = 9 \log (1 + i)$$

---

[6]It appears the Excel® **EFFECT** function yields results identical to those obtained mathematically. However, if calculations are carried out to more decimal places, the Excel® solution tends to be greater than the actual value. In Appendix 2.A, we show that the effective annual interest rate is 12.7496851579% when the nominal annual interest rate is 12 percent and when the number of compounding periods in a year approaches infinity. When calculated mathematically to ten-decimal-place accuracy, 12 percent compounded every second has an effective annual interest rate of 12.74968514 percent versus 12.74968522 percent when calculated using the **EFFECT** function. Compounding an infinite number of times in a year establishes an upper bound on the effective annual interest rate (12.7496851579 percent). Therefore, the Excel® solution of 12.74968522 percent, which is greater than the upper bound, cannot be correct. Even though Excel® is not always "accurate," we continue to use the **EFFECT** function in future chapters.

Dividing both sides by 9, taking the antilog of the result, and solving for i gives

$$i = 0.046$$

Thus, the 6-month interest rate is approximately 4.6 percent. Computing the effective annual interest rate yields

$$\begin{aligned} i_{eff} &= (1+i)^2 - 1 \\ &= (1.046)^2 - 1 \\ &= 0.0943 \end{aligned}$$

The effective annual interest rate for the loan transaction was approximately 9.43 percent.

Instead of using logarithms, we could have searched the interest tables for a value of i that yielded a value of 1.50 for the $(F|P\ i\%,9)$ factor. With interpolation, i is approximately 4.6 percent. The computation of the effective annual interest rate follows that used for the effective annual interest rate of 9.2 percent compounded semiannually.

 The Excel® **RATE** worksheet function can be used to determine the effective annual interest rate for the loan transaction. The **RATE** function has the following parameters: number of interest periods, size of uniform payment, present value, future value, *type*, and *guess*. The latter two parameters can be skipped for the example, as can the size of the annual payment.[7]

For the example, entering **=RATE(4.5,,-1000,1500)** in any cell in an Excel® spreadsheet yields the following result: 9.4287 percent.

EXAMPLE 2.39 Making Monthly House Payments

Greg Wilhelm borrowed $100,000 to purchase a house. He agreed to repay the loan with equal monthly payments over a 30-year period at a nominal annual interest rate of 6 percent. His monthly payment on the 30-year loan was calculated as follows:

$$\begin{aligned} A &= \$100,000(A|P\ 0.5\%,360) \\ &= \$100,000(0.0059955) \\ &= \$599.55 \end{aligned}$$

 or, using the Excel® **PMT** worksheet function,

$$A = \textbf{PMT(0.06/12,360,-100000)} = \$599.55$$

However, there were $2,000 closing fees on the loan that he had to pay. If he chose to finance the closing costs, then his monthly payment would be

$$\begin{aligned} A &= \$102,000(A|P\ 0.5\%,360) \\ &= \$102,000(0.0059955) \\ &= \$611.54 \end{aligned}$$

 or

$$A = \textbf{PMT(0.06/12,360,-102000)} = \$611.54$$

---

[7]As we shall find later in Example 13.31, the Excel® **RATE** function does not always yield a solution when a solution exists. For example, if $P = -\$115$, $A = \$45$, and $n = 10$, then

$$\textbf{=RATE(10,45,-115)} = \text{\#NUM!}$$

However, the Excel® **IRR** worksheet function can be used to obtain the correct value: 37.51 percent.

What was the effective annual interest rate on the loan? If he made 360 payments of $611.54/month for $100,000, then the rate would be

$$i_{eff} = \text{EFFECT}(12*\text{RATE}(360,611.54,-100000),12) = 6.364\%$$

2-6 WHEN COMPOUNDING AND CASH FLOW FREQUENCIES DIFFER

In the previous example, the frequency of compounding coincided with the frequency of cash flows—for example, monthly compounding and monthly cash flows. What if they are not the same?

Two approaches can be used to solve problems when the compounding frequency and the cash flow frequency differ. With the first approach, it is assumed that money deposited during a compounding period earns no interest, whereas the second approach assumes that money earns interest regardless of when it is deposited. We adopt the second approach, because it is consistent with other *DCF* assumptions made throughout the text.

When compounding frequency and cash flow frequency differ, the following approach is taken. Let r denote the nominal annual interest rate for money and m denote the number of compounding periods in a year; let k denote the number of cash flows in a year, and let i denote the interest rate per cash flow period. The value of i is obtained as follows:

$$i = (1 + r/m)^{m/k} - 1 \tag{2.47}$$

Equation 2.47 results from setting the effective annual interest rate for the stated compounding frequency of money equal to that for the cash flow frequency:

$$(1 + i)^k - 1 = (1 + r/m)^m - 1$$

and solving for i.

EXAMPLE 2.40   When Cash Flow Frequency Does Not Match Compounding Frequency

What size monthly payments should occur when $10,000 is borrowed at 8 percent per year compounded quarterly and the loan is repaid with 36 equal monthly payments?

From Equation 2.47, $r = 0.08$, $m = 4$, and $k = 12$. Therefore,

$$i = (1 + 0.08/4)^{4/12} - 1$$
$$= 0.006623 \text{ or } 0.6623\%/\text{month}$$

Knowing the monthly interest rate, the monthly payment can be determined:

$$A = \$10,000(A|P\,0.6623\%,36)$$
$$= \$10,000[(0.006623)(1.006623)^{36}]/[(1.006623)^{36} - 1]$$
$$= \$313.12$$

Using the Excel® **PMT** worksheet function,

$$A = \text{PMT}(1.02^{\wedge}(1/3)-1,36,-10000) = \$313.12.$$

The Excel® worksheet financial functions used in this chapter are summarized in Table 2.7.

TABLE 2.7
Summary of Selected Excel® Worksheet Financial Functions.

To Find	Given	Worksheet Function	Cell Entry
P	i, n, F	PV	$=\text{PV}(i\%,n,,-F)$
P	i, n, A	PV	$=\text{PV}(i\%,n,-A)$
P	i, n, F, A	PV	$=\text{PV}(i\%,n,-A,-F)$
P	$i, A_1, A_2, \ldots, A_n$	NPV	$=\text{NPV}(i\%,A_1,A_2,\ldots,A_n)$
F	i, n, P	FV	$=\text{FV}(i\%,n,,-P)$
F	i, n, A	FV	$=\text{FV}(i\%,n,-A)$
F	i, n, P, A	FV	$=\text{FV}(i\%,n,-A,-P)$
A	i, n, P	PMT	$=\text{PMT}(i\%,n,-P)$
A	i, n, F	PMT	$=\text{PMT}(i\%,n,,-F)$
A	i, n, P, F	PMT	$=\text{PMT}(i\%,n,-P,-F)$
i	n, P, A	RATE	$=\text{RATE}(n,A,-P)$
i	n, P, F	RATE	$=\text{RATE}(n,,-P,F)$
i	n, A, F	RATE	$=\text{RATE}(n,A,,-F)$
i	n, P, A, F	RATE	$=\text{RATE}(n,A,-P,F)$
n	i, P, A	NPER	$=\text{NPER}(i\%,A,-P)$
n	i, P, F	NPER	$=\text{NPER}(i\%,,-P,F)$
n	i, A, F	NPER	$=\text{NPER}(i\%,-A,,F)$
n	i, P, A, F	NPER	$=\text{NPER}(i\%,A,-P,F)$
i_{eff}	r, m	EFFECT	$=\text{EFFECT}(r\%,m)$

2-7 SPECIAL AND LIMITING CASES OF TIME VALUE OF MONEY FACTORS

It is instructive to consider certain special and limiting cases of the *TVOM* factors. Several of the relationships presented below have been discussed previously in the text and are summarized here for convenience. Others (particularly the limiting cases) are new and may require some reflective thought. Derivations or proofs of the relationships are left as exercises.

2.7.1 Mathematical Relationships

The following equations represent mathematical relationships that hold among the *TVOM* factors. While proofs of each can be derived mathematically, it is perhaps more instructive to intuitively rationalize the relationships using simple examples and cash flow diagrams.

Inverse Relationships

$$(F|P\ i\%,n) = \frac{1}{(P|F\ i\%,n)} \tag{2.48}$$

$$(A|P\ i\%,n) = \frac{1}{(P|A\ i\%,n)} \tag{2.49}$$

$$(A|F\ i\%,n) = \frac{1}{(F|A\ i\%,n)} \tag{2.50}$$

Series-to-Series and Series-to-Single-Sum Relationships

$$(A|P\,i\%,n) = (A|F\,i\%,n) + i \tag{2.51}$$

$$(P|A\,i\%,n) = \sum_{t=1}^{n} A(1+i)^{-t} \tag{2.52}$$

Single Sum Timing Relationships

$$(P|F\,i\%,n+m) = (P|F\,i\%,n)(P|F\,i\%,m) \tag{2.53}$$

$$(P|F\,i\%,n-m) = (P|F\,i\%,n)(F|P\,i\%,m) \tag{2.54}$$

$$(P|F\,i\%,nm) = (P|F\,i\%,n)^{m} \tag{2.55}$$

$$(P|F\,i\%,nm) = (P|F\,i\%,m)^{n} \tag{2.56}$$

2.7.2 Limiting Cases

Table 2.8 presents limiting cases of *TVOM* relationships. Each row should be considered independently. In each case, the expression in the left column approaches the result in the right column as the limiting condition in the middle column is approached. In each case, all variables except the limiting condition variable are assumed to hold constant.

2.7.3 Special Cases for $n = 1$

The following equations represent special cases that hold when the value of n is equal to 1.

$$(P|G\,i\%,1) = 0 \tag{2.57}$$

$$(A|G\,i\%,1) = 0 \tag{2.58}$$

$$(A|P\,i\%,1) = (F|P\,i\%,1) = 1 + i \tag{2.59}$$

$$(A|F\,i\%,1) = (F|A\,i\%,1) = 1 \tag{2.60}$$

TABLE 2.8
Limiting Cases.

Expression	Variable and Limit	Result
$F = P(F|P\,i\%,n)$	$n \to \infty$	$F \to \infty$
$F = P(F|P\,i\%,n)$	$i \to 0$	$F \to P$
$P = F(P|F\,i\%,n)$	$n \to \infty$	$P \to 0$
$P = F(P|F\,i\%,n)$	$i \to 0$	$P \to F$
$A = P(A|P\,i\%,n)$	$n \to \infty$	$A \to Pi$
$A = P(A|P\,i\%,n)$	$i \to 0$	$A \to P/n$
$P = A(P|A\,i\%,n)$	$n \to \infty$	$P \to A/i$
$P = A(P|A\,i\%,n)$	$i \to 0$	$P \to nA$
$F = A(F|A\,i\%,n)$	$n \to \infty$	$F \to \infty$
$F = A(F|A\,i\%,n)$	$i \to 0$	$F \to nA$
$A = F(A|F\,i\%,n)$	$n \to \infty$	$A \to 0$
$A = F(A|F\,i\%,n)$	$i \to 0$	$A \to F/n$

2-8 SUMMARY

This chapter established the foundation for the rest of the text. Basic compound interest formulas, which will be used throughout the book, were developed and illustrated with numerous examples. From the examples presented, we learned

1. how powerful compounding of money can be in personal investing;

2. the power of compounding is maximized by investing sooner, not later;

3. how to perform basic mathematical operations involving single sums of money and series of cash flows;

4. how to transform a present sum into a future sum, a future sum into a present sum, a present sum into a uniform series of cash flows, a uniform series of cash flows into a present sum, a future sum into a uniform series of cash flows, a uniform series of cash flows into a future sum, a gradient series into a present sum, a gradient series into a uniform series, a geometric series into a present sum, and a geometric series into a future sum;

5. how to mathematically perform economic transformations using tabulated values of the compound interest factors found in Appendix A, as well as using several Excel® worksheet functions;

6. how to calculate the effective annual interest rate and use it to deal with cash flow frequencies differing from the compounding frequency; and

7. the Excel® **GOAL SEEK** and **SOLVER** tools will not always produce accurate solutions because of premature terminations of searches used by each tool.

Hopefully you feel very confident in your ability to perform the basic calculations covered in the chapter. If not, then you will soon learn that *mastering the material in this chapter is essential to understanding what comes in the following chapters.* If you do not master the material in Chapter 2 before moving into subsequent chapters, you will struggle with what awaits you. Good luck!

Pit Stop #2—Hang On!

1. True of False: If money is worth 5% compounded annually to you, then you should prefer to receive $2,750 today than to receive $3,500 five years from today.

2. True or False: If money is worth 7% compounded annually to you, then you should prefer to receive $1,000,000 thirty years from now than to receive $200,000 today.

3. True of False: If money is worth 6% compounded annually to you, then you should prefer to receive $1750 per year for 5 years than to receive $1000 per year for 10 years, assuming the first receipt occurs one year from today in both cases.

4. True or False: If money is worth 7% compounded annually to you, then you would prefer to receive $2,200 each year for 5 years than to receive $4,000 the first year, $3,000 the second year, $2,000 the third year, $1,000 the fourth year, and $0 the fifth year.

5. True of False: If money has a time value of 8% compounded annually, you should prefer to receive a uniform series of ten $1,000 cash flows over the interval [1,10] to receiving a uniform series of ten $1,260 cash flows over the interval [4,13].

CONTINUOUS COMPOUND INTEREST CALCULATIONS

In the discussion of the effective annual interest rate in Section 2.5, we noted that the more frequently compounding occurs, the greater the effective annual interest rate. When reviewing Example 2.37, you might have wondered why we considered compounding every hour, every minute, and every second. In today's global economy, money moves around the world 24-7 and is "put to work" for businesses as soon as it is received. With electronic data interchange (EDI), businesses like Wal-Mart reimburse suppliers on a near continuous basis.

If one wishes to account explicitly for daily or hourly compounding, then *continuous compounding* is appropriate. *Continuous compounding* means that each year is divided into an infinite number of interest periods. Mathematically, the single payment compound amount factor is given by

$$\lim_{m \to \infty} (1 + r/m)^{mn} = e^{rn} \qquad (2.A.1)$$

where n is the number of years, m is the number of interest periods per year, and r is the nominal annual interest rate. Given P, r, and n, the value of F can be computed using continuous compounding as follows:

$$F = P\,e^{rn} \qquad (2.A.2)$$

or

$$F = P(F|P\,r\%,n)_\infty \qquad (2.A.3)$$

where $(F|P\,r\%,n)_\infty$ denotes the *continuous compounding, single sum, future worth factor*. The subscript ∞ is provided to denote that continuous compounding is being used. Selected interest tables for continuous compounding are given in Appendix B.

EXAMPLE 2.A.1 Continuous Compounding Example

If \$2,000 is invested in a fund that pays interest at a rate of 12 percent compounded continuously, after 5 years the cumulative amount in the fund will total

$$F = P(F|P\,12\%,5)_\infty$$
$$= \$2,000(1.82212)$$
$$= \$3,644.24$$

Thus, a withdrawal of \$3,644.24 will deplete the fund after 5 years.

The effective annual interest rate under continuous compounding is easily obtained using the relation

$$i_{eff} = e^r - 1 \qquad (2.A.4)$$

or

$$i_{eff} = (F|P\,r\%,1)_\infty - 1 \qquad (2.A.5)$$

To illustrate, if interest is 12 percent compounded continuously, then the effective annual interest rate is given by

$$i_{eff} = (F|P\,12\%,1)_\infty - 1$$
$$= 0.127496851579$$

Thus, 12.7496851579 percent compounded annually is equivalent to 12 percent compounded continuously.

The inverse relationship between F and P indicates that

$$P = Fe^{-rn} \qquad (2.A.6)$$

or

$$P = F(P|F\,r\%,n)_\infty \qquad (2.A.7)$$

where $(P|F\,r\%,n)_\infty$ is called the *continuous compounding, single sum, present worth factor.*

2.A-1 DISCRETE FLOWS

If it is assumed that cash flows are discretely spaced over time, then the continuous compounding relations for the uniform, gradient, and geometric series can be obtained. Substituting e^{-rn} for $(1+i)^{-n}$, $e^r - 1$ for i, and e^{rn} for $(1+i)^n$ in the remaining discrete compounding formulas yields the continuous compounding interest factors summarized in Table 2.A.1. Values for these factors are provided in Appendix B.

EXAMPLE 2.A.2 Continuous Compounding with a Uniform Series of Cash Flows

To illustrate the use of continuous compounding interest factors, suppose $1,000 is deposited each year into an account that pays interest at a rate of 12 percent compounded continuously. Determine both the amount in the account immediately after the tenth deposit and the present worth equivalent for 10 deposits.

The amount in the fund immediately after the tenth deposit is given by the relation

$$F = \$1,000(F|A\,12\%,10)_\infty$$
$$= \$1,000(18.19744)$$
$$= \$18,197.44$$

TABLE 2.A.1
Summary of Continuous Compounding Interest Factors for Discrete Flows.

To Find	Given	Factor	Symbol
P	F	e^{-rn}	$(P\|F\ r,n)_{\infty}$
F	P	e^{rn}	$(F\|P\ r,n)_{\infty}$
F	A	$\dfrac{e^{rn} - 1}{e^{r} - 1}$	$(F\|A\ r,n)_{\infty}$
A	F	$\dfrac{e^{r} - 1}{e^{rn} - 1}$	$(A\|F\ r,n)_{\infty}$
P	A	$\dfrac{e^{rn} - 1}{e^{rn}(e^{r} - 1)}$	$(P\|A\ r,n)_{\infty}$
A	P	$\dfrac{e^{rn}(e^{r} - 1)}{e^{rn} - 1}$	$(A\|P\ r,n)_{\infty}$
P	G	$\dfrac{e^{rn} - 1 - n(e^{r} - 1)}{e^{rn}(e^{r} - 1)^{2}}$	$(P\|G\ r,n)_{\infty}$
A	G	$\dfrac{1}{e^{r} - 1} - \dfrac{n}{e^{rn} - 1}$	$(A\|G\ r,n)_{\infty}$
P	A_1, c	$\dfrac{1 - e^{(c-r)n}}{e^{r} - e^{c}}$	$(P\|A_1\ r,c,n)_{\infty}{}^{*}$
F	A_1, c	$\dfrac{e^{rn} - e^{cn}}{e^{r} - e^{c}}$	$(F\|A_1\ r,c,n)_{\infty}{}^{*}$

$*r \neq c.$

The present worth equivalent of the 10 deposits is obtained using the relation

$$P = \$1{,}000(P|A\ 12\%,10)_{\infty}$$
$$= \$1{,}000(5.48097)$$
$$= \$5{,}480.97$$

Excel® does not include worksheet functions that explicitly deal with continuous compounding. However, in the case of discrete flow, one can enter as the interest rate exp(0.12)-1. Using the Excel® **FV** and **PV** worksheet functions for the example gives

$$F = \textbf{FV(exp(0.12)-1,10,-1000)} = \$18{,}197.44$$

and

$$P = \textbf{PV(exp(0.12)-1,10,-1000)} = \$5480.97$$

In the case of geometric series, the size of the tth cash flow will be assumed to be given by

$$A_t = A_{t-1}e^{c} \quad t = 2, \cdots, n \tag{2.A.8}$$

or, equivalently,

$$A_t = A_1 e^{(t-1)c} \quad t = 1, \cdots, n \tag{2.A.9}$$

where c is the nominal compound rate of increase in the cash flow's size. The resulting expressions for the *continuous compounding, geometric series present worth factor* and the *continuous compounding, geometric series future worth factor* are given, respectively, by $(P|A_1\ r\%,c\%,n)_\infty$ and $(F|A_1\ r\%,c\%,n)_\infty$, as given in Table 2.A.1 for the case of $r \neq c$. As an exercise, you may wish to derive the appropriate expression when $r = c$.

EXAMPLE 2.A.3 Continuous Compounding with a Geometric Series

An individual receives an annual bonus and deposits it in a savings account that pays 8 percent compounded continuously. The size of the bonus increases each year at a rate of 10 percent compounded continuously; the initial deposit is $500. Determine how much will be in the fund immediately after the tenth deposit.

In this case, $A_1 = \$500$, $r = 8\%$, $c = 10\%$, and $n = 10$. Thus, the value of F is given by

$$F = \$500(F|A_1\ 8\%,10\%,10)_\infty$$
$$= \$500(22.51619)$$
$$= \$11,258.09$$

Comparing the result with that obtained in Example 2.31, the effect of continuous compounding increases the amount in the fund by $11,258.09 - \$10,870.45 = \$387.64$

Since the differences in discrete and continuous compounding are not usually great, it is not uncommon to see discrete compounding used when continuous compounding is more appropriate. The arguments given for this are that errors in estimating cash flows will probably offset any attempts to be very precise by using continuous compounding and that the interest rate used in discrete compounding is actually the effective annual interest rate resulting from continuous compounding.

2.A-2 CONTINUOUS FLOW

Thus far, only discrete cash flows have been considered. It was assumed that cash flows occurred at, say, the end of the year. In some cases, money is expended throughout the year on a somewhat uniform basis. Costs of labor, carrying inventory, and operating and maintenance equipment are typical examples. Others include capital improvement projects that conserve energy or water or that process steam.

Consequently, as a mathematical convenience, instead of assuming that money flows in discrete increments at the end of monthly, weekly, daily, or hourly time periods, it is assumed that money flows continuously at a uniform rate during the time period. Instead of having a uniform series of discrete cash flows of magnitude A, it is assumed that a *total* of $\overline{A}$ dollars flows uniformly and continuously throughout a given time period. Such an approach to modeling cash flows is referred to as the *continuous flow* approach.

To illustrate the continuous flow concept, suppose you are to divide $1,000 into k equal amounts to be deposited at equally spaced points in time during a year. The interest rate per period is defined to be $r\%/k$, where r is the nominal rate. Thus, the present worth of a series of k equal amounts is given by

$$P = \frac{\$1,000}{k}\left(P|A\ \frac{r\%}{k},k\right)$$

or

$$P = \frac{\$1,000}{k} \left[\frac{(1 + (r/k))^k - 1}{(r/k)(1 + (r/k)^k} \right]$$

which reduces to

$$P = \frac{\$1,000}{k} \left[\frac{1}{r} - \frac{1}{r(1 + (r/k))^k} \right]$$

Taking the limit of P as k approaches infinity gives

$$\lim_{k \to \infty} P = \$1,000 \left(\frac{1}{r} - \frac{1}{(re^r)} \right)$$

or

$$P = \$1,000(e^r - 1)/(re^r)$$

In general, for n years,

$$P = \overline{A}(e^{rn} - 1)/(re^{rn}) \qquad (2.A.10)$$

or

$$P = \overline{A}(P|\overline{A} \, r\%,n) \qquad (2.A.11)$$

where $(P|\overline{A} \, r\%,n)$ is referred to as the *continuous flow, continuous compounding uniform series present worth factor* and is tabulated in Appendix B. (We do not include the subscript ∞ to denote continuous compounding due to the presence of continuous flow, denoted by $\overline{A}$.)

The remaining continuous flow, continuous compound interest factors are summarized in Table 2.A.2. Values of the factors are given in Appendix B for various values of r and n. With continuous flow and continuous compounding, the continuous annual cash flow, $\overline{A}$, is equivalent to $Ar/(e^r - 1)$, when discrete flow and continuous compounding is used. Hence, the discrete flow equivalent of $\overline{A}$ is given by

$$A = \overline{A}(e^r - 1)/r$$

TABLE 2.A.2			
Summary of Continuous Compounding Interest Factors for Continuous Flows.			
Find	Given	Factor	Symbol
P	$\overline{A}$	$(e^{rn}-1)/(re^{rn})$	$(P|\overline{A} \, r\%,n)$
$\overline{A}$	P	$re^{rn}/(e^{rn} - 1)$	$(\overline{A}|P \, r\%,n)$
F	$\overline{A}$	$(e^{rn} - 1)/r$	$(F|\overline{A} \, r\%,n)$
$\overline{A}$	F	$r/(e^{rn} - 1)$	$(\overline{A}|F \, r\%,n)$

or

$$A = \overline{A}(F|\overline{A}\ r\%,1)$$

EXAMPLE 2.A.4 A Continuous Flow, Continuous Compounding Example

What are the present worth and future worth equivalents of a uniform series of continuous cash flows totaling $10,000/year for 10 years when interest is compounded continuously at a rate of 20 percent/year?

The present worth equivalent is given by

$$\begin{aligned} P &= \$10,000(P|\overline{A}\ 20\%,10) \\ &= \$10,000(4.32332) \\ &= \$43,233.20 \end{aligned}$$

The future worth equivalent is given by

$$\begin{aligned} F &= \$10,000(F|\overline{A}\ 20\%,10) \\ &= \$10,000(31.94528) \\ &= \$319,452.80 \end{aligned}$$

To use the **PV** and **FV** functions, $e^{0.2} - 1$ is the interest rate and $\overline{A}(e^{0.2} - 1)/0.2$ is the uniform series payment. For the example,

$$P = PV(exp(0.2)\text{-}1,10,\text{-}10000*(exp(0.2)\text{-}1)/0.2) = \$43,233.24$$

and

$$F = FV(exp(0.2)\text{-}1,10,\text{-}10000*(exp(0.2)\text{-}1)/0.2) = \$319,452.80$$

We placed continuous compounding and continuous flow in an appendix to Chapter 2 because of its limited use in industry and government. Although there are many practical applications for which continuous compounding and continuous flow are reasonable approximations, few organizations incorporate them in their engineering economic analyses. However, because some do and because you might encounter a situation where continuous compounding and/or flow are used, we provided this material to familiarize you with the mathematics involved.

FE-LIKE PROBLEMS

1. A deposit of $3,000 is made in a savings account that pays 7.5 percent interest compounded annually. How much money will be available to the depositor at the end of 16 years?

   a. $8,877

   b. $10,258

   c. $9,542

   d. $943

2. The plan was to leave $5,000 on deposit in a savings account for 15 years at 6.5 percent interest compounded annually. It became necessary to withdraw $1,500 at the end of the fifth year. How much will be on deposit at the end of the 15-year period?

   a. $11,359

   b. $9,359

   c. $12,043

   d. $10,043

3. A child receives $100,000 as a gift, which is deposited in a bank account earning 6 percent compounded semiannually. If $5,000 is withdrawn at the end of each half year, how long will the money last?

   a. 21 years

   b. 15.5 years

   c. 25 years

   d. 18 years

4. Your company seeks to take over Good Deal Company. Your company's offer for Good Deal is for $3,000,000 in cash upon signing the agreement followed by 10 annual payments of $300,000 starting 1 year later. The time value of money is 10 percent. What is the present worth of your company's offer?

   a. $3,000,000

   b. $2,281,830

   c. $4,843,380

   d. $5,281,830

5. If you want to triple your money at an interest rate of 6 percent per year compounded annually, how many years would you have to leave the money in the account?

   a. 12 years

   b. 19 years

   c. 32 years

   d. Cannot be determined without knowing the amount invested

6. Let F be the accumulated sum, P the principal invested, i the annual compound interest rate, and n the number of years. Which of the following correctly relates these quantities?

   a. $F = P(1 + in)$

   b. $F = P(1 + i)^n$

   c. $F = P(1 + n)^i$

   d. $F = P(1 + ni)^{n-1}$

7. The maintenance costs of a car increase by $200 each year. This cash flow pattern is best described by which of the following?

   a. Gradient series

   b. Geometric series

   c. Infinite series

   d. Uniform series

8. If you invest $5,000 three years from now, how much will be in the account 15 years from now if $i = 10$ percent compounded annually?

   a. $8,053

   b. $15,692

   c. $20,886

   d. $27,800

9. The president of a growing engineering firm wishes to give each of 20 employees a holiday bonus. How much must be deposited each month for a year at a 12 percent nominal rate, compounded monthly, so that each employee will receive a $2,500 bonus?

   a. $2,070

   b. $3,840

   c. $3,940

   d. $4,170

10. What is the annual interest rate if a simple interest loan of $10,000 for 4 years charges a total of $2,800 interest? The loan is repaid with a single payment at the end of year 4.

    a. 7 percent

    b. 28 percent

    c. i such that $12,800 = 10,000(F|P\,i\%,4)$

    d. Cannot be determined from the information given

11. What is the effective annual interest rate if the nominal annual interest rate is 24 percent per year compounded monthly?

    a. 2 percent

    b. 24 percent

    c. 26.82 percent

    d. 27.12 percent

12. Under what circumstances are the effective annual interest rate and the period interest rate equal?

    a. Never true

    b. If the number of compounding periods per year is 1

    c. If the number of compounding periods per year is infinite

    d. Always true

13. Consider the following cash flow diagram. What is the value of X if the present worth of the diagram is $400 and the interest rate is 15 percent compounded annually?

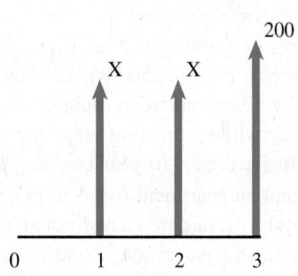

a. $246

b. $165

c. $200

d. $146

14. A young engineer calculated that monthly payments of $A are required to pay off a $5,000 loan for n years at i% interest, compounded annually. If the engineer decides to borrow $10,000 instead with the same n and i%, her monthly payments will be $2A.

a. True

b. False

c. Cannot be determined without knowing the value of n and i

d. Cannot be determined without knowing the value of n or i

PROBLEMS

Section 2.1

1. What words comprise the acronym "*DCF*"? Describe/define what it means in 10 words or less.

2. State the four *DCF* rules.

3. You are offered $200 now plus $100 a year from now for your used computer. Since the sum of those two amounts is $300, the buyer suggests simply waiting and giving you $300 a year from now. You know and trust the buyer, and you typically earn 5 percent per year on your money. So, is the offer fair and equitable?

4. You are offered $500 now plus $500 one year from now. You can earn 6 percent per year on your money.

   a. It is suggested that a single fair amount be paid now. What do you consider fair?

   b. It is suggested that a single fair amount be paid 1 year from now. What do you consider fair?

Section 2.2

5. Pooi Phan needs $2,000 to pay off her bills. She borrows this amount from a bank with plans to pay it back over the next 4 years at $X per year. Draw a cash flow diagram from the bank's perspective.

6. Today you borrow $10,000 to pay for your expected college costs over the next 4 years, including a master's degree. Two years from now, you determine that you need an additional $4,000, so you borrow this amount. Starting 4 years from the original loan (2 years from the second loan), you begin to repay your combined debt by making annual payments of $2,880. You will make these payments for 10 years. Draw a cash flow diagram of this situation from your perspective.

7. Kaelyn borrows $30,000 from her grandfather today to cover her college expenses. She agrees to repay the loan, with the first payment due 5 years from today in the amount of $2,000. No payment is made at the end of year 6. Starting 7 years from today, a series of five annual end-of-year payments is made, with the first in the amount of $X. Each subsequent payment is $1,500 greater than the previous payment. Draw the cash flow diagram of this transaction from the grandfather's perspective.

8. David is borrowing $150,000 from Hartford Bank to open a road and off-road bicycle shop. Since David expects it to take a few years before the shop earns a sizeable profit, he has arranged for no payments on the loan until the end of the fourth year. The first and second payments are due 4 and 5 years, respectively, from today in the amounts of $20,000 each. Starting at the end of year 6, a series of 4 annual end-of-year payments will be made. The first of these is $X. Each subsequent payment is $8,000 greater than the previous payment. Draw the cash flow diagram from David's perspective.

9. Mercruiser purchases a used, recently upgraded computer numerical control (CNC) machine for turning operations. It costs $50,000, and since the machine will increase productivity, the company expects to increase sales by $7,000 per year. Maintenance costs are $1,000 per year starting 1 year after purchase. Every 5 years, the machine will require a software upgrade costing $5,000. Draw the cash flow diagram for the scenario described if Mercruiser uses a 10-year planning horizon.

10. You rent an apartment for $550 per month, payable at the beginning of the month. An initial deposit of $450 is required. Utilities are an additional $150 per month payable at the end of the month. The deposit is refundable at the time you move out, assuming a clean apartment in good condition. Draw a monthly cash flow diagram, assuming you keep the apartment for 12 full months.

11. Rodeo Jeans are stonewashed under a contract with independent USA Denim Company. USA Denim purchased 2 semiautomatic machines that cost $19,000 each at $(t = 0)$. Annual operating and maintenance costs are $15,000 per machine. Two years after purchasing the machines, USA Denim made them fully automatic at a cost of $12,000 per machine. In the fully automatic mode, the operating and maintenance costs are $6,000 the first year, increasing by $1,000 each year thereafter. The contract with Rodeo Company is for 8 years. Draw the cash flow diagram for all of USA Denim's investment and other costs assuming the contract will not be extended beyond 8 years.

12. A laser-cutting machine is purchased today for $23,000. There are no maintenance costs for the next 2 years. Maintenance at the end of year 3 is expected to be $2,000, with the subsequent years' maintenance costs each exceeding the previous year's by $1,000. An increase in revenues of $14,000 per year is expected. The planning horizon is 6 years. Draw the cash flow diagram.

13. Draw a cash flow diagram depicting the net cash flows associated with the purchase, operation, and disposition of a synthetic rubber-blending machine. The cash flow components are shown below. Your *CFD* should have only one arrow at any given time period, reflecting the net of that period's cash flows.

At $t = 0$ (now), purchase blender for $62,000.

At $t = 0$, install at cost of $8,000.

At $t = 1$, savings generated by blender is $10,000.

At $t = 1$, maintenance costs are $800.

At $t = 2$, savings generated by blender are $12,000.

At $t = 2$, maintenance costs are $1,200.

At $t = 3$, savings generated by blender is $18,000.

At $t = 3$, maintenance costs are $1,600.

At $t = 4, 5, 6, 7, 8, 9, 10$, savings generated are $24,000 and maintenance is $4,000.

At $t = 10$, the blender is sold for $8,000.

At $t = 10$, blender removal costs are $1,600.

Sections 2.3 and 2.4

14. You want to withdraw a single sum of $8,000 from an account at the end of 12 years. This withdrawal will deplete the account.

   a. What single sum of money must you deposit today if the account earns 5 percent simple interest? (2.3)

   b. What single sum of money must you deposit today if the account earns 5 percent compound interest? (2.4)

15. You have $10,000 to invest for 5 years. Your local bank has the following accounts available:

   Account 1 for $500 or over: 5.5 percent per year
     simple interest

   Account 2 for $2,000 or over: 5 percent per year
     compound interest

   Account 3 for $6,000 or over: 6.5 percent per year
     simple interest

   Account 4 for $10,000 or over 6 percent per year
     compound interest

   Construct a table showing the projected amount of money in each account at the end of each of the 5 years. Which do you prefer? (2.3 and 2.4)

16. A sum of $1,000 is borrowed today. The loan is to be paid off with interest at the end of 3 years with no payments made in between. Calculate the total interest paid using:

   a. Simple interest of 8 percent per year (2.3)

   b. Compound interest of 8 percent per year (2.4)

17. A $3,000 loan is to be made over 5 years with 12 percent interest. Determine how much will be required to pay off the loan plus interest if

   a. simple interest is used. (2.3)

   b. compound interest is used. (2.4)

18. Trevor needs a new computer for college. His uncle lends him $1,000 at 5 percent interest for 3 years.
    a. What is the total payment after 3 years if simple interest is used? (2.3)
    b. How much of the total payment is simple interest? (2.3)
    c. What is the total payment after 3 years if compound interest is used? (2.4)
    d. How much of the total payment is compound interest? (2.4)

19. Jayjeet wants to purchase a car but needs $5,000 to do so. His uncle Eswar offers to loan him the money at 8 percent compounded yearly. Uncle Shankar offers to loan him the money at 9 percent simple interest. If both loans are to be paid in a lump sum in 5 years, which loan should Jayjeet use? (2.3 and 2.4)

20. For each of the parts below, you want to withdraw $8,000 from an account at the end of 10 years.
    a. What single sum of money must you deposit today if the account earns 8 percent compound interest? (2.4)
    b. What value of simple interest yields the same single sum of money as determined in part (a)? (2.3)

21. You decide to place $12,000 on deposit for 4 years. The bank offers you 6 percent compounded annually.
    a. What is the total amount of money in the account at the end of 4 years? (2.4)
    b. What value of simple interest would be necessary to have the same amount of money in the account at the end of 4 years? (2.3)

22. If Kathy borrows $11,000 to remodel her beach house at 7 percent compounded annually for 5 years, what is the principal, the interest, and the final amount paid if all are paid at the end of year 5? (2.4)

23. A man lends $2,500 at 8 percent per year simple interest for 4 years. At the end of this time, he invests the entire amount (principal plus interest) at 6 percent compounded annually for 9 years. How much money will he have at the end of the 13-year period? (2.3 and 2.4)

24. You need to borrow $10,000, which you will pay back in 4 years. Your local bank has the following four loan accounts available:

Account	Interest (Percent)	Interest Type
1	7	Compounded annually
2	7.5	Simple
3	7.5	Compounded annually
4	8.25	Simple

Regardless of the account chosen, you will not pay back any money until the end of the fourth year. Construct a table showing the projected loan balance (i.e., the amount you owe) for each account at the end of each of the 4 years. If your objective is to repay the least amount of money, which account do you prefer? (2.3 and 2.4)

Section 2.4.1

25. Develop a single spreadsheet that allows you to calculate $F|P$ and $P|F$ factors. For each cell where the calculation is performed, place above it a small "control panel" that allows you to enter whatever numbers you need to perform the calculation. For example, for the $F|P$ factor, your control panel must include i and n. Test each of your factors against the tables in Appendix A to ensure they work right. Keep this handy. It will be useful to you.

26. Emma loans Austin $25,000 with interest compounded at a rate of 8 percent per year. How much will Austin owe Emma if he repays the loan at the end of 5 years?

27. Charlotte wishes to accumulate $100,000 in a savings account in 10 years. If she wishes to make a single deposit today and the bank pays 4 percent compounded annually on deposits of this size, how much should Charlotte deposit in the account?

28. How much will a $25,000 investment today be worth in 10 years if it earns 7 percent annual compound interest?

29. What deposit today is required for it to be worth $150,000 in 25 years if the deposit earns 5 percent annual compound interest?

30. On August 1, 1958, first-class postage for a 1-ounce envelope was 4¢. On August 1, 2007, a first-class stamp for the same envelope cost 41¢. What was the annual compound increase in the cost of first-class postage during the 49-year period?

31. How much money can be withdrawn at the end of the investment period if
    a. $1,000 is invested at 8 percent/year compounded annually for 10 years?
    b. $5,000 is invested at 11 percent/year compounded annually for 4 years?
    c. $13,000 is invested at 9 percent/year compounded annually for 7 years?
    d. $25,000 is invested at 10 percent/year compounded annually for 3 years?

32. How much money would have to be deposited today to accumulate
    a. $10,000 after 6 years if the investment earns 5%/year compounded annually.
    b. $6,500 after 4 years if the investment earns 8 percent/year compounded annually? 4777
    c. $3,400 after 12 years if the investment earns 6 percent/year compounded annually? 1689
    d. $13,500 after 5 years if the investment earns 10 percent/year compounded annually? 8382

33. What will be the amount accumulated by each of the following present investments?
    a. $3,000 invested for 7 years at 14 percent compounded annually
    b. $1,600 invested for 17 years at 12% compounded annually
    c. $20,000 invested for 38 years at 16 percent compounded annually
    d. $3,500 invested for 71 years at 8 percent compounded annually
    e. $5,000 invested for 34 years at 11.5 percent compounded annually

34. What is the present value of the following future receipts?
    a. $19,000 five years from now at 9 percent compounded annually 12349
    b. $8,300 twelve years from now at 15 percent compounded annually 1551
    c. $6,200 fifty-three years from now at 12 percent compounded annually 15.
    d. $13,000 eighteen years from now at 19.2 percent compounded annually 551
    e. $5,000 ten years from now at 8 percent compounded annually

35. What rate of interest compounded annually is involved if
    a. an investment of $10,000 made now will result in a receipt of $23,674 ten years from now?
    b. an investment of $2,000 made 18 years ago has increased in value to $15,380?
    c. an investment of $2,500 made now will result in a receipt of $4,212 five years from now?

36. What present amount of money must be deposited at 11 percent interest compounded annually to grow to $15,000 in 9 years? Give your answer to the nearest penny.
    a. Use the tables provided in Appendix A.
    b. Use the formula, either in a spreadsheet or using a calculator.
    c. Use the PV function in Excel®.

37. For your twenty-first birthday, your grandfather offers you a gift of $1,000 today. However, you have the choice of waiting 3 years and receiving $1,500 or waiting 5 years and receiving $3,000. If your money grows at a rate of 8 percent compounded annually, which alternative should you choose?

38. Jason takes out a loan at 10 percent compounded annually for 7 years. At the end of this period, he pays off the loan at a value of $23,384.61. What amount did he borrow? 12,000

39. Calculate using the interest formula the factor $(P|F\ 11.5\%, 37)$. Compare that to the result using Excel®'s PV function.

40. You want to withdraw a single sum amount of $6,000 from an account at the end of 7 years. This withdrawal will zero out the account. What single sum of money deposited today is required if the account earns 12 percent per year compounded annually?
    a. Use the tables provided in Appendix A.
    b. Use the $P|F$ formula directly in Excel® or your calculator.
    c. Use an appropriate Excel® function.

41. If $5,000 is borrowed today and $8,955 is paid back in 10 years, what interest rate compounded annually has been earned?

42. If you invest $1,500 today and withdraw $2,500 in 3 years, what interest rate was earned?

43. If you have $2,500 to invest and need to withdraw $4,430 at some time in the future, what is the minimum number of whole years to leave the money invested at 5 percent?

44. At what interest rate will money
    a. double itself in 10 years? 7.1%
    b. triple itself in 10 years? 12%
    c. quadruple itself in 10 years? 15%

 45. With interest at 9 percent compounded annually, what is the fewest number of years (integer-valued) required for money to double in magnitude?

46. With interest at 6 percent compounded annually, what is the fewest number of years (integer-valued) required for money to triple in magnitude?

 47. What is the smallest integer-valued annual compound interest that will result in an investment tripling in value in less than or equal to 10 years?

48. How long, to the nearest year, does it take an investment at 6 percent compounded annually to (nearly, more or less)
    a. double itself?
    b. triple itself?
    c. quadruple itself?

49. Use the six approaches from Example 2.10 to determine to the nearest year how long it takes for an investment to double if the interest is compounded annually at the following rates:
    a. 5 percent
    b. 7 percent
    c. 10 percent
    d. 15 percent
    e. 20 percent

 50. You purchase a quarter section (160 acres) of land for $176,000 today and sell it in exactly 9 years for $525,000 at auction. At what annual compound rate did the value of your land grow?

 51. If you deposit $5,000 four years from today, how much can you withdraw 10 years from today if interest is 8.5 percent per year compounded annually?

52. You want to have $15 million available when you retire in 40 years (if you think that is exorbitant, wait until you learn about inflation in Chapter 12). If your money can grow in a high-performing stock index fund at a rate of 12 percent per year, how much would you have to invest today?

Section 2.4.2

 53. Ben deposits $5,000 now into an account that earns 7.5 percent interest compounded annually. He then deposits $1,000 per year at the end of the first and second years. How much will the account contain 10 years after the initial deposit?

54. If you invest $2,000 today, $3,000 in 2 years, $4,000 in 5 years, and $1,000 in 7 years, how much will be in the bank 15 years from today if interest is 6 percent compounded annually?

 55. If you invest $2,000 today, withdraw $1,000 in 3 years, deposit $3,000 in 5 years, deposit $1,500 in 8 years, and withdraw the entire sum 3 years after the final deposit, how much will you withdraw? Interest is 7 percent per year.

56. The cash flow profile for an investment is given below, and the interest rate is 6.5 percent compounded annually.

EOY	0	1	2	3	4	5	6	7
Cash Flow	$0	−$500	$200	$400	−$300	$500	−$200	$100

    a. Find the future worth of this cash flow series using the actual cash flows.
    b. Find the present worth of this series using the actual cash flows.
    c. Find the present worth using the future worth.

57. The cash flow profile for an investment is given below, and the interest rate is 8 percent compounded annually.

EOY	0	1	2	3	4	5	6
Cash Flow	$0	$500	−$200	$600	$300	−$100	$200

  a. Find the present worth of this series using the actual cash flows.

  b. Find the future worth of this cash flow series using the actual cash flows.

  c. Find the future worth using the present worth.

  d. Find the worth of the series at EOY 4 using the individual cash flows.

  e. Find the present worth using the worth at EOY 4.

58. Renaldo borrows $8,000 from his aunt today to help pay for college expenses. He agrees to repay the loan according to the following schedule, at a rate of 6 percent/year compounded annually.

End of Year	0	1	2	3	4	5	6	7	8
Cash Flow	$8,000	$0	$0	$0	$0	−$X	−($X + 100)	−($X + 400)	−$2X

  a. Draw the cash flow diagram from Renaldo's perspective.

  b. Find the value of X such that the loan is fully repaid with the last payment.

  c. What is the dollar amount of each of the 4 payments?

59. Ken loans his grandson Rex $20,000 at 5.5 percent per year to help pay for executive chef schooling in Florida. Rex requires 3 years of schooling before beginning to earn a salary. He agrees to pay Ken back the loan following the schedule below:

End of Year	0	1	2	3	4	5	6	7	8
Cash Flow	$20,000	$0	$0	$0	−$X	−$2X	−$3X	−$4X	−$5X

  a. Draw the cash flow diagram from Ken's perspective.

  b. Find the value of X such that the loan is fully repaid with the last payment.

  c. What is the dollar amount of each of the 5 payments?

  d. Quite by surprise, following successful on-time completion of all payments, Ken gives back to Rex all interest paid. What is the amount of Ken's check?

60. An investment has the following cash flow series where interest is 8 percent:

End of Year	0	1	2	3	4	5	6	7	8
Cash Flow	$300	$300	$600	−$500	−$300	$0	$800	$700	$600

  a. Determine the present worth of the series.

  b. Determine the future worth of the series at the end of year 8.

  c. Find the worth of the series at the end of year 2.

61. An investment has the following cash flow series where interest is 5 percent:

End of Year	0	1	2	3	4	5	6	7	8
Cash Flow	$150	$300	$450	$0	−$500	$0	$600	$700	$800

  a. Determine the present worth of the series.

  b. Determine the future worth of the series at the end of year 8.

  c. Find the worth of the series at the end of year 6.

62. The manager at a Sherwin-Williams store has decided to purchase a new $30,000 paint-mixing machine with hi-tech instrumentation for matching color and other components. The machine may be paid for in one of two ways: (1) pay the full price now, less a 3 percent discount, or (2) pay $5,000 now, $8,000 one year from now, and $6,000 at the end of each of the next 4 years. If interest is 12 percent compounded annually, determine the best way for the manager to make the purchase.

Section 2.4.2.1

63. Develop a single spreadsheet that allows you to calculate any of the $P|A$, $A|P$ $F|A$, or $A|F$ factors. For each cell where the calculation is performed, place above it a small "control panel" that allows you to enter whatever numbers you need to perform the calculation. For example, for the $F|A$ factor, your control panel must include i and n. Test each of your factors against the tables in Appendix A to ensure they work right. Keep this handy. It will be useful to you.

64. If you borrow $40,000 at 9 percent annual compound interest and pay it back with 7 equal annual payments, what will be the size of each payment if the first payment occurs 1 year after borrowing the $40,000?

65. Sara Beth made annual deposits of $5,000 in an account that paid 4 percent compounded annually. How much money should be in the account immediately after her tenth deposit?

66. Jason has been making equal annual payments of $7,500 to repay a college loan. He has just made an annual payment and now wants to pay off the rest of the loan immediately. He has eight payments remaining. With an annual compound interest rate of 6 percent, how much should Jason pay?

67. Adriana wishes to accumulate $2,000,000 in 35 years. If 35 end-of-year deposits are made into an account that pays interest at a rate of 7 percent compounded annually, what size deposit is required each year to meet Adriana's stated objective?

68. Juan borrows $25,000 at 7 percent compounded annually. If the loan is repaid in five equal annual payments, what will be the size of Juan's payments if the first payment is made 1 year after borrowing the money?

69. Each year, $7,500 is invested at 4 percent annual compound interest.
     a. What is the value of the investment portfolio after 20 years? After 25 years? After 30 years?
     b. Repeat part (a) with the investment at 5 percent annual compound interest.
     c. Based upon your answers to (a) and (b), what conclusions can be drawn regarding the impact of the interest earned versus the duration of the investment?

70. An amount equal to $50,000 is borrowed at 7 percent annual compound interest.
     a. What size equal annual payment is required if the first of five payments is made 1 year after receiving the $50,000?
     b. What size payment is required if the first of five payments is not made until 4 years after receipt?

71. Using a 5 percent annual compound interest rate, what investment today is needed in order to withdraw $5,000 annually
     a. for 10 years?
     b. for 10 years if the first withdrawal does not occur for 3 years?

72. If money is worth more than 0 percent to you, would you rather receive $10,000/year for 5 years or receive $5,000/year for 10 years? What is your preference if you must pay these amounts, rather than receive them?

73. What uniform series over the interval [1,8] will be equivalent to a uniform series of $10,000 cash flows over the interval [3,10] based on
     a. a 6 percent annual compound interest rate?
     b. a 10 percent annual compound interest rate?

74. What uniform series over the interval [11,20] will be equivalent to uniform series of $10,000 cash flows over the interval [1,10] based on
     a. a 6 percent annual compound interest rate?
     b. A 10 percent annual compound interest rate?

75. You deposit $1,000 in a fund at the end of each year for 10 years. The fund pays 5 percent compounded annually. How much money is available to withdraw immediately after your last deposit?

76. Eight equal deposits of $1,000 are made at the end of each year into a fund paying 8 percent per year.
    a. What is the present worth 1 year before the first deposit?
    b. What is the future worth immediately after the last deposit?
    c. What is the future worth 3 years after the last deposit?

77. In planning for your retirement, you would like to withdraw $60,000 per year for 10 years. The first withdrawal will occur 20 years from today.
    a. What amount must you invest today if your return is 10 percent per year?
    b. What amount must you invest today if your return is 15 percent per year?

78. You purchase a house for $250,000 directly from the buyer who owns the home outright. You pay a 20 percent down payment. You sign a first mortgage, and the buyer agrees to finance the remaining $200,000 at 7 percent annual compound interest with annual end-of-year payments over 12 years. How much is a single yearly payment?

79. How much money can be withdrawn at the end of the investment period if
    a. $4,000 is invested at the end of each of 3 years at 5 percent/year compounded annually, with the lump sum then shifted into an investment paying 8 percent/year for 5 additional years?
    b. $12,000 is invested at the end of each of 10 years at 10 percent/year compounded annually, with the lump sum then shifted into an investment paying 5 percent/year for 3 additional years?
    c. $18,000 is invested at the end of each of 5 years at 9 percent/year compounded annually, with the lump sum then shifted into an investment paying 7 percent/year for 8 additional years?

80. How much money can be withdrawn at the end of 15 years if
    a. $2,000 is deposited at the end of each year and earns 5 percent/year compounded annually?
    b. $3,000 is deposited at the end of each year for 10 years and no deposits are made thereafter, where the fund earns 8 percent?
    c. $2,000 is deposited at the end of years 1 through 5, $4,000 is deposited at the end of years 6 through 10, and $6,000 is deposited at the end of years 11 through 15, with all deposits earning 8 percent?

81. Determine the present worth of 5 equal annual deposits of $1,200 at the end of years 1 through 5, followed by 4 equal annual withdrawals of $700 at the end of years 4 through 7. Note that both years 4 and 5 will have a deposit and a withdrawal. Interest is 5 percent.

82. You take out a loan to buy a new audio system. Your equal annual payments are 20 percent of the amount you borrowed. The interest rate on the loan is 7 percent compounded annually.
    a. Determine the number of years you will be required to make payments (may be a non-whole year such as 4.791, for example).
    b. If you make the same payment for an integer number of years, rounding up from your answer in part (a), what interest rate will you be paying?

83. You take out a loan to build a swimming pool in your new home's backyard. Your equal annual payments are 1/6 of the amount you borrowed. If it will take you 7 years to fully repay the loan, what is the interest rate on the loan?

84. You decide to open an IRS-approved retirement account at your local brokerage firm. Your best estimate is that it will earn 9 percent. At the end of each year for the next 25 years, you will deposit $4,000 per year into the account (25 total deposits). Three years after the last deposit, you will begin making annual withdrawals.
    a. How much money is in the account 1 year before the first withdrawal?
    b. If you want to make 30 annual withdrawals, what amount will you be able to withdraw each year?
    c. If you want the account to last forever, what amount will you be able to withdraw each year?

85. You plan to open a retirement account. Your employer will match 50 percent of your deposits up to a limit on the match of $2,500 per year. You believe the fund will earn 12 percent per year over the next 30 years, and you will make 30 deposits of $5,000, plus 50 percent employer matching, totaling $7,500 per year.
    a. How much money will be in the account immediately after the last deposit?
    b. How much total money will you put into the fund?
    c. How much total money will your employer put into the fund?
    d. How much will be the total investment earnings?

e. If you want the account to last for 30 years (30 withdrawals), starting 1 year after the last deposit, what amount will you be able to withdraw each year?

f. If you want the account to last forever, what amount will you be able to withdraw each year?

86. Janie deposits $10,000 in the bank today. Starting 3 years from now, she makes equal withdrawals of $1,000 for 5 years and then withdraws the remaining amount 10 years from now. How much will she be able to withdraw 10 years from now, assuming the bank pays 6 percent compounded annually?

87. Fishing Designs has arranged to borrow $15,000 today at 12 percent interest. The loan is to be repaid with end-of-year payments of $3,000 at the end of years 1 through 4. At the end of year 5, the remainder will be paid. What is the year 5 payment?

88. You deposit X in an account on your twenty-fifth, thirtieth, and thirty-fifth birthdays. The account pays 9 percent. You intend to withdraw your savings in 10 equal annual withdrawals on your forty-first, forty-second, . . . ,fiftieth birthdays, just depleting your account. After making the withdrawal on your forty-fifth birthday, you have $32,801.60 left in the account. What is X?

89. You put $20,000 on deposit on your thirtieth birthday at 5 percent compounded annually. On your fortieth birthday, the account begins earning 6 percent. Then on your fiftieth birthday, it begins earning 7 percent. You plan to withdraw equal annual amounts on your sixty-first, sixty-second, . . . , seventieth birthdays.

a. How much will be your annual withdrawal?

b. On your sixty-fifth birthday, you decide to withdraw the entire amount remaining. How much do you withdraw?

90. Determine the equivalent annual cash flow of this series at 10 percent interest:

End of Year	0	1	2	3	4	5	6	7	8
Cash Flow	−$2,500	$3,000	$4,500	$0	−$5,000	$0	−$1,000	$7,000	$3,000

91. Develop a mathematical relationship for finding the accumulated amount F at the *end* of n years that will result from a series of n beginning-of-year payments each equal to B if these payments are placed in an account for which the interest rate is $i\%/year$.

a. Express the relationship between F and B in terms of the factors listed in the tables of Appendix A.

b. Express the relationship between F and B in terms of i and n.

c. Demonstrate that your answers to (a) and (b) are equivalent by calculating the value of F using $B = \$1,000$, $n = 5$, and $n = 10$ percent for each approach.

Section 2.4.2.2 (Use of a gradient factor is expected in each problem)

92. Develop a single spreadsheet that allows you to calculate the $P|G$, $F|G$, and $A|G$ factors. For each cell where the calculation is performed, place above it a small "control panel" that allows you to enter whatever numbers you need to perform the calculation. For example, for the $P|G$ factor, your control panel must include i and n. Test the $P|G$ and $A|G$ factors against the tables in Appendix A to ensure they work right. Keep this handy. It will be useful to you.

93. You want to be able to withdraw $800 from a savings account at the end of year 1, $900 at the end of year 2, $1,000 at the end of year 3, and so on over a total of 5 years. How much money must be on deposit right now, at the end of year 0, to just deplete the account after the 5 withdrawals if interest is 5 percent compounded annually?

94. Deposits are made at the end of years 1 through 7 into an account paying 6 percent per year interest. The deposits start at $5,000 and increase by $1,000 each year. How much will be in the account immediately after the last deposit?

95. A small company wishes to set up a fund that can be used for technology purchases over the next 6 years. Their forecast is for $12,000 to be needed at the end of year 1, decreasing by $2,000 each year thereafter. The fund earns 8 percent per year. How much money must be deposited to the fund at the end of year 0 to just deplete the fund after the last withdrawal?

96. An easy payment plan offered by a local electronics store for your new audio system calls for payments of $2,000, $2,500, $3,000, and $3,500 at the ends of years 1 through 4, respectively. Your money is well invested and earns a consistent 10 percent per year.

a. What is the present worth of these payments?

b. If you prefer to make equal annual payments having the same present worth, how much would they be?

97. A person you trust asks you to loan them $2,000 at the end of year 1, $1,000 at the end of year 2, nothing in year 3, and then they will pay you $1,000 in year 4, $2,000 in year 5, and $3,000 in year 6. They note that you will pay out a total of $3,000 to them, and then they will pay back $6,000 to you, allowing you to "double your money!" If you make 12 percent per year on your investments, determine the present worth of this series of cash flows.

98. Consider the following cash flow profile:

EOY	Cash Flow	EOY	Cash Flow	EOY	Cash Flow
0	−$75,000	3	+$9,000	6	+$18,000
1	+$3,000	4	+$12,000	7	+$21,000
2	+$6,000	5	+$15,000	8	+$24,000

Using a gradient series factor, determine the present worth equivalent for the cash flow series using an annual compound interest rate of

a. 6 percent.

b. 7 percent.

99. On Juan's twenty-sixth birthday, he deposited $7,500 in a retirement account. Each year thereafter, he deposited $1,000 more than the previous year. Using a gradient series factor, determine how much was in the account immediately after his thirty-fifth deposit if

a. the account earned annual compound interest of 5 percent.

b. the account earned annual compound interest of 6 percent.

100. A $90,000 investment is made. Over a 5-year period, a return of $30,000 occurs at the end of the first year. Each successive year yields a return that is $3,000 less than the previous year's return. If money is worth 5 percent, use a gradient series factor to determine the equivalent present worth for the investment.

101. What single sum of money occurring at $t = 5$ will be equivalent to a cash flow series consisting of $7,000 at $t = 1$, $6,000 at $t = 2$, $5,000 at $t = 3$, $4,000 at $t = 4$, $3,000 at $t = 5$, $2,000 at $t = 6$, and $1,000 at $t = 7$, based on an interest rate of

a. 6 percent.

b. 10 percent.

102. Consider the following cash flow profile:

EOY	Cash Flow	EOY	Cash Flow	EOY	Cash Flow
0	−$50,000	3	+$11,000	6	+$8,000
1	+$13,000	4	+$10,000	7	+$7,000
2	+$12,000	5	+$9,000	8	+$6,000

What is the present worth equivalent for the cash flow series with an interest rate of 12 percent?

103. In Problem 102, using an interest rate of 10 percent, what uniform series over the closed interval [1,8] is equivalent to the cash flow profile shown?

104. In Problem 102, using an interest rate of 8 percent, what single sum of money occurring at the end of year 8 is equivalent to the cash flow profile shown?

105. In Problem 102, with an interest rate of 6 percent, what increasing gradient series is equivalent to the cash flow profile shown if the gradient series sought has a value of X at EOY $= 1$ and a value of $8X$ at EOY $= 8$?

106. Consider the following cash flow profile:

EOY	Cash Flow	EOY	Cash Flow	EOY	Cash Flow
0	−$45,000	3	+$10,000	6	+$7,000
1	+$12,000	4	+$9,000	7	+$6,000
2	+$11,000	5	+$8,000	8	+$5,000

With a compounded annual interest rate of 6 percent, what single sum of money at the end of the sixth year will be equivalent to the cash flow series?

107. In Problem 106, what uniform annual series over [4,7] will be equivalent to the cash flow profile if money is worth 6 percent compounded annually?

108. In Problem 106, suppose the positive-valued cash flows are replaced by a positive gradient series. If the cash flow at end-of-year 8 is $10,000, what first year payment and gradient step make the cash flow profiles equivalent?

WILEY 109. Maintenance costs on a certain piece of equipment are estimated to be $500, $600, $700, $800, and $900 at the end of years 1, 2, 3, 4, and 5, respectively. The time value of money rate is 8 percent compounded annually.

    a. What is the present value of the maintenance costs?

    b. What is the uniform annual equivalent maintenance cost?

110. A series of 25 end-of-year deposits is made that begins with $1,000 at the end of year 1 and increases at the rate of $200 per year with a 12 percent interest rate compounded annually.

    a. What amount can be withdrawn at $t = 25$?

    b. What uniform annual series of deposits $(n = 25)$ would result in the same accumulated balance at $t = 25$?

WILEY 111. A series of 10 end-of-year deposits is made that begins with $7,000 at the end of year 1 and decreases at the rate of $300 per year with 10 percent interest.

    a. What amount could be withdrawn at $t = 10$?

    b. What uniform annual series of deposits $(n = 10)$ would result in the same accumulated balance at the end of year 10?

112. Miller Machining needs to purchase a piece of machinery to be able to compete on a new contract with a first-tier automotive supplier. The machinery will cost $140,000, and the owner arranges to borrow the entire amount at 8 percent interest. The initial payment 1 year after purchase is $11,000 with successive payments increasing each year by $X. The last payment is to be made 6 years after the purchase.

    a. By how much ($X) does the payment increase each year?

    b. What is the amount of the final payment?

    c. Suppose that, at the last minute, the company decides to purchase the same machinery at the same rate (8 percent), with payments decreasing by $7,500 each year. How much is the first payment?

113. Lee Chiew is borrowing $170,000 from AsiaBankUSA to open Asian Health Foods in Virginia. She agrees to repay the loan at 10 percent compounded annually. Since she expects it to take a few years to be consistently making more than her expenses, she has arranged for minimal "good faith" payments of $10,000 at the end of each of the first 4 years. Beginning with the fifth year's payment, she will increase the amount from $10,000 to $10,000 + X, then pay $10,000 + 2X at year 6, continuing to increase by X each year until the loan is paid in full at the end of year 9.

    a. How much is $X?

    b. What is the dollar amount of the last payment?

    c. Each payment consists of principal plus interest. The total principal paid will be $170,000. How much total interest is included in the payments Lee Chiew will make?

114. What single sum of money at the end of year 3 is equivalent to a payment series of $10,000 the first year, $9,000 the second year, . . . ,down to $6,000 the fifth year? Assume that money has a time value of 10 percent/year compounded annually.

WILEY 115. Consider a loan of $10,000 and the following pattern of cash flows.

End of Year	0	1	2	3	4
Cash Flow	−$10,000	$3,000	$4,000	$5,000	$6,000

    a. What is the interest rate that makes the present worth equal to $0.00?

    b. Using the interest rate determined in part (a) and leaving the −$10,000 at year 0 in place, determine the equal annual incomes that are equivalent to the gradient series in years 1, 2, 3, and 4?

116. Piyush has recently inherited 20 million INR (Indian rupees) from his late uncle Scrooge. To keep Piyush from spending his money immediately, Scrooge made arrangements for the inheritance to be deposited at the time of his death into an account paying 5 percent. Further arrangements instructed the bank to pay Piyush 2 million INR at the end of year 1, 2 million + X INR at the end of year 2, 2 million + 2X INR at the end of the year 3, 2 million + 3X INR at the end of year 4, and so on for a period of 10 years, just depleting the fund after the tenth payment.

    a. What is the value of X?

    b. How much is in the fund immediately after the fifth withdrawal?

117. Consider the following series of cash flows:

End of Year	−1	0	1	2	3	4	5	6	7	8	9	10
Cash Flow	$1,200	$1,000	$800	$500	$500	$500	$500	$0	−$800	−$800	$0	$1,500

Clearly set up an expression and determine the value of a lump sum equivalent amount of the above cash flows at year 5 if $i = 7$ percent. Use at least one each of the following factors:

$$A|G\,i\%,n; P|A\,i\%,n; F|A\,i\%,n; F|P\,i\%,n; P|F\,i\%,n$$

118. A cash flow profile starts with $2,000 and increases by $1,000 each year up to $21,000 at time 20. Then it starts again with $21,000 at time 21 and decreases by $1,000 each year to $2,000 at year 40. You desire to convert it to an equivalent gradient series beginning at year 1 with $$X$ and continuing through year 40 with $500 increases each year (ending at $$X + 19,500$ at time 40). Interest is 8 percent compounded annually. What is X?

119. Your friend claims that the following series of payments is absolutely worthless since they add up to $0:

End of Year	0	1	2	3	4	5	6	7	8	9	10
Cash Flow	$100	$80	$60	$40	$20	$0	$−20	−$40	−$60	−$80	−$100

The time value of money is 18 percent. Determine the present value of these cash flows.

120. Below is an equation to compute the present value of a cash flow series. Determine the cash flow profile that is implied by the equation.

$$P = 800 + 950(P|A\,i\%,4) - 450(P|G\,i\%,4) - 600(P|A\,i\%,3)(P|F\,i\%,4)$$

121. Below is an equation to compute the present value of a cash flow series. Determine the cash flow profile that is implied by the equation.

$$P = -7,000 + [1,850 + 200(A|G\,8\%,6)](P|A\,8\%,6)(P|F\,8\%,4)$$

122. Develop a mathematical relationship for finding the accumulated amount F at the *end* of n years of a gradient series where the interest is $i\%$. Put differently, you already have access to a $(P|G\,i\%,n)$ factor. Develop an $(F|G\,i\%,n)$ factor.

    a. Express the $(F|G\,i\%,n)$ factor in terms of the existing factors listed in the tables of Appendix A.

    b. Express the $(F|G\,i\%,n)$ factor in terms of i and n.

    c. Demonstrate that your answers to (a) and (b) are equivalent by calculating the value of F using a first payment of $0, increasing by $1,000 each year with $n = 5$ and $i = 10$ percent for each approach.

Section 2.4.2.3

123. Develop a single spreadsheet that allows you to calculate the $(P|A_1\,i\%,j\%,n)$, $(F|A_1,i\%\,j\%, n)$, and $(A|A_1\,i\%,j\%,n)$ factors. (Note that the $(A|A_1\,i\%\,j\%,n)$ factor is not in Appendix A.) For each cell where the calculation is performed, place above it a small "control panel" that allows you to enter whatever numbers you need to perform the calculation. For example, for the $(P|A_1\,i\%,j\%,n)$ factor, your control panel must include i, j, and n. Test the first two factors using $i = 7$ percent, $j = 5$ percent, and $n = 10$ against the tables in Appendix A to ensure they work right. Then, using $A_1 = \$1,000$, $i = 7$ percent, and $j = 5$ percent, calculate A using the third factor and check it against $(P|A_1\,i\%,j\%,n)*(A|P\,i\%,n)$. Keep this handy. It will be useful to you.

124. Suppose you make 30 annual investments in a fund that pays 5 percent compounded annually. If your first deposit is $7,500 and each successive deposit is 5 percent greater than the preceding deposit, how much will be in the fund immediately after the thirtieth deposit?

125. In Problem 124, how much will be in the fund immediately after the thirtieth deposit if the fund pays 6 percent compounded annually and each successive deposit is 6 percent greater than the preceding deposit?

126. On Juan's twenty-sixth birthday, he invested $7,500 in a retirement account. Each year thereafter, he deposited 8 percent more than the previous deposit. The account paid annual compound interest of 5 percent. How much was in the account immediately after his thirty-fifth deposit?

127. In Problem 126, if Juan decided to wait 10 years before investing for retirement, how much would he have to invest on his thirty-sixth birthday to have the same account balance on his sixtieth birthday?

128. In Problem 126, what uniform annual investment is required to achieve the same account balance?

129. A $90,000 investment is made. Over a 5-year period, a return of $30,000 occurs at the end of the first year. Each successive year yields a return that is 10 percent less than the previous year's return. If money is worth 5 percent, what is the equivalent present worth for the investment?

130. Consider the following cash flow profile:

EOY	Cash Flow	EOY	Cash Flow	EOY	Cash Flow
0	−$45,000	3	+$10,000	6	+$7,000
1	+$12,000	4	+$9,000	7	+$6,000
2	+$11,000	5	+$8,000	8	+$5,000

Suppose the positive-valued cash flows are now replaced by a geometric series. If the cash flow at end-of-year 1 is $10,000, what geometric rate is required for the cash flow profiles to be equivalent? Interest is at a compounded annual rate of 6 percent.

131. On your child's first birthday, you open an account to fund her college education. You deposit $2,000 to open the account. Each year, on her birthday, you make another deposit, with each being 10 percent larger than the previous deposit. The account pays interest at 5 percent per year compounded annually. How much money is in the account immediately after the deposit on her eighteenth birthday?

132. You are preparing the business plan for a new company. A net revenue analysis covering the first 6 years is required for obtaining financing. Net revenue in year 1 is expected to be $50,000 and increase by 15 percent each year thereafter. If $i = 12$ percent and the net revenue is assumed to be an end-of-year cash flow, what is the present value of the cash flow series over the 6 years?

133. A famous high-volume calculus text generates royalties beginning with $60,000 in the first year and declining each year by 40 percent of the previous year due to used sales and competition. The author is on a 4-year cycle of revision. Determine the present worth of one complete cycle of royalties if the author's time value of money is 7 percent.

134. A cash flow series is increasing geometrically at a rate of 6 percent per year. The initial cash flow at $t = 1$ is $1,000. The increasing payments end at $t = 20$. The interest rate in effect is 15 percent compounded annually. Find the present amount at $t = 0$ that is equivalent to this cash flow series.

135. You want to be able to withdraw $1,000 from a savings account at the end of year 1, with withdrawals increasing by 10 percent each year thereafter over a total of 5 years. How much money must be on deposit right now, at the end of year 0, to just deplete the account after the five withdrawals if interest is 5 percent compounded annually?

136. Deposits are made at the end of years 1 through 7 into an account paying 5 percent per year interest. The deposits start at $4,000 and increase by 15 percent each year. How much will be in the account immediately after the last deposit?

137. A small company wishes to set up a fund that can be used for technology purchases over the next 6 years. Their forecast is for $9,000 to be needed at the end of year 1, increasing by 5 percent each year thereafter. The fund earns 10 percent per year. How much money must be deposited to the fund at the end of year 0 to just deplete the fund after the last withdrawal?

138. An easy payment plan offered by a local electronics store for your new audio system calls for payments of $2,000 at the end of year 1, increasing by 15 percent each year thereafter through year 4. Your money is well invested and earns a consistent 10 percent per year.

    a. What is the present worth of these payments?

    b. If you prefer to make equal annual payments having the same present worth, how much would they be?

139. Maintenance on a test track simulator used to "exercise" vehicles 24/7 for engineering reliability analyses is expected to require $14,000 the first year increasing by 10 percent each year thereafter during its 5-year life. Interest is 15 percent.

    a. Determine the present worth of this series of expenditures.

    b. What is the equal annual amount that has the same present worth?

140. Upon the birth of your son, you open an account to fund his college education. You deposit $1,500 to open the account. Each year, on his birthday, you make another deposit, each being 15 percent larger than the previous deposit. The last deposit is on his seventeenth birthday. The account has earnings of 6 percent per year compounded annually. How much money is in the account on his eighteenth birthday, one year after the last of eighteen deposits?

141. You are helping a friend prepare a business plan for his already-prospering consultancy. Net revenue in year 1 is expected to be $140,000, increasing by 10% each year thereafter. If $i = 15\%$ and the net revenue is assumed to be an end-of-year flow, what is the present value of the cash flow series over a 5 year planning period?

142. In a new highly automated factory, labor costs are expected to decrease at an annual rate of 5 percent; material costs will increase at an annual rate of 4 percent; overhead costs will increase at 8 percent. The labor, material, and overhead costs at the end of year 1 are $2 million, $3 million, and $1.6 million, respectively. The time value of money rate is 11 percent, and the time horizon is 7 years.

    a. Determine the dollar value for *each cost category* (labor, material, overhead) for *each year* and determine the *total cost* for *each year*. (Hint: Use a spreadsheet!)

    b. Determine the present worth of each cost category and the total cost.

    c. Determine the annual worth over 7 years that is equivalent to the present worth of the total cost.

143. Susan gets a job upon completion of her MSME degree with a mechanisms design firm. Her starting salary is $70,000; each successive year she gets a 5 percent raise. Assuming she deposits 10 percent of her salary each year into a fund earning 8 percent interest, how much money will she have in 10 years to donate to her university?

144. A boat is purchased by financing $50,000. The loan is to be paid over a 5-year period with annual payments based on a 15 percent compounding rate per year. Each successive payment is scheduled to be 10 percent greater than the previous one.

    a. Determine the size of the smallest payment.

    b. Determine the size of the largest payment.

145. Carlson Photography receives royalties based on the use of their photographs with a major client. Every year, the client makes deposits in Carlson's bank account that earns 6 percent compounded annually. The client increases the amount they deposit into the Carlson account by 4 percent per year. If the client initially gives Carlson $15,000, how much will the account have in 5 years?

Section 2.5

146. Develop a single spreadsheet that allows you to (1) calculate the effective annual interest rate given the nominal annual interest rate and the number of compounding periods per year, and (2) calculate the nominal annual interest rate given the effective annual interest rate and the number of compounding periods per year. Use the "control panel" approach that allows you to enter whatever numbers you need to perform the calculation. Keep this handy. It will be useful to you.

147. What equal monthly investment is required over a 40-year period to achieve a balance of $2,000,000 in an investment account that pays monthly interest of ¾ percent?

148. How many monthly payments are required to repay a loan of $12,000 with an interest rate of ¾ percent per month and end-of-month payments of $400?

149. What is the effective annual interest rate for 10 percent compounded (a) semiannually, (b) every 4 months, (c) quarterly, (d) every other month, (e) monthly?

150. What is the effective annual interest rate for 5 percent compounded (a) semiannually, (b) every 4 months, (c) quarterly, (d) every other month, (e) monthly?

151. A total of $50,000 is borrowed and repaid with 60 monthly payments, with the first payment occurring 1 month after receipt of the $50,000. The stated interest rate is 6 percent compounded monthly. What monthly payment should be made?

152. A refrigerator sold for $500. The store financed it by charging 0.5 percent monthly interest on the unpaid balance. If the refrigerator is paid for with 30 equal end-of-month payments,
    a. what will be the size of the monthly payments?
    b. what will be the size of the monthly payments if the first payment is not made until 1 year after the purchase?

153. If you deposit $4,000 into an account paying 6 percent per year compounded semiannually, how much will you have in the account after 10 years?

154. How much money must be deposited now in order to withdraw $10,000 in 4 years if interest is 5 percent compounded quarterly?

155. You invest $10,000 in a fund that pays 7 percent per year for 5 years. How much is in the fund at the end of 5 years if (forgetting leap years and making "convenient" assumptions)
    a. compounding is annual?
    b. compounding is quarterly?
    c. compounding is monthly?
    d. compounding is daily?

156. How much money must be invested in an account that pays 6 percent per year interest to be worth $20,000 at the end of 8 years if (forgetting leap years and making "convenient" assumptions)
    a. interest is compounded annually?
    b. interest is compounded semiannually?
    c. interest is compounded quarterly?
    d. interest is compounded monthly?
    e. interest is compounded weekly?
    f. interest is compounded daily?
    g. interest is compounded hourly?
    h. interest is compounded minutely?
    i. interest is compounded secondly?

157. You decide to open a retirement account at your local bank that pays 8 percent/year/month (8 percent per year compounded monthly). For the next 20 years, you will deposit $400 per month into the account, with all deposits and withdrawals occurring at month's end. On the day of the last deposit, you will retire. Your expenses during the first year of retirement will be covered by your company's retirement plan. As such, your first withdrawal from your retirement account will occur on the day exactly 12 months after the last deposit.
    a. What monthly withdrawal can you make if you want the account to last 15 years?
    b. What monthly withdrawal can you make if you want the account to last forever (with infinite withdrawals)?

158. Wei Min opens a retirement account that pays 8 percent/year/month. For the next 30 years, he deposits $300 per month into it, with all deposits occurring at the end of the month. On the day of the last deposit, Wei Min retires. As a benefit to retirees, the bank increases the interest rate to 12 percent/year/quarter from that time on. His first withdrawal will occur exactly 2 years after his last deposit. He then plans to make equal quarterly withdrawals from the account.
    a. What is the balance of the account immediately after the last monthly deposit?
    b. What is the balance of the account one quarter before the first quarterly withdrawal?
    c. What quarterly amounts can be withdrawn to last for 15 years?

159. You borrow $2,000 from Gougo's, a well-known loan consolidation outfit. The loan is an "unbelievably low" 2.5 percent per month compounded monthly. You have 2 years to pay back the loan.
    a. What is the nominal interest rate?
    b. What is the effective interest rate?
    c. If you wait until the end of year 2 to pay it off in one lump sum, how much must you pay? Use the "period interest rate" approach.
    d. If you wait until the end of year 2 to pay it off in one lump sum, how much must you pay? Use the "effective interest rate" approach.
    e. Of your payment in parts (c) or (d), how much is interest?
    f. Suppose you make equal end-of-month payments. How much is the monthly amount?

160. Naihui and Haiyan deposit $250 into their joint account at the end of each month. They want to have a total of $12,000 in their account after 40 months.

    a. What monthly rate of interest must they earn?

    b. What nominal annual rate of interest must they earn?

    c. What effective annual rate of interest must they earn?

161. You have your eyes on a new automobile costing $25,000. If you wrote a check for the $25,000, you could drive off in your new car. However, you don't have it and must finance $20,000 through the dealership at 15 percent/year/month over a 5-year period. The dealer then proceeds to add on a 1.25 percent loan initiation fee of $250. Also, they have a prepaid loan closeout fee of another $250. Then there is the paperwork filing and storage fee of another $100 and another prepaid loan maintenance fee of only $8/ month or $480. At this point, they are speaking very fast and assure you that these little "required" amounts are routine and can be rolled into your loan. They figure your monthly payment for the $20,000 loan as $A = \$21,080(A|P\ 1.25\%,60) = \$501.49$.

    a. What is the monthly rate of "interest" you are really paying for the $20,000 loan?

    b. What is the nominal annual "interest" rate you are really paying for the $20,000 loan?

    c. What is the effective annual "interest" rate you are really paying for the $20,000 loan?

162. You are down on your luck and need a loan, quick! You locate Mr. Loa N. Shark who advertises weekly loans for "an almost imperceptibly small rate" of only 3 percent, prepaid at the time of loan. You sign over your Federal tax refund for $1,000 to Mr. Shark, with proof that it is correct and will be forthcoming from the IRS in 1 week.

    a. How much money does Mr. Shark hand you?

    b. How much weekly interest are you really paying?

    c. What is the nominal annual interest rate?

    d. What is the effective annual interest rate?

163. Your boss, who never took an engineering economy course, is buying a new house and needs your help in answering some questions. The loan amount will be in the "jumbo loan" category of $600,000 at (1) 7 percent per year compounded monthly over 30 years, or (2) 6.625 percent compounded monthly over 15 years. There are no loan initiation fees, points paid, or other charges. Prepayment, if desired, can be done without penalty.

    a. What is the monthly payment for plan (1)?

    b. What is the monthly payment for plan (2)?

    c. What is the effective annual interest rate for plan (1)?

    d. What is the effective annual interest rate for plan (2)?

    e. What is the total interest paid over the life of loan (1)?

    f. What is the total interest paid over the life of loan (2)?

Section 2.6

164. A total of $50,000 is borrowed and repaid with 60 *monthly* payments, with the first payment occurring 1 month after receipt of the $50,000. The stated interest rate is 6 percent compounded *quarterly*. What monthly payment is required?

165. David and Tami deposit $150 into their joint account at the end of each *month*. If their account earns 6 percent per year compounded *quarterly*, how long will it take them to have a total of $20,000 in their savings account?

166. Mario and Claudia deposit $300 into their joint account at the end of each *quarter*. If their account earns 7 percent/ year/*month* (7 percent per year compounded *monthly*), how long will it take them to have a total of $15,000 in their savings account?

167. Mario and Claudia deposit $100 into their joint account at the end of each *month*. If their account earns 7 percent/year/ *quarter* (7 percent per year compounded *quarterly*), how long will it take them to have a total of $15,000 in their savings account?

168. Daniel deposits $20,000 into an account earning interest at 6 percent per year compounded monthly. He wishes to withdraw $1,200 at the end of each *quarter*. For how many *quarters* can he make these withdrawals?

169. Daniel deposits $20,000 into an account earning interest at 6 percent per year compounded quarterly. He wishes to withdraw $400 at the end of each *month*. For how many *months* can he make these withdrawals?

Section 2.7

170. Show the following mathematically:

    a. Using equation 2.9, show mathematically that Equation 2.53 is correct.

    b. Using Equations 2.8 and 2.9, show mathematically that Equation 2.54 is correct.

    c. Using Equation 2.9, show mathematically that Equations 2.55 and 2.56 are correct.

171. Show that Equations 2.57 through 2.60 are correct, using

    a. a cash flow diagram.

    b. the mathematical formulas for each of the factors given.

Appendix 2.A

172. An interest rate is given as 5 percent per year nominal. Determine the effective annual rate if

    a. compounding is annual.

    b. compounding is daily.

    c. compounding is continuous.

173. An interest rate is given as 10 percent per year nominal. Determine the effective annual rate if

    a. compounding is annual.

    b. compounding is daily.

    c. compounding is continuous.

174. How much will $10,000 amount to after 5 years if interest is 10 percent per year compounded continuously?

175. What amount must be placed on deposit today to equal $15,000 in 4 years at 15 percent per year compounded continuously?

176. Equal end-of-period semiannual payments of $500 are made to a fund paying a nominal 10 percent per year compounded continuously.

    a. What will the fund amount to after 7 years?

    b. What is the present worth equivalent of the total set of payments? Use the $500 payments in your calculation.

    c. What is the present worth equivalent of the total set of payments? Use the future worth from part (a) in your calculation.

177. Semiannual deposits, beginning with $500 and increasing by $100 with each subsequent deposit, are made into a fund paying a nominal 10 percent per year compounded continuously.

    a. What will the fund amount to after 7 years?

    b. What is the present worth equivalent of the total set of deposits?

    c. What is the equal semiannual equivalent amount of the deposits?

178. Semiannual deposits beginning with $500 and increasing by a continuously compounded 20 percent, are made to a fund paying a nominal 10 percent per year compounded continuously.

    a. What will the fund amount to after 7 years?

    b. What is the present worth equivalent of the total set of deposits?

    c. What is the equal semiannual equivalent amount of the deposits?

179. A continuous uniform series of deposits totaling $1,000 per year are made into a fund paying 10 percent compounded continuously.

    a. What will the fund amount to after 7 years?

    b. What is the present worth equivalent of the total set of deposits?

180. What continuous uniform series of cash flows over 7 years can be paid out of a fund having $20,000 at the present (or time 0) if interest is 10 percent compounded continuously?

Chapter 3

BORROWING, LENDING, AND INVESTING

Now, and in the future, you will find the material in this chapter to be quite useful, as will the members of this multidisciplinary team from the University of Arkansas, who designed, built, and launched a solar powered boat to compete in the Solar Splash (http://www.solarsplash.com/index.php). (Courtesy of the College of Engineering at the University of Arkansas)

Samuel Washington

Fifteen years after graduating in electrical engineering and accepting employment with Texas Instruments, Samuel Washington decides to establish a consulting business. Although he has invested wisely for the past 15 years, the value of his investments is only $325,000. After developing a business plan, he realizes he will need $250,000 on hand initially, plus $150,000 each successive year, to cover the expenses of an office and an assistant. He is unsure about how much of his own money he should use and how much to borrow. In talking to the loan officer of a local bank, he learns that the bank will charge him annual compound interest of 6 percent for a 5-year loan period or 5.5 percent for a 10-year loan period. Over the past 10 years, Samuel earned an average of 5.25 percent annually on his investments; he believes he will continue to earn at least that amount on his investment portfolio. If he borrows money, he can repay the loan in several ways: pay accumulated interest monthly, plus pay the principal at the end of the loan period; make equal monthly payments; make monthly payments that increase like a gradient series; make monthly payments that increase like a geometric series; or make a lump sum payment at the end of the loan period. Since this is a business investment, any interest paid can be deducted from his taxable income.

With one exception, in this chapter you will learn how to analyze the financial needs Samuel Washington faces. How to incorporate income tax effects in his analysis is reserved for Chapter 10. In addition to learning how to perform the analysis Samuel performed, you will learn how to deal with different compounding frequencies, how to analyze various bond transactions, and how to determine the amount of each loan payment that is an interest versus a principal payment. Throughout the chapter, we show you how to perform the analyses using tabulated values of compound interest factors and using Excel®'s financial functions.

3-1   INTRODUCTION

The material presented in this chapter will prove useful in any financial transaction that occurs over a period of time. Borrowing, lending, and investing money are financial transactions that lend themselves to analysis using material found in this chapter.

Many of the examples in Chapter 2 dealt with borrowing, lending, and investing money. In this chapter, we build on the foundation established in Chapter 2 (which we hope you mastered!). If you have difficulty understanding the material, then you should review one or more sections in the previous chapter.

Our study of borrowing, lending, and investing begins by considering four equivalent loan payment plans that aren't necessarily equivalent insofar as the borrower is concerned. Next, we consider alternative methods of financing a house purchase. Our treatment of borrowing and lending concludes with a consideration of the amount of each loan payment that is an interest payment and the amount that reduces the unpaid principal of the loan.

In our consideration of investing, we do not recommend individual investments for you to make. Instead, we present techniques you can use to evaluate alternative investment strategies.

Our principal investment reminder is this: *Remember the tortoise!* In the fable of the tortoise and the hare, the tortoise won, because *steady wins the race!* We believe steady and consistent investment over a long period of time is the best strategy. In Chapter 2, we emphasized the importance of investing sooner rather than later. Remember, n is in the exponent—it plays a greater role than does i!

3-2   FOUR METHODS OF REPAYING LOANS

In borrowing money, there are many ways a loan can be repaid. However, we will consider the following four payment plans:

1. Pay the accumulated interest at the end of each interest period, and pay the principal at the end of the loan period.

2. Make equal principal payments, plus interest on the unpaid balance at the end of each interest period.

3. Make equal end-of-period payments.

4. Make a single payment of principal and interest at the end of the loan period.

The following example illustrates each method.

Four Loan Payment Plans

1. Pay interest each period, but make no principal payment until the end of the loan period

2. Make equal end-of-period principal payments and pay interest each period on the unpaid balance at the beginning of the period

3. Make equal end-of-period payments over the loan period

4. Make no payment until the end of the loan period

EXAMPLE 3.1   Four Loan Payment Plans

An owner of a small business borrows $10,000 at 15 percent annual compound interest. The loan is to be repaid over a 5-year period using one of the four possible payment plans described above. Payments are made at the end of the year.

Plan 1: As shown in Figure 3.1 and Table 3.1, $1,500 interest payments are made each year, and the $10,000 principal is paid at the end of 5 years. The cash flow profile for end

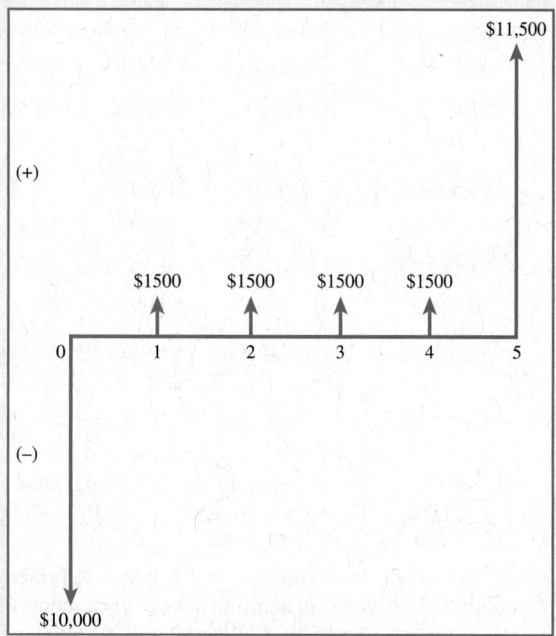

FIGURE 3.1

Lender's *CFD* for Payment Plan 1 in Example 3.1.

TABLE 3.1

Cash Flow Profiles for Four Payment Plans in Example 3.1.

A	B	C	D	E	F	G	H
Payment Plan	End of Year	Interest Accrued During Year	Total Money Owed Before Yearly Payment	Interest Payment	Principal Payment	Total Payment	Total Money Owed After Yearly Payment
1	0						$10,000.00
	1	$1,500.00	$11,500.00	$1,500.00	$0.00	$1,500.00	$10,000.00
	2	$1,500.00	$11,500.00	$1,500.00	$0.00	$1,500.00	$10,000.00
	3	$1,500.00	$11,500.00	$1,500.00	$0.00	$1,500.00	$10,000.00
	4	$1,500.00	$11,500.00	$1,500.00	$0.00	$1,500.00	$10,000.00
	5	$1,500.00	$11,500.00	$1,500.00	$10,000.00	$11,500.00	$0.00
2	0						$10,000.00
	1	$1,500.00	$11,500.00	$1,500.00	$2,000.00	$3,500.00	$8,000.00
	2	$1,200.00	$9,200.00	$1,200.00	$2,000.00	$3,200.00	$6,000.00
	3	$900.00	$6,900.00	$900.00	$2,000.00	$2,900.00	$4,000.00
	4	$600.00	$4,600.00	$600.00	$2,000.00	$2,600.00	$2,000.00
	5	$300.00	$2,300.00	$300.00	$2,000.00	$2,300.00	$0.00
3	0						$10,000.00
	1	$1,500.00	$11,500.00	$1,500.00	$1,483.16	$2,983.16	$8,516.84
	2	$1,277.53	$9,794.37	$1,277.53	$1,705.63	$2,983.16	$6,811.22
	3	$1,021.68	$7,832.90	$1,021.68	$1,961.47	$2,983.16	$4,849.74
	4	$727.46	$5,577.20	$727.46	$2,255.69	$2,983.16	$2,594.05
	5	$389.11	$2,983.16	$389.11	$2,594.05	$2,983.16	$0.00
4	0						$10,000.00
	1	$1,500.00	$11,500.00	$0.00	$0.00	$0.00	$11,500.00
	2	$1,725.00	$13,225.00	$0.00	$0.00	$0.00	$13,225.00
	3	$1,983.75	$15,208.75	$0.00	$0.00	$0.00	$15,208.75
	4	$2,281.31	$17,490.06	$0.00	$0.00	$0.00	$17,490.06
	5	$2,623.51	$20,113.57	$10,113.57	$10,000.00	$20,113.57	$0.00

of year t was developed using the following relations among columns in Table 3.1: $C_t = 0.15H_{t-1}$; $D_t = C_t + H_{t-1}$; $E_t = C_t$; $F_t = \$0.00$ for $t = 1, \ldots, 4$; $F_5 = \$10,000$; $G_t = E_t + F_t$; and $H_t = D_t - G_t$.

Plan 2: As shown in Figure 3.2 and Table 3.1, principal payments of $2,000 are made each year for 5 years, in addition to yearly payments of the interest on the unpaid balance (i.e., payments of $3,500, $3,200, $2,900, $2,600, and $2,300). The cash flow profile for end of year t was developed using the following relations: $C_t = 0.15H_{t-1}$; $D_t = C_t + H_{t-1}$; $E_t = C_t$; $F_t = \$2,000$ for $t = 1, \ldots, 5$; $G_t = E_t + F_t$; and $H_t = D_t - G_t$.

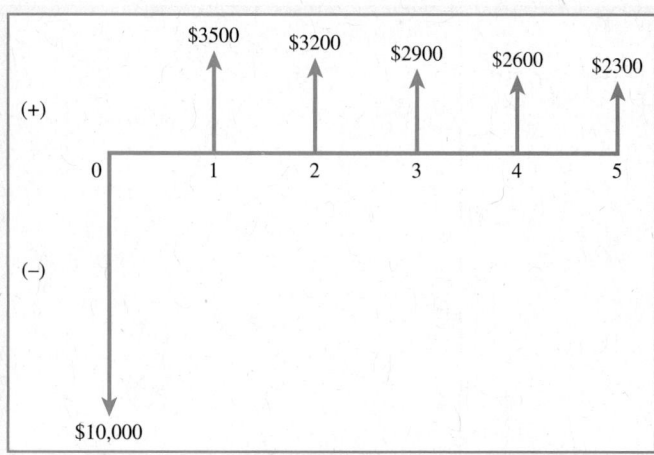

FIGURE 3.2
Lender's *CFD* for Payment Plan 2 in Example 3.1.

Plan 3: As shown in Figure 3.3 and Table 3.1, five equal annual payments are made totaling

$$A = \$10,000(A|P\,15\%,5) = \$2,983.20$$

or, using Excel®,

$$A = \text{PMT}(15\%,5,-10000) = \$2983.16$$

The cash flow profile for end of year t was developed using the following relations: $C_t = 0.15\,H_{t-1}$; $D_t = C_t + H_{t-1}$; $E_t = C_t$; $G_t = \$2,983.16$ for $t = 1, \ldots, 5$; $F_t = G_t - E_t$; and $H_t = D_t - G_t$.

Plan 4: As shown in Figure 3.4 and Table 3.1, after 5 years, make a single payment of

$$F = \$10,000(F|P\,15\%,5) = \$20,113.60$$

or, using Excel®,

$$F = \text{FV}(15\%,5,,-10000) = \$20,113.57$$

The cash flow profile for end of year t was developed using the following relations: $C_t = 0.15\,H_{t-1}$; $D_t = C_t + H_{t-1}$; $E_t = F_t = 0$ for $t = 1, \ldots, 4$; $E_5 = \$10,000(1.15)^5 - \$10,000$; $F_5 = \$10,000.00$; $G_t = E_t + F_t$; and $H_t = D_t - G_t$.

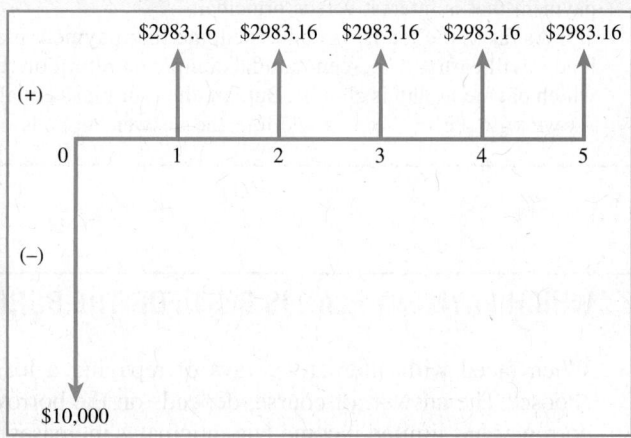

FIGURE 3.3
Lender's *CFD* for Payment Plan 3 in Example 3.1.

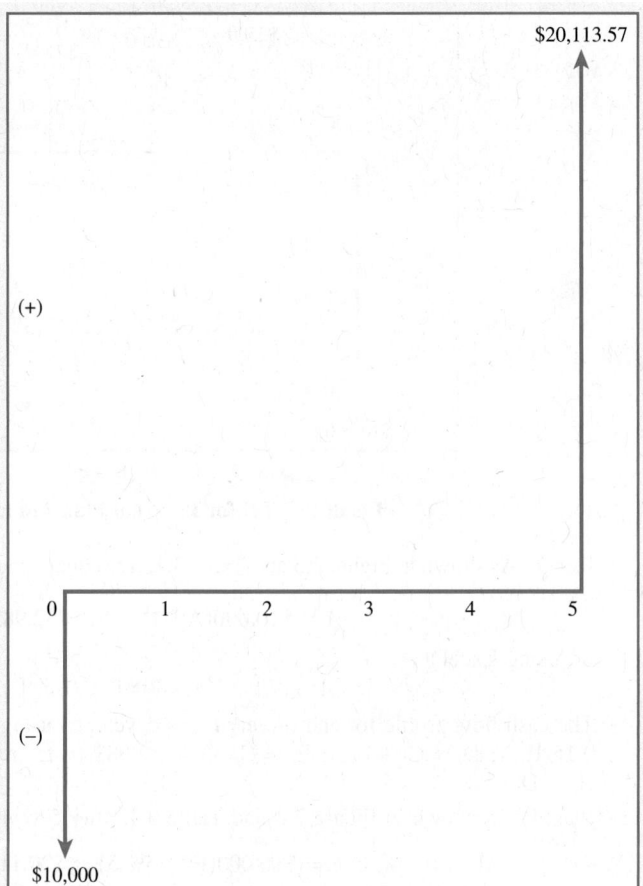

FIGURE 3.4
Lender's *CFD* for Payment Plan 4 in Example 3.1.

Except for payment Plan 3, the development of each cash flow profile was quite straightforward. In Section 3.5, we show how to determine the amount of each uniform payment that is interest versus principal.

As far as the lender is concerned, the four payment plans are equally desirable. The lender will earn a 15 percent annual compound return on the $10,000 loan, regardless of which payment plan is chosen. But, are the four plans equally preferred by the borrower? As we will see in the next section, the answer depends on the borrower's *TVOM*.

3-3 WHICH PAYMENT PLAN IS BEST FOR THE BORROWER?

When faced with alternative ways of repaying a loan, which should the borrower choose? The answer, of course, depends on the borrower's financial situation. If the borrower has limited income but anticipates increases in future income, then it might be necessary to keep the initial payments as small as possible; Plan 1 and Plan 4 would be the most appealing in this circumstance.

As noted in the previous example, the four payment plans provided the lender with a 15 percent return on the $10,000 loan. However, what about the borrower? Which payment plan minimizes the present worth of the payments made by the borrower? The answer depends on the relationship between the lender's interest rate and the borrower's *TVOM*.

EXAMPLE 3.2 Which Payment Plan Is Best (for the Borrower)?

Suppose in the previous example, where the borrower's *TVOM* is 15 percent, that the lender's interest rate is less than 15 percent, equal to 15 percent, or more than 15 percent. Which payment plan would the borrower prefer?

Table 3.2 contains the present worth of the loan payments the borrower made for the four payment plans. The borrower's present worth for the loan transaction, when the lender charges $i\%$, is given as follows for each payment plan:

$$PW_1(15\%) = \$10,000 - \$10,000(i)(P|A\,15\%,5) - \$10,000(P|F\,15\%,5)$$

$$PW_2(15\%) = \$10,000 - (\$2,000 + \$10,000(i))(P|A\,15\%,5) + \$2,000(i)(P|G\,15\%,5)$$

$$PW_3(15\%) = \$10,000 - \$10,000(A|P\,i\%,5)(P|A\,15\%,5)$$

$$PW_4(15\%) = \$10,000 - \$10,000(F|P\,i\%,5)(P|F\,15\%,5)$$

 The present worth given in Table 3.2 was obtained using Excel®'s **NPV** function for three values of the lender's interest rate: 10 percent; 15 percent; and 20 percent.

As expected, when the borrower's *TVOM* equals the lender's interest rate, the present worth is the same for all payment plans. However, when the lender's interest rate on the loan is less than the borrower's *TVOM*, the preferred payment plan is Method 4: *Make a single payment of principal and interest at the end of the loan period.* When the lender's

TABLE 3.2
Borrower' Present Worth of $10,000 Loan with Four Payment Plans.

| End of Year | Lender's Interest Rate = 10% | | | |
	Plan 1	Plan 2	Plan 3	Plan 4
0	$10,000.00	$10,000.00	$10,000.00	$10,000.00
1	−$1,000.00	−$3,000.00	−$2,637.97	$0.00
2	−$1,000.00	−$2,800.00	−$2,637.97	$0.00
3	−$1,000.00	−$2,600.00	−$2,637.97	$0.00
4	−$1,000.00	−$2,400.00	−$2,637.97	$0.00
5	−$11,000.00	−$2,200.00	−$2,637.97	−$16,105.10
PW(15%)	$1,676.08	$1,098.56	$1,157.10	$1,992.92

(Continued)

TABLE 3.2
(Continued)

Lender's Interest Rate = 15%

End of Year	Plan 1	Plan 2	Plan 3	Plan 4
0	$10,000.00	$10,000.00	$10,000.00	$10,000.00
1	−$1,500.00	−$3,500.00	−$2,983.16	$0.00
2	−$1,500.00	−$3,200.00	−$2,983.16	$0.00
3	−$1,500.00	−$2,900.00	−$2,983.16	$0.00
4	−$1,500.00	−$2,600.00	−$2,983.16	$0.00
5	−$11,500.00	−$2,300.00	−$2,983.16	−$20,113.57
PW(15%)	$0.00	$0.00	$0.00	$0.00

Lender's Interest Rate = 20%

End of Year	Plan 1	Plan 2	Plan 3	Plan 4
0	$10,000.00	$10,000.00	$10,000.00	$10,000.00
1	−$2,000.00	−$4,000.00	−$3,343.80	$0.00
2	−$2,000.00	−$3,600.00	−$3,343.80	$0.00
3	−$2,000.00	−$3,200.00	−$3,343.80	$0.00
4	−$2,000.00	−$2,800.00	−$3,343.80	$0.00
5	−$12,000.00	−$2,400.00	−$3,343.80	−$24,883.20
PW(15%)	−$1,676.08	−$1,098.56	−$1,208.93	−$2,371.35

interest rate is greater than the borrower's *TVOM*, the preferred payment plan is Plan 2: *Make equal principal payments, plus interest on the unpaid balance at the end of the period.*

The borrower's *TVOM* reflects the value of the borrower's money. A convenient way to think of the borrower's *TVOM* is what is being earned on his or her investments. When faced with liquidating an investment that is earning an annual return of 10 percent to purchase something costing $10,000 versus borrowing the money at a 15 percent annual compound interest rate, the borrower wants to reduce the unpaid principal quickly. Of the four payment plans considered, Plan 2 reduces unpaid principal the quickest. Similarly, if the borrower's investments are earning 20 percent, then it is desirable to delay paying any money as long as possible; Plan 4 delays paying money until the end of the loan period.

Figure 3.5 illustrates how the four payment plans differ for different values of the lender's interest rate on the loan. Notice, the preferences do not change: Plan 2 is preferred when a lender's interest rate is greater than the borrower's *TVOM*; Plan 4 is preferred when a lender's interest rate is less than the borrower's *TVOM*. (We revisit the four payment plans in Chapter 10, where we address deducting interest paid from taxable income; in Chapter 12 we consider the impact of inflation on the preferred payment plan.)

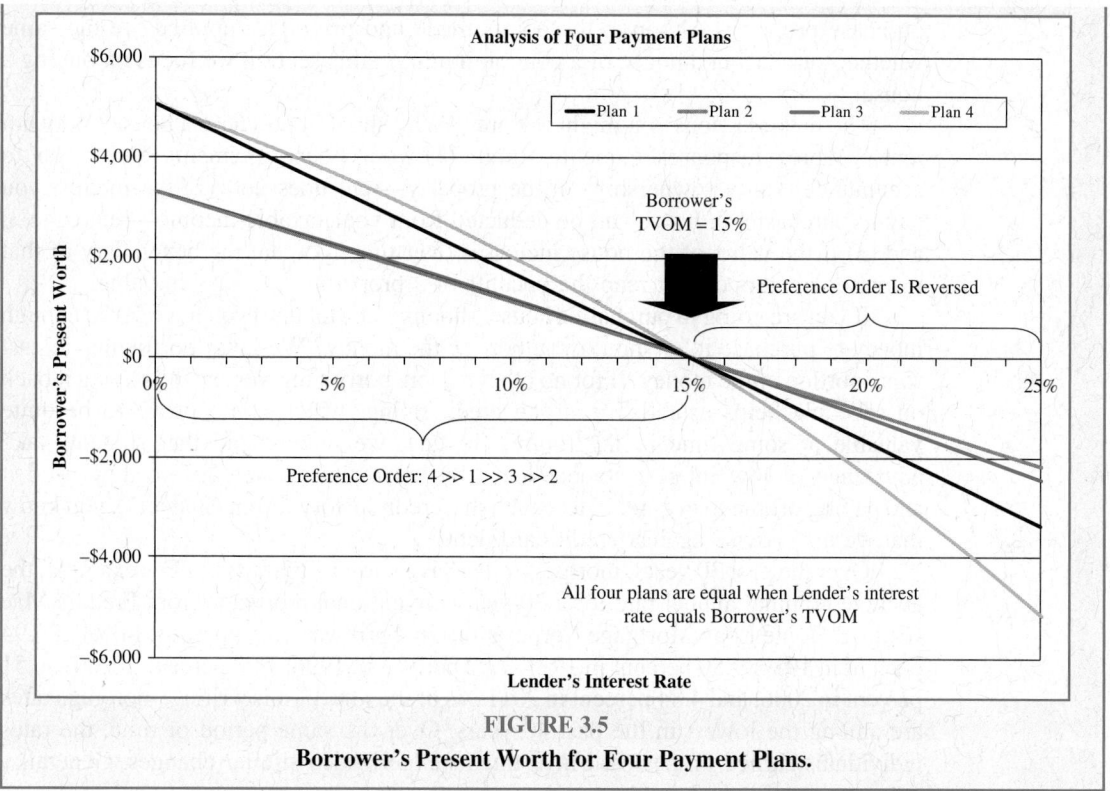

FIGURE 3.5
Borrower's Present Worth for Four Payment Plans.

The Borrower's Preferred Payment Plan

- Plan 4 is preferred if lender's interest rate < borrower's *TVOM*
- Plan 2 is preferred if lender's interest rate > borrower's *TVOM*

3-4 REAL ESTATE INVESTMENT

Because buying a home is usually the largest purchase a person makes in his or her lifetime, and because so many students ask questions about financing such a purchase, we will focus specifically on that topic in this section. There is no shortage of literature available to educate a first-time home buyer; likewise, numerous Web sites provide a wealth of information that can prove helpful to someone contemplating spending thousands of dollars on real estate. (*Buying Your Home: Settlement Costs & Helpful Information*, published by the U.S. Department of Housing and Urban Development, is a good starting point, as is the HUD Web site: www.hud.gov.)

Before getting into the nitty-gritty of determining payment sizes, a disclaimer is in order: This text treats briefly the subject of purchasing real estate, and the interest rates we use are unlikely to be representative of the rate you will pay when you purchase property. Although the points made and principles applied are the same whether purchasing a house or a condominium, in this section we focus on buying a house.

The first questions you might ask are, ''Why should I purchase a house? Why not rent?'' Three responses come to mind: (1) your house payments allow you to accumulate equity (ownership) in the property—rent does not; (2) the interest you pay in purchasing a house can be deducted from your taxable income—rent cannot; and (3) if the value of the house increases over time, you are the beneficiary of that increase—renters do not reap the benefits of a property's increase in value.

If you are going to purchase a house, should you wait until you have saved enough money to purchase it, or should you borrow the money? We favor borrowing at least some portion of the money. If for no other reason, borrowing money and paying it back on schedule helps establish a strong credit rating, which could prove to be quite valuable at some time in the future. (In fact, we recommend that students take advantage of low interest student loans by borrowing money before they need it and paying off the loan quickly to establish a credit history. From Chapter 2, you know that we also advise against credit card debt!)

Over the past 30 years, mortgage rates have varied significantly. For example, the average nominal annual rate for a 30-year conventional mortgage from Freddie Mac (Federal Home Loan Mortgage Corporation) in April was 15.58 percent in 1981, 9.94 percent in 1986, 9.50 percent in 1991, 7.92 percent in 1996, 7.08 percent in 2001, 6.51 percent in 2006, and 4.84 percent in 2011. As of the time of this writing, mortgage rates are among the lowest in the past 40 years. Over the same period of time, the rates individuals earned on personal investments experienced similar changes. Generally, returns on individual investments are greater than 30-year conventional mortgage rates. However, we cannot guarantee that you will earn more on your investments than the interest rate you will pay in purchasing a house.

When you visit with a mortgage broker, a loan officer at a bank, a savings and loan officer, or the Web sites of any number of financial institutions, you will find many different ways available to finance a house purchase. For example, the following mortgage alternatives are available at Arvest Bank:

1. 30-year conventional fixed rate mortgage
2. 15-year conventional fixed rate mortgage
3. 30-year Federal Housing Authority (FHA) mortgage
4. 15-year FHA mortgage
5. 30-year Veterans Authority (VA) mortgage
6. 3/1 30-year Adjustable Rate Mortgage (ARM), adjustable annually, with a 3-year duration
7. 5/1 30-year ARM, adjustable annually, with a 5-year duration

The financial transaction in securing the mortgage is called a *closing*. At the closing, a number of financial charges occur, including but not limited to an appraisal fee, a credit report, hazard insurance premium, title insurance fees, government recording charges, state tax, tax service fee, flood certification, underwriting fee, interest, and a settlement or closing fee. For a mortgage in the amount of $225,000, such charges might total more than $4,000.00. Depending on the buyer's financial situation, these costs might be included in the amount borrowed from the lending institution or agent. If not, then the buyer must be prepared to pay such costs at closing.

Loan payments for conventional fixed rate mortgages are calculated in the same way that we did in Chapter 2 using the $(A|P \ i\%, n)$ factor. As mentioned, financial institutions add closing costs. They also charge what are called "points." These are one-time charges that occur when the loan is initiated. One "point" equals 1 percent of the loan amount. The number of points is negotiable - typically, trade-offs occur between points and the interest rate charged (i.e., the lower the interest rate, the greater the number of points the lender charges).

One of the payment plans considered previously, Plan 1, is an interest-only loan, meaning that interest-only payments are made until the final payment, and it is usually limited to 5 or 10 years. A related loan is a "balloon" loan, which includes equal monthly payments, usually based on a lower rate than a conventional mortgage, and requires a lump sum (balloon) payment at the end of the loan period. Plan 3 is a conventional loan. Interestingly, banks and mortgage institutions typically do not have alternatives akin to Plans 2 or 4, which (depending on the borrower's *TVOM*) minimize the borrower's present worth equivalent of loan payments. Plans 2 and 4, however, are used in corporate financing.

Interest-only and balloon loans are popular for young professionals who expect salary increases and promotions. Their thinking goes something like this: when our disposable income is significantly greater, we will refinance the house and begin making payments that will generate equity in the property. Interest-only and balloon loans are also popular for persons who do not expect to own the house for many years. Since the average ownership for a house is less than 5 years, they expect to either sell the house and upgrade to another in the same city or be transferred to another city within a 5-year period. Building equity is not as important as being able to deduct the interest from taxable income and benefit from the appreciated value of the property within the 5-year period. Finally, interest-only and balloon payments are appealing to those who believe current interest rates are higher than they will be in a few years. Rather than become "locked in" with a high interest rate, such buyers plan to refinance when interest rates drop.

Similar arguments lead some buyers to use ARMs. In contrast to conventional, interest only, and balloon loans, where the interest rate is fixed, the interest rate for an ARM can increase or decrease over time. Typically, the interest rate for an ARM changes with the overall economy. Generally, the interest rate applied to the ARM is linked to an index, such as 1-, 3-, or 5-year U.S. Treasury securities or LIBOR (London InterBank Offered Rate). In addition, as noted by the Federal Reserve Board, "Another common index is the national or regional average cost of funds to savings and loan associations.... You should ask what index will be used and how often it changes. Also ask how it has behaved in the past and where it is published."

"To determine the interest rate on an ARM, lenders add to the index rate a few percentage points called the 'margin.' The amount of the margin can differ from one lender to another, but it is usually constant over the life of the loan."[1]

The amount the interest rate can increase at the end of an adjustment period is usually capped. The federal government requires a limit be placed on the maximum interest rate that can be charged during the life of the loan. Also, some ARMs place limits on the number of times the interest rate can increase in a given period of time.

---

[1]*Consumer Handbook on Adjustable Rate Mortgages,* Federal Reserve Board, Office of Thrift Supervision, Item 2196 (9402); to order call: 800-530-9393.

EXAMPLE 3.3 Buying and Selling a House

To purchase a house that cost $325,000, Adriana Lopez made a $100,000 down payment. She financed the remaining $225,000 using a 30-year conventional loan at a 5 percent per annum compounded monthly interest rate with 0 points and no additional closing costs. How much were her monthly payments? If she sold the house for $395,000 after 5 years, how much equity would she have had in the house at the time of its sale?

The monthly house payment is computed to be:

$$A = \$225{,}000(\text{A}|\text{P } 5/12\%,360) = \$225{,}000(0.00537) = \$1{,}208.25$$
$$=\text{PMT}(0.05/12,360,-225000) = \$1{,}207.85$$

The unpaid balance on the loan after 5 years is given by the present worth of the remaining 300 monthly payments:

$$P = \$1{,}208.25(\text{P}|\text{A } 5/12\%,300) = \$1{,}208.25(171.06005) = \$206{,}683.31$$
$$=\text{PV}(0.05/12,300,-\text{PMT}(0.05/12,360,-225000)) = \$206{,}614.65$$

The equity in the house equals the difference in its value ($395,000) and the unpaid balance on the loan ($206,614.65), or $188,385.35. Of this amount, $170,000 is due to a combination of appreciation in the house's value and the down payment. The 60 loan payments contributed only $188,385.35 − $170,000.00 = $18,385.35 toward equity. Interestingly (or perhaps depressingly if you are a home owner), over the 5-year period, the home owner made payments totaling $72,741.00, of which $54,085.65 was interest.

Numerous Web sites are available for obtaining up-to-date information on mortgage rates. Figure 3.6 is an example of how an online loan calculator might look. After entering the data for Ms. Lopez's house purchase, the monthly payment of $1,496.93 was obtained. Mortgage payment calculators are available on numerous Web sites, including Arvest Bank, Bank of America, Bloomberg, CNNMoney, SunTrust, USA Today, and Wells Fargo. Notice, in our example, 5 percent is a nominal annual rate, not the effective annual interest rate. The effective annual interest rate for 5 percent per annum compounded monthly is:

$$i_{eff} = (1 + 0.05/12)^{12} - 1 = 0.05116, \text{ or } 5.116\%$$
$$=\text{EFFECT}(5\%,12) = 0.05116, \text{ or } 5.116\%$$

Various financial calculators are available, including an APR calculator. APR stands for annual percentage rate. Figure 3.7 contains the Truth in Lending Disclosure Statement for Ms. Adriana Lopez's 30-year conventional mortgage. As required by the U.S. Department of Housing and Urban Development, the statement "... will show you the 'Annual Percentage Rate' ('APR') and other payment information for the loan you have applied for. The APR takes into account not only the interest rate, but also the points, mortgage broker fees and certain other fees that you have to pay. Ask for the APR before you apply to help you shop for the loan that is best for you. Also ask if your

---

Mortgage Payment Calculator

Home Price	$325,000.00
Down Payment	$100,000.00
Total Loan Amount	$225,000.00
Annual Interest Rate	5.00%
Loan Term	30 years

Calculate Results

Your monthly payment will be $1,207.85.

Total Charges:

Total Payments	$434,824.96
Interest Compounding	Monthly
Total Finance Charge	$209,824.96

FIGURE 3.6

Prototype of a Monthly Loan Payment Calculator

loan will have a charge or fee for paying all or part of the loan before payment is due ('prepayment penalty'). You may be able to negotiate the terms of the prepayment penalty."[2]

For fixed rate loans, the APR calculation is relatively straightforward. However, for variable rate loans (ARMs), the assumptions made regarding future interest rates are unlikely to reflect what will occur. The APR was developed to assist the borrower in comparing alternative mortgage costs. However, from the borrower's perspective, we believe knowing the APR is not nearly as important as knowing the size of the monthly payment and the effective annual interest rate.

Unfortunately, many variations exist in how APR values are calculated. The differences in results may well be due to differences in assumptions concerning, among others: (1) when the first payment is to be made (immediately, in 30 days, or in 45 days), (2) whether interest is prepaid (at the beginning of the month) or postpaid (at the end of the month), (3) whether points are applied only to the loan principal or to the sum of the loan principal and "other" closing costs, (4) the number of days considered in a year (365 versus 360—the product of 30 days per month and 12 months per year), and (5) the number of decimal points included in the calculations.

Basically, the U.S. Congress mandated that lenders quote an "annual percentage rate" that incorporates into the calculation any additional costs incurred at the closing of the loan. The APR calculation is supposed to include any fee that is designated as a pre-paid finance charge; these fees typically include origination fees, discount points, processing fees, underwriting fees, and mortgage insurance - the latter might be required, depending on the size of the down payment relative to the purchase price for

---

[2]*Buying Your Home: Settlement Costs & Helpful Information,* U.S. Department of Housing and Urban Development, Office of Housing—Federal Housing Commission, Item 1583 (9706); to order call: 800-530-9393.

TRUTH-IN-LENDING DISCLOSURE

NAME(S)/ADDRESS(ES) OF BORROWER(S) ("Borrower," "I," "You," or "Your") **ADRIANA LOPEZ** **3826 RAZORBACK CIRCLE** **FAYETTEVILLE, AR 72702**	NAME/ADDRESS OF LENDER (CREDITOR) ("Lender," "Us," or "Our")

PROPERTY ADDRESS **AR Benton**			
LOAN NUMBER **0007439177**	TRANSACTION DATE	**May 26, 2011**	☒ Preliminary ☐ Final

Words, numbers or phrases preceded by a ☐ are applicable only if the ☐ is marked. ☐ All numerical disclosures except the late payment disclosure are estimates.

ANNUAL PERCENTAGE RATE	FINANCE CHARGE	Amount Financed	Total of Payments
The cost of your credit as a yearly rate. **4.9067**%	The dollar amount the credit will cost you. **$ 204,924.69**	The amount of credit provided to you or on your behalf. **$ 223,733.23**	The amount you will have paid after you have made all payments as scheduled. **$428,657.92**

☐ Interest on the amount of credit outstanding during the construction period will be paid   , followed by:

INTEREST RATE AND PAYMENT SUMMARY

	Rate & Monthly Payment
Interest Rate	4.8750%
Principal + Interest Payment	$ 1,190.72
Est. Taxes + Insurance	N/A
Total Est. Monthly Payment	**$ 1,190.72**

VARIABLE RATE:
☐ This transaction is subject to a variable rate feature. Variable rate disclosures have been provided at an earlier time.

PAYABLE ON DEMAND: ☐ This obligation is payable on demand. ☐ The disclosures are based on an assumed maturity of one year.

INSURANCE: You may obtain property insurance from anyone acceptable to Lender.

SECURITY: You are giving a security interest in the real property and any of the following items which are checked:
☐ Goods being purchased. ☐ Funds on deposit with Lender. ☐ Collateral securing other loans with us may also secure this loan.
☐ Other (Specify)

LATE CHARGE: If you are more than **15** days late in making any payment, in addition to your payment, you will pay a late charge of:
☐ the lesser of ☐ the greater of ☐ an amount equal to ☐ **$59.54**   or ☐   **5.0000**% of the payment in default.

PREPAYMENT: If you pay off early, you   ☐ may   ☒ will not   have to pay a penalty.
                     ☐ may   ☒ will not   be entitled to a refund of part of the finance charge.

ASSUMPTION: If this loan is to purchase and is secured by your principal dwelling, and if checked here, ☒ someone buying your dwelling cannot assume the remainder of this purchase money mortgage loan on the original terms. If this loan is to purchase and is secured by your principal dwelling, and if checked here, ☐ someone buying your dwelling may, subject to conditions, be allowed to assume the remainder of this purchase money mortgage loan.

See your contract documents for any additional information about nonpayment, default, any required repayment in full before the scheduled date, prepayment refunds and penalties and Creditor's policy regarding assumption of the obligation.
There is no guarantee that you will be able to refinance to lower your rate and payments.
You are not required to complete this agreement merely because you have received these disclosures or signed a loan application.
☒ Please refer to the "Good Faith Estimate" for a breakdown of fees,   ☐ Please refer to the Itemization of Amount Financed Statement.
     charges and amount financed.

SIGNATURES: By signing you acknowledge receipt of a completed copy of this disclosure. You understand that this is not a contract and does not reflect all of the terms and conditions of the mortgage transaction to which the disclosures reflected on this form relate.

X_____	X_____
ADRIANA LOPEZ DATE	DATE
X_____	X_____
DATE	DATE

FIGURE 3.7

Truth in Lending Disclosure Form

the house. Only fees directly associated with the loan are supposed to be included in the APR calculation. Hence, the APR calculation does not include attorney fees and, other possible costs not directly associated with the loan.

    Among the various approaches used to compute the APR, we will consider two that we have encountered. The first approach, which we call *additive*, determines the nominal annual rate that equates (1) the payment that would be made when the closing costs are added to the amount borrowed with (2) the amount borrowed. The second approach, which we call *subtractive*, determines the nominal annual rate that equates

(1) the payment that would be made without considering closing costs with (2) the difference in the amount borrowed and the closing costs.

To illustrate the approaches used, let

n = number of monthly payments to be made

i = monthly interest rate

P = amount borrowed

c_o = closing costs, other than points

p_1 = points applied to the amount borrowed

p_2 = points applied to "other" closing costs

C = closing costs, including points and "other" closing costs
$= p_1 P + (1 + p_2)c_o$

$$A_{add} = \text{payment, including closing costs}$$
$$= (P + C)(A|P\,i\%,n) = \text{PMT}(i\%,n,-(P+C)) \tag{3.1}$$

$$A_{sub} = \text{payment, excluding closing costs}$$
$$= P(A|P\,i\%,n) = \text{PMT}(i\%,n,-P) \tag{3.2}$$

APR_{add} = nominal annual percentage rate using the *additive* approach

APR_{sub} = nominal annual percentage rate using the *subtractive* approach

Mathematically, the *additive* approach determines the *APR* as follows:

$$APR_{add} = \text{RATE}(n,-A_{add},P)*12 \tag{3.3}$$

Mathematically, the subtractive approach is determined as follows:

$$APR_{sub} = \text{RATE}(n,-A_{sub},P-C)*12 \tag{3.4}$$

Among the *APR* calculators available, we will use eFunda's (www.efunda.com) to illustrate variations in calculating the *APR* for fixed rate loans. (A Web-based *APR* calculator for adjustable rate mortgages is available at http://www.dinkytown.net.)

EXAMPLE 3.4 Paying Closing Costs

For the house purchase considered in the previous example, suppose Ms. Lopez had to pay 1 point to the lender at closing. Since 1 point is 1 percent of the loan amount, the closing cost would be $2,250. Ms. Lopez can choose to pay the money at the time of closing or she can add it to the loan and finance it under the loan's terms. If she decides to finance the closing costs, she is effectively borrowing $227,250, not $225,000. As shown below, the new monthly payment will be $1,219.93.

$$A = \$227,250(A|P\,5/12\%,360) = \$1,219.93$$

If the lending institution uses the *additive* approach, what will the *APR* be?

$n = 360$, $i = 0.05/12$, $P = \$225,000$, $c_o = \$0$, $p_1 = 1\%$,

$p_2 = 0\%$, $C = 0.01(\$225,000) = \$2,250$, and $A_{add} = (\$225,000 + \$2,250)(A|P\,5/12\%,360)$

$= \text{PMT}(0.05/12,360,-(225000+2250)) = \$1,219.93$

The *additive* approach assumes Ms. Lopez receives $225,000 but makes monthly payments based on borrowing $227,250 from the lending agency. The *APR* is defined to be the nominal annual rate that equates over the loan period (360 months) the $225,000 borrowed from the lending institution with the monthly payment ($1,219.93) required to repay the sum of the closing costs ($2,250) and the amount borrowed ($225,000). From Equation 3.3,

$$APR_{add} = \text{RATE}(360, -\text{PMT}(.05/12, 360, -(225000+2250)), 225000) * 12 = 5.0876\%$$

Entering the required data in eFunda's *APR* calculator (Figure 3.8) yields an APR value of 5.0876% (Figure 3.9). Notice, eFunda uses the Newton-Raphson method of successive approximations to find the root of the polynomial; we use the Excel® **RATE** function.

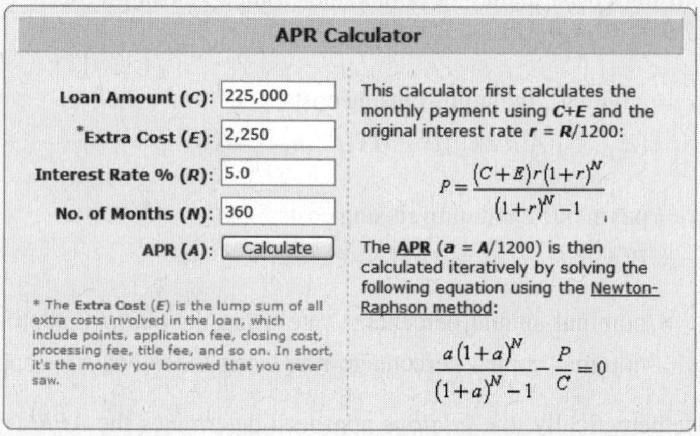

APR Calculator

Loan Amount (*C*): 225,000

*Extra Cost (*E*): 2,250

Interest Rate % (*R*): 5.0

No. of Months (*N*): 360

APR (*A*): [Calculate]

* The **Extra Cost** (*E*) is the lump sum of all extra costs involved in the loan, which include points, application fee, closing cost, processing fee, title fee, and so on. In short, it's the money you borrowed that you never saw.

This calculator first calculates the monthly payment using *C+E* and the original interest rate *r* = *R*/1200:

$$P = \frac{(C+E)r(1+r)^N}{(1+r)^N - 1}$$

The **APR** (*a* = *A*/1200) is then calculated iteratively by solving the following equation using the Newton-Raphson method:

$$\frac{a(1+a)^N}{(1+a)^N - 1} - \frac{P}{C} = 0$$

FIGURE 3.8

Data Entered Using eFunda's APR Calculator and APR Value Obtained.

APR Calculator

Loan Amount (*C*): 225,000

Extra Cost (*E*): 2,250

Interest Rate % (*R*): 5

No. of Months (*N*): 360

[Calculate Again]

APR: 5.0876 %

Monthly Payment: $1,219.93

Total Payment: $439,173.77

Total Interest: $214,173.77

Detailed Payoff Schedule

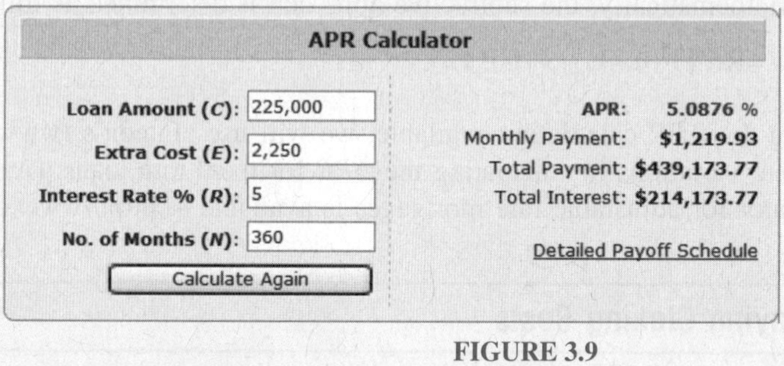

FIGURE 3.9

Second Data Set Entered in eFunda's APR Calculator and APR Value Obtained.

The formula used by eFunda, as shown in Figure 3.8, is identical to the solution procedure we use. Namely, the formula for *P* in Figure 3.8 is the mathematical equivalent of the $(A|P\ i\%, n)$ factor we use to compute the monthly payment.

EXAMPLE 3.5 Other Closing Costs

Suppose Ms. Lopez has to pay $1,000 in closing costs but no points. What will be the size of her monthly payment, her *APR*, and her effective annual interest rate?

If Ms. Lopez finances the $1,000 closing costs, then she finances $226,000. As shown below, her monthly payment will be $1,213.22. (Note, this agrees with eFunda's calculation in Figure 3.10.)

$$A = (\$225,000 + \$1,000)(A|P\,5/12\%,360) = \$1,213.22$$
$$=\text{PMT}(.05/12,360,-226000) = \$1,213.22$$

Continuing with the *additive* approach,

$$n = 360,\ i = 0.05/12,\ P = \$225,000, c_o = \$1,000,\ p_1 = 0\%,\ p_2 = 0\%,$$
$$C = \$1,000,\ \text{and}\ A_{add} = \$226,000(A|P\,5/12\%,360)$$
$$=\text{PMT}(.05/12,360,-226000) = \$1,213.22$$

APR Calculator	
Loan Amount (*C*): 225,000	APR: 5.0390 %
Extra Cost (*E*): 1,000	Monthly Payment: $1,213.22
Interest Rate % (*R*): 5	Total Payment: $436,758.07
No. of Months (*N*): 360	Total Interest: $211,758.07
Calculate Again	Detailed Payoff Schedule

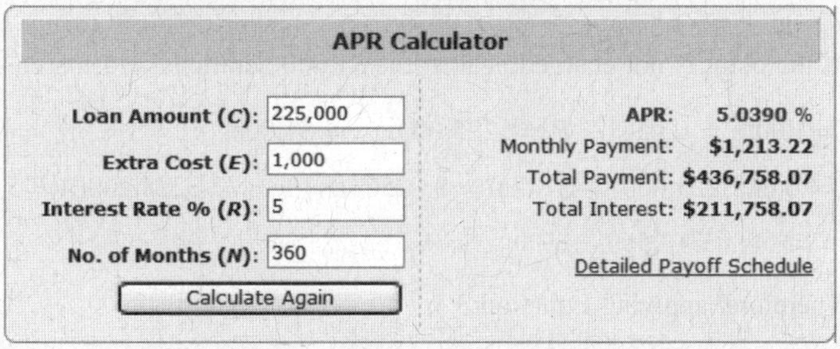

FIGURE 3.10

Third Data Set Entered in eFunda's APR Calculator and APR Value Obtained.

Therefore, applying Equation 3.3,

$$APR_{add} = \text{RATE}(360,-\text{PMT}(.05/12,360,-226000),225000)*12 = 5.0390\%$$

(The eFunda *APR* calculator gives the same result, as shown in Figure 3.10.)

The effective annual interest rate is obtained by noting that Ms. Lopez borrowed $225,000 and made monthly payments of $1,213.22. Therefore, her effective annual interest rate is obtained as follows:

$$i_{eff} = (1+\text{RATE}(360,-\text{PMT}(.05/12,360,-226000),225000))^{\wedge}12-1 = 5.1570\%$$

EXAMPLE 3.6 APR Calculation

If Ms. Lopez has to pay $1,000 in closing costs, plus 1 point, what is the size of her monthly payment, what is her APR, and what is her effective annual interest rate?

If she finances both the additional costs and the point, and if the point is not applied to the sum of the loan amount and the additional $1,000 closing cost, then she actually finances $225,000 + $1,000 + $2,250, or $228,250.00. As shown below, her monthly payment is $1,225.30. (Note this agrees with eFunda's calculation in Figure 3.11.)

$$A = (\$225,000 + 3,250(A|P\ 5/12\%,360) = \$1,225.30$$
$$=\text{PMT}(.05/12,360,-228250) = \$1,225.30$$

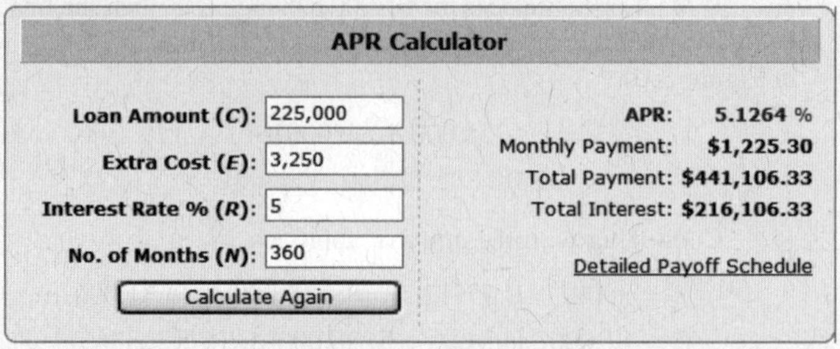

FIGURE 3.11

eFunda, Inc. *APR* Calculator with the *APR* Formula Used.

If the point is not charged against the $1,000 additional closing cost,

$$n = 360, \ i = 0.05/12, \ P = \$225{,}000, \ c_o = \$1{,}000, \ p_1 = 1\%, \ p_2 = 0\%,$$

$$C = 0.01(\$225{,}000) + \$1{,}000 = \$3{,}250, \text{ and } A_{add} = \$228{,}250(A|P \ 5/12\%,360)$$

$$=\text{PMT}(.05/12,360,-225000-3250) = \$1{,}225.30$$

Therefore, applying Equation 3.3,

$$APR_{add} = \text{RATE}(360,-\text{PMT}(.07/12,360,-228250),225000)*12 = 5.1264\%$$

As shown in Figure 3.11, eFunda's APR calculator yields the same result. The effective annual interest rate will be:

$$i_{eff} = (1+\text{RATE}(360,-\text{PMT}(.05/12,360,-228250),225000))^{\wedge}12\text{-}1 = 5.2486\%$$

For example, if the point is charged to the additional closing cost, such that $p_2 = 1\%$, $C = 0.01(\$225{,}000) + 1.01(\$1000) = \$3{,}260$, and $A_{add} = \$228{,}260(A|P \ 5/12\%,360)$

$$=\text{PMT}(.05/12,360,-225000-3260) = \$1{,}225.35$$

Then, applying Equation 3.3,

$$APR_{add} = \text{RATE}(360,-\text{PMT}(.05/12,360,-225000-3260),225000)*12 = 5.1268\%$$

Using eFunda's Advanced APR Calculator, entering the data for the example (Figure 3.12) and calculating the value of APR_{add} yields the same result that we obtained (Figure 3.13).
The effective annual interest rate will be:

$$i_{eff} = (1+\text{RATE}(360,-\text{PMT}(.05/12,360,-228260),225000))^{\wedge}12\text{-}1 = 5.2490\%$$

Notice, from Figure 3.12, the eFunda advanced APR calculator allows the payment and compounding frequencies to differ. To use Equations 3.3 and 3.4 in such a case, the interest rate for the calculations is obtained from Equation 2.47 on page 85.

Now, let's consider how the APR values differ when a *subtractive* approach is used. The *subtractive* approach assumes that Ms. Lopez pays the closing costs at the time of closing, receives $225,000 from the lending institution (which she pays to the owner of the house), and makes monthly payments based on borrowing $225,000. Hence, her net cash flow at the time of the transaction is $225,000 less than the closing costs.

We can use Equation 3.4 to obtain APR_{sub} values. Since, for both the *additive* and the *subtractive* approaches, the monthly rate obtained using the Excel® **RATE** function is

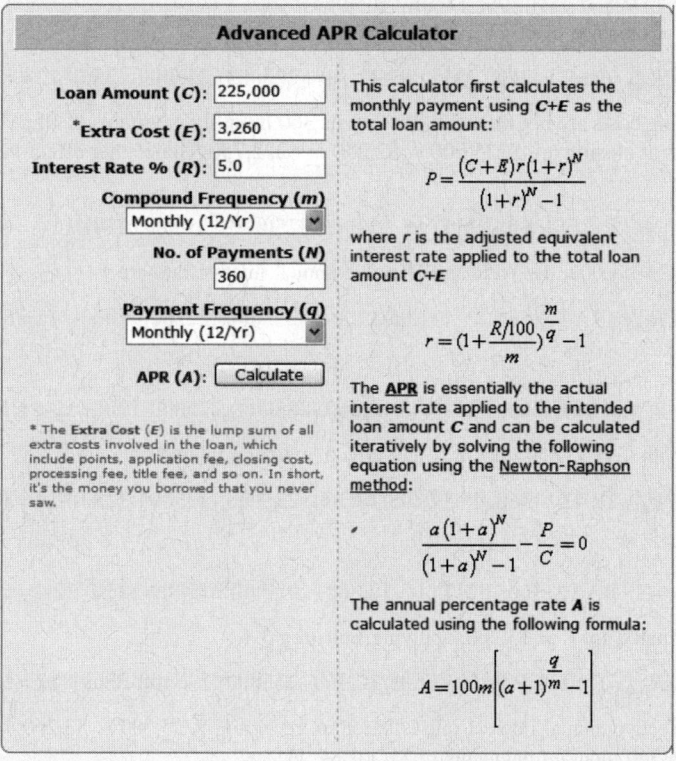

FIGURE 3.12

eFunda, Inc. *APR* Calculator and *APR* Value Obtained.

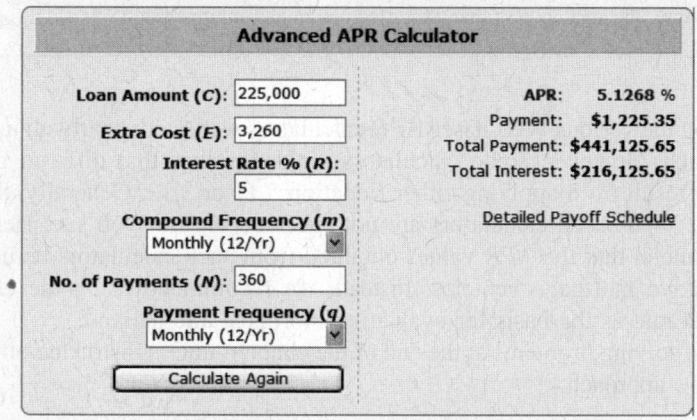

FIGURE 3.13

eFunda, Inc. *APR* Value When $p_1 = p_2 = 1\%$ and $c_o = \$1000$.

identical to the monthly rate used to compute the effective annual interest rate, we can also easily calculate the effective annual interest rates.

For Ms. Lopez's mortgage examples, $n = 360$, $i = 0.05/12\%$, $P = \$225,000$, and four values of C are considered. For all cases, with the subtractive approach,

$$A_{sub} = \$225,000(A|P\ 5/12\%,360)$$
$$= \text{PMT}(0.05/12,360,-225000) = \$1,207.85$$

For the case of C = \$2,250, applying Equation 3.4,

$$APR_{sub} = \text{RATE}(360,-\text{PMT}(.05/12,360,-225000),225000-2250)*12 = 5.0885\%$$

If closing costs are not financed, she makes 360 monthly payments of \$1,207.85, but her net receipts at closing are \$225,000 − \$2,250 or \$222,750. Hence, her effective annual interest rate is:

$$i_{eff} = (1+\text{RATE}(360,-\text{PMT}(.05/12,360,-225000),225000-2250)^{\wedge}12-1 = 5.2089\%$$

When C = \$1,000, the APR and effective annual interest rate are

$$APR_{sub} = \text{RATE}(360,-\text{PMT}(.05/12,360,-225000),225000-1000)*12 = 5.0392\%$$

and

$$i_{eff} = (1+\text{RATE}(360,-\text{PMT}(.05/12,360,-225000),225000-1000)^{\wedge}12-1 = 5.1572\%$$

With C = \$3,250, the APR and effective annual interest rate are

$$APR_{sub} = \text{RATE}(360,-\text{PMT}(.05/12,360,-225000),225000-3250)*12 = 5.1283\%$$

and

$$i_{eff} = (1+\text{RATE}(360,-\text{PMT}(.05/12,360,-225000),225000-3250)^{\wedge}12-1 = 5.2506\%$$

Finally, for C = \$3,260, applying Equation 3.4,

$$APR_{sub} = \text{RATE}(360,-\text{PMT}(.05/12,360,-225000),225000-3260)*12 = 5.1287\%$$

The effective annual interest rate is based on receiving \$225,000 − \$3,260, or \$221,740, and making 360 monthly payments of \$1,207.85. Hence,

$$i_{eff} = (1+\text{RATE}(360,-\text{PMT}(.05/12,360,-225000),225000-3260)^{\wedge}12-1 = 5.2510\%$$

Notice that APR_{add} is less than APR_{sub}. Furthermore, since the annual percentage rate is a nominal annual rate, the APR is less than the effective annual interest rate.

Among the various Web-based *APR* calculators we tested, nearly all used the *additive* approach. However, some calculators yielded values that differed from those that would result from applying either Equation 3.11 or 3.12. Generally, the assumptions behind Web-based calculators are not specified on the Web site. Hence, we do not recommend that the *APR* values obtained from such calculators be used to evaluate alternative mortgage vehicles. Instead, we recommend using the effective annual interest rate as the basis for evaluating mortgage alternatives.

In solving problems at the end of the chapter, unless instructed otherwise, use the *additive* approach.

EXAMPLE 3.7 Imputing Administrative Costs from the APR

Suppose a lending institution approved Ms. Lopez for a 30-year conventional 5 percent fixed rate loan, which would include 0.157 in points plus other administrative costs, and the *APR* on the loan would be 5.095 percent. Excluding points and other closing costs, her monthly payment would be \$5.366 per \$1,000 borrowed. How much were they charging her in administrative costs?

Since she knew that the lending institution computed the *APR* by deducting closing costs from the amount borrowed, she used Excel's **PV** function to calculate the present value on which the *APR* was calculated. Letting *BASE* denote the base amount on which the *APR* is calculated, she obtained the following results:

$$BASE = \$5.366(\$225,000)(P|A\ 5.095/12\%,360)/\$1,000 = \$222,494.52$$
$$\mathbf{=PV(0.05095/12,360,-5.366)*225000/1000 = \$222,494.52}$$

Therefore, administrative costs plus points equal the difference in \$225,000 and \$222,494.52, or \$2,505.48. Assuming points do not apply to other closing costs, since 0.157 points on a \$225,000 loan equals \$353.25, the administrative costs totaled \$2,505.48 −\$353.25, or \$2,152.23.

EXAMPLE 3.8 Selecting a Mortgage Plan

A professional couple has decided to purchase a house for \$450,000. They made a down payment of \$100,000. After meeting with representatives of several banks and mortgage brokers, they narrowed the choice of mortgages to the following: a 30-year fixed rate mortgage; a 30-year ARM; and a 5-year interest-only loan. The conventional 30-year fixed rate mortgage will have a 7 percent annual nominal rate and includes 0.157 points. Other loan-related closing costs total \$1,000. The 30-year ARM has the following parameters: The rate will be locked in after 7 years; it begins with a 6.5 percent interest rate and will not change for a year; it will not increase by more than 100 basis points (100 basis points equals 1 percent) annually; and it will not increase by more than 500 basis points over the 7-year period. The 30-year ARM has 1.28 points and other loan-related closing costs totaling \$850. The 35-year interest-only loan has a 6.1 percent annual nominal rate and 1.753 points, plus additional loan-related closing costs of \$7,500. The nominal annual *TVOM* for the couple is 10 percent. Which of the three should the couple choose? (For now, we ignore the effects of income taxes; in Chapter 10, we return to the example and examine the impact income taxes has on choosing a financing method.)

The conventional 30-year fixed rate mortgage will have monthly payments of

$$A = [\$350,000(1.00157) + \$1,000](A|P\ 7/12\%,360) = \$2,337.80$$
$$\mathbf{=PMT(.07/12,360,-350000*1.00157-1000) = \$2,338.87}$$

The 30-year ARM will have monthly payments the first year equal to

$$A = [\$350,000(1.0128) + \$850](A\ P\ 6.5/12\%,360) = \$2,245.69$$
$$\mathbf{=PMT(.065/12,360,-350000*1.0128-850) = \$2,245.93}$$

The 5-year interest-only, loan will have monthly payments the first year equal to

$$A = (0.061/12)[\$350,000(1.01753) + \$7,500] = \$1,848.48$$

The couple expects to be in the house for no more than 5 years. Over that period of time, they do not anticipate a reduction in interest rates. Their "optimistic" scenario is for the interest rates to remain unchanged for 5 years; their "pessimistic" scenario is for the interest rates to increase by 100 basis points each of the next 4 years.

The couple performed the following present worth analysis:

30-Year Conventional Loan

$$PW = -\$2,338.87(P|A\,10/12\%,60) - \$2,338.87(P|A\,7/12\%,300)(P|F\,10/12\%,60)$$

$$= -\$311,209.32$$

$$=PV(.10/12,60,2338.87)+PV(.10/12,60,-PV(.07/12,300,2338.87))$$

$$=-\$311,208.86$$

30-Year ARM Loan (Optimistic Case)

$$PW = -\$2,245.93(P|A10/12\%,60) - \$2,245.93(P|A\,6.5/12\%,300)(P|F\,10/12\%,60)$$

$$= -\$307,873.67$$

$$=PV(.10/12,60,2245.93)+PV(.10/12,60,,-PV(.065/12,300,2245.93))$$

$$=-\$307,873.20$$

30-Year ARM Loan (Pessimistic Case)

Assuming the interest rate increases the maximum of 100 basis points a year over a 5-year period, the monthly payments will be as shown in Table 3.3. The resulting PW, also shown in Table 3.3, is −$331,937.56. To understand the calculations performed, consider the 12 monthly payments in the fifth year. Since the nominal annual interest rate in the fifth year is 10.5 percent, the size of the monthly payment is obtained by computing the present worth of

TABLE 3.3
Monthly Payments for a 30-Year ARM Loan.

	A	B	C	D	E
1	Year	Nominal Annual Interest Rate	Size of Monthly Payment	PW(10/12%)	Excel® Calculation for PW(10/12%)
2	1	6.50%	$2,245.93	−$25,546.32	=PV(0.10/12,12,-C2)
3	2	7.50%	$2,479.61	−$25,530.89	=PV(0.10/12,12*(A3-1),,-PV(0.10/12,12,-C3))
4	3	8.50%	$2,717.46	−$25,327.72	=PV(0.10/12,12*(A4-1),,-PV(0.10/12,12,-C4))
5	4	9.50%	$2,958.52	−$24,960.81	=PV(0.10/12,12*(A5-1),,-PV(0.10/12,12,-C5))
6	5	10.50%	$3,201.98	−$24,454.17	=PV(0.10/12,12*(A6-1),,-PV(0.10/12,12,-C6))
7	> 5	10.50%	$3,201.98	−$206,117.66	=PV(0.10/12,60,,-PV(0.105/12,300,-C7))
8			Sum =	−$331,937.56	
9					
10			=PMT(B4/12,336,-PV(B3/12,336,-C3))		
11					
12					
13			=PMT(B7/12,300,-PV(B6/12,300,-C6))		
14					

the 312 remaining payments that were based on a nominal annual interest rate of 9.5 percent and then spreading them out over 312 months using a nominal annual rate of 10.5 percent. Hence,

$$A = \$2,958.52(P|A\ 9.5\%/12,312)(A|P\ 10.5/12\%,312) = \$3,202.56$$

$$\mathbf{=PMT(0.105/12,312,-PV(0.095/12,312,-2958.52)) = \$3,201.98}$$

Since the investment ends after 5 years, no increase in the interest rate will occur for future payments. Therefore, from the lender's perspective, at the time of the house's sale at the end of the fifth year, the present worth of the remaining 300 payments is

$$PW = -\$3,201.98(P|A\ 10.5/12\%,300) = -\$339,127.53$$

The professional couple's present worth of the 300 unpaid payments is given by

$$PW = -\$3,201.98(P|A\ 10.5/12\%,300)(P|F\ 10/12\%,60) = -\$206,118.32$$

$$\mathbf{=PV(0.10/12,60,-PV(0.105/12,300,-3201.98)) = -\$206,117.84}$$

(The 18¢ difference in this Excel® result and that shown in Table 3.3 is due to round-off error in the size of the monthly payment.)

For the 12 payments of \$3,201.98 made during the fifth year, the professional couple's present worth is

$$PW = -\$3,201.98(P|A\ 10/12\%,12)(P|F\ 10/12\%,48) = -\$24,454.12$$

$$\mathbf{=PV(0.10/12,48,,\ PV(0.10/12,12,-3201.98)) = -\$24,454.19}$$

(The 2¢ difference in this Excel® result and that shown in Table 3.3 is due to round-off error in the size of the monthly payment.)

5-Year Interest-Only Loan

$$PW = -\$1,848.48(P|A\ 10/12\%,60) - [\$350,000(1.01753)$$

$$+ \$7,500](P|F\ 10/12\%,60) = -\$307,990.82$$

$$\mathbf{=PV(0.10/12,60,(0.061/12)*(350000*1.01753+7500))}$$

$$\mathbf{+PV(0.10/12,60,,\ 350000*1.01753+7500) = -\$308,012.92}$$

Regarding the 30-year conventional loan, the couple made 60 monthly payments of \$2,338.87. After 5 years of making payments, the couple will owe \$330,919.47 on the loan. The present worth equivalent of the payments made is −\$119,536.56; the present worth equivalent of what they will owe at the time of the sale of the house is −\$239,308.16. Thus, the net present worth is −\$358,844.72.

For the 30-year ARM, the calculation for the optimistic case is identical to that for the 30-year conventional loan, except for the differences in closing costs and a lender's nominal annual interest rate of 6.5 percent, instead of 7 percent. For the pessimistic case, each year a new monthly payment is calculated for the number of years remaining on the loan; the interest rate used is 100 basis points greater than for the previous year. After 5 years, with a 10.5 percent nominal rate, the monthly payments for the future years equal \$3,201.98. As shown in Table 3.3, the present worth of the unpaid loan balance at the assumed time of the house's sale is $382,713.97. In essence, the couple lost ground over the 5-year period because of the assumed increases in the interest rate.

For the 5-year interest-only loan, the analysis is quite simple. Equal monthly payments of $1,848.48 are made for 60 months. Since the couple only paid interest on the loan principal, plus points and additional closing costs, they will owe a total of $363,635.50 when they sell the house. The present worth of the 60 payments made is −$94,473.40; the present worth of the unpaid loan principal is −$262,967.13. Thus, the net present worth for the interest-only loan is −$357,440.52.

The couple concluded that the risks of increases in interest rates offset the advantages of the 30-year ARM. For that reason, they eliminated the ARM from further consideration. The $1,404.30 difference in the present worths of the conventional and interest-only loans was almost insignificant. However, they decided to choose the interest-only loan. (Interestingly, if they had pursued a 30-year 7/1 ARM or a 30-year 5/1 ARM, the ARM might have been the preferred alternative, depending on the closing costs and interest rate. A 7/1 ARM locks in the interest rate for the first 7 years and, thereafter, adjusts the interest rate annually based on the index used.)

Perhaps you wondered why we did not include in the analysis the amount received if the house was sold after 5 years. Recalling Principle 7 from Chapter 1, it was not necessary for the couple to include how much they received for the house, since it does not depend on the method of loan financing.

Excluding the ARM, based on a 10% *TVOM* for the buyer, if M denotes the number of months the couple keeps the house, the present worth of the payments for the two alternatives will be

$$PW_{\text{conventional}} = -\$2,338.87[(P|A\ 10/12\%,M)$$
$$+ (P|A\ 7/12\%,360 - M)(P|F\ 10/12\%,M)]$$
$$PW_{\text{interest-only}} = -\$1,848.48(P|A\ 10/12\%,M)$$
$$- [\$350,000(1.01753) + \$7,500](P|F\ 10/12\%,M)$$

Table 3.4 provides the present worths for a range of values of M. For most of the values considered, the interest-only loan is preferred.

TABLE 3.4
Present Worth of Loan Payments for Two Types of 30-Year Loans.

| M | Type Loan | | Greatest PW? |
	Conventional	Interest Only	
12	−$3,41,598.22	−$3,50,192.93	Conventional
24	−$3,32,684.74	−$3,38,024.55	Conventional
36	−$3,24,708.24	−$3,27,009.58	Conventional
48	−$3,17,577.20	−$3,17,038.69	Interest Only
60	−$3,11,208.86	−$3,08,012.92	Interest Only
72	−$3,05,528.38	−$2,99,842.68	Interest Only
84	−$3,00,468.08	−$2,92,446.88	Interest Only
96	−$2,95,966.78	−$2,85,752.11	Interest Only

108	−$2,91,969.17	−$2,79,691.92	Interest Only
120	−$2,88,425.24	−$2,74,206.16	Interest Only
132	−$2,85,289.79	−$2,69,240.38	Interest Only
144	−$2,82,521.98	−$2,64,745.29	Interest Only
156	−$2,80,084.89	−$2,60,676.29	Interest Only
168	−$2,77,945.17	−$2,56,992.97	Interest Only
180	−$2,76,072.67	−$2,53,658.79	Interest Only
192	−$2,74,440.19	−$2,50,640.64	Interest Only
204	−$2,73,023.14	−$2,47,908.58	Interest Only
216	−$2,71,799.31	−$2,45,435.49	Interest Only
228	−$2,70,748.66	−$2,43,196.81	Interest Only
240	−$2,69,853.09	−$2,41,170.33	Interest Only
252	−$2,69,096.29	−$2,39,335.94	Interest Only
264	−$2,68,463.51	−$2,37,675.42	Interest Only
276	−$2,67,941.46	−$2,36,172.30	Interest Only
288	−$2,67,518.16	−$2,34,811.66	Interest Only
300	−$2,67,182.81	−$2,33,579.99	Interest Only

Principle #7

Consider only differences in cash flows among investment alternatives.

Because you might find the balloon loan attractive, we have provided another prototype of a financial calculator that you might find online. It computes the monthly payment for a balloon loan.

EXAMPLE 3.9   A Balloon Loan

Suppose Adriana Lopez pays closing costs and uses a balloon loan to finance $225,000 at a 4.75 percent annual nominal rate with monthly payments based on a 30-year loan and a balloon payment after 10 years. As shown in Figure 3.14, monthly payments of $1,173.71 and a balloon payment of $182,798.61 after 10 years are required. (As an exercise, verify these results.)

Balloon Mortgage Payments

Home Price	$325,000.00
Down Payment	$100,000.00
Amortized Over	30 years
Balloon Payment after	10 years
Interest Rate	4.75%

Calculate Results

Your monthly payment will be $1,173.71.

Your balloon payment will be $182,798.61.

Total Charges:

Total Loan Amount	$225,000.00
Total Payments	$139,671.49
Total Interest	$97,470.10

FIGURE 3.14

Prototype of an Interest-Only Loan Payment Calculator

Often, closing costs will make the difference in the borrower's choice of the mortgage vehicle to use. Table 3.5 provides data obtained from an Arvest Bank online calculator for Ms. Lopez's $225,000 mortgage. If the down payment is less than 20 percent of the property cost, the federal government requires the buyer to purchase mortgage insurance. Table 3.5 includes alternatives with a down payment greater than 20 percent and without mortgage insurance (1 & 2), with a 10 percent down payment and mortgage insurance premiums included in the loan payment (3 & 4), with a 10 percent down payment and mortgage insurance premiums paid separately at closing (5 & 6), FHA mortgages with the minimum down payment required (7 & 8), a VA loan (9), and 30-year ARMs that adjust annually and include a down payment that is greater than 20 percent (10 & 11).

Since mortgage rates and points differ depending on the down payment, alternatives are provided for down payments of $100,000 and $25,000. To maintain the same amount financed ($225,000), the purchase price of the house was reduced to $250,000 for the 10 percent down payment alternatives.

Using a nominal annual time value of money of 6.5 percent for Ms. Lopez, the present worth was computed for payments of principal and interest (PIP) and for payments that included taxes and insurance (PITI), where applicable. The present

TABLE 3.5
Present Worth Comparison of Several Mortgage Alternatives.

Some Representative Mortgage Alternatives	Interest Rate	APR	Points	Prepaid Finance Costs	Principal and Interest Payment plus Monthly Mortgage Insurance if Applicable (PIP)	Total Payment including taxes and insurance (PITI)*****	PW (PIP) per $000 Financed	PW(PITI) per $000 Financed
Conventional 30 year fixed rate *	4.8750	4.9067	0.000	$1,266.77	$1,190.72	$1,499.05	$608.48	$766.04
Purchase Price $325,000	4.7500	4.8470	0.750	$2,942.71	$1,173.71	$1,482.04	$599.80	$613.68
Loan Amount $225,000	4.6250	4.7981	1.625	$4,899.90	$1,156.81	$1,465.14	$591.18	$606.70
Over 20% down, no MI	4.5000	4.7380	2.375	$6,575.85	$1,140.04	$1,448.37	$582.63	$599.77
Conventional 15 year fixed rate *	4.1250	4.2158	0.250	$1,759.92	$1,678.43	$1,986.76	$856.35	$1,013.66
Purchase Price $325,000	4.0000	4.1648	0.750	$2,873.36	$1,664.30	$1,972.63	$849.14	$1,006.45
Loan Amount $225,000	3.8750	4.1514	1.500	$4,549.31	$1,650.24	$1,958.57	$841.96	$999.27
Over 20% down, no MI	3.7500	4.1195	3.750	$5,944.00	$1,636.25	$1,944.58	$834.83	$992.14
Conventional 30 year fixed rate **	4.875	5.2266	0.000	$1,266.77	$1,297.60	$1,535.10	$663.09	$784.46
Purchase Price $250,000	4.750	5.1630	0.750	$2,942.71	$1,280.59	$1,518.09	$654.42	$775.79
Loan Amount $225,000	4.625	5.1136	1.625	$4,899.90	$1,263.69	$1,501.19	$645.81	$767.18
10% down, MI included in monthly payment ($106.88)	4.500	5.0494	2.375	$6,575.85	$1,246.92	$1,484.42	$637.25	$758.63
Conventional 15 year fixed rate **	4.125	4.4381	0.250	$1,759.92	$1,789.06	$2,097.39	$912.79	$1,070.10
Purchase Price $250,000	4.000	4.3881	0.750	$2,873.36	$1,774.96	$2,083.26	$905.60	$1,062.89
Loan Amount $225,000	3.875	4.3697	1.500	$4,549.31	$1,760.87	$2,069.20	$898.41	$1,055.72
10% down, MI included in monthly payment ($110.63)	3.750	4.3391	2.125	$5,944.00	$1,746.88	$2,055.21	$891.27	$1,048.58
Conventional 30 year fixed rate ***	4.875	5.0154	0.000	$4,084.90	$1,205.60	$1,443.10	$608.48	$728.35
Purchase Price $250,000	4.750	4.9553	0.750	$5,760.70	$1,188.38	$1,425.88	$599.80	$719.68
Loan Amount $225,000 Adjusted Loan Amount $227,812	4.625	4.9061	1.625	$7,717.75	$1,171.27	$1,408.77	$591.19	$711.06
10% down, MI financed into loan amount	4.500	4.8456	2.375	$9,393.55	$1,154.29	$1,391.79	$582.63	$702.51
Conventional 15 year fixed rate ***	4.125	4.3706	0.250	$4,126.43	$1,696.05	$1,933.55	$856.35	$976.26
Purchase Price $250,000	4.000	4.3194	0.750	$5,239.75	$1,681.77	$1,919.27	$849.14	$969.05
Loan Amount $225,000 Adjusted Loan Amount $227,362	3.875	4.3059	1.500	$6,915.57	$1,667.56	$1,905.06	$841.96	$961.88
10% down, MI financed into loan amount	3.750	4.2739	2.125	$8,310.14	$1,653.43	$1,890.93	$834.83	$954.74
FHA 30 year fixed rate ****	4.500	5.1709	0.000	$3,416.26	$1,367.07	$1,604.57	$651.60	$764.80
Purchase Price $250,000	4.375	5.1248	0.875	$5,515.51	$1,350.26	$1,587.76	$643.61	$1,188.07
Loan Amount $225,000								
Adjusted Loan Amount $227,250								
10% down, 1% MI financed in loan and 1.15% monthly MI in payment								
FHA 15 year fixed rate ****	4.000	4.2829	0.000	$3,369.56	$1,727.82	$1,965.32	$881.54	$1,002.72

(Continued)

TABLE 3.5
(Continued)

Some Representative Mortgage Alternatives	Interest Rate	APR	Points	Prepaid Finance Costs	Principal and Interest Payment plus Monthly Mortgage Insurance if Applicable (PIP)	Total Payment including taxes and insurance (PITI)[*****]	PW (PIP) per $000 Financed	PW(PITI) per $000 Financed
Purchase Price $250,000	3.500	4.1791	2.500	$9,354.12	$1,671.45	$1,908.95	$852.78	$973.96
Loan Amount $225,000								
Adjusted Loan Amount $227,250								
10% down, 1% MI financed in loan and .25% monthly MI in payment								
VA 30 year fixed rate[******]	4.500	4.7144	0.250	$6,783.27	$1,293.95	$1,531.45	$582.63	$689.58
Purchase Price $250,000	4.375	4.6635	1.125	$8,957.65	$1,275.05	$1,512.55	$574.14	$681.09
Loan Amount $255,375 (100% plus 2.15% VA funding fee)	4.250	4.5688	1.500	$9,882.03	$1,256.29	$1,493.79	$565.71	$672.66
ARM 3/1 30 YR [*]	3.250	3.0835	0.000	$1,116.51	$979.21	$1,287.54		
Purchase Price $325,000	2.875	3.0795	1.000	$3,331.84	$933.51	$1,241.84		
Loan Amount $225,000								
Over 20% down, no MI								
ARM 5/1 30 YR [*]	3.750	3.2920	0.000	$1,162.75	$1,042.01	$1,350.34		
Purchase Price $325,000	3.375	3.2395	1.000	$3,378.07	$994.72	$1,303.05		
Loan Amount $225,000								
Over 20% down, no MI								

[*]$100,000 Down payment

[**]10% Down payment, monthly mortgage insurance payment
　　　　30 yr MMI $106.88 included in loan payment
　　　　15 yr MMI $110.63 included in loan payment

[***]10% Down payment, up front mortgage insurance premium.
　　　　30 year UPFMIP $2,812.50 - Financed back into the loan amount; adjusted loan amount $227,812
　　　　15 year UPFMIP $2,362.50 - Financed back into the loan amount; adjusted loan amount $227,362

[****]10% Down payment - up front mortgage insurance premium is 1% of the loan amount, financed back into the loan
　　　　30 year MMI is 1.15% *base loan amount, included in loan payment
　　　　15 year MMI is .25% * base loan amount, included in loan payment

[*****]Total Payment includes taxes and insurance. Taxes based on 1% of purchase price minus $350 applicable Arkansas homestead tax credit

[******]VA loan is standard 100% financing plus 2.15% VA funding fee financed into the loan
　　　　Combined monthly taxes and insurance $308.33 for $325,000 purchase price and $237.50 for $250,000 purchase price

worth was calculated for a 15-year period. (Our reason for using the same loan period for the present worth calculations becomes clear in Chapter 5.) The most attractive PIP alternative for Ms. Lopez is the 30-year fully financed VA loan at a nominal annual rate of 4.25%; the least attractive PIP alternative is a 15-year conventional loan with a 10 percent down payment and a 4.125% nominal annual rate. For PITI payments, the most attractive is a 30-year conventional loan with a $100,000 down payment and a 4.5 percent nominal annual rate; the least attractive is a 30-year FHA loan with a 10 percent down payment and a 4.375 percent nominal annual rate.

The rates in Table 3.5 were effective on May 24, 2011. As mentioned earlier in this section, interest rates change frequently. Likewise, closing costs vary among financial institutions. Therefore, you should not conclude that the information provided in Table 3.5 will be accurate if and when you purchase a house.

We did not include ARM alternatives in the comparison. Our decision to exclude them was not due to reservations about the loan vehicle. Instead, we felt uncomfortable making assumptions about future interest rates.

Because the ARM is a viable option (we have used it with good results), you should consult with mortgage brokers or loan officers at one or more banks and learn what the assumptions are behind their APR estimates. Also, at the time of your mortgage decision, you should assess the interest rate climate and make your own judgments about the likelihood of changes in the interest rates over your planning horizon.

Unfortunately, too many people take on greater debt than they can afford. "Late Payments on Mortgage Rise," a May 18, 2006, article in the Wall Street Journal by Ruth Simon, opened with, "Soaring housing prices and aggressive mortgage lending have saddled home buyers with ever greater levels of debt, and early signs are now emerging that more people are unable to keep up with their monthly mortgage payments.

"Recent studies by several Wall Street firms point to rising delinquency rates on home mortgages that were issued last year, a period when lenders were pushing hard to keep business going as interest rates and home prices were rising. The increase in late loan payments comes as more buyers have been forced to stretch financially to afford ever costlier houses in recent years, and many homeowners have increased debt by tapping their home equity. Analysts say that laxer lending standards on the part of mortgage lenders also resulted in higher debt loads, which some borrowers are now struggling to repay."

The 2006 article was a harbinger of the sub-prime lending rate problem that resulted in a global credit crunch in late 2007 and throughout 2008. As of this writing, the housing market and financial institutions are still recovering from the worst financial condition in 80 years, due largely to lending institutions loaning money to individuals who could not afford the loans they received.

As noted at the beginning of this section, investments in houses and condominiums can be among the best investments you make. However, there is no guarantee that you will be able to sell your home *when* you want for *what* (the price) you want.

3-5   INTEREST PAYMENTS AND PRINCIPAL PAYMENTS

Recall our consideration of four payment plans for a loan of $10,000. The first, second, and third payment plans paid interest each year on the unpaid balance of the loan. Since the balance was not reduced with the first plan, payments equaled the product of the interest rate (15 percent) and the loan principal ($10,000). Since the second plan included equal payments of principal ($2,000), the interest payments were a decreasing gradient series with a gradient step ($300) equal to the product of the interest rate (15 percent) and the payment against principal. Since the third plan included equal-sized payments ($2,983.16), as the unpaid balance decreased, the amount of a payment that was interest decreased.

In Section 3.3, we learned that the equal-sized payment plan did not minimize the present worth of borrower's payments if the borrower's *TVOM* differed from the interest rate charged by the lender. However, Plan 3 is the most popular way to repay conventional loans.

Likewise, we mentioned previously that interest paid on a person's primary residence and interest paid by businesses can be deducted from taxable income. In

Chapter 10, we will examine the after-tax effects of borrowing money. However, here we will determine the amount of each equal-sized payment that is interest and the amount that is a reduction of principal or increase in equity. (In general, *equity* is defined as the difference in the loan principal and the unpaid balance; however, in the case of purchasing a house, it is the difference in the value of the property and the amount owed on the loan, since the down payment is an equity component. We will use *equity* and *principal* interchangeably in this section.)

3.5.1   Immediate Payment Loans

Typically, when money is borrowed, the first payment is made one interest period after receipt of the money. Here, we consider loans of this type, which we call *immediate payment loans*.

EXAMPLE 3.10   Paying Off a Loan Early

Recall Example 3.1 and the $10,000 loan for 5 years at 15 percent annual compound interest. After making the second payment, suppose the borrower decided to pay off the loan's balance. How much would be owed? If the borrower had paid off the balance after the first payment, how much would have been owed? What do you deduce from these results?

To determine how much is owed immediately after making the second payment, we compute the present worth of the remaining payments. Since it is the amount owed the lender, we use the lender's interest rate of 15 percent in computing the present worth of the three remaining payments: $2,983.16(P|A\ 15\%,3) = \$2,983.16(2.28323) = \$6,811.24$. Using Excel®'s financial functions, $=PV(15\%,3,-PMT(15\%,5,-10000))$ $=\$6,811.22$. (The 2¢ difference in results is due to round-off errors in the tables in Appendix A.)

The amount owed immediately after the first payment is obtained as follows: $2,983.16(P|A\ 15\%,4) = \$2,983.16(2.85498) = \$8,516.86$. Using Excel®'s financial functions, $=PV(15\%,4,-PMT(15\%,5,-10000)) = \$8,516.84$. (The 2¢ difference in results is due to round-off errors in the tables in Appendix A.)

The difference in the loan principal ($10,000) and the unpaid balance immediately after the first payment ($8,516.84) equals $1,483.16. It is not a coincidence that this is also the difference in the loan payment ($2,983.16) and the $1,500 in interest on the unpaid balance during the first year, $10,000(0.15). Thus, the first payment includes a $1,500 interest payment and a $1,483.16 payment to reduce the unpaid principal. (The latter is also called an *equity payment*.)

The difference in the unpaid balance after the first payment ($8,516.84) and the unpaid balance after the second payment ($6,811.22) equals $1,705.62, which indicates the second payment reduced the unpaid principal by $1,705.62. (Note: the 1¢ difference in this result and the result shown in the next example is due to a limit of two decimal places for currency values in Excel®.)

From the example, we learn that the difference in unpaid balances for consecutive years is the amount of a payment that reduces principal or is an equity payment. The following example presents another avenue for determining the amount of a loan payment that is a principal or equity payment.

EXAMPLE 3.11   Interest and Principal Payments in a Loan

Continuing to consider the $10,000 loan for 5 years at 15 percent annual compound interest, we wish to determine the amount of each payment that is interest and the amount that is a payment against principal or an equity payment.

Recall, the equal annual payment size was calculated to be $2,983.16. As shown in Table 3.6, the first payment consists of $10,000(0.15), or $1,500, in interest and a $1,483.16 principal or equity payment. The unpaid balance after the first payment is $10,000 −$1,483.16, or $8,516.84.

The second payment consists of $8,516.84(0.15), or $1,277.53, in interest and a $1,705.63 principal payment. The unpaid balance after the second payment is $6,811.22.

The third payment consists of $6,811.22(0.15), or $1,021.68, in interest and a $1,961.47 principal payment. The unpaid balance after the third payment is $4,849.74.

The fourth payment consists of $4,849.74(0.15), or $727.46, in interest and a $2,255.69 principal payment. The unpaid balance after the fourth payment is $2,594.05.

The fifth payment consists of $2,595.05(0.15), or $389.11, in interest and a $2,594.05 principal payment. The unpaid balance after the final payment, as expected, is zero.

TABLE 3.6
Interest and Equity Portions of a Loan Payment in Example 3.11.

Year	Beginning Balance	Loan Payment	Interest Payment	Principal Payment	Ending Balance
1	$10,000.00	$2,983.16	$1,500.00	$1,483.16	$8,516.84
2	$8,516.84	$2,983.16	$1,277.53	$1,705.63	$6,811.22
3	$6,811.22	$2,983.16	$1,021.68	$1,961.47	$4,849.74
4	$4,849.74	$2,983.16	$727.46	$2,255.69	$2,594.05
5	$2,594.05	$2,983.16	$389.11	$2,594.05	$0.00

Note: the loan payment was calculated using Excel®'s PMT function; $A_t = A_{t-1}$; $C_t = 0.15 A_t$; $D_t = B_t - C_t$; $E_t = A_t - D_t$

The results from this example can be generalized as follows: if P is borrowed (at $t = 0$) with a period interest rate of $i\%$/period for n periods and is to be repaid in n equal end-of-period payments (starting at $t = 1$), then the amount of the payments, A, can be determined by the relationship $A = P(A|P\, i\%,n)$. For any given payment, part of the payment goes to pay interest and the remaining part reduces the principal amount (unpaid balance). While the payments remain constant at A, the portions of each payment that go to pay interest and to reduce the principal vary over time.

The amount of principal remaining to be repaid immediately after making payment at time t can be found by stripping off the interest on the remaining $(n - t)$ payments. Letting U_t denote the unpaid principal after making t payments, we have

$$U_t = A(P|A\, i\%,n - t) \tag{3.5}$$

where A, n, and i are defined as noted above.

A related quantity is the payoff quantity. Payoff$_t$ is the total amount required to pay off the loan at time t, including both the current payment and the unpaid balance.

$$\text{Payoff}_t = A + U_t = A + A(P|A\ i\%,n-t) \tag{3.6}$$

$$= A[1 + (P|A\ i\%,n-t)] \tag{3.7}$$

The interest accrued during any payment period is given by the product of the unpaid balance at the beginning of the period and the period interest rate. Letting I_t denote the portion of payment t that goes to pay interest, we have

$$I_t = iU_{t-1} \tag{3.8}$$

Substituting the results of Equation 3.5 into Equation 3.8, the following relationship can be derived.

$$I_t = A[1 - (P|F\ i\%,n-t+1)] \tag{3.9}$$

The portion of the payment that does not pay accrued interest goes to principal reduction. Letting P_t denote the portion of payment t that is a principal payment (goes to reduce principal), we have

$$P_t = A - I_t \tag{3.10}$$

or

$$P_t = A(P|F\ i\%,n-t+1) \tag{3.11}$$

Excel® has two financial functions that apply directly to this material: **IPMT** and **PPMT**. The **IPMT** worksheet function determines the amount of a periodic payment that is interest and has the following parameters: interest rate, period for which the value is sought, number of periodic payments made, present amount, future amount, and *type*. The **PPMT** worksheet function determines the amount of a periodic payment that reduces the unpaid principal on a loan; it has the same parameters as **IPMT**. For conventional loans, the future amount and *type* parameters are not needed.

EXAMPLE 3.12 Purchasing a Car

Sara Beth Brakmann wants to purchase a used car in excellent condition. She has decided on a car with low mileage that will cost $20,000. After considering several alternatives, she identified a local lending source that will charge her an interest rate of 6 percent per annum compounded monthly for a 48-month loan: (a) What will be the size of her monthly payments? (b) What will be the remaining balance on her loan immediately after making her twenty-fourth payment? (c) If she chooses to pay off the loan at the time of her thirty-sixth payment, how much must she pay? (d) What portion of her twelfth payment is interest? (e) What portion of her twelfth payment is an equity payment?

a. $A = P(A|P\,i\%,n)$

Period interest rate = 6 percent/12 months = 0.5 percent/month

$n = 48$ months

$A = \$20,000(A|P\,0.5\%,48)$

$= \$20,000(0.02349)$

$= \$469.80$

$= PMT(0.5\%,48,-20000)$

$= \$469.70$

b. $U_t = A(P|A\,i\%,n-t) = n = 48 \quad t = 24 \quad n-t = 48-24 = 24$

$U_{24} = A(P|A\,0.5\%,24)$

$= \$469.80(22.56287)$

$= \$10,600.04$

$= PV(0.5\%,24,-PMT(0.5\%,48,-20000))$

$= \$10,597.79$

c. $\text{Payoff}_t = A + A(P|A\,i\%,n-t)$

$n = 48 \quad t = 36 \quad n-t = 48-36 = 12$

$\text{Payoff}_{36} = A + A(P|A\,0.5\%,12) = \$469.80 + \$469.80(11.61893) = \$5,928.37$

$= PV(0.5\%,12,-PMT(0.5\%,48,-20000))+PMT(0.5\%,48,-20000)$

$= \$5,927.12$

d. $I_t = i\,U_{t-1}$

$n = 48 \quad t = 12 \quad t-1 = 12-1 = 11$

$U_{11} = A(P|A\,0.5\%,37) = \$469.80(33.70250) = \$15,833.44$

$I_{12} = 0.005(\$15,833.44) = \$79.17$

$= IPMT(0.5\%,12,48,-20000) = \$79.15$

e. $P_t = A - I_t$

$t = 12$

$P_{12} = A - I_{12}$

$= \$469.80 - \$79.17 = \$390.63$

$= PPMT(0.5\%,12,48,-20000) = \$390.55$

EXAMPLE 3.13   Applying Equations 3.9 and 3.11

Recall the \$10,000 loan at 15 percent annual compound interest for 5 years. Values for I_t and P_t for $t = 1, \ldots, 5$ were determined previously in Example 3.11 and summarized in Table 3.6. Show that the same values (except for round-off error in the interest tables) are obtained using Equations 3.9 and 3.11.

The results are summarized in Table 3.7.

TABLE 3.7
Interest and Equity Payments Using Equations 3.9 and 3.11 and the Excel® IPMT and PPMT Worksheet Functions.

t	A	$(P\|F\,15\%,5-t+1)$	I_t	IPMT	P_t	PPMT
1	$2,983.16	0.4972	$1,499.93	$1,500.00	$1,483.23	$1,483.16
2	$2,983.16	0.5718	$1,277.39	$1,277.53	$1,705.77	$1,705.63
3	$2,983.16	0.6575	$1,021.73	$1,021.68	$1,961.43	$1,961.47
4	$2,983.16	0.7561	$727.59	$727.46	$2,255.57	$2,255.69
5	$2,983.16	0.8696	$389.00	$389.11	$2,594.16	$2,594.05

EXAMPLE 3.14   Calculating Interest Payments

Recall, Ms. Lopez's purchase of a house. Over the 3-year period, how much interest would she pay each year? Her monthly payments are $1,207.85

The amount of principal paid during the first year can be obtained by subtracting the present worth of the payments made the last 29 years from the loan principal, i.e.,

$$P_1 = \$225,000.00 - \$1,207.85(P|A\,5/12\%,348) = \$3,319.57$$

Since 12 payments of $1,207.85 were made, a total of $14,494.18 was paid. Therefore, $14,494.18 − $3,319.57, or $11,174.61, was paid in interest. (Figure 3.15 shows a prototype of an online calculator that can be used to determine the

Tax Deduction					
Total Home Loan Amount				$225,000.00	
Annual Interest Rate				5.00%	
Loan Term				30 years	
Calculate Results					
Tax Deduction Amount per Year					
Year 1	$11,174.61	Year 11	$9,026.82	Year 21	$5,489.38
Year 2	$11,004.78	Year 12	$8,747.10	Year 22	$5,028.68
Year 3	$10,826.25	Year 13	$8,453.06	Year 23	$4,544.40
Year 4	$10,638.59	Year 14	$8,143.99	Year 24	$4,035.35
Year 5	$10,441.33	Year 15	$7,819.10	Year 25	$3,500.26
Year 6	$10,233.98	Year 16	$7,477.59	Year 26	$2,937.79
Year 7	$10,016.02	Year 17	$7,118.61	Year 27	$2,346.54
Year 8	$9,786.91	Year 18	$6,741.26	Year 28	$1,725.05
Year 9	$9,546.08	Year 19	$6,344.61	Year 29	$1,071.75
Year 10	$9,292.92	Year 20	$5,927.66	Year 30	$385.04

FIGURE 3.15
Prototype of a Tax Deduction Calculator

amount of interest paid each year. Entering the data for the example yields the result shown.)

To determine the amount of interest paid annually over the 30-year period, we developed a spreadsheet, as shown in Figure 3.16.

	A	B	C	D	E	F	G	H	I	J
	Year	PW of Remaining Payments	Δ PW of Remaining Payments	Interest Paid						
1										
2	0	$225,000.00								
3	1	$221,680.43	$3,319.57	$11,174.61						
4	2	$218,191.02	$3,489.41	$11,004.78						
5	3	$214,523.09	$3,667.93	$10,826.25						
6	4	$210,667.50	$3,855.59	$10,638.59						
7	5	$206,614.65	$4,052.85	$10,441.33						
8	6	$202,354.45	$4,260.20	$10,233.98		=PV(0.07/12,360-12*A8,-PMT(0.07/12,360,-225000))				
9	7	$197,876.28	$4,478.16	$10,016.02						
10	8	$193,169.01	$4,707.27	$9,786.01		=B9-B10				
11	9	$188,220.91	$4,948.11	$9,546.08						
12	10	$183,019.65	$5,201.26	$9,292.92		=12*PMT(0.07/12,360,-225000)-C12				
13	11	$177,552.28	$5,467.37	$9,026.82						
14	12	$171,805.19	$5,747.09	$8,747.10						
15	13	$165,764.07	$6,041.12	$8,453.06						
16	14	$159,413.88	$6,350.19	$8,143.99						
17	15	$152,738.79	$6,675.08	$7,819.10						
18	16	$145,722.20	$7,016.59	$7,477.59						
19	17	$138,346.63	$7,375.57	$7,118.61						
20	18	$130,593.70	$7,752.92	$6,741.26						
21	19	$122,444.13	$8,149.58	$6,344.61						
22	20	$113,877.60	$8,566.53	$5,927.66						
23	21	$104,872.80	$9,004.80	$5,489.38						
24	22	$95,407.29	$9,465.51	$5,028.68						
25	23	$85,457.51	$9,949.78	$4,544.40						
26	24	$74,998.68	$10,458.83	$4,035.35						
27	25	$64,004.75	$10,993.92	$3,500.26						
28	26	$52,448.36	$11,556.39	$2,937.79						
29	27	$40,300.72	$12,147.64	$2,346.54						
30	28	$27,531.58	$12,769.14	$1,725.05						
31	29	$14,109.15	$13,422.43	$1,071.75						
32	30	$0.00	$14,109.15	$385.04						

B8 fx =PV(0.05/12,360-12*A8,-PMT(0.05/12,360,-225000))

FIGURE 3.16

Interest Paid by Ms. Lopez Over a 30-Year Period.

3.5.2 Deferred Payment Loans

Repayment of loans does not always begin one interest period after receipt of the principal. For any number of reasons, some individuals and organizations arrange to delay the beginning of payment for several interest periods. Such loans are called *deferred payment loans* and are the subject of this section.

Determining the amount of a deferred payment that is interest versus equity is not as straightforward as it is for immediate payment loans. Unfortunately, Equations 3.9 and 3.11 and the Excel® **IPMT** and **PPMT** worksheet functions cannot be used for all deferred payments. However, a tabular approach similar to Table 3.6 can be used in all situations. (*Importantly, until the accumulated interest resulting from deferring payments is paid, no principal payments occur.*)

EXAMPLE 3.15 Interest and Equity in Deferred Payments

Suppose the first payment for the $10,000 loan, considered previously, will not occur until 4 years after receipt of the principal amount. However, five equal annual payments will be made to repay the loan. How much of each payment will be interest and principal?

The size of the new, deferred payments will be

$$A_d = \$10,000(F|P\ 15\%,3)(A|P\ 15\%,5)$$
$$= \$10,000(1.52088)(0.29832) = \$4,537.09$$
$$= \text{PMT}(15\%,5,-\text{FV}(15\%,3,,-10000)) = \$4,537.01$$

Table 3.8 summarizes the calculations to determine the amount of each payment that will be interest and equity. Since no payments are made until 4 years after receiving the $10,000, the amount owed *immediately before making the first deferred payment* equals $10,000(F|P 15%,4), or $17,490.10 (based on the compound interest values given in Appendix A) or **$17,490.06** (using Excel®'s **FV** function).

The first deduction from a payment is the interest on the unpaid balance. Since the amount owed ($17,490.06) includes $7,490.06 in accumulated interest, which is greater than a full payment ($4,537.01), all of the first payment is an interest payment.

Likewise, the amount owed before making the second payment ($14,896.01) includes accumulated interest of $4,896.01, which is also greater than a full payment ($4,537.01). Therefore, all of the second payment is an interest payment.

The amount owed for the third payment ($11,912.86) includes accumulated unpaid interest totaling $1,912.86, which is less than a full payment ($4,537.01).

TABLE 3.8
Interest and Equity Payments in a Deferred Payment Loan.

	A	B	C	D	E	F	G	H	I
Beginning of Year	Unpaid Balance Before Payment	Interest During Year	Unpaid Interest Before Payment	Amount Owed	Loan Payment	Interest Payment	Principal Payment	Unpaid Interest After Payment	Unpaid Balance After Payment
1	$10,000.00	$1,500.00	$1,500.00	$11,500.00	$0.00	$0.00	$0.00	$1,500.00	$11,500.00
2	$11,500.00	$1,725.00	$3,225.00	$13,225.00	$0.00	$0.00	$0.00	$3,225.00	$13,225.00
3	$13,225.00	$1,983.75	$5,208.75	$15,208.75	$0.00	$0.00	$0.00	$5,208.75	$15,208.75
4	$15,208.75	$2,281.31	$7,490.06	$17,490.06	$4,537.01	$4,537.01	$0.00	$2,953.06	$12,953.06
5	$12,953.06	$1,942.96	$4,896.01	$14,896.01	$4,537.01	$4,537.01	$0.00	$359.01	$10,359.01
6	$10,359.01	$1,553.85	$1,912.86	$11,912.86	$4,537.01	$1,912.86	$2,624.15	$0.00	$7,375.85
7	$7,375.85	$1,106.38	$1,106.38	$8,482.23	$4,537.01	$1,106.38	$3,430.63	$0.00	$3,945.22
8	$3,945.22	$591.78	$591.78	$4,537.01	$4,537.01	$591.78	$3,945.22	$0.00	$0.00
	$A_t = I_{t-1}$	0.15^*A_t	$C_t = B_t + H_{t-1}$	$D_t = A_t + B_t$	E_t	$F_t = \min(C_t, E_t)$	$G_t = E_t - F_t$	$H_t = C_t - F_t$	$I_t = D_t - E_t$

Therefore, the $1,912.86 in accumulated interest is an interest payment; the $2,624.15 remaining in the $4,537.01 payment reduces principal.

Just before making the fourth payment, $8,482.23 is owed, $1,106.38 of which is unpaid interest. Therefore, the $1,106.38 in interest earned during the year is deducted from the payment, and the $3,430.63 balance reduces principal.

Finally, the amount owed just before the fifth and final payment is made totals $4,537.01, the size of a payment. The interest charged during the year equals $591.78. Therefore, the balance of $3,945.22 is a principal payment and reduces the unpaid balance to zero.

To formalize the computation of interest payments and principal payments when deferred payments are made on a loan, we introduce the following notation. Let

Princ = loan principal

IR = interest rate on the loan

UB = unpaid balance at the beginning of the interest period

UIB = unpaid accumulated interest immediately before making a payment

UIA = unpaid accumulated interest immediately after making a payment

AO = amount owed just before making a payment

Int = interest earned during the period = UB*IR

A_d = size of the deferred payment

IPmt = amount of the payment that is an interest payment

PPmt = amount of the payment that is a principal payment = A_d − IPmt

As illustrated in the previous example and reflected in Table 3.8,

$$IPmt = \min(UIB, A_d) \tag{3.12}$$

The amount of a payment that is interest is either the accumulated interest immediately before making a payment or the entire payment, whichever is the lesser. The difference in the payment and the interest payment is the principal payment.

Since the first thing paid in a loan payment is accumulated interest, when a uniform series of payments is made on a deferred payment loan, another approach can be used to determine the amount of principal and the amount of interest in a deferred payment. To motivate the approach, from Table 3.8 we notice that Equation 3.9 can be used to determine the amount of interest in payments 4 and 5, but not in payment 3.

Let P denote the amount borrowed, i denote the interest rate on the loan, k denote the deferral period, n denote the number of payments to be made, A_d denote the size of the deferred payment, T denote the *transition payment*, and N_d denote the *integer portion* of the number of payments of size A_d required to pay off P. Therefore,

$$A_d = P(F|P\,i\%,k)(A|P\,i\%,n) \tag{3.13}$$

and

$$T = n - N_d \tag{3.14}$$

N_d is the largest value of n for which $(P|A\,i\%,n) \leq P/A_d$. Using Excel®,

$$N_d = \textbf{ROUNDDOWN(NPER}(i\%, A_d, P),0) \tag{3.15}$$

Payments $1, \ldots, T - 1$ will be interest-only payments. Therefore, as noted, the amount of interest in payments $T + 1, \ldots, n$ can be obtained using Equation 3.9. The portions of payment T, the transition payment, that are principal and interest are:

$$PPmt_T = P - A_d(P|A\ i\%, N_d) \qquad (3.16)$$

and

$$IPmt_T = A_d - PPmt_T \qquad (3.17)$$

EXAMPLE 3.16   An Alternative Approach

To determine the amount of each deferred payment that is interest and principal, we continue to consider the $10,000 loan, with 15 percent annual interest and five equal annual payments. As before, the first payment occurs 4 years after receipt of the $10,000. Hence, $i = 15\%$, $P = \$10,000$, $k = 3$, $n = 5$, and, using the Excel® results in Example 3.15, $A_d = \$4,537.01$. Dividing the amount borrowed by the deferred payment gives $10,000/$4,537.01 = 2.20406. From Table A-a-19 on page 843, $(P|A\ 15\%,2) = 1.62571$ and $(P|A\ 15\%,3) = 2.28323$. Therefore, $N_d = 2$ and $T = 5 - 2 = 3$.

Since $T = 3$, payments 1 and 2 are *interest-only payments* and Equations 3.9 and 3.11 or Excel's IPMT and PPMT worksheet functions can be used for payments 4 and 5. For payment 3, $PPmt_3 = \$10,000 - \$4,537.01(P|A\ 15\%,2) = \$2,624.14$ or, using Excel, $\$2,624.15 = 10000 + PV(15\%,2,PMT(15\%,5,FV(15\%,3,10000)))$. Therefore, $IPmt_3 = \$4,537.01 - \$2,624.15 = \$1,912.86$. The results are given in Table 3.9.

TABLE 3.9

Alternative Method of Calculating Equity and Interest Payments in a Deferred Loan.

Payment	Deferred Payment	Type of Payment	Principal Payment	Interest Payment
1	$4,537.01	Interest-only	$P_1 = \$0.00$	$I_1 = \$4,537.01 - \$0.00 = \$4,537.01$
2	$4,537.01	Interest-only	$P_2 = \$0.00$	$I_2 = \$4,537.01 - \$0.00 = \$4,537.01$
3	$4,537.01	Transition	$P_3 = \$10,000 - \$4,537.01(P|A\ 15\%,2) = \$2,624.14$	$I_3 = \$4,537.01 - \$2,624.14 = \$1,912.87$
			$P_3 = 10000 + PV(15\%,2,PMT(15\%,5,FV(15\%,3,,10000)))$ $= \$2,624.15$	$I_3 = \$4,537.01 - \$2,624.15$ $= \$1,912.86$
4	$4,537.01	Normal	$P_4 = \$4,537.01(P|F\ 15\%, 5 - 4 + 1) = \$3,430.61$	$I_4 = \$4,537.01 - \$3,430.61 = \$1,106.40$
			$P_4 = PPMT(15\%,4,5,FV(15\%,3,,10000))$ $= \$3,430.63$	$I_4 = IPMT(15\%,4,5,FV(15\%,3,,10000))$ $= \$1,106.38$
5	$4,537.01	Normal	$P_5 = \$4,537.01(P|F\ 15\%, 5 - 5 + 1) = \$3,945.25$	$I_5 = \$4,537.01 - \$3,945.25 = \$591.76$
			$P_5 = PPMT(15\%,5,5,FV(15\%,3,,10000))$ $= \$3,945.22$	$I_5 = IPMT(15\%,5,5,FV(15\%,3,,10000))$ $= \$591.78$

3-6   RETIREMENT PLANNING

The most important message regarding retirement planning is to start sooner rather than later. Wealth maximization is more likely to occur if you take advantage of the exponent (n) in the compound amount factor than if you rely on the annual return (i) you receive on

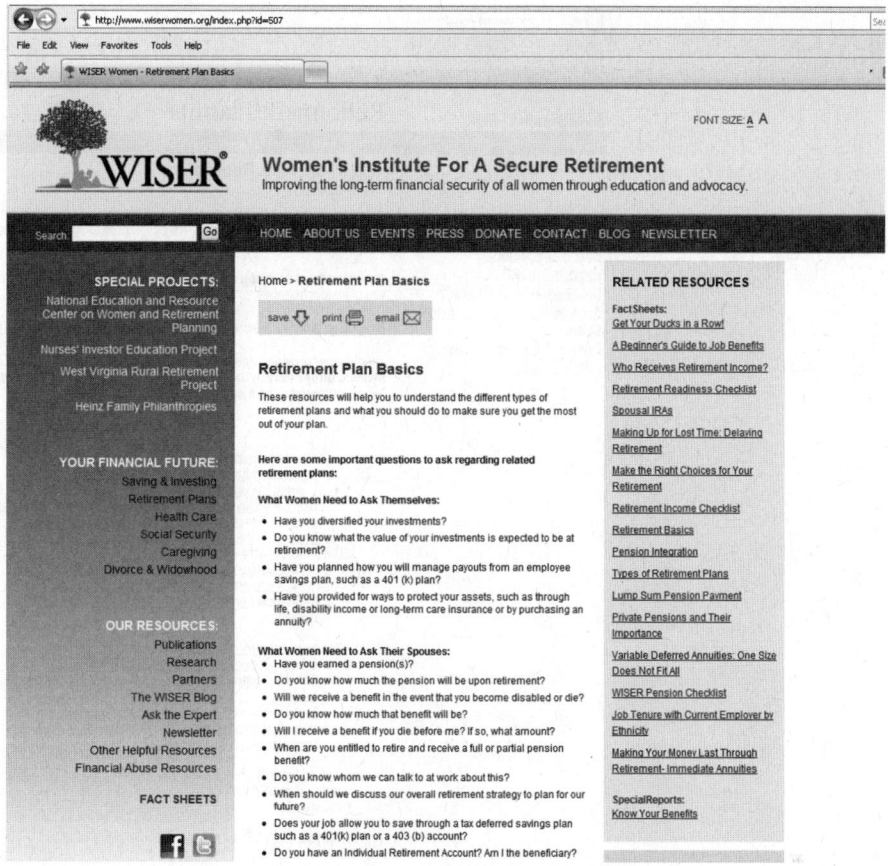

FIGURE 3.17

Information on Retirement Planning Available on Women's Institute for a Secure Retirement (WISER) Web Site.

your investments. Also, fewer employers provide defined benefit retirement plans for their employees—instead, they rely on employees to do their own retirement planning.

Numerous retirement-planning websites are available. Figures 3.17 and 3.18 are examples. Also, books, magazines, and newspapers provide abundant information on retirement planning. Consider, for example, the *USA Today*, June 30, 2006, article "Retirement Calculators Can Help You Prepare for the Future," by Christine Dugas. The article included the following: "Retirement may or may not be a long way off, but it never hurts to find out if you're on the right track. Even if you'd rather not pay a financial planner, there are free online retirement calculators that can help you check out your progress." The article described four calculators from NASD.com, AARP.org, EBRI.org, and T.RowePrice.com. Also, a retirement planning calculator is available on the *USA Today* Web site.

As you begin to think more seriously about investing for retirement, you might find one or more of the available retirement-planning calculators to be helpful. However, behind any calculator are assumptions that might not match your personal circumstances. For that reason, we suggest you perform your own calculations, using the tools and techniques provided in the text. If nothing else, it will serve to validate the results obtained using the calculators.

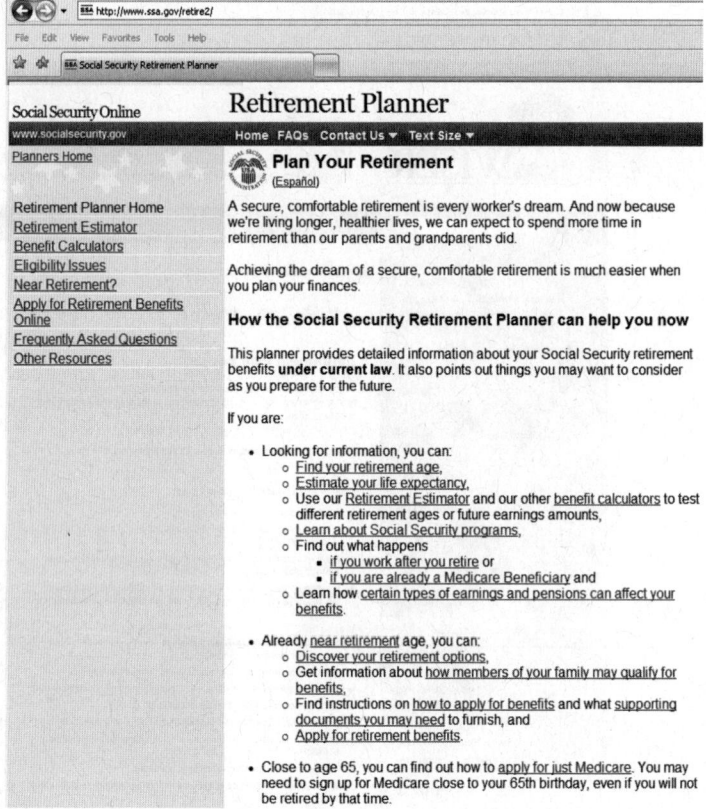

FIGURE 3.18

U.S. Government Social Security Administration Web Site for Retirement Planning.

What kind of salary increases might you experience over your engineering career? How you fare salary-wise depends very much on how effective you are in your job. Also, timing and luck seem to play a big factor. Most people will have several changes of employment during their career. Even in the matter of annual income, we are reminded of Principle 9: *Risks and rewards tend to be positively correlated.*

Principle #9

Risks and rewards tend to be positively correlated.

How much money you make is not nearly as important as what you do with it. Many people increase their standard of living as rapidly as they increase their income. In fact, too many increase their standard of living faster than their income.

In the end, for many, it will be a matter of choices. While it is true that everyone has 24 hours in a day, many spend their time and others invest it. Those who invest their time are very productive and usually quite successful professionally. The same is true of money: Some spend it while others invest it. You can choose to spend your money on things that depreciate, like vehicles, sound systems, big-screen televisions, and the like, or you can invest your money in things that appreciate, such as real estate, stocks, bonds, certificates of deposit (CDs), and so forth.

We are reminded of an excellent book by William T. Morris, titled *How to Get Rich, Slowly, But Almost Surely.*[3] The book's underlying thesis is to take advantage of the power of compounding by starting now with your investments. Any year that is lost is very difficult to make up. The following examples illustrate this point.

EXAMPLE 3.17 **The Power of Compounding Illustrated**

Immediately after beginning her engineering career, Maria establishes an investment plan and invests 10 percent of her $60,000 salary. If her salary increases by 10 percent per year over her professional career and she is able to earn 8 percent annually on her investments, how much will be in her investment account after 40 years if she continues to invest 10 percent of her salary?

$$F = \$6,000(F|A_1\ 8\%,10\%,40)$$
$$= \$6,000(1176.73670)$$
$$= \$7,060,420.00$$

EXAMPLE 3.18 **Losing Time Is Losing Money**

Franklin decides to postpone investing until he can "comfortably" do so. His salary is identical to Maria's and increases 10 percent annually. If he waits 20 years to begin investing and earns 8 percent on his investments, what must be the size of his initial investment in order to accumulate the same amount in his investment account?

After 20 years, his salary will be $60,000(F|P 10\%,20)$, or $403,650.00. If he invests 10 percent of his salary for 20 years at 8 percent annually, he will accumulate

$$F = \$40,365.00(F|A_1\ 8\%,10\%,20)$$
$$= \$40,365.00(103.32714)$$
$$= \$4,170,800$$

To achieve a balance of $7,060,420, Franklin must initially invest an additional amount equal to

$$P = (\$7,060,420 - \$4,170,800)(P|F\ 8\%,20)$$
$$= \$2,889,620(0.21455)$$
$$= \$619,968.00$$

(How will Franklin be able to invest more than $600,000, since he waited 20 years until he could "comfortably" invest?)

---

[3]Morris, William T., *How to Get Rich Slowly, But Almost Surely: Adventures in Applying the Decision Sciences,* Reston Publishing Company, Inc., Reston, VA, 1973.

A considerable number of studies have shown that an individual's lifetime income is highly correlated with education level. Because we have been asked frequently if graduate education can be justified economically, we thought it would be instructive to examine the economic impact of a bachelor's degree in engineering, a master's degree in engineering, or a doctorate in engineering versus having a high school diploma. We do not believe anyone should choose to major in engineering or to pursue graduate work simply because of money. However, neither do we believe an individual who so chooses should mistakenly believe that it is an unwise choice from an economic perspective. Although there are many variables that affect the economic analysis of the education alternatives, the following example illustrates how one might go about performing such economic analyses.

EXAMPLE 3.19 Justifying an Engineering Degree

Five alternatives will be considered in this example:

A. Graduating from high school at age 18 and beginning work, making $18,000 the first year, with 4 percent annual increases over a 48-year period, and retiring at age 65

B. Pursuing an engineering degree, paying $10,000 annually for tuition, fees, and books, graduating in 4 years, beginning employment at an annual salary of $60,000, receiving 6 percent annual increases in salary over a 44-year period, and retiring at age 65

C. Pursuing a bachelor's and master's degree in engineering, paying $10,000 annually for tuition, fees, and books for 4 years and $12,000 annually for 2 years, graduating with a master's degree 2 years after receiving the bachelor's degree, beginning employment at an annual salary of $75,000, receiving 7 percent annual increases in salary over a 42-year period, and retiring at age 65

D. Pursuing a bachelor's and a doctoral degree in engineering, paying $10,000 annually for tuition, fees, and books for 4 years and $12,000 annually for 4 years, graduating with a doctorate 4 years after receiving the bachelor's degree, beginning employment at an annual salary of $90,000, receiving 8 percent annual increases in salary over a 40-year period, and retiring at age 65

E. Pursuing a bachelor's and a doctoral degree in engineering, paying $10,000 annually for tuition, fees, and books for 4 years, receiving a $25,000 graduate assistantship for 4 years while pursuing the doctoral degree, graduating after 4 years of doctoral study, beginning employment at an annual salary of $90,000, receiving 8 percent annual increases in salary over a 40-year period, and retiring at age 65

Based on a time value of money of 8 percent compounded annually, the present worth of earnings until age 65 for each alternative is as follows:

$$PW(A) = \$18{,}000(P|A_1\ 8\%,4\%,48) = \$18{,}000[1 - (1.04)^{48}(1.08)^{-48}]/(0.08 - 0.04)$$
$$= \$376{,}468.65$$

$$PW(B) = -\$10{,}000(P|A\ 8\%,4) + \$60{,}000(P|A_1\ 8\%,6\%,44)(P|F\ 8\%,4)$$
$$= -\$10{,}000(3.31213) + \$60{,}000$$
$$\times\ \{[1 - (1.06)^{44}(1.08)^{-44}]/(0.08 - 0.06)\}(0.73503)$$
$$= \$1{,}203{,}158.00\ (\$1{,}203{,}157.29\ \text{with Excel®})$$

$$PW(C) = -\$10,000(P|A\,8\%,6) - \$2,000(P|A\,8\%,2)(P|F\,8\%,4)$$
$$+ \$75,000(P|A_1\,8\%,7\%,42)(P|F\,8\%,6)$$
$$= -\$10,000(4.62288) - \$2,000(1.78326)(0.73503)$$
$$+ \$75,000\{[1 - (1.07)^{42}(1.08)^{-42}]/(0.08 - 0.07)\}(0.63017)$$
$$= \$1,479,708.00\ (\textbf{\$1,479,707.57 with Excel®})$$

$$PW(D) = -\$10,000(P|A\,8\%,8) - \$2,000(P|A\,8\%,4)(P|F\,8\%,4)$$
$$+ \$90,000(P|A_1\,8\%,8\%,40)(P|F\,8\%,8)$$
$$= -\$10,000(5.74664) - \$2,000(3.31213)(0.73503)$$
$$+ \$90,000(40/1.08)(0.54027)$$
$$= \$1,738,565.00\ (\textbf{\$1,738,560.87 with Excel®})$$

$$PW(E) = -\$10,000(P|A\,8\%,8) + \$25,000(P|A\,8\%,4)(P|F\,8\%,4)$$
$$+ \$90,000(P|A_1\,8\%,8\%,40)(P|F\,8\%,8)$$
$$= -\$10,000(5.74664) + \$25,000(3.31213)(0.73503)$$
$$+ \$90,000(40/1.08)(0.54027)$$
$$= \$1,804,296.00\ (\textbf{\$1,828,637.82 with Excel®})$$

Clearly, obtaining the PhD in engineering while on a graduate assistantship yields the greatest present worth. Although that option is not available to all students, it is obvious that completing the bachelor's degree is far superior, economically, to having only a high school diploma.

Why was $10,000 used for tuition and fees for the bachelor's degree, when the average full cost of attendance at a national public research university exceeds $16,000? We did not include ''normal living costs'' of room, board, travel, laundry, and so on, since similar costs would be incurred if the person was working instead of attending college.

If the $10,000 tuition and fee costs for undergraduate studies and $12,000 tuition and fee costs for graduate studies are incorrect, it is relatively easy to substitute more accurate numbers. The same is true for the first year's salary under each scenario, as well as the annual increases in salary and the *TVOM* used.

Why did we use different growth rates for annual incomes for different education levels attained? Generally, different career options are available, depending on education level. While not everyone will experience the growth rates used in the

TABLE 3.10
Present Worth of Lifetime Earnings with Various Education Levels.

j	HS	BS	MS	PhD-1	PhD-2
4%	$376,469	$859,907	$890,581	$884,626	$974,703
5%	$444,795	$1,011,322	$1,044,015	$1,033,237	$1,123,314
6%	$533,070	$1,203,157	$1,236,488	$1,217,791	$1,307,868
7%	$648,262	$1,448,207	$1,479,708	$1,448,476	$1,538,552
8%	$800,000	$1,763,618	$1,789,144	$1,738,561	$1,828,638
9%	$1,001,587	$2,172,416	$2,185,273	$2,105,355	$2,195,432
10%	$1,271,457	$2,705,569	$2,695,224	$2,571,457	$2,661,534

Note: PhD-1 denotes PhD student not on assistantship; PhD-2 denotes PhD student on assistantship

example, our experience is that the rates of increase for total annual income are quite reasonable estimates. Of course, individual circumstances will differ. For that reason, we examined the effect on present worth for various growth rates, as shown in Table 3.10.

If the growth rate in annual income is independent of education level, the greatest present worth occurs with the doctoral degree, coupled with an assistantship. If an assistantship is not available, the master's degree is the preferred alternative.

EXAMPLE 3.20   Planning for Your Retirement

After deciding to start an investment program for your future retirement, you set about designing an Excel® spreadsheet to assist in your planning. What data will you need?

At a minimum, it will be helpful to estimate the amount you plan to invest each year, the number of years you anticipate investing before retiring, and the annual return you expect to receive on your investments. We have found it helpful to create one spreadsheet based on the amount invested each year increasing as a geometric series and one that increases as a gradient series.

A first attempt at developing a "geometric series spreadsheet" might look like that in Figure 3.19. After entering values for the three parameters, the "filled in" spreadsheet will

G30		fx	=G29*(1+G&)+F30					
	A	B	C	D	E	F	G	H
1		Geometric Series Personal Investment Planner						
2								
3	Name:					Date:		
5			Amount invested the first year ($):				$0.00	
6			Annual increase in amount invested (%):				0.00%	
7			Annual return on investment (%):				0.00%	
9	Investment Year	Amount Invested	Account Balance		Investment Year	Amount Invested	Account Balance	
10	0	$0.00	$0.00		21	$0.00	$0.00	
11	1	$0.00	$0.00		22	$0.00	$0.00	
12	2	$0.00	$0.00		23	$0.00	$0.00	
13	3	$0.00	$0.00		24	$0.00	$0.00	
14	4	$0.00	$0.00		25	$0.00	$0.00	
15	5	$0.00	$0.00		26	$0.00	$0.00	
16	6	$0.00	$0.00		27	$0.00	$0.00	
17	7	$0.00	$0.00		28	$0.00	$0.00	
18	8	$0.00	$0.00		29	$0.00	$0.00	
19	9	$0.00	$0.00		30	$0.00	$0.00	
20	10	$0.00	$0.00		31	$0.00	$0.00	
21	11	$0.00	$0.00		32	$0.00	$0.00	
22	12	$0.00	$0.00		33	$0.00	$0.00	
23	13	$0.00	$0.00		34	$0.00	$0.00	
24	14	$0.00	$0.00		35	$0.00	$0.00	
25	15	$0.00	$0.00		36	$0.00	$0.00	
26	16	$0.00	$0.00		37	$0.00	$0.00	
27	17	$0.00	$0.00		38	$0.00	$0.00	
28	18	$0.00	$0.00		39	$0.00	$0.00	
29	19	$0.00	$0.00		40	$0.00	$0.00	
30	20	$0.00	$0.00		41	$0.00	$0.00	

FIGURE 3.19
Retirement Planning Spreadsheet.

look like the one in Figure 3.20. (Notice how simple it is to play around with the investment plan. You can try various values for the percent of your income you choose to invest and the return you expect to receive on your investments.)

| A1 | fx Geometric Series Personal Investment Planner |

	A	B	C	D	E	F	G	H	I	J
1		**Geometric Series Personal Investment Planner**								
2										
3	Name:					Date:				
4										
5			Amount invested the first year ($):				$4,500.00			
6			Annual increase in amount invested (%):				8.00%			
7			Annual return on investment (%):				6.00%			
8										
9	Investment Year	Amount Invested	Account Balance		Investment Year	Amount Invested	Account Balance			
10	0	$4,500.00	$4,500.00		21	$22,652.25	$412,425.67			
11	1	$4,860.00	$9,630.00		22	$24,464.43	$461,635.65			
12	2	$5,248.80	$15,456.60		23	$26,421.59	$515,755.37			
13	3	$5,668.70	$22,052.70		24	$28,535.31	$575,236.01			
14	4	$6,122.20	$29,498.06		25	$30,818.14	$640,568.31			
15	5	$6,611.98	$37,879.92		26	$33,283.59	$712,285.99			
16	6	$7,140.93	$47,293.65		27	$35,946.28	$790,969.43			
17	7	$7,712.21	$57,843.48		28	$38,821.98	$877,249.57			
18	8	$8,329.19	$69,643.28		29	$41,927.74	$971,812.29	←=G17*(1+$G$7)+F18		
19	9	$8,995.52	$82,817.39		30	$45,281.96	$1,075,402.98			
20	10	$9,715.16	$97,501.60		31	$48,904.51	$1,188,831.67			
21	11	$10,492.38	$113,844.07		32	$52,816.87	$1,312,978.44			
22	12	$11,331.77	$132,006.48		33	$57,042.22	$1,448,799.37			
23	13	$12,238.31	$152,165.18		34	$61,605.60	$1,597,332.04	←=F22*(1+$G$6)		
24	14	$13,217.37	$174,512.46		35	$66,534.05	$1,759,706.96			
25	15	$14,274.76	$199,257.97		36	$71,856.77	$1,937,146.15			
26	16	$15,416.74	$226,630.19		37	$77,605.32	$2,130,980.24			
27	17	$16,650.08	$256,878.08		38	$83,813.74	$2,342,652.79			
28	18	$17,982.09	$290,272.85		39	$90,518.84	$2,573,730.80			
29	19	$19,420.65	$327,109.88		40	$97,760.35	$2,825,915.00			
30	20	$20,974.31	$367,710.78		41	$105,581.17	$3,101,051.07			

FIGURE 3.20

Completed Retirement Planning Spreadsheet.

As shown in the following example, the spreadsheet allows you to set an investment goal and then determine what the values of the parameters have to be in order to achieve the goal.

EXAMPLE 3.21   Becoming a Multimillionaire

Suppose you place $4,500 in an investment account. If you increase the magnitude of your investment by 8 percent each year, how much must you earn annually on your investments in order to have an investment portfolio that totals $4,000,000 after 35 years?

From Figure 3.21, you see that a value of 0 percent was entered in cell G7. Excel®'s **GOAL SEEK** tool is used with the following parameter values:

Set cell: G24

To value: 2000000

By changing cell: G7

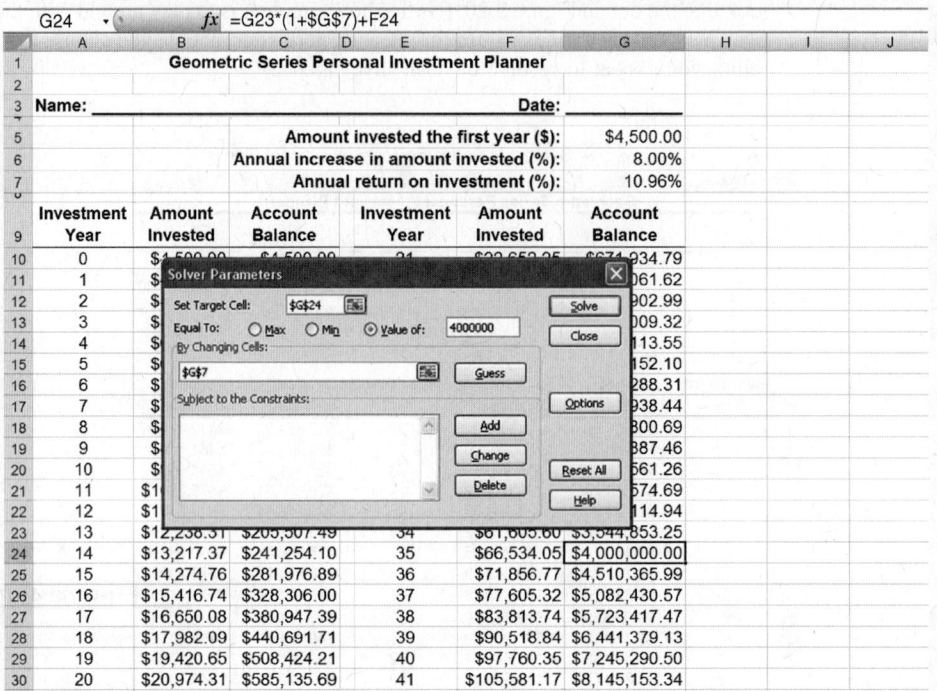

FIGURE 3.21

Applying the Excel® SOLVER Tool in Retirement Planning.

The solution obtained using GOAL SEEK is 10.96 percent. Notice, if this return is achieved and the other parameters are realized, by working an additional 5 years (for a total of 40 years), the portfolio totals $7,245,290.50. (This example can also be solved using Excel®'s SOLVER tool.)

As an exercise, create a spreadsheet based on a gradient series. While you are at it, you might as well build one for a geometric series, because we are confident you will be using it in the future.

3-7 EQUIVALENCE AND INDIFFERENCE

Throughout Chapter 2 and the preceding sections in this chapter, we have used the term *equivalence* without defining precisely what it meant. This was done intentionally in order to subtly introduce the notion that two cash flow series or profiles are equivalent at some specified interest rate $k\%$, if their present worths are equal using an interest rate of $k\%$. We will now define *equivalence* and a related concept, *indifference*, more formally and will discuss their importance in engineering economic analyses.

3.7.1 Equivalence

In engineering economic analyses, *equivalence* means "the state of being equal in value." The concept is primarily applied in the comparison of two or more cash flow profiles. Specifically, two (or more) cash flow profiles are *equivalent* if their time value of money worths at a common point in time are equal.

Question: Are the following two cash flows equivalent at 15 percent/year?
Cash Flow 1: Receive $1,322.50 two years from today
Cash Flow 2: Receive $1,000 today

Analysis Approach 1: Compare worths at $t = 0$ (present worth)

$$PW(1) = \$1,322.50(P|F\ 15\%,2)$$
$$= \$1,322.50(0.756147) = \$1,000.00$$

$$=PV(15\%,2,,-1322.5)$$
$$=\$1,000.00$$
$$PW(2) = \$1,000.00$$

Answer: Cash Flow 1 and Cash Flow 2 are equivalent.

Analysis Approach 2: Compare worths at $t = 2$ (future worth)

$$FW(1) = \$1,322.50$$
$$FW(2) = \$1,000.00(F|P\ 15\%,2)$$
$$= \$1,000.00(1.32250) = \$1,322.50$$

$$=FV(15\%,2,,-1000) = \$1,322.50$$

Answer: Cash Flow 1 and Cash Flow 2 are equivalent.

Analysis Approach 3: Compare worths at $t = 1$

$$W_1(1) = \$1,322.50(P|F\ 15\%,1)$$
$$= \$1,322.50(0.869565) = \$1,150.00$$

$$=PV(15\%,1,,-1322.5) = \$1,150.00$$
$$W_1(2) = \$1,000.00(F|P\ 15\%,1)$$
$$= \$1,000.00(1.1500) = \$1,150.00$$

$$=FV(15\%,1,,-1000) = \$1,150.00$$

Answer: Cash Flow 1 and Cash Flow 2 are equivalent.

Analysis Approach 4: Compare worths at $t = 6$

$$W_6(1) = \$1,322.50(F|P\ 15\%,4)$$
$$= \$1,322.50(1.749006) = \$2,313.06$$

$$=FV(15\%,\ 4,,-1322.5) = \$2,313.06$$
$$W_6(2) = \$1,000.00(F|P\ 15\%,6)$$
$$= \$1,000.00(2.31306) = \$2,3130.06$$

$$=FV(15\%,\ 6,,-1000) = \$2,313.06$$

Answer: Cash Flow 1 and Cash Flow 2 are equivalent.

Notice, we did not obtain values for the compound interest factors from the interest tables in Appendix A because of possible round-off errors. Instead, we calculated the value of each factor to six decimal places in order to demonstrate that equivalency existed. (That is why the Excel® results were identical to the calculated results.)

Also, notice that the selection of the point in time, t, at which the comparison is made is completely arbitrary. Clearly, however, some choices are more intuitively appealing (and computationally simpler) than others ($t = 0$ and $t = 2$ in the above example).

EXAMPLE 3.22   A Single-Sum Equivalency at an Intermediate Point of a Cash Flow Profile

What single sum of money at $t = 6$ is equivalent to the cash flow profile shown in Figure 3.22 if $i = 10\%$?

The present worth of the cash flow profile is given by

$$PW = -\$400(P|F\ 10\%,1) + \$100(P|A\ 10\%,3)(P|F\ 10\%,1)$$
$$+ \$100(P|A\ 10\%,3)(P|F\ 10\%,5)$$
$$= -\$400(0.90909) + \$100(2.48685)(0.90909) + \$100(2.48685)(0.62092)$$
$$= \$16.85$$

Moving \$16.85 forward in time to $t = 6$ gives

$$W_{t=6} = \$16.85(F|P\ 10\%,6)$$
$$= \$16.85(1.77156) = \$29.85$$

Thus, at 10 percent, a positive-valued cash flow of \$29.85 at $t = 6$ is equivalent to the cash flow profile shown in Figure 3.22.

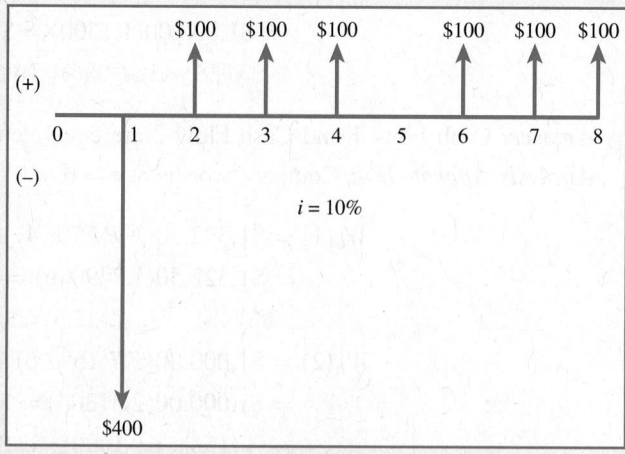

FIGURE 3.22

CFD **for Example 3.22.**

EXAMPLE 3.23   A Uniform Series Equivalency of a Decreasing Gradient Series

Using an 8 percent discount rate, what uniform series over five periods, [1,5], is equivalent to the cash flow profile given in Figure 3.23a?

The cash flow profile in Figure 3.23a consists of the difference in a uniform series of $500 and a gradient series, with $G = \$100$. As shown in Figure 3.23b, a uniform series equivalent of the cash flow profile can be obtained over the interval [2,6] as follows:

$$A = \$500 - \$100(A|G\,8\%,5)$$
$$= \$500 - \$100(1.84647)$$
$$= \$315.35$$

To convert a uniform series over the interval [2,6] to an equivalent uniform series over the interval [1,5], the entire series must be shifted backward in time one time unit. From *DCF Rule #4*, we move money backward in time one time unit by dividing by 1 plus the interest rate. Hence, as shown in Figure 3.23c, the equivalent worth over the interval [1,5] is

$$W_{[1,5]} = \$315.35(P|F\,8\%,1)$$
$$= \$315.35(0.92593)$$
$$= \$291.99$$

Consequently, a uniform series of $291.99 over the interval [1,5] is equivalent to the cash flow profile given in Figure 3.23a. (If you have doubts concerning the equivalence, compare their present worths using an 8 percent interest rate.)

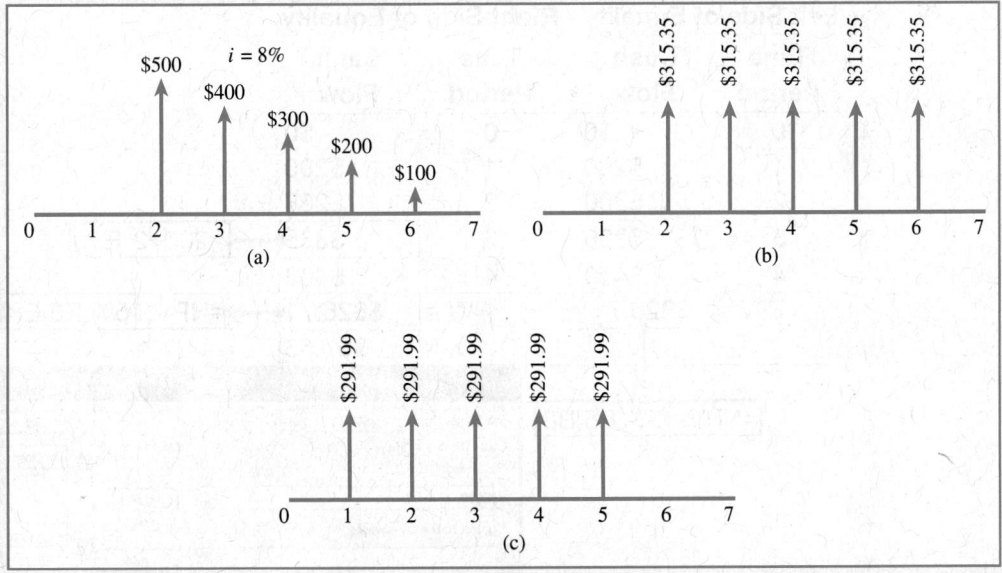

FIGURE 3.23

CFDs for Example 3.23.

EXAMPLE 3.24 Determining an Equivalent Gradient Step

Consider Figure 3.24. Determine the value of X that makes the two cash flow profiles equivalent using a *TVOM* of 15 percent.

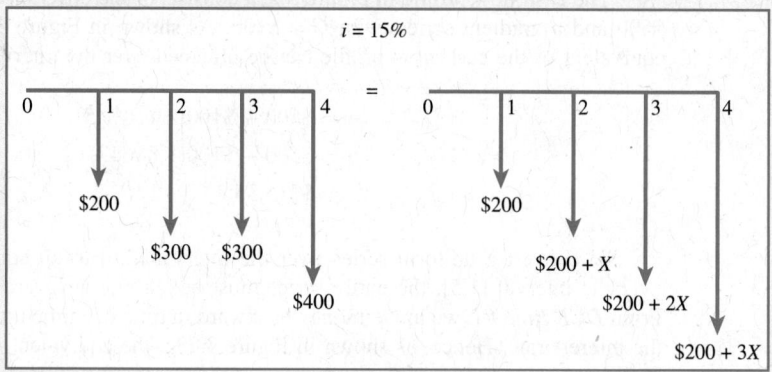

FIGURE 3.24

***CFD*s for Example 3.24.**

Equating the future worths of the two cash flow profiles at $t = 4$ gives

$$\$200(F|A\ 15\%,4) + \$100(F|A\ 15\%,3) + \$100 = [\$200 + X(A|G\ 15\%,4)](F|A\ 15\%,4)$$

Eliminating the common term of $\$200(F|A\ 15\%,4)$ yields

$$\$100(3.47250) + \$100 = X(1.32626)(4.99338)$$

Solving for X gives a value of $\$67.53$.

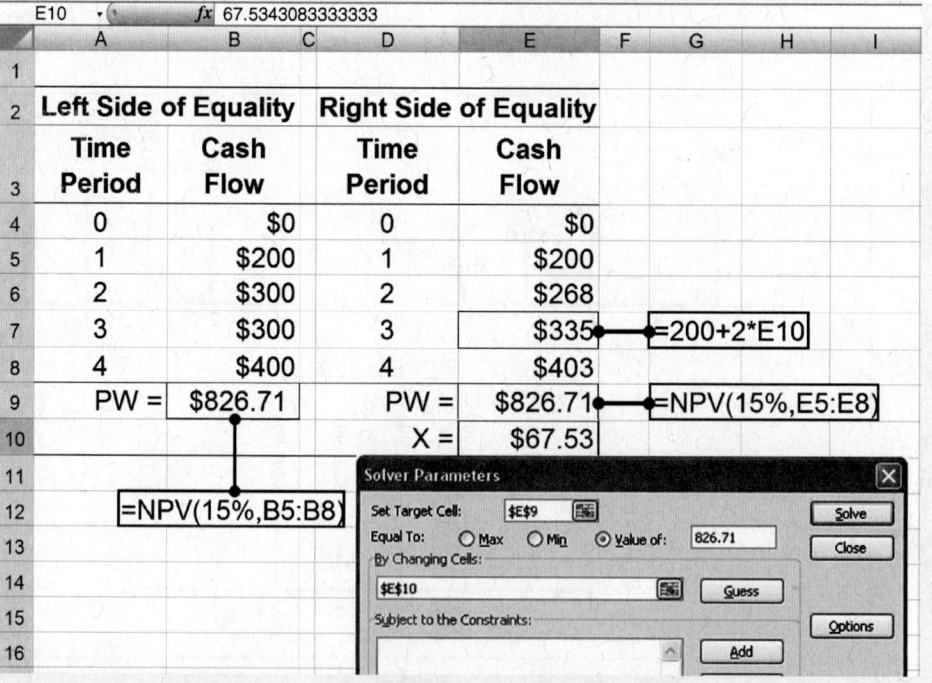

FIGURE 3.25

Using the Excel® SOLVER Tool to Solve Example 3.24.

This example offers an opportunity to use either Excel®'s **SOLVER** tool or Excel®'s **GOAL SEEK** tool. To use **SOLVER**, the data are entered in a spreadsheet as shown in Figure 3.25. The present worth of the cash flows to the left of the equality in Figure 3.25 is set equal to the present worth of the cash flows to the right of the equality.

Notice, the unknown is given by cell E10. The target cell, E9, is to be made equal to $826.71, which is the present worth of the equality's left-hand side. The cash flows on the equality's right-hand side appropriately include the value of cell E10. When **SOLVER** is applied, the value in cell E10 is changed to $67.53 with the result that the present worth in cell B9 equals the present worth in cell E9.

EXAMPLE 3.25   Determining an Equivalent Interest Rate

For what interest (discount) rate are the two cash flow profiles shown in Figure 3.26 equivalent?

Converting each cash flow profile to a uniform series over the interval [1,5] gives

$$-\$4{,}000(A|P\,i\%,5) + \$1{,}500 = -\$7{,}000(A|P\,i\%,5) + \$1{,}500 + \$500(A|G\,i\%,5)$$

or

$$\$3{,}000(A|P\,i\%,5) = \$500(A|G\,i\%,5)$$

which reduces to

$$(A|G\,i\%,5) = 6(A|P\,i\%,5)$$

Searching through the interest tables at $n = 5$, the value of the $(A|G\,i\%,5)$ factor is six times the value of the $(A|P\,i\%,5)$ factor for an interest rate between 12 percent and 15 percent. Specifically, with a 12 percent interest rate,

$$(A|G\,12\%,5) - 6(A|P\,12\%,5) = 1.77459 - 6(0.27741) = 0.11013$$

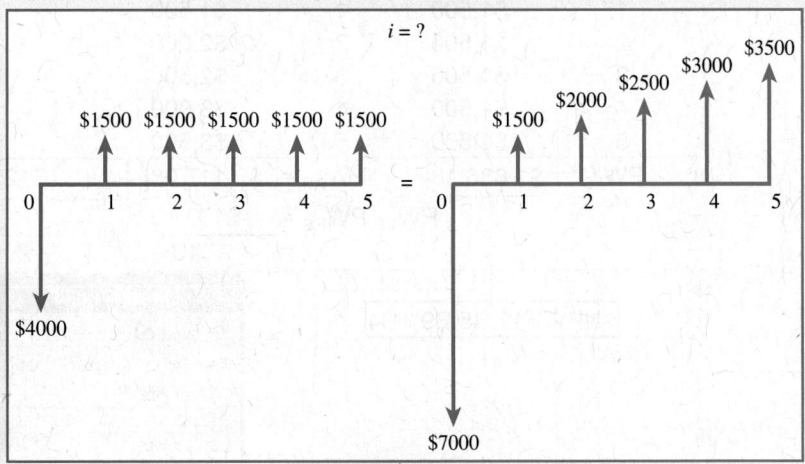

FIGURE 3.26

*CFD*s for Example 3.25.

and, using a 15 percent interest rate,

$$(A|G\,15\%,5) - 6(A|P\,15\%,5) = 1.72281 - 6(0.29832) = -0.06711$$

Interpolating for i gives

$$i = 0.12 + (0.15 - 0.12)(0.11013)/(0.11013 + 0.06711)$$

or

$$i = 0.138641$$

Therefore, using a discount rate of approximately 13.8641 percent will establish an equivalence relationship between the cash flow profiles given in Figure 3.26.

Excel® can be used to determine the equivalency. As shown in Figure 3.27, we set the present worth of the equality's left-hand side equal to its right-hand side. Excel®'s **NPV** function is used to compute the present worth of each cash flow stream. In cell E11 is entered the difference in the present worth of the left-hand side (B10) and the present worth of the right-hand side (E10). Each present worth is calculated using a value for the interest rate given in cell E12.

Using the Excel® **SOLVER** tool, the target cell is set to E11. (Since we want the two present worths to be equal, E11 must equal zero.) In order to make E11 equal 0, cell E12's value, the interest rate, must be changed. We initialize the underlying search performed by **SOLVER** by setting E12 equal to 10 percent. After applying **SOLVER**, as shown in Figure 3.28, a value of 13.8677 percent is obtained for the interest rate, which is quite close to the value obtained by interpolating values obtained from tables in Appendix A. (The Excel® **GOAL SEEK** tool can also be used to solve the example.)

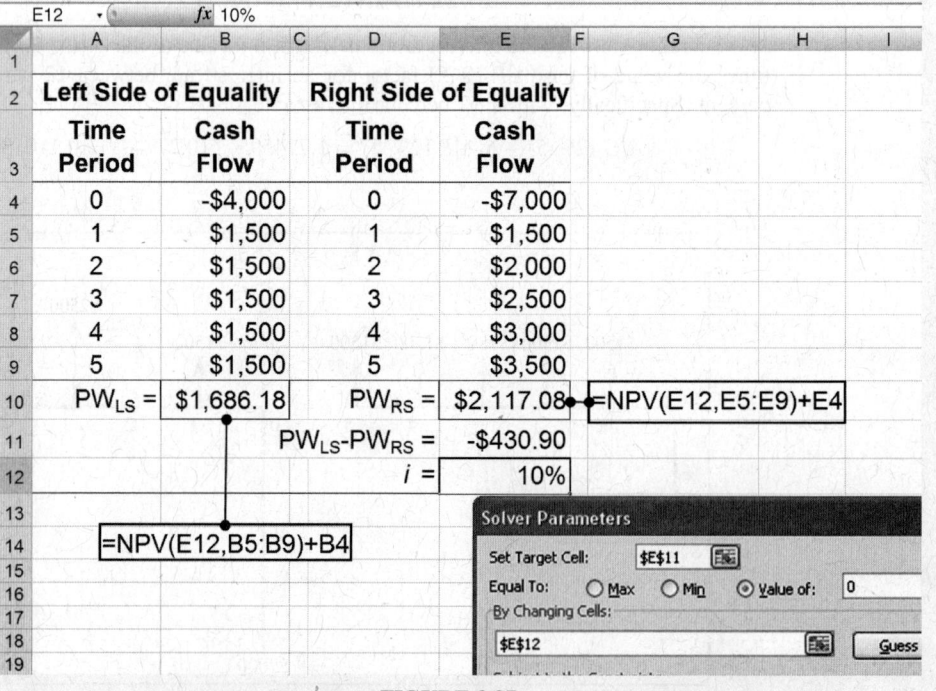

FIGURE 3.27

Using the Excel® SOLVER Tool to Solve Example 3.25.

E11	▾	fx =B10-E10				
	A	B	C	D	E	F
1						
2	**Left Side of Equality**			**Right Side of Equality**		
3	**Time Period**	**Cash Flow**		**Time Period**	**Cash Flow**	
4	0	-$4,000		0	-$7,000	
5	1	$1,500		1	$1,500	
6	2	$1,500		2	$2,000	
7	3	$1,500		3	$2,500	
8	4	$1,500		4	$3,000	
9	5	$1,500		5	$3,500	
10	PW$_{LS}$ =	$1,166.04		PW$_{RS}$ =	$1,166.04	
11				PW$_{LS}$-PW$_{RS}$ =	$0.00	
12				i =	13.8677%	

FIGURE 3.28
Solution to Example 3.25.

3.7.2 Indifference

A concept that is closely related to equivalence is *indifference*. In engineering economic analyses, *indifference* means "to have no preference." The concept is primarily applied in the comparison of two or more cash flow profiles. Specifically, a potential investor is *indifferent* between two (or more) cash flow profiles if they are equivalent.

Question: Given the following two cash flows at 15 percent/year, which do you prefer?
Cash Flow 1: Receive $1,322.50 two years from today
Cash Flow 2: Receive $1,000 today

Answer: Based on the equivalence calculations above, given these two choices, you should be indifferent if your *TVOM* is 15 percent.

3.7.3 Applying the Concepts of Equivalence and Indifference

The concept of equivalence can be used to break a large, complex problem into a series of smaller, more manageable ones. This is done by taking advantage of the fact that, in calculating the economic worth of a cash flow profile, any part of the profile can be replaced by an *equivalent* representation without altering the profile's worth at an arbitrary point in time.

Question: You are given a choice between (1) receiving $P today or (2) receiving $2,000 per year for 5 years starting at $t = 3$. What must the value of P be for you to be indifferent between the two choices if $i = 10$ percent/year?

Analysis Approach: To be indifferent between the choices, P must have a value such that the two alternatives are equivalent at 10 percent/year. If we select $t = 0$ as the common point in time upon which to base the analysis (present worth approach), then the analysis proceeds as follows:

$$PW(\text{Alt } 1) = P$$

$$PW(\text{Alt } 2) = ?$$

Step 1 — Replace the uniform series ($t = 3$ to 7) with an equivalant single sum,

V_2, at $t = 2$ (why $t = 2$?): $V_2 = \$2,000(P|A\ 10\%,5) = \$2,000(3.79079) = \$7,581.58$

Note, since the cash flows were positive, V_2 must also be positive for equivalence to hold.

Step 2 — Replace the single sum, V_2, with an equivalent value, V_0, at $t = 0$:

$$PW(\text{Alt } 2) = V_0 = V_2(P|F\ 10\%,2) = \$7,581.58(0.82645) = \$6,265.80$$

Answer: To be indifferent between the two alternatives, they must be equivalent at $t = 0$. To be equivalent, P must have a value of $6,265.80.

3-8 PURCHASING AND SELLING BONDS

Previously, we said we would not make recommendations regarding particular investments for you to pursue. Then we discussed real estate investing, and now we are about to discuss purchasing and selling bonds. You probably have doubts about our veracity. In our defense, consideration of real estate and bond transactions is not due to their relative attractiveness in an investment portfolio but because they are great vehicles for applying the *DCF* models developed in Chapter 2, and they prepare you for what lies ahead in other chapters. Specifically, bond problems are considered in engineering economic analysis texts for the following reasons:

1. Bond problems illustrate the notion of equivalence covered in the previous section—that is, a bond's purchase price is equivalent to the returns from the bond at an appropriate compound interest rate. Hence, they are a useful mechanism for demonstrating a number of the *TVOM* calculations developed earlier.

2. Bond problems are convenient investment opportunities and will be used to motivate our presentations in Chapters 5, 6, 7, and 8 of various measures of the economic worths of investment alternatives.

3. The issuance and sale of bonds is a mechanism by which capital may be raised to finance engineering investments; as such, they contribute to the firm's overall cost of capital, as discussed in Chapter 4.

4. Bonds represent investment opportunities, which many individual investors choose to include in their personal financial plans.

An organizational unit desiring to raise capital may issue bonds totaling, say, $1 million, $5 million, $25 million, or more. A financial brokerage firm usually handles the issue on a commission basis and sells smaller amounts to other organizational units or individual investors. Individual bonds are normally issued in even denominations such as $500, $1,000, or $5,000. The stated value on the individual bond is termed the *face* or *par value*. The par value is to be repaid by the issuing organization at the end of a specified period of time, say 5, 10, 15, 20, or even 50 years. Thus, the issuing unit is obligated to *redeem* the bond at par value at *maturity*. Furthermore, the issuing unit is obligated to pay a stipulated *bond rate* on the face value during the interim between date of issuance and date of redemption. This might be 10 percent payable quarterly, 9½ percent payable semiannually, 11 percent payable annually, and so forth. For the purpose of the following problems, it is emphasized that *the bond rate applies to the par value of the bond*.

EXAMPLE 3.26   Determining the Annual Return on a Bond Transaction

Charlotte purchases five $1,000, 5-year bonds on the date of issuance for $5,000. The stated bond rate is 10 percent semiannually, and the interest payments are received on schedule until the bonds are redeemed at maturity for $5,000. The bond rate per interest period is 10%/2 = 5%. Thus, Charlotte receives $(0.10/2)(\$5,000) = \$250$ payments every 6 months. A *CFD* for the duration of the investment is given in Figure 3.29, where time periods are 6-month intervals.

Note, from Figure 3.29, that the $5,000 expenditure at $t = 0$ yields $250 each semiannual interest period for 10 semiannual periods and a $5,000 redemption value at $t = 10$. Thus, the $5,000 investment at $t = 0$ yielded the revenues from $t = 1$ through $t = 10$. What annual interest rate or *return on investment* did the $5,000 bond investment yield?

One might intuitively answer the question posed by stating that the $5,000 investment was exactly returned (no loss or gain in capital) at redemption, and since during the interim an interest rate of 10 percent semiannual was received, then the yield *must* be 10 percent semiannual. Accepting this argument for the moment, one might further pose certain hypotheses concerning the transaction. For instance, it is hypothesized that the $5,000 at $t = 0$ is equivalent (has the same present worth) to the revenue cash flows if the

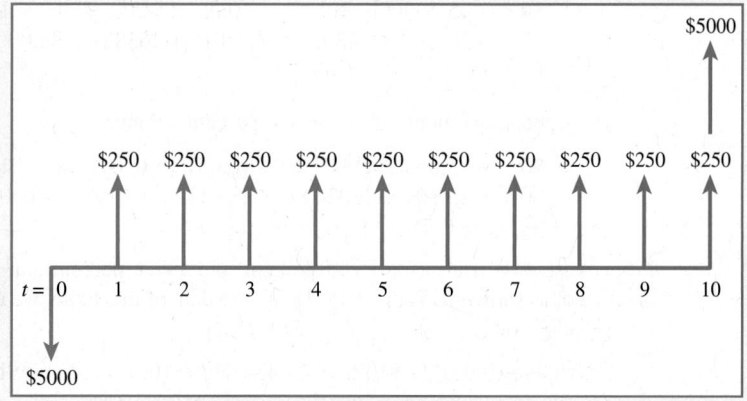

FIGURE 3.29

CFD **for a $5000, 10% Semiannual, 10-Year Bond Investment.**

TVOM is 10 percent compounded semiannually. That this hypothesis is true is shown by the relation

$$P = A(P|A\ 5\%,10) + F(P|F\ 5\%,10)$$

or

$$\$5,000 = (0.05)(\$5,000)(7.72173) + \$5,000(0.61391),$$

and

$$\$5,000 = \$4,999.98$$

(The 2¢ difference is due to round-off errors in the interest tables.)

Since the bond earns 10 percent compounded semiannually, the annual effective return on the bond is $(1.05)^2 - 1$, or 10.25 percent.

A second hypothesis concerning the transaction is that if more than the par value is paid for the bonds at $t = 0$ and all revenue figures remain the same, then a return on investment less than the bond rate of 10 percent semiannual will be received on the bond investment. For example, if \$5,500 was paid for the 5 bonds at $t = 0$, the present worth of the \$5,500 expenditure is not equal (equivalent) to the present worth of the revenues at a 10 percent semiannual yield. This is shown by

$$\$5,500 \neq (0.05)(\$5,000)(P|A\ 5\%,10) + \$5,000(P|F\ 5\%,10)$$
$$\$5,500 \neq \$250(7.72173) + \$5,000(0.61391)$$
$$\$5,500 \neq \$4,999.98$$

This result now raises the pertinent question, What is the rate of return on the bond investment if \$5,500 is paid for the bond and the revenues remain the same? Intuition may suggest that the yield will be less that 10 percent semiannual, because the purchase value of \$5,500 decreases (a loss of investment capital) to \$5,000 on redemption. Furthermore, the semiannual payments of \$250 are not equal to 5 percent of the \$5,500 purchase price. In order to answer the question more precisely, let us answer the alternate question of, What interest rate per period (or yield per period) will make the future worth of all cash flows equal to zero? That is, what interest rate satisfies the following equation?

$$\$0 = -\$5,500(F|P\ i\%,10) + (0.05)(\$5,000)(F|A\ i\%,10) + \$5,000$$

The solution to the above equation gives the answer to the original question, and the task is to solve for the positive roots of the polynomial. However, an approximate solution to avoid such tedium is trial and error. An iterative procedure follows.

For $i = 3$ percent/6-month period (or 6 percent semiannual),

$$\$0 < -\$5,500(F|P\ 3\%,10) + (0.05)(\$5,000)(F|A\ 3\%,10) + \$5,000$$
$$\$0 < -\$5,500(1.34392) + (\$250)(11.46388) + \$5,000$$
$$\$0 < \$474.41$$

For $i = 4$ percent/6-month period (or 8 percent semiannual),

$$\$0 > -\$5,500(F|P\ 4\%,10) + (0.05)(\$5,000)(F|A\ 4\%,10) + \$5,000$$
$$\$0 > -\$5,500(1.48024) + (\$250)(12.00611) + \$5,000$$
$$\$0 > -\$139.79$$

From these two trials (for $i = 3$ percent and $i = 4$ percent), the future worth of \$0 is bracketed, as shown in Table 3.11. Using the data of this table, we can solve for X by linear interpolation, or

$$(0.04 - 0.03)/(-\$139.79 - \$474.41) = (0.04 - X)/(-\$139.79 - \$0.00)$$

or

$$X = 0.37724 \quad \text{or} \quad 3.7724\%/6\text{-month period}$$

TABLE 3.11 Bond Yield Interpolation			
For $i =$	0.03	X	0.04
FW of revenues $=$	$474.53	$0.00	-$139.58

Thus, the equivalent yield on the 45,500 investment in the bonds is approximately $3.7724\%(2) = 7.5448\%$ compounded semiannually, for an effective annual yield of $[(1 + 0.037724)^2 - 1]$ $(100\%) = 7.6871\%$. The figures support the a priori intuition of a return on investment less than 10 percent compounded semiannually, and the second hypothesis is accepted.

This example fits perfectly the Excel® **RATE** worksheet function. Recall, the syntax for **RATE** is **RATE(nper,pmt,pv,fv,type,guess)**. By entering the following in any Excel® cell,

$$=\textbf{RATE(10,250,-5500,5000)}$$

the result obtained is 3.781 percent every 6 months. Hence, the effective annual yield on the bond transaction is given by

$$i_{eff} = \textbf{(1+RATE(10,250,-5500,5000)}^\wedge\textbf{2-1}$$

or **7.704** percent, which is a more accurate value than that obtained by interpolation.

Bond problems arise in economic analysis, because many bonds trade daily through financial markets. Bonds may be purchased for less than, greater than, or equal to par value, depending on the economic environment. They may also be sold for less than, greater than, or equal to par value. Furthermore, once purchased, bonds may be kept for a variable number of interest periods before being sold or redeemed. A variety of situations can occur, but there are only three basic types of bond problems. These will be presented after formalizing the discussion thus far. We now employ the following notation:

P = the purchase price of a bond

F = the sales price (or redemption value) of a bond

V = the par or face value of a bond

r = the bond rate (coupon rate) per interest period

i = the yield rate (return on investment or rate of return) per interest period

n = the number of interest (coupon) payments received by the bondholder

$A = Vr$ = the interest or coupon payment received per interest period

The general expression relating these terms is

$$P = Vr(P|A\ i\%,n) + F(P|F\ i\%,n) \qquad (3.18)$$

$$\boxed{P = Vr(P|A\ i\%,n) + F(P|F\ i\%,n)}$$

Three types of bond problems are considered:

1. Given *P, r, n, V,* and a desired *i,* find the sales price *F.*
2. Given *F, r, n, V,* and a desired *i,* find the purchase price *P.*
3. Given *P, F, r, n,* and *V,* find the yield rate *i* that has been realized.

Each of these cases is illustrated in the following examples.

EXAMPLE 3.27 Determining the Selling Price for a Bond

On January 1, 2012, Austin plans to pay $1,050 for a $1,000, 12 percent semiannual bond, which he will keep for 3 years, receive six coupon payments, and sell it. How much should he sell the bond for in order to receive a yield of 10 percent compounded semiannually? The *CFD* for the example is given in Figure 3.30.

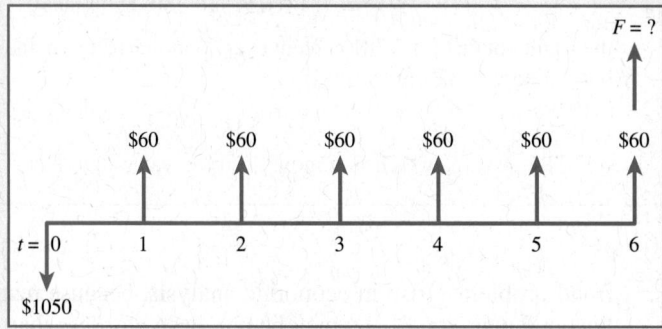

FIGURE 3.30
***CFD* for a $1000 Bond Investment–Determining the Sales Price.**

The present worth for the bond investment is given by

$$P = Vr(P|A\,5\%,6) + F(P|F\,5\%,6)$$

or

$$\$1,050 = (\$1,000)(0.06)(5.07569) + F(0.74622)$$

Solving for *F* yields a value of $998.98. As long as the selling price at the end of 3 years is at least $998.98, the bond will yield a return of at least 10 percent compounded semiannually.

The Excel® FV worksheet function is well suited for this example. Recall the syntax for the **FV** worksheet function is **FV(rate,nper,pmt,pv,type)**. Therefore, entering

$$=\text{FV}(5\%,6,60,-1050)$$

into any cell in an Excel® spreadsheet will produce the following result: **$998.99**. (The 1¢ difference in results is due to round-off errors in the interest tables.)

EXAMPLE 3.28 Determining the Purchase Price for a Bond

Emma is planning to purchase a $1,000, 12 percent semiannual bond, hold it for 3 years, receive six coupon payments, and redeem it at par value. What is the maximum amount she should pay for the bond if she wants to earn at least 14 percent compounded semiannually on her investment? A *CFD* for the planned investment is given in Figure 3.31.

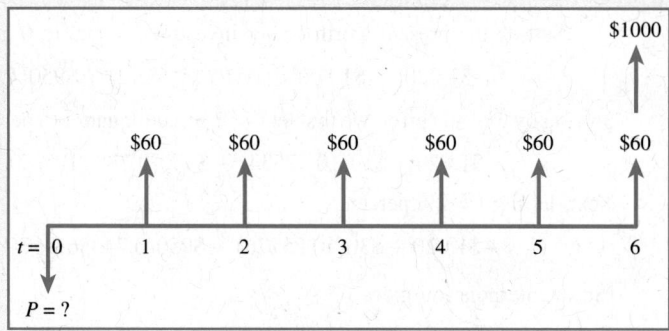

FIGURE 3.31

CFD for a $1000 Bond Investment–Determining the Purchase Price.

The present worth for the bond investment is given by

$$P = Vr(P|A\,7\%,6) + F(P|F\,7\%,6)$$

or

$$P = (\$1,000)(0.06)(4.76654) + \$1,000(0.66634)$$

Solving for P yields a value of $952.33. As long as the purchase price is no greater than $952.33, Emma's rate of return on her investment will be at least 14 percent compounded semiannually.

 The Excel® **PV** worksheet function matches perfectly with this bond calculation. Recall the **PV** syntax is **PV(rate,nper,pmt,fv,type)**. Therefore, entering

$$=\text{PV}(7\%,6,\text{-}60,\text{-}1000)$$

in any cell in an Excel® spreadsheet will give the answer sought: **$952.33**.

EXAMPLE 3.29   Determining the Rate of Return for a Bond Investment

Sara Beth purchased a $1,000, 12 percent quarterly bond for $1,020, kept it for 3 years, received twelve coupon payments, and sold it for $950. What was her quarterly yield on her bond investment? What was her effective annual rate of return? The *CFD* for the investment is given in Figure 3.32.

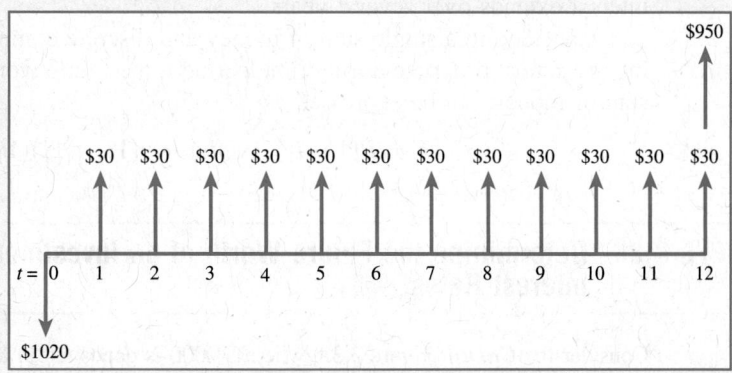

FIGURE 3.32

CFD for a $1000 Bond Investment–Determining the Annual Yield.

Setting the present worth of her investment equal to 0 gives

$$-\$1,020 + (\$1,000)(0.03)(P|A\ i\%,12) + \$950(P|F\ i\%,12) = \$0$$

Solving by trial and error, we first let $i = 2$ percent/quarter (8 percent compounded quarterly):

$$-\$1,020 + \$30(10.57534) + \$950(0.78849) > \$0 \quad \$46.3257 > \$0$$

Next, letting $i = 2\frac{1}{2}$ percent,

$$-\$1,020 + \$30(10.25776) + \$950(0.74356) < \$0 - \$5.8852 < \$0$$

Linear interpolation gives

$$0.02 + 0.005(\$46.3257)/(\$46.3257 + \$5.8852) = 0.024436$$

or 2.4436 percent/quarter (9.7746 percent compounded quarterly).

The effective annual return is

$$i_{eff} = [(1 + 0.024436)^4 - 1]100\% = 10.1387\%$$

 The Excel® **RATE** and **EFFECT** worksheet functions are ideally suited for this example. Recall, **RATE(nper,pmt,pv,fv,type,guess)** and **EFFECT(nominal_rate,npery)**, where **npery** is a truncated integer and denotes the number of compounding periods in a year.

Therefore, entering the following in any cell of an Excel® spreadsheet will yield the quarterly rate:

$$i_{qtr} = \textbf{RATE}(12,30,\text{-}1020,950) = 2.442\%$$

Embedding the **RATE** function in the **EFFECT** function allows us to calculate the effective annual return on the bond transaction:

$$i_{eff} = \textbf{EFFECT}(4*\textbf{RATE}(12,30,\text{-}1020,950),4) = 10.132\%$$

3-9 VARIABLE INTEREST RATES

Except for the adjustable rate mortgage discussion in Section 3.4, thus far we have considered interest rates to be fixed over the duration of the financial transaction. Recent experience indicates that such a situation is not likely if the time period of interest extends over several years.

Considering a single sum of money and discrete compounding, if i_t denotes the interest rate appropriate during time period t, the future worth equivalent for a single sum of money can be expressed as

$$F = P(1 + i_1)(1 + i_2) \cdots (1 + i_{n-1})(1 + i_n)$$

EXAMPLE 3.30 Determining the Future Worth of an Investment with Variable Interest Rates

Consider the *CFD* in Figure 3.33, where $1,000 is deposited in a savings account paying interest at an annual compounding rate of 8 percent for the first 3 years, 10 percent for the next 4 years, and 12 percent for the next 2 years. Note how the cash flow diagram has been

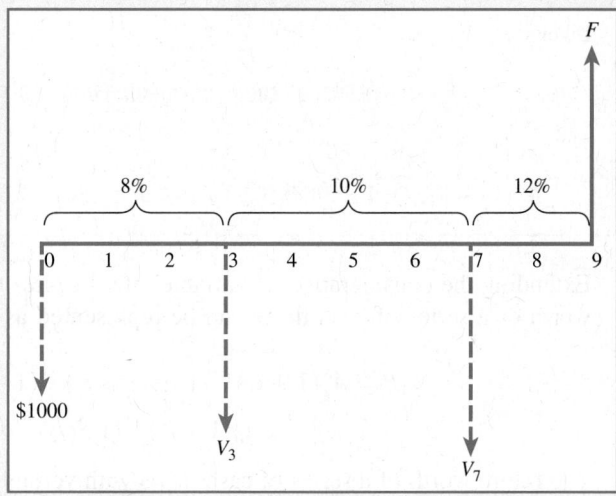

FIGURE 3.33

***CFD* for Variable Interest Rate Example 3.30.**

modified to incorporate variable interest rates. How much should be in the fund at the end of the 9-year investment period?

Letting V_t denote the account's value at the end of time period t, we see that

$$V_3 = \$1,000(F|P\,8\%,3)$$
$$= \$1,000(1.25971)$$
$$= \$1,259.71$$

Likewise,

$$V_7 = \$1,259.71(F|P\,10\%,4)$$
$$= \$1,259.71(1.46410)$$
$$= \$1,844.34$$

Similarly,

$$V_9 = \$1,844.34(F|P\,12\%,2)$$
$$= \$1,844.34(1.25440)$$
$$= \$2,313.54$$

Hence, $F = \$2,313.54$.

Alternately, the amount in the account at the end of 9 years is given by

$$F = \$1,000(1.08)(1.08)(1.08)(1.10)(1.10)(1.10)(1.10)(1.12)(1.12)$$
$$= \$2,313.55$$

(The 1¢ difference is due to round-off errors in the interest tables.)

 This example provides an opportunity to use an Excel® worksheet function not previously used in this text: **FVSCHEDULE**. Its syntax is **FVSCHEDULE(principal, schedule)**, and it is applied to single cash flows. For the example,

$$V_3 = \textbf{FVSCHEDULE}(1000,\{0.08,0.08,0.08\}) = \$1259.71$$

Likewise,

$$V_7 = \text{FVSCHEDULE}(1000, \{0.08, 0.08, 0.08, 0.1, 0.1, 0.1, 0.1\}) = \$1844.34$$

and

$$F = \text{FVSCHEDULE}(1000, \{0.08, 0.08, 0.08, 0.1, 0.1, 0.1, 0.1, 0.12, 0.12\}) = \$2313.55$$

Extending the consideration of variable interest rates to cash flow series, the present worth of a series of cash flows can be represented as

$$
\begin{aligned}
P = &A_1(1 + i_1)^{-1} + A_2(1 + i_1)^{-1}(1 + i_2)^{-1} \\
&+ \cdots + A_n(1 + i_1)^{-1}(1 + i_2)^{-1} \cdots (1 + i_n)^{-1}
\end{aligned}
\tag{3.19}
$$

The future worth of a series of cash flows with variable interest rates can be given as

$$
\begin{aligned}
F = &A_n + A_{n-1}(1 + i_n) + A_{n-2}(1 + i_{n-1})(1 + i_n) \\
&+ \cdots + A_1(1 + i_2)^{-1}(1 + i_3)^{-1} \cdots (1 + i_{n-1})(1 + i_n)
\end{aligned}
\tag{3.20}
$$

EXAMPLE 3.31   A Cash Flow Series with Variable Interest Rates

Consider the *CFD* given in Figure 3.34 with the appropriate interest rates indicated. Determine the present worth, future worth, and uniform series equivalents for the cash flow series.

Computing the present worth gives

$$
\begin{aligned}
P = &\$200(P|F\,10\%,1) - \$200(P|F\,10\%,1)(P|F\,10\%,1) \\
&+ \$300(P|F\,8\%,1)(P|F\,10\%,1)(P|F\,10\%,1) \\
&+ \$200(P|F\,12\%,1)(P|F\,8\%,1)(P|F\,8\%,1)(P|F\,10\%,1)(P|F\,10\%,1) \\
= &\$200(P|F\,10\%,1) - \$200(P|F\,10\%,2) + \$300(P|F\,8\%,1)(P|F\,10\%,2) \\
&+ \$200(P|F\,12\%,1)(P|F\,8\%,2)(P|F\,10\%,1) = \$372.63
\end{aligned}
$$

The future worth is given by

$$
\begin{aligned}
F = &\$200 + \$300(F|P\,8\%,1)(F|P\,12\%,1) - \$200(F|P\,8\%,2)(F|P\,12\%,1) \\
&+ \$200(F|P\,10\%,1)(F|P\,8\%,2)(F|P\,12\%,1) \\
= &\$200 + \$300(1.08000)(1.12000) - \$200(1.16640)(1.12000) \\
&+ \$200(1.10000)(1.16640)(1.12000) = \$589.01
\end{aligned}
$$

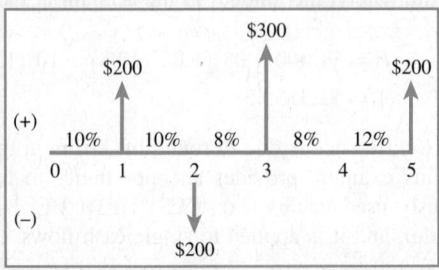

FIGURE 3.34

***CFD* for Variable Interest Rate Example 3.31.**

D16	▾	fx =D15/(1+B15)+C16			
	A	B	C	D	E

End of Period	Interest Rate During Period	End of Period Cash Flow	Sequential Movement	
5	12%	$200.00	=C3	
4	8%	$0.00	=D3/(1+B3)+C4	
3	8%	$300.00	=D4/(1+B4)+C5	
2	10%	-$200.00	=D5/(1+B5)+C6	
1	10%	$200.00	=D6/(1+B6)+C7	
0			=D7/(1+B7)+C8	

End of Period	Interest Rate During Period	End of Period Cash Flow	Sequential Movement	
5	12%	$200.00	$200.00	
4	8%	$0.00	$178.57	
3	8%	$300.00	$465.34	
2	10%	-$200.00	$230.87	
1	10%	$200.00	$409.89	
0			$372.62	= PW

FIGURE 3.35

Excel® Solution for the Present Worth in Example 3.31.

The uniform series equivalent is obtained as follows:

$$P = A(P|F\ 10\%,1) + A(P|F\ 10\%,2) + A(P|F\ 8\%,1)(P|F\ 10\%,2)$$
$$+ A(P|F\ 8\%,2)(P|F\ 10\%,2) + A(P|F\ 12\%,1)(P|F\ 8\%,2)(P|F\ 10\%,2)$$
$$\$372.63 = A[(0.90909) + (0.82645) + (0.92593)(0.82645) + (0.85734)(0.82645)$$
$$+ (0.89286)(0.85734)(0.82645)] = 3.841958A$$
$$A = \$96.99$$

Thus, $96.99/time period for five time periods is equivalent to the original cash flow series.

To obtain the present worth using Excel®, we recommend a spreadsheet of the type shown in Figure 3.35. The spreadsheet's upper portion provides the formulas used in column E. Notice, the years are shown in reverse order. Basically, the cash flow shown at the end of period 5 is moved forward one time period, and its value is added to the cash flow that occurs at the end of period 4. The sum is moved forward one time period and added to the cash flow occurring at the end of period 3. The new sum is moved forward one time period and added to the cash flow at the end of period 2. The sum is moved forward one time period and added to the cash flow at the end of period 1. Finally, the sum of equivalent cash flows at the end of period 1 is moved forward one time period to obtain the present worth of $372.62. (The 1¢ difference is due to round-off error in the interest tables.)

To obtain the future worth, Excel®'s **FVSCHEDULE** is appropriate. Specifically,

$$F = \text{FVSCHEDULE}(200,\{0.1,0.08,0.08,0.12\})$$
$$-\text{FVSCHEDULE}(200,\{0.08,0.08,0.12\})$$
$$+\text{FVSCHEDULE}(300,\{0.08,0.12\})+200$$
$$= \$589.01$$

Alternately, a spreadsheet can be used, as shown in Figure 3.36. An approach similar to that used to calculate the present worth was used to calculate the future worth. As seen, the same answer was obtained: **$589.01**.

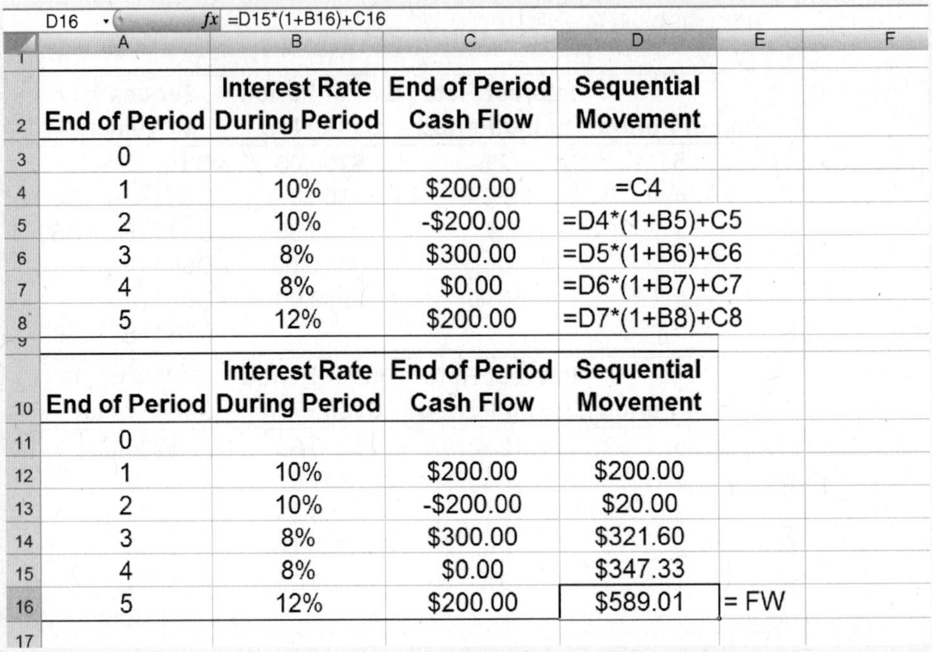

D16	▾	fx =D15*(1+B16)+C16				
	A	B	C	D	E	F
2	End of Period	Interest Rate During Period	End of Period Cash Flow	Sequential Movement		
3	0					
4	1	10%	$200.00	=C4		
5	2	10%	-$200.00	=D4*(1+B5)+C5		
6	3	8%	$300.00	=D5*(1+B6)+C6		
7	4	8%	$0.00	=D6*(1+B7)+C7		
8	5	12%	$200.00	=D7*(1+B8)+C8		
10	End of Period	Interest Rate During Period	End of Period Cash Flow	Sequential Movement		
11	0					
12	1	10%	$200.00	$200.00		
13	2	10%	-$200.00	$20.00		
14	3	8%	$300.00	$321.60		
15	4	8%	$0.00	$347.33		
16	5	12%	$200.00	$589.01	= FW	
17						

FIGURE 3.36

Excel® Solution for the Future Worth in Example 3.31.

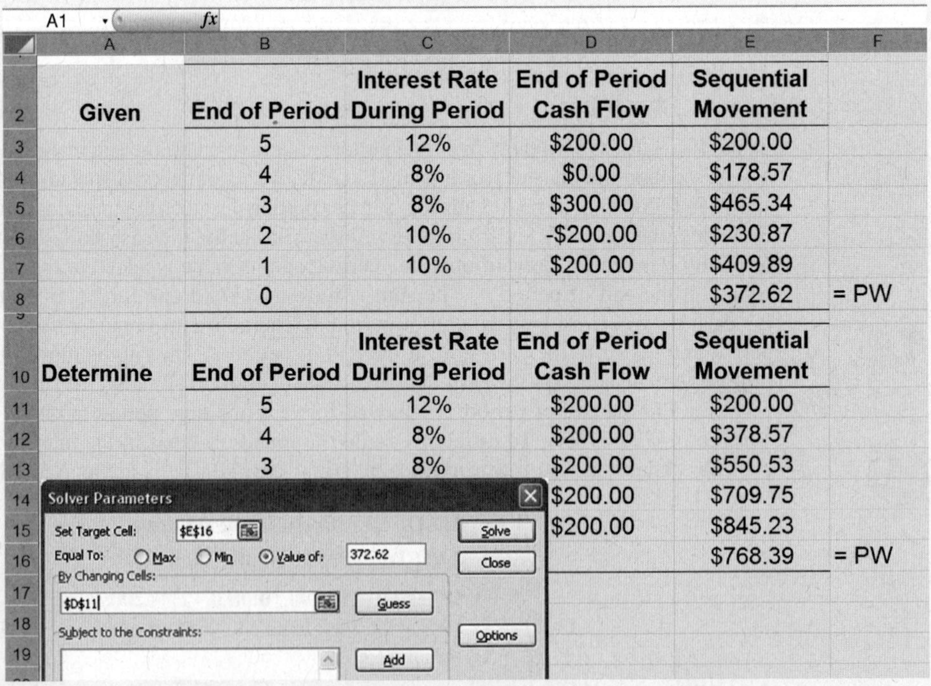

A1	▾	fx				
	A	B	C	D	E	F
2	Given	End of Period	Interest Rate During Period	End of Period Cash Flow	Sequential Movement	
3		5	12%	$200.00	$200.00	
4		4	8%	$0.00	$178.57	
5		3	8%	$300.00	$465.34	
6		2	10%	-$200.00	$230.87	
7		1	10%	$200.00	$409.89	
8		0			$372.62	= PW
10	Determine	End of Period	Interest Rate During Period	End of Period Cash Flow	Sequential Movement	
11		5	12%	$200.00	$200.00	
12		4	8%	$200.00	$378.57	
13		3	8%	$200.00	$550.53	
14				$200.00	$709.75	
15				$200.00	$845.23	
16					$768.39	= PW

Solver Parameters

Set Target Cell: $E$16

Equal To: ○ Max ○ Min ⊙ Value of: 372.62

By Changing Cells:

$D$11

Subject to the Constraints:

Solve Close Guess Options Add

FIGURE 3.37

Excel® SOLVER Set Up to Determine the Uniform Series Equivalent in Example 3.31.

To obtain the uniform series equivalent for the cash flow profile, the Excel® SOLVER tool was used. First, as indicated in Figure 3.37, a near-duplicate spreadsheet was created with entries D12 thru D16 being equal—specifically, D13 thru D16 were set equal to D12, the cell to be changed by SOLVER in making the target cell, E17, equal the $372.62 present worth for the original cash flow profile. As shown in Figure 3.38, a uniform series of $96.99 has the same present worth as the original cash flow series. (GOAL SEEK can be used instead of SOLVER. Also, we could have solved for the uniform annual series that yielded a future worth equal to $589.01.)

D11		fx 96.9874920950741				
	A	B	C	D	E	F
2	**Given**	**End of Period**	**Interest Rate During Period**	**End of Period Cash Flow**	**Sequential Movement**	
3		5	12%	$200.00	$200.00	
4		4	8%	$0.00	$178.57	
5		3	8%	$300.00	$465.34	
6		2	10%	-$200.00	$230.87	
7		1	10%	$200.00	$409.89	
8		0			$372.62	= PW
10	**Determine**	**End of Period**	**Interest Rate During Period**	**End of Period Cash Flow**	**Sequential Movement**	
11		5	12%	$96.99	$96.99	
12		4	8%	$96.99	$183.58	
13		3	8%	$96.99	$266.97	
14		2	10%	$96.99	$344.18	
15		1	10%	$96.99	$409.88	
16		0			$372.62	= PW
17						
18						
19						

FIGURE 3.38
Excel® SOLVER Solution for the Uniform Series Equivalent in Example 3.31.

3-10 SUMMARY

In some ways, reading this chapter is like drinking from a fire hose—a lot of material comes rather quickly. Don't become discouraged. Everything in the book tends to build on itself. Most of the concepts introduced in this chapter will be revisited at least once in the coming chapters.

The significant points from the chapter are the following:

1. *Start investing NOW.* This might be the most important thing anyone will learn from this book. Don't wait until some future time to begin investing; start investing now!

2. *All forms of debt are not equal.* The analysis of the four payment plans demonstrated that not all payment plans that are equivalent from a lender's perspective

are equivalent from a borrower's perspective. When borrowing money, it is important to analyze the economic worth of alternative payment plans. It is also important to understand the differences among the payment plans, as well as the economic penalty of not choosing the least expensive option. Also, remember, *the effective interest rate is an important tool*—use it to compare alternative forms of raising the funds needed to live, to attend college, and to purchase property. Also remember: Credit card debt is one of the most expensive options. College students should always contact the college's financial aid office to learn what low-cost student loans are available. Low-interest student loans are usually available, allowing expensive debt to be consolidated and replaced with far less expensive debt.

3. *There is a vast amount of helpful material available online.* Do your homework before you approach a financial institution for a loan; before you purchase a new or used car; and before you choose a mutual fund, stock, or bond for investment.

4. *Excel® has available a wide range of worksheet functions that can be used in performing engineering economic analyses* and personal financial analyses. Ten Excel® worksheet functions used in this chapter include **EFFECT, FV, FVSCHEDULE, IPMT, NPER, NPV, PMT, PPMT, PV**, and **RATE**. Also, Excel®'s **SOLVER** and **GOAL SEEK** tools were used to solve some rather complicated examples.

5. *How mortgage payments are calculated.* Be on the lookout for the "hidden costs" that show up at a loan's closing. Also remember, *many of the closing costs are negotiable*, regardless of what others might tell you.

6. *Interest rates will change over time.* However, the basic *DCF* rules can be used in analyzing the financial impact of changing interest rates on investments and loans.

7. *It's your money; manage it wisely.* If you do, you'll accomplish William T. Morris' goal of getting rich slowly but almost surely.

Excel® Worksheet Functions Used*

- **PV**(**rate,nper,pmt**,fv,type)
- **PMT**(**rate,nper,pv**,fv,type)
- **FV**(**rate,nper,pmt**,pv,type)
- **RATE**(**nper,pmt,pv**,fv,type,guess)
- **NPV**(**rate,value1**,value2,...)
- **EFFECT**(**nominal_rate,npery**)
- **FVSCHEDULE**(**principal,schedule**)
- **IPMT**(**rate,per,nper,pv**,fv,type)
- **PPMT**(**rate,per,nper,pv**,fv,type)
- **NPER**(**rate,pmt,pv**,fv,type)

*IRR will be used in Chapter 8; **SOLVER** and **GOAL SEEK** are tools, not worksheet functions

Pit Stop #3—Checking Your Vital Signs!

1. True or False: If you can earn 8% on your investments and you can borrow money at an annual compound rate of 6%, then (of the four payment plans described in the chapter) you would prefer to repay the loan with equal monthly payments.

2. True or False: In purchasing a house, the points and other closing costs you pay are included in the stated interest rate for a 30-year conventional loan.

3. True or False: The annual percentage rate is the same as the effective annual interest rate.

4. True or False: When repaying a loan with equal monthly payments, the amount of interest and the amount of principal in a loan payment remain proportionally the same over the loan period.

5. True or False: If you purchase a $1,000, 8% semiannual bond for $1,000 and sell it after 5 years for $1,000, then your effective annual yield on the bond is 8%.

Tutoring problem available (at instructor's discretion) in *WileyPLUS*.

Problem available (at instructor's discretion) in *WileyPLUS*.

Worked Problem Video available in *WileyPLUS*.

FE-LIKE PROBLEMS

1. When repaying a loan using Plan 1 (interest each period; principal only at end), what can be said about the payments?

    a. The interest payments will decrease by a constant amount each period.

    b. The interest payments will increase by a constant amount each period.

    c. The interest payments will either increase or decrease, but not necessarily by a constant amount each period.

    d. The interest payments will remain constant from period to period.

2. When repaying a loan using Plan 3 (equal end-of-period payments), which of the following is true?

    a. Interest payments will increase and principal payments will decrease from period to period.

    b. Interest payments will decrease and principal payments will increase from period to period.

    c. Interest payments and principal payments will both increase from period to period.

    d. Interest payments and principal payments will both decrease from period to period.

3. When repaying a loan using the four plans presented in Chapter 3 (assuming no taxes and no inflation), what can be said about the borrower's preferred payment plan?

    a. Since Plan 3 is most commonly used, it is the preferred method.

    b. Plan 2 is preferred if the borrower's *TVOM* < lender's interest rate; Plan 4 is preferred otherwise.

    c. Plan 4 is preferred if the borrower's *TVOM* < lender's interest rate; Plan 2 is preferred otherwise.

    d. Plan 1 and 3 are equally advantageous to the borrower.

4. A house is to be purchased for $180,000 with a 10 percent down payment, thereby financing $162,000 with a home loan and mortgage. There are no points or other closing charges associated with the loan. A conventional 30-year loan is used at 7.5 percent, resulting in monthly payments of $1,132.73. The interest portion of the first monthly payment will be what?

    a. $1,012.50

    b. $682.73

    c. $120.23

    d. Answer cannot be determined without more information

5. A house is to be purchased for $270,000 with a 5 percent down payment, thereby financing $256,500 with a home loan

and mortgage. There are 2 points assessed, and there are additional closing charges of $3,500, with both points and additional charges being included in the loan. A conventional 30-year loan is used at 7.5 percent, resulting in monthly payments of $1,853.83. Which of the following statements is false?

a. The loan will be figured on a total of $265,130 borrowed.

b. There can (unfortunately) be multiple methods of computing the APR (annual percentage rate) on such a loan, yielding (usually slightly) different answers.

c. The effective interest rate will exceed 7.5 percent.

d. The APR will be less than 7.5 percent.

6. You want to purchase a house and have done a thorough job identifying many different local and Web-based financing plans. Various plans have different up-front charges, which you intend to roll into the loan, thereby paying no loan-related charges out of your pocket at time of closing. Your best estimate is that you will be in the house for only 5 years, at which time you will sell it and move on. Right now, you want to determine the most economically advantageous financing plan. Your approach should be to calculate which of the following for each financing alternative?

a. Determine all payments you will make over the 5 years, including the loan "payoff" at the end of the 5 years, and determine the PW using your *TVOM*; select the largest (least negative) PW.

b. Determine all payments you will make over the 5 years, including the loan "payoff" at the end of the 5 years, and determine the PW using the loan rate of interest; select the largest (least negative) PW.

c. Determine the PW at your *TVOM* of the estimated market value of the house after 5 years, less all monthly payments you will make over the 5 years; select the largest PW.

d. Determine the PW at your loan rate of interest of the estimated market value of the house after 5 years, less all monthly payments you will make over the 5 years; select the largest PW.

7. Consider a 7/1 ARM loan, starting at 5 percent with potential up-or-down yearly increments of 1 percent in the rate. Why is such an ARM loan potentially economically dangerous?

a. Actually, many people have financed their house with an ARM, and such loans are not considered potentially economically dangerous.

b. The loan interest rate can increase without limit over the life of the loan.

c. The loan interest rate for the example mentioned can start at 5 percent and increase to as much as

12 percent after 7 years, effectively doubling (+/−) the monthly payment.

d. The economic risk of an ARM loan is neutralized, because it is just as likely that the interest rate for the example mentioned could go down each year by the maximum amount.

8. One of your financing options is a balloon loan on a $200,000 thirty-year mortgage with monthly payments and an interest rate of 7.5 percent per year. Which of the following statements is correct?

a. Monthly payments are $1,500, and a balloon payment is $200,000 after 30 years.

b. Monthly payments are $1,500, and a balloon payment is more than $200,000 after 30 years.

c. Monthly payments are $1,250, and a balloon payment is $200,000 only after 30 years.

d. Monthly payments are $1,250, and balloon payment is $200,000 at any time the loan is paid off.

9. You borrow $5,000 at 10 percent per year and will pay off the loan in three equal annual payments starting 1 year after the loan is made. The end-of-year payments are $2,010.57. Which of the following is true for your payment at the end of year 2?

a. Interest is $500 and principal is $1,510.57.

b. Interest is $450 and principal is $1,560.57.

c. Interest is $348.94 and principal is $1,661.63.

d. Interest is $182.78 and principal is $1,827.79.

10. You borrow $10,000 at 15 percent per year and will pay off the loan in three equal annual payments with the first occurring at the end of the fourth year after the loan is made. The three equal annual payments will be $6,661.08. Which of the following is true for your first payment at the end of year 4?

a. Interest = $6,661.08; principal = $0.00.

b. Interest = $2,281.31; principal = $4,379.77.

c. Interest = $1,500; principal = $5,161.08

d. Interest = $0.00; principal = $6,661.08

11. You are looking ahead to retirement and desire to invest 7 percent of your salary in investments earning 6 percent. You expect your salary to increase at 5 percent per year throughout your working life of 35 years. If you are now earning $50,000 and you will make your first investment at the end of this year, which of the following is the correct estimate of the future value of your investments at retirement?

a. $F = \$3,500(F|P\ 6\%,35)$
   $\qquad + \$175(A|G\ 6\%,35)(F|A\ 6\%,35)$

b. $F = \$3,500(F|A_1\ 6\%,5\%,35)$

c. $F = \$3,500(F|A_1\ 5\%,6\%,35)$

d. $F = \$3,500(P|A_1\ 6\%,5\%,35)(A|P\ 6\%,35)$

12. What series of equal annual payments is equivalent to a series of decreasing payments as follows: $5,000, $4,000, $3,000, $2,000, $1,000 if the interest rate is 10 percent per year?

   a. $3,000

   b. $\$3,000(1 + 0.1) = \$3,300$

   c. $[\$5,000(F|P\ 10\%,4) + \$4,000(F|P\ 10\%,3)$
       $+ \$3,000(F|P\ 10\%,2) + \$2,000(F|P\ 10\%,1)$
       $+ 1,000]/5$

   d. $\$5,000(A|P\ 10\%,5) - \$1,000(A|G\ 10\%,5)$

13. You purchase a $10,000 bond with a bond rate of 6 percent per year payable semiannually for 2 years. You pay $9,600 for the bond. Which statement is correct?

   a. Semiannual cash flows will be −$9,600, $300, $300, $300, $9,900, and the bond will earn more than 10 percent.

   b. Semiannual cash flows will be −$9,600, $300, $300, $300, $9,900, and the bond will earn less than 10 percent.

   c. Semiannual cash flows will be −$9,600, $300, $300, $300, $10,300, and the bond will earn more than 10 percent.

   d. Semiannual cash flows will be −$9,600, $300, $300, $300, $10,300, and the bond will earn less than 10 percent.

14. Consider a cash flow and interest profile as shown:

	Year 0	Year 1	Year 2	Year 3
Cash Flow at End of Year	−$1,000	$3,000	$2,000	$1,000
Interest Rate during Year	NA	6%	8%	10%

The worth of these cash flows at the end of year 3 is

   a. $5,000.

   b. $5,504.72.

   c. $5,994.56.

   d. $5,440.

PROBLEMS

Section 3.2

1. You have decided to purchase a small tract of land for building a new home on the outskirts of town. You have some money available but need a loan of $18,000 to make the purchase. The land will be owner-financed over 4 years with end-of-year payments. The interest rate is 9 percent. Develop an Excel® table to illustrate the payment amounts and schedule for the loan, assuming payback follows

   a. Plan 1: Pay the accumulated interest at the end of each interest period and repay the principal at the end of the loan period.

   b. Plan 2: Make equal principal payments, plus interest on the unpaid balance at the end of the period.

   c. Plan 3: Make equal end-of-period payments.

   d. Plan 4: Make a single payment of principal and interest at the end of the loan period.

   e. A different plan: Pay $3,000 principal at the end of the first year, then $4,000, $5,000, and $6,000 at the end of years 2, 3, 4, plus the accumulated interest at the end of each interest period.

2. You need a good preowned car following college. For the car you want, you need a loan of $12,000. With your limited credit record and the best rate available to you being 10 percent, you have decided to get creative. You know your grandparents are financially comfortable and are invested rather conservatively. You guess their average return is 7 percent or less. You propose, and they accept, the win-win proposition that they loan you the $12,000 at 8.5 percent, splitting the difference between their 7 percent and your best alternative, 10 percent. End-of-year payments will be made. Your grandparents want to see some different repayment schedules over 5 years. Develop an Excel® table to illustrate to show your grandparents various cash flow profiles, assuming payback follows

   a. Plan 1: Pay the accumulated interest at the end of each interest period and repay the principal at the end of the loan period.

   b. Plan 2: Make equal principal payments, plus interest on the unpaid balance at the end of the period.

   c. Plan 3: Make equal end-of-period payments.

   d. Plan 4: Make a single payment of principal and interest at the end of the loan period.

   e. A different plan: Pay an amount of principal at the end of the first year, then increase it each year thereafter by 20 percent, just paying off the loan principal at the end of the fifth year. In addition, pay the accumulated interest at the end of each interest period.

3. J&J Cattle has purchased a quarter section of land for $160,000. They make a down payment of $20,000, and the remainder of the purchase price ($140,000) is financed at 12 percent compounded quarterly with quarterly payments over 2 years. Develop an Excel® table to illustrate the payment amounts and schedule for the loan, assuming payback follows

   a. Plan 1: Pay the accumulated interest at the end of each interest period and repay the principal at the end of the loan period.

   b. Plan 2: Make equal principal payments, plus interest on the unpaid balance at the end of the period.

   c. Plan 3: Make equal end-of-period payments.

   d. Plan 4: Make a single payment of principal and interest at the end of the loan period.

   e. A different plan: Pay off the principal per the table below. In addition, pay the accumulated interest at the end of each interest period.

Quarter	1	2	3	4	5	6	7	8
Principal	X	$2X$	$3X$	$4X$	$4X$	$3X$	$2X$	X

4. Upon graduation, Steven purchases a new home theater system for his apartment. To finance the system, he "borrows" $5,000 from a new credit card at 21 percent per year compounded monthly. He fully intends to pay off the "loan" in 1 year while making monthly payments. Develop an Excel® table to illustrate the payment amounts and schedule for the loan, assuming payback follows

   a. Plan 1: Pay the accumulated interest at the end of each interest period and repay the principal at the end of the loan period.

   b. Plan 2: Make equal principal payments, plus interest on the unpaid balance at the end of the period.

   c. Plan 3: Make equal end-of-period payments.

   d. Plan 4: Make a single payment of principal and interest at the end of the loan period.

   e. A different plan: Pay X in principal at the end of months 1, 2, and 3; pay $2X$ at the end of months 4, 5, and 6; then $3X$ at 7, 8, 9; and finally $4X$ at 10,11,12. In addition, pay the accumulated interest at the end of each interest period.

Section 3.3

5. Refer to Problem 1. For each of the five payment schedules, determine the present worth of the loan payments made by the borrower. Use an Excel® spreadsheet and program it such that you can enter different interest rates for the borrower's time value of money (*TVOM*). Use *TVOM* rates of 5 percent, 9 percent, and 13 percent.

6. Refer to Problem 2. For each of the five payment schedules, determine the present worth of the loan payments made by the borrower. Use an Excel® spreadsheet and program it such that you can enter different interest rates for the borrower's *TVOM*. Use *TVOM* rates of 4 percent, 8.5 percent, and 13 percent.

7. Refer to Problem 3. For each of the five payment schedules, determine the present worth of the loan payments made by the borrower. Use an Excel® spreadsheet and program it such that you can enter different interest rates for the borrower's *TVOM*. Use *TVOM* rates of 7 percent, 12 percent, and 17 percent compounded quarterly.

8. Refer to Problem 4. For each of the payment schedules, determine the present worth of the loan payments made by the borrower. Use an Excel® spreadsheet and program it such that you can enter different interest rates for the borrower's *TVOM*. Use *TVOM* rates of 6 percent, 21 percent, and 36 percent compounded monthly.

9. Your money is tied up and you need to borrow $10,000. The following two alternatives are available at different banks: (1) Pay $3,311.61 at the end of each year for 5 years, starting at the end of the first year (5 payments total at 18 percent nominal per year compounded monthly which equates to 19.56 percent effective); or (2) pay $253.93 at the end of each month for 5 years, starting at the end of the first month (60 payments total at 18 percent nominal per year compounded monthly). Which will result in the smaller PW of payments to you if

a. your *TVOM* is 9 percent nominal per year compounded monthly?

b. your *TVOM* is 25 percent nominal per year compounded monthly?

10. Your money is tied up and you need to borrow $10,000. The following two alternatives are being offered by the lender: (1) pay $3,288.91 at the end of each year for 5 years, starting at the end of the first year (5 payments total at 18 percent nominal per year compounded quarterly which equates to 19.25% effective); or (2) pay $X at the end of each quarter for 6 years, starting at the end of the first quarter (24 payments total at 18 percent nominal per year compounded quarterly). Determine the value of $X that will make Alternative 2 equally desirable to Alternative 1 if

a. your *TVOM* is 8 percent nominal per year compounded quarterly.

b. your *TVOM* is 22 percent nominal per year compounded quarterly.

Section 3.4

11. Go to the U.S. Department of Housing and Urban Development (HUD) Web site at www.hud.gov and identify the three topics under ''Homes'' that are of interest to you. For each of the three topics, tell briefly (15 words or less) what you personally find useful.

12. Do a Google search on something like home loans; mortgage lenders; home financing; fixed loans; ARM and spend 10 minutes seeing what you can learn about available home loans. Give the URL of any Web site you visit and tell briefly (30 to 50 words) what you learned or found interesting.

13. Do a Google search on something like financial calculators; mortgage calculators; loan calculators; or similar. Locate one to your liking and put into it a loan of $225,000 at 7 percent over 360 months. Submit evidence of having used a Web-based financial calculator for this exercise, whether or not you got the correct result of $1,496.93 per month.

14. A recent engineering graduate is relocating after 3 years on the job. History shows that subsequent assignments with the company last for 4 to 6 years before moving on to a new location for additional experience and broadening. The graduate wishes to buy a new home costing $200,000, make a 5 percent down payment, and finance the remaining $190,000. The rate quoted for a conventional 30-year loan is 6.8230 percent interest with no points and no other closing costs.

a. What is the amount of the monthly payment? Calculate this using both Excel® and one of the Web-based calculators.

b. If, immediately after the sixtieth payment (5 years), the graduate is asked to move, what will be the unpaid balance on the loan?

c. Use Excel®'s EFFECT function (or RATE function) to determine the effective annual interest rate for the loan.

d. Determine the APR using both Excel® and one of the Web-based calculators.

15. A midcareer professional couple is interested in purchasing a new home costing $750,000. They can afford a 20 percent, or $150,000, down payment, leaving $600,000 to be borrowed, a loan in the ''jumbo'' category. They prefer to have a conventional loan, and one lender has offered a 30-year loan at 6.9932 percent with no points and no other closing costs.

a. What is the amount of the monthly payment? Calculate this using both Excel® and one of the Web-based calculators.

b. If, immediately after the one hundred twentieth payment (10 years), the professional couple decides to sell the house, what will be the unpaid balance on the loan?

c. Use Excel®'s EFFECT function (or RATE function) to determine the effective annual interest rate for the loan.

d. Determine the APR using Excel® and one of the Web-based calculators.

16. A recent civil engineering graduate wishes to buy a new home costing $200,000, make a 5 percent down payment, and finance the remaining $190,000. The rate quoted for a conventional 30-year loan is 6.4495 percent interest with 1.625 points and no other closing costs.

a. What is the amount of the monthly payment if the points are paid at the time of closing and not added to the loan? Calculate this using both Excel® and one of the Web-based calculators.

    b. What is the amount of the monthly payment if the points are added to the loan? Calculate this using both Excel® and one of the Web-based calculators.

    c. If, immediately after the sixtieth payment (5 years), the graduate is asked to move, what will be the unpaid balance on the loan with the points added to the loan?

    d. Determine the effective annual interest rate for the loan with the points added to the loan.

    e. Use the additive approach to determine the APR (see Example 3.6) using both Excel® and one of the Web-based calculators.

17. A professional couple wishes to purchase a new home costing $750,000, make a 20 percent down payment, and finance the remaining $600,000. The rate quoted for a conventional 30-year loan is 6.5084 percent interest with 1.875 points and no other closing costs.

    a. What is the amount of the monthly payment if the points are paid at the time of closing and not added to the loan? Calculate this using both Excel® and one of the Web-based calculators.

    b. What is the amount of the monthly payment if the points are added to the loan? Calculate this using both Excel® and one of the Web-based calculators.

    c. If, immediately after the one hundred twentieth payment (10 years), the professional couple decides to sell the house, what will be the unpaid balance on the loan with the points added to it?

    d. Determine the effective annual interest rate for the loan with points added to it.

    e. Use the additive approach to determine the APR (see Example 3.6) using both Excel® and one of the Web-based calculators.

18. A contact engineer in petrochemicals wishes to buy a new home costing $200,000, make a 5 percent down payment, and finance the remaining $190,000. The rate quoted for a conventional 30-year loan is 5.8750 percent interest with 2.75 points (applied to only the $190,000) and $6,570 in other closing costs.

    a. What is the amount of the monthly payment if the points and other costs at closing are not added to the loan? Calculate this using both Excel® and one of the Web-based calculators.

    b. What is the amount of the monthly payment if the points and other costs at closing are added to the loan? Calculate this using both Excel® and one of the Web-based calculators.

    c. If, immediately after the sixtieth payment (5 years), the graduate is asked to move, what will be the unpaid balance on the loan with the points and other closing costs added to it?

    d. Determine the effective annual interest rate for the loan with points and other costs at closing added to it.

    e. Use the additive approach to determine the APR (see Example 3.6) using both Excel® and one of the Web-based calculators.

19. A two-executive professional couple wishes to purchase a new home costing $750,000, make a 20 percent down payment, and finance the remaining $600,000. The rate quoted for a conventional 30-year loan is 6 percent interest with 3.125 points (applied to only the $600,000) and $16,159 in other closing costs.

    a. What is the amount of the monthly payment if the points and other costs at closing are not added to the loan? Calculate this using both Excel® and one of the Web-based calculators.

    b. What is the amount of the monthly payment if the points and other closing costs are added to the loan? Calculate this using both Excel® and one of the Web-based calculators.

    c. If, immediately after the one hundred twentieth payment (10 years), the professional couple decides to sell the house, what will be the unpaid balance on the loan with the points and other closing costs added to it?

    d. Determine the effective annual interest rate for the loan with points and other closing costs added to it.

    e. Use the additive approach to determine the APR (see Example 3.6) using both Excel® and one of the Web-based calculators.

20. An environmental engineer wishes to buy a new home costing $200,000, make a 5 percent down payment, and finance the remaining $190,000. The rate quoted for a conventional 15-year loan is 5.5 percent interest with 2.625 points (applied to only the $190,000) and $6,444.50 in other closing costs.

    a. What is the amount of the monthly payment if the points and other closing costs are not added to the loan? Calculate this using both Excel® and one of the Web-based calculators.

    b. What is the amount of the monthly payment if the points and other closing costs are added to the loan? Calculate this using both Excel® and one of the Web-based calculators.

    c. If, immediately after the sixtieth payment (5 years), the graduate is asked to move, what will be the unpaid balance on the loan with the points and other closing costs added to it?

    d. Determine the effective annual interest rate for the loan with points and other closing costs added to it.

    e. Use the additive approach to determine the APR (see Example 3.6) using both Excel® and one of the Web-based calculators.

21. A couple nearing retirement wishes to purchase a new home costing $750,000, make a 20 percent down payment, and finance the remaining $600,000. The conventional 15-year loan rate is 5.6250 percent with 3 points and $15,974 in other closing costs. Points are applied to other closing costs, too.

    a. What is the amount of the monthly payment if the points and other closing costs are not added to the loan? Calculate this using both Excel® and one of the Web-based calculators.

    b. What is the amount of the monthly payment if the points and other closing costs are added to the loan? Calculate this using both Excel® and one of the Web-based calculators.

    c. If, immediately after the one hundred twentieth payment (10 years), the professional couple decides to sell the house, what will be the unpaid balance on the loan, including points and other closing costs.

    d. Determine the effective annual interest rate for the loan with points and other closing costs added to it.

    e. Use the additive approach to determine the APR (see Example 3.6) using both Excel® and one of the Web-based calculators.

22. You have settled on a house for $180,000 and need a loan for $171,000. You have been offered a $171,000 loan for 6.25 percent, plus 2.375 points (applied to only the $171,000), plus ''administrative costs'' that have not been quantified. You are told that the APR is 7.233 percent. Determine the ''administrative costs.''

23. A new engineering department head is joining the university and during a visit has made an offer on a home for $350,000 with a 20 percent down payment. The offer has been accepted pending success in obtaining a satisfactory loan. A loan for $280,000 has been offered for 6.125 percent plus 3 points and ''administrative costs'' that have not been quantified. The APR is quoted as 6.517 percent. Determine the ''administrative costs.'' Points apply to only the $280,000.

24. The Chopras wish to purchase a new house, even though they plan to be in it for only 6 years. The house costs $550,000, and they will make a $55,000 down payment, leaving $495,000 to be financed. They are considering three loans, and in all cases points apply to only the $495,000: (1) a 30-year jumbo conventional for 6.875 percent with 0.25 points plus $14,344.50 in other closing costs, (2) a 30-year jumbo ARM loan at 6 percent over 30 years with 0.125 points plus $13,558.25 in other closing costs, and (3) a 30-year interest-only balloon loan at 5.5 percent, 0.625 points plus $45,769 in other closing costs. The ARM in part (2) can go either up or down by 75 basis points per year (0.750 percent), they wish to evaluate it both (i) remaining constant over the 6 years, and (ii) under the worst-case result where it starts at 6 percent and in the second and each subsequent year increases by 0.750 percent.

    a. For each loan, determine the monthly payment (years 1 through 6 for the ARM).

    b. Perform a PW analysis on each of the four scenarios, assuming the Chopras continue to own the house exactly 6 years. Their *TVOM* is 8 percent.

25. You are planning to pursue a MS degree in engineering. The program will require 2 years, at which time you will likely go to work in the same city. You have decided to purchase a house and live in it for 3 years. The house costs $90,000, and after a down payment of $4,500 you will finance $85,500. You want to consider both low payment loans and those requiring the lowest cash to close. You are considering three loans and in all cases points apply to only the $85,500: (1) a 30-year conventional for 6.750 percent with 0.125 points plus $4,065.13 in other closing costs, (2) a 30-year ARM loan at 5.250 percent with 2.375 points plus $5,991 in other closing costs, and (3) a 30-year balloon loan at 4.850 percent, 1.100 points, plus $6,500 in other closing costs. The ARM in part (2) can go either up or down by 100 basis points per year (1 percent) and will be ''locked in'' after 3 years, you wish to evaluate the ARM both (i) remaining constant over the 3 years, and (ii) under the worst-case result where it starts at 5.250 percent and in the second and third years it increases by 1 percent.

    a. For each loan, determine the monthly payment (years 1 through 3 for the ARM).

    b. Perform a PW analysis, assuming you continue to own the house exactly 3 years. Your *TVOM* is 5.3 percent.

Section 3.5

26. In order to buy a car, you borrow $25,000 from a friend at 12 percent/year compounded monthly for 4 years. You plan to repay the loan with 48 equal monthly payments.

   a. How much are the monthly payments?

   b. How much interest is in the twenty-third payment?

   c. What is the remaining balance after the thirty-seventh payment?

   d. Three and a half years after borrowing the money, you decide to pay off the loan. You have not yet made the payment due at that time. What is the payoff amount for the loan?

 27. CTL (Concrete Testing Lab) borrowed $80,000 for new equipment at 8 percent per year, compounded quarterly. It is to be paid back over 3 years in equal quarterly payments. For each part below, use both the interest tables and the Excel® financial functions. Compare answers between the two.

   a. How much interest is in the sixth payment?

   b. How much principal is in the sixth payment?

   c. What principal is owed immediately following the sixth payment?

28. Med Diagnostics Inc. borrowed $200,000 from a lender for a new blood analyzer module to improve accuracy and consistency of its tests. The rate was 6 percent, 2 percent above the prime rate. The loan was to be paid back in equal monthly amounts over 7 years.

   a. How much is the monthly payment?

   b. Two years (24 months) of payments have been made. What is the principal remaining after 2 years?

   c. The prime rate has now risen, and the bank can make loans to other customers, if it has the available capital, for 8.5 percent payable in equal monthly payments. The bank contacts Med Diagnostics and offers to let them pay off the loan immediately for the amount owed at the end of year 2, less X. What is the range of X that would be beneficial to both the bank and Med Diagnostics?

29. Upon graduation, Jeffrey Feldhusen borrows $15,000 to finance a late model used car. The loan is made by a family member who wishes to have equal annual payments at 9 percent over 4 years.

   a. How much are the annual payments?

   b. How many total dollars of interest does Jeffrey pay over the life of the loan?

   c. How much of the second payment goes to pay interest?

   d. How much of the second payment goes to pay principal?

   e. Develop a table similar to that of Table 3.7. Do your answers to Parts a, c, and d agree?

30. In order to pay for school, you borrow $22,000 at 12 percent/year compounded monthly. You do not pay back any of it until the end of the first month following year 4, and you intend to have it paid off by the end of year 7.

   a. What are your monthly payments during years 5, 6, and 7?

   b. How much interest is in the sixtieth month's payment? How much principal?

   c. How much interest is in the sixty-fourth month's payment? How much principal?

   d. How much interest is in the sixty-eighth month's payment? How much principal?

   e. You are doing very well after graduation and decide to pay off the loan in full at the time you make your twenty-fourth payment in the seventy-second month. For how much do you write the check, including the twenty-fourth payment?

31. Aerotron Electronics has just bought a used delivery truck for $15,000. The small business paid $1,000 down and financed the rest, with the agreement to pay nothing for the entire first year and then to pay $536.83 at the end of each month over years 2, 3, and 4 (first payment is in thirteenth month).

   a. What nominal interest rate is Aerotron paying on the loan?

   b. What effective interest rate are they paying?

   c. How much of the fourteenth month's payment is interest? How much is principal?

   d. How much of the eighteenth month's payment is interest? How much is principal?

   e. How much of the twenty-second month's payment is interest? How much is principal?

32. BioElectroMechanical Systems (BEMS) is a start-up company with high potential and little available cash. They obtain $500,000 for necessary technology from a venture capitalist who charges them 24 percent compounded monthly. The agreement calls for no payment until the end of the first month of the fourth year, with equal monthly payments thereafter for 3 complete years (36 payments).

a. How much are the monthly payments?

b. What is the total interest paid to the lender?

c. What is the total principal paid to the lender?

d. If BEMS is doing incredibly well and would like to pay off the debt immediately after making the twenty-fourth payment in month 60, how much must they pay?

Section 3.6

33. Catherine Valentine wants to start saving for retirement as soon as she gets a job upon graduation with an MS degree at age 24. She plans to deposit $1,500 at the end of her first year of work, at age 25, and increase the amount she saves by the same percentage as her salary increases. She thinks her salary increases will be about 6 percent per year and that her money will earn 5 percent per year. How much will she have in the account right after her deposit when she is 60 years old?

34. Shortly after completing his MS degree in engineering, Jerry Dechert wanted to initiate a retirement plan. He decided to use a 15 percent mix of blue chip individual stocks, 50 percent mutual funds, 20 percent municipal bonds, and 15 percent CDs, investing 10 percent of his gross income using a payroll deduction plan (he correctly reasoned that if the money was never in his pocket, he would never miss it). Although he invests new money on a monthly basis, he treats all inflows and outflows as if they occurred at the end of the year. Jerry anticipates earnings of 7.5 percent per year. Starting at a salary of $60,000 and estimating annual increases of 6 percent over a 40-year working career, how much money can Jerry expect to have in the fund at that time?

35. Recall Problem 34. Shortly before Jerry got under way with his job and investment plan, he met Jennifer. All of a sudden, he decided to put the retirement plan on hold, reasoning that 40 years is a long way off. After getting married, having two kids, two cars, an upscale house, and saving absolutely $0, he realized that at age 37 he was getting very old. Fortunately, his career was on track with the raises. Also, he still liked his investment plan and decided to get started exactly 15 years behind schedule, leaving only 25 years for investment.

    a. How much money can Jerry expect to have in the fund after 25 years?

    b. What additional increment of "starting money" would Jerry need to invest right now (1 year before his first deposit) to end up after 25 years where he would have been if he had started his investments as originally planned?

    c. What lesson is to be learned from your result in part (b)?

36. Let's build a spreadsheet that will help you evaluate some very basic retirement issues in short order. Put each of the following in its own cell—kind of a "control panel" approach: (1) Starting yearly salary during (consider at end of) year 1; (2) increase in salary per year in percent; (3) percentage of your salary that you will invest; (4) growth of investments per year in percent; (5) amount of money you would like to have today if you retired; and (6) rate in percent per year that things cost more to buy. (Note that [6] is what we will call the *general inflation rate* in Chapter 1.2). Now build your spreadsheet with the following columns:

    A: Year—from 0 up to about 45.

    B: My Age—in year 0, put your age at the time you begin investing, and increase it to about your age plus 45.

    C: Desired Amount—In year 0, put the number in cell 5. Increase it each year by the percentage in cell 6.

    D: Earnings—In year 0, put the number in cell 1. Increase it each year by the percentage in cell 2 up to the year/age at which you wish to retire.

    E: Investment—Column D for year increased by the percentage in cell 3.

    F: Accumulated Investments—in year 0, put 0; in subsequent years, put the previous year's value increased by the percentage in cell 4, plus the current year's investment from column E.

      Evaluate your spreadsheet using cell 1: $60,000; Cell 2: 10%; Cell 3: 10%; Cell 4: 8%; Cell 5: $2,000,000; Cell 6: 3.5%. You should get $619,962.84 at the end of year 20.

37. Go to the Fidelity, CNN, Edward Jones, SmartMoney, AARP, and so on, retirement worksheets. Put in financial information that applies to you, your expectations, and your desires. In a category that you do not understand, try to

Wikipedia it or Google it. At the very least, play with the unknown category to determine whether or not it has a large influence. If so, set it conservatively. Copy your input sheet and analysis results.

38. Go to the Fidelity, CNN, Edward Jones, SmartMoney, AARP, and so on, retirement worksheets. Put in financial information that applies to someone between 40 and 60 such as a parent, aunt/uncle, and so on, to the best of your knowledge. You may have to guess at their financial holdings, expectations, and desires. In a category that you do not understand, try to Wikipedia it or Google it. At the very least, play with the unknown category to determine whether or not it has a large influence. If so, set it conservatively. Copy your input sheet and analysis results.

39. Josh is graduating at the end of the academic year with a BS degree in engineering. He already has an offer with a good company for $58,000. He has learned that those who continue along a technical path in the company typically receive increases of 6 percent per year. Now that Josh smells the diploma and the money, he is ready to get out and make his mark in the company. Josh's family, however, have encouraged him to consider completing a MS degree, thereby deferring employment for 2 years. Josh has learned that in the same company, those with an MS degree who remain on a technical path earn increases of 7.2 percent. With a graduate assistantship, Josh will have to pay only $8,000 per year out of his own pocket. He will be 23 when he graduates with the BS degree, 25 when he completes an MS degree, and 65 when he retires. All salaries and costs are considered to occur at the end of the year. Based on the PW of salaries and costs at Josh's *TVOM* of 7 percent, what must his minimum starting salary be to justify staying for the MS degree?

Section 3.7

40. An automobile is priced at $7,000. A buyer may purchase the car for $6,500 now, or alternatively, the buyer can make a down payment of $1,000 now and pay the remaining $6,000 in eight equal quarterly payments (over 2 years) at 8 percent compounded quarterly.

   a. If the buyer's *TVOM* is 10 percent per year compounded quarterly, would the buyer prefer to pay the $6,500 outright, or make the down payment and the quarterly payments?

   b. What is the effective annual *TVOM* at which these two payment options are equivalent?

41. Consider the following two cash flow series of payments: Series A is a geometric series increasing at a rate of 8 percent per year. The initial cash payment at the end of year 1 is $1,000. The payments occur annually for 5 years. Series B is a uniform series with payments of value X occurring annually at the end of years 1 through 5. You must make the payments in either Series A or Series B.

   a. Determine the value of X for which these two series are equivalent if your *TVOM* is $i = 6.5$ percent.

   b. If your *TVOM* is 8 percent, would you be indifferent between these two series of payments? If not, which do you prefer?

   c. If your *TVOM* is 5 percent, would you be indifferent between these two series of payments? If not, which do you prefer?

42. Kinnunen Company wishes to give its customers three options on payments for office equipment when the initial purchase price is over a certain amount. For example, the following three payment plans are options on a typical purchase, and Kinnunen wants to be sure they are equivalent at their *TVOM* of 14 percent. Determine the values of Q and R.

End of Year	Option 1	Option 2	Option 3
0	$0	$0	$0
1	1,800	Q	R
2	1,800	2Q	(1.1)R
3	1,800	3Q	$(1.1)^2$R
4	1,800	4Q	$(1.1)^3$R
5	1,800	5Q	$(1.1)^4$R

43. Consider the following three cash flow series:

End of Year	Cash Flow Series A	Cash Flow Series B	Cash Flow Series C
0	−$1,000	−$2,500	Y
1	X	3,000	Y
2	1.5X	2,500	Y
3	2.0X	2,000	2Y
4	2.5X	1,500	2Y
5	3.0X	1,000	2Y

Determine the values of X and Y so that all three cash flows are equivalent at an interest rate of 15 percent per year compounded yearly.

44. Consider the following three cash flow series:

End of Year	Cash Flow Series A	Cash Flow Series B	Cash Flow Series C
0	3.0X$	$1,000	2Y
1	2.5X	1,500	2Y
2	2.0X	2,000	2Y
3	1.5X	2,500	Y
4	1.0X	3,000	Y
5	−1,000	−2,500	Y

Determine the values of X and Y so that you are indifferent between all three cash flows if your *TVOM* is 11% per year compounded yearly.

45. Zetterberg Builders is given two options for making payments on a brush hog. Find the value of X such that they would be indifferent between the two cash flow profiles if their *TVOM* is 12 percent per year compounded yearly.

End of Year	Series 1	Series 2
0	$150	$0
1	$200	$0
2	$250	35X$
3	$300	25X$
4	$0	15X$
5	$0	5X$

Section 3.8

46. Dr. Sivaraman is considering purchasing a $10,000 bond with a bond coupon rate of 7 percent per year with semiannual interest payments (3.5 percent payable every 6 months). The bond has a life of 15 years, and it is being issued at a discount of $1,500. Dr. Sivaraman wants to make 15 percent per year compounded semiannually on his investment. Determine the interest rate he would earn if he purchases the bond. Should Dr. Sivaraman invest in it?

47. Lucy Lampkin wants to purchase a bond with a face value of $7,000 and a bond rate of 6 percent per year, payable at 3 percent semiannually. The bond has a remaining life of 5 years. If Lucy wants to earn at least 8 percent per year compounded semiannually, at what range of prices should she be willing to purchase the bond?

48. A 15-year bond having a face value of $5,000 and a coupon rate of 6 percent per 6 months payable semiannually was purchased for $7,000 eight years ago, and the sixteenth interest payment was just made. What can it be sold for now if a buyer's desired return is 4 percent per 6 months?

49. You have just purchased a municipal bond with a $10,000 par value for $9,500. You purchased it immediately after the previous owner received a semiannual interest payment. The bond rate is 6.6 percent per year payable semiannually. You plan to hold the bond for 5 years, selling the bond immediately after you receive the interest payment. If your desired nominal yield is 12 percent per year compounded semiannually, what will be your minimum selling price for the bond?

50. You wish to purchase a $1,000 bond from a friend who needs the money. There are 7 years remaining until the bond matures, and interest payments are quarterly. You decide to offer $750.08 for the bond, because you want to earn exactly 16 percent per year compounded quarterly on the investment. What is the annual bond rate of interest?

51. Leann just sold a $10,000 par value bond for $9,800. The bond interest rate was 6 percent per year payable quarterly. Leann owned the bond for 3 years. The first interest payment she received was 3 months after she bought the bond. She sold it immediately after receiving her twelfth interest payment. Leann's yield on the bond was 12 percent per year compounded quarterly. Determine the price she paid when she purchased the bond.

52. A bond is purchased for $8,628.12. It is kept for 5 years, and interest is received at the end of each year. Immediately following the owner's receipt of the fifth interest payment, the owner sells the bond for $500 more than its par value. The bond rate of interest is 8 percent, and the owner's money yields a 10 percent interest rate.

    a. Draw a clear, completely labeled cash flow diagram of the entire bond transaction using dollar amounts where they are known and using $X to represent the bond's face value.

    b. Determine the bond's face value.

53. A bond is purchased for $9,855.57. It is kept for 5 years, and interest is received at the end of each year. Immediately following the owner's receipt of the fifth interest payment, the owner sells the bond for $500 less than its par value. The bond rate of interest is 8 percent, and the owner's money yields a 10 percent interest rate.

    a. Draw a clear, completely labeled cash flow diagram of the entire bond transaction using dollar amounts where they are known and using $X to represent the bond's face value.

    b. Determine the bond's face value.

54. A $20,000 municipal bond is offered for sale at $18,000. The bond interest rate is 6 percent per year payable semiannually. The bond will mature and be redeemed at face value 5 years from now. If you purchase the bond, the first premium you will receive is 6 months from today. You have decided that you will invest $18,000 in the bond if your effective annual yield is at least 8.16 percent. Will you buy this bond? Why or why not?

55. Shannon purchases a bond for $1,142.38. The bond matures in 3 years, and she will redeem it at its face value of $1,200. Interest premiums are paid annually. If Shannon will earn a yield of 12 percent/year compounded yearly, what is the bond interest rate?

Section 3.9

56. Sydney just opened a savings account with an initial deposit of $2,500. The interest rate starts at 2 percent compounded annually and doubles every 4 years.

    a. How much will Sydney have in the account after 10 years?

    b. What constant interest rate compounded annually will provide the same sum in the account after 10 years?

57. Charlie has $10,000 to invest for a period of 5 years. The following three alternatives are available to him:

    • Account 1 pays 4 percent for year 1, 6 percent for year 2, 8 percent for year 3, 10 percent for year 4, and 12 percent for year 5, all with annual compounding.

    • Account 2 pays 12 percent for year 1, 10 percent for year 2, 8 percent for year 3, 6 percent for year 4, and 4 percent for year 5, all with annual compounding.

    • Account 3 pays interest at the rate of 7.96294 percent per year for all 5 years.

    Based on the available balance at the end of year 5, which alternative is Charlie's best choice?

58. You have $2,000 that you want to invest at the beginning of each of 5 years. The following alternatives are available to you:

- An investment that pays 7 percent for year 1, 6 percent for year 2, 5 percent for year 3, 4 percent for year 4, and 3 percent for year 5.
- An account that pays 3 percent for year 1, 4 percent for year 2, 5 percent for year 3, 6 percent for year 4, and 7 percent for year 5.
- An account that pays 5 percent per year each year.

On the basis of available balance at the end of year 5, which alternative is the best choice?

59. Jimmy deposits $4,000 now, $2,500 three years from now, and $5,000 six years from now. Interest is 5 percent for the first 3 years and 7 percent for the last 3 years.

   a. How much money will be in the fund at the end of 6 years?

   b. What is the present worth of the fund?

   c. What is the uniform series equivalent of the fund (uniform cash flow at end of years 1–6)?

60. Consider the following cash flows and interest rates:

End of Year	Interest Rate during Period	Cash Flow at End of Period
0		$0
1	10%	$2,000
2	8%	−$3,000
3	12%	$4,000

   a. Determine the future worth of this series of cash flows.

   b. Determine the present worth of this series of cash flows.

   c. Determine a 3-year uniform annual series that is equivalent to the original series.

Chapter 4

ESTABLISHING THE PLANNING HORIZON AND THE MINIMUM ATTRACTIVE RATE OF RETURN

Located in Kingsport, Tennessee, Eastman Chemical Company's Tennessee Operations is one of the largest chemicals manufacturing sites in North America. The site has more than 550 buildings and approximately 4,000 acres of land. The main plant covers 900 acres. (Courtesy of Eastman Chemical Company)

Eastman Chemical Company

Eastman Chemical Company manufactures and sells a broad portfolio of chemicals, plastics, and fibers globally. Eastman began business in Kingsport, Tennessee, in 1920 for the purpose of producing chemicals for Eastman Kodak Company's photographic business. On December 31, 1993, Kodak spun off its chemicals businesses and created the new independent corporation Eastman Chemical Company. Headquartered in Kingsport, Tennessee, Eastman is the world's largest producer of PET (polyethylene terephthalate) polymers for packaging and is a major supplier of cellulose acetate fibers.

Eastman has four business segments: coatings, adhesives, specialty polymers and inks; fibers; performance chemicals and intermediates; and specialty plastics. In 2010, Eastman had sales revenue of $5.8 billion. A global manufacturer and supplier, it has a total employment of approximately 10,000, with 16 manufacturing sites in 9 countries.

In general, chemical companies are in a cyclical business. Business cycles tend to be driven by mismatches in global capacity and global demand. Historically, when chemical companies add new manufacturing capacity to meet growing global demand, the total global capacity exceeds demand, causing prices to drop and profitability to suffer. To achieve economies of scale, new plants and expansions of existing plants tend to be quite large and require sizeable investments. As a result, capital investment decisions have to be made very carefully.

In the early 1960s, Tennessee Eastman Company was losing market share in acetate yarn, because it was unable to economically justify the investment needed to install modern manufacturing technology used by its competitors, which included Dupont and Celanese. The principal reason it could not justify the expenditures was a corporate mandate stating that any capital investment had to be recovered, ignoring the *TVOM*, within 2 years. It would take longer than 2 years to purchase and install the new equipment, to train employees in its use, to regain the confidence of customers and achieve profitable sales levels, and to achieve levels of productivity that would allow competitive pricing. Therefore, it was not possible for Tennessee Eastman Company to obtain the corporate approval to invest the money needed to modernize its production operations.

Faced with an imminent decision to exit the business, a bright financial analyst, Stan Wells, presented upper management with the results of his analysis. Based on a 10-year planning horizon and a 15 percent after-tax minimum attractive rate of return (*MARR*), he performed after-tax present worth and rate of return analyses. His extraordinary results stunned upper management. Wells showed how profitable the business would be if the company adopted a longer planning horizon and discounted cash flow methods. Management immediately scrapped the use of a 2-year payback requirement and accepted his recommendation to use *DCF* methods in economic justifications. As you will see later in the chapter, Eastman continues to use *DCF* methods. (Stan Wells advanced within Eastman Kodak's financial organization and later became the chief financial officer of Xerox Corporation.)

I n the previous two chapters, we focused more on personal financial planning than on engineering economic analysis, because we knew you would be more motivated to learn the material if you saw how it significantly impacts wealth generation. While we will continue to relate the material in the text to personal financial decision making, we shift focus now to business decision making.

4-1 INTRODUCTION

In performing engineering economic analyses, two critical parameters are often taken for granted: the duration of the planning horizon and the time value of money to be used.[1] Decisions regarding both are particularly challenging for multinational firms that encounter entirely different cost structures, labor practices, and governmental regulations around the world. Because judgments are involved in assigning values to both parameters, decisions regarding their values are often made arbitrarily.

Of the three estimates needed in performing an engineering economic analysis (cash flows, planning horizon, and the *MARR*), estimating values of cash flows is far more definitive. In contrast to decisions regarding the planning horizon and the *MARR*, when estimating cash flows, at least you are making decisions that can be shown to be either correct or incorrect. But what about the length of the planning horizon? How do you know if your decision is correct? Will it matter if the planning horizon is too short or too long? Does it matter whether it is 5 years, 10 years, or 15 years?

[1] Hereafter, we will usually refer to the time value of money as the *hurdle rate* or the *minimum attractive rate of return*. In the case of the latter, we denote it *MARR*.

Systematic Economic Analysis Technique

1. Identify the investment alternatives
2. Define the planning horizon
3. Specify the discount rate
4. Estimate the cash flows
5. Compare the alternatives
6. Perform supplementary analyses
7. Select the preferred investment

The same questions arise regarding the *MARR*. Will it matter if it is smaller or larger than it should be? Should the same value be used for all analyses? What adjustments should be made country to country for multinational firms?

In this chapter, you will learn why decisions regarding the planning horizon and the *MARR* are important. You will also learn how to make choices regarding each for particular situations, and you will become familiar with the approach Eastman Chemical Company uses in establishing the value of the *MARR*.

4-2   CHOOSING THE PLANNING HORIZON

As noted in Chapter 1, the planning horizon defines the period of time over which the comparison of investment alternatives is to occur; it is the width of the window through which you look to assess the economic performances of the alternatives. The planning horizon's length can be less than, greater than, or equal to the useful lives of the investment alternatives being considered. The ideal circumstance is for the useful lives to coincide in duration with the planning horizon. If, on the other hand, the planning horizon is longer than one or more lives of the alternatives, then explicit decisions must be made regarding the ''gap'' that exists between the end of an alternative's useful life and the end of the planning horizon. What about the remaining case of the planning horizon being shorter than the longest-lived alternative? In this case, estimated values of unused lives of the alternatives are required.

Occasionally, no decision is required regarding the duration of a planning horizon. Consider the following situations:

1. A building is being leased, and it is known that the building's owner will not renew it after 5 years; hence, there is minimal uncertainty regarding the length of time a lease holder will benefit from any improvements made to the building.

2. Various alternative ways of securing office space for an election campaign headquarters are being evaluated; there is little uncertainty regarding the duration of occupancy since the date of the election is known.

3. A one-shot investment opportunity arises; the only choices are to do it or don't do it. The terms of the investment will dictate the length of the planning horizon.

4. The time for which the needed investment exists is incredibly long (e.g., a dam or a bridge).

5. The firm or organization mandates the duration of the planning horizon (e.g., 10 years).

Recall, in Section 3.4, after working several examples, we presented in Table 3.5 the results of a comparison of 31 mortgage alternatives. In computing the present worth of the borrower's payments, we chose a 15-year planning horizon. Why 15 years? Why didn't we compute the present worth for each alternative, regardless of the loan duration?

Principle #8

In performing engineering economic analyses, use a common period of time in the comparison of the investment alternatives.

The alternatives under consideration included 15-year, 30-year, and 40-year mortgages. To ensure that no biases were introduced by comparing relatively short-term mortgages with relatively long-term ones, we wanted to use a common time frame for the comparison. (Recall Principle #8: *Compare investment alternatives over a common period of time.*) In this case, it was relatively simple to determine what the payoff amounts would be after 15 years for the 30-year and 40-year mortgages. Unfortunately, as you will see, when dealing with unequal-lived alternatives, it is not necessarily easy to determine the value, at the end of the planning horizon, of alternatives with lives that exceed the planning horizon.

When the lives of investment alternatives differ, six general approaches are used in determining the planning horizon's length:

1. Set the planning horizon equal to the shortest life among the alternatives
2. Set the planning horizon equal to the longest life among the alternatives
3. Set the planning horizon equal to the least common multiple of the lives of the various alternatives
4. Use a standard length horizon, such as 10 years
5. Set the planning horizon equal to the period of time that best fits the organization's need for the investment
6. Use an infinitely long planning horizon

The least common multiple of lives is a popular choice for the planning horizon's length. When it is used, the assumption is made that each alternative's cash flow profile

---

Planning Horizon Durations (When Alternatives Have Unequal Lives)

- Shortest life
- Longest life
- Least common multiple of lives
- Standard length
- Length of time for which the investment is needed
- Forever

repeats in the future until all investment alternatives under consideration conclude at the same time. Such an assumption might be practical for some applications but can prove untenable for others.

EXAMPLE 4.1 Selecting the Planning Horizon

A construction engineer has been asked to recommend an excavator for acquisition. Three alternatives have been identified, having the characteristics shown in Table 4.1. What are the planning horizon options? For each, what are the advantages and disadvantages? If a *MARR* of 12 percent is used, which alternative is recommended?

Notice, Alternative A has a useful life of 4 years, Alternative B has a useful life of 5 years, and Alternative C has a useful life of 6 years. What is the least common multiple of 4, 5, and 6? The answer is 60. It does not seem realistic to assume that identical cash flow profiles will repeat over a period of 60 years. Some argue that successive replacements might differ, but they will change proportionately. Even if you buy the argument, which we don't, what is the likelihood the equipment suppliers will still be in business 40 or 50 years in the future? (For example, Digital Equipment and Data General are no longer supplying computers. Motorola is no longer manufacturing television sets. Eastern Airlines is no longer flying.) Also, what is the likelihood you will still need the equipment's service 60 years in the future? Because change occurs so frequently in the business world, using a 60-year planning horizon for the acquisition of any kind of equipment does not seem wise.

Nevertheless, if a least common multiple of lives planning horizon is adopted, based on the data provided in Table 4.1 and as depicted in Figure 4.1, the following present worth analysis is applicable:

$$PW_A(12\%) = -\$15,500 - \$8,750(P|A\ 12\%,60) - \$13,000[(P|F\ 12\%,4)$$
$$+ (P|F\ 12\%,8) + \cdots + (P|F\ 12\%,56)] + \$2,500(P|F\ 12\%,60)$$
$$= -\$110,959.97$$

$$PW_B(12\%) = -\$20,250 - \$5,850(P|A\ 12\%,60) - \$17,250[(P|F\ 12\%,5)$$
$$+ (P|F\ 12\%,10) + \cdots + (P|F\ 12\%,55)] + \$3,000(P|F12\%,60)$$
$$= -\$91,525.57$$

$$PW_C(12\%) = -\$30,750 - \$3,175(P|A\ 12\%,60) - \$27,500[(P|F\ 12\%,6)$$
$$+ (P|F\ 12\%,12) + \cdots + (P|F\ 12\%,54)] + \$3,250(P|F\ 12\%,60)$$
$$= -\$85,352.36$$

Alternative C has the least negative present worth, so it would be recommended.

TABLE 4.1
Data for Example 4.1.

Excavator Alternative	Useful Life	Initial Investment	Annual Operating Cost	Terminal Salvage Value
A	4 yrs	$15,500	$8,750	$2,500
B	5 yrs	$20,250	$5,850	$3,000
C	6 yrs	$30,750	$3,175	$3,250

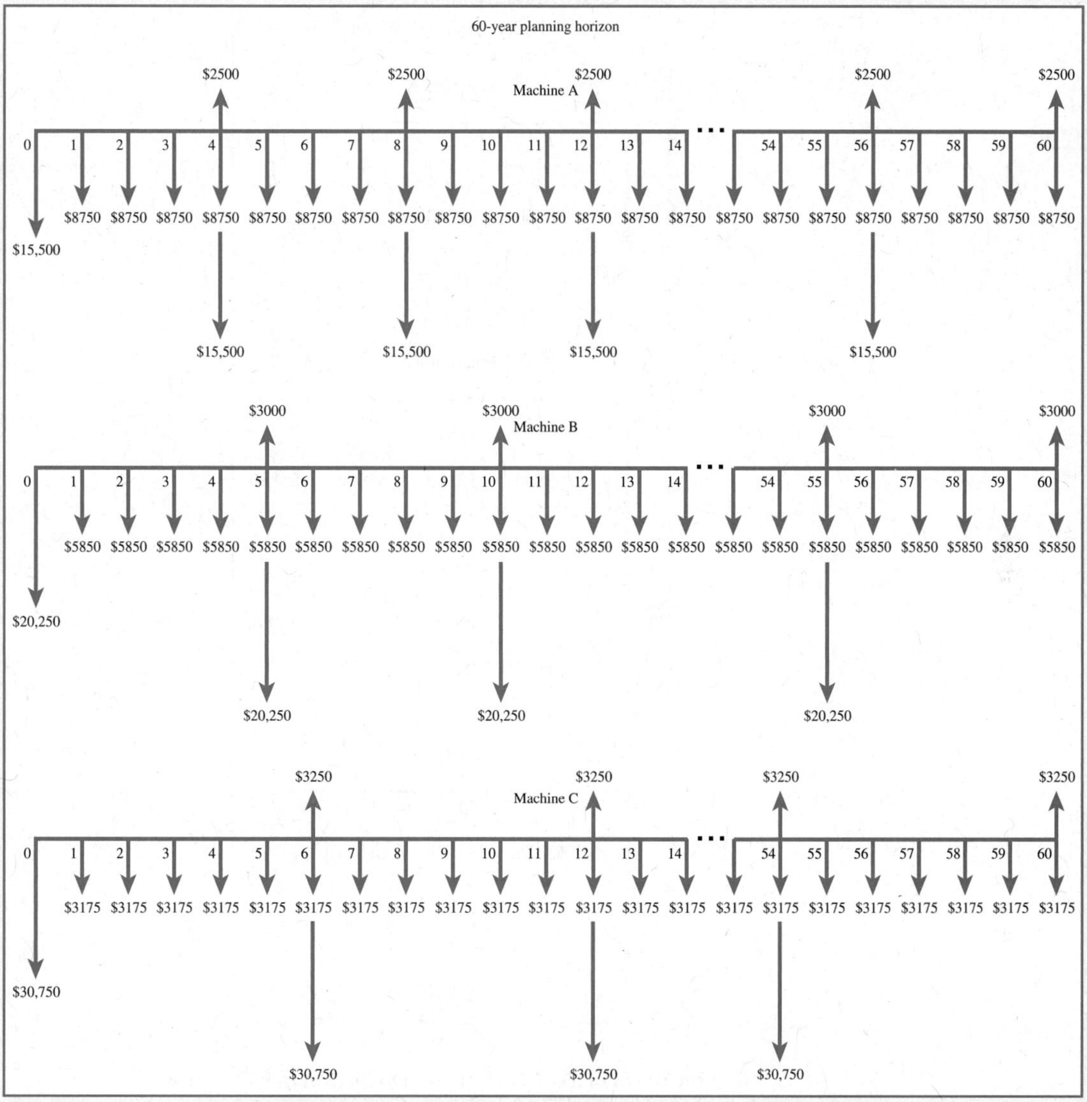

60-year planning horizon

$2500 $2500 $2500 $2500 $2500

Machine A

0 | 1 | 2 | 3 | 4 | 5 | 6 | 7 | 8 | 9 | 10 | 11 | 12 | 13 | 14 | ... | 54 | 55 | 56 | 57 | 58 | 59 | 60

$8750 $8750 $8750 $8750 $8750 $8750 $8750 $8750 $8750 $8750 $8750 $8750 $8750 $8750 $8750 $8750 $8750 $8750 $8750 $8750 $8750

$15,500

$15,500 $15,500 $15,500 $15,500

$3000 $3000 $3000 $3000

Machine B

0 | 1 | 2 | 3 | 4 | 5 | 6 | 7 | 8 | 9 | 10 | 11 | 12 | 13 | 14 | ... | 54 | 55 | 56 | 57 | 58 | 59 | 60

$5850 $5850 $5850 $5850 $5850 $5850 $5850 $5850 $5850 $5850 $5850 $5850 $5850 $5850 $5850 $5850 $5850 $5850 $5850 $5850 $5850

$20,250

$20,250 $20,250 $20,250

$3250 $3250 $3250 $3250

Machine C

0 | 1 | 2 | 3 | 4 | 5 | 6 | 7 | 8 | 9 | 10 | 11 | 12 | 13 | 14 | ... | 54 | 55 | 56 | 57 | 58 | 59 | 60

$3175 $3175 $3175 $3175 $3175 $3175 $3175 $3175 $3175 $3175 $3175 $3175 $3175 $3175 $3175 $3175 $3175 $3175 $3175 $3175 $3175

$30,750

$30,750 $30,750 $30,750

FIGURE 4.1

***CFD* for the Least Common Multiple of Lives Planning Horizon in Example 4.1.**

Using the shortest life to establish the planning horizon's length, it would be 4 years. With a 4-year planning horizon, one must estimate the value of the one remaining year of useful service for Alternative B; at the end of its useful life, it will have a salvage value of $3,000—perhaps it will be worth $6,000 after 4 years of use. Similarly, one must estimate the value of the 2 years of useful service available with Alternative C; at the end of 6 years of service, it will have a value of $3,250—perhaps it will be worth $11,000 after 4 years use. The *CFD* for a 4-year planning horizon is given in Figure 4.2.

Based on the salvage value estimates for the remaining useful lives for Alternatives B and C, the following present worth analysis holds:

$$PW_A(12\%) = -\$15,500 - \$8,750(P|A\ 12\%,4) + \$2,500(P|F\ 12\%,4) = -\$40,488.01$$
$$= -PV(12\%,4,-8750,2500)-15500 = -\$40,488.01$$

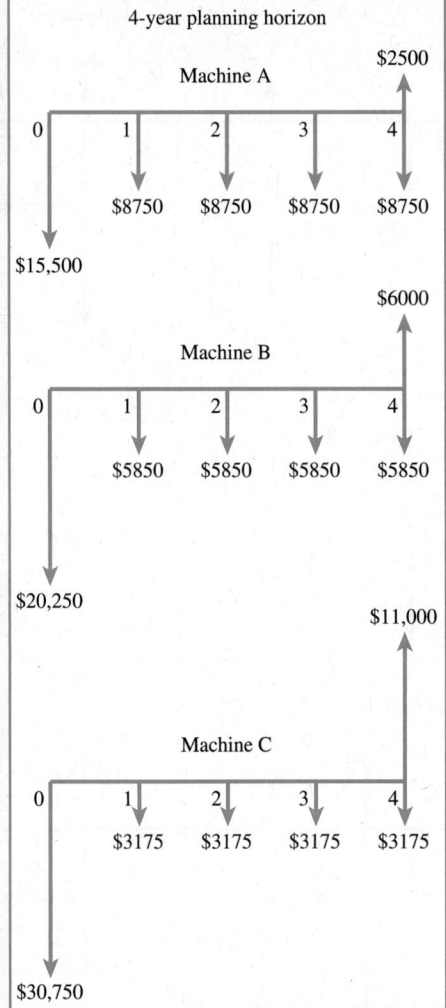

FIGURE 4.2

***CFD* for the Shortest-Lived Planning Horizon in Example 4.1.**

$$PW_B(12\%) = -\$20,250 - \$5,850(P|A\ 12\%,4) + \$6,000(P|F\ 12\%,4) = -\$34,205.38$$
$$=\text{-PV}(12\%,4,-5850,6000)-20250 = -\$34,205.39$$

$$PW_C(12\%) = -\$30,750 - \$3,175(P|A\ 12\%,4) + \$11,000(P|F\ 12\%,4) = -\$33,402.87$$
$$=\text{-PV}(12\%,4,-3175,11000)-30750 = -\$33,402.89$$

Alternative C continues to have the greatest present worth, so it would be recommended.

Using the longest life as the basis for the planning horizon, it will be 6 years. In this case, decisions must be made about the 2-year gap for Alternative A and the 1-year gap for Alternative B. Will identical replacements be made? If so, what will be their monetary values at the end of the planning horizon? In the case of Alternative A, if replaced with an identical excavator at the same cost as the original, it might have a value of $9,000 after 2 years of use; for Alternative B, if replaced with an identical excavator at the same cost as the original, it might have a value of $14,500 after 1 year of use.

Assuming replacements have identical cash flow profiles as their predecessors and using the salvage value estimates given for the remaining useful lives for Alternatives A and B, the *CFD* will be as shown in Figure 4.3. The following present worth analysis holds:

$$PW_A(12\%) = -\$15,500 - \$8,750(P|A\ 12\%,6) - \$13,000(P|F\ 12\%,4)$$
$$+ \$9,000(P|F\ 12\%,6) = -\$55,176.93$$
$$=-PV(12\%,6,-8750,9000)-15500+PV(12\%,4,,13000)$$
$$=-\$55,176.87$$

$$PW_B(12\%) = -\$20,250 - \$5,850(P|A\ 12\%,6) - \$17,250(P|F\ 12\%,5)$$
$$+ \$14,500(P|F\ 12\%,6) = -\$46,743.78$$
$$=-PV(12\%,6,-5850,14500)-20250+PV(12\%,5,,17250)$$
$$=-\$46,743.69$$

$$PW_C(12\%) = -\$30,750 - \$3,175(P|A\ 12\%,6)$$
$$+ \$3,250(P|F\ 12\%,6) = -\$42,157.18$$
$$=-PV(12\%,6,-3175,3250)-30750 = -\$42,157.17$$

As before, Alternative C has the most favorable present worth and is recommended.

Next, we consider the impact of a "standard planning horizon" of 10 years on the recommendation. As before, we assume identical replacements will occur. For Alternative A, 10 years represents two complete life cycles and a one-half life cycle. For the latter, we assume a salvage value of $9,000, as was done for the 6-year planning horizon case. For Alternative B, 10 years represents two complete life cycles. For Alternative C, 10 years represents one full life cycle and one partial life cycle; the 4-year remaining life for the replacement will result in a salvage value of $11,000, as with the 4-year planning horizon case. Based on the *CFD* in Figure 4.4, the present worths for the alternatives will be

$$PW_A(12\%) = -\$15,500 - \$8,750(P|A\ 12\%,10) - \$13,000(P|F\ 12\%,4)$$
$$- \$13,000(P|F\ 12\%,8) + \$9,000(P|F\ 12\%,10) = -\$75,553.90$$
$$=-PV(12\%,10,-8750,9000)-15500+PV(12\%,4,,13000)$$
$$+PV(12\%,8,,13000)=-\$75,553.91$$

$$PW_B(12\%) = -\$20,250 - \$5,850(P|A\ 12\%,10) - \$17,250(P|F\ 12\%,5)$$
$$+ \$3,000(P|F\ 12\%,10) = -\$62,126.04$$
$$=-PV(12\%,10,-5850,3000)-20250+PV(12\%,5,,17250)$$
$$=-\$62,126.00$$

$$PW_C(12\%) = -\$30,750 - \$3,175(P|A\ 12\%,10) - \$27,500(P|F\ 12\%,6)$$
$$+ \$11,000(P|F\ 12\%,10) = -\$59,080.10$$
$$=-PV(12\%,10,-3175,11000)-30750+PV(12\%,6,,27500)$$
$$=-\$59,080.11$$

Again, Alternative C is preferred, based on a present worth analysis.

Finally, we consider the infinitely long planning horizon. Obviously, for many investments, it makes no sense to assume an indefinite planning horizon. However, when the least common multiple of lives is quite long, using an infinitely long planning horizon will yield a reasonably good approximation.

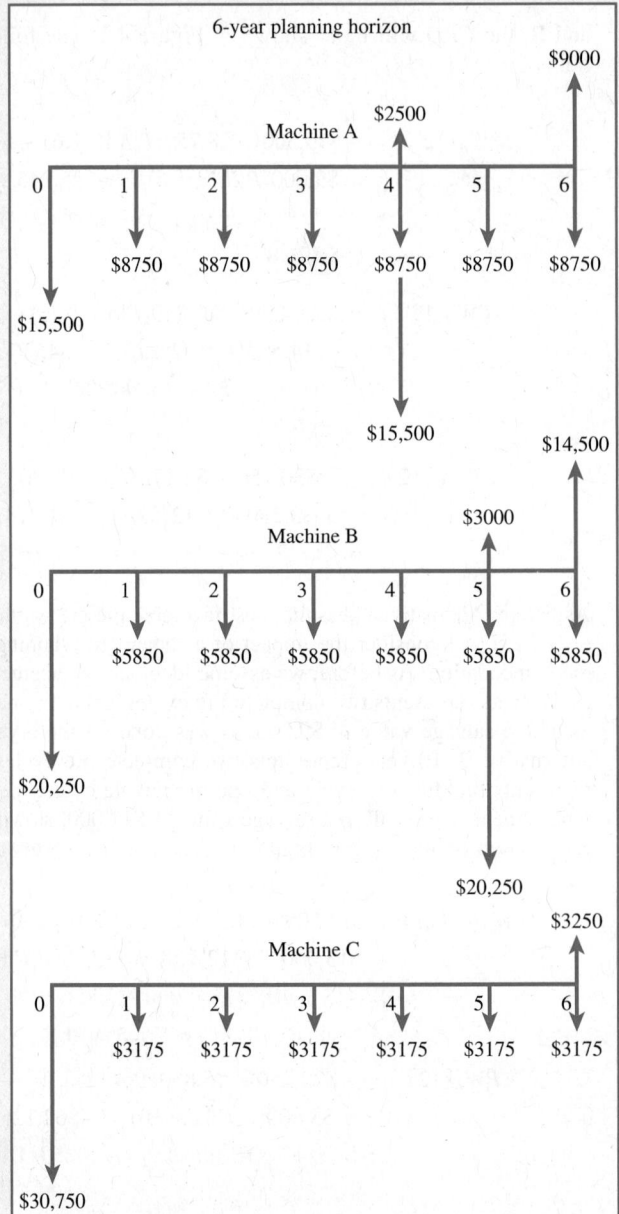

FIGURE 4.3

***CFD* for the Longest-Lived Planning Horizon in Example 4.1.**

Since equipment will be replaced indefinitely, it is not possible to compute the present worth of an infinitely long cash flow stream. Instead, we compute the value of an equivalent uniform annual series, which we call the *annual worth,* for each investment alternative. Furthermore, by assuming identical replacements, all we have to do is calculate the annual worth of one life cycle for each alternative. The analysis is as follows:

$$AW_A(12\%) = -\$15,500(A|P\ 12\%,4) - \$8,750 + \$2,500(A|F\ 12\%,4) = -\$13,329.99$$
$$= \text{PMT}(12\%,4,15500,-2500)-8750 = -\$13,330.05$$

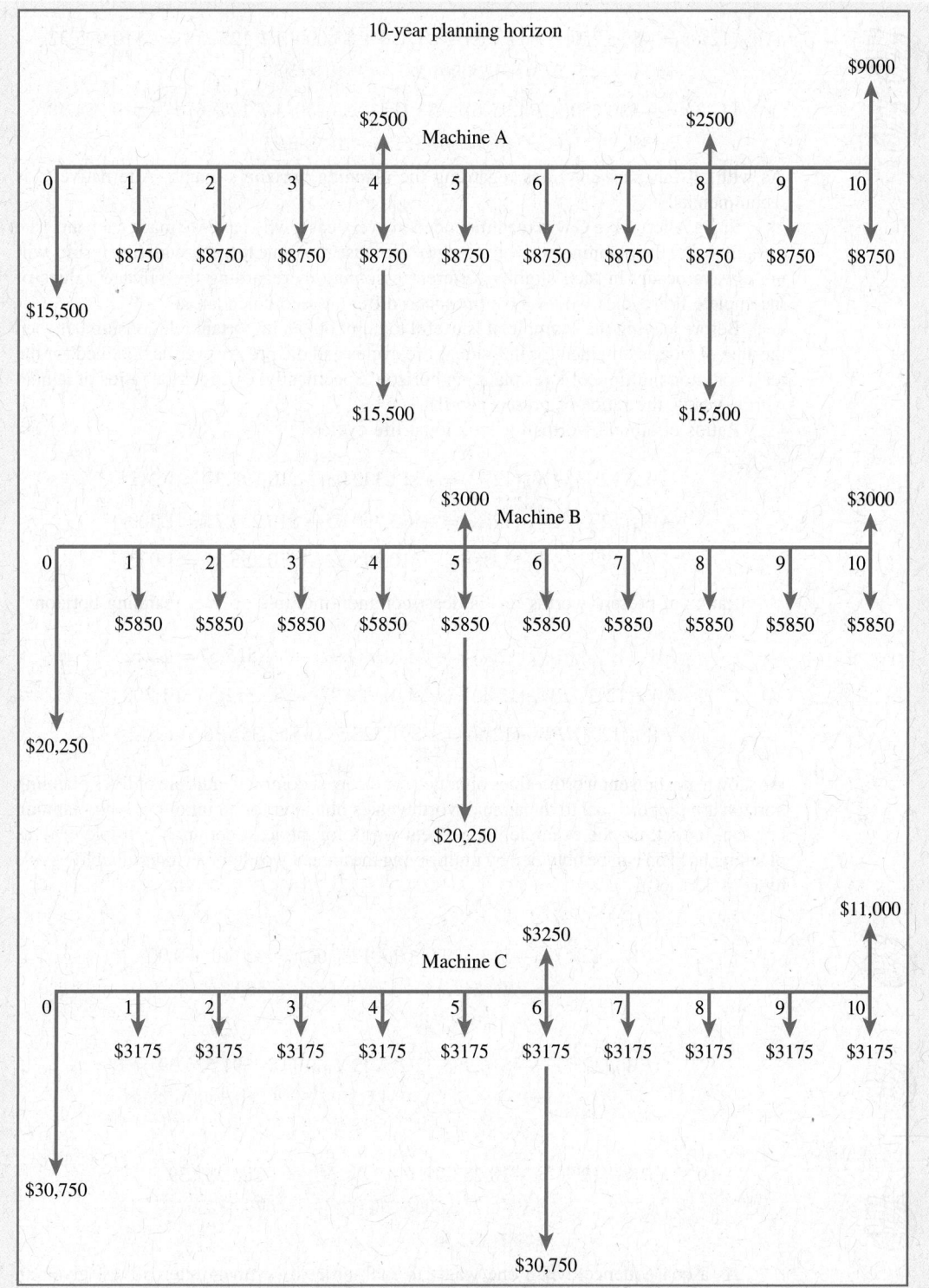

FIGURE 4.4
CFD **for the 10-year Standard Planning Horizon in Example 4.1.**

$$AW_B(12\%) = -\$20,250(A|P\,12\%,5) - \$5,850 + \$3,000(A|F\,12\%,5) = -\$10,995.32$$
$$=\text{PMT}(12\%,5,20250,-3000)-5850 = -\$10,995.32$$

$$AW_C(12\%) = -\$30,750(A|P\,12\%,6) - \$3,175 + \$3,250(A|F\,12\%,6) = -\$10,254.38$$
$$=\text{PMT}(12\%,6,30750,-3250)-3175 = -\$10,253.71$$

As with all other assumptions regarding the planning horizon's length, Alternative C is recommended.

Since Alternative C was recommended in every case, why have we made such an issue over choosing the planning horizon's length? Because the same recommendation results will not always occur. In fact, slightly different assumptions regarding the salvage values of incomplete life cycles would have produced different recommendations.

Before leaving the example, it is useful to point out an important relationship between the annual worths obtained for individual life cycles and the present worths obtained for the least common multiple of lives planning horizon. Specifically, consider the ratios of annual worths versus the ratios of present worths:

Ratios of annual worths for individual life cycles:

$$AW_A(12\%)/AW_B(12\%) = -\$13,330.05/-\$10,995.32 = 1.212$$

$$AW_A(12\%)/AW_C(12\%) = -\$13,330.05/-\$10,253.71 = 1.300$$

$$AW_B(12\%)/AW_C(12\%) = -\$10,995.32/-\$10,253.71 = 1.072$$

Ratios of present worths for the least-common-multiple-of-lives planning horizon:

$$PW_A(12\%)/PW_B(12\%) = -\$110,959.97/-\$91,525.57 = 1.212$$

$$PW_A(12\%)/PW_C(12\%) = -\$110,959.97/-\$85,352.36 = 1.300$$

$$PW_B(12\%)/PW_C(12\%) = -\$91,525.57/-\$85,352.36 = 1.072$$

As shown, the present worth values obtained for the least common multiple of lives planning horizon are proportional to the annual worth values obtained for an infinitely long planning horizon. In fact, for the example, the present worth for the least common multiple of lives planning horizon can be obtained by multiplying the annual worth for an individual life cycle by $(P|A\,12\%,60)$.

$$PW_A(12\%) = -\$13,330.05(P|A\,12\%,60) = -\$110,960.00$$
$$=\text{-PV}(12\%,60,\text{-PMT}(12\%,4,-15500,2500)-8750)$$
$$=\text{-}\$110,959.72$$

$$PW_B(12\%) = -\$10,995.32(P|A\,12\%,60) = -\$91,525.59$$
$$=\text{-PV}(12\%,60,\text{-PMT}(12\%,5,-20250,3000)-5850)$$
$$=\text{-}\$91,525.57$$

$$PW_C(12\%) = -10,253.71(P|A\,12\%,60) = -\$85,352.39$$
$$=\text{-PV}(12\%,60,\text{-PMT}(12\%,6,-30750,3250)-3175)$$
$$=\text{-}\$85,352.36$$

As a consequence, when one wants to rank-order investment alternatives, given an indefinitely long planning horizon or a least common multiple of lives planning horizon, one can rank-order their annual worths for individual life cycles. We will say more about this in Chapter 7.

EXAMPLE 4.2   Selecting the Planning Horizon with One-Shot Investments

As a second illustration of the planning horizon selection process, consider the two cash flow diagrams given in Figure 4.5. The two alternatives are *one-shot investments*. We are unable to predict what investment alternatives will be available in the future, but we do anticipate that recovered capital can be reinvested and earn a 15 percent return.

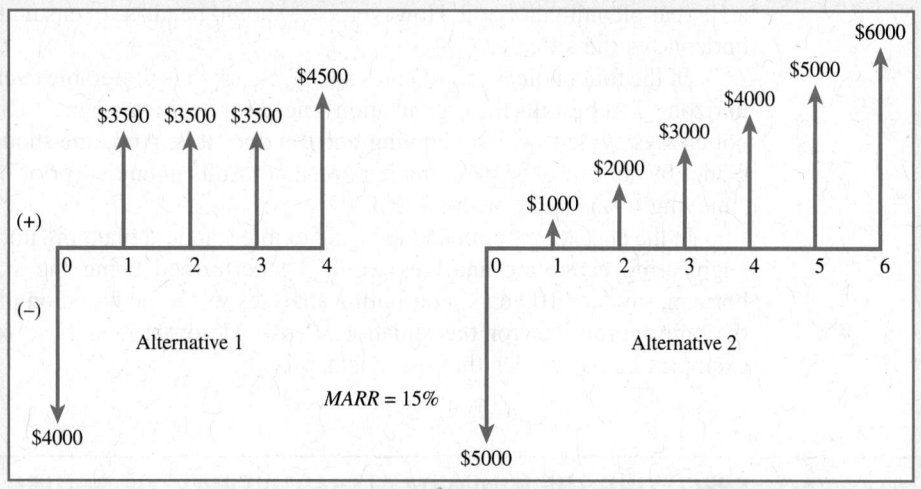

· FIGURE 4.5

*CFD*s for Example 4.2.

For this type of situation, a 6-year planning horizon is suggested, with zero cash flows occurring in years 5 and 6 with Alternative 1. At the end of 6 years, the net future worths for the two alternatives will be

$$FW_1(15\%) = \$4,500(F|P\ 15\%,2) + \$3,500(P|A\ 15\%,3)(F|P\ 15\%,6) - \$4,000(F|P\ 15\%,6)$$
$$= \$4,500(1.32250) + \$3,500(2.28323)(2.31306) - \$4,000(2.31306)$$
$$= \$15,183.38$$
$$= FV(15\%,6,,-PV(15\%,4,-3500,-1000)+4000) = \$15,183.34$$

$$FW_2(15\%) = \$1,000(F|A\ 15\%,6) + \$1,000(A|G\ 15\%,6)(F|A\ 15\%,6) - \$5,000(F|P\ 15\%,6)$$
$$= \$1,000(8.75374) + \$1,000(2.09719)(8.75374) - \$5,000(2.31306)$$
$$= \$15,546.70$$
$$= FV(15\%,6,,-NPV(15\%,1000,2000,3000,4000,5000,6000)+5000)$$
$$= \$15,546.69$$

Thus, we would recommend Alternative 2.

If we did not give careful thought to the situation involved and simply calculated the annual worth over 4- and 6-year horizons, respectively, annual values of $2,299.20 and $1,776.20 would result in favor of Alternative 1. This would be comparable to blindly assuming a least common multiple of lives planning horizon of 12 years, with identical cash flows in repeating life cycles. Hence, it is important to consider the particular situation involved and specify the planning horizon instead of employing a rule of thumb for establishing planning horizons that does not consider the nature of the investments.

Except for special cases, where the planning horizon's length is evident from the investment situation, we prefer to use standard planning horizons. Typically, when performing economic justifications for businesses and governmental agencies, we use a 10-year planning horizon. However, care should be taken to ensure that the planning horizon fits the situation.

Of the four choices offered previously, clearly it is preferable to choose a planning horizon "that best fits the organization's need for the investment." Unfortunately, it is not always evident which planning horizon does this. And, one should avoid playing games by choosing the planning horizon that results in one's a priori recommendation "moving to the head of the line."

In the end, we recommend using a flexible standard planning horizon. All routine engineering economic analyses would be performed using the standard planning horizon, say 5 or 10 years; nonroutine analyses would be based on planning horizons that are appropriate for the situation. Pepsi, Motorola, and Eastman Chemical are examples of companies that use this approach.

4-3   SPECIFYING THE MINIMUM ATTRACTIVE RATE OF RETURN

From the text's beginning, we have repeatedly emphasized the first rule of discounted cash flow analysis: Money has a time value. In each of the previous chapters, we have examined investment opportunities, but always using an interest rate to compound (move forward in time) or discount (move backward in time) cash flows. Later in the text, we explore the sensitivity of interest rate changes on the economic viability of investments. For now, we ask you to accept the following statement: *The value used for the minimum attractive rate of return matters*. In fact, it matters a lot!

Determining the correct value to use for the *MARR* has been the subject of an enormous amount of research. Many master's theses and doctoral dissertations have been written on the subject. Hundreds of articles have appeared in research journals on the topic, and a vast number of books have devoted thousands of pages to it.

It is *not* this text's objective to be the authoritative source on determining the appropriate *MARR* value for an organization. Rather, it is to provide you with a clear understanding of the issues that should be considered when making the determination. In the process, we will share what one multinational firm provides its engineers to help them choose an appropriate *MARR* value.

Since any investment will consume some portion of a firm's scarce resources, it is important for the investment to earn more than it costs to obtain the investment capital. (A firm's cost of obtaining capital is called its *cost of capital*. Motorola defines *cost of capital* as the "economic cost of attracting and retaining various forms of capital from investors who require a rate of return commensurate with the risk of their investment.")

As noted in Chapter 1, it is important for the *MARR* to be greater than the cost of capital. In addition, the *MARR* should reflect the *opportunity cost* associated with

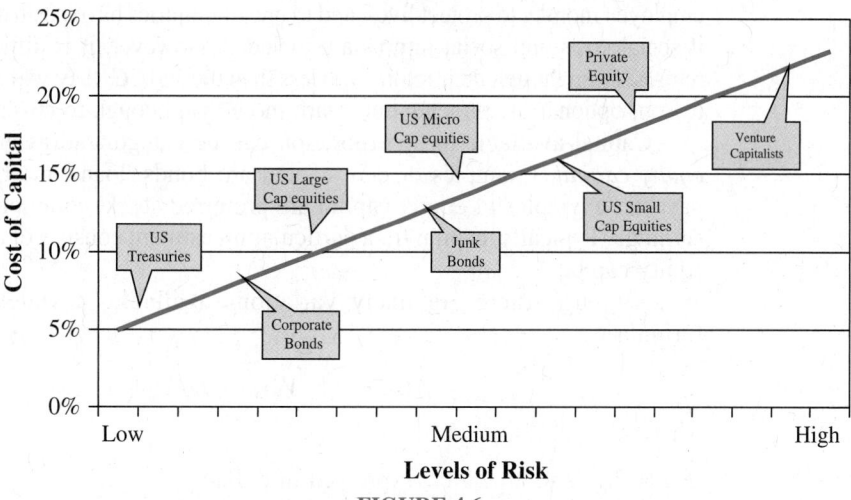

Costs of Various Surces of U.S. Capital Versus Levels of Risk Assumed.

investing in the candidate alternative as opposed to investing in other available alternatives. In fact, we assume investment capital not committed to the candidate alternative is earning a return at least equal to the *MARR*.

> ## Principle #9
>
> Risks and returns tend to be positively correlated.

Generally, a company has available multiple sources of capital: loans, bonds, stocks, and so on. Each has a different cost associated with it. As an example, Figure 4.6 displays various sources of capital and illustrates the different interest rates or returns associated with them. The capital with the lowest cost, U.S. treasuries, are also considered to have the lowest risk; in fact, an average over some number of months of the yields on 10-year U.S. treasury notes is often used as a surrogate measure of capital's risk-free cost. Next, in terms of risk, come corporate bonds; again risk and cost are positively correlated. (Recall Principle #9 from Chapter 1: *Risks and returns tend to be positively correlated.* Figure 4.6 supports the principle.) The most expensive capital shown is venture capital (VC); because it is often the "last resort" source of capital, the investments it supports tend to have the highest risks.

4.3.1 Weighted Average Cost of Capital

Because they have multiple sources of capital, firms typically calculate the *weighted average cost of capital* (*WACC*) and use it to establish a lower bound on the *MARR*. It is only a lower bound because certain unprofitable investment will be required. A firm must make such investments for nonmonetary reasons; examples include investments in environmental compliance equipment, safety devices, and recreational facilities for employees.

Investments made to ensure compliance with governmental regulations, to enhance employee morale, to protect lives, and to prevent injuries have positive returns, particularly if social costs and social returns are included. However, it is difficult to quantify such returns. Even though their returns are less than the *WACC*, they will still be made. For this reason, optional investments must earn more than enough to cover the *WACC*.

Capital available to a corporation can be categorized as either *debt capital* or *equity capital*. Examples of debt capital are bonds, loans, mortgages, and accounts payable; examples of equity capital are preferred stock, common stock, and retained earnings. Typically, capital for a particular investment consists of a mixture of debt and equity capital.

Although there are many variations available, a widely accepted *WACC* formula is

$$WACC = (E/V)i_e + (D/V)i_d(1 - itr) \qquad (4.1)$$

where

$E =$ a firm's total equity, expressed in dollars

$D =$ a firm's total debt and leases, expressed in dollars

$V = E + D$, a firm's total invested capital

$i_e =$ cost of equity or expected rate of return on equity, expressed in percent

$i_d =$ cost of debt or expected rate of return on borrowing, expressed in percent

$itr =$ corporate tax rate

Weighted Average Cost of Capital (*WACC*)

$$WACC = (E/V)i_e + (D/V)i_d(1 - itr)$$

Notice, the costs associated with debt capital are deductible from taxable income. However, the costs associated with equity capital are not deductible. As a result, $(1 - itr)$ is associated with debt capital but not equity capital.

An impressive body of scholarly research on topics associated with the cost of capital has resulted in Nobel Memorial Prizes in Economic Sciences being awarded to several economists, including Harry Markowitz, Merton Miller, Franco Modigliani, and William F. Sharpe. A Web search on their names reveals an impressive legacy from their work.

As with real estate investments, a vast number of Web sites treat the subject of the weighted average cost of capital. An example of an online calculator for the *WACC*, albeit using different notation and a different approach, is shown in Figure 4.7. For a more extensive and advanced treatment of cost of capital calculations, see Park and Sharp.[2]

---

[2]Park, Chan S. and Gunter P. Sharp-Bette, *Advanced Engineering Economics,* John Wiley & Sons, New York, NY, 1990.

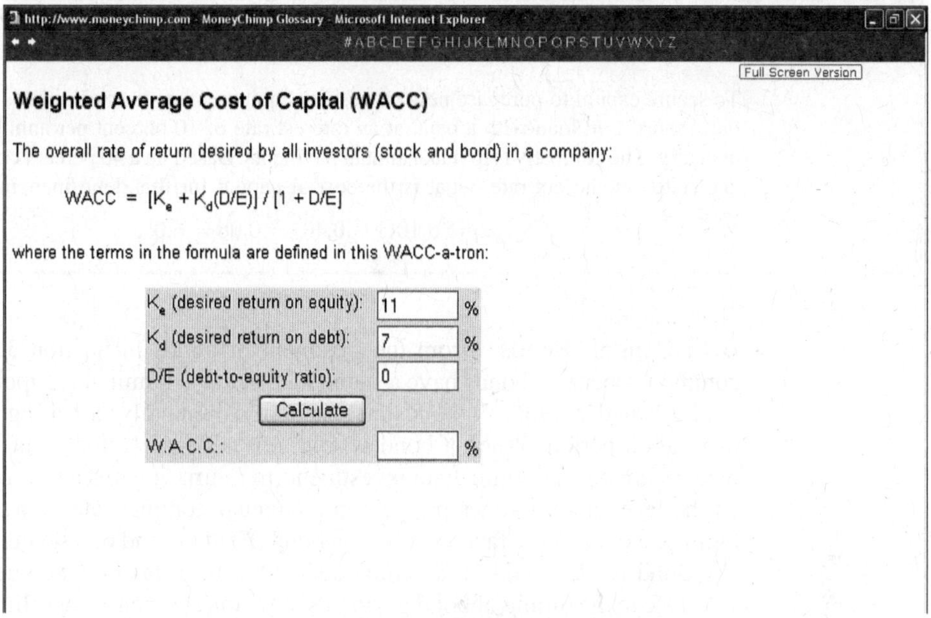

FIGURE 4.7

WACC **On-Line Calculator Available At http://www.moneychimp.com.**

Debt Capital: Loans   Debt capital such as that derived from issuing bonds or securing loans or mortgages results in a specific obligation to pay back both interest and principal. A short-term loan may be obtained from a bank or an insurance company. The interest paid for using the money is a cost of capital. Fortunately, not all of the interest is lost. As noted previously, interest is tax-deductible.[3] Hence, even though we pay $I in interest during a year, the $I may be subtracted from taxable income, resulting in a tax savings of $I \times itr$, where itr is the combined state and federal income tax rate. Since interest is deductible, every $1 spent on interest costs $1(1 - itr)$, after taxes. Therefore, for a simple loan, the effective after-tax interest rate, k_l, can be approximated by

$$k_l = \{[1 + (r/m)]^m - 1\}(1 - itr) \tag{4.2}$$

where, as in Equation 2.46, r is the nominal annual interest rate and m is the number of interest periods per year.

An alternate form of Equation 4.2 is preferred by a number of authors.[4]

---

[3]Tax effects are considered briefly, since income taxes are treated in considerable detail in Chapter 10. We present a "quick and dirty" approach to compute the *WACC*, since we do not explicitly account for quarterly tax payments and do not match midyear debt cash flows with midyear tax cash flows.

[4]The following alternate form is preferred by some:

$$k_l = [1 + (r/m)(1 - itr)]^m - 1.$$

The alternate formulation assumes taxes are paid every m periods during the year (e.g., quarterly). Hence, the tax deductions occur more frequently than annually. Similar modifications are made to the other calculations of the cost of debt capital. In the text, we assume annual cash flows for corporate tax purposes.

EXAMPLE 4.3 Cost of Capital for a Loan

To secure capital to purchase new processing equipment, a small chemicals company takes out a short-term loan with a bank at an interest rate of 10 percent per annum compounded annually. The company is to make annual payments. Based on a 40 percent combined federal and state income tax rate, what is the cost of capital for this debt financing?

$$k_l = 0.10(1 - 0.40) = 0.06 = 6.0\%$$

Debt Capital: Bonds From the treatment of bonds in Section 3.8, we know that common debenture bonds have a stated face value, a nominal (coupon) annual interest rate, a stated number of bond interest periods annually, a selling price (P), and a maturation period. When a bond is sold, not necessarily for its face value, the firm receives money for immediate investment. In return, it gives a promise to pay interest on the face value m times per year at an annual nominal rate r. In addition, the firm promises to repay the face value of the bond (F) at the end of a specified period of time (n). Bond interest paid by a firm is deductible from taxable income.

Due to the timing of bond payments, additional expenses of selling and redeeming bonds, and the various strategies used to discount bonds, obtaining an exact value for the cost of capital from bonds can be quite complicated. For that reason, we will only *approximate* the cost of bond capital.

Recall, from the discussion of bonds in Section 3.8, and particularly Example 3.28, the effective annual yield from a bond is the value of i_b for which

$$P - Fr(P|A\ i_b\%,n) - F(P|F\ i_b\%,n) = 0 \qquad (4.3)$$

Assuming annual tax payments, the after-tax cost of bond capital is approximated by

$$k_b \approx i_b(1 - itr) \qquad (4.4)$$

where, as before, *itr* denotes the combined state and federal income tax rate.

EXAMPLE 4.4 Cost of Capital for Bonds

To raise capital for a new plastics extrusion plant, a company issues $50 million of bonds, each bond having a par value of $1,000, an annual bond rate of 8 percent, and a 10-year life. As an incentive for the bonds to be purchased quickly, the company offers them at $985. If the firm's incremental income tax rate is 40 percent, what is the effective after-tax interest rate for the bonds?

Solving for i_b is facilitated by using Excel®'s **RATE** worksheet function:

$$i_b = \text{RATE}(10,80,-985,1000) = 8.226\%$$

Assuming annual tax payments, the after-tax annual effective yield on the bonds will be

$$k_b \approx 0.08226(0.60) \approx 4.9356\%$$

Debt Capital: Accounts Payable Although seldom included in cost of capital calculations by large corporations, it is not uncommon for small- and medium-sized firms to use their accounts payable as a source of capital. (Accounts payable will be treated in Chapter 16. For our purposes, it represents the money owed for goods or services received.)

To provide incentives for customers to pay their bills promptly, many vendors discount the amount owed if payment occurs within a specified period of time. As an example, a 1 percent or 2 percent discount applies if payment is made within 10 or 14 days of receipt of the invoice for goods or services; otherwise, payment in full is usually due within 45 or 60 days of the invoice's date. If payment is not made within the 10-day window, the customer, in effect, is borrowing money from the vendor.

In developing a formula for calculating the cost of capital for accounts payable, let

D_1 = the number of days after invoice receipt by which payment must occur to obtain the discount

D_2 = the number of days normally taken to pay invoices

d = the discount on the invoice

The cost of capital secured through delayed payment of accounts payable (k_{ap}) is

$$k_{ap} = \left\{ [1/(1-d)]^{365/(D_2 - D_1)} - 1 \right\}(1 - itr) \tag{4.5}$$

(Anything paid for goods and services is included in cost of sales, and the expenditures are deductible from income for tax purposes.)

EXAMPLE 4.5 Cost of Capital for Accounts Payable

The Majestic Music Company purchased a large number of musical instruments for $75,000. The invoice offered a 1.5 percent discount if payment was made within 10 days of the invoice's date; full payment was due within 45 days. Failure to pay fully within the 45-day period would result in a penalty of 5 basis points (0.05 percent) compounded daily. If the music company always pays its invoices in full before the end of the maximum penalty-free period, what will be its cost of capital received in the form of deferred payment of money owed to vendors?

Basically, the music company forgoes a 1.5 percent reduction in the cost of goods received in order to have the money available for 35 additional days. The company pays

$$100\%/98.5\% - 1.0 = 0.01523 = 1.523\%$$

for use of the money for 35 days.

Hence, the firm either pays $75,000(0.985) = $73,875 ten days after receiving the invoice or $75,000 forty-five days after receiving the invoice. We can obtain the daily interest rate that equates the two amounts over the 35-day period as follows:

$$\$75,000 = \$73,875(1 + i_{35})^{35}$$

Solving for i_{35} gives a value of 0.0432 percent. Therefore, the before-tax effective annual interest rate is

$$(1.000432)^{365} - 1 = 17.0714\%$$

Since every dollar spent on the musical equipment costs Majestic Music Company 60¢ after taxes, the after-tax effective annual interest rate is

$$0.170714(0.6) = 0.102428 \text{ or } 10.2428\%,$$

which is the result obtained when using Equation 4.5.

Equity Capital: Preferred Stock   Preferred stock, as the name implies, receives preferred treatment in comparison with common stock. In the event of bankruptcy, preferred stock "stands ahead" of common stock in the line of creditors. Owners of corporate debt, however, are "in line" ahead of owners of equity capital (i.e., since bond interest and principal repayment have a higher priority than dividend payments on preferred and common stock, the pecking order is well established).

Preferred stock carries with it a commitment to pay a stated dividend. Letting PSD denote the magnitude of the preferred stock dividend, C_{ps} denote the cost of selling a share of preferred stock, and P_{ps} denote the share price of preferred stock at the time of issuance, the equity interest rate for preferred stock, e_{ps}, will be

$$e_{ps} = PSD/(P_{ps} - C_{ps}) \tag{4.6}$$

In contrast to debt capital, the costs associated with equity capital are not deductible from income for tax purposes. Since dividends are paid from after-tax earnings by corporations, the cost of equity capital is relatively simple to calculate.

EXAMPLE 4.6   Cost of Capital for Preferred Stock

A company issues preferred stock that pays an annual dividend of $15; a share of preferred stock is sold by the company for $230; it has to pay $5 per share to sell it. What is the cost of capital for the preferred stock?

$$e_{ps} = \$15/(\$230 - \$5) = 6.667\%$$

Equity Capital: Common Stock   In determining the cost of capital derived from common stock, remember that shareholders expect more than dividend returns from common stock. Admittedly, owners of "value" stocks often buy the stock because of its dividends. However, owners of "growth" stocks expect to profit more from the increase in share price than from dividends. In fact, many stocks do not pay dividends at all; instead, they rely on the increase in the stock's value to attract buyers of their stock. Unlike preferred stock, common stock does not guarantee dividends will be paid.

To incorporate aspects of growth in share price in the cost of capital calculation, the following model has been proposed for common stock:

$$e_{cs} = CSD/P_{cs} + g \tag{4.7}$$

where *CSD* denotes the magnitude of common stock dividends, P_{cs} denotes the market value of a share of common stock, and *g* denotes the growth rate for the price of a share of common stock.

The growth rate can be estimated by the ratio of retained earnings to share price. However, retained earnings is the difference in earnings per share and the dividend per share. Hence, the cost of capital for common stock can be approximated by

$$e_{cs} \approx EPS/P_{cs} \tag{4.8}$$

where *EPS* is earnings per share after interest and taxes. Because of this relationship, many corporate CEOs focus on growing earnings per share. They believe that is the best way to increase the price of common stock.

EXAMPLE 4.7   Estimating the Cost of Capital from Common Stock

Logility, a logistics software firm, had an average *EPS* of 55¢ during a 2-year period. Its common stock price, over the same period, averaged $9.75. It pays no dividends. Based on Equation 4.8, what is an approximation for its cost of capital for common stock?

$$e_{cs} \approx EPS/P_{cs} = \$0.55/\$9.75 = 5.64\%$$

An alternative approach that several corporations use to establish the cost of equity capital, based on the capital asset pricing model (CAPM), is discussed in Appendix 4.A.

Equity Capital: Retained Earnings   Another source of equity capital is the earnings retained within the company and not declared as dividends. Even though this money appears to be free, there is a cost of capital. After all, shareholders are the company's owners. Therefore, the retained earnings are theirs. The cost of using retained earnings for investment carries an opportunity cost—the cost of dividends forgone by the stockholders from their own earnings. Hence, one estimate of the cost of capital for retained earnings (e_{re}) is

$$e_{re} \approx CSD/P_{cs}, \tag{4.9}$$

because retained earnings are owned by the stockholders, the owners of the business. *Therefore, it is reasonable to assign the same opportunity cost to retained earnings as assigned to common stock. Therefore, when valuing equity capital, we add retained earnings to the market value of common stock.*

Weighted Average Cost of Capital   The weighted average cost of capital is simply the sum product of the fraction (p) of total capital represented by a source of capital and the cost of capital (k) for the source. In our case,

$$WACC = p_l k_l + p_b k_b + p_{ap} k_{ap} + p_{ps} e_{ps} + p_{cs+re} e_{cs+re} \tag{4.10}$$

where $p_l + p_b + p_{ap} + p_{ps} + p_{cs+re} = 1$ and $cs + re$ denotes the sum of retained earnings and the market value of common stock.

EXAMPLE 4.8   Computing the *WACC*

The capital structure of a firm is made up as follows:

Sources of Capital	Funding	Fraction	After-Tax Cost of Capital
Loans	$1,000,000	9.259%	9.3%
Bonds	$1,800,000	16.667%	5.5%
Common Stocks	$8,000,000	74.074%	9.8%

What is the firm's *WACC*?

$$WACC = 0.09259(9.3\%) + 0.16667(5.5\%) + 0.74074(9.8\%)$$
$$WACC = 9.037\%$$

The foregoing implicitly assumed either zero inflation or an inflation-based cost of capital. Robert Kaplan,[5] a distinguished accounting professor at the Harvard Business School, noted that studies of returns to investors in equity and fixed-income markets during the period from 1926 to 1984 indicated that the average total return from a diversified portfolio of common stock was 11.7 percent/year; fixed-income securities averaged nominal before-tax returns of less than 5 percent/year. However, both figures included the effect of inflation over the same period. Factoring out the impact of inflation, the returns were approximately 8.5 percent and 1.5 percent, respectively. Kaplan concluded that "a mixture of debt and equity financing produces a total real cost of capital less than 8%." He contended that one of the primary reasons American industry tends to underinvest in capital improvements is the use of an overly large discount rate in discounting future cash flows.

Regarding the use of *DCF* methods, Kaplan observed that it "most often goes wrong when companies set arbitrarily high hurdle rates for evaluating new investment projects." He added, "The discounting function serves only to make cash flows received in the future equivalent to cash flows received now. For this narrow purpose—the only purpose, really, of discounted cash flows—companies should use a discount rate based on the project's opportunity cost of capital (that is, the return available in the capital markets for investments of the same risk)."

4.3.2   Eastman Chemical Company's Hurdle Rate Calculator

As noted at the chapter's beginning, for more than 40 years, Eastman Chemical Company has used *DCF* methods to justify capital investments. At the heart of its financial decision making is the *MARR*, which Eastman calls the *hurdle rate*. But the hurdle rate's foundation is the cost of capital. Not only is the cost of capital used to establish the hurdle rate, but it is also used by Eastman to provide incentives for all employees. Five percent of each employee's base salary is placed in a bonus pool that will not be distributed unless the company earns a return for the shareholders greater than its cost of capital. A side benefit of the incentive program is that every

---

[5]Kaplan, R. S., "Must CIM be Justified by Faith Alone?" *Harvard Business Review, 64* (2), March–April 1986, pp. 87–95.

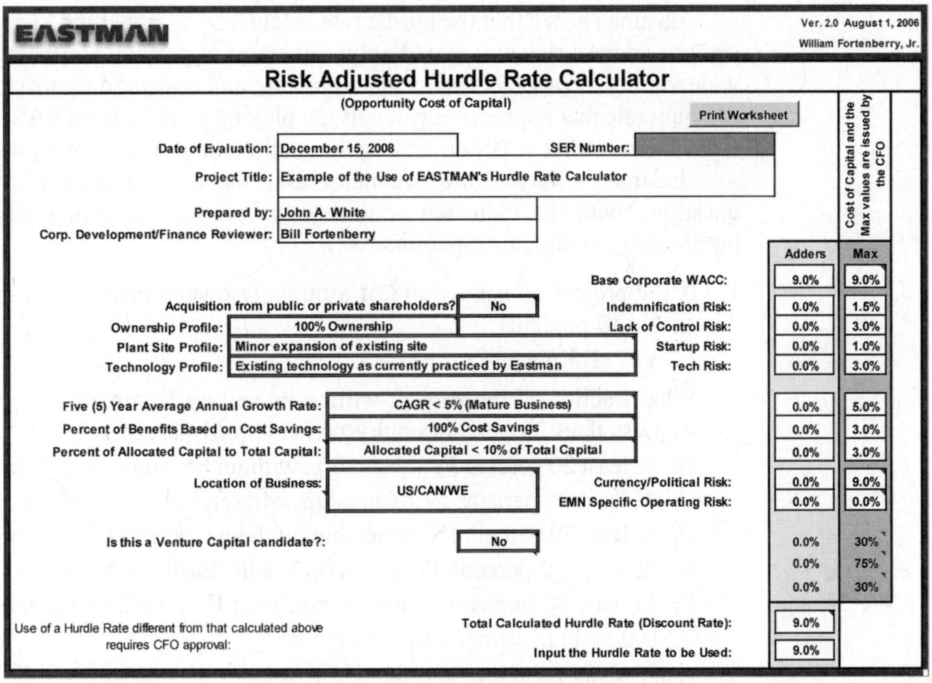

EASTMAN

Ver. 2.0 August 1, 2006
William Fortenberry, Jr.

Risk Adjusted Hurdle Rate Calculator
(Opportunity Cost of Capital)

Print Worksheet

Cost of Capital and the Max values are issued by the CFO

Date of Evaluation: December 15, 2008   SER Number:

Project Title: Example of the Use of EASTMAN's Hurdle Rate Calculator

Prepared by: John A. White
Corp. Development/Finance Reviewer: Bill Fortenberry

		Adders	Max
Base Corporate WACC:		9.0%	9.0%
Acquisition from public or private shareholders? **No**	Indemnification Risk:	0.0%	1.5%
Ownership Profile: 100% Ownership	Lack of Control Risk:	0.0%	3.0%
Plant Site Profile: Minor expansion of existing site	Startup Risk:	0.0%	1.0%
Technology Profile: Existing technology as currently practiced by Eastman	Tech Risk:	0.0%	3.0%
Five (5) Year Average Annual Growth Rate: CAGR < 5% (Mature Business)		0.0%	5.0%
Percent of Benefits Based on Cost Savings: 100% Cost Savings		0.0%	3.0%
Percent of Allocated Capital to Total Capital: Allocated Capital < 10% of Total Capital		0.0%	3.0%
Location of Business: US/CAN/WE	Currency/Political Risk:	0.0%	9.0%
	EMN Specific Operating Risk:	0.0%	0.0%
Is this a Venture Capital candidate?: **No**		0.0%	30%
		0.0%	75%
		0.0%	30%

Use of a Hurdle Rate different from that calculated above requires CFO approval:

Total Calculated Hurdle Rate (Discount Rate): 9.0%

Input the Hurdle Rate to be Used: 9.0%

FIGURE 4.8
Eastman Chemical Company Hurdle Rate (*MARR*) Calculator.

employee understands the importance of the firm being profitable—it impacts their pocketbooks!

In establishing hurdle rates for capital justifications, Eastman communicates to its engineers that the hurdle rate used in a particular economic justification should "be appropriate for the uncertainties inherent in specific projects; be appropriate for the risks inherent in specific projects; support corporate objectives; and be consistently applied across the company."[6]

To facilitate consistent application, Eastman developed an Excel®-based hurdle rate calculator, illustrated in Figure 4.8. Eastman communicated to its engineers that "the hurdle rate calculator is to be used for all projects for which a return is calculated. Eastman's CFO provides the elements for the calculator and any subsequent updates to ensure consistency with management's targets. Corporate Development and Business Finance units are responsible for appropriate use of the hurdle rate calculator: all hurdle rate calculations should be reviewed by the appropriate Corporate Development or Business Finance personnel before presentation to management, and a copy of the calculation is to be attached to each relevant economic analysis. Recognize that the relationship of a project's estimated return to its hurdle rate is only one factor that is considered when accepting or rejecting that project. Other factors would include corporate initiatives, value of options created, health and safety, etc."[7]

---

[6]From presentation materials shared with the authors by Brian Ferguson, chairman and chief executive officer, Eastman Chemical Company.
[7]Ibid.

Eastman noted that the hurdle rate calculator is "a method to apply some level of rigor to address risk and uncertainty; a method to provide consistent application in a wide variety of projects across the company; and a method to provide a risk adjusted discount rate that appropriately levels the playing field for most EASTMAN projects." It also noted what it is not: "an automated method to accept or reject projects."[8]

Eastman's hurdle rate calculator asks the user to answer the following nine questions, with the indicated options for responses (percentages added to the base hurdle rate are shown in parentheses):

1. Is the project an acquisition of a publicly owned business?
   A. No (0 percent)
   B. Yes (1.5 percent)

2. What fraction of the project will be owned by Eastman?
   A. Less than 20 percent equity ownership (3 percent)
   B. At least 20 percent JV ownership, without Eastman having control (2.5 percent)
   C. At least 35 percent JV ownership, without Eastman having control (2 percent)
   D. At least 50 percent JV ownership, without Eastman having control (1.5 percent)
   E. At least 50 percent JV ownership, with Eastman having control (1 percent)
   F. At least 80 percent JV ownership, with Eastman having control (0.5 percent)
   G. 100 percent ownership (0 percent)

3. What is the profile of the plant site?
   A. Adequately addressed by decision and risk analysis probabilities (0 percent)
   B. Debottleneck of existing site (0 percent)
   C. Minor expansion of existing site (0 percent)
   D. Major expansion of existing site (0.2 percent)
   E. New plant at third-party "condo" site (0.5 percent)
   F. New plant at greenfield site (1 percent)

4. What is the profile of the technology to be used?
   A. Adequately addressed by decision and risk analysis probabilities (0 percent)
   B. Existing technology as currently practiced by Eastman (0 percent)
   C. Slightly different application of practiced Eastman technology (0.5 percent)
   D. Licensed technology as currently practiced widely by industry (0.8 percent)
   E. Licensed technology with limited use by industry (1.5 percent)
   F. New technology (3 percent)

5. What is the estimated 5-year compound annual growth rate (CAGR) for revenue?
   A. Negative CAGR (declining business; 0.7 percent)
   B. CAGR $\leq$ 5 percent (mature business; 0 percent)
   C. 5 percent < CAGR $\leq$ 8 percent (twice GDP; 1.2 percent)
   D. 8 percent < CAGR $\leq$ 10 percent (aggressive growth; 2.1 percent)
   E. 10 percent < CAGR $\leq$ 15 percent (cycle recovery; 2.8 percent)
   F. 15 percent < CAGR $\leq$ 25 percent (established new product; 4.2 percent)
   G. 25 percent < CAGR $\leq$ 35 percent (venture capital candidate; 7 percent)
   H. 35 percent < CAGR (seed money candidate; 10 percent)

[8]Ibid.

6. What mix of cost savings versus revenue growth is used in the justification?
   A. 100 percent cost savings (0 percent)
   B. 80 percent/20 percent (0.6 percent)
   C. 60 percent/40 percent (1.2 percent)
   D. 40 percent/60 percent (1.8 percent)
   E. 20 percent/80 percent (2.4 percent)
   F. 100 percent revenue growth (3 percent)

7. What fraction of total capital is allocated capital?
   A. Less than 10 percent (0 percent)
   B. From 10 percent to 25 percent (−0.6 percent)
   C. From 26 percent to 45 percent (−1.2 percent)
   D. From 46 percent to 65 percent (−1.8 percent)
   E. From 66 percent to 85 percent (−2.4 percent)
   F. Greater than 85 percent (−3 percent)

8. Where is the expenditure of capital located?
   A. In the U.S., Australia, Belgium, Canada, France, Germany, Hong Kong, Italy, Japan, the Netherlands, New Zealand, Portugal, Singapore, Spain, Switzerland, Taiwan, and the United Kingdom (0%)
   B. In Chile, Malaysia, and South Korea (0.5%)
   C. In the Czech Republic, Hungary, Israel, Mexico, South Africa, and Thailand (1.0%)
   D. In Egypt and India (1.5%)
   E. In Brazil, China, Columbia, and Indonesia (2.0%)
   F. In the Philippines, Turkey, and Vietnam (2.5%)
   G. In Russia (3.0%)
   H. In Argentina (3.5%)
   I. In Venezuela (10%), and other country or mix of countries (10%)

9. Is this a venture capital candidate?
   A. No (0 percent)
   B. Yes (30 percent minimum venture capital risk)

   (1) It is a seed stage candidate (105%)
   (2) It is a midstage candidate (70%)
   (3) It is a late (expansion capital) stage (45%)
   (4) It is IPO imminent (30%)

The hurdle rate calculation begins with Eastman's *WACC* as a base. (Alternatives are 8 percent, 8.5 percent, 9 percent, 9.5 percent, and 10 percent.) Answers to all but Question 7 add to the base; the answer to Question 7 can subtract from the base.

If the answer to the first question is no, then nothing is added to the base. However, if the answer is yes, and the project involves the acquisition of a publicly traded company, then 1.5 percent is added to the base. The increment is in recognition of the increased level of risk when there is no surviving, viable entity to offer indemnities or "reps and warranties" about the condition of the business.

With respect to the second question, Eastman recognizes "the increased uncertainty of potential outcomes when control is less than complete."

The third question serves to categorize the investment in terms of the site. The options range from increasing capacity at existing sites (called *debottlenecking* in the chemical industry) to a new plant at a new site. An added option indicates sophisticated probabilistic modeling has been used to quantify the risks and uncertainties associated with the project. The hurdle rate calculator comes with the reminder, "Significant projects should utilize the Decision & Risk process to highlight and quantify probability ranges around specific uncertainties leading to optimum decision paths, ranges of potential outcomes, and the expected NPV and IRR." (More will be said about this in Chapter 13.)

The fourth question addresses the type technology being acquired. The options range from tried-and-true technology that Eastman has used to technology that is new to the site and new to the industry. As with the plant site profile, the technology profile includes the option of decision and risk analysis.

Sales growth is addressed in the fifth question. It accounts for "the inherent uncertainty in forecasting 'super normal' growth of revenues." The growth adjustment is designed to account for approximately one-half of the CAGR above twice the growth rate of the gross domestic product (GDP). For a CAGR of 5 percent or less, no increment is added to the hurdle rate. Greater increments are added as estimates of the CAGR increase, because Eastman's postaudits of major capital expenditures showed that revenue estimates tended to be overestimated. Increasing the hurdle rate is intended to compensate for overly optimistic estimates of revenues accompanying capital expenditures.

The sixth question relates to the source of the cash flows used to justify the expenditure. Based on experience and formal postaudits of capital investments made in the past, Eastman concluded that engineers' estimates of cost reductions were much more accurate than their estimates of revenue growth. As a result, the hurdle rate calculator has built into it an assumption of an 80 percent chance of achieving the revenue growth but a 100 percent chance of achieving the cost savings.

The seventh question provides an opportunity for *deductions* from the base. It addresses the capital expenditure profile for the project. The possible reduction in the base rate is in recognition of the probability of delaying the decision to spend support capital. The adjustment is based on a 30 percent chance that allocated support capital will not be spent.

What is meant by *allocated capital*? When queried, Eastman management responded that Eastman Chemical Company is highly integrated. As a result, a special expenditure request (SER) will often be submitted to expand an existing plant. As a result, supporting services might be required. Examples of these include utilities (electricity, steam, water, nitrogen, compressed air, etc.), fire protection (hydrants, additional centralized equipment, etc.), equipment for administrative support (office space, computers, etc.), and, in some cases, added manufacturing capacity for a shared raw material.

The incremental nature of added support services is such that it is difficult to pinpoint the product or expansion project that causes Eastman to add administrative personnel, space, or equipment to accommodate growth. Also, when utilities and manufacturing equipment are added, the company prefers to add sufficient capacity to meet longer-term expansion needs, rather than add them piecemeal. As a result, they prefer to fund large-scale, highly efficient designs that can support multiple projects at lower costs.

Management is confident the company will continue to grow and expand. Consequently, they do not want the company to have to wait until sufficient downstream expansion projects have been approved before funding the supporting investments needed. To do so would drive the company toward funding smaller, less efficient supporting infrastructure to meet the required timing of specific expansion projects.

How does Eastman deal with this ''chicken and egg'' challenge? One approach is to have a higher hurdle rate for all expansion projects and to ignore the added cost (unless the expansion project is bundled with its support project[s]). Another approach is to calculate a capacity reservation fee based on the estimated capital cost of the next increment of a particular support service. To the extent an expansion project uses units of the ''next increment,'' that portion of the estimated capital cost of the support service is allocated to the expansion project. This assures that all projects are evaluated on a similar basis. Eastman adopted the latter approach.

By using allocated capital, if a project is unsuccessful (which occasionally happens), the project can be canceled and the company will not have to spend the allocated portion of the capital. The Eastman hurdle rate calculator incorporates historical data regarding the likelihood of allocated capital being spent in support of an SER. Because of the probability it will not be spent, reductions in the hurdle rate can occur.

The eighth question addresses the currency risks of non-U.S. installations. It recognizes the increased (relative to the United States) political risk to investment returns in non-U.S. countries. The country premium is based on interest rate premiums that are charged in the country. They are not exchange rates or inflation differentials but accommodations for the potential future risk of conversion of the local currency into dollars. Country premiums are updated semiannually. Because of changing global conditions, we have seen countries go from ''most favored nation'' levels in which the premium was 5 percent to the premium being 10 percent in a period of 5 years; over a similar time frame, another country moved from a premium of 6.5 percent to 1.5 percent.

The final question addresses the stage of any joint ventures. If the project is a candidate for venture capital, all but one of the earlier questions are moot; only the question of location survives. The hurdle rate for venture capital projects equals the country premium plus the maximum of a minimum venture capital risk and the sum of a venture capital stage risk and a liquidity risk. Values of the parameters are updated by the new business ventures organization. For the version of the hurdle rate calculator we used, the minimum VC risk is 30 percent; the values for VC stage risk and liquidity risk depend on the type of venture capital project being justified. Four VC stages are included in the calculator: seed stage, midstage, late stage, and initial public offering (IPO) imminent stage.

Values of the hurdle rate calculator's various parameters are updated periodically, as well as when economic, political, and other changes occur that would affect levels of risk for the company. As noted on the spreadsheet, if the hurdle rate used differs from the total calculated hurdle rate, then the chief financial officer's approval is required.

EXAMPLE 4.9 Eastman's Hurdle Rate Calculator

A team of process engineers has proposed to spend $2.5 million on a cost savings project. When they entered the data in the Eastman hurdle rate calculator, they obtained a calculated value of 9 percent, as shown in Figure 4.8. Note, debottlenecking of an existing site, using existing technology, was proposed. Also, notice that a base *WACC* of 9 percent was entered. The base corporate *WACC* changes over time; corporate finance managers are responsible for keeping the hurdle rate calculator updated.

EXAMPLE 4.10 Hurdle Rate Calculation for a Cost Savings Investment

The plant manager of a major manufacturing site has proposed the installation of new technology in an effort to significantly expand the production capacity at the site. It is a 100 percent cost savings proposal. Assuming a base corporate *WACC* of 8.5 percent, the hurdle rate to be used in the economic justification is calculated as follows:

Base Corporate *WACC*: 8.5 percent
1. Indemnification risk: 0.0
2. Lack of control risk: 0.0
3. Start-up risk: 0.0
4. Technology risk: 3.0
5. 5-year average AGR: 0.0
6. Percent benefits based on cost savings: 0.0
7. Percent allocated capital to total capital: 0.0
8. Currency/political risk: 0.0
9. EMN specific operating risk: 0.0

Total Calculated Hurdle Rate 11.5 percent

EXAMPLE 4.11 Hurdle Rate Calculation for a Revenue Enhancing Investment

A business development team has proposed the expenditure of $8.5 million to produce a new specialty chemical at an existing site (a major expansion). Since it is a new business venture, the justification is based on new revenue generated for the company and in anticipation of a 7 percent CAGR for revenue. After entering the data in the Eastman hurdle rate calculator (which includes a 9.5 percent base corporate *WACC*), a value of 13.9 percent is obtained. To the base are added 0.2 percent (due to the major expansion of an existing site), 1.2 percent (due to a CAGR of 7 percent for revenue), and 3 percent (due to the expansion being based solely on revenue growth), for a total of 13.9 percent.

EXAMPLE 4.12 Hurdle Rate Calculation for a China Joint Venture

The vice president for strategic planning, together with members from the business team and manufacturing, are exploring a joint venture in China with Eastman owning 40 percent and not having control of the joint venture. In anticipation of synergies among the joint owners of the business, it was estimated that 20 percent of the benefits would result from cost savings and 80 percent would result from new revenue. Also, it was estimated that revenue would grow at a 6 percent compound annual growth rate over the next 5 years. After using the Eastman hurdle rate calculator, the VP approached the CFO with a request for approval to use a hurdle rate of 17.6 percent in performing the economic justification for the joint venture. The hurdle rate is obtained by adding to the 9 percent base the following amounts: 2 percent (due to 40 percent ownership); 0.5 percent (due to new plant at third-party "condo" site); 0.5 percent (due to slightly different application of Eastman technology); 1.2 percent (due to 6 percent CAGR); 2.4 percent (due to 20 percent/80 percent cost savings and revenue mix); and 2 percent (due to location in China).

EXAMPLE 4.13   Hurdle Rate Calculation for a Venture Capital Investment

Researchers in the R&D labs for a multinational chemicals company have discovered a by-product that does not fit into the company's long-term business plans. The plan is to spin off the business when it has been proven that the product can be produced in large quantities at required quality and cost levels. The product is viewed to be a seed-stage candidate for venture capital (VC) financing. To determine the *MARR* to be used in evaluating the new venture's economics, the Eastman hurdle rate calculator was used. It yielded a value of 105 percent, as shown in Figure 4.9.

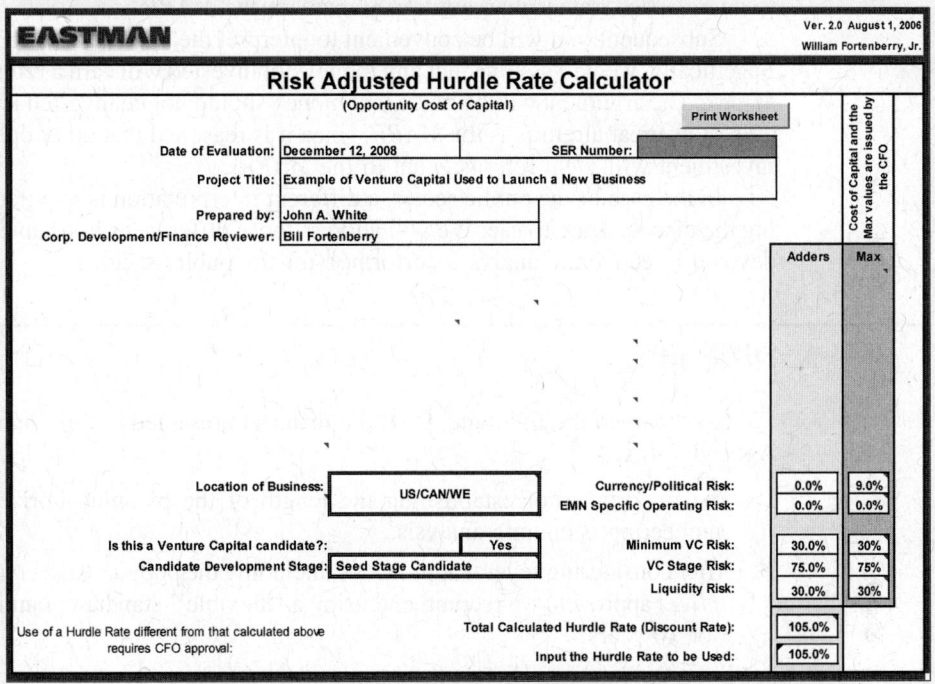

FIGURE 4.9

**Eastman Chemical Company Hurdle Rate Calculator Used to Solve Example 4.13
(Courtesy of Eastman Chemical Company).**

The foregoing analysis implicitly assumed either zero inflation or an inflation-based cost of capital. It is important for the cost of capital to reflect the true cost of capital to the firm during the future investment period. For this reason, we prefer to determine the cost of capital *absent* inflation effects. In Chapter 12, we examine the impact of inflation on engineering economic analyses. Likewise, we will provide a more complete coverage of income tax effects on economic justification in Chapter 10.

Eastman Chemical Company's hurdle rate calculator identified several considerations that impact the choice of a minimum attractive rate of return. Not all companies use a systematic approach similar to Eastman's. Instead, some establish the *MARR* by

1. adding a fixed percentage to the firm's cost of capital;
2. using the rate of return actually achieved over the past 5 years;
3. using different values for different planning horizon durations;
4. using different values for different magnitudes of investment;

5. using different values for new ventures than for cost reduction projects;

6. varying the value, depending on the overall economic condition of the firm; and

7. using the average stockholder's return on investment for companies in the same industry sector.

Although many companies increase the value of the *MARR* as the risks associated with the project increase, an alternate approach is to deal with risk explicitly by using techniques presented in Chapter 13. Merck, PepsiCo, and Eastman are examples of firms that utilize decision trees, Monte Carlo simulation, and other probabilistic tools to address risk, rather than arbitrarily increase the *MARR*.

Subsequently, it will be convenient to interpret the *MARR* as an opportunity cost. Specifically, we will assume that any money not invested will earn a return equal to the *MARR*. The argument will be made that money should not be invested if it cannot earn at least as great a return as the *MARR*, since it is reasoned that other opportunities for investment will yield returns equal to the *MARR*.

In the case of the public sector, a different interpretation is required in determining the discount rate to use. We will address those differences in Chapter 14, which is devoted to economic analyses performed for the public sector.

4-4   SUMMARY

We have learned the following from the material presented in this chapter, including Appendix 4.A:

1. The importance of establishing the length of the planning horizon used in an engineering economic analysis.

2. After considering several approaches, including the popular *least common multiple of lives* approach, we recommend using a "flexible" standard planning horizon of 5 or 10 years.

3. Some investments dictate the length of the planning horizon.

Turning to the *MARR*, we learned

1. that a *weighted average cost of capital* (*WACC*) is a popular basis for calculating the *MARR* value;

2. that any value chosen for the *MARR* should reflect opportunities for investment elsewhere (i.e., opportunity costs);

3. that a company typically has multiple sources of capital;

4. how to apply *DCF* methods to obtain the after-tax cost of capital for each source of capital, including both debt and equity capital;

5. how Eastman Chemical Company establishes the *MARR*, which it calls the *hurdle rate*; and

6. that additions are made to Eastman's historical weighted average cost of capital based on the levels and types of risks involved.

7. how the *capital asset pricing model* (*CAPM*) is used to determine the cost of equity capital;

8. the important role β plays in *CAPM*;

9. that there are multiple ways to calculate β;

10. that *predicted beta* is used by investment banks and many corporations;

Hopefully, along the way, you found learning this material to be a lot of fun. We have found it to be so.

Pit Stop #4—Take a Deep Breath!

1. True or False: When dealing with multiple alternatives having unequal lives, the planning horizon equals the least common multiple of lives.

2. True or False: The *MARR* should be at least as great as the firm's weighted cost of capital and should reflect the opportunity cost for money.

3. True or False: Among the various sources of capital, U.S. large cap equities have a lower cost of capital than do U.S. small cap equities.

4. True or False: If the before-tax WACC $= 5.4\%$ and the income tax rate is 40%, then the after-tax WACC $= 9\%$.

5. True or False: The cost of debt capital needs to reflect the tax deductibility of costs of debt.

6. True or False: The Eastman hurdle rate calculator can be used for any company and under any conditions that are specifically targeted by the calculator.

7. True or False: A company's beta can be used to accurately forecast its stock price during the coming year.

8. True or False: Historical beta values are not impacted by rare events that might adversely affect a firm's stock price.

9. True or False: The Federal Reserve Bank's prime lending rate should be used for the risk-free rate in the capital asset pricing model.

10. True or False: When using the Eastman hurdle rate calculator, if venture capital is being sought, the hurdle rate obtained will not be affected by ownership, plant site, or technology profiles.

CAPITAL ASSET PRICING MODEL

An alternative approach to estimating the cost of capital for common stock is the capital asset pricing model (CAPM). A product of his doctoral research, William F. Sharpe earned the Nobel Prize for CAPM in 1990.

As with *WACC*, CAPM is the subject of numerous Web sites, as well as considerable debate concerning its accuracy and continued relevancy. Rather than contribute to the debate, we point you to the Internet and invite you to do your own exploration. A good place to begin is with an interview of William F. Sharpe by Jonathan Burton, reprinted by permission from *Dow Jones Asset Manager*, May/June 1998, pp. 20–28, and found online at www.stanford.edu/~wfsharpe/art/djam/djam.htm.

An overview of CAPM is available at www.investopedia.com/articles/06/CAPM .asp.

The following is also worth visiting: http://en.wikipedia.org/wiki/Capital_asset_ pricing_model.

We include CAPM in a treatment of the cost of capital because Sharpe's research showed that the return on an individual or a portfolio of stocks should equal its cost of capital. As noted, investors in common stock are rewarded in two ways: value and growth. Stated a different way, common stock investors are compensated through the time value of money and risk. The latter relates to the volatility of stock prices over time. Sharpe's model quantifies the common stock relationship between risks and returns.

The underlying formula for CAPM is

$$E(r_{cs}) = r_f + \beta[E(r_m) - r_f] \tag{4.A.1}$$

where

$E(r_{cs}) =$ expected return for the common stock in question

$r_f =$ risk-free interest rate (e.g., 4 percent)

$E(r_m) =$ expected return of the stock market or of a stock portfolio that is representative of the overall market

$$\beta = Cov(r_{cs}, \ r_m)/\mathrm{Var}(r_m)$$

Essentially, Equation 4.A.1 indicates that the risk-adjusted discount rate or cost of capital for common stock is equal to the sum of a risk-free return and a risk premium. The risk premium equals the stock's beta (β) times the market's expected excess return over the risk-free return. Beta is a measure of a stock's volatility relative to the overall market or a portfolio; mathematically, beta is equal to the ratio of the covariance of the common stock in question and the market or portfolio proxy for the market and the variance of the market or portfolio. A common proxy for the market is Standard and Poor's 500 index.

Capital Asset Pricing Model (*CAPM*)

$$E(r_{cs}) = r_f + \beta[E(r_m) - r_f]$$

Today, *beta* is a part of financial analysts' vocabularies. Since the 1970s, within the investment community, beta has become the most widely accepted and applied measure of risk. It is common to hear people talk about a particular stock's β-value. If $\beta < 1.0$, the stock in question is less volatile than the market and less of a premium is expected in return; if $\beta > 1.0$, the stock is more volatile than the market and a larger premium is expected from the stock; if $\beta = 0$, the common stock is equivalent to a risk-free investment.

In the CAPM formula, β values indicate how a stock will change as the market changes. For example, if a stock's $\beta = 1.25$ and the market rises by 10 percent, then the stock's price should increase by 12.5 percent; likewise, if the market decreases by 8 percent, then the stock price should decrease by 8% (1.25) or 10 percent.

Once you know a stock's β, the expected annual return for the market, and the risk-free rate, you can calculate the expected 1-year return for the stock. As shown in Figure 4.A.1, moneychim.com provides an online CAPM calculator. However, it is simple enough to solve Equation 4.A.1 once you know the value of β for a particular stock.

Notice, in Equation 4.A.1, a linear relationship exists between β and $E(e_{cs})$. In the finance literature, the straight line is known as the *security market line* (SML). When securities are plotted, if they are above the SML, then they are overvalued; if they fall below the line, they are undervalued. Of course, this will not hold for any security at specific points in time, since the theory is based on expected values.

Since it first appeared, a number of alternative formulations of beta have been developed. Comparisons of the alternative with *historical beta* (β_h) have been made, and claims of improved predictability have been made relative to stock prices. One alternative that has gained considerable use is one developed by Barra;[9] it is called *predicted beta* (β_p), also known as *fundamental beta*. According to its developers, β_p forecasts a stock's sensitivity to the market before the fact by adjusting β_h for such factors as industry exposure, growth, earnings variability, financial leverage, size, volatility, and momentum.

The *predicted beta* was developed in response to a belief that historical betas measured past relationships of a firm's returns and the returns of the market without recognizing that a firm's return at any point in time can be adversely impacted by a rare event. For example, when United Airlines (UAL) sold its hotel and rental car businesses in the late 1980s, the risk profile for UAL changed significantly. The devastating events in Bhopal, India, in 1984, did not reflect Union Carbide's year-in and year-out performance. The predicted beta factors out the effects of a rare occurrence, whereas its impact would continue to be included in the calculations of historical beta.

Barra updates its predicted beta values monthly; updates include significant changes in a company's risk structure. Historical beta does not reflect divestitures and acquisitions; it is sensitive to specific, one-time events that impact the firm or the overall market. Financial firms, such as Bank of America, Goldman Sachs, J. P. Morgan Chase, and Morgan Stanley, use the predicted beta in valuing companies for acquisition or sale. Many corporations also use the predicted beta to compute their cost of equity capital.

---

[9]For information, contact MSCI Barra, Wall Street Plaza, 88 Pine Street, 2nd Floor, New York, NY 10005 or www.barra.com.

CAPM Calculator

Valuation with the Capital Asset Pricing Model uses a variation of discounted cash flows; only instead of giving yourself a "margin of safety" by being conservative in your earnings estimates, you use a varying discount rate that gets bigger to compensate for your investment's riskiness. There are different ways to measure risk; the original CAPM defined risk in terms of volatility, as measured by the investment's beta coefficient. The formula is:

$K_c = R_f + beta \times (K_m - R_f)$
where
K_c is the risk-adjusted discount rate (also known as the Cost of Capital);
R_f is the rate of a "risk-free" investment, i.e. cash;
K_m is the return rate of a market benchmark, like the S&P 500.

You can think of K_c as the expected return rate you would require before you would be interested in this particular investment at this particular price. The idea is that investors require higher levels of expected returns to compensate them for higher expected risk; the CAPM formula is a simple equation to express that idea.

Here is a calculator to let you try it out. You can find values for beta via the box below.

Benchmark Return Rates	
Return available on an appropriate market benchmark investment (like the S&P 500):	11 %
Return available on a risk-free investment (cash, or government bond):	5.00 %
Risk Factor	
Your investment's Beta (relative to the market benchmark above):	
Results	
Risk-adjusted discount rate:	%
Carry result to DCF calculator...	

Find Beta

Ticker:

You now plug this value for the discount rate into the discounted cash flow calculator - ignoring the advice underneath it about using conservative estimates for earnings.

Analysts sometimes use a more complicated value for beta, that grows with a company's debt level. There is also lots of controversy about whether beta, which measures past volatility, is sufficient or even relevant in predicting future risk. William F. Sharpe, who invented CAPM, discusses these issues in an online interview.

One big caveat: the sophistication of the sliding discount rate makes this approach potentially dangerous. If you get creative enough with the discount rate and long-term growth expectations,

FIGURE 4.A.1

**On-line *CAPM* Calculator Available at http://www.moneychimp.com/articles/valuation/
capm.htm.**

Values of historical beta are available from several financial institutions. Table 4.A.1 provides values of β_h and β_p for 40 corporations over a 3-year period; the β_h and β_p values were obtained using a fee-based service from MSCI Barra.

Values used by firms for r_f are usually arrived at by using the yield on 10-year U.S. Treasury notes as a surrogate for a risk-free return. Depending on the economy's condition, r_f values range from 2 percent to 5.25 percent. In mid-2008, a value between 4.5 percent and 5 percent for r_f was not unreasonable.

Values used for the market risk premium, $[E(r_m) - r_f]$, typically range from 3 percent to 8 percent. The value depends on the period of time considered and whether arithmetic or geometric averages are used. In mid-2008, 6 percent was commonly used for the market risk premium.

TABLE 4.A.1
Historical and Predicted Beta Values for Forty U.S. Corporations.

Corporation	2006		2007		2008		2009		2010		2011	
	β_h	β_p	β_h	β_p	β_h	β_p	β_h	β_p	β_h	β_p	β_h	β_p
Boeing	1.04	1.03	0.91	0.90	1.39	1.14	1.24	1.25	1.27	1.10	1.27	1.01
Abbott Labs	0.65	0.63	0.21	0.59	0.14	0.37	0.20	0.54	0.22	0.60	0.30	0.58
Apple	1.52	1.50	1.32	1.33	2.36	1.35	1.67	0.87	1.50	0.87	1.33	0.98
AT&T	0.95	0.73	1.51	0.93	1.03	0.89	0.63	0.72	0.69	0.69	0.66	0.70
Caterpillar	1.58	1.25	1.46	1.29	1.32	1.22	1.76	1.65	1.77	1.35	1.73	1.37
Cisco	1.11	1.22	1.71	1.21	1.51	1.06	1.17	0.90	1.24	0.94	1.21	1.34
Coca Cola	0.75	0.46	0.66	0.52	0.72	0.57	0.59	0.52	0.59	0.52	0.60	0.51
Deere	1.54	1.29	1.27	1.45	1.47	1.39	1.75	1.69	1.56	1.31	1.53	1.37
Dell Computer	0.94	1.35	1.14	1.04	1.23	1.06	1.41	1.31	1.35	1.27	1.41	1.19
Dupont	1.11	0.96	1.13	1.02	0.98	1.02	1.36	1.31	1.37	1.09	1.39	1.04
Eastman Chemical	1.34	1.06	0.94	1.02	0.93	1.05	1.86	1.35	1.87	1.19	1.92	1.15
Exxon/Mobil	1.20	1.00	0.84	1.00	0.92	0.82	0.50	0.84	0.47	1.01	0.48	0.95
Federal Express	1.10	1.03	0.48	0.98	0.85	1.11	0.99	1.14	1.17	1.12	1.17	1.01
Ford	1.51	1.71	1.94	1.86	2.39	2.34	2.62	1.95	2.53	1.84	2.41	1.76
General Electric	0.84	0.89	0.71	0.93	0.63	1.15	1.43	1.62	1.57	1.46	1.64	1.35
General Motors	1.31	2.00	1.06	1.73	2.01	2.19	NA	NA	NA	NA	NA	1.65
Hewlett Packard	1.18	1.20	1.85	0.97	0.13	0.47	1.04	0.79	1.04	0.86	1.01	1.13
Home Depot	1.17	1.06	1.44	1.05	0.87	1.27	0.65	0.90	0.74	1.07	0.78	0.95
IBM	1.01	0.84	1.64	0.87	0.99	0.72	0.79	0.69	0.75	0.62	0.72	0.68
Intel	1.26	1.68	1.85	1.45	1.64	1.05	1.18	0.74	1.15	0.83	1.12	0.96
J. B. Hunt Transport	1.28	1.32	1.07	1.33	0.66	1.11	1.06	1.04	0.95	1.03	0.94	1.00
Johnson & Johnson	0.60	0.55	0.20	0.54	0.39	0.35	0.53	0.54	0.58	0.52	0.60	0.61
Lockheed Martin	0.75	0.64	0.03	0.67	0.62	0.76	1.09	0.83	1.04	0.90	0.96	0.89
Lowe's	1.21	0.93	0.89	1.05	1.14	1.27	0.97	0.98	1.06	1.15	1.01	1.07
Merck	0.59	0.77	0.85	0.83	0.85	0.79	0.81	0.70	0.80	0.64	0.72	0.64
Microsoft	0.93	1.18	1.18	0.97	0.95	0.87	1.01	0.80	1.04	0.94	1.04	0.89
Motorola	1.44	1.44	1.36	1.46	2.14	1.80	1.97	1.32	1.75	1.36	1.71	1.14
Pepsi Cola	0.58	0.50	1.42	0.60	0.33	0.46	0.53	0.53	0.53	0.51	0.55	0.51
Pfizer	1.08	0.83	0.76	0.79	0.69	0.67	0.70	0.69	0.69	0.81	0.69	0.75
Procter & Gamble	0.59	0.64	0.24	0.53	0.66	0.56	0.56	0.69	0.56	0.59	0.51	0.64
Southwest Airlines	0.89	1.60	0.99	1.55	0.10	1.26	0.87	1.04	1.07	0.87	1.08	0.93
Starbuck's	1.01	0.99	0.70	1.30	1.22	1.25	1.20	1.08	1.30	0.94	1.25	0.98
Target	0.80	0.94	1.28	0.97	0.83	1.16	1.16	1.01	1.04	0.90	0.94	0.97
Texas Instruments	1.47	1.52	2.00	1.50	1.85	1.11	1.16	0.79	1.09	0.82	1.07	0.94
Tyco	1.17	1.19	1.29	1.04	0.68	1.21	1.25	1.22	1.25	1.01	1.17	1.12
Tyson Foods	0.72	0.98	0.90	0.96	0.88	1.20	1.38	1.08	1.19	1.06	1.17	1.04
United Parcel Service	0.89	0.83	0.53	0.90	0.86	0.96	0.80	0.90	0.83	0.91	0.82	0.81
United Technologies	1.05	0.99	0.73	0.87	1.06	1.03	0.95	0.98	0.99	0.98	1.01	0.97
Wal-Mart	0.84	0.82	0.60	0.84	0.14	0.74	0.20	0.64	0.28	0.64	0.33	0.63
Xerox	1.15	1.02	1.90	0.99	0.88	0.87	1.44	1.31	1.47	1.30	1.58	1.31

Source: Barra (July, 2006; June, 2007; June, 2008; June, 2009; June, 2010; June, 2011)
Note: Historical beta results are based on a 12-60-month regression against the S&P 500 depending on data availability
2011 data represents Motorola Solutions for Motorola

EXAMPLE 4.A.1 Effect of Market Return and Beta on Cost of Equity Capital

Using the CAPM, determine the change in the expected return on a stock having a risk-free return of 5 percent and values of β ranging from 0 to 2 when the expected overall market return is 8 percent, 9 percent, 10 percent, 11 percent, and 12 percent.

Figure 4.A.2 provides the security market lines for the five expected market return values. Notice how the slope of the SML changes with changes in the expected overall market return. Also, notice that when β equals 0, the expected return is the risk-free market return, regardless of the expected overall market return. Finally, notice that when β equals 1, the expected return is the expected overall market return, regardless of the risk-free market return.

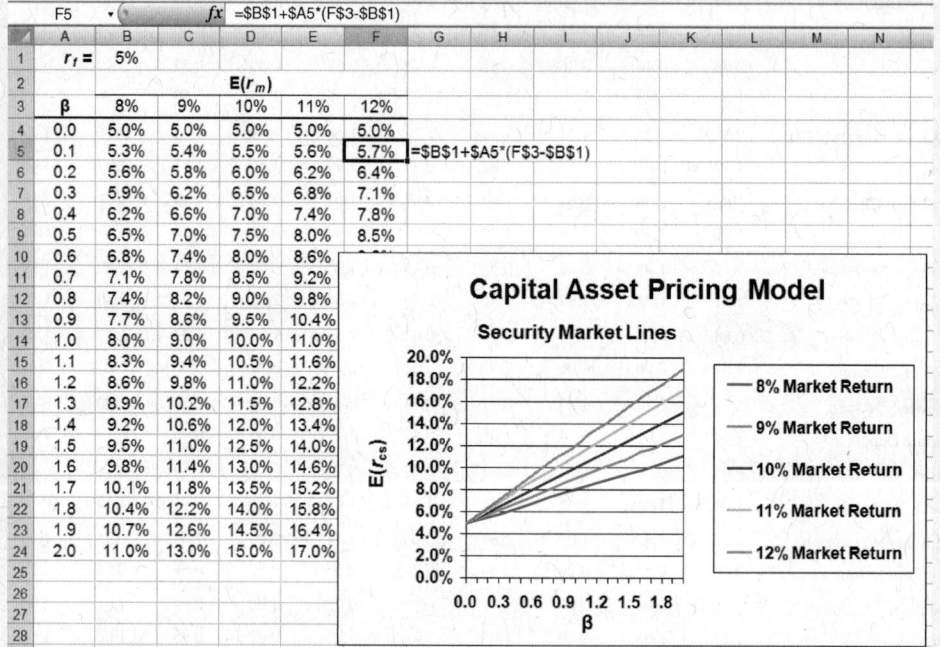

F5		fx	=$B$1+$A5*(F$3-$B$1)					

	A	B	C	D	E	F	G
1	r_f =	5%					
2				$E(r_m)$			
3	β	8%	9%	10%	11%	12%	
4	0.0	5.0%	5.0%	5.0%	5.0%	5.0%	
5	0.1	5.3%	5.4%	5.5%	5.6%	5.7%	=$B$1+$A5*(F$3-$B$1)
6	0.2	5.6%	5.8%	6.0%	6.2%	6.4%	
7	0.3	5.9%	6.2%	6.5%	6.8%	7.1%	
8	0.4	6.2%	6.6%	7.0%	7.4%	7.8%	
9	0.5	6.5%	7.0%	7.5%	8.0%	8.5%	
10	0.6	6.8%	7.4%	8.0%	8.6%		
11	0.7	7.1%	7.8%	8.5%	9.2%		
12	0.8	7.4%	8.2%	9.0%	9.8%		
13	0.9	7.7%	8.6%	9.5%	10.4%		
14	1.0	8.0%	9.0%	10.0%	11.0%		
15	1.1	8.3%	9.4%	10.5%	11.6%		
16	1.2	8.6%	9.8%	11.0%	12.2%		
17	1.3	8.9%	10.2%	11.5%	12.8%		
18	1.4	9.2%	10.6%	12.0%	13.4%		
19	1.5	9.5%	11.0%	12.5%	14.0%		
20	1.6	9.8%	11.4%	13.0%	14.6%		
21	1.7	10.1%	11.8%	13.5%	15.2%		
22	1.8	10.4%	12.2%	14.0%	15.8%		
23	1.9	10.7%	12.6%	14.5%	16.4%		
24	2.0	11.0%	13.0%	15.0%	17.0%		
25							
26							
27							
28							

FIGURE 4.A.2
Security Market Lines for Three Market Return Values in the *CAPM* Formula.

EXAMPLE 4.A.2 PepsiCo's *WACC*

PepsiCo determines its cost of capital using a *WACC* approach. To estimate the cost of debt capital, current market estimates are used and are updated quarterly. A recent estimate of the after-tax cost of debt produced a result of 4 percent.

To estimate the cost of equity capital, PepsiCo uses CAPM. Recently, a 10-year risk-free rate of 5 percent, an expected market return of 10 percent, and a β of 0.75 were used. The risk-free rate is based on the 10-year U.S. Treasury yield. The value of the risk-free rate is updated quarterly; the value of β is based on a 5-year historical record.

Using PepsiCo's values of the CAPM parameters, what is its cost of equity?

$$E(r_{cs}) = 5\% + 0.75(10\% - 5\%) = 8.75\%$$

Based on a 70/30 split between equity and debt capital, what is PepsiCo's *WACC*?

$$WACC = 0.7(8.75) + 0.3(4) = 7.325\%$$

FE-LIKE PROBLEMS

1. When using the "shortest life" planning horizon, what issue should you explicitly consider for alternatives whose cash flow profiles extend longer than the "shortest life"?
   a. Determination of salvage values for truncated cash flows
   b. The validity of the assumption that cash flow profiles are repetitive
   c. Both (a) and (b)
   d. Neither (a) nor (b)

2. Given the following information about sources of capital, what is the appropriate weighted average cost of capital to use in determining *MARR*?

Source	Before-TaxCost	After-TaxCost	Proportion of Total Funds
Loans	10%	6.6%	0.20
Bonds	15%	9.9%	0.50
Retained Earnings	—	12%	0.30

   a. 9.87 percent
   b. 10.55 percent
   c. 12.42 percent
   d. 13.10 percent

3. When using the "longest life" planning horizon, what issue(s) might you have to consider for alternatives whose cash flow profiles are shorter than the "longest life"?
   a. Determination of salvage values for any truncated cash flows
   b. The validity of the assumption that cash flow profiles are repetitive
   c. Both (a) and (b)
   d. Neither (a) nor (b)

4. Kooche Company plans to invest $1,000,000 in projects next year. Of that, $700,000 will be provided through debt capital with a before-tax cost of 7.3 percent. The remaining $300,000 will be provided through equity capital at a cost of 6.5 percent. Kooche's corporate tax rate is 40 percent. What is the weighted average cost of capital?
   a. 5.02 percent
   b. 6.50 percent
   c. 7.06 percent
   d. 13.80 percent

5. Three alternatives are being considered. Alternative A has a useful life of 3 years; Alternative B, 5 years; and Alternative C, 6 years. Using the longest life approach, what is the planning horizon?
   a. 6 years
   b. 14 years
   c. 18 years
   d. 30 years

6. Three alternatives are being considered. Alternative A has a useful life of 5 years; Alternative B, 6 years; and Alternative C, 8 years. Using the least-common-multiple approach, what is the planning horizon?
   a. 30 years
   b. 48 years
   c. 120 years
   d. 240 years

7. Three alternatives are being considered. Alternative A has a useful life of 6 years; Alternative B, 2 years; and Alternative C, 3 years. What is the difference (in years) between the planning horizons determined by the longest life approach and the least-common-multiple approach?
   a. 0 years
   b. 6 years
   c. 12 years
   d. 30 years

8. Which of the following best represents the relationship between the weighted average cost of capital (*WACC*) and the minimum attractive rate of return (*MARR*)?
   a. *WACC* and *MARR* are unrelated.
   b. *WACC* is a lower bound for *MARR*.
   c. *WACC* is an upper bound for *MARR*.
   d. $MARR \leq WACC$.

9. Which of the following is true about the minimum attractive rate of return (*MARR*) used in judging the economic value of projects?
   a. *MARR* has no bearing on engineering projects.
   b. *MARR* is the same for all companies.
   c. *MARR* is usually much smaller than the interest rate used in discounted cash flow analysis.
   d. The value of *MARR* is usually determined by management and is based on many factors.

10. The after-tax cost of capital for a loan is less than the effective interest rate on the loan for which following reason?

a. Discounting

b. Inflation

c. *MARR*

d. Tax deductions

11. The "weights" in the weighted average cost of capital (*WACC*) approach are usually determined based on which of the following?

    a. 1/*n* where *n* is the number of sources

    b. Negotiations with fund providers

    c. Proportion of funds obtained from each source

    d. The ratio of the after-tax cost for each source

12. Within the context of engineering economy, beta (β) symbolizes which of the following?

a. The corporate tax rate

b. The price of a company's preferred stock

c. The ratio of common stock price to preferred stock price

d. The volatility of a stock relative to the overall market

13. When calculating the weighted average cost of capital, the costs of which of the following types of capital include a $(1 - T)$ multiplier, where T is the effective tax rate?

    a. Debt capital

    b. Equity capital

    c. Both (a) and (b)

    d. Neither (a) nor (b)

PROBLEMS

Section 4.1

1. For each of the following categories, describe some of the difficulties that you would face in estimating appropriate values to be used in conducting an economic analysis.

    a. Cash flows

    b. *MARR*

    c. Planning horizon

2. Reconsider the categories in Question 1. What sources of information would you consult in order to develop the most accurate estimates for an economic analysis?

Section 4.2

3. If an annual worth analysis is used to compare alternatives having different lives, what implicit assumption is being made about the planning horizon?

 4. Consider the net cash flows (NCF) and salvage values (SV) shown below for each of the two feasible alternatives for an economic analysis. Alternatives 1 and 2 have lives of 3 and 5 years, respectively. Assume each alternative can be renewed indefinitely with the same NCF and SV profiles.

	Alternative 1		Alternative 2	
EOY	NCF1	SV1	NCF2	SV2
0	−$50,000	$50,000	−$80,000	$80,000
1	$25,000	$25,000	$35,000	$50,000
2	$30,000	$10,000	$45,000	$20,000
3	$35,000	$0	$50,000	$10,000
4			$55,000	$0
5			$60,000	$0

    a. If the least-common-multiple-of-lives approach is used, specify the planning horizon and the complete set of cash flows for each alternative.

b. If the shortest life approach is used, specify the planning horizon and the complete set of cash flows for each alternative.

c. If a fixed planning horizon of 2 years is used, specify the complete set of cash flows for each alternative.

5. Three alternatives are being considered to attract new clients to a health club. A jogging track has an expected useful life of 8 years; a stationary bike 4 years, and a treadmill 6 years. What is the length of the planning horizon for each of the following approaches?

a. Least-common-multiple planning horizon

b. Shortest life planning horizon

c. Longest life planning horizon

6. Consider the net cash flows (NCF) and salvage values (SV) shown below. Assume the alternatives can be indefinitely renewed with the same cash flows and salvage values. Specify the planning horizon and complete set of cash flows for each alternative using each of the following:

EOY	Alternative 1		Alternative 2	
	NCF	SV	NCF	SV
0	−$100	$100	−$70	$70
1	$20	$40	$30	$50
2	$20	$20	$40	$30
3	$40		$50	
4	$60			

a. Least common multiple of lives

b. Shortest life among alternatives

c. Longest life among alternatives

7. Alternatives 1, 2, and 3 have lives of 3, 4, and 6 years, respectively. Their net cash flow (NCF) and salvage value (SV) profiles are as follows:

EOY	Alternative 1		Alternative 2		Alternative 3	
	NCF1	SV1	NCF2	SV2	NCF3	SV3
0	−$20,000	−	−$40,000	$40,000	−$70,000	$70,000
1	$8,000	−	$20,000	$30,000	$30,000	$50,000
2	$8,000	−	$20,000	$20,000	$30,000	$30,000
3	$28,000	−	$20,000	$10,000	$30,000	$20,000
4			$20,000	0	$30,000	$10,000
5					$30,000	$5,000
6					$30,000	$2,000

Additional explanation is necessary: the NCF profile of Alternative 1 that is shown above is the net result of a $20,000/year lease payment payable at the beginning of each year, plus an end-of-year net revenue of $28,000. This lease arrangement may be renewed in 3-year increments; however, premature cancellation of the lease results in a lease termination penalty (cost) of $10,000 at the time of cancellation.

The NCFs of all other alternatives are expected to repeat indefinitely as shown.

a. If a least-common-multiple-of-lives approach is to be used, specify the planning horizon and the complete set of cash flows for each alternative.

b. Repeat (a) using the shortest life approach.

    c. Repeat (a) using the longest life approach.

    d. Repeat (a) using a standard planning horizon of 2 years.

    e. Repeat (a) using a standard planning horizon of 5 years.

8. Three assets are being considered. Assets A, B, and C have natural lives of 4, 5, and 6 years and first costs of $12,000, $20,000, and $30,000, respectively. There will be no salvage value at the end of each asset's life. Market value decreases in a straight-line manner for each. Identical assets will be used to succeed themselves if the planning horizon exceeds their natural life. The assets are needed for a strategic venture that is expected to last 7 years.

    a. What is the most appropriate planning horizon for evaluation of these assets?

    b. What is the salvage value of each alternative at the end of the planning horizon determined in (a)?

9. Two alternatives, Alpha and Beta, have the net cash flow (NCF) and salvage value (SV) profiles shown in the table below for their first cycles. Both alternatives can be repeated; however, the cash flow profiles and salvage value will change. Renewal of Alpha will cost 50 percent more for the initial investment (i.e., first cost will be $150,000 for the second cycle). Salvage values are adjusted based on the new first cost within each cycle. Further renewals of Alpha will cause the initial investment to increase 50 percent over the previous cycle. Annual revenues for Alpha are expected to continue increasing $10,000 per year indefinitely. Renewals of Beta will cost 60 percent more for the initial investment for each renewal. Salvage values for each cycle are adjusted based on each cycle's initial cost. Annual revenues for Beta are expected to continue increasing at $10,000 per year indefinitely.

Specify the complete set of cash flows for each of the following planning horizons:

	Alpha		Beta	
EOY	**NCF**	**SV (% of First Cost)**	**NCF**	**SV (% of First Cost)**
0	−$100,000	100%	−$160,000	100%
1	50,000	50%	80,000	62.5%
2	60,000	20%	90,000	25%
3	70,000	0%	100,000	12.5%

    a. 2 years

    b. 3 years

    c. 4 years

    d. 5 years

    e. 10 years

10. Consider the two one-shot investment alternatives shown in the table below. Neither alternative is expected to be available again in the future, but it is expected that investment options returning *MARR* will always be available.

EOY	0	1	2	3	4	5	6	7
Alternative W	−$100,000	$20,000	$20,000	$50,000	$80,000	$110,000		
Alternative X	−$150,000	$40,000	$45,000	$50,000	$55,000	$60,000	$65,000	$70,000

Determine the following.

    a. What is the length of the planning horizon?

    b. What measure of worth is preferred?

    c. What measure of worth should be avoided?

    d. Which alternative is preferred if *MARR* is 8 percent?

11. The city planning commission would like to create a fund to provide maintenance on a newly constructed bridge over Rain Swollen Creek. The commission estimates that it will cost $2,000/year to maintain the bridge. A one-time deposit is to be made today into the fund to pay for all expected future maintenance expenses. Each year, starting 1 year from now, the maintenance costs will be withdrawn from the fund. The city expects that it can invest the money in the fund to earn 5 percent per year.

   a. If the planning horizon is 10 years, how much must be deposited into the fund?
   b. If the planning horizon is 20 years, how much must be deposited into the fund?
   c. If the planning horizon is 30 years, how much must be deposited into the fund?
   d. If the planning horizon is 40 years, how much must be deposited into the fund?
   e. If the planning horizon is 50 years, how much must be deposited into the fund?
   f. If the planning horizon is infinite, how much must be deposited into the fund?
   g. If the commission rounds all fund requests to the nearest thousand, at what planning horizon does the fund deposit become equivalent to an infinite horizon?

12. Reconsider Problem 11. Plot a graph that shows the planning horizon as the independent variable and the required deposit as the dependent variable. Plot planning horizons from 1 to 250 with a step size of 1.

13. Enhance your plot from Problem 12 with the following:
   a. Add a curve to your plot for 4 percent interest
   b. Add a curve to your plot for 6 percent interest
   c. Add a curve to your plot for 15 percent interest
   d. What generalizations can you make from your plot?

Section 4.3

14. A company's board of directors is considering the plan for capital expenditures. A director asks the chief financial officer how the appropriate rate of return is set for evaluating capital expenditures. The CFO responds that the company uses the after-tax weighted average cost of capital and that the current value is 13 percent. If the combined tax rate is 45 percent, the before-tax cost of borrowed capital is 14 percent, and equity comprises 60 percent of the capitalization of the company, what is the percent return to shareholders?

15. To help fund an addition to your house, you borrow $5,000 from your bank. The conditions of your loan state that the interest rate is 10 percent compounded monthly. Assuming a tax rate of 40 percent (paid annually), determine the following:
   a. The effective before-tax cost of capital
   b. The effective after-tax cost of capital

16. Anderson Machines' common stock has a present trading price of $75/share. An annual dividend of $10/share is paid to all shareholders.
   a. If the share price has been stable over the past 3 years, determine the cost of equity capital.
   b. If the share price has been increasing at an annualized rate of 4 percent, determine the cost of equity capital.

17. Thumbtack's capital structure is shown in table below. If taxes are paid annually and Thumbtack's combined tax rate is 36 percent, determine the weighted average cost of capital.

Loans	12%/yr/semi	$3,000,000
Bonds	8%/yr/qtr	$4,500,000
Common Stock	$72/share price; $8/shr/yr dividend; 1%/yr share price growth	$2,000,000
Retained Earnings		$1,500,000

18. Due to the need for expanded production, Wilson and Wilson Company decides to build a new factory. The company decides to fund the investment from the sources listed below.

Source	Funding
Loan	$3,750,000
Bonds	$750,000
Common Stock	$5,000,000
Retained Earnings	$500,000

The loan has a before-tax effective annual rate of 10.25 percent. The bonds have an after-tax effective annual rate of 7 percent. The stock price is stable and is currently trading at $200/share with a $14 annual dividend. Wilson and Wilson is in a 35 percent tax bracket and pays taxes annually. Determine the weighted average cost of capital.

19. Reconsider Problem 18. Management has decided that the $5 million raised through stock should be split between common stock and preferred stock. Common stock will be used to raise $3,000,000 and preferred stock $2,000,000. The characteristics of the common stock will not change as a result of the preferred stock offering. The preferred stock will sell for $100/share, pay an annual dividend of $5/share, and have a cost of selling of $6 per share. The loan and the bonds remain unchanged. Determine the new weighted average cost of capital.

20. Great Eats needs $2,000,000 to finance a new restaurant in Mytown. The project will be funded from the following sources.

Source	Funding	Cost of Funding
Loan	$700,000	8%/yr/mo
Bonds	$500,000	6%/yr/qtr
Common Stock	$400,000	$0.75 dividend/yr 5%/yr stock price growth rate
Retained Earnings	$400,000	

Great Eats' effective tax rate is 34 percent with taxes paid annually. Current stock price is $15/share. Management determines *MARR* based on the weighted average cost of capital plus a constant. Currently the constant is 4 percent (i.e., if *WACC* is 6 percent, *MARR* is 10 percent). Determine the appropriate value of *MARR* for evaluating the project.

21. The management of Could Do Better has asked you to explain the concept of weighted average cost of capital. In particular, they are confused that you are encouraging the use of debt capital to fund projects even though the CFO's data shows that the cost of debt capital is higher than the cost of equity capital. The CFO's data are shown below.

Cost of Debt Capital (before tax)	12%
Cost of Equity Capital	10%
Effective Tax Rate	36%

a. In preparation for your presentation, you create a graph whose x-axis is Percent of Funds from Debt Capital from 0 to 100 with a step size of 10. The y-axis is Cost of Capital. There are five curves on your chart: (1) Cost of Debt Capital before Tax, (2) Cost of Equity Capital, (3) Cost of Debt Capital After Tax, (4) Weighted Average Cost of Capital Before Tax, and (5) Weighted Average Cost of Capital After Tax.

b. Using your chart, (i) explain why the end points of curves (4) and (5) fall where they do, (ii) explain why one of the slopes of curves (4) and (5) is positive and one is negative, and (iii) defend your recommendation encouraging the use of debt capital.

22. To become more globally competitive, the Ajax Manufacturing Corporation needs to invest $1,000,000 in new equipment. After careful analysis, the corporate engineering economist has determined that in order for the investment to be attractive, the cost of capital should be no greater than 10.509 percent. The investment is to be financed through a combination of two sources: (1) a bank loan and (2) company common stock. The bank loan, regardless of amount, has

a before-tax effective interest rate of 9.60 percent/yr/yr. Company stock is selling for a stable price of $100/share and pays an annual dividend of $11.90. Ajax's effective tax rate is 34 percent with taxes paid annually. If the cost of capital is to be exactly 10.509 percent, how much of the investment should be financed from each source?

23. Lahoma Enterprises, Inc., needs $15 million to finance a major product development. The project will be financed from the following sources:

Source	Amount	Comments
Loans	$2,600,000	14%/yr with semiannual compounding
Bonds	$4,100,000	12% bond interest rate, quarterly premiums
Stock	$5,000,000	$6.50 dividend on selling price of $65/share
Retained Earnings	$3,300,000	

Lahoma Enterprises' effective tax rate is 34 percent with taxes paid annually. The stock price is stable. Management determines *MARR* based on the weighted average cost of capital plus 8 percent (i.e., if the weight average cost of capital is 12 percent, *MARR* is 20 percent). Determine the appropriate value of *MARR* for evaluating this project.

24. Repeat Problem 23 assuming that the stock price is growing at 3 percent per year.

25. Repeat Problem 23 assuming the stock offering will be preferred stock rather than common stock. The preferred stock will sell for $120/share, pay a $9 annual dividend, and have a cost of selling of $0.50 per share.

26. The GOJO Steam Cleaning Corporation is preparing to purchase a new mobile steam cleaning fleet for $5,500,000. The proposed sources of capital are $2,000,000 from a bank loan, $1,000,000 from a bond offering, $1,000,000 from the sale of common stock, and $1,500,000 from retained earnings. The specifics for each source are listed below. GOJO is a growing company with a stock price growth rate of 8 percent per year. GOJO is in a 36 percent tax bracket and pays taxes annually. Determine the weighted average cost of capital.

Bank Loan	15% before-tax interest rate
Bond Issuance	12% bond interest rate with quarterly premiums
Stock Sale	$2.00 dividends on a selling price of $70 per share

27. Harold's U-Store-It is using a loan to finance the construction of a new storage facility. The loan is for $1,000,000 to be repaid over 20 years with annual payments. The mortgage interest rate is 5 percent/yr. Harold's effective tax rate is 45 percent. What is the cost of capital for the loan?

28. S&R Catering is selling bonds to finance a new franchise in Yukon. The total amount of funding is $500,000 with each bond having a face value of $500 and a 10-year life. The annual bond interest rate is 6 percent with premiums paid annually. The bonds are expected to sell at face value. If S&R's effective tax rate is 36 percent, determine the effective after-tax cost of the bonds if taxes are paid annually.

29. Repeat Problem 28 assuming that S&R enhances the bonds by raising the interest rate to 7 percent and discounting the selling price by 10 percent of the face value.

30. Cowboy Construction buys materials on account from Highes. Highes offers a 2 percent discount for invoices paid within 10 days. Full payment is due within 90 days. Cowboy Construction routinely pays its invoices on the ninetieth day. If Cowboy's effective tax rate is 42 percent, what is the cost of capital for accounts payable?

31. Repeat Problem 30 assuming that Highes has changed its invoice terms such that full payment is due within 60 days. Cowboy Construction pays invoices in full on the sixtieth day.

32. A team of Eastman Chemical Company's process engineers has proposed a minor expansion project for an existing 100 percent ownership plant located in Canada. The expansion of this mature business will utilize a licensed

technology that is currently practiced widely by industry. Twenty percent of the justification is based on cost savings with the remainder attributed to revenue growth. The project is not a venture capital candidate, and 50 percent of the funds required are allocated capital. Based on the Eastman hurdle rate calculator and a base rate of 9 percent, what discount rate should be used for this project?

 33. Eastman's vice president for strategic planning, together with members from the business team and manufacturing, are exploring the possibility of building a greenfield plant through a joint venture in Brazil. Eastman would operate the plant and maintain a 51 percent controlling interest. The plant would support a mature business, and the technology to be used is an existing technology already employed by Eastman. No allocated capital or venture capital would be used. In anticipation of synergies among the joint owners of the business, it is estimated that 20 percent of the benefits would result from cost savings, and 80 percent would result from new revenue. Based on the Eastman hurdle rate calculator and a base rate of 9 percent, what discount rate should be used for this project?

34. Reconsider Problem 33. Due to an economic downturn, one of the joint venture partners has withdrawn from the project. The remaining partners have agreed to redistribute the withdrawing partner's share. The result for Eastman is an increase in ownership from 51 percent to 82 percent. What discount rate should be used for the project?

35. Reconsider Problem 33. Due to political unrest in Brazil, the CFO has suggested that either the joint venture be moved to Chile or that the location risk factor for Brazil be increased by adding an additional 0.5 percent risk premium. What discount rate should be used for the project under each of these two cases?

Appendix

36. Interpret the meaning of each of the following:
    a. β less than one
    b. β equals 0
    c. β equals 1
    d. β greater than 1

37. Using Table 4.A.1 as a guide, respond to the following questions based on the 2007 Predicted β.
    a. Which corporation has the lowest volatility?
    b. Which corporation has the highest volatility?
    c. Consider the three corporations with the three lowest volatilities. What do they have in common?
    d. Consider the two corporations with the two highest volatilities. What do they have in common?
    e. Which corporation has the largest difference (positive or negative) between its historical and predicted beta? Given the comparative values of the two betas, how would you characterize the "rare event" (positive, negative, or neutral from an investor's perspective)?

38. Using the CAPM model, calculate the cost of equity capital for each of the following situations:
    a. Risk-free rate is 6 percent, expected market return is 11 percent, β is 0.75
    b. Risk-free rate is 6 percent, expected market return is 11 percent, β is 0.90
    c. Risk-free rate is 6 percent, expected market return is 11 percent, β is 1.20
    d. Risk-free rate is 6 percent, expected market return is 11 percent, β is 0.00
    e. Risk-free rate is 6 percent, expected market return is 11 percent, β is 1.00

39. For each situation, calculate the *WACC*:
    a. Risk-free rate is 5 percent, expected market return is 11 percent, β is 0.75, after-tax cost of debt capital is 5 percent, split between debt/equity capital is 60/40
    b. Risk-free rate is 5 percent, expected market return is 11 percent, β is 0.90, after-tax cost of debt capital is 4 percent, split between debt/equity capital is 50/50
    c. Risk-free rate is 5 percent, expected market return is 11 percent, β is 1.20, after-tax cost of debt capital is 6 percent, split between debt/equity capital is 20/80
    d. Risk-free rate is 5 percent, expected market return is 11 percent, β is 0.00, after-tax cost of debt capital is 6 percent, split between debt/equity capital is 80/20
    e. Risk-free rate is 5 percent, expected market return is 11 percent, β is 1.00, after-tax cost of debt capital is 5 percent, split between debt/equity capital is 60/40

Chapter 5

PRESENT WORTH ANALYSIS

ConocoPhillips employs thousands of engineers. This example, from offshore drilling and exploration at the Ekofisk Field in the Norwegian North Sea, demonstrates the need for considerable engineering expertise at ConocoPhillips. (Courtesy of ConocoPhillips)

ConocoPhillips

ConocoPhillips is the third-largest integrated energy company in the United States, based on market capitalization and oil and natural gas proved reserves and production; it is also the second-largest refiner in the United States. Worldwide, of non-government-controlled companies, ConocoPhillips has the seventh-largest proved reserves and is the fourth-largest refiner. An international, integrated energy company, it is known globally for its technological expertise in exploration and production, reservoir management and exploitation, 3-D seismic technology, high-grade petroleum coke upgrading, and sulfur removal.

Headquartered in Houston, Texas, ConocoPhillips operates in more than 30 countries. As of December 31, 2010, the company had 29,700 employees worldwide and assets of $156 billion. Its capital expenditures and investments in 2010 totaled $9.8 billion; total revenues were $198.7 billion. Its debt-to-capital ratio at the end of 2010 was 25 percent, versus 31 percent at the end of 2009.

The company's worldwide core business activities include: petroleum exploration and production; petroleum refining, marketing, supply, and transportation; and natural gas gathering, processing, and marketing. Also, the company invests in emerging businesses—power generation, carbon-to-liquids, technology solutions, and emerging technologies such as renewable fuels and alternative energy sources—that provide current and potential future growth opportunities.

In its Form 10-K for 2010, the company provided the following comments regarding "standardized measure of discounted future net cash flows relating to proved oil and gas reserve quantities:" "In accordance with SEC and FASB requirements, amounts for 2010 and 2009 were computed using 12-month average prices and end-of-year costs (adjusted only for existing contractual changes), appropriate statutory tax rates and a prescribed 10 percent discount factor. Twelve-month average prices are calculated on the unweighted arithmetic average of the first-day-of-the-month price for each month within the 12-month period prior to the end of the reporting period. . . . For all years, continuation of year-end economic conditions was assumed. The calculations were based on estimates of proved reserves, which are revised over time as new data become available.''

ConocoPhillips and numerous other organizations rely on present worth analysis in making investment decisions. To list the other firms that use present worth analysis would surely require listing every organization that uses discounted cash flow methods.

Present worth analysis is the most popular DCF method of comparing investments. That is why we chose to use it in every previous chapter: in Chapter 1, it was used to demonstrate the use of time value of money in Examples 1.1 and 1.2; in Chapter 2, it was used to solve many examples, including Examples 2.11 and 2.12; in Chapter 3, it was used frequently in the examples, including the comparison of the four loan repayment methods (Examples 3.2 and 3.3) and the three mortgage plans (Example 3.8); and in Chapter 4, it was used to demonstrate the challenges involved in choosing a planning horizon when alternatives have differing lives (Example 4.1).

5-1 INTRODUCTION

Variously referred to as *present worth, present value*, and *net present value*, present worth analysis is used to evaluate alternative investments in equipment, facilities, land, and so forth, and it is used by corporations and investment bankers to assess mergers, acquisitions, and divestitures (MAD) of companies and divisions of companies. For example, an investment banking firm, Goldman Sachs, was retained by Eastman Chemical Company to assist them in analyzing the costs and benefits to shareholders of splitting the business into two separate companies (chemicals and plastics); although the board of directors ultimately decided not to split the company, present worth analysis was at the heart of Goldman Sachs's work. Likewise, when Russell Corporation retained Goldman Sachs to evaluate an offer from Berkshire Hathaway to acquire the firm, present worth analysis was the principal analytical tool used to organize and present the information needed by the board of directors to make a decision regarding the offer. (The board of directors recommended acceptance of the offer by the shareholders; the shareholders voted affirmatively; and Russell Corporation was acquired by Berkshire Hathaway on August 1, 2006.)

In this chapter, you will learn how results obtained from present worth analysis compare with other methods of measuring economic worth. You will also learn about two measures that are extensions of the present worth method.

5-2 COMPARING ALTERNATIVES

Recall, the fifth step in the 7-step process described in Chapter 1 for performing an engineering economic analysis: *compare the alternatives.* Implicit in this step is a decision regarding the method(s) to be used in making the comparison. The choice of method carries with it a selection of a measure of economic worth.

Systematic Economic Analysis Technique

1. Identify the investment alternatives
2. Define the planning horizon
3. Specify the discount rate
4. Estimate the cash flows
5. **Compare the alternatives**
6. Perform supplementary analyses
7. Select the preferred investment

5.2.1 Measures of Economic Worth

As their names imply, present worth, future worth, and annual worth are measures of economic worth. If you decide to use present worth analysis to compare alternatives, then you have indicated a preference for the use of a single sum of money at a time called "the present" as the basis for comparison; and, in the absence of other nonmonetary considerations, you have chosen as your criterion the maximization of present worth. Alternatively, if you decide to use future worth analysis, then you prefer to use a single sum equivalent at a time called "the future" as the basis for comparison. If, instead of expressing an investment's economic worth as a single sum equivalent—as with present worth and future worth—you prefer to think in terms of an annualized figure, then annual worth would be preferred. Some prefer to express the net economic worth as a rate or percentage—similar to how the cost of capital is expressed; for them, internal rate of return or external rate of return would be preferred. Finally, some prefer to have the net economic worth stated as a percentage of the investment required—the benefit/cost ratio is one method of providing such information.

In this and the next three chapters, we examine eight *DCF* methods used in comparing investment alternatives: present worth, future worth, annual worth, internal rate of return, external rate of return, modified internal rate of return, discounted payback period, and capitalized worth. In Chapter 14, we examine a ninth method, benefit/cost ratio, used in public sector analysis.

The nine *DCF* methods may be described briefly as follows:

1. The present worth (PW) method converts all cash flows to a single sum equivalent at time zero using $i = MARR$.
2. The future worth (FW) method converts all cash flows to a single sum equivalent at the end of the planning horizon using $i = MARR$.
3. The annual worth (AW) method converts all cash flows to an equivalent uniform annual series of cash flows over the planning horizon using $i = MARR$.
4. The internal rate of return (IRR) method determines the interest rate that yields a future worth (or present worth or annual worth) of zero.

5. The external rate of return (ERR) method determines the interest rate that equates the future worth of the invested capital to the future worth of recovered capital (when the latter is computed using the *MARR*.)

6. The modified internal rate of return (MIRR) method determines the interest rate that equates the present worth of invested capital (where the present worth is computed using a finance rate) to the future worth of recovered capital (where the future worth is computed using the *MARR*.)

7. The discounted payback period (*DPBP*) method determines how long it takes for the cumulative present worth to be positive using $i = MARR$.

8. The capitalized worth (CW) determines the present worth (using $i = MARR$) when the planning horizon is infinitely long.

9. The benefit/cost ratio (B/C) method determines the ratio of the present worth of benefits (savings or positive-valued cash flows) to the negative of the present worth of the investment(s) (or negative-valued cash flows) using $i = MARR$.

5.2.2   Ranking and Incremental Methods of Economic Worth

The nine *DCF* methods can be divided into two groups: *ranking* and *incremental* methods.

- Present worth, future worth, annual worth, and capitalized worth are ranking methods; as such, the alternative having the greatest *PW*, *FW*, *AW*, or *CW* over the planning horizon is the economic choice and would be recommended, absent nonmonetary criteria.[1] *DPBP* is also a ranking method, but the goal is to identify the investment alternative with the *smallest* value; however, it is not equivalent to the other ranking methods. From the discussion on planning horizons in Chapter 4, we know that *CW* will be equivalent to *PW*, *FW*, and *AW* if the planning horizon is infinitely long or equal to the least common multiple of lives of the various investment alternatives; otherwise, it is not equivalent to them. *PW*, *FW*, and *AW* are equivalent measures of economic worth; hence, the same recommendation will occur, regardless of which method is used.

- Internal rate of return, external rate of return, modified internal rate of return, and benefit/cost ratio are incremental methods; as such, the preferred alternative is that which satisfies Principle #6: *Money should continue to be invested as long as each additional increment of investment yields a return that is greater than the investor's TVOM.* The *IRR*, *ERR*, and B/C methods are equivalent economic worth methods; as such, the same investment will be recommended, regardless of the method used.

- Six of the nine economic worth methods are equivalent. CW, MIRR, and *DPBP* are not guaranteed to result in a recommendation that is identical to that obtained using any of the six equivalent economic worth methods.

- Incremental solutions that are equivalent to ranking solutions can be obtained using *PW*, *FW*, *AW*, and *CW*. However, there seems to be little reason to employ the more cumbersome incremental solution, since it is much simpler to compute the value of the

---

[1]Rather than make the statement "absent nonmonetary criteria" every time we indicate which investment is recommended, henceforth we assume that the single criterion is monetary and the objective is to maximize economic worth.

PW, *FW*, *AW*, or *CW* and recommend the one having the greatest value over the planning horizon.

Principle #6

Continue to invest as long as each additional increment of investment yields a return that is greater than the investor's *TVOM*.

5.2.3   Before-Tax or After-Tax Analysis?

In using a measure of economic worth to compare investment alternatives, you can employ either *before-tax* or *after-tax* cash flows. However, be consistent! It is *either/or* but *not both* in the same analysis. If the comparison is based on before-tax cash flows, then use a *before-tax MARR*; likewise, if the comparison is based on after-tax cash flows, then use an *after-tax MARR*.

In Chapter 4, the cost of capital calculations incorporated the effects of income taxes. Hence, an after-tax *MARR* was obtained. Also, the Eastman hurdle rate calculator yielded after-tax hurdle rates.

Although we believe it is usually best to perform after-tax economic justifications, we will not cover tax issues until after discussing a variety of methods used to compare economic alternatives. Consequently, in this and the following three chapters, you may consider the analyses to be either before-tax (with before-tax cash flows and a before-tax *MARR*) or after-tax (with after-tax cash flows and an after-tax *MARR*).

Depending on the application, it might be necessary to convert an after-tax rate to a before-tax rate. Recall, in Chapter 4 the weighted average cost of capital was given by Equation 4.1:

$$WACC = (E/V)i_e + (D/V)i_d(1 - itr)$$

where i_e is the expected after-tax return on equity capital, i_d is the before-tax return on debt capital, and *itr* is the combined state and federal income tax rate. To convert the before-tax rate to an after-tax rate, the before-tax rate was multiplied by 1 minus the income tax rate; likewise, to convert an after-tax rate to a before-tax rate, the after-tax rate is divided by 1 minus the income tax rate.[2] Hence, to convert a before-tax *MARR* to an after-tax *MARR*

$$MARR_{BT} \approx MARR_{AT}/(1 - itr) \tag{5.1}$$

EXAMPLE 5.1   Converting an After-Tax *MARR* to a Before-Tax *MARR*

Using Eastman's hurdle rate calculator (described in Chapter 4) for a new plant at a greenfield site, the after-tax *MARR* is determined to be equal to 10 percent. If the firm's incremental income tax rate is 40 percent, what before-tax *MARR* should be used?

$$MARR_{BT} \approx 0.10/(1 - 0.40)$$
$$\approx 0.1667 = 16.67\%$$

---

[2]The conversion is an approximation and not always a good one, as we show in Chapter 10.

5.2.4 Equal or Unequal Lives?

Frequently in the engineering economy literature, the subject of equal-lived versus unequal-lived alternatives is discussed. We addressed this in Chapter 4. However, it is useful to summarize our position on this matter. When comparing investment alternatives, they must be compared over a common time period, called the *planning horizon*. (Recall Principle # 8: *Compare investment alternatives over a common period of time*.) If the duration of the planning horizon differs from the useful lives of the alternatives, then (at the end of the planning horizon) cash flow estimates must be provided for the terminal or salvage values for alternatives with lives greater than the planning horizon; for alternatives having useful lives less than the planning horizon, replacement decisions must be made and cash flow estimates must be provided for the replacements.

> ## Principle #8
>
> Compare investment alternatives over a common period of time.

5.2.5 A Single Alternative

"A single alternative" is an oxymoron. If there is no choice, then there is no alternative. However, when we consider "a single alternative," we are considering doing something versus doing nothing. Recall, in Chapter 1 we noted that the "do nothing" alternative can be an expensive one, because revenues could be declining and costs could be increasing while you are doing nothing. Eastman's acetate yarn experience in the early 1960s, described in the introduction to Chapter 4, is a perfect example of how expensive the do-nothing alternative can be.

Assuming the do-nothing alternative is feasible, you have two options when faced with the question *Should I invest in an opportunity or not?* Invest or don't invest. In evaluating the "invest" option, we assume that the cash flow estimates reflect the differences in doing nothing versus doing something. On that basis,

- when using *PW*, *FW*, and *AW*, we choose to "do something" if the measure of economic worth has a value greater than zero;[3]
- when using the *B/C* method, we choose to "do something" if the *B/C* ratio is greater than 1; and
- when using the IRR, ERR, and MIRR methods, we choose to "do something" if the measure of economic worth has a value greater than the *MARR*.

(For *DPBP*, the decision to invest or not depends on the prescribed acceptable value.) Implicit in the $XW > 0$ (for $X = P, F, A$, and C), $XRR > MARR$ (for $X = I, E$, and MI), and $B/C > 1.0$-requirement is an *opportunity cost* assumption. Namely, we assume we are currently earning a return on our money equal to the *MARR*. Therefore, the decision to invest in a particular opportunity reduces to the following: *Will we make more money by investing here or by leaving our money in an investment pool that earns*

---

[3]As discussed in Section 5.7.1, $CW > 0$ is not a viable test, since the do-nothing alternative is not feasible for most of its applications.

a return equal to the MARR? If we will not make more money by investing in the opportunity in question, then we should leave our money in the investment pool. We also assume the investment in question has risks comparable to those of the investment pool.

5-3 PRESENT WORTH: SINGLE ALTERNATIVE

WILEY
VIDEO LESSON

As noted, when using the present worth method to evaluate whether an investment should be made, the decision depends on whether the present worth is positive. If so, then the investment is recommended. Recalling our work in Chapter 2, the present worth of an investment can be expressed mathematically as follows:

$$PW = \sum_{t=0}^{n} A_t (1+i)^{-t} \tag{5.2}$$

where i is the minimum attractive rate of return (*MARR*).

EXAMPLE 5.2   **A Single Investment Opportunity**

To automatically insert electronic components in printed circuit boards for a cell phone production line, a $500,000 surface mount placement (SMP) machine is being evaluated by a manufacturing engineer at Motorola. Over the 10-year planning horizon, it is estimated that the SMP machine will produce annual after-tax cost savings of $92,500. The engineer estimates the machine will be worth $50,000 at the end of the 10-year period. Based on the firm's 10 percent after-tax *MARR*, should the investment be made?

From our work in Chapter 2, we compute the present worth for the investment:

$$PW = -\$500,000 + \$92,500(P|A\ 10\%,10) + \$50,000(P|F\ 10\%,10)$$
$$= -\$500,000 + \$92,500(6.14457) + \$50,000(0.38554)$$
$$= \$87,649.73$$

or, using Excel®,

$$PW = PV(10\%,10,-92500,-50000)-500000$$
$$= \$87,649.62$$

Since $PW > \$0$, the investment is recommended.

With a present worth of **$87,649.62**, there can be little doubt that the investment is a good one for the company. However, it is useful to examine how the present worth behaves over the 10-year period.

Figure 5.1 shows that the present worth begins at −$500,000 with the purchase of the new machine and increases over the planning horizon to a final value of **$87,649.62**. Notice that the investment "loses money" (has a negative present worth) for the first 8 years. It is only in the ninth year that the present worth becomes positive. Therefore, if something unforeseen occurred, causing the company to abandon the investment before the ninth year, would the investment still be profitable? The answer to the question depends on the SMP machine's salvage value at the time it is abandoned.

	B14	▾	fx	=NPV(B1,B4:B13)+B3	
	A	B	C	D	
1	**MARR =**	**10%**	**(ignores salvage value until EOY = 10)**		
2	**EOY**	**CF**	**Cum(PW)**		
3	0	-$500,000	-$500,000.00	=B3	
4	1	$92,500	-$415,909.09	=NPV($B$1,$B$4:B4)+$B$3	
5	2	$92,500	-$339,462.81	=NPV($B$1,$B$4:B5)+$B$3	
6	3	$92,500	-$269,966.19	=NPV($B$1,$B$4:B6)+$B$3	
7	4	$92,500	-$206,787.45	=NPV($B$1,$B$4:B7)+$B$3	
8	5	$92,500	-$149,352.22	=NPV($B$1,$B$4:B8)+$B$3	
9	6	$92,500	-$97,138.39	=NPV($B$1,$B$4:B9)+$B$3	
10	7	$92,500	-$49,671.26	=NPV($B$1,$B$4:B10)+$B$3	
11	8	$92,500	-$6,519.33	=NPV($B$1,$B$4:B11)+$B$3	
12	9	$92,500	$32,709.70	=NPV($B$1,$B$4:B12)+$B$3	
13	10	$142,500	$87,649.62	=NPV($B$1,$B$4:B13)+$B$3	
14	**PW =**	$87,649.62	=NPV(B1,B4:B13)+B3		
15					

FIGURE 5.1
Plot of Cumulative Present Worth Over the Planning Horizon.

$$PW(i\%) = \sum_{i=0}^{n} A_t(1+i)^{-t}$$

5-4 PRESENT WORTH: MULTIPLE ALTERNATIVES

Ranking Approach. As a ranking method, *PW* is easily applied when choosing the preferred alternative from among several mutually exclusive alternatives: choose the one with the greatest *PW* over the planning horizon. Mathematically, the objective is

$$\underset{\forall j}{\text{Maximize }} PW_j = \sum_{t=0}^{n} A_{jt}(1 + MARR)^{-t} \qquad (5.3)$$

$$\underset{\forall j}{\text{Maximize }} PW_j(i\%) = \sum_{i=0}^{n} A_{jt}(1+i)^{-t}$$

EXAMPLE 5.3 Choosing Between Two Alternatives

Entertainment Engineers, Inc., is an Ohio-based design engineering firm that, among other things, designs rides for amusement and theme parks all over the world. The rides range in complexity from very simple rides for young children to extremely sophisticated rides for adults. Entertainment Engineers employs aerospace, civil, electrical, industrial, materials, and mechanical engineers. Two alternative designs are under consideration for a new ride called the Scream Machine at a theme park located in Florida. The two candidate designs differ in complexity, cost, and predicted revenue. The first alternative design (A) will require an investment of $300,000 and is estimated to produce after-tax revenue of $55,000 annually over a 10-year planning horizon. The second alternative design (B) will require an investment of $450,000 and is expected to generate annual after-tax revenue of $80,000. A negligible salvage value is assumed for both designs. Theme park management could decide to "do nothing"; if so, the present worth of doing nothing will be zero. An after-tax *MARR* of 10 percent is used. Which alternative design, if either, should the theme park select?

Letting A denote the alternative design for the $300,000 initial investment and B denote the other alternative, the present worth of each is shown below:

Alternative A

$$PW_A = -\$300,000 + \$55,000(P|A\ 10\%,10)$$
$$= -\$300,000 + \$55,000(6.14457)$$
$$= \$37,951.35 > \$0.00 \text{ (therefore, } A \text{ is better than doing nothing)}$$

or, using Excel®,

$$PW_A = \text{PV}(10\%,10,-55000)-300000$$
$$= \$37,951.19 > \$0.00 \text{ (therefore, } A \text{ is better than doing nothing)}$$

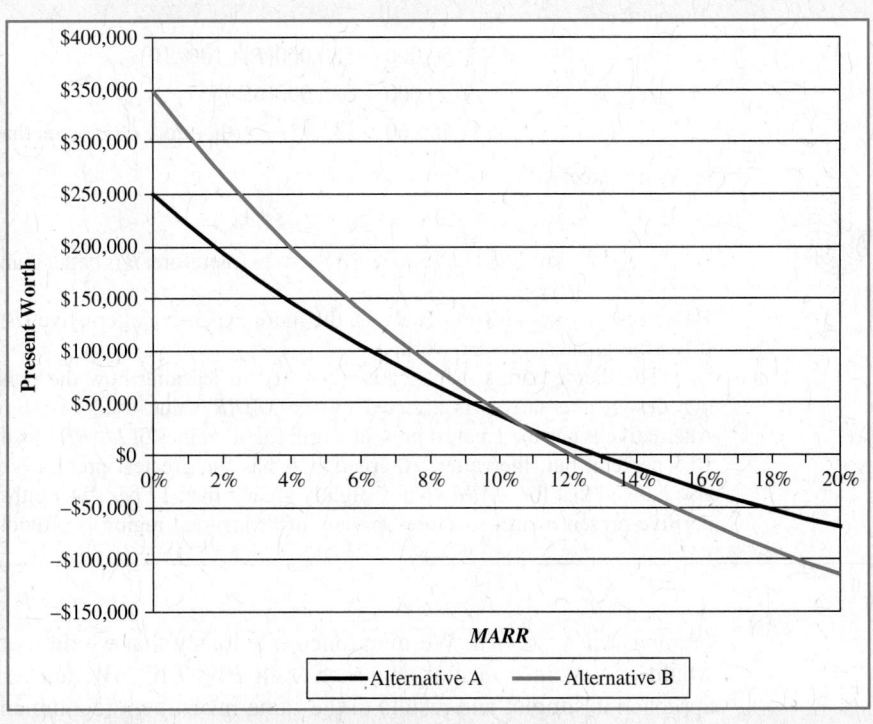

FIGURE 5.2
Plot of Present Worths for Example 5.3.

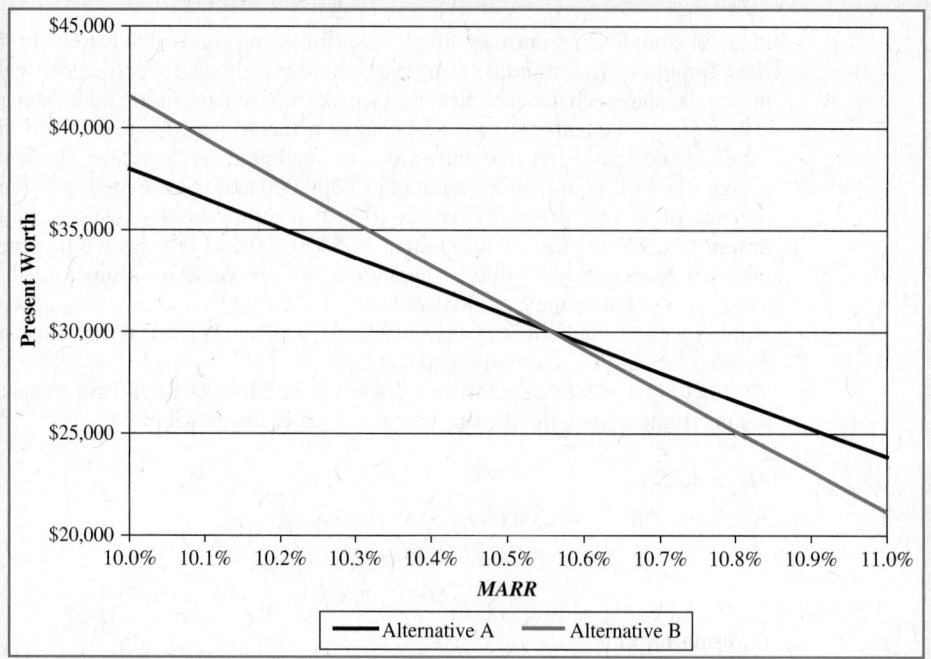

FIGURE 5.3

Close-up of Critical Region of Figure 5.2.

Alternative B

$$PW_B = -\$450,000 + \$80,000(P|A\ 10\%,10)$$

$$= -\$450,000 + \$80,000(6.14457)$$

$$= \$41,565.60 > \$37,951.35 \text{ (therefore, } B \text{ is better than } A)$$

or, using Excel®,

$$PW_B = PV(10\%,10,-80000)-450000$$

$$= \$41,565.37 > \$37,951.19 \text{ (therefore, } B \text{ is better than } A)$$

Based on the present worth analysis, the more expensive alternative (*B*) is recommended. It has the greatest present worth.

The theme park's manager is interested in learning how the present worth for the two design alternatives is affected by the *MARR* value used. As shown in Figure 5.2, Alternative B has the greatest present worth for all values of *MARR* less than approximately 10.5 percent, but, thereafter, Alternative A has the greatest present worth. The manager also noticed that for *MARR* values slightly greater than 12 percent, neither alternative has a positive present worth. A close-up view of the critical region is provided in Figure 5.3.

Incremental Approach. We mentioned previously that we did not know why anyone would use an incremental approach with *PW*, *FW*, *AW*, and *CW*, since a ranking approach is simpler and results in the same investment recommendation. Rather than ask you to accept on faith our claim, we will use an incremental approach to solve the example problem. In doing so, we apply the incremental algorithm shown in Figure 5.4 for all but *PBP* and *DPBP* among the *DCF* economic worth methods.

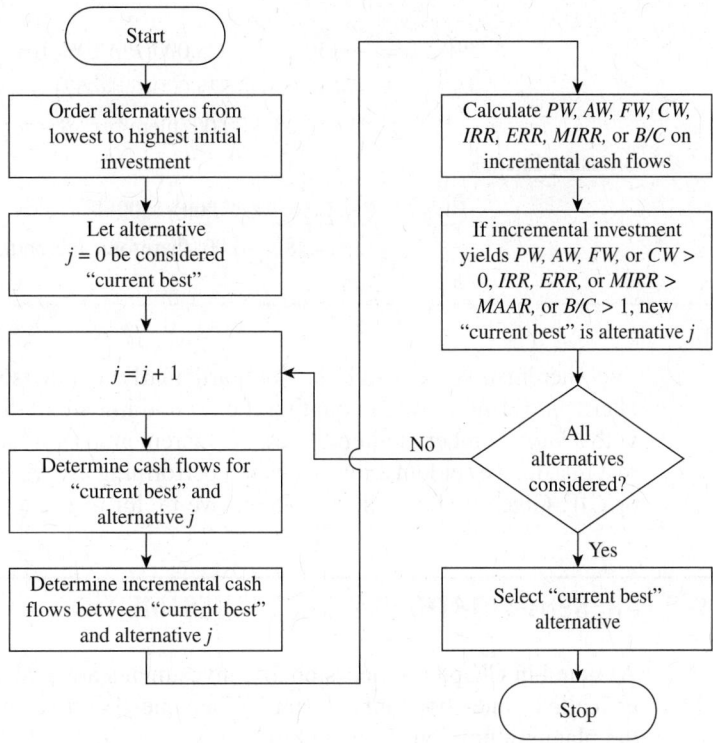

FIGURE 5.4

Flow Chart of Incremental Comparison of Investment Alternatives.

EXAMPLE 5.4   Incremental Solution to Example 5.3

To perform an incremental analysis of the two designs being considered for a new ride in a theme park, in rank order of initial investment, Alternative A is considered first. Its present worth is computed; if it is greater than 0, the present worth of the difference in cash flows between Alternatives B and A is computed; if it is greater than 0, Alternative B is recommended; otherwise, Alternative A is recommended. If the present worth of Alternative A is not greater than 0, then the present worth of Alternative B would be computed; if it is greater than 0, Alternative B is recommended; otherwise, the do-nothing alternative is recommended.

$$PW_A = -\$300{,}000 + \$55{,}000(P|A\ 10\%,10)$$
$$= -\$300{,}000 + \$55{,}000(6.14457)$$
$$= \$37{,}951.35 > \$0.00 \text{ (therefore, } A \text{ is better than doing nothing)}$$

or, using Excel®,

$$PW_A = \textbf{PV(10\%,10,-55000)-300000}$$
$$= \mathbf{\$37{,}951.19} > \$0.00 \text{ (therefore, } A \text{ is better than doing nothing)}$$

Next, we consider the incremental investment of $150,000, which yields an incremental annual cash flow of $25,000.

$$PW_{B-A} = -\$150,000 + \$25,000(P|A\ 10\%,10)$$
$$= -\$150,000 + \$25,000(6.14457)$$
$$= \$3,614.25 > \$0.00\ (\text{therefore, } B \text{ is better than } A)$$

or, using Excel®,

$$PW_{B-A} = \text{PV}(10\%,10,\text{-}25000)\text{-}150000$$
$$= \$3614.18 > \$0.00\ (\text{therefore, } B \text{ is better than } A)$$

The incremental approach is not particularly cumbersome with two investment alternatives (three, when counting the do-nothing alternative). However, when faced with a large number of alternatives, the incremental approach can become tedious. For that reason, we seldom employ it when performing analyses using either *PW*, *FW*, *AW*, or *CW*. Given a choice in the matter, we prefer to use a ranking approach.

5-5 PRESENT WORTH: ONE-SHOT INVESTMENTS

As noted in Chapter 4, occasionally, investments are available only once. Such cases are called "one-shot" investments. When one-shot investments are being considered, the planning horizon is defined to be equal to the longest life among the investment alternatives. Then, the present worth is computed for each alternative.

EXAMPLE 5.5 Selecting from Among Multiple One-Shot Investments

In Chapter 4, we considered the two cash flow diagrams given in Figure 5.5. Both alternatives are *one-shot investments*. As such, we cannot predict what investment alternatives might be available in the future. However, the minimum attractive rate of return, 15 percent, reflects the opportunity to reinvest recovered capital.

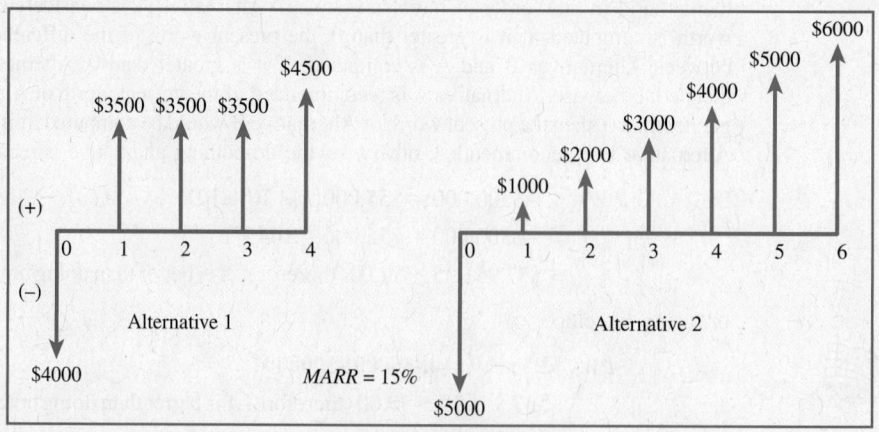

FIGURE 5.5
CFDs for Example 5.5.

For the one-shot investments in question, a 6-year planning horizon is to be used, with zero cash flows occurring in years 5 and 6 for Alternative 1. Using present worth analysis, the following results are obtained:

$$PW_1(15\%) = -\$4,000 + \$3,500(P|A\ 15\%,4) + \$1,000(P|F\ 15\%,4)$$
$$= -\$4,000 + \$3,500(2.85498) + \$1,000(0.57175)$$
$$= \$6,564.18$$
$$= NPV(15\%,3500,3500,3500,4500)\text{-}4000$$
$$= \$6564.18$$

$$PW_2(15\%) = -\$5,000 + \$1,000(P|A\ 15\%,6) + \$1,000(P|G\ 15\%,6)$$
$$= -\$5,000 + \$1,000(3.78448) + \$1,000(7.93678)$$
$$= \$6,721.26$$
$$= NPV(15\%,1000,2000,3000,4000,5000,6000)\text{-}5000$$
$$= \$6721.26$$

Thus, we would recommend Alternative 2.

5-6 DISCOUNTED PAYBACK PERIOD: SINGLE ALTERNATIVE

WILEY
VIDEO LESSON

In solving Example 5.1, we showed in Figure 5.1 how cumulative present worth increased over the life of the investment in a surface mount placement machine. Specifically, it increased from −$500,000 at the beginning of the 10-year investment period to a final value of **$87,649.62** at the end of the planning horizon. We pointed out that the cumulative present worth did not become positive until the ninth year of the investment. The time required for an investment to be fully recovered, including the time value of money, is the time required for the cumulative present worth to equal 0; it is called the *discounted payback period (DPBP)* for an investment. In this and the next section, we determine the *DPBP* for single and multiple investment alternatives.

EXAMPLE 5.6   A Closer Look at the Single Investment Opportunity

In Example 5.2, suppose Motorola management asked the manufacturing engineer to determine how long it takes for the new SHP machine to recover fully its initial cost of $500,000, including the *TVOM*.

Recall from Chapter 2 that the Excel® **NPER** worksheet function can be used to determine how long it takes for the $500,000 investment to be recovered, based on an annual return of $92,500. What is not known, however, is what the SMP machine's salvage value will be if its useful life is less than the 10-year planning horizon. To provide management with more information regarding the recovery period, the manufacturing engineer did the following analysis.

First, the engineer used the Excel® **NPER** worksheet function, assuming a negligible salvage value:

yrs to recover the investment $= NPER(10\%,92500,\text{-}500000) = 8.16$ years

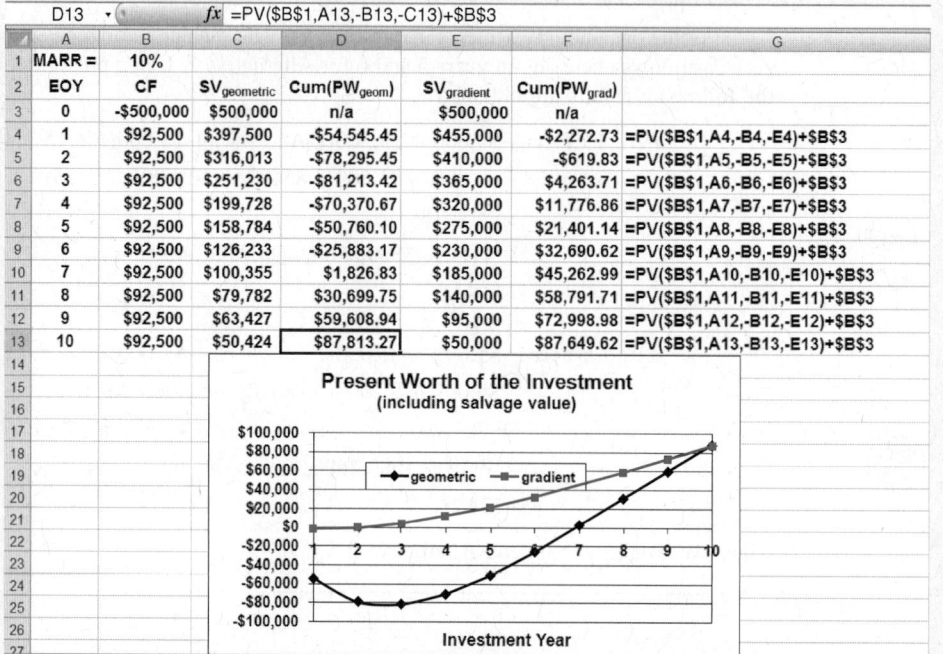

	D13	▾		*fx*	=PV($B$1,A13,-B13,-C13)+$B$3	
	A	B	C	D	E	F	G
1	MARR =	10%					
2	EOY	CF	SV$_{geometric}$	Cum(PW$_{geom}$)	SV$_{gradient}$	Cum(PW$_{grad}$)	
3	0	-$500,000	$500,000	n/a	$500,000	n/a	
4	1	$92,500	$397,500	-$54,545.45	$455,000	-$2,272.73	=PV($B$1,A4,-B4,-E4)+$B$3
5	2	$92,500	$316,013	-$78,295.45	$410,000	-$619.83	=PV($B$1,A5,-B5,-E5)+$B$3
6	3	$92,500	$251,230	-$81,213.42	$365,000	$4,263.71	=PV($B$1,A6,-B6,-E6)+$B$3
7	4	$92,500	$199,728	-$70,370.67	$320,000	$11,776.86	=PV($B$1,A7,-B7,-E7)+$B$3
8	5	$92,500	$158,784	-$50,760.10	$275,000	$21,401.14	=PV($B$1,A8,-B8,-E8)+$B$3
9	6	$92,500	$126,233	-$25,883.17	$230,000	$32,690.62	=PV($B$1,A9,-B9,-E9)+$B$3
10	7	$92,500	$100,355	$1,826.83	$185,000	$45,262.99	=PV($B$1,A10,-B10,-E10)+$B$3
11	8	$92,500	$79,782	$30,699.75	$140,000	$58,791.71	=PV($B$1,A11,-B11,-E11)+$B$3
12	9	$92,500	$63,427	$59,608.94	$95,000	$72,998.98	=PV($B$1,A12,-B12,-E12)+$B$3
13	10	$92,500	$50,424	$87,813.27	$50,000	$87,649.62	=PV($B$1,A13,-B13,-E13)+$B$3

FIGURE 5.6
Plot of Cumulative Present Worths for Example 5.6.

Next, the engineer estimated the salvage value if the machine was sold at any time before the end of the planning horizon. Not knowing exactly how the salvage value would decrease with use, the engineer made two approximations: The salvage value decreases as a geometric series, and the salvage value decreases as a gradient series. The engineer computed the geometric rate required to yield a $50,000 salvage value after 10 years and obtained a value of 20.6 percent; then, he computed the gradient step required and obtained a value of $45,000. (As an exercise, you should verify the engineer's calculations.) Using the salvage values shown in Figure 5.6, the engineer calculated the present worth, assuming the SMP machine was kept for 1, 2, ... , 10 years.

Based on the salvage value decreasing at a geometric rate of 20.6 percent each year, as shown in Figure 5.6, the investment in the new SMP machine is fully recovered during the seventh year. Based on the salvage value decreasing at a gradient rate of $45,000 per year, the investment is fully recovered during the third year.

Management was much more comfortable making the $500,000 investment after learning that the present worth over the planning horizon was $87,649.62 and that, if things went badly, the investment would be fully recovered in no more than 7 years and, possibly, as quickly as 3 years, depending on the salvage value for the SMP machine.

The calculations just performed are also performed by Eastman Chemical Company. The year in which the cumulative present worth equals 0 is called by Eastman the *net present value payback year*. We, and numerous other authors and engineering economists, call it the *discounted payback period* (*DPBP*).

We do not recommend using *DPBP* to identify the investment that is to be made from among a set of mutually exclusive investment alternatives. Instead, we recommend it be used as a supplemental tool, just as it was used in the SMP example. If used as a stand-alone measure of economic worth, it is difficult to understand how one would decide if the *DPBP* value obtained was acceptable or not. Such decisions would have to be arbitrary, since we know of no rational basis for saying, in the case of the previous example, that a *DPBP* value of 5 is acceptable but a value of 6 is not. (Recall the challenge faced by Tennessee Eastman Company when it was required to recover the investment in 2 years or less, ignoring the time value of money.)

As we will find, using *DPBP* as the basis for selecting the best investment from among multiple mutually exclusive investment alternatives can lead to a very different selection than will occur when using any of the other *DCF* measures of economic worth.

As illustrated in the example, if the salvage value for an investment of P in an asset is negligible, regardless of how long the asset is used, then the Excel® **NPER** worksheet function can be used to determine the *DPBP*, when the annual returns are a uniform annual series of A,

$$DPBP = \mathrm{NPER}\,(MARR, A, -P)$$

If, on the other hand, salvage value decreases with usage according to some mathematical relationship, then the Excel® **SOLVER** and **GOAL SEEK** tools can be used to determine the *DPBP*. In the previous example, salvage value was assumed to decline either geometrically or "gradiently." The following example illustrates the calculations involved in determining the *DPBP* for the SMP investment.

EXAMPLE 5.7   Using the Excel® SOLVER Tool to Calculate the DPBP

To determine the *DPBP* for the SMP investment, as shown in Figure 5.7, a spreadsheet is created with the input parameters shown. When salvage value decreases at an annual rate of 20.6 percent, the formula for salvage value after n years of use is $\$500,000(0.794)^n$. Likewise, when it decreases by $\$45,000$ each year, the salvage value after n years is $\$500,000 - \$45,000n$.

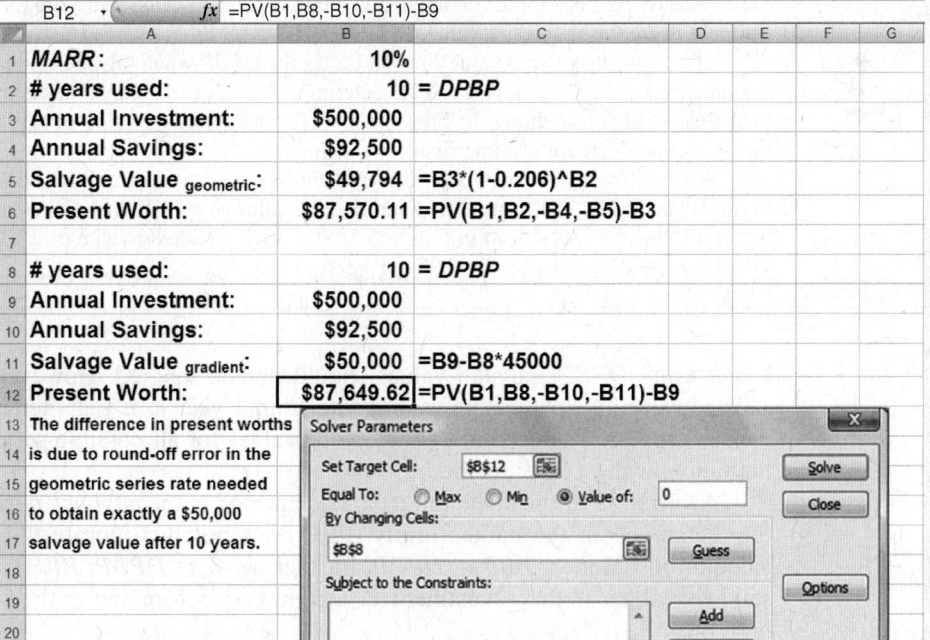

FIGURE 5.7

Excel® SOLVER Set Up to Calculate the *DPBP* in Example 5.7 with Gradient Decrease in Salvage Value.

	B12	▾		fx	=PV(B1,B8,-B10,-B11)-B9	

	A	B	C
1	*MARR* :	10%	
2	# years used:	6.95187521	= *DPBP*
3	Annual Investment:	$500,000	
4	Annual Savings:	$92,500	
5	Salvage Value _geometric_:	$100,585	=B3*(1-0.206)^B2
6	Present Worth:	$0.00	=PV(B1,B2,-B4,-B5)-B3
7			
8	# years used:	2.16997447	= *DPBP*
9	Annual Investment:	$500,000	
10	Annual Savings:	$92,500	
11	Salvage Value _gradient_:	$402,351	=B9-B8*45000
12	Present Worth:	$0.00	=PV(B1,B8,-B10,-B11)-B9
13			

FIGURE 5.8

Excel® SOLVER Solutions for the *DPBP* in Example 5.7 with Geometric and Gradient Decreases in Salvage Value.

To determine the *DPBP*, the value of *n* that makes *PW* equal zero can be obtained using SOLVER, twice: once for the geometric decrease in salvage value and again for the gradient or linear decrease in salvage value.

After entering a "trial value" in cell B2 for the *DPBP* when salvage value decreases as a geometric series, SOLVER is used to determine the value of B2 that makes present worth (cell B6) equal 0. As shown in Figure 5.8, SOLVER yields a value of 6.95 years when salvage value decreases geometrically over time.

When salvage value decreases as a gradient series, a "trial value" for *DPBP* is entered in cell B8 and SOLVER is used to determine the value of cell B8 that makes present worth (cell B12) equal 0. As shown in Figure 5.8, SOLVER yielded a value of 2.17 years when salvage value decreases by $45,000 per year.

When using *DPBP*, salvage values should not be ignored. However, determining salvage values for periods of use ranging from 1 year to *n* years tends to be a very inexact process. The need to know salvage values for all possible periods of use is a limitation of the *DPBP* method.

A variation of the discounted payback period is the *payback period* (*PBP*). As the difference in the names imply, PBP does not incorporate the *TVOM* in its calculations. Hence, *PBP* ≤ *DPBP*. Further, as with *DPBP*, *PBP* tends to ignore salvage values if the investment is terminated before the end of the planning horizon.

In essence, *PBP* users assume a value of zero for the *MARR* and the salvage value. Since *PBP* violates the first rule laid down in the text, it should come as no surprise that we have little good to say about it, only that it can be used as a "tie breaker" when two or more alternatives have essentially the same *PW*. (Eastman Chemical Company calculates the *PBP*; they call it the *cash payback year*. However, they only use it as a supplemental tool.)

Yet, *PBP* is very, very popular. Why? The following reasons are given by its advocates:

- It is simple mathematically—does not require interest rate calculations.
- It does not require a decision concerning the *MARR*.
- It is much more easily explained and understood than are *DCF* methods.
- It reflects a manager's attitudes when capital is limited.
- It provides a hedge against uncertainty of future cash flows.
- It provides a rough measure of the liquidity of an investment.

EXAMPLE 5.8   Solving for *PBP*

For the $500,000 investment in a surface mount placement machine that yields annual savings of $92,500, the *PBP* is easily obtained:

$$PBP = \$500{,}000/\$92{,}500 = 5.4054 \text{ years}$$

Alternately, using Excel®,

$$PBP = \text{NPER}(0\%,92500,\text{-}500000) = 5.4054 \text{ years}$$

Notice, the $50,000 salvage value at the end of 10 years of use is ignored in the calculation.

5-7   DISCOUNTED PAYBACK PERIOD: MULTIPLE ALTERNATIVES

We have emphasized the use of *DPBP* as a supplemental tool when comparing investment alternatives. We do not recommend it as the sole basis for choosing the preferred alternative. To understand why, consider the following example.

EXAMPLE 5.9   Using *DPBP* When Choosing Among Three Alternatives

Recall the previous example involving a theme park and two design alternatives. Now we add a third design alternative, which requires an initial investment of $150,000 and will produce annual after-tax revenue represented by a decreasing gradient series, with a revenue of $45,000 the first year and decreasing by $5,000 per year to a final value of 0 in the last year. Which alternative has the smallest *DPBP*?

The present worths for the three alternatives (*A*, *B*, and *C*), for *DPBP* years is given by

$$PW_A = -\$300{,}000 + \$55{,}000(P|A\ 10\%, DPBP_A)$$

$$PW_B = -\$450{,}000 + \$80{,}000(P|A\ 10\%, DPBP_B)$$

$$PW_C = -\$150{,}000 + \$45{,}000(P|A\ 10\%, DPBP_C) - \$5{,}000(P|G\ 10\%, DPBP_C)$$

B2	▾ (	*fx*	6.2731483493823		
	A	B	C	D	
1	*MARR =*	10%			
2	*DPBP =*	6.273148349			
3	(*P|G MARR,DPBP*) =	10.5029			
4	Initial Investment =	$150,000.00			
5	First Year Savings =	$45,000.00			
6	Gradient Step =	-$5,000.00			
7	Present Worth =	$0.00			
8					
9	=(1-(1+B1*B2)*(1+B1)^-B2)/B1^2				

Solver Parameters

Set Target Cell: $B$7

Equal To: ○ Max ○ Min ● Value of: 0

By Changing Cells: $B$2

Subject to the Constraints:

[Solve] [Close] [Guess] [Options] [Add]

FIGURE 5.9

Excel® SOLVER Solution for DPBP$_C$ in Example 5.9.

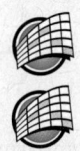 The Excel® **NPER** function can be used to solve for the values of $DPBP_A$ and $DPBP_B$ that equates the present worth to 0:

$$DPBP_A = \text{NPER}(10\%,-55000,300000) = 8.273 \text{ years}$$
$$DPBP_B = \text{NPER}(10\%,-80000,450000) = 8.674 \text{ years}$$

 The Excel® **SOLVER** tool is used to obtain the value of $DPBP_C$, as shown in Figure 5.9.

$$DPBP_C = 6.273 \text{ years}$$

Based on the discounted payback period, the rank-ordered preference for the alternatives is C, B, A—exactly the reverse order of their present worth values. The present worth for C can be shown to be

$$PW_C = -\$150,000 + \$45,000(P\|A\ 10\%,10) - \$5,000(P\|G\ 10\%,10)$$
$$= -\$150,000 + \$45,000(6.14457) - \$5,000(22.89134)$$
$$= \$12,048.95$$

or, using Excel®,

$$PW_C = 1000*\text{NPV}(10\%,45,40,35,30,25,20,15,10,5,0)-150000$$
$$= \$12,048.81$$

whereas, using Excel®, $PW_A = \$37,951.19$ and $PW_B = \$41,565.37$.

Figure 5.10 illustrates how the three present worths change over the duration of the planning horizon.

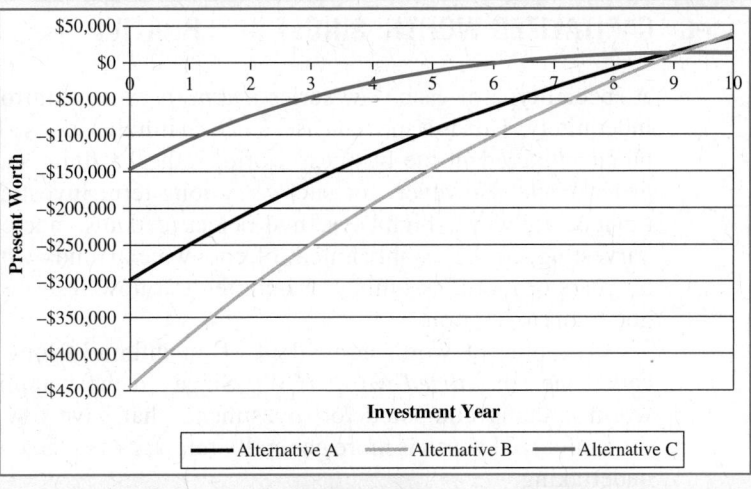

FIGURE 5.10
Discounted Payback Period Analysis for Example 5.9.

As the previous example illustrated, the *DPBP* can lead to wrong conclusions regarding the investment alternative that maximizes economic worth. The following example illustrates the same is true for the *PBP*. Like the *DPBP*, *PBP ignores everything after the payback period!*

EXAMPLE 5.10 Payback Period Analysis for Three Investments

Three investments are available, but only one can be pursued. The first requires an investment of $10,000 and produces returns of $5,000 per year for 2 years; thereafter, nothing is received until the end of the fifth year, at which time $1,000 is received. The second alternative requires an investment of $10,000 and produces returns of $5,000 the first year, $4,000 the second year, $3,000 the third year, $2,000 the fourth year, and $1,000 the fifth, and final, year. The third alternative requires an investment of $10,000 and produces returns of $2,500 each year for 5 years, plus a return of the original investment at the end of the 5-year investment period.

As shown in Table 5.1, the *PBP* rank ordering of the investments is $1 \gg 2 \gg 3$, where "$\gg$" means "is better than." Using PW analysis, the rank ordering is $3 \gg 2 \gg 1$, the exact opposite ranking of *PBP*. Enough said!

TABLE 5.1
Payback Period and Present Worth Solutions for Example 5.8.

EOY	CF(1)	CumCF(1)	CF(2)	CumCF(2)	CF(3)	CumCF(3)
0	−$10,000	−$10,000	−$10,000	−$10,000	−$10,000	−$10,000
1	$5,000	−$5,000	$5,000	−$5,000	$2,500	−$7,500
2	$5,000	$0	$4,000	−$1,000	$2,500	−$5,000
3	$0	$0	$3,000	$2,000	$2,500	−$2,500
4	$0	$0	$2,000	$4,000	$2,500	$0
5	$1,000	$1,000	$1,000	$5,000	$12,500	$12,500
PBP =		2 yrs		2.33 yrs		4 yrs
PW(10%) =	−$701.39		$2,092.13		$5,686.18	

5-8 CAPITALIZED WORTH: SINGLE ALTERNATIVE

WILEY
VIDEO LESSON

A special type of cash flow series is a *perpetuity*, a uniform series that continues indefinitely. This is a special case, since an infinite series of cash flows would rarely be encountered in the business world; rather, a finite series of cash flows is the general rule. However, for such very long-term investment projects as bridges, tunnels, railways, highways, hydroelectric dams, nuclear power plants, forest harvesting, or the establishment of endowment funds where the estimated life is 50 years or more, assuming an infinite cash flow series exists will generally be a good approximation.

The present worth equivalent of an infinitely long series of cash flows is called the *capitalized worth (CW)*. Since, in most applications, the capitalized worth is being computed for investments that have few if any positive returns, the capitalized worth is more generally referred to as the *capitalized cost (CC)* of an undertaking.

The *capitalized worth method* is applicable only if there is reason to believe a series of cash flows will extend indefinitely into the future. Because it does not use the same planning horizon as PW, FW, and AW, there is no reason to assume that the results will be the same as those that would occur when using a finite planning horizon. However, when operating at the limit of mathematical relationships, assumptions should not be made too quickly.

Recall that Table 2.8 presented limiting cases for the discrete compounding factors studied in Chapter 2. Notice, if one wants to compute the present worth of an infinitely long uniform series of cash flows, which we call *capitalized worth*, then

$$CW = A(P|A\ i\%,\infty) = A/i \tag{5.4}$$

Therefore, if the project in question involves an indefinite repetition of a life cycle, then *one can convert the life cycle costs to an annual equivalent and divide the result by the MARR to obtain the CW.*

As with the other measures of economic worth, capitalized worth can be used in the absence of alternatives. However, since capitalized worth calculations are generally performed when the do-nothing alternative is not feasible, the requirement that $CW > \$0.00$ in deciding whether or not to proceed with the investment is not appropriate. If only costs occur, then our objective is to minimize capitalized cost.

Our consideration of a single alternative is merely to show how the *CW* is calculated, not to show how one uses it in deciding whether to "invest" or "not invest." And, we will use capitalized cost (*CC*) instead of capitalized worth as the measure of merit.

EXAMPLE 5.11 Keeping the Capital Dome Bright and Shiny

Every 10 years, the dome of the state capital building has to be cleaned, sandblasted, and retouched. It costs $750,000 to complete the work. Using a 5 percent *MARR*, what is the capitalized cost for refurbishing the capital dome?

$$CC = \$750,000 + \$750,000(P|F\ 5\%,10) + \$750,000(P|F\ 5\%,20) + \cdots$$

or

$$CC = \$750{,}000(A|P\,5\%,10)/0.05$$
$$= \$750{,}000(0.12950)/0.05$$
$$= \$1{,}942{,}500$$

Alternatively,

$$CC = \$750{,}000 + \$750{,}000(A|F\,5\%,10)/0.05$$
$$= \$750{,}000 + \$750{,}000(0.07950)/0.05$$
$$= \$1{,}942{,}500$$

The alternative approach yielded the same result because of the following relationship between the $A|P$ and $A|F$ factors: $(A|P\,i\%,n) = (A|F\,i\%,n) + i$.

A useful interpretation of the CC is the following: If \$1,942,500 was deposited in a fund that paid 5 percent annual compound interest, then \$750,000 could be paid out every 10 years, forever, to cover the cost of cleaning the capital dome.

EXAMPLE 5.12   Capitalized Cost for Highway Construction

A new highway is to be constructed, and asphalt paving will be used. The asphalt will cost \$150 per foot, including the material and the paving operation. Due to the heavy usage expected, the asphalt is expected to last 5 years before requiring resurfacing. It is anticipated that the cost of resurfacing will remain the same per foot. Concrete drainage ditches will be installed on each side of the highway; they will each cost \$7.75 per foot to install. Ditches will have to be replaced every 15 years; the cost of replacing them will also be \$7.75 per foot. Four pipe culverts will be installed every mile; each culvert will cost \$8,000 and will last 10 years; replacement culverts will cost \$10,000 each, indefinitely. Annual maintenance of the highway will cost \$9,000 per mile. Cleaning each culvert will cost \$1,250 per year. Cleaning and maintaining each ditch will cost \$3.75 per foot per year. Determine the capitalized cost (CC) per mile of highway using a *MARR* of 5 percent.

First, let's compute the capitalized cost of paving the road and the ditches. Since paving must occur every 5 years, there are two approaches that can be used: (1) convert the initial paving of the highway and ditches to an annual equivalent and then divide by the *MARR* to obtain the capitalized cost, or (2) treat the initial paving as a present cost and convert the resurfacing and replacing costs to an annual equivalent and then divide by the *MARR* to obtain the capitalized cost of resurfacing. The following results:

1. CC(paving/mile) $= 5{,}280\,\text{ft/mi}[\$150/ft(A|P\,5\%,5) + \$7.75/ft(A|P\,5\%,15)]/(0.05)$

   $= \$3{,}737{,}409$

   =(PMT(5%,5,-5280*150)+PMT(5%,15,-5280*7.75))/0.05

   =$3,737,487

2. CC(paving/mile) $= 5{,}280\,\text{ft/mi}\{\$150/ft[1 + (A|F\,5\%,5)]$

   $+ \$7.75/ft[1 + (A|F\,5\%,15)]\}/(0.05) = \$3{,}737{,}409$

   =5280*(150+PMT(5%,5,,-150)/0.05+7.75

   +PMT(5%,15,,-7.75)/0.05)

   =$3,737,487

To complete the example, we add the capitalized cost for maintaining the highway and ditches, plus the installation and maintenance of the culverts:

$$CC(\text{maintenance/mile}) = \$9,000/0.05 = \$180,000$$

$$CC(\text{ditches/mile}) = [(2)(5,280\,\text{ft/mi})(\$3.75/\text{ft})]/(0.05) = \$792,000$$

$$CC(\text{culverts/mile}) = (4)[\$8,000 + \$1,250/0.05 + \$10,000(A|F\,5\%,10)/0.05]$$
$$= \$195,600$$

$$=4^*(8000+1250/0.05+PMT(5\%,10,,-10000)/0.05)$$
$$=\$195,604$$

Therefore,

$$CC(\text{highway/mile}) = \$3,737,487 + \$180,000 + \$792,000 + \$195,604$$
$$= \$4,905,091$$

The capitalized cost for paving the highway and ditches is $3,737,487. The capitalized cost to maintain the highway and ditches is $972,000. The capitalized cost to install culverts every 10 years and maintain them annually is obtained by using the alternative approach in Example 5.11, since the replacement costs differ from the initial installation cost; the result is a capitalized cost of $195,604. Therefore, the overall capitalized cost to build and maintain the highway is $4,905,091 per highway mile.

(Based on state highway estimates, the initial cost to construct a 4-lane divided highway comparable to interstates is currently approximately $25 million per highway mile. The initial cost to construct a 2-lane highway, as above, is approximately $1 million per highway mile, depending on terrain and a host of other factors. Hence, the cost estimates provided above are somewhat conservative.)

EXAMPLE 5.13 Endowing Scholarships at a University

A full scholarship at a state land-grant university costs $12,500 per year. If the payout from the endowment is 4.5 percent per year and you want to endow a scholarship, what size gift is required?

To generate $12,500 annually forever, a gift of $12,500/0.045, or $277,777.78, is required.

With an endowment, the principal is never spent. Some donors want their gift to be used for many years but not necessarily forever. Quasi-endowments are managed very much like endowments, except portions of the principal can be spent over time. Generally, the period of time for which a quasi-endowment is intended to provide support exceeds 50 years. The following example illustrates a quasi-endowment.

EXAMPLE 5.14 Using a Quasi-Endowment to Fund a Scholarship

Suppose a donor is asked to establish a quasi-endowment that will be used to support a scholarship for a period of 100 years. Here, we assume that the quasi-endowment grows at a rate of 9 percent per year, and any amount can be spent in support of a scholarship as long as the balance is not depleted within a 100-year planning horizon. Also, we assume a $12,500 scholarship is provided the first year, but the magnitude of the scholarship increases at the same rate that tuition and fees increase. We assume tuition and fees

L29 fx =L28*(1+$H$1)-K29

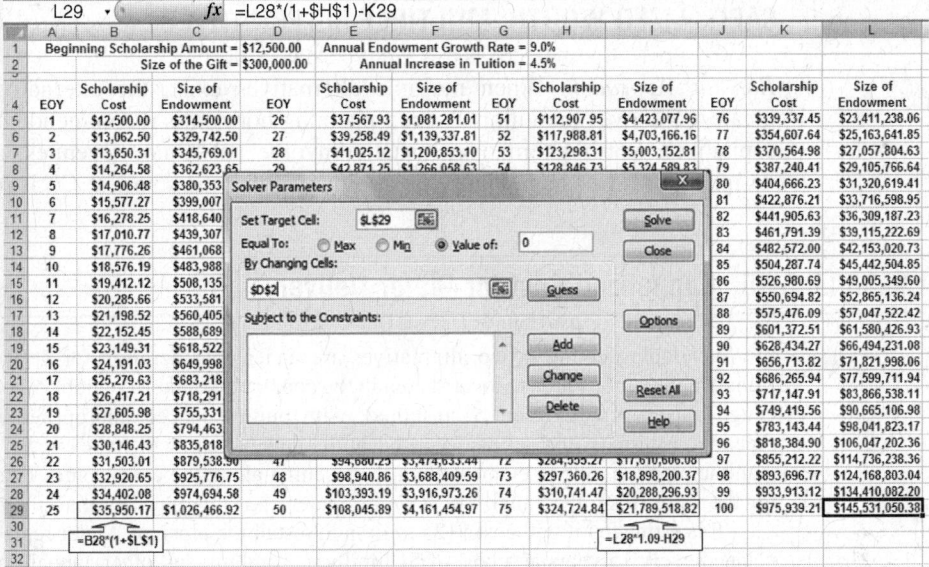

FIGURE 5.11

Set Up to Use the Excel® SOLVER Tool to Compute Gift Size for a Scholarship.

increase at an annual rate of 4.5 percent. What size gift is needed to fund the scholarship for 100 years?

As shown in Figure 5.11, a spreadsheet was designed, showing a 4.5 percent annual increase in the scholarship's size and a 9 percent growth in the quasi-endowment's size. It was designed to allow the two parameter values to be changed to accommodate the institution. Also, the initial size of the scholarship is a parameter. As shown in Figure 5.12, using the Excel® SOLVER tool, a $273,678.79 gift will support the scholarship for 100 years.

L29 fx =L28*(1+$H$1)-K29

| Beginning Scholarship Amount = $12,500.00 | | Annual Endowment Growth Rate = 9.0% | | | | | | | | |
| Size of the Gift = $273,678.79 | | Annual Increase in Tuition = 4.5% | | | | | | | | |
EOY	Scholarship Cost	Size of Endowment	EOY	Scholarship Cost	Size of Endowment	EOY	Scholarship Cost	Size of Endowment	EOY	Scholarship Cost	Size of Endowment
1	$12,500.00	$285,809.88	26	$37,567.93	$833,883.79	51	$112,907.95	$2,289,751.77	76	$339,337.45	$5,015,394.26
2	$13,062.50	$298,470.27	27	$39,258.49	$869,674.84	52	$117,988.81	$2,377,840.62	77	$354,607.64	$5,112,172.10
3	$13,650.31	$311,682.28	28	$41,025.12	$906,920.46	53	$123,298.31	$2,468,547.97	78	$370,564.98	$5,201,702.61
4	$14,264.58	$325,469.11	29	$42,871.25	$945,672.05	54	$128,846.73	$2,561,870.55	79	$387,240.41	$5,282,615.44
5	$14,906.48	$339,854.85	30	$44,800.46	$985,982.08	55	$134,644.83	$2,657,794.07	80	$404,666.23	$5,353,384.60
6	$15,577.27	$354,864.51	31	$46,816.48	$1,027,903.99	56	$140,703.85	$2,756,291.68	81	$422,876.21	$5,412,313.01
7	$16,278.25	$370,524.06	32	$48,923.22	$1,071,492.13	57	$147,035.53	$2,857,322.41	82	$441,905.63	$5,457,515.55
8	$17,010.77	$386,860.46	33	$51,124.76	$1,116,801.66	58	$153,652.12	$2,960,829.30	83	$461,791.39	$5,486,900.56
9	$17,776.26	$403,901.64	34	$53,425.38	$1,163,888.43	59	$160,566.47	$3,066,737.47	84	$482,572.00	$5,498,149.61
10	$18,576.19	$421,676.60	35	$55,829.52	$1,212,808.87	60	$167,791.96	$3,174,951.88	85	$504,287.74	$5,488,695.33
11	$19,412.12	$440,215.37	36	$58,341.85	$1,263,619.82	61	$175,342.60	$3,285,354.95	86	$526,980.69	$5,455,697.22
12	$20,285.66	$459,549.09	37	$60,967.23	$1,316,378.38	62	$183,233.02	$3,397,803.88	87	$550,694.82	$5,396,015.15
13	$21,198.52	$479,709.99	38	$63,710.76	$1,371,141.68	63	$191,478.50	$3,512,127.72	88	$575,476.09	$5,306,180.43
14	$22,152.45	$500,731.44	39	$66,577.74	$1,427,966.69	64	$200,095.03	$3,628,124.19	89	$601,372.51	$5,182,364.16
15	$23,149.31	$522,647.96	40	$69,573.74	$1,486,909.95	65	$209,099.31	$3,745,556.05	90	$628,434.27	$5,020,342.66
16	$24,191.03	$545,495.25	41	$72,704.56	$1,548,027.29	66	$218,508.78	$3,864,147.32	91	$656,713.82	$4,815,459.68
17	$25,279.63	$569,310.19	42	$75,976.26	$1,611,373.48	67	$228,341.68	$3,983,578.90	92	$686,265.94	$4,562,585.11
18	$26,417.21	$594,130.90	43	$79,395.19	$1,677,001.90	68	$238,617.05	$4,103,483.95	93	$717,147.91	$4,256,069.87
19	$27,605.98	$619,996.70	44	$82,967.98	$1,744,964.10	69	$249,354.82	$4,223,442.69	94	$749,419.56	$3,889,696.59
20	$28,848.25	$646,948.14	45	$86,701.54	$1,815,309.33	70	$260,575.78	$4,342,976.74	95	$783,143.44	$3,456,625.85
21	$30,146.43	$675,027.05	46	$90,603.11	$1,888,084.06	71	$272,301.69	$4,461,542.96	96	$818,384.90	$2,949,337.28
22	$31,503.01	$704,276.47	47	$94,680.25	$1,963,331.38	72	$284,555.27	$4,578,526.55	97	$855,212.22	$2,359,565.42
23	$32,920.65	$734,740.70	48	$98,940.86	$2,041,090.35	73	$297,360.26	$4,693,233.68	98	$893,696.77	$1,678,229.54
24	$34,402.08	$766,465.29	49	$103,393.19	$2,121,395.29	74	$310,741.47	$4,804,883.25	99	$933,913.12	$895,357.07
25	$35,950.17	$799,496.99	50	$108,045.89	$2,204,274.98	75	$324,724.84	$4,912,597.90	100	$975,939.21	$0.00

FIGURE 5.12

Excel® SOLVER Solution to Example 5.13.

5-9 CAPITALIZED WORTH: MULTIPLE ALTERNATIVES

Ranking Approach. When multiple alternatives exist, the alternative having the greatest *CW* over the infinitely long planning horizon is recommended. Again, since capitalized worth alternatives usually involve costs, not revenues, and costs are designated with positive signs, the alternative with the smallest *CC* is recommended.

EXAMPLE 5.15 Capitalized Cost for Water Delivery

In a developing country, two alternatives are under consideration for delivering water from a mountainous area to an arid area in the country's southern region. A coated heavy-gauge plastic pipeline can be installed, with pumps spaced appropriately along the pipeline. Alternatively, a canal can be built; however, it will have greater water loss than the pipeline, due to evaporation and poaching along the canal route. To compensate for the water loss, the canal will have a greater carrying capacity than the pipeline.

It is estimated it will cost $125 million to install the pipeline. Major replacements are planned every 15 years at a cost of $10 million. Pumping and other annual operating and maintenance costs are estimated to be $5 million.

The canal will cost $200 million to construct; its annual operating and maintenance costs are anticipated to be $1 million. Major upgrades of the canal are anticipated every 10 years, at a cost of $5 million.

Based on a 5 percent *MARR* and an infinitely long planning horizon, which alternative has the lowest capitalized cost?

Pipeline

$$CC = \$125{,}000{,}000 + [\$10{,}000{,}000(A|F\,5\%,15) + \$5{,}000{,}000]/0.05$$
$$= \$234{,}268{,}000.00$$

=125000000+(PMT(5%,15,,-10000000)+5000000)/0.05

=$234,268,457.52

Canal

$$CC = \$200{,}000{,}000 + [\$5{,}000{,}000(A|F\,5\%,10) + \$1{,}000{,}000]/0.05$$
$$= \$227{,}950{,}000.00$$

=200000000+(PMT(5%,10,,-5000000)+1000000)/0.05

=$227,950,457.50

The canal has the smallest capitalized cost and would be recommended.

Incremental Approach. An incremental approach can be employed when using capitalized worth to compare investment alternatives. The following example illustrates the use of an incremental approach when there are no positive-valued cash flows.

EXAMPLE 5.16 Incremental Analysis of the Water Delivery Alternatives

Continuing with the previous example, we first rank order the alternatives in increasing order of initial investment. Hence, the pipeline is considered first. Its capitalized cost is determined, as in Example 5.15.

Pipeline

$$CC_P = \$125,000,000 + [\$10,000,000(A|F\ 5\%,15) + \$5,000,000]/0.05$$
$$= \$234,268,000$$

$$=125000000+(PMT(5\%,15,,-10000000)+5000000)/0.05$$
$$=\$234,268,458$$

Next, we consider the incremental investment (and costs) required to go from the pipeline to the canal.

Canal–Pipeline

$$CC_{C-P} = (\$200,000,000 - \$125,000,000 + [\$5,000,000(A|F\ 5\%,10)$$
$$- \$10,000,000(A|F\ 5\%,15) + \$1,000,000 - \$5,00,000]/0.05$$
$$= -\$6,318,000$$

$$=200000000-125000000+(PMT(5\%,10,,-5000000)$$
$$-PMT(5\%,15,,-10000000)+1000000-5000000)/0.05$$
$$=-\$6,318,000$$

Since the incremental cost is negative, a positive worth results from the incremental investment. Therefore, the canal is recommended.

5-10   SUMMARY

After having used present worth analysis in each previous chapter, some might have wondered if anything new would be presented in this chapter. If so, then they found that many new topics were covered, not only with respect to present worth but also with all the measures of economic worth addressed in this text.

In this chapter, we learned the following:

1. Present worth analysis is the most popular discounted cash flow measure of economic worth.

2. The nine *DCF* methods of comparing investment alternatives can be separated into ranking methods and incremental methods, with present worth being a ranking method.

3. All four "worth measures" (present worth, future worth, annual worth, and capitalized worth) can also be applied using incremental analysis.

4. When applied correctly, *PW, FW, AW, CW, IRR, ERR,* and *B/C* will result in a consistent recommendation of the preferred alternative.

5. We do not advise using *DPBP* and *PBP* to choose the alternative recommended for funding.

6. Since *DPBP* and *PBP* are not guaranteed to produce the same recommendation as the other measures of economic worth, they should *not* be used as the sole basis for such recommendations—instead, they should be used as supplemental methods.

7. When choosing among mutually exclusive alternatives and when seeking to maximize economic worth, recommend the alternative with the greatest present worth over the planning horizon.

8. Capitalized worth is the present worth of an infinitely long cash flow series and is used for extraordinarily long and indefinite planning horizons.

9. When performing *before-tax* analyses, use a *before-tax MARR*; likewise, when *after-tax* analyses are performed, use an *after-tax MARR*.

10. To convert a before-tax *MARR* to an after-tax *MARR*, an approximation is obtained by dividing the before-tax *MARR* by 1 minus the marginal income tax rate.

After reading this chapter, it should be apparent that a critical decision when using present worth analysis is the length of the planning horizon. Another important factor is the type of investment being considered. A third factor is the life of each investment alternative.

1. For one-shot investments, determine the present worth of each investment. If the mutually exclusive investments have unequal lives, so be it. Investments having lives less than that of the longest-lived investment are assigned cash flows of 0 for the years following their lives.

2. When investments are not one-shot and their lives are unequal, specify the duration of the planning horizon, make decisions regarding cash flows and any necessary replacements during the planning horizon, and determine the present worth over the planning horizon.

Pit Stop #5—Open Road Ahead!

1. True or False: Present worth analysis is the most popular *DCF* measure of economic worth.

2. True or False: Unless non-monetary considerations dictate otherwise, choose the mutually exclusive investment alternative that has the greatest present worth, regardless of the lives of the alternatives.

3. True or False: When using present worth analysis to evaluate the economic viability of mutually exclusive alternatives, use a common period of time in the comparison.

4. True or False: If $PW > MARR = 20\%$, then $DPBP < 5$ years.

5. True or False: $DPBP \geq PBP$.

6. True or False: If $CW > 0$, then $PW > 0$.

7. True or False: If $PW(A) > PW(B)$, then $FW(A) > FW(B)$, $AW(A) > AW(B)$, $CW(A) > CW(B)$, $DPBP(A) < DPBP(B)$, and $PBP(A) < PBP(B)$.

8. True or False: *PW, FW, AW, CW*, and *B/C* are ranking methods; therefore, the alternative having the greatest *PW, FW, AW, CW*, or *B/C* should be recommended.

9. True or False: If $PW(A) > PW(B) > \$0$ and $PBP(A) < DPBP(B)$, then $DPBP(A) > PBP(B)$.

10. True or False: The "do nothing" alternative always has negligible incremental costs and revenues.

Tutoring problem available (at instructor's discretion) in *WileyPLUS*.

 Problem available (at instructor's discretion) in *WileyPLUS*.

 Worked Problem Video available in *WileyPLUS*.

FE-LIKE PROBLEMS

1. When using present worth to evaluate the attractiveness of a single investment alternative, what value is the calculated PW compared to?

   a. 0.0

   b. *MARR*

   c. 1.0

   d. WACC

2. A natural gas well is projected to produce $200,000 in profit during its first year of operation, $190,000 the second year, $180,000 the third year, and so on, continuing this pattern. If the well is expected to produce for a total of 10 years, and the effective annual interest rate is 8 percent, which of the following most closely represents the present worth of the well?

   a. $1,770,000

   b. $1,508,000

   c. $1,253,000

   d. $1,082,000

3. The present worth of a multiyear investment with all positive cash flows (incomes) other than the initial investment is $PW = \$10,000$ at $MARR = i\%$. If *MARR* changes to $(i + 1)\%$, the present worth will be

   a. Less than $10,000.

   b. Equal to $10,000.

   c. Greater than $10,000.

   d. Cannot determine without the cash flow profile and a value for i

4. Consider the following cash flow diagram. Which of the expressions is not valid for the present worth?

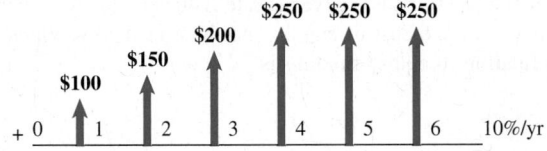

   a. $P = 100(P|A\ 10\%,6) + 50(P|G\ 10\%,3)$
      $+150(P|A\ 10\%,3)(P|F\ 10\%,3)$

   b. $P = 100(P|A\ 10\%,3) + 50(P|G\ 10\%,3)$
      $+250(P|A\ 10\%,3)(P|F\ 10\%,3)$

   c. $P = 250(P|A\ 10\%,6) - 50(P|G\ 10\%,3)$

   d. $P = 100(P|A\ 10\%,4) + 50(P|G\ 10\%,4)$
      $+250(P|A\ 10\%,2)(P|F\ 10\%,4)$

5. Ivan, an industrial engineering student, is working on a homework problem for Engineering Economy. He needs to calculate the PW at 12 percent of a cash flow series with $1,000 at $t = 3$, $1,500 at $t = 4$, and $2,000 at $t = 5$. If Ivan uses the equation $P = 1,000(P|A\ 12\%,3) + 500(P|G\ 12\%,3)$, where is the P now located?

   a. $t = 4$

   b. $t = 2$

   c. $t = 1$

   d. $t = 0$

6. The owner of a cemetery plans to offer a perpetual care service for grave sites. The owner estimates that it will cost $120 per year to maintain a grave site. If the interest rate is 8 percent, what one-time fee should the owner charge for the perpetual care service?

   a. $96

   b. $120

   c. $1,500

   d. $12,000

7. Consider a palletizer at a bottling plant that has a first cost of $150,000, operating and maintenance costs of $17,500 per year, and an estimated net salvage value of $25,000 at the end of 30 years. Assume an interest rate of 8 percent. What is the present equivalent cost of the investment if the planning horizon is 30 years?

   a. $335,000

   b. $344,500

c. $360,000

d. $395,500

8. The heat loss through the windows of a home is estimated to cost the homeowner $412 per year in wasted energy. Thermal windows will reduce heat loss by 93 percent and can be installed for $1,232. The windows will have no salvage value at the end of their estimated life of 8 years. Determine the net present equivalent value of the windows if the interest rate is 10 percent.

a. $412

b. $812

c. $1,044

d. $1,834

 9. An inline filter has an estimated life of 9 years. By adding a purifier to the filter, savings of $300 in annual operating costs can be obtained. Annual interest on capital is 8 percent. Compute the maximum expenditure justifiable for the purifier.

a. $24

b. $33

c. $300

d. $1,875

10. The city council has approved the building of a new bridge over Running Water Creek. The bridge will cost $17,000 for initial construction and have an annual maintenance cost of $1,000. The council plans to withdraw money from the city's Bridges and Highways account to open a special account to cover the initial construction and to fund a perpetuity to cover the maintenance costs forever. How much money must be withdrawn from the Bridges and Highways account if the city can expect to earn 5 percent on the special account?

a. $1,000

b. $17,000

c. $18,000

d. $37,000

11. Two projects, A and B, are analyzed using ranking present worth analysis with *MARR* at *i*%. It is found that PW(A) > PW(B). If *MARR* is changed to $(i + 1)$%, what will be the relationship between PW(A) and PW(B)?

a. PW(A) > PW(B)

b. PW(A) = PW(B)

c. PW(A) < PW(B)

d. Cannot be determined without the cash flow profiles

PROBLEMS

Section 5.1

1. Use the Internet to access Home Depot's most recent annual report.
   a. What evidence did you find that Home Depot continues to rely on present worth analysis in its corporate decision making?
   b. Does Home Depot refer specifically to "present worth" analysis? If not, what alternative term is used?

2. Use the Internet to access ConocoPhillips's most recent annual report.
   a. What evidence do you find that ConocoPhillips continues to rely on present worth analysis in its corporate decision making?
   b. Does ConocoPhillips refer specifically to "present worth" analysis? If not, what alternative term is used?

3. Use an Internet search engine to identify three companies or agencies (other than those mentioned in the chapter) that use present worth analysis to make business decisions as evidenced in their annual reports.

Section 5.2

4. Allister Company uses both debt capital and equity capital to fund new projects. The before-tax cost of debt capital is 12 percent. The cost of equity capital is 10 percent. Allister's effective tax rate is 40 percent. For each of the following cases, calculate the before-tax weighted average cost of capital and the after-tax weighted average cost of capital. The percentage ratio of debt funding to equity funding is

   a. 0/100.
   b. 25/75.
   c. 50/50.

d. 75/25.

e. 100/0.

5. Reconsider the results you obtained for the Allister Company in Problem 4. Assume that Allister's uses the WACC for *MARR*.

    a. For each case (a through e), use the estimation equation given in Equation 5.1 and your result for after-tax WACC to calculate an estimate of before-tax WACC.

    b. What conclusions can you draw from your calculations about the accuracy of the estimations as the split between debt and equity changes?

    c. Would your answer to (b) have been different if you had used Equation 5.1 to estimate after-tax WACC based on before-tax WACC for each case?

6. GeoWorld Systems uses a subset of the following questions during the interview process for new engineers. For each of the following cases, determine if "the project" or "do nothing" is preferred. The value of *MARR* in each case is 14 percent.

    a. The present worth of the project is $1,367.

    b. The internal rate of return of the project is 12.9 percent.

    c. The annual worth of the project is −$632.

    d. The benefit cost ratio of the project is 1.08.

    e. The future worth of the project is $3.75.

    f. The external rate of return of the project is 15.3 percent.

    g. The present worth of the project is −$47.

    h. The internal rate of return of the project is 14.7 percent.

    i. The annual worth of the project is $6,775.

    j. The benefit cost ratio of the project is 0.97.

    k. The future worth of the project is −$13,470.

    l. The external rate of return of the project is 3.7 percent.

    m. For the cases (if any) in which "do nothing" was preferred, what assumption is being made about the return generated by the "uninvested" funds?

    n. Is it possible that the values stated in (a) and (b) were correctly calculated on the same project? If not, why?

    o. Is it possible that the values stated in (c) and (d) were correctly calculated on the same project? If not, why?

    p. What do you know must be true about the present worth for the project in (j)?

    q. What do you know must be true about the internal rate of return for the project in (j)?

 7. Match the measures of worth in the first column with an appropriate definition from the second column.

Measure of Worth	Definitions
(a) Annual worth	(1) Converts all cash flows to a single sum equivalent at $t =$ (planning horizon) using $i = MARR$
(b) Discounted payback period	(2) Converts all cash flows to a single sum equivalent at $t = 0$ using $i = MARR$
(c) Capitalized worth	(3) Converts all cash flows to an equivalent uniform series over the planning horizon
(d) External rate of return	(4) Determines an interest rate that yields a PW (or FW or AW) of 0
(e) Future worth	(5) Determines how long it takes for the cumulative present worth to be positive at $i = MARR$
(f) Internal rate of return	(6) Determines the interest rate that equates the future worth of invested capital to the future worth of recovered capital invested at $i = MARR$
(g) Present worth	(7) Determines the PW when the planning horizon is infinitely long

8. Match the measures of worth in the first column with an appropriate decision rule for preferring a project over "do nothing."

Measure of Worth	Decision Rule
(a) Annual worth	(1) Measure of worth is greater than 0
(b) Benefit/cost ratio	(2) Measure of worth is greater than 1
(c) External rate of return	(3) Measure of worth is greater than *MARR*
(d) Future worth	
(e) Internal rate of return	
(f) Present worth	

Section 5.3

 9. Bailey, Inc., is considering buying a new gang punch that would allow them to produce circuit boards more efficiently. The punch has a first cost of $100,000 and a useful life of 15 years. At the end of its useful life, the punch has no salvage value. Annual labor costs would increase $2,000 using the gang punch, but annual raw material costs would decrease $12,000. *MARR* is 5 percent/year.

    a. What is the present worth of this investment?

    b. What is the decision rule for judging the attractiveness of investments based on present worth?

    c. Should Bailey buy the gang punch?

10. Repeat Problem 9 assuming that floor support and vibration dampening must be added for the gang punch. These one-time first costs are estimated to be $35,000.

11. Repeat Problem 9 assuming that the cost of capital has increased due to weak market conditions and *MARR* is now 6 percent/year.

 12. Carlisle Company has been cited and must invest in equipment to reduce stack emissions or face EPA fines of $18,500 per year. An emission reduction filter will cost $75,000 and will have an expected life of 5 years. Carlisle's *MARR* is 10 percent/year.

    a. What is the present worth of this investment?

    b. What is the decision rule for judging the attractiveness of investments based on present worth?

    c. Is the filter economically justified?

    d. State at least one noneconomic factor that might influence this decision.

13. Repeat parts (a) through (c) of Problem 12 assuming that Carlisle's board of directors has decided that since this action is based on a Federal government citation, no financial gain should be expected and the appropriate value of *MARR* is 0.

 14. DuraTech Manufacturing is evaluating a process improvement project. The estimated receipts and disbursements associated with the project are shown below. *MARR* is 6 percent/year.

End of Year	Receipts	Disbursements
0	$0	$5,000
1	$0	$200
2	$2,000	$300
3	$4,000	$600
4	$3,000	$1,000
5	$1,600	$1,500

    a. What is the present worth of this investment?

    b. What is the decision rule for judging the attractiveness of investments based on present worth?

    c. Should DuraTech implement the proposed process improvement?

15. Eddie's Precision Machine Shop is insured for $700,000. The present yearly insurance premium is $1.00 per $100 of coverage. A sprinkler system with an estimated life of 20 years and no salvage value can be installed for $20,000. Annual maintenance costs for the sprinkler system are $400. If the sprinkler system is installed, the system must be included in the shop's value for insurance purposes, but the insurance premium will reduce to $0.40 per $100 of coverage. Eddie uses a *MARR* of 15 percent/year.

   a. What is the present worth of this investment?

   b. What is the decision rule for judging the attractiveness of investments based on present worth?

   c. Is the sprinkler system economically justified?

16. Fabco, Inc., is considering purchasing flow valves that will reduce annual operating costs by $10,000 per year for the next 12 years. Fabco's *MARR* is 7 percent/year. Using a present worth approach, determine the maximum amount Fabco should be willing to pay for the valves.

17. Galvanized Products is considering purchasing a new computer system for their enterprise data management system. The vendor has quoted a purchase price of $100,000. Galvanized Products is planning to borrow one-fourth of the purchase price from a bank at 15 percent compounded annually. The loan is to be repaid using equal annual payments over a 3-year period. The computer system is expected to last 5 years and has a salvage value of $5,000 at that time. Over the 5-year period, Galvanized Products expects to pay a technician $25,000 per year to maintain the system but will save $55,000 per year through increased efficiencies. Galvanized Products uses a *MARR* of 18 percent/year to evaluate investments.

   a. What is the present worth of this investment?

   b. What is the decision rule for judging the attractiveness of investments based on present worth?

   c. Should the new computer system be purchased?

18. Quilts R Us (QRU) is considering an investment in a new patterning attachment with the cash flow profile shown in the table below. QRU's *MARR* is 13.5 percent/year.

EOY	0	1	2	3	4	5	6	7
Cash Flow	−$1,400	$0	$500	$500	$500	$500	$0	$500
EOY	8	9	10	11	12	13	14	15
Cash Flow	$600	$700	$800	$900	−$1,000	−$2,000	−$3,000	$1,400

   a. What is the present worth of this investment?

   b. What is the decision rule for judging the attractiveness of investments based on present worth?

   c. Should QRU invest?

19. Imagineering, Inc., is considering an investment in CAD-CAM compatible design software with the cash flow profile shown in the table below. Imagineering's *MARR* is 18 percent/year.

EOY	0	1	2	3	4	5	6	7
Cash Flow (M$)	−$12	−$1	$5	$2	$5	$5	$2	$5

   a. What is the present worth of this investment?

   b. What is the decision rule for judging the attractiveness of investments based on present worth?

   c. Should Imagineering invest?

20. Jupiter's is considering investing time and administrative expense on an effort that promises one large payoff in the future, followed by additional expenses over a 10-year horizon. The cash flow profile is shown in the table below. Jupiter's *MARR* is 12 percent/year.

EOY	0	1	2	3	4	5	6	7	8	9	10
Cash Flow (K$)	−$2	−$10	−$12	−$14	−$16	−$18	$200	−$10	−$12	−$14	−$100

a. What is the present worth of this investment?

b. What is the decision rule for judging the attractiveness of investments based on present worth?

c. Should Jupiter invest?

WILEY + **21.** Aerotron Electronics is considering purchasing a water filtration system to assist in circuit board manufacturing. The
VS system costs $40,000. It has an expected life of 7 years at which time its salvage value will be $7,500. Operating and maintenance expenses are estimated to be $2,000 per year. If the filtration system is not purchased, Aerotron Electronics will have to pay Bay City $12,000 per year for water purification. If the system is purchased, no water purification from Bay City will be needed. Aerotron Electronics must borrow half of the purchase price, but they cannot start repaying the loan for 2 years. The bank has agreed to three equal annual payments, with the first payment due at the end of year 2. The loan interest rate is 8 percent compounded annually. Aerotron Electronics' *MARR* is 10 percent compounded annually.

a. What is the present worth of this investment?

b. What is the decision rule for judging the attractiveness of investments based on present worth?

c. Should Aerotron Electronics buy the water filtration system?

22. Home Innovation is evaluating a new product design. The estimated receipts and disbursements associated with the new product are shown below. *MARR* is 10 percent/year.

End of Year	0	1	2	3	4	5
Receipts	$0	$600	$600	$700	$700	$700
Disbursements	$1,000	$300	$300	$300	$300	$300

a. What is the present worth of this investment?

b. What is the decision rule for judging the attractiveness of investments based on present worth?

c. Should Home Innovation pursue this new product?

WILEY + **23.** A design change being considered by Mayberry, Inc., will cost $6,000 and will result in an annual savings of $1,000 per year for the 6-year life of the project. A cost of $2,000 will be avoided at the project's end as a result of the change. *MARR* is 8 percent/year.

a. What is the present worth of this investment?

b. What is the decision rule for judging the attractiveness of investments based on present worth?

c. Should Mayberry implement the design change?

WILEY + **24.** Nancy's Notions pays a delivery firm to distribute its products in the metro area. Delivery costs are $30,000 per
VS year. Nancy can buy a used truck for $10,000 that will be adequate for the next 3 years. Operating and maintenance costs are estimated to be $25,000 per year. At the end of 3 years, the used truck will have an estimated salvage value of $3,000. Nancy's *MARR* is 24 percent/year.

a. What is the present worth of this investment?

b. What is the decision rule for judging the attractiveness of investments based on present worth?

c. Should Nancy buy the truck?

Section 5.4

WILEY + **25.** The engineering team at Manuel's Manufacturing, Inc., is planning to purchase an enterprise resource planning (ERP) system. The software and installation from Vendor A costs $380,000 initially and is expected to increase revenue $125,000 per year every year. The software and installation from Vendor B costs $280,000 and is expected to increase revenue $95,000 per year. Manuel's uses a 4-year planning horizon and a 10 percent per year *MARR*.

a. What is the present worth of each investment?

b. What is the decision rule for determining the preferred investment based on present worth ranking?

c. Which ERP system should Manuel purchase?

26. Reconsider Problem 25. Determine which ERP system should be purchased based on an incremental present worth analysis.

27. Nadine Chelesvig has patented her invention. She is offering a potential manufacturer two contracts for the exclusive right to manufacture and market her product. Plan A calls for an immediate single lump sum payment to her of $30,000. Plan B calls for an annual payment of $1,000 plus a royalty of $0.50 per unit sold. The remaining life of the patent is 10 years. Nadine uses a *MARR* of 10 percent/year.

    a. What must be the uniform annual sales volume of the product for Nadine to be indifferent between the contracts, based on a present worth analysis?

    b. If the sales volume is below the volume determined in (a), which contract would the manufacturer prefer?

28. Octavia Bakery is planning to purchase one of two ovens. The expected cash flows for each oven are shown below. *MARR* is 8 percent/year.

	Model 127B	Model 334A
Initial Investment	$50,000	$80,000
Estimated Life	10	5
End of Life Salvage	$10,000	$0
Annual Income	$19,400	$26,000
Annual Expense	$10,000	$6,000

    a. Based on a 10-year planning horizon, what is the present worth of each investment?

    b. What is the decision rule for determining the preferred investment based on present worth ranking?

    c. Which oven should Octavia purchase?

29. Reconsider Problem 28. Determine which oven should be purchased based on an incremental present worth analysis.

30. Parker County Community College (PCCC) is trying to determine whether to use no insulation or to use insulation that is either 1 inch thick or 2 inches thick on its steam pipes. The heat loss from the pipes without insulation is expected to cost $1.50 per year per foot of pipe. A 1-inch thick insulated covering will eliminate 89 percent of the loss and will cost $0.40 per foot. A 2-inch thick insulated covering will eliminate 92 percent of the loss and will cost $0.85 per foot. PCCC Physical Plant Services estimates that there are 250,000 feet of steam pipe on campus. The PCCC Accounting Office requires a 10 percent/year return to justify capital expenditures. The insulation has a life expectancy of 10 years. Determine which insulation (if any) should be purchased using a ranking present worth analysis.

31. Reconsider Problem 30. Determine which insulation (if any) should be purchased based on an incremental present worth analysis.

32. Quantum Logistics, Inc., a wholesale distributor, is considering the construction of a new warehouse to serve the southeastern geographic region near the Alabama–Georgia border. There are three cities being considered. After site visits and a budget analysis, the expected income and costs associated with locating in each of the cities have been determined. The life of the warehouse is expected to be 12 years and *MARR* is 15 percent/year.

City	Initial Cost	Net Annual Income
Lagrange	$1,260,000	$480,000
Auburn	$1,000,000	$410,000
Anniston	$1,620,000	$520,000

    a. What is the present worth of each site?

    b. What is the decision rule for determining the preferred site based on present worth ranking?

    c. Which city should be recommended?

33. Reconsider Problem 32. Determine which city should be recommended based on an incremental present worth analysis.

34. DelRay Foods must purchase a new gumdrop machine. Two machines are available. Machine 7745 has a first cost of $10,000, an estimated life of 10 years, a salvage value of $1,000, and annual operating costs estimated at $0.01 per 1,000 gumdrops. Machine A37Y has a first cost of $8,000, a life of 10 years, and no salvage value. Its annual operating costs will be $300 regardless of the number of gumdrops produced. *MARR* is 6 percent/year, and 30 million gumdrops are produced each year.

    a. What is the present worth of each machine?

    b. What is the decision rule for determining the preferred machine based on present worth ranking?

    c. Which machine should be recommended?

35. Reconsider Problem 34. Determine which machine should be recommended based on an incremental present worth analysis.

36. Two storage structures, given code names Y and Z, are being considered for a military base located in Sontaga. The military uses a 5 percent/year expected rate of return and a 24-year life for decisions of this type. The relevant characteristics for each structure are shown below.

	Structure Y	**Structure Z**
First Cost	$4,500	$10,000
Estimated Life	12 years	24 years
Estimated Salvage Value	None	$1,800
Annual Maintenance Cost	$1,000	$720

    a. What is the present worth of each machine?

    b. What is the decision rule for determining the preferred machine based on present worth ranking?

    c. Which structure should be recommended?

 37. Tempura, Inc., is considering two projects. Project A requires an investment of $50,000. Estimated annual receipts for 20 years are $20,000; estimated annual costs are $12,500. An alternative project, B, requires an investment of $75,000, has annual receipts for 20 years of $28,000, and has annual costs of $18,000. Assume both projects have a zero salvage value and that *MARR* is 12 percent/year.

    a. What is the present worth of each project?

    b. Which project should be recommended?

38. Final Finishing is considering three mutually exclusive alternatives for a new polisher. Each alternative has an expected life of 10 years and no salvage value. Polisher 1 requires an initial investment of $20,000 and provides annual benefits of $4,465. Polisher 2 requires an initial investment of $10,000 and provides annual benefits of $1,770. Polisher 3 requires an initial investment of $15,000 and provides annual benefits of $3,580. *MARR* is 15 percent/year.

    a. What is the present worth of each polisher?

    b. Which polisher should be recommended?

 39. Xanadu Mining is considering three mutually exclusive alternatives, as shown in the table below. *MARR* is 10 percent/year.

EOY	A001	B002	C003
0	−$210	−$110	−$160
1	$80	$60	$80
2	$90	$60	$80
3	$100	$60	$80
4	$110	$70	$80

a. What is the present worth of each alternative?

b. Which alternative should be recommended?

40. Yani has $12,000 for investment purposes. His bank has offered the following three choices:

a. A special savings certificate that will pay $100 each month for 5 years and a lump sum payment at the end of 5 years of $13,000

b. Buy a share of a racehorse for $12,000 that will be worth $20,000 in 5 years

c. Put the money in a savings account that will have an interest rate of 12 percent per year compounded monthly.

Use a present worth analysis to make a recommendation to Yani.

41. Two numerically controlled drill presses are being considered by the production department of Zunni's Manufacturing; one must be selected. Comparison data is shown in the table below. *MARR* is 10 percent/year.

	Drill Press T	Drill Press M
Initial Investment	$20,000	$30,000
Estimated Life	10 years	10 years
Estimated Salvage Value	$5,000	$7,000
Annual Operating Cost	$12,000	$6,000
Annual Maintenance Cost	$2,000	$4,000

a. What is the present worth of each drill press?

b. Which drill press should be recommended?

42. Alpha Electronics can purchase a needed service for $90 per unit. The same service can be provided by equipment that costs $100,000 and that will have a salvage value of 0 at the end of 10 years. Annual operating costs for the equipment will be $7,000 per year plus $25 per unit produced. *MARR* is 12 percent/year.

a. Based on a present worth analysis, should the equipment be purchased if the expected production is 200 units/year?

b. Based on a present worth analysis, should the equipment be purchased if the expected demand is 500 units/year?

c. Determine the breakeven value for annual production that will return *MARR* on the investment in the new equipment.

43. On-Site Testing Service has received four investment proposals for consideration. Two of the proposals, X1 and X2, are mutually exclusive. The other two proposals, Y1 and Y2 are also mutually exclusive. Proposal Y1 is contingent on X1, and Y2 is contingent on X2. Other than these restrictions, any combination of proposals (including null) is feasible. *MARR* is 10 percent/year. The expected cash flows for the proposals are shown below. A present worth analysis is to be conducted.

End of Year	X1	X2	Y1	Y2
0	−$10,000	−$15,000	−$6,000	−$9,000
1 through 8	$1,600	$2,600	$2,500	$3,500

a. List all the alternatives to be considered.

b. Determine which (if any) proposals On-Site Testing should accept.

44. Dark Skies Observatory is considering several options to purchase a new deep-space telescope. Revenue would be generated from the telescope by selling "time and use" slots to various researchers around the world. Four possible telescopes have been identified in addition to the possibility of not buying a telescope if none are financially attractive. The table below details the characteristics of each telescope. A present worth ranking analysis is to be performed.

	T1	T2	T3	T4
Useful Life	10 years	10 years	10 years	10 years
First Cost	$600,000	$800,000	$470,000	$540,000
Salvage Value	$70,000	$130,000	$65,000	$200,000
Annual Revenue	$400,000	$600,000	$260,000	$320,000
Annual Expenses	$130,000	$270,000	$70,000	$120,000

    a. Determine the preferred telescope if *MARR* is 25 percent/year.

    b. Determine the preferred telescope if *MARR* is 42 percent/year.

45. Reconsider Problem 44 using an incremental present worth analysis.

46. Delta Dawn's Bakery is considering purchasing a new van to deliver bread. The van will cost $18,000. Two-thirds ($12,000) of this cost will be borrowed. The loan is to be repaid with four equal annual payments (first payment at $t = 1$) based on an interest rate of 4 percent/year. It is anticipated that the van will be used for 6 years and then sold for a salvage value of $500. Annual operating and maintenance expenses for the van over the 6-year life are estimated to be $700 per year. If the van is purchased, Delta will realize a cost savings of $3,800 per year. Delta uses a *MARR* of 6 percent/year. Based on a present worth analysis, is the purchase of the van economically attractive?

47. Several years ago, a man won $27 million in the state lottery. To pay off the winner, the state planned to make an initial $1 million payment immediately followed by equal annual payments of $1.3 million at the end of each year for the next 20 years. Just before receiving any money, the man offered to sell the winning ticket back to the state for a one-time immediate payment of $14.4 million. If the state uses a 6 percent/year *MARR*, should it accept the man's offer? Use a present worth analysis.

48. Allied Electronics must purchase a new automatic soldering machine to meet increased demand for its electronic goods. Of all the machines considered, management has narrowed the choices to the following three, which are mutually exclusive:

	Machine 1	Machine 2	Machine 3
Initial Cost	$800,000	$650,000	$575,000
Annual Operating Cost	$50,000	$90,000	$105,000
Salvage Value	$40,000	$32,500	$28,750

Allied Electronics uses a 4-year planning horizon, and *MARR* is 12 percent/year. Based on a present worth analysis, determine which machine should be purchased.

49. The management of Brawn Engineering is considering three alternatives to satisfy an OSHA requirement for safety gates in the machine shop. Each gate will completely satisfy the requirement, so no combinations need to be considered. The first costs, operating costs, and salvage values over a 5-year planning horizon are shown below. Using a present worth analysis with a *MARR* of 20 percent/year, determine the preferred gate.

End of Year	Gate 1	Gate 2	Gate 3
0	−$15,000	−$19,000	−$24,000
1	−$6,500	−$5,600	−$4,000
2	−$6,500	−$5,600	−$4,000
3	−$6,500	−$5,600	−$4,000
4	−$6,500	−$5,600	−$4,000
5	−$6,500 + $0	−$5,600 + $2,000	−$4,000 + $5,000

50. RealTurf is considering purchasing an automatic sprinkler system for its sod farm by borrowing the entire $30,000 purchase price. The loan would be repaid with four equal annual payments at an interest rate of 12 percent/year. It is anticipated that the sprinkler system would be used for 9 years and then sold for a salvage value of $2,000. Annual operating and maintenance expenses for the system over the 9-year life are estimated to be $9,000 per year. If the new system is purchased, cost savings of $15,000 per year will be realized over the present manual watering system. RealTurf uses a *MARR* of 15 percent/year for economic decision making. Based on a present worth analysis, is the purchase of the new sprinkler system economically attractive?

51. Orpheum Productions in Nevada is considering three mutually exclusive alternatives for lighting enhancements to one of its recording studios. Each enhancement will increase revenues by attracting directors who prefer this lighting style. The cash flow details, in thousands of dollars, for these enhancements are shown in the chart below. *MARR* is 10 percent/year. Based on a present worth analysis, which alternative (if any) should be implemented?

End of Year	Light Bar	Sliding Spots	Reflected Beam
0	−$6,000	−$14,000	−$20,000
1	$2,000	$3,500	$0
2	$2,000	$3,500	$2,300
3	$2,000	$3,500	$4,600
4	$2,000	$3,500	$6,900
5	$2,000	$3,500	$9,200
6	$2,000	$3,500	$11,500

52. Deep Seas Submarine must implement a new engine in its submarines to meet the needs of clients who desire quieter operation. Two designs, both technologically feasible, have been created, and Deep Seas wishes to know which one to pursue. Design 1 would require an up-front manufacturing cost of $15,000,000 and will cost $2,500,000 per year for 3 years to swap out the engines in all its current submarines. Design 2 will cost $20,000,000 up front, but due to a higher degree of compatibility will only require $1,500,000 per year to implement. *MARR* is 10 percent/year. Based on a present worth analysis, determine which design should be chosen.

53. Calisto Launch Services is an independent space corporation and has been contracted to develop and launch one of two different satellites. Initial equipment will cost $750,000 for the first satellite and $850,000 for the second. Development will take 5 years at an expected cost of $150,000 per year for the first satellite; $120,000 per year for the second. The same launch vehicle can be used for either satellite and will cost $275,000 at the time of the launch 5 years from now. At the conclusion of the launch, the contracting company will pay Calisto $2,500,000 for either satellite.

Calisto is also considering whether they should consider launching both satellites. Because Calisto would have to upgrade its facilities to handle two concurrent projects, the initial costs would rise by $150,000 in addition to the first costs of each satellite. Calisto would need to hire additional engineers and workers, raising the yearly costs to a total of $400,000. An additional compartment would be added to the launch vehicle at an additional cost of $75,000. As an incentive to do both, the contracting company will pay for both launches plus a bonus of $1,000,000. Using a present worth analysis with a *MARR* of 10 percent/year, what should Calisto Launch Services do?

54. Baon Chemicals Unlimited purchases a computer-controlled filter for $100,000. Half of the purchase price is borrowed from a bank at 15 percent compounded annually. The loan is to be paid back with equal annual payments over a 5-year period. The filter is expected to last 10 years, at which time it will have a salvage value of $10,000. Over the 10-year period, the operating and maintenance costs are expected to equal $20,000 in year 1 and increase by $1,500/year each year thereafter. By making the investment, annual fines of $50,000 for pollution will be avoided. Baon expects to earn 12 percent compounded annually on its investments. Based on a present worth analysis, determine whether purchasing the filter is economically justified.

55. Value Lodges owns an economy motel chain and is considering building a new 200-unit motel. The cost to build the motel is estimated at $8,000,000; Value Lodges estimates furnishings for the motel will cost an additional $700,000

and will require replacement every 5 years. Annual operating and maintenance costs for the motel are estimated to be $800,000. The average rental rate for a unit is anticipated to be $40/day. Value Lodges expects the motel to have a life of 15 years and a salvage value of $900,000 at the end of 15 years. This estimated salvage value assumes that the furnishings are not new. Furnishings have no salvage value at the end of each 5-year replacement interval. Assuming average daily occupancy percentages of 50 percent, 60 percent, 70 percent, and 80 percent for years 1 through 4, respectively, and 90 percent for the fifth through fifteenth years, *MARR* of 12 percent/year, 365 operating days/year, and ignoring the cost of land, should the motel be built? Base your decision on a present worth analysis.

56. Nu Things, Inc., is considering an investment in a business venture with the following anticipated cash flow results:

EOY	Cash Flow	EOY	Cash Flow	EOY	Cash Flow
0	−$70,000	7	14,000	14	7,000
1	20,000	8	13,000	15	6,000
2	19,000	9	12,000	16	5,000
3	18,000	10	11,000	17	4,000
4	17,000	11	10,000	18	3,000
5	16,000	12	9,000	19	2,000
6	15,000	13	8,000	20	1,000

Assume *MARR* is 20 percent per year. Based on a present worth analysis, (1) determine the investment's worth, (2) state whether or not your results indicate the investment should be undertaken, and (3) state the decision rule you used to arrive at this conclusion.

57. Reconsider the data from Problem 56.

a. Plot a graph of PW versus *MARR*, where *MARR* varies from 0 percent to 50 percent by 1 percent increments. PW should be on the *y*-axis and *MARR* on the *x*-axis.

b. Explain the significance of the *y*-axis intercept.

c. Explain the significance of the *x*-axis intercept.

58. Packaging equipment for Xi Cling Wrap is expected to result in end-of-year net savings of $23,000 per year for 3 years. The equipment can be purchased for $60,000 and will have a market value of $10,000 after 3 years. Alternatively, the equipment can be leased for $21,000 per year, payable at the beginning of each year. Xi Cling's *MARR* is 10 percent/year. Based on a present worth analysis, determine if the packaging equipment should be purchased or leased.

59. An environmental consultant is considering the installation of a water storage tank for a client. The tank is estimated to have an initial cost of $426,000, and annual maintenance costs are estimated to be $6,400 per year. As an alternative, a holding pond can be provided a short distance away at an initial cost of $180,000 for the pond plus $90,000 for pumps and piping. Annual operating and maintenance costs for the pumps and holding pond are estimated to be $17,000. The planning horizon is 20 years, and at that time, neither alternative has any salvage value. Determine the preferred alternative based on a present worth analysis with a *MARR* of 20 percent/year.

60. A civil engineer is considering two pumps for an irrigation system. Pump A can be purchased for $19,400 with annual operating and maintenance expenses estimated to be $7,000. Alternatively, Pump B can be purchased for $15,000 with annual operating and maintenance costs estimated to be $8,400. A 10-year planning horizon is to be used. Salvage value for each pump at the end of the tenth year is estimated to be 10 percent of the purchase price. *MARR* is 12 percent/year. Determine the preferred alternative based on a present worth analysis.

Section 5.5

61. Consider the two one-shot investment alternatives shown in the table below. Neither alternative is expected to be available again in the future. *MARR* is 11 percent/year. Based on a present worth analysis, which alternative is preferred?

EOY	Alternative W	Alternative X
0	−$100,000	−$150,000
1	$20,000	$40,000
2	$20,000	$45,000
3	$50,000	$50,000
4	$80,000	$55,000
5	$110,000	$60,000
6		$65,000
7		$70,000

62. Two new opportunities are being considered for a venture capital firm. Both are one-time opportunities with no option for renewal. The firm uses a 12 percent/year expected rate of return for decisions of this type. The relevant characteristics for each option are shown below. Based on a present worth analysis, which option is preferred?

	Option 1	Option 2
Initial Investment	$100,000	$75,000
Estimated Life	12 years	9 years
Expected Annual Return	$16,500	$14,300

63. Technology Innovations is planning to purchase one of two chip insertion machines. Due to the pace of technological change in this area, it is realistic to assume that these are one-shot investments. The expected cash flows for each machine are shown below. *MARR* is 8 percent/year. Based on a present worth analysis, which machine is preferred?

	E Series	M Series
Initial Investment	$40,000	$60,000
Estimated Life	7	5
End of Life Salvage	$10,000	$0
Annual Income	$19,400	$26,000
Annual Expense	$10,000	$6,000

64. Consider the net cash flow profiles shown below for each of three one-shot alternatives to be considered in an economic analysis. *MARR* is 10 percent/year. Based on a present worth analysis, which alternative is preferred?

EOY	Alternative 1	Alternative 2	Alternative 3
0	−$50,000	−$90,000	−$100,000
1	$40,000	$35,000	$70,000
2	$50,000	$40,000	$65,000
3	$60,000	$45,000	$60,000
4		$50,000	$55,000
5		$55,000	

Section 5.6

 65. Reconsider Problem 9 (repeated here). Bailey, Inc., is considering buying a new gang punch that would allow them to produce circuit boards more efficiently. The punch has a first cost of $100,000 and a useful life of 15 years. At the end of its useful life, the punch has no salvage value. Labor costs would increase $2,000 per year using the gang punch, but raw material costs would decrease $12,000 per year. *MARR* is 5 percent/year.

    a. What is the discounted payback period for this investment?

    b. If the maximum attractive *DPBP* is 3 years, what is the decision rule for judging the worth of this investment?

    c. Should Bailey buy the gang punch based on *DPBP*?

66. Repeat Problem 65 using payback period with no discounting (*PBP*).

    a. What is the payback period for this investment?

    b. If the maximum attractive *PBP* is 3 years, what is the decision rule for judging the worth of this investment?

    c. Should Bailey buy the gang punch based on *PBP*?

    d. Compare your recommendations resulting from Problems 9, 65, and 66. Are they consistent? What recommendation would you make to Bailey?

67. Reconsider Problem 22 (repeated here). Home Innovations is evaluating a new product design. The estimated receipts and disbursements associated with the new product are shown below. *MARR* is 10 percent/year.

End of Year	Receipts	Disbursements
0	$0	$1,000
1	$600	$300
2	$600	$300
3	$700	$300
4	$700	$300
5	$700	$300

    a. What is the discounted payback period for this investment?

    b. If the maximum attractive *DPBP* is 3 years, what is the decision rule for judging the worth of this investment?

    c. Should Home Innovations buy the gang punch based on *DPBP*?

68. Repeat Problem 67 using payback period with no discounting (*PBP*).

    a. What is the payback period for this investment?

    b. If the maximum attractive *PBP* is 3 years, what is the decision rule for judging the worth of this investment?

    c. Should Home Innovations pursue this new product based on *PBP*?

    d. Compare your recommendations resulting from Problems 22, 67, and 68. Are they consistent? What recommendation would you make to Home Innovations?

Section 5.7

 69. Reconsider Problem 25 (repeated here). The engineering team at Manuel's Manufacturing, Inc., is planning to purchase an enterprise resource planning (ERP) system. The software and installation from Vendor A costs $380,000 initially and is expected to increase revenue $125,000 per year every year. The software and installation from Vendor B costs $280,000 and is expected to increase revenue $95,000 per year. Manuel's uses a 4-year planning horizon and a 10 percent per year *MARR*.

    a. What is the discounted payback period of each investment?

    b. Which ERP system should Manuel purchase if his decision rule is to select the system with the shortest *DPBP*?

    c. Does this decision agree or disagree with the results of the present worth analysis in Problem 25?

70. Reconsider Problem 28 (repeated here). Octavia Bakery is planning to purchase one of two ovens. The expected cash flows for each oven are shown below. *MARR* is 8 percent/year.

	Model 127B	Model 334A
Initial Investment	$50,000	$80,000
Estimated Life	10	5
End of Life Salvage	$10,000	$0
Annual Income	$19,400	$26,000
Annual Expense	$10,000	$6,000

a. What is the discounted payback period for each investment?

b. Which oven should Octavia Bakery purchase if they wish to minimize the *DPBP*?

c. Is this recommendation consistent with a present worth analysis recommendation in Problem 28?

71. Reconsider Problem 32 (repeated here). Quantum Logistics, Inc., a wholesale distributor, is considering the construction of a new warehouse to serve the southeastern geographic region near the Alabama–Georgia border. There are three cities being considered. After site visits and a budget analysis, the expected income and costs associated with locating in each of the cities have been determined. The life of the warehouse is expected to be 12 years, and *MARR* is 15 percent/year.

City	Initial Cost	Net Annual Income
Lagrange	$1,260,000	$480,000
Auburn	$1,000,000	$410,000
Anniston	$1,620,000	$520,000

a. What is the discounted payback period for each location?

b. Which city should Quantum Logistics select if they wish to minimize the *DPBP*?

c. Is this recommendation consistent with a present worth analysis recommendation in Problem 32?

Sections 5.8 and 5.9

72. A municipality is planning on constructing a water treatment plant at an initial cost of $10,000,000. Every 5 years, major repairs and cleanup are required at a cost of $2,000,000. Due to the necessity to remove sludge and make minor repairs, annual costs of operating the treatment plant are estimated to be $700,000, $775,000, $850,000, $925,000, and $1,000,000 each year leading up to the 5-year major repair and cleanup. Based on a 4 percent/year *TVOM*, what is the capitalized cost for the water treatment plant?

73. Two incinerators are being considered by a waste management company. Design A has an initial cost of $2,500,000, has annual operating and maintenance costs of $800,000, and requires overhauls every 5 years at a cost of $1,250,000. Design B is more sophisticated, including computer controls; it has an initial cost of $5,750,000, has annual operating and maintenance costs of $600,000, and requires overhauls every 10 years at a cost of $3,000,000. Using a 5 percent/year interest rate, determine the capitalized cost for each design and recommend which should be chosen.

74. A flood control project at Pleasant Valley dam is projected to cost $2,000,000 today, have annual maintenance costs of $50,000, and have major inspection and upkeep after each 5-year interval costing $250,000. If the interest rate is 10 percent/year, determine the capitalized cost.

75. The gaming commission is introducing a new lottery game called Infinite Progresso. The winner of the Infinite Progresso jackpot will receive $1,000 at the end of January, $2,000 at the end of February, $3,000 at the end of March, and so on up to $12,000 at the end of December. At the beginning of the next year, the sequence repeats starting at $1,000 in January and ending at $12,000 in December. This annual sequence of payments repeats indefinitely. If the gaming commission expects to sell a minimum of 1 million tickets, what is the minimum price they can charge for the tickets to break even, assuming the commission earns 6 percent/year/month on its investments and there is exactly one winning ticket.

76. A generous benefactor donates $500,000 to a state university. The donation is to be used to fund student scholarships. Determine the dollar amount of scholarships that can be given out each year under each of the following conditions. The state university earns 4 percent per year on its investments.

   a. The donation is a quasi-endowment designed to last 20 years.

   b. The donation is a quasi-endowment designed to last 30 years.

   c. The donation is a quasi-endowment designed to last 50 years.

   d. The donation is an endowment designed to last forever.

77. Reconsider the data from Problem 76. Plot a graph of scholarship dollars versus number of years, where the number of years varies from 1 year to 100 years by 2-year increments. Dollars should be on the *y*-axis and years on the *x*-axis.

78. A prospective venture has the following cash flow profile over a 5-year horizon. What is the capitalized worth at 6 percent/year assuming the pattern repeats indefinitely?

End of Year	Receipts	Disbursements
0	$100	$1,100
1	$300	$50
2	$500	$250
3	$400	$150
4	$350	$100
5	$250	$0

79. You decide to open an individual retirement account (IRA) at your local bank that pays 8 percent/year compounded annually. At the end of each of the next 40 years, you will deposit $4,000 into the account. Three years after your last deposit, you will begin making annual withdrawals. What annual amount will you be able to withdraw if you want the withdrawals to last

   a. 20 years?

   b. 30 years?

   c. forever?

80. Barnard College is about to bury a time capsule. To maintain and protect the time capsule in perpetuity, three options are available. Barnard's *MARR* is 6 percent/year. Based on a capitalized cost analysis, which option is preferred?

Costs	Pay-Me-Now	Pay-Me-Later	Pay-Me-Forever
First Cost	$5,000	$1,000	$0
Recurring Costs	$0	$1,000 every 5 years	$250 every year

Chapter 6

FUTURE WORTH

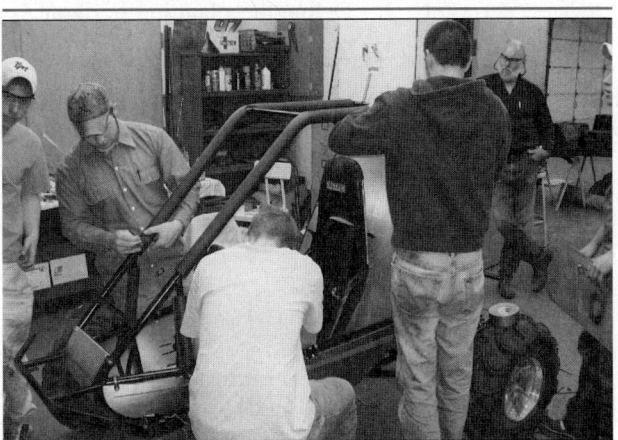

Regardless of your major and regardless of your plans concerning graduate school, don't put off planning for your future. These Oklahoma State University engineering students have spent hundreds of hours designing and building their entry in the Society of Automotive Engineers national Baja car competition. You should give at least this much thought to your future. (Courtesy of the College of Engineering, Architecture and Technology at Oklahoma State University)

Josh Liu

Josh Liu has been investing in the stock market for several years, beginning when he was a freshman in high school. His recent investments in Google and Akamai stock have been quite successful. Based on a stellar academic record as an undergraduate engineering student, Josh is contemplating graduate school, with interests in pursuing an MBA or a master's in engineering. Due to his interests in investments, Josh has a keen interest in financial engineering and possibly working on Wall Street following completion of his master's degree.

With an eye toward the future, Josh is interested in knowing what annual investments and annual returns on investments are required for him to amass an investment portfolio valued at $2 million within 30 years. He is also interested in knowing how long it will take for him to achieve a net worth in excess of $1 million.

Not only do individual investors establish financial goals for the future, but so do businesses. Although we are not aware of firms using future worth analysis as the principal tool to measure the economic worth of investment alternatives, future worth is used as a supplement to present worth in an engineering economic analysis. Also, some firms use future worth analysis to estimate terminal values in business acquisition analysis. The most popular use of future worth analysis is in retirement planning.

> ### Systematic Economic Analysis Technique
>
> 1. Identify the investment alternatives
> 2. Define the planning horizon
> 3. Specify the discount rate
> 4. Estimate the cash flows
> 5. **Compare the alternatives**
> 6. Perform supplementary analyses
> 7. Select the preferred investment

6-1   INTRODUCTION

In this chapter, we continue the discussion of using measures of economic worth in comparing mutually exclusive investment alternatives. In the previous chapter, we considered two worth measures: present worth and capitalized worth. Now we focus on what is variously referred to as *future worth, future value,* and *terminal value.* Future worth analysis uses the *MARR* to express the economic worth of a set of cash flows, occurring over the planning horizon, as a single equivalent value at an ending or termination time called "the future."

In the previous chapter, we noted that many investors prefer to express the economic worth of the set of cash flows as a single monetary sum at a point in time called "the present." To obtain the single sum equivalent, we discount cash flows that occur at various points in time in the future. Hence, the name *discounted cash flow analysis.*

As popular as discounting money is, we have found that people have far more difficulty understanding discounting than compounding. For many, it is easier to grasp the notion of money growing in value as one moves forward in time, rather than shrinking in value as one moves backward in time. For them, future worth analysis is more intuitively appealing than present worth analysis.

Yet another reason for performing future worth analysis is goal setting. When performing financial planning, many individuals are interested in knowing what the value of their investment portfolio will be at some particular point in the future. For them, future worth is more relevant than present worth.

For investors, the following important distinction exists between present worth and future worth analyses: Present worth analysis brings money to the point in time when the decision will be made, the present; future worth analysis takes money to the point in time when it will be enjoyed, the future.

In the chapter, we learn how to make decisions regarding the economic viability of a single investment using future worth analysis. We also learn how to determine the point in time when an investment begins to "make money." In addition, we learn how to use future worth analysis to choose from among multiple investment alternatives the one having the greatest economic worth. And, finally, we learn how to maximize the value of an investment portfolio by considering both the money invested in a particular alternative *and* the available capital that is not invested.

6-2   FUTURE WORTH: SINGLE ALTERNATIVE

Recalling our work in Chapter 2 and letting i denote the *MARR*, the future worth of an investment can be expressed mathematically as follows:

$$FW = \sum_{t=0}^{n} A_t (1 + MARR)^{n-t} \tag{6.1}$$

As with present worth analysis, the decision to pursue an investment opportunity is dependent on $FW > 0$. If the future worth is positive, then the investment will be recommended.

EXAMPLE 6.1   A Single Investment Opportunity

In Chapter 5, we considered the acquisition of a new surface mount placement (SMP) machine having an initial cost of $500,000. It was anticipated that the investment would result in annual operating and maintenance costs being reduced by $92,500 per year, after taxes. The manufacturing engineer estimated the machine would be worth $50,000 at the end of the 10-year planning horizon. Using a 10 percent after-tax *MARR* and future worth analysis, should the investment be made?

The future worth for the investment will be

$$FW = -\$500,000(F|P\ 10\%,10) + \$92,500(F|A\ 10\%,10) + \$50,000$$
$$= -\$500,000(2.59374) + \$92,500(15.93742) + \$50,000$$
$$= \$227,341.40$$

or, using Excel®,

$$FW = \text{FV}(10\%,10,-92500,500000)+50000=\$227,340.55$$

Since $FW > \$0$, the investment is recommended.

The FW of **$227,340.55** assumes the investment will be continued for 10 years. What if the planning horizon is less than 10 years? Will it still be a good investment? These questions are addressed in the following example.

EXAMPLE 6.2   A Closer Look at the Single Investment Opportunity

Suppose there is some uncertainty regarding the length of time the SMP machine will be used. Further, suppose the salvage value decreases with usage; specifically, suppose the salvage value either decreases geometrically at a rate of 20.6 percent per year or decreases by $45,000 per year.

As shown in Figure 6.1, when salvage value decreases geometrically, the future worth decreases during the first 2 years of the investment; then it begins to increase, becoming positive in 6.95 years. As expected, the future worth grows exponentially after its minimum point at 3.21 years.

How did we know future worth equals 0 in 6.95 years, if salvage value decreases geometrically? Recall, 6.95 years is the value for DPBP obtained in Example 5.4. The same result is obtained if cumulative future worth, rather than cumulative present worth, is used to define DPBP. As shown in Figure 6.2, the Excel® **SOLVER** tool can be used to obtain the number of years required for the SMP investment to be recovered, including the time value of money.

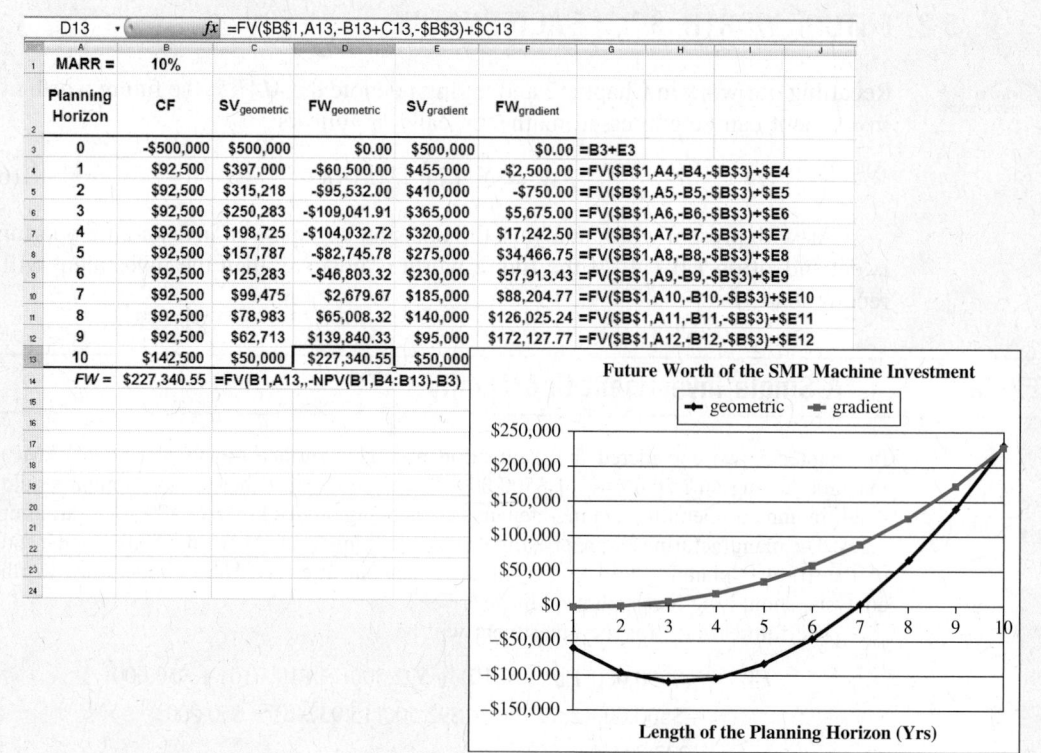

	D13	▾	fx =FV($B$1,A13,-B13+C13,-$B$3)+$C13			

	A	B	C	D	E	F	G
1	MARR =	10%					
2	Planning Horizon	CF	SV$_{geometric}$	FW$_{geometric}$	SV$_{gradient}$	FW$_{gradient}$	
3	0	-$500,000	$500,000	$0.00	$500,000	$0.00	=B3+E3
4	1	$92,500	$397,000	-$60,500.00	$455,000	-$2,500.00	=FV($B$1,A4,-B4,-$B$3)+$E4
5	2	$92,500	$315,218	-$95,532.00	$410,000	-$750.00	=FV($B$1,A5,-B5,-$B$3)+$E5
6	3	$92,500	$250,283	-$109,041.91	$365,000	$5,675.00	=FV($B$1,A6,-B6,-$B$3)+$E6
7	4	$92,500	$198,725	-$104,032.72	$320,000	$17,242.50	=FV($B$1,A7,-B7,-$B$3)+$E7
8	5	$92,500	$157,787	-$82,745.78	$275,000	$34,466.75	=FV($B$1,A8,-B8,-$B$3)+$E8
9	6	$92,500	$125,283	-$46,803.32	$230,000	$57,913.43	=FV($B$1,A9,-B9,-$B$3)+$E9
10	7	$92,500	$99,475	$2,679.67	$185,000	$88,204.77	=FV($B$1,A10,-B10,-$B$3)+$E10
11	8	$92,500	$78,983	$65,008.32	$140,000	$126,025.24	=FV($B$1,A11,-B11,-$B$3)+$E11
12	9	$92,500	$62,713	$139,840.33	$95,000	$172,127.77	=FV($B$1,A12,-B12,-$B$3)+$E12
13	10	$142,500	$50,000	$227,340.55	$50,000		
14	FW =	$227,340.55	=FV(B1,A13,,-NPV(B1,B4:B13)-B3)				

Future Worth of the SMP Machine Investment

FIGURE 6.1

Future Worth for Alternative Salvage Values in Example 6.2.

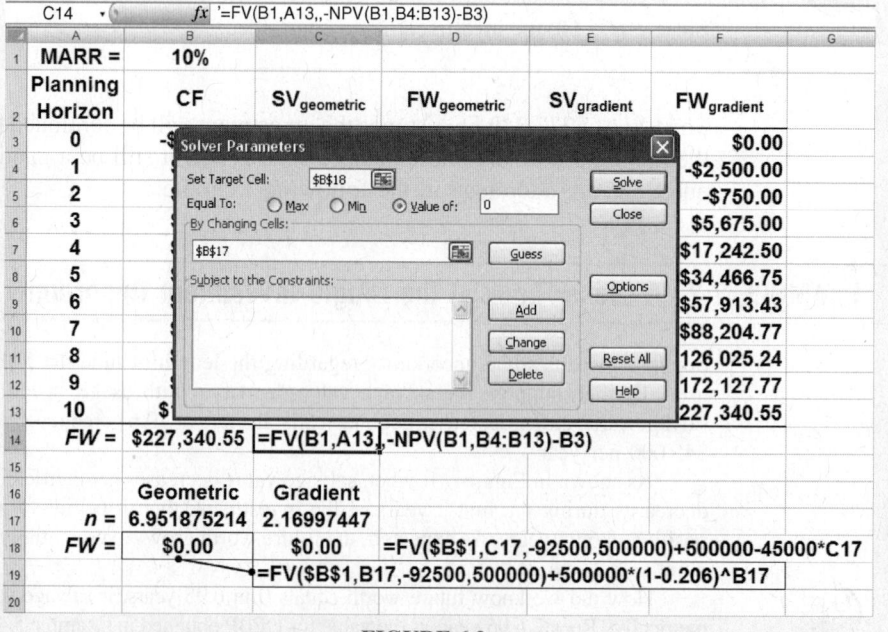

	C14	▾	fx '=FV(B1,A13,,-NPV(B1,B4:B13)-B3)			

	A	B	C	D	E	F	G
1	MARR =	10%					
2	Planning Horizon	CF	SV$_{geometric}$	FW$_{geometric}$	SV$_{gradient}$	FW$_{gradient}$	
3	0					$0.00	
4	1					-$2,500.00	
5	2					-$750.00	
6	3					$5,675.00	
7	4					$17,242.50	
8	5					$34,466.75	
9	6					$57,913.43	
10	7					$88,204.77	
11	8					126,025.24	
12	9					172,127.77	
13	10					227,340.55	
14	FW =	$227,340.55	=FV(B1,A13,,-NPV(B1,B4:B13)-B3)				
16		Geometric	Gradient				
17	n =	6.951875214	2.16997447				
18	FW =	$0.00	$0.00	=FV($B$1,C17,-92500,500000)+500000-45000*C17			
19			=FV($B$1,B17,-92500,500000)+500000*(1-0.206)^B17				

FIGURE 6.2

Using the Excel® SOLVER Tool to Determine Number of Years Required to Recover the SMP Investment.

How did we know future worth achieved its minimum value at 3.21 years? We used the Excel® SOLVER tool, as shown in Figure 6.3, to determine the value of n that minimizes future worth when salvage value decreases geometrically.

	B14 ▾	fx =FV(B1,A13,,-NPV(B1,B4:B13)-B3					
	A	B	C	D	E	F	G
1	MARR =	10%					
2	Planning Horizon	CF	SV$_{geometric}$	FW$_{geometric}$	Solver Parameters		
3	0	-$500,000	$500,000	$0.00	Set Target Cell: $B$17		
4	1	$92,500	$397,164	-$60,335.90	Equal To: ○ Max ⊙ Min ○ Value of: 0		
5	2	$92,500	$315,479	-$95,271.36	By Changing Cells:		
6	3	$92,500	$250,594	-$108,731.42	$B$16		Gu
7	4	$92,500	$199,054	-$103,703.95	Subject to the Constraints:		
8	5	$92,500	$158,114	-$82,419.40			A
9	6	$92,500	$125,594	-$46,492.29			
10	7	$92,500	$99,763	$2,967.85			Cha
11	8	$92,500	$79,245	$65,269.88			Del
12	9	$92,500	$62,946	$140,074.01			
13	10	$142,500	$50,000	$227,340.55			
14	FW =	$227,340.55	=FV(B1,A13,,-NPV(B1,B4:B13)-B3)				
15							
16	n =	3.20992665					
17	FW =	-$109,440.80	=FV(10%,B16,-92500,500000)+500000*(1-0.206)^B16				
18							
19							
20							

FIGURE 6.3

Using the Excel® SOLVER Tool to Determine the Length of Service that Minimizes Future Worth.

We noted previously that future worth analysis is appropriate when planning to achieve a particular financial goal at some point in the future. The following example illustrates the use of future worth analysis in financial planning.

$$FW(i\%) = \sum_{t=0}^{n} A_t (1 + i)^{n-t}$$

EXAMPLE 6.3   Achieving a Financial Goal

A recent engineering graduate decided to begin an investment program at the age of 23, with the hope of achieving an investment goal of $5 million by age 58. If a gradient series describes the engineer's investment pattern over the 35-year period and if the annual return on the engineer's investments is approximately 6.5 percent, what gradient step is required to achieve the goal if the first of the 36 investments equals $5,000?

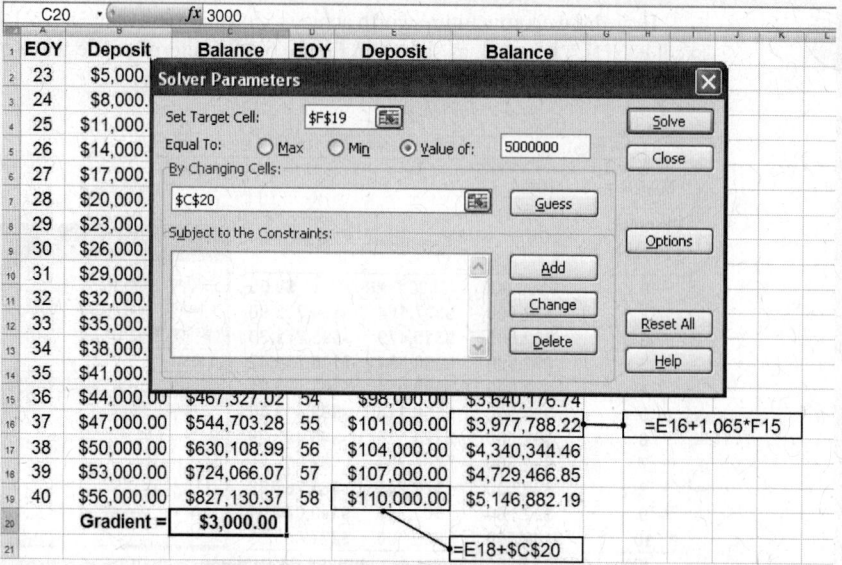

C20	▾	*fx* 3000				
EOY	Deposit	Balance	EOY	Deposit	Balance	

EOY	Deposit	Balance	EOY	Deposit	Balance
23	$5,000.				
24	$8,000.				
25	$11,000.				
26	$14,000.				
27	$17,000.				
28	$20,000.				
29	$23,000.				
30	$26,000.				
31	$29,000.				
32	$32,000.				
33	$35,000.				
34	$38,000.				
35	$41,000.				
36	$44,000.00	$467,327.02	54	$98,000.00	$3,640,176.74
37	$47,000.00	$544,703.28	55	$101,000.00	$3,977,788.22
38	$50,000.00	$630,108.99	56	$104,000.00	$4,340,344.46
39	$53,000.00	$724,066.07	57	$107,000.00	$4,729,466.85
40	$56,000.00	$827,130.37	58	$110,000.00	$5,146,882.19
	Gradient =	$3,000.00			

=E16+1.065*F15

=E18+$C$20

Solver Parameters

Set Target Cell: $F$19

Equal To: ◯ Max ◯ Min ◉ Value of: 5000000

By Changing Cells:

$C$20

Subject to the Constraints:

Solve · Close · Guess · Options · Add · Change · Reset All · Delete · Help

FIGURE 6.4

Set Up to Use the Excel® SOLVER Tool to Determine the Gradient Step Needed to Achieve a Financial Goal.

Since the investment's future worth is given and the unknown is the size of the gradient step (G), the following equation is to be solved for G:

$$G = [\$5,000,000(A|F\,6.5\%,36) - \$5,000]/(A|G\,6.5\%,36)$$

where

$$(A|F\,6.5\%,36) = 0.065/[(1.065)^{36} - 1] = 0.0075133$$

and

$$(A|G\,6.5\%,36) = \{(1.065)^{36} - [1 + 36(0.065)]\}/\{0.065[(1.065)^{36} - 1]\} = 11.22339$$

Therefore,

$$G = [\$5,000,000(0.0075133) - \$5,000]/11.22339 = \$2,901.66$$

SOLVER can be used to solve for G. As shown in Figure 6.4, we let cell C20 contain the value of G. Then we generate the deposits by adding C20 to the preceding deposit. The balance in the investment account is computed by adding the most recent deposit to the product of the previous balance and 1.065. After 36 years, when the engineer is 58, the balance is to be $5 million. (If $G = \$3,000$, the final balance is $5,146,882.19.)

Figure 6.5 contains the solution obtained using SOLVER. Notice, SOLVER is set up to make F19 equal 5000000 by changing C20. As shown, if $G = \$2,901.67$, then a $5 million balance will occur in the investment account after 36 years.

What if the investments do not earn 6.5 percent? To gain an understanding of the impact on the future worth of the investments, Figure 6.6 was developed, showing the growth in the investment portfolio over time for various annual returns on the investment, where the formula for $(F|G\,i\%,n)$ is given in Equation 2.39 in Chapter 2. In anticipation of annual returns being between 6 and 8 percent, the engineer anticipates the size of the investment portfolio will be between $4.6 million and $6.4 million after the thirty-sixth deposit.

Next, the engineer considered the effect on the future worth of the investment portfolio if annual investments increase as a geometric series. Using the formula for $(F|A_1\,i\%,j\%,n)$,

| F19 | | fx | =E19+1.065*F18 | | | | | | | | |

	A	B	C	D	E	F	G	H	I	J	K
1	EOY	Deposit	Balance	EOY	Deposit	Balance					
2	23	$5,000.00	$5,000.00	41	$57,230.10	$914,908.38					
3	24	$7,901.67	$13,226.67	42	$60,131.77	$1,034,509.19					
4	25	$10,803.34	$24,889.75	43	$63,033.44	$1,164,785.73					
5	26	$13,705.02	$40,212.60	44	$65,935.11	$1,306,431.92					
6	27	$16,606.69	$59,433.11	45	$68,836.79	$1,460,186.78					
7	28	$19,508.36	$82,804.62	46	$71,738.46	$1,626,837.37					
8	29	$22,410.03	$110,596.95	47	$74,640.13	$1,807,221.93					
9	30	$25,311.70	$143,097.46	48	$77,541.80	$2,002,233.16					
10	31	$28,213.38	$180,612.17	49	$80,443.47	$2,212,821.79					
11	32	$31,115.05	$223,467.01	50	$83,345.15	$2,440,000.35					
12	33	$34,016.72	$272,009.09	51	$86,246.82	$2,684,847.19					
13	34	$36,918.39	$326,608.07	52	$89,148.49	$2,948,510.75					
14	35	$39,820.06	$387,657.66	53	$92,050.16	$3,232,214.11					
15	36	$42,721.74	$455,577.14	54	$94,951.83	$3,537,259.86					
16	37	$45,623.41	$530,813.07	55	$97,853.51	$3,865,035.26	=E16+1.065*F15				
17	38	$48,525.08	$613,841.00	56	$100,755.18	$4,217,017.73					
18	39	$51,426.75	$705,167.41	57	$103,656.85	$4,594,780.73					
19	40	$54,328.43	$805,331.72	58	$106,558.52	$5,000,000.00					
20		Gradient =	$2,901.67								
21						=E18+$C$20					

FIGURE 6.5

Excel® SOLVER Solution to Example 6.3.

| B14 | | fx | =FV(A14,36,-5000)+2901.67206*(((1+A14)^36-(1+36*A14))/A14^2) |

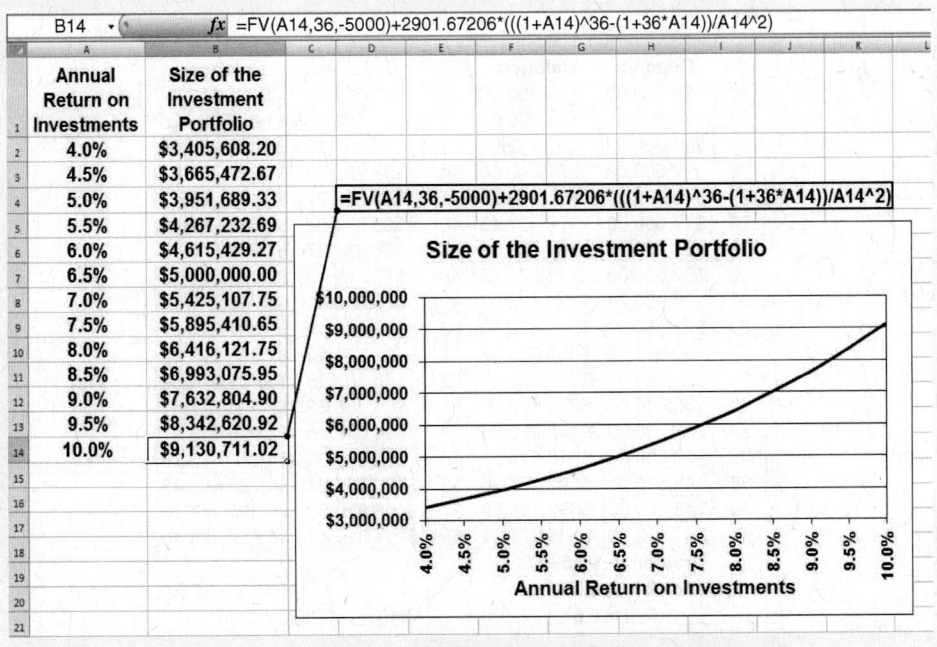

	A	B	C	D	E	F	G	H	I	J	K	L
1	Annual Return on Investments	Size of the Investment Portfolio										
2	4.0%	$3,405,608.20										
3	4.5%	$3,665,472.67										
4	5.0%	$3,951,689.33	=FV(A14,36,-5000)+2901.67206*(((1+A14)^36-(1+36*A14))/A14^2)									
5	5.5%	$4,267,232.69										
6	6.0%	$4,615,429.27		Size of the Investment Portfolio								
7	6.5%	$5,000,000.00										
8	7.0%	$5,425,107.75	$10,000,000									
9	7.5%	$5,895,410.65	$9,000,000									
10	8.0%	$6,416,121.75	$8,000,000									
11	8.5%	$6,993,075.95	$7,000,000									
12	9.0%	$7,632,804.90	$6,000,000									
13	9.5%	$8,342,620.92										
14	10.0%	$9,130,711.02	$5,000,000									

FIGURE 6.6

Impact of Annual Returns on an Investment Portfolio.

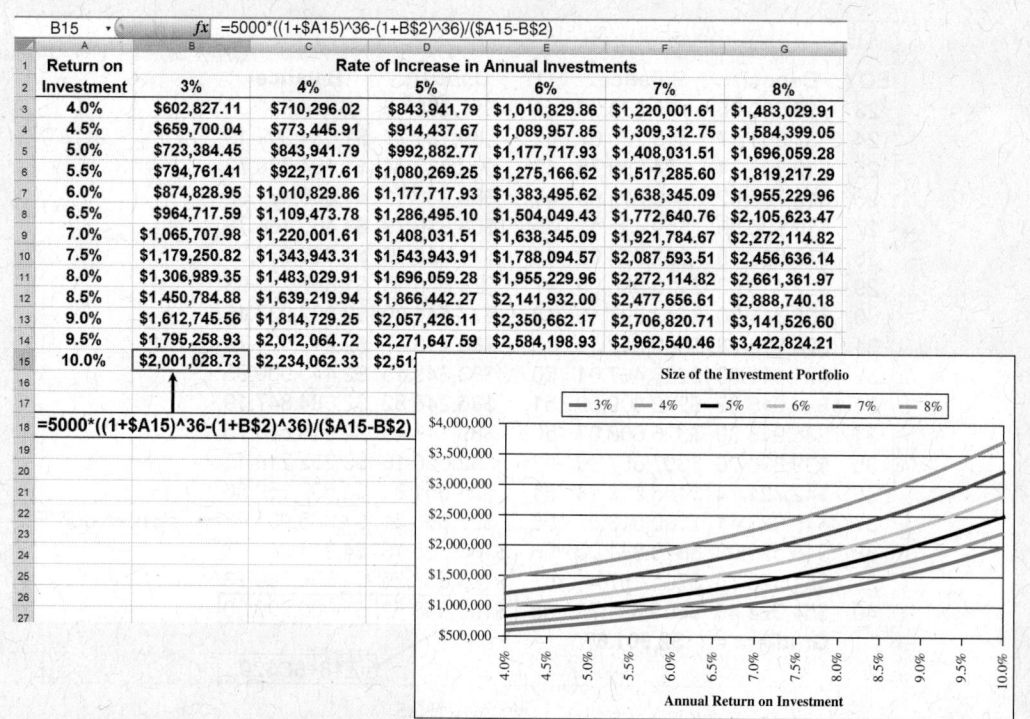

B15	▼(	*fx*	=5000*((1+$A15)^36-(1+B$2)^36)/($A15-B$2)			
	A	B	C	D	E	F	G

	Return on	Rate of Increase in Annual Investments					
1	Return on	Rate of Increase in Annual Investments					
2	Investment	3%	4%	5%	6%	7%	8%
3	4.0%	$602,827.11	$710,296.02	$843,941.79	$1,010,829.86	$1,220,001.61	$1,483,029.91
4	4.5%	$659,700.04	$773,445.91	$914,437.67	$1,089,957.85	$1,309,312.75	$1,584,399.05
5	5.0%	$723,384.45	$843,941.79	$992,882.77	$1,177,717.93	$1,408,031.51	$1,696,059.28
6	5.5%	$794,761.41	$922,717.61	$1,080,269.25	$1,275,166.62	$1,517,285.60	$1,819,217.29
7	6.0%	$874,828.95	$1,010,829.86	$1,177,717.93	$1,383,495.62	$1,638,345.09	$1,955,229.96
8	6.5%	$964,717.59	$1,109,473.78	$1,286,495.10	$1,504,049.43	$1,772,640.76	$2,105,623.47
9	7.0%	$1,065,707.98	$1,220,001.61	$1,408,031.51	$1,638,345.09	$1,921,784.67	$2,272,114.82
10	7.5%	$1,179,250.82	$1,343,943.31	$1,543,943.91	$1,788,094.57	$2,087,593.51	$2,456,636.14
11	8.0%	$1,306,989.35	$1,483,029.91	$1,696,059.28	$1,955,229.96	$2,272,114.82	$2,661,361.97
12	8.5%	$1,450,784.88	$1,639,219.94	$1,866,442.27	$2,141,932.00	$2,477,656.61	$2,888,740.18
13	9.0%	$1,612,745.56	$1,814,729.25	$2,057,426.11	$2,350,662.17	$2,706,820.71	$3,141,526.60
14	9.5%	$1,795,258.93	$2,012,064.72	$2,271,647.59	$2,584,198.93	$2,962,540.46	$3,422,824.21
15	10.0%	$2,001,028.73	$2,234,062.33	$2,51...			
16							
17							
18	=5000*((1+$A15)^36-(1+B$2)^36)/($A15-B$2)						

FIGURE 6.7

Impact on Future Worth of Annual Investments Increasing at Various Geometric Series Rates.

B18	▼(	*fx*	=B17+$C$20			
	A	B	C	D	E	F	G	H	I	J	K

	EOY	Deposit	Balance	EOY	Deposit	Balance					
1	EOY	Deposit	Balance	EOY	Deposit	Balance					
2	23	$5,000.00	$5,000.00	41	$49,875.00	$908,552.04					
3	24	$7,500.00	$12,900.00	42	$52,368.75	$1,033,604.96	=E2*(1+$C$21)				
4	25	$10,000.00	$23,932.00	43	$54,987.19	$1,171,280.54					
5	26	$12,500.00	$38,346.56	44	$57,736.55	$1,322,719.53					
6	27	$15,000.00	$56,414.28	45	$60,623.37	$1,489,160.47					
7	28	$17,500.00	$78,427.43	46	$63,654.54	$1,671,947.85					
8	29	$20,000.00	$104,701.62	47	$66,837.27	$1,872,540.94					
9	30	$22,500.00	$135,577.75	48	$70,179.13	$2,092,523.35					
10	31	$25,000.00	$171,423.97	49	$73,688.09	$2,333,613.31					
11	32	$27,500.00	$212,637.89	50	$77,372.49	$2,597,674.87					
12	33	$30,000.00	$259,648.92	51	$81,241.12	$2,886,729.98					
13	34	$32,500.00	$312,920.83	52	$85,303.18	$3,202,971.56					
14	35	$35,000.00	$372,954.50	53	$89,568.33	$3,548,777.61					
15	36	$37,500.00	$440,290.86	54	$94,046.75	$3,926,726.57					
16	37	$40,000.00	$515,514.13	55	$98,749.09	$4,339,613.79	=E16+(1+$C$22)*F15				
17	38	$42,500.00	$599,255.26	56	$103,686.54	$4,790,469.43					
18	39	$45,000.00	$692,195.68	57	$108,870.87	$5,282,577.86					
19	40	$47,500.00	$795,071.34	58	$114,314.41	$5,819,498.50					
20		Gradient =	$2,500.00								
21		Geometric =	5.0%			=E18*(1+$C$21)					
22		ROI =	8.0%		=B19+(1+$C$22)*C18						
23											

FIGURE 6.8

**Impact on Future Worth of Combination of Gradient and Geometric Increases
in Annual Investments.**

| G11 ▾ | *fx* | =(FV($A11,18,-5000)+2500*(((1+$A11)^18-(1+18*$A11))/$A11^2))*(1+$A11)^18+((5000+17*2500)*1+$A11)* |

	A	B	C	D	E	F	G
1	**Annual Return on**	**Rate of Increase in Annual Investments**					
2	**Investment**	**3%**	**4%**	**5%**	**6%**	**7%**	**8%**
3	4.0%	$2,809,930.78	$2,959,850.36	$3,127,030.79	$3,313,582.98	$3,521,875.02	$3,754,562.56
4	4.5%	$3,033,555.95	$3,187,706.58	$3,359,454.70	$3,550,941.57	$3,764,568.52	$4,003,027.53
5	5.0%	$3,280,374.71	$3,438,924.71	$3,615,418.73	$3,812,029.08	$4,031,191.05	$4,275,633.74
6	5.5%	$3,553,040.23	$3,716,165.42	$3,897,591.39	$4,099,522.22	$4,324,427.91	$4,575,075.48
7	6.0%	$3,854,522.48	$4,022,406.54	$4,208,958.72	$4,416,415.60	$4,647,282.67	$4,904,365.72
8	6.5%	$4,188,146.69	$4,360,981.51	$4,552,862.75	$4,766,060.22	$5,003,115.70	$5,266,874.60
9	7.0%	$4,557,636.45	$4,735,622.51	$4,933,044.62	$5,152,206.59	$5,395,687.32	$5,666,372.68
10	7.5%	$4,967,162.09	$5,150,508.86	$5,353,693.05	$5,579,053.23	$5,829,206.24	$6,107,079.37
11	8.0%	$5,421,394.89	$5,610,321.25	$5,819,498.50	$6,051,300.83	$6,308,383.87	$6,593,717.23
12	8.5%	$5,925,567.82	$6,120,302.47	$6,335,714.06	$6,574,213.18	$6,838,495.16	$7,131,572.86
13	9.0%	$6,485,543.71	$6,686,325.65	$6,908,223.56	$7,153,685.29	$7,425,446.76	$7,726,565.11
14	9.5%	$7,107,891.57	$7,314,970.55	$7,543,617.97	$7,796,319.81	$8,075,853.54	$8,385,321.53
15	10.0%	$7,799,972.13	$8,013,609.17	$8,249,281.01	$8,509,512.68	$8,797,124.16	$9,115,264.07
16							
17							
18							
19	=(5000+2500*((1+$A15)^18-(1+18*$A15))/($A15*((1+$A15)^18-1)))*(((1+$A15)^18-1)/$A15)*(1+$A15)^18						
20	+47500*(1+B$2)*((1+$A15)^18-(1+B$2)^18)/($A15-B$2)						
21							

FIGURE 6.9

Using a Combination of Gradient and Geometric Series to Achieve a Financial Goal.

given in Equation 2.45 in Chapter 2, the engineer considered annual increases ranging from 3 to 8 percent. The future worth results obtained are shown in Figure 6.7.

Noting that the investment portfolio would not reach the $5 million level desired when a geometric series was used, the engineer decided to consider a combination of gradient and geometric series. Specifically, the second through eighteenth investments are $2,500 greater than the previous investment; thereafter, each investment increases at a geometric rate. Figure 6.8 shows the deposits and the investment account balance with an 8 percent return on investment and a 5 percent geometric rate of increase in the annual investment over an 18-year period. Figures 6.9 and 6.10 provide the results for a range of values for the return on investment and geometric rate of increase in annual investments.

The engineer felt confident the $5 million investment goal would be achieved as long as the annual deposits continued to increase along the lines considered in the analysis.

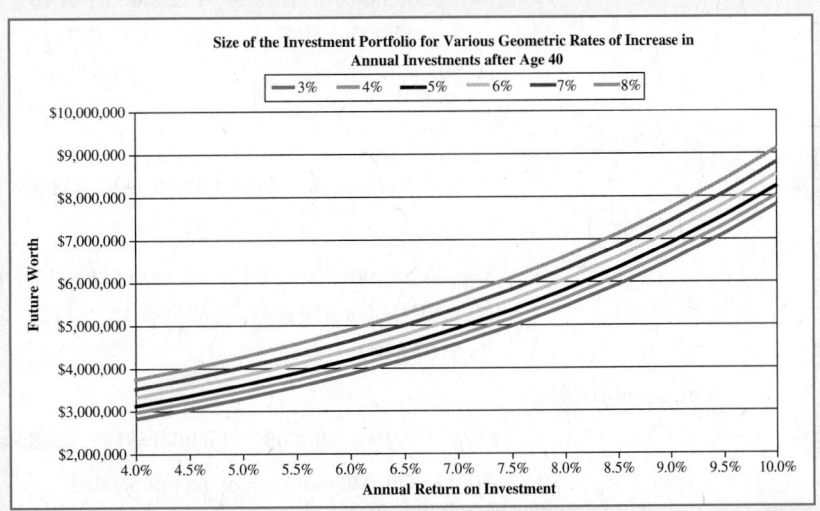

FIGURE 6.10

Future Worth of an Investment Portfolio for Various Returns on Investment and Geometric Increases in Annual Investments.

6-3 FUTURE WORTH: MULTIPLE ALTERNATIVES

Ranking Approach. When attempting to determine the preferred alternative from among multiple mutually exclusive alternatives and when using future worth as the measure of economic worth, choose the alternative that maximizes FW. Mathematically, letting *MARR* denote the interest rate used, the objective is to

$$\underset{\forall j}{\text{Maximize }} FW_j = \sum_{t=0}^{n} A_{jt}(1 + MARR)^{n-t} \tag{6.2}$$

$$\underset{\forall j}{\textit{Maximize }} FW_j(i\%) = \sum_{t=0}^{n} A_{jt}(1 + i)^{n-t}$$

EXAMPLE 6.4   Using Future Worth to Choose Between Two Alternatives

Recall in Chapter 5, we compared economically two design alternatives (A and B) for a new ride (the Scream Machine) at a theme park (Example 5.8). Alternative A required a $300,000 investment, produced after-tax net annual revenue of $55,000, and had a negligible salvage value at the end of the 10-year planning horizon. Alternative B required a $450,000 investment, generated after-tax net annual revenue of $80,000, and also had a negligible salvage value at the end of the 10-year planning horizon. The do-nothing alternative is feasible. Based on an after-tax *MARR* of 10 percent and using a future worth analysis, which alternative, if any, is the economic choice? (The do-nothing alternative is assumed to have a future worth of $0.)

$$FW_A = -\$300,000(F|P\,10\%,10) + \$55,000(F|A\,10\%,10)$$
$$= -\$300,000(2.59374) + \$55,000(15.93742)$$
$$= \$98,436.10$$

or, using Excel®,

$$FW_A = \text{FV}(10\%,10,-55000,300000) = \$98,435.62$$

Likewise,

$$FW_B = -\$450,000(F|P\,10\%,10) + \$80,000(F|A\,10\%,10)$$
$$= -\$450,000(2.59374) + \$80,000(15.93742)$$
$$= \$107,810.60$$

or, using Excel®,

$$FW_B = \text{FV}(10\%,10,-80000,450000) = \$107,809.86$$

Since $FW_B > FW_A > \$0$, Design Alternative B is recommended.

    To determine how future worth changes during the planning horizon, we estimate the salvage values of the two design alternatives if they are used for n years, with $n = 1, 2, \ldots, 9$. We know the salvage value at $n = 10$; it is $0. To use a negative geometric

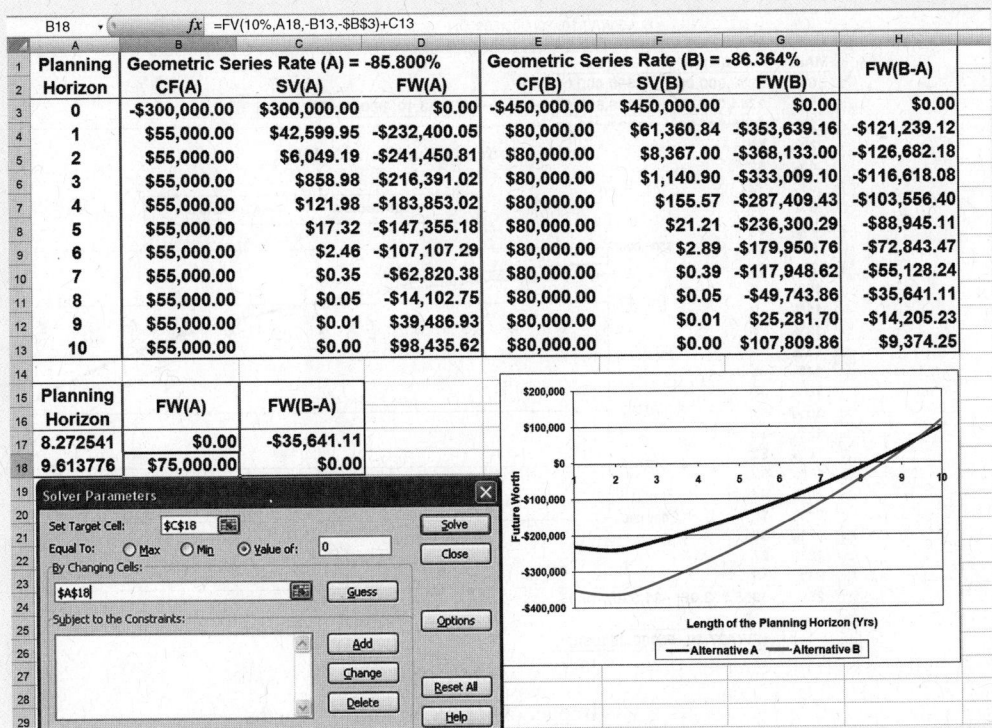

| B18 | ▾ | fx | =FV(10%,A18,-B13,-$B$3)+C13 | | | | |

| | Planning | Geometric Series Rate (A) = -85.800% | | | Geometric Series Rate (B) = -86.364% | | | FW(B-A) |
	Horizon	CF(A)	SV(A)	FW(A)	CF(B)	SV(B)	FW(B)	
3	0	-$300,000.00	$300,000.00	$0.00	-$450,000.00	$450,000.00	$0.00	$0.00
4	1	$55,000.00	$42,599.95	-$232,400.05	$80,000.00	$61,360.84	-$353,639.16	-$121,239.12
5	2	$55,000.00	$6,049.19	-$241,450.81	$80,000.00	$8,367.00	-$368,133.00	-$126,682.18
6	3	$55,000.00	$858.98	-$216,391.02	$80,000.00	$1,140.90	-$333,009.10	-$116,618.08
7	4	$55,000.00	$121.98	-$183,853.02	$80,000.00	$155.57	-$287,409.43	-$103,556.40
8	5	$55,000.00	$17.32	-$147,355.18	$80,000.00	$21.21	-$236,300.29	-$88,945.11
9	6	$55,000.00	$2.46	-$107,107.29	$80,000.00	$2.89	-$179,950.76	-$72,843.47
10	7	$55,000.00	$0.35	-$62,820.38	$80,000.00	$0.39	-$117,948.62	-$55,128.24
11	8	$55,000.00	$0.05	-$14,102.75	$80,000.00	$0.05	-$49,743.86	-$35,641.11
12	9	$55,000.00	$0.01	$39,486.93	$80,000.00	$0.01	$25,281.70	-$14,205.23
13	10	$55,000.00	$0.00	$98,435.62	$80,000.00	$0.00	$107,809.86	$9,374.25

	Planning Horizon	FW(A)	FW(B-A)
17	8.272541	$0.00	-$35,641.11
18	9.613776	$75,000.00	$0.00

FIGURE 6.11

Future Worth Analysis of the Theme Park Design Example.

series to approximate the decline in salvage value over time, we compute the rate needed for the salvage values to decrease from the initial investment to a value of 0.1¢ after 10 years.

$$\text{Geometric Series Rate}_A = \text{RATE}(10,-300000,0.001) = -85.800\%$$

$$\text{Geometric Series Rate}_B = \text{RATE}(10,-450000,0.001) = -86.364\%$$

Figure 6.11 includes the salvage values for each alternative, as well as the future worth for each alternative if its service were limited to any number of years less than 10. Note that the future worth for Alternative A is $98,435.62 after 10 years; it is $107,809.86 for Alternative B after 10 years.

Of particular interest is the strength of Alternative A versus Alternative B for planning horizons less than 9.6138 years. However, for values of n less than 8.2725 years, the do-nothing alternative is preferred to Design A. For values of n between 8.2725 and 9.1638, Design A is preferred; for values of n greater than 9.1638, Design B is preferred. (As shown in Figure 6.11, **SOLVER** was used to determine the values of n that made FW(A) and FW(B–A) equal 0.)

Clearly, determining the planning horizon's length plays a critical role in selecting the preferred design for the new ride in the theme park. Neither design is attractive economically for planning horizons less than 8.2725 years.

To further illustrate the differences in the economic performance of Alternatives A and B, Figure 6.12 depicts the future worth for each alternative for various values of the *MARR*. Notice, for *MARR* = 10 percent, $FW(B) > FW(A)$; and for *MARR* = 12 percent, $FW(B) < FW(A)$. In Chapter 8, we show that $FW(B) = FW(A)$ for *MARR* = 10.56 percent.

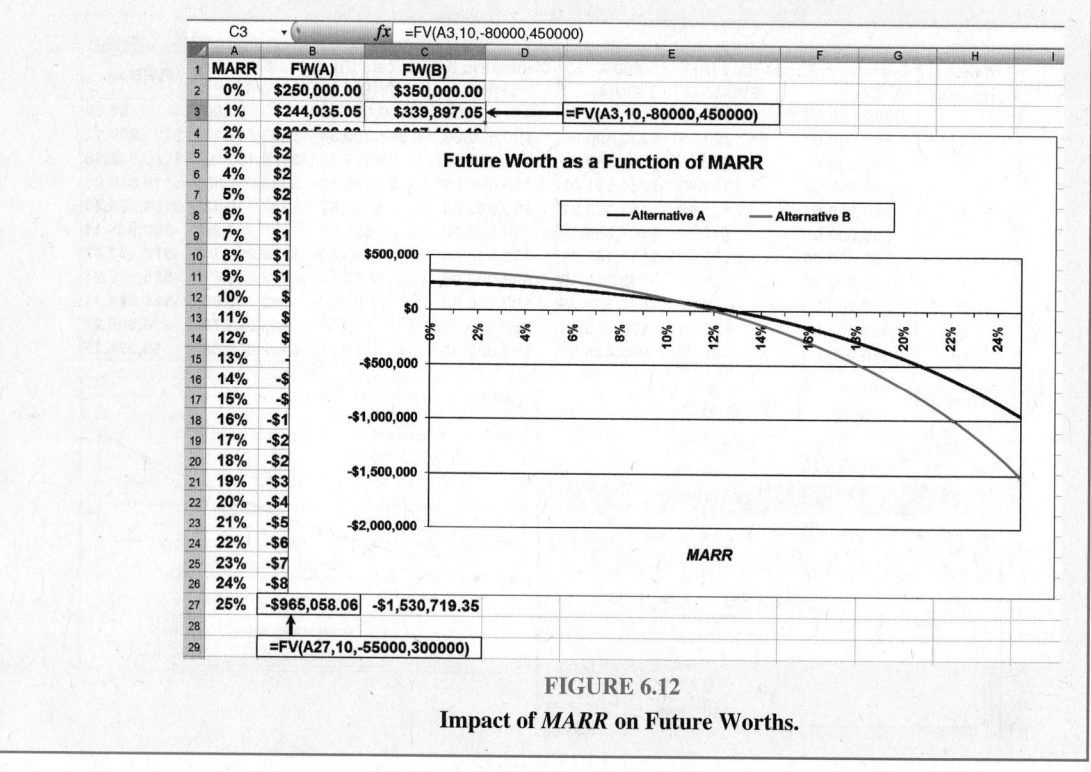

FIGURE 6.12

Impact of *MARR* on Future Worths.

EXAMPLE 6.5 Choosing a Retirement Plan

During a meeting with a human resources representative of her new employer, a recent engineering graduate learns that she needs to choose between two retirement plans. One plan involves investments that are matched by the employer; the plan is managed by a committee of employees in the firm. Another option is to establish an investment plan that she will manage. In both cases, deposits are tax-deferred; also in both cases, withdrawal of funds before age 62 will result in a significant financial penalty. Her current age is 22.

Under the first plan, up to 4 percent of an employee's annual compensation is matched by the employer. Funds are invested in a mix of securities, including the company's own stock; however, no more than 20 percent of the investment portfolio is allowed to be invested in the firm's stock. The portfolio includes a mix of stocks, bonds, and U.S. Treasury notes. Over the past 15 years, the investment portfolio has increased in value at an annual compound rate of 6 percent.

Alternatively, individuals can manage their own investment portfolios. Although there are limits on the investments that can be made, a number of riskier choices are available. Individuals who choose to manage their own portfolio have to pay a management fee of 1.5 percent of the annual deposits to the fund. The company still matches up to 4 percent of the employee's annual compensation.

After considering the investments available, the new employee narrows the choices to a set of investments that historically have earned between 2 and 12 percent annually. If the employee's current salary is $55,000, she invests the maximum allowed (4 percent), and her annual salary increases at an annual rate of 5 percent, which retirement plan should she choose?

Under the first plan, her investment portfolio will have the following value after 40 years:

$$FW_1 = 2(0.04)(\$55,000)(F|A_1\ 6\%,5\%,40)$$
$$= \$4,400[(1.06)^{40} - (1.05)^{40}]/(0.06 - 0.05)$$
$$= \$1,428,120.90$$

Under the second plan, in the pessimistic case (earns 2 percent/year), her investment portfolio will have the following value after 40 years:

$$FW_{2p} = 2(0.04)(\$55,000)(0.985)(F|A_1\ 2\%,5\%,40)$$
$$= \$4,334[(1.02)^{40} - (1.05)^{40}]/(0.02 - 0.05)$$
$$= \$698,055.57$$

Under the second plan, in the optimistic case (earns 12 percent/year), her investment portfolio will have the following value after 40 years:

$$FW_{2o} = 2(0.04)(\$55,000)(0.985)(F|A_1\ 12\%,5\%,40)$$
$$= \$4,334[(1.12)^{40} - (1.05)^{40}]/(0.12 - 0.05)$$
$$= \$5,325,308.50$$

After giving the matter considerable thought, she decided to choose the second plan and manage her own investment portfolio. What would you have done?

Incremental Approach. As with present worth, future worth can be applied using incremental analysis. But, as was noted in Chapter 5, we do not know why anyone would choose to use incremental analysis, since a ranking approach is simpler to use. However, we will apply incremental analysis to solve the example involving the Scream Machine.

EXAMPLE 6.6   Incremental Solution to Example 6.4

Let's use the incremental approach depicted in Figure 5.7 to analyze the choice of designs for the Scream Machine. Recall, Alternative A requires a $300,000 investment and has net annual after-tax revenue of $55,000; Alternative B requires a $450,000 investment and has net annual after-tax revenue of $80,000. A 10 percent *MARR* is required over a 10-year planning horizon. The design alternatives are considered in increasing order of investment. Hence, Alternative A is considered first. As demonstrated previously, its FW is **$98,435.62**, based on an Excel® solution. (Since $FW_A > \$0$, Alternative A is preferred to doing nothing.) Next, we compute the FW of the difference in cash flows between Alternatives B and A.

$$FW_{B-A} = -\$150,000(F|P\ 10\%,10) + \$25,000(F|A\ 10\%,10)$$
$$= -\$150,000(2.59374) + \$25,000(15.93742)$$
$$= \$9,374.50$$

or, as shown in Figure 6.13, using Excel®,

$$FW_{B-A} = \text{FV}(10\%,10,-25000,150000) = \$9,374.25$$

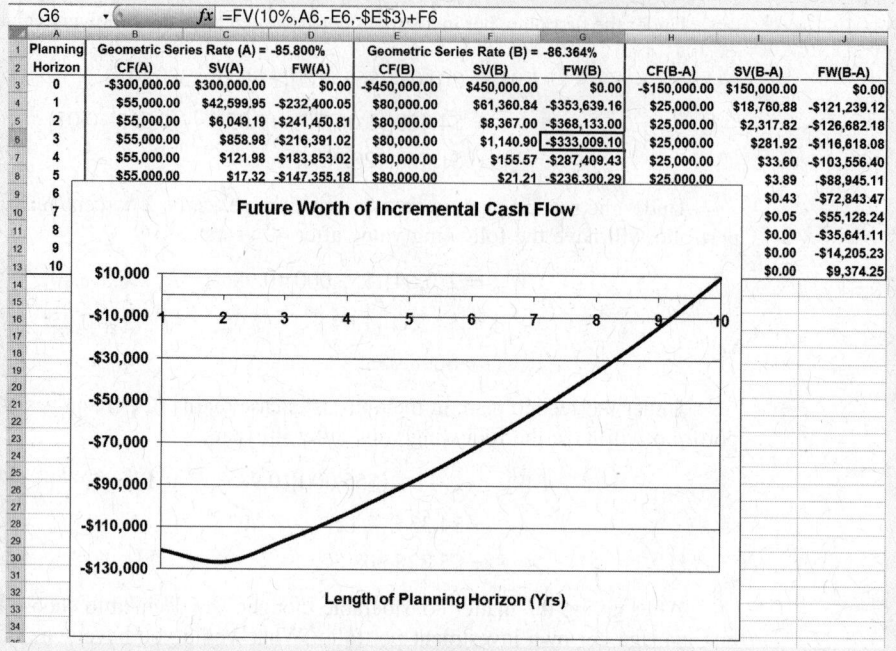

G6	▼		fx	=FV(10%,A6,-E6,-$E$3)+F6					
	A	B	C	D	E	F	G	H	I	J

FIGURE 6.13

Incremental Analysis for Example 6.6.

Since $FW_{B-A} > \$0$, Alternative B is preferred to Alternative A. Since there are no more alternatives to consider, Alternative B is recommended.

For various salvage values, Figure 6.13 contains plots of the future worth of the incremental cash flows. As shown, a future worth of $9,374.25 occurs at the end of the tenth year. (As an exercise, use the Excel® **SOLVER** tool to determine the point during the planning horizon when future worth of the incremental cash flows is minimized.)

Figure 6.14 depicts the future worth of the incremental cash flows for various *MARR* values. Notice, for *MARR* values less than 10 percent, the future worth is positive;

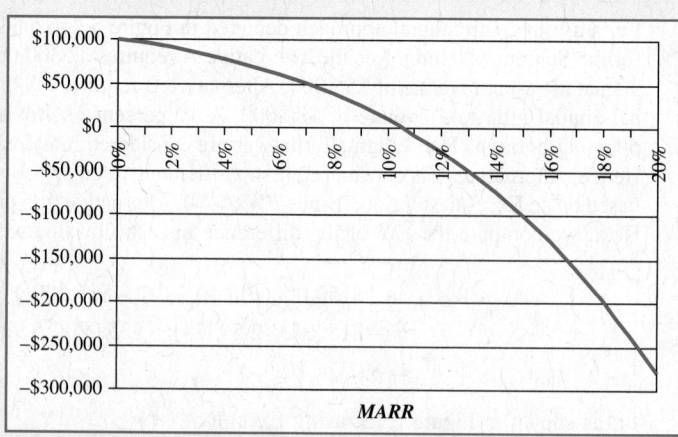

FIGURE 6.14

Future Worth of the $150,000 Incremental Investment.

for *MARR* values greater than 11 percent, the future worth is negative. (In Chapter 8, we determine the interest rate that equates to 0 the future worth of the incremental cash flows and call it the *internal rate of return on the incremental investment.*)

6-4   MAXIMIZING THE INVESTMENT PORTFOLIO

Recall, previously we noted that it is assumed that any money not invested in a candidate alternative remains in an investment pool and earns a return equal to the *MARR*. Future worth is a convenient means of demonstrating the equivalence of ranking investments on the basis of their present or future worths and maximizing the value of the investment portfolio at the end of the planning horizon, *including the money in the investment pool.*

EXAMPLE 6.7   **Future Worth of the Portfolio**

In the case of the two design alternatives (A and B) for the Scream Machine, the most expensive one required a $450,000 investment. For the design alternative to be feasible, $450,000 must have been available for investment. If it is not invested in a new ride at the theme park, it could be invested and earn 10 percent annual compound returns. If this was done, the future worth for the do-nothing alternative (*DN*) would be

$$FW_{DN} = \$450,000(F|P\,10\%,10) = \$450,000(2.59374) = \$1,167,183.00$$

or, using Excel®,

$$FW_{DN} = \text{FV}(10\%,10,,-450000) = \$1,167,184.11$$

The $450,000 invested in Design Alternative B will result in annual revenue of $80,000. If the recovered funds are added to the investment pool, in 10 years they will be worth

$$FW_B = \$80,000(F|A\,10\%,10) = \$80,000(15.93742) = \$1,274,993.60$$

or, using Excel®,

$$FW_B = \text{FV}(10\%,10,-80000) = \$1,274,993.97$$

If Design Alternative A is chosen for investment, $55,000 will be recovered annually for 10 years. Placing the $55,000 in the investment pool will result in a future value of

$$FW_A = \$55,000(F|A\,10\%,10) = \$55,000(15.93742) = \$876,558.10$$

or, using Excel®,

$$FW_A = \text{FV}(10\%,10,-55000) = \$876,558.35$$

In addition, since $450,000 was available and only $300,000 was required for Alternative A, $150,000 of residual capital (*RC*) remains in the investment pool and earns an annual return of 10 percent. Therefore, the $150,000 will grow at a rate of 10 percent compounded annually to achieve a value of

$$FW_{RC} = \$150,000(F|P\,10\%,10) = \$150,000(2.59374) = \$389,061$$

or, using Excel®,

$$FW_{RC} = \text{FV}(10\%,10,,-150000) = \$389,061.37$$

Hence, if Design Alternative A is chosen, the investment portfolio will total $876,558.10 + $389,061.00, or $1,265,619.10. Or, using Excel®, the investment portfolio will total **$876,558.35 + $389,061.37**, or **$1,265,619.72**.

In summary, if neither design is selected, the investment portfolio will have a value, based on results from Excel®, of **$1,167,184.11**. If Design B is installed, the investment portfolio will have a value of **$1,274,993.97**. If Design A is installed, the total value of the investment portfolio will be **$1,265,619.72**. Hence, to maximize the investment portfolio, Design B should be selected, and the overall investment portfolio will be **$1,274,993.97 - $1,265,619.72**, or **$9374.25** greater than if Design A is purchased. (We revisit the investment portfolio argument in Chapter 8.)

6-5   MORE ON UNEQUAL LIVES

Previously, we emphasized the importance of comparing investment alternatives over a common period of time. (Recall Principle 8: *Compare investment alternatives over a common period of time.*) Using a planning horizon is one way of ensuring that this principle is not violated.

Principle #8

Compare investment alternatives over a common period of time.

When a situation occurs in which the various alternatives have unequal lives, if future worth analysis is used, it becomes obvious that decisions must be made regarding the length of time over which the analysis is to be performed. For example, if faced with three investment alternatives having individual lives of 4, 5, and 6 years, one could easily (but incorrectly) compute the present worths of individual life cycles, since each of the alternatives has a common beginning point, called "the present." However, if this is done with future worth, it becomes obvious that a worth at $t = 4$ is being compared with one at $t = 5$ and another at $t = 6$.

Notice, future worth analysis can be useful in analyzing the economic performances of unequal-lived alternatives, because it forces one to think about Principle 8. (Since we devoted considerable space to the topic when discussing planning horizons in Chapter 4, we will not dwell on the subject of unequal lives in this chapter.)

EXAMPLE 6.8   Dealing with Unequal Lives

Three mutually exclusive investment alternatives exist. The first alternative requires an investment of $10,000; it will yield annual returns of $5,000 for 3 years, plus a terminal value of $5,000 at the end of the third year. The second alternative requires a $14,500 investment; it will yield annual returns of $5,000 for 6 years. The third alternative is also a 6-year investment; it requires a $20,000 investment and will yield annual returns equal to a $3,000 gradient series. If the investor's *MARR* is 12 percent, which, if either, of the alternatives should be chosen in order to maximize the investor's future worth?

TABLE 6.1
Data for Example 6.9.

EOY	CF(1)	CF(2)	CF(3)
0	−$10,000	−$14,500	−$20,000
1	$5,000	$5,000	$0
2	$5,000	$5,000	$3,000
3	$10,000	$5,000	$6,000
4		$5,000	$9,000
5		$5,000	$12,000
6		$5,000	$15,000

Table 6.1 contains the cash flows for the three investments. Before calculating the future worths for the alternatives, an important question must be answered: What planning horizon should be used?

The obvious answer is a 6-year planning horizon. But, if that is the choice, then another question must be answered: What assumptions will be made concerning Alternative 1 for years 4, 5, and 6?

If a present worth analysis was requested, it would have been tempting to compute the present worths of the alternatives, with the present worth for Alternative 1 based on the four cash flows shown. To do so assumes cash flows of $0 during years 4, 5, and 6. Is that a reasonable assumption?

Let's examine two possible solutions to the investment alternative. First, assume Alternative 1 is a one-shot investment opportunity, and nothing comparable to it will be available during years 4, 5, and 6. In that case, the future worth will be

$$FW_1 = -\$10,000(F|P\ 12\%,6) + [\$5,000(F|A\ 12\%,3) + \$5,000](F|P\ 12\%,3)$$
$$= -\$10,000(1.97382) + [\$5,000(3.37440) + \$5,000](1.40493)$$
$$= \$10,990.43$$

or, using Excel®,

$$FW_1 = FV(12\%,6,-5000,10000) + FV(12\%,3,5000,-5000) = \$10,990.36$$

Similarly, for Alternative 2,

$$FW_2 = -\$14,500(F|P\ 12\%,6) + \$5,000(F|A\ 12\%,6)$$
$$= -\$14,500(1.97382) + \$5,000(8.11519)$$
$$= \$11,955.56$$

or, using Excel®,

$$FW_2 = FV(12\%,6,-5000,14500) = \$11,955.52$$

Likewise, for Alternative 3,

$$FW_3 = -\$20,000(F|P\ 12\%,6) + \$3,000(A|G\ 12\%,6)(F|A\ 12\%,6)$$
$$= -\$20,000(1.97382) + \$3,000(2.17205)(8.11519)$$
$$= \$13,403.40$$

TABLE 6.2
Alternate Data for the First Investment in Example 6.9.

EOY	CF(1')	CF(2)	CF(3)
0	−$10,000	−$14,500	−$20,000
1	$5,000	$5,000	$0
2	$5,000	$5,000	$3,000
3	$0	$5,000	$6,000
4	$5,000	$5,000	$9,000
5	$5,000	$5,000	$12,000
6	$10,000	$5,000	$15,000

or, using Excel®,

$$FW_3 = FV(12\%,6,,-1000*NPV(12\%,0,3,6,9,12,15)+20000) = \$13,403.27$$

Based on the future worth analysis, the third investment is preferred; the first investment is least attractive financially.

Now, assume equally attractive investment opportunities will be available in 3 years when the first investment ends. By fully recovering the initial investment in the third year, funds will be available to repeat the investment, as shown in Table 6.2. The future worth for the repetition of Investment 1 will be

$$FW_1 = -\$10,000(F|P\,12\%,6) + \$5,000(F|A\,12\%,6) - \$5,000(F|P\,12\%,3) + \$5,000$$
$$= -\$10,000(1.97382) + \$5,000(8.11519) - \$5,000(1.40493) + \$5,000$$
$$= \$18,813.10$$

or, using Excel®,

$$FW_1 = FV(12\%,6,-5000,10000)+FV(12\%,3,,5000)+5000 = \$18,813.08$$

If the investment can be repeated in 3 years, then the first investment is preferred. If it cannot be repeated, then the third investment should be chosen.

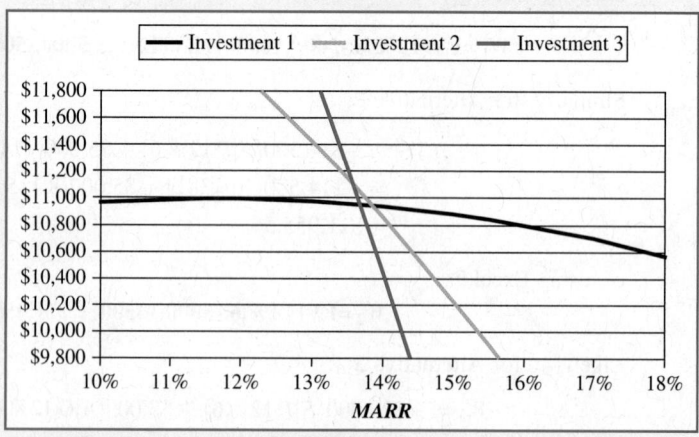

FIGURE 6.15
Close-Up of the Future Worth for Each Alternative in Example 6.8.

What should the investor do? Recall, when the *MARR* of 12 percent was established, it was to reflect what the investor could do with money not invested in one of the three alternatives. The *MARR* reflects the opportunity for returns of comparable risk available to the investor. Hence, there is no reason to expect that an equally attractive investment will be available in 3 years. If there is reason to expect such opportunities, then the *MARR* was set too low.

To gain an increased understanding of how the three alternatives perform for various *MARR* values, see Figure 6.15. From the close-up of the region defined by the future worth between \$9,800 and \$11,800, it is obvious that the first investment is preferred if *MARR* ≥ 14.5 percent. In such a case, the assumption of repeatability is not needed to justify the investment.

In the end, the choice comes down to what we believe the future holds. As for us, we fall back on the selection of the *MARR*. If it truly is 12 percent, then the third investment should be chosen; if the *MARR* is greater than 14.5 percent, then the first investment should be chosen. (As we stated in Chapter 4, the *MARR* value matters!)

6-6   SUMMARY

The following are the important messages of this chapter:

1. Future worth analysis has advantages over other measures of economic merit.
2. Future worth analysis facilitates financial goal-setting, particularly when an individual or firm desires to achieve a particular investment goal by a certain point in time (e.g., to achieve a net worth of \$5 million within 25 years).
3. Some people find it easier to understand the concept of compounding than the concept of discounting.
4. Present worth brings money to a point in time (the present) at which the decision will be made, while future worth takes money to a point in time (the future) at which the money will begin to be enjoyed.
5. Future worth analysis yields the same result as would occur when maximizing an investment portfolio, when the residual capital remains in an investment pool and earns a return equal to the *MARR*.
6. When investments have unequal lives, future worth analysis requires explicit decisions regarding cash flows during a common period of time—the planning horizon.

Pit Stop #6—Put the Pedal to the Metal!

 1. True or False: Future worth analysis is the most popular *DCF* measure of economic worth.
 2. True or False: Unless non-monetary considerations dictate otherwise, choose the mutually exclusive investment alternative that has the greatest future worth, regardless of the lives of the alternatives.
3. True or False: If $FW > 0$ when the $MARR = 20\%$, then $DPBP < 5$ years.
4. True or False: If $FW < 0$, then $PW < 0$.
 5. True or False: If $FW(A) > FW(B)$, then $DPBP(A) < DPBP(B)$, and $PBP(A) < PBP(B)$.

6. True or False: When using future worth analysis with mutually exclusive alternatives having unequal lives, always use a planning horizon equal to the least common multiple of lives.

 Tutoring problem available (at instructor's discretion) in *WileyPLUS*.

 Problem available (at instructor's discretion) in *WileyPLUS*.

 Worked Problem Video available in *WileyPLUS*.

FE-LIKE PROBLEMS

 1. Moving money forward in time while accounting for the time value of money is referred to as
   a. weighted average cost of capital.
   b. minimum attractive rate of return.
   c. discounting.
   d. compounding.

2. When using future worth to evaluate the attractiveness of a single investment alternative, what value is the calculated FW compared to?
   a. 0.0
   b. 1.0
   c. *MARR*
   d. WACC

 3. If you invest $3,000 three years from now, how much will be in the account 15 years from now if $i = 8$ percent compounded annually?
   a. $3,500
   b. $7,555
   c. $9,415
   d. $9,516

4. Consider a palletizer at a bottling plant that has a first cost of $150,000, has operating and maintenance costs of $17,500 per year, and an estimated net salvage value of $25,000 at the end of 30 years. Assume an interest rate of 8 percent/year. What is the future equivalent cost of the investment if the planning horizon is 30 years?
   a. $3,371,000
   b. $3,467,000
   c. $3,623,000
   d. $3,980,000

5. Five thousand dollars is deposited in an account that pays 6 percent interest per year. Two years from today, another $5,000 is deposited. Five years from today, $10,000 is withdrawn from the account. How much money is in the account 6 years from today?
   a. $0
   b. $2,646
   c. $2,805
   d. $3,056

6. Scott wants to accumulate $2,500 over a period of 7 years so that a cash payment can be made for roof maintenance on his summer cottage. To have this amount when it is needed, he will make annual deposits at the end of each year into a savings account that earns 8 percent annual interest per year. How much must each annual deposit be?
   a. . $244
   b. $259
   c. $280
   d. $357

7. Which of the following expressions will correctly determine the future worth of the following general cash flow series at time 7?

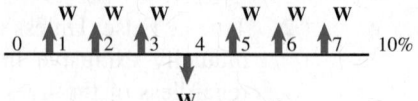

   a. $W(F|A\ 10\%,3)(F|P\ 10\%,4)$
      $- W(F|P\ 10\%,3) + W(F|A\ 10\%,3)$
   b. $W(F|A\ 10\%,3)(F|P\ 10\%,3)$
      $- W(F|P\ 10\%,3) + W(F|A\ 10\%,3)$

c. $W(F|A\ 10\%,7) - (F|P\ 10\%,4)$

d. None of the above

8. A piece of machinery costs $20,000 and has an estimated life of 8 years and a scrap value of $2,000. What uniform annual amount must be set aside at the end of each of the 8 years for replacement if the interest rate is 4 percent/year?

   a. $1,953

   b. $2,174

   c. $2,250

   d. $2,492

9. How much money would be accumulated in 5 years with an initial deposit of $10,000 if the account earned interest at 12 percent per year for the first 3 years and at 15 percent per year for the last 2 years?

   a. $17,623

   b. $18,580

   c. $18,836

   d. $19,078

10. A deposit of $800 is planned for the end of each year into an account paying 8 percent/year compounded annually. The deposits were not made for the tenth and eleventh years. All other deposits were made as planned. What amount will be in the account after the deposit at the end of year 25?

    a. $55.397

    b. $55,397

c. $59,537

d. $53,597

11. Consider the time value of money factors $(F|P\ i\%,n)$ and $(F|P\ i/12\%,12n)$. Assume $i > 0$ and $n > 0$. What can be said about the value of these factors?

    a. These factors are always equal.

    b. These factors are never equal.

    c. Cannot determine without knowing either i or n

    d. Cannot determine without knowing both i and n

12. The present worth of an alternative is 0. What do we know about the value of the future worth?

    a. $FW < 0$

    b. $FW = 0$

    c. $FW > 0$

    d. Cannot be determined without cash flows

13. On the day your daughter is born, you deposit $1,000 in a college savings account that earns 8 percent compounded annually. On each of her birthdays thereafter, up to and including her eighteenth birthday, you deposit an additional $1,000. How much money is in the college account the day after her eighteenth birthday?

    a. $37,450

    b. $38,950

    c. $41,450

    d. $46,800

PROBLEMS

Note to Instructors and Students

Many of the problems in this chapter are similar to problems in previous chapters. This similarity is intentional. It is designed to illustrate the use of different measures of merit on the same problem.

Section 6.1

1. Compare and contrast the terms *discounting* and *compounding*.

2. Determine whether each of the following is true or false. In each case, assume P is located at $t = 0$ and F is located at $t = n$.

   a. $F = F(P|F\ i\%,n)(F|P\ i\%,n)$

   b. $F = P(F|P\ i\%,n + 10)(P|F\ i\%,10)$

   c. $F = P(F|P\ i\%,n + 10)/(F|P\ i\%,10)$

   d. $F = P^*(F|P\ i\%,n - 5)(F|P\ i\%,5)$

   e. $F = P(F|P\ i - 2\%,n)(F|P\ 2\%,n)$

   f. $F = P(F|P\ i\%,n - 3) + P(F|P\ i\%,3)$

3. What do you know about the mathematical value of a project's future worth, relative to zero, under each of the following conditions?

   a. The present worth of the project is greater than 0.

   b. The present worth of the project is equal to 0.

   c. The present worth of the project is less than 0.

Section 6.2

4. A 22-year-old engineering graduate wants to accumulate $2,000,000 to be available when she retires 40 years from today. She investigates several investment options and decides to invest in a stock market index fund after discovering that the long-term average return for the stock market is 10.4 percent per year. Since this will be a tax-sheltered account, she plans to ignore the impact of taxes.

    a. If she plans to make 40 uniform annual deposits starting 1 year from today, what is the dollar amount of the required deposits?

    b. If she makes the first of the 40 deposits starting today rather than 1 year from today, what is the dollar amount of the required deposits?

    c. If she plans to make the first payment 1 year from today and each annual payment will be $200 greater than the previous year's payment,

    (i) what is the dollar amount of the first deposit?

    (ii) what is the dollar amount of the last deposit?

    d. If she plans to make the first payment 1 year from today and each annual payment will be 5 percent greater than the previous year's payment,

    (i) what is the dollar amount of the first deposit?

    (ii) what is the dollar amount of the last deposit?

5. Reconsider the situation described in Problem 4. Assume that rather than annual deposits, she makes monthly deposits. The first deposit will be 1 month from today, and the last deposit will be 40 years from today. Assume that the stock market return is 10.4 percent per year compounded monthly.

    a. If she plans to make uniform monthly deposits, what is the dollar amount of the monthly deposit?

    b. If she earns a 4 percent annual raise each year throughout her career (starting 1 year from today) and adjusts her monthly deposits by the same 4 percent each year, how much will be in the account immediately after the last deposit?

6. You decide to set up a college fund for your 10-year-old child and plan to make annual deposits into the account each year on your child's birthday. Because "other things" consistently use more of your money than anticipated, your deposits are actually somewhat erratic. One year even resulted in a withdrawal. The account earns 5 percent per year.

Birthday	10	11	12	13	14	15	16	17	18
Deposit	$1,000	$1,000	$2,000	$1,500	−$1,500	$3,000	$2,500	$2,000	$2,000

    a. How much is in the account immediately after the deposit on your child's eighteenth birthday?

    b. How much would you have needed to deposit on each birthday to accumulate the same total if you had started on your child's tenth birthday and made equal annual deposits with no withdrawals?

    c. How much would you have needed to deposit on each birthday to accumulate the same total if you had started on your child's first birthday and made equal annual deposits with no withdrawals?

 7. An investment has the following cash flow profile. *MARR* is 12 percent/year. What is the minimum value of *X* such that the investment is attractive based on a future worth measure of merit?

End of Year	0	1	2	3	4
Cash Flow	−$30,000	$6,000	$13,500	$X	$13,500

8. Jeff has $10,000 to invest for a period of 5 years. The following account is available at his bank. The account pays 4 percent/year for year one, 6 percent/year for year two, 8 percent/year for years three and four, and 12 percent/year for year five. How much will be in the account at the end of the fifth year?

LEY ⊕ **9.** You decide to open an individual retirement account (IRA) at your local bank that pays 9 percent/year/month. For the next 30 years, starting 1 month from today, you will deposit $200 per month into the account. On the day of the last deposit, you will retire. As a benefit to retirees, the bank increases the interest rate on this account to 12 percent/year/month on the day they retire. It remains at this rate from that time on. You do not make any withdrawals for the first 2 years after you retire. Two years after you retire, you will begin making monthly withdrawals from your IRA. You plan to make equal monthly withdrawals from the account.

  a. What is the balance in the account immediately after the last deposit?

  b. What is the balance in the account 1 month prior to making the first withdrawal?

  c. What monthly amount can be withdrawn if you want the withdrawals to last for 15 years?

  d. What monthly amount can be withdrawn if you want the withdrawals to last forever?

10. You decide to open an individual retirement account (IRA) at your local stockbroker that pays 10 percent/year/year for the life of the account. You deposit $2,000 today to open the account. For the next 41 years, you will deposit $2,000 per year into the account at the end of each year. There are a total of forty-two $2,000 deposits. Exactly 1 year after the last deposit, you will start making withdrawals.

  a. What is the balance in the account immediately after the last deposit?

  b. What annual withdrawal can you make if you want the withdrawals to last 15 years?

  c. What annual withdrawal can you make if you want the withdrawals to last 20 years?

  d. What annual withdrawal can you make if you want the withdrawals to last 25 years?

LEY ⊕ **11.** You decide to open an individual retirement account (IRA) at your local bank that pays 8 percent/year/year. At the end of each of the next 40 years, you will deposit $2,000 per year into the account (40 total deposits). Three years after the last deposit, you will begin making annual withdrawals. If you want the account to last 30 years (30 withdrawals), what amount will you be able to withdraw each year?

12. You decide to open an individual retirement account (IRA) at your local bank that pays 8 percent/year/month. For the next 30 years, you will deposit $225 per month into the account. Assume that all deposits and withdrawals to the account occur at the end of the month. On the day of the last deposit, you will retire. Your expenses for the first year of your retirement will be covered by a company lump sum retirement bonus; thus, your first withdrawal from your IRA will occur on the day exactly 12 months after the last deposit. What monthly withdrawal can you make if you want the account to last

  a. 15 years?

  b. 25 years?

  c. 40 years?

  d. forever?

LEY ⊕ **13.** Your local bank is offering a new type of retirement savings account. An initial deposit is made to the account when it is opened. This money and any accumulated interest must be left in the account for 25 years. No additional deposits can be made. On the day the account is opened and on each annual anniversary of the initial deposit, the account balance is reviewed and the following terms apply:

- If the account balance is less than or equal to $20,000, interest for the next annual period is 7 percent/year compounded annually.

- If the account balance is greater than $20,000 but less than or equal to $40,000, interest for the next annual period is 10 percent/year compounded quarterly.

- If the account balance is greater than $40,000, interest for the next annual period is 12 percent/year compounded monthly.

    You decide to open an account under these terms today with $10,000. How much money will you withdraw when the account is closed 25 years from today?

14. You have $10,000 that you must invest for a period of 4 years. The following account is available at your bank. The account pays 14 percent/year/year for years one and three, 15.5 percent/year/year for year two, and 15 percent/year/quarter for year four.

  a. What is the balance in the account at the end of year 4?

  b. An Internet bank offers the same type of account, but the order of the interest rates is reversed (i.e., the Internet bank pays 15 percent/year/quarter, 15.5 percent/year/year, and 14 percent/year/year in years 1, 2, 3, and 4, respectively). If you plan to leave your money on deposit for the entire 4 years regardless of the bank you choose, should you switch banks? Explain.

WILEY ⊕ **15.** On your child's first birthday, you open an account to fund his college education. You deposit $300 to open the account. Each year, on his birthday, you make another deposit. Each subsequent deposit is 8 percent larger than the previous. The account pays interest at 5 percent/year compounded annually. How much money is in the account immediately after the deposit on his eighteenth birthday?

WILEY ⊕ **16.** Financial planners (and engineering economists) unanimously encourage people to start early in planning for retirement.
VS To illustrate this point, they frequently produce a table similar to the one below. Fill in the blank cells in this table assuming that your goal is to have $1,000,000 on your sixty-fifth birthday and that deposits start on the birthday shown and continue annually in the same amount on each birthday up to and including your sixty-fifth birthday. Assume that interest is compounded annually at 10 percent/year.

Birthday of First Deposit	25	30	35	40	45	50	55	60	65
Amount of Required Annual Deposit									$1,000,000

WILEY ⊕ **17.** Financial planners (and engineering economists) unanimously encourage people to seek out the highest rate of
VS return possible within their personal level of risk tolerance. To illustrate this point, they frequently produce a table similar to the one below. Fill in the blank cells in this table assuming that your goal is to have $1,000,000 on your sixty-fifth birthday and that deposits start on your twenty-sixth birthday and continue annually in the same amount on each birthday up to and including your sixty-fifth birthday.

Interest Rate Earned	Amount of Required Annual Deposit
4 percent/year	
5 percent/year	
6 percent/year	
7 percent/year	
8 percent/year	
9 percent/year	

WILEY ⊕ **18.** Bailey, Inc., is considering buying a new gang punch that would allow them to produce circuit boards more
VS efficiently. The punch has a first cost of $100,000 and a useful life of 15 years. At the end of its useful life, the punch has no salvage value. Annual labor costs would increase $2,000 using the gang punch, but annual raw material costs would decrease $12,000. *MARR* is 5 percent/year.

a. What is the future worth of this investment?

b. What is the decision rule for judging the attractiveness of investments based on future worth?

c. Should Bailey buy the gang punch?

WILEY ⊕ **19.** Carlisle Company has been cited and must invest in equipment to reduce stack emissions or face EPA fines of $18,500 per year. An emission reduction filter will cost $75,000 and have an expected life of 5 years. Carlisle's *MARR* is 10 percent/year.

a. What is the future worth of this investment?

b. What is the decision rule for judging the attractiveness of investments based on future worth?

c. Is the filter economically justified?

20. DuraTech Manufacturing is evaluating a process improvement project. The estimated receipts and disbursements associated with the project are shown below. *MARR* is 6 percent/year.

End of Year	0	1	2	3	4	5
Receipts	$0	$0	$2,000	$4,000	$3,000	$1,600
Disbursements	$5,000	$200	$300	$600	$1,000	$1,500

    a. What is the future worth of this investment?

    b. What is the decision rule for judging the attractiveness of investments based on future worth?

    c. Should DuraTech implement the proposed process improvement?

21. Eddie's Precision Machine Shop is insured for $700,000. The present yearly insurance premium is $1.00 per $100 of coverage. A sprinkler system with an estimated life of 20 years and no salvage value can be installed for $20,000. Annual maintenance costs for the sprinkler system are $400. If the sprinkler system is installed, the system must be included in the shop's value for insurance purposes, but the insurance premium will reduce to $0.40 per $100 of coverage. Eddie uses a *MARR* of 15 percent/year.

    a. What is the future worth of this investment?

    b. What is the decision rule for judging the attractiveness of investments based on future worth?

    c. Is the sprinkler system economically justified?

22. Fabco, Inc., is considering the purchase of flow valves that will reduce annual operating costs by $10,000 per year for the next 12 years. Fabco's *MARR* is 7 percent/year. Using a future worth approach, determine the maximum amount Fabco should be willing to pay for the valves.

23. Galvanized Products is considering the purchase of a new computer system for their enterprise data management system. The vendor has quoted a purchase price of $100,000. Galvanized Products is planning to borrow one-fourth of the purchase price from a bank at 15 percent compounded annually. The loan is to be repaid using equal annual payments over a 3-year period. The computer system is expected to last 5 years and has a salvage value of $5,000 at that time. Over the 5-year period, Galvanized Products expects to pay a technician $25,000 per year to maintain the system but will save $55,000 per year through increased efficiencies. Galvanized Products uses a *MARR* of 18 percent/year to evaluate investments.

    a. What is the future worth of this investment?

    b. What is the decision rule for judging the attractiveness of investments based on future worth?

    c. Should the new computer system be purchased?

24. Quilts R Us (QRU) is considering an investment in a new patterning attachment with the cash flow profile shown in the table below. QRU's *MARR* is 13.5 percent/year.

EOY	0	1	2	3	4	5	6	7
Cash Flow	−$1,400	$0	$500	$500	$500	$500	$0	$500
EOY	8	9	10	11	12	13	14	15
Cash Flow	$600	$700	$800	$900	−$1,000	−$2,000	−$3,000	$1,400

    a. What is the future worth of this investment?

    b. What is the decision rule for judging the attractiveness of investments based on future worth?

    c. Should QRU invest?

WILEY VS ⊕ **25.** Imagineering, Inc., is considering an investment in CAD-CAM compatible design software with the cash flow profile shown in the table below. Imagineering's *MARR* is 18 percent/year.

EOY	0	1	2	3	4	5	6	7
Cash Flow (M$)	−$12	−$1	$5	$2	$5	$5	$2	$5

    a. What is the future worth of this investment?

    b. What is the decision rule for judging the attractiveness of investments based on future worth?

    c. Should Imagineering invest?

26. Jupiter's is considering investing time and administrative expense on an effort that promises one large payoff in the future, followed by additional expenses over a 10-year horizon. The cash flow profile is shown in the table below. Jupiter's *MARR* is 12 percent/year.

EOY	0	1	2	3	4	5	6	7	8	9	10
Cash Flow (K$)	−$2	−$10	−$12	−$14	−$16	−$18	$200	−$10	−$12	−$14	−$100

    a. What is the future worth of this investment?

    b. What is the decision rule for judging the attractiveness of investments based on future worth?

    c. Should Jupiter invest?

WILEY ⊕ **27.** Aerotron Electronics is considering the purchase of a water filtration system to assist in circuit board manufacturing. The system costs $40,000. It has an expected life of 7 years at which time its salvage value will be $7,500. Operating and maintenance expenses are estimated to be $2,000 per year. If the filtration system is not purchased, Aerotron Electronics will have to pay Bay City $12,000 per year for water purification. If the system is purchased, no water purification from Bay City will be needed. Aerotron Electronics must borrow half of the purchase price, but they cannot start repaying the loan for 2 years. The bank has agreed to three equal annual payments, with the first payment due at the end of year 2. The loan interest rate is 8 percent compounded annually. Aerotron Electronics' *MARR* is 10 percent compounded annually.

    a. What is the future worth of this investment?

    b. What is the decision rule for judging the attractiveness of investments based on future worth?

    c. Should Aerotron Electronics buy the water filtration system?

28. Home Innovation is evaluating a new product design. The estimated receipts and disbursements associated with the new product are shown below. *MARR* is 10 percent/year.

End of Year	0	1	2	3	4	5
Receipts	$0	$600	$600	$700	$700	$700
Disbursements	$1,000	$300	$300	$300	$300	$300

    a. What is the future worth of this investment?

    b. What is the decision rule for judging the attractiveness of investments based on future worth?

    c. Should Home Innovation pursue this new product?

LEY ⊕ 29. A design change being considered by Mayberry, Inc., will cost $6,000 and will result in an annual savings of $1,000 per year for the 6-year life of the project. A cost of $2,000 will be avoided at the end of the project as a result of the change. *MARR* is 8 percent/year.

a. What is the future worth of this investment?

b. What is the decision rule for judging the attractiveness of investments based on future worth?

c. Should Mayberry implement the design change?

30. Nancy's Notions pays a delivery firm to distribute its products in the metro area. Delivery costs are $30,000 per year. Nancy can buy a used truck for $10,000 that will be adequate for the next 3 years. Operating and maintenance costs are estimated to be $25,000 per year. At the end of 3 years, the used truck will have an estimated salvage value of $3,000. Nancy's *MARR* is 24 percent/year.

a. What is the future worth of this investment?

b. What is the decision rule for judging the attractiveness of investments based on future worth?

c. Should Nancy buy the truck?

Section 6.3

LEY ⊕ 31. The following three investment opportunities are available. The returns for each investment for each year vary, but the first cost of each is $20,000. Based on a future worth analysis, which investment is preferred? *MARR* is 9 percent/year.

End of Year	Investment 1	Investment 2	Investment 3
1	$8,000	$11,000	$9,500
2	$9,000	$10,000	$9,500
3	$10,000	$9,000	$9,500
4	$11,000	$8,000	$9,500

32. Reconsider the data of Problem 31.

a. For each of the investments, calculate the average annual return without considering the time value of money.

b. Describe the pattern exhibited by the returns for each investment with respect to your result in part (a).

c. Are your results from (b) and the FWs from Problem 31 consistent with the concept of the time value of money? Explain.

LEY ⊕ 33. This problem is related to Problem 8. Jeff has $10,000 to invest for a period of 5 years. The following three alternatives are available at his bank:

a. Account 1 pays 4 percent/year/year for year one, 6 percent/year/year for year two, 8 percent/year/year for years three and four, and 12 percent/year/year for year five.

b. Account 2 pays 6 percent/year compounded monthly for all 5 years.

c. Account 3 pays interest at the rate of 8 percent/year compounded semiannually for all 5 years.

Based on the available balance at the end of year 5, which alternative is Jeff's best choice?

34. The engineering team at Manuel's Manufacturing, Inc., is planning to purchase an enterprise resource planning (ERP) system. The software and installation from Vendor A costs $380,000 initially and is expected to increase revenue $125,000 per year every year. The software and installation from Vendor B costs $280,000 and is expected to increase revenue $95,000 per year. Manuel's uses a 4-year planning horizon and a 10 percent per year *MARR*.

a. What is the future worth of each investment?

b. What is the decision rule for determining the preferred investment based on future worth ranking?

c. Which ERP system should Manuel purchase?

35. Reconsider Problem 34. Determine which ERP system should be purchased based on an incremental future worth analysis.

36. Nadine Chelesvig has patented her invention. She is offering a potential manufacturer two contracts for the exclusive right to manufacture and market her product. Plan A calls for an immediate single lump sum payment to her of $30,000. Plan B calls for an annual payment of $1,000 plus a royalty of $0.50 per unit sold. The remaining life of the patent is 10 years. Nadine uses a *MARR* of 10 percent/year. What must be the uniform annual sales volume of the product for Nadine to be indifferent between the contracts based on a future worth analysis?

37. Parker County Community College (PCCC) is trying to determine whether to use no insulation or to use insulation that is either 1 inch thick or 2 inches thick on its steam pipes. The heat loss from the pipes without insulation is expected to cost $1.50 per year per foot of pipe. A 1-inch thick insulated covering will eliminate 89 percent of the loss and will cost $0.40 per foot. A 2-inch thick insulated covering will eliminate 92 percent of the loss and will cost $0.85 per foot. PCCC Physical Plant Services estimates that there are 250,000 feet of steam pipe on campus. The PCCC Accounting Office requires a 10 percent/year return to justify capital expenditures. The insulation has a life expectancy of 10 years. Determine which insulation (if any) should be purchased using a ranking future worth analysis.

38. Reconsider Problem 37. Determine which insulation (if any) should be purchased based on an incremental future worth analysis.

 39. Quantum Logistics, Inc., a wholesale distributor, is considering the construction of a new warehouse to serve the southeastern geographic region near the Alabama–Georgia border. There are three cities being considered. After site visits and a budget analysis, the expected income and costs associated with locating in each of the cities have been determined. The life of the warehouse is expected to be 12 years and *MARR* is 15 percent/year.

City	Initial Cost	Net Annual Income
Lagrange	$1,260,000	$480,000
Auburn	$1,000,000	$410,000
Anniston	$1,620,000	$520,000

   a. What is the future worth of each site?

   b. What is the decision rule for determining the preferred site based on future worth ranking?

   c. Which city should be recommended?

40. Reconsider Problem 39. Determine which city should be recommended based on an incremental future worth analysis.

 41. DelRay Foods must purchase a new gumdrop machine. Two machines are available. Machine 7745 has a first cost of $10,000, an estimated life of 10 years, a salvage value of $1,000, and annual operating costs estimated at $0.01 per 1,000 gumdrops. Machine A37Y has a first cost of $8,000, a life of 10 years, and no salvage value. Its annual operating costs will be $300 regardless of the number of gumdrops produced. *MARR* is 6 percent/year, and 30 million gumdrops are produced each year.

   a. What is the future worth of each machine?

   b. What is the decision rule for determining the preferred machine based on future worth ranking?

   c. Which machine should be recommended?

42. Reconsider Problem 41. Determine which machine should be recommended based on an incremental future worth analysis.

43. Tempura, Inc., is considering two projects. Project A requires an investment of $50,000. Estimated annual receipts for 20 years are $20,000; estimated annual costs are $12,500. An alternative project, B, requires an investment of $75,000, has annual receipts for 20 years of $28,000, and has annual costs of $18,000. Assume both projects have a zero salvage value and that *MARR* is 12 percent/year.

   a. What is the future worth of each project?

   b. Which project should be recommended?

LEY ● 44. Final Finishing is considering three mutually exclusive alternatives for a new polisher. Each alternative has an expected life of 10 years and no salvage value. Polisher 1 requires an initial investment of $20,000 and provides annual benefits of $4,465. Polisher 2 requires an initial investment of $10,000 and provides annual benefits of $1,770. Polisher 3 requires an initial investment of $15,000 and provides annual benefits of $3,580. *MARR* is 15 percent/year.

   a. What is the future worth of each polisher?

   b. Which polisher should be recommended?

LEY ● 45. Xanadu Mining is considering three mutually exclusive alternatives, as shown in the table below. *MARR* is 10 percent/year.

EOY	0	1	2	3	4
A001	−$210	$80	$90	$100	$110
B002	−$110	$60	$60	$60	$70
C003	−$160	$80	$80	$80	$80

   a. What is the future worth of each alternative?

   b. Which alternative should be recommended?

 46. Yani has $12,000 for investment purposes. His bank has offered the following three choices.

   a. A special savings certificate that will pay $100 each month for 5 years and a lump sum payment at the end of 5 years of $13,000

   b. Buy a share of a racehorse for $12,000 that will be worth $20,000 in 5 years

   c. Put the money in a savings account that will have an interest rate of 12 percent per year compounded monthly. Use a future worth analysis to make a recommendation to Yani.

LEY ● 47. Two numerically controlled drill presses are being considered by the production department of Zunni's Manufacturing; one must be selected. Comparison data is shown in the table below. *MARR* is 10 percent/year.

	Drill Press T	Drill Press M
Initial Investment	$20,000	$30,000
Estimated Life	10 years	10 years
Estimated Salvage Value	$5,000	$7,000
Annual Operating Cost	$12,000	$6,000
Annual Maintenance Cost	$2,000	$4,000

   a. What is the future worth of each drill press?

   b. Which drill press should be recommended?

 48. Alpha Electronics can purchase a needed service for $90 per unit. The same service can be provided by equipment that costs $100,000 and that will have a salvage value of zero at the end of 10 years. Annual operating costs for the equipment will be $7,000 per year plus $25 per unit produced. *MARR* is 12 percent/year.

   a. Based on a future worth analysis, should the equipment be purchased if the expected production is 200 units/year?

   b. Based on a future worth analysis, should the equipment be purchased if the expected production is 500 units/year?

   c. Determine the breakeven value for annual production that will return *MARR* on the investment in the new equipment.

49. On-Site Testing Service has received four proposals for consideration. Two of the proposals, X1 and X2, are mutually exclusive. The other two proposals, Y1 and Y2, are also mutually exclusive. Proposal Y1 is contingent on X1, and Y2 is contingent on X2. Other than these restrictions, any combination of proposals (including null) is feasible. *MARR* is 10 percent/year. The expected cash flows for the proposals are shown below. A future worth analysis is to be conducted.

End of Year	X1	X2	Y1	Y2
0	−$10,000	−$15,000	−$6,000	−$9,000
1 through 8	$1,600	$2,600	$2,500	$3,500

   a. List all the alternatives to be considered.

   b. Determine which (if any) proposals On-Site Testing should accept.

 50. Dark Skies Observatory is considering several options to purchase a new deep-space telescope. Revenue would be generated from the telescope by selling "time and use" slots to various researchers around the world. Four possible telescopes have been identified in addition to the possibility of not buying a telescope if none are financially attractive. The table below details the characteristics of each telescope. A future worth ranking analysis is to be performed.

	T1	T2	T3	T4
Useful Life	10 years	10 years	10 years	10 years
First Cost	$600,000	$800,000	$470,000	$540,000
Salvage Value	$70,000	$130,000	$65,000	$200,000
Annual Revenue	$400,000	$600,000	$260,000	$320,000
Annual Expenses	$130,000	$270,000	$70,000	$120,000

   a. Determine the preferred telescope if *MARR* is 25 percent/year.

   b. Determine the preferred telescope if *MARR* is 42 percent/year.

51. Reconsider Problem 50 using an incremental future worth analysis.

52. Delta Dawn's Bakery is considering purchasing a new van to deliver bread. The van will cost $18,000. Two-thirds ($12,000) of this cost will be borrowed. The loan is to be repaid with four equal annual payments (first payment at $t = 1$) based on an interest rate of 4 percent/year. It is anticipated that the van will be used for 6 years and then sold for a salvage value of $500. Annual operating and maintenance expenses for the van over the 6-year life are estimated to be $700 per year. If the van is purchased, Delta will realize a cost savings of $3,800 per year. Delta uses a *MARR* of 6 percent/year. Based on a future worth analysis, is the purchase of the van economically attractive?

 53. Several years ago, a man won $27 million in the state lottery. To pay off the winner, the state planned to make an initial $1 million payment today followed by equal annual payments of $1.3 million at the end of each year for the next 20 years. Just before receiving any money, the man offered to sell the winning ticket back to the state for a one-time immediate payment of $14.4 million. If the state uses a 6 percent/year *MARR*, should it accept the man's offer? Use a future worth analysis.

54. Allied Electronics must purchase a new automatic soldering machine to meet increased demand for its electronic goods. Of all the machines considered, management has narrowed the choices to the following three which are mutually exclusive:

	Machine 1	Machine 2	Machine 3
Initial Cost	$800,000	$650,000	$575,000
Annual Operating Cost	$50,000	$90,000	$105,000
Salvage Value	$40,000	$32,500	$28,750

Allied Electronics uses a 4-year planning horizon, and *MARR* is 12 percent/year. Based on a future worth analysis, determine which machine should be purchased.

LEY ⊕ 55. The management of Brawn Engineering is considering three alternatives to satisfy an OSHA requirement for safety gates in the machine shop. Each gate will completely satisfy the requirement, so no combinations need to be considered. The first costs, operating costs, and salvage values over a 5-year planning horizon are shown below. Using a future worth analysis with a *MARR* of 20 percent/year, determine the preferred gate.

End of Year	Gate 1	Gate 2	Gate 3
0	−$15,000	−$19,000	−$24,000
1	−$6,500	−$5,600	−$4,000
2	−$6,500	−$5,600	−$4,000
3	−$6,500	−$5,600	−$4,000
4	−$6,500	−$5,600	−$4,000
5	−$6,500 + $0	−$5,600 + $2,000	−$4,000 + $5,000

56. RealTurf is considering purchasing an automatic sprinkler system for its sod farm by borrowing the entire $30,000 purchase price. The loan would be repaid with four equal annual payments at an interest rate of 12 percent/year. It is anticipated that the sprinkler system would be used for 9 years and then sold for a salvage value of $2,000. Annual operating and maintenance expenses for the system over the 9-year life are estimated to be $9,000 per year. If the new system is purchased, cost savings of $15,000 per year will be realized over the present manual watering system. RealTurf uses a *MARR* of 15 percent/year for economic decision making. Based on a future worth analysis, is the purchase of the new sprinkler system economically attractive?

LEY ⊕ 57. Orpheum Productions in Nevada is considering three mutually exclusive alternatives for lighting enhancements to one of its recording studios. Each enhancement will increase revenues by attracting directors who prefer this lighting style. The cash flow details, in thousands of dollars, for these enhancements are shown in the chart below. *MARR* is 10 percent/year. Based on a future worth analysis, which alternative (if any) should be implemented?

End of Year	Light Bar	Sliding Spots	Reflected Beam
0	−$6,000	−$14,000	−$20,000
1	$2,000	$3,500	$0
2	$2,000	$3,500	$2,300
3	$2,000	$3,500	$4,600
4	$2,000	$3,500	$6,900
5	$2,000	$3,500	$9,200
6	$2,000	$3,500	$11,500

58. Deep Seas Submarine must implement a new engine in its submarines to meet the needs of clients who desire quieter operation. Two designs, both technologically feasible, have been created, and Deep Seas wishes to know which one to pursue. Design 1 would require an up-front manufacturing cost of $15,000,000 and will cost $2,500,000 per year for 3 years to swap out the engines in all its current submarines. Design 2 will cost $20,000,000 up front, but due to a higher degree of compatibility will only require $1,500,000 per year to implement. *MARR* is 10 percent/year. Based on a future worth analysis, determine which design should be chosen.

WILEY 59. Calisto Launch Services is an independent space corporation and has been contracted to develop and launch one of two different satellites. Initial equipment will cost $750,000 for the first satellite and $850,000 for the second. Development will take 5 years at an expected cost of $150,000 per year for the first satellite; $120,000 per year for the second. The same launch vehicle can be used for either satellite and will cost $275,000 at the time of the launch 5 years from now. At the conclusion of the launch, the contracting company will pay Calisto $2,500,000 for either satellite.

Calisto is also considering whether they should launch both satellites. Because Calisto would have to upgrade its facilities to handle two concurrent projects, the initial costs would rise by $150,000 in addition to the first costs of each satellite. Calisto would need to hire additional engineers and workers, raising the yearly costs to a total of $400,000. An additional compartment would be added to the launch vehicle at an additional cost of $75,000. As an incentive to do both, the contracting company will pay for both launches plus a bonus of $1,000,000. Using a future worth analysis with a *MARR* of 10 percent/year, what should Calisto Launch Services do?

60. Baon Chemicals Unlimited purchases a computer-controlled filter for $100,000. Half of the purchase price is borrowed from a bank at 15 percent compounded annually. The loan is to be paid back with equal annual payments over a 5-year period. The filter is expected to last 10 years, at which time it will have a salvage value of $10,000. Over the 10-year period, the operating and maintenance costs are expected to equal $20,000 in year 1 and increase by $1,500/year each year thereafter. By making the investment, annual fines of $50,000 for pollution will be avoided. Baon expects to earn 12 percent compounded annually on its investments. Based on a future worth analysis, determine whether purchasing the filter is economically justified.

WILEY 61. Value Lodges owns an economy motel chain and is considering building a new 200-unit motel. The cost to build GO the motel is estimated at $8,000,000; Value Lodges estimates furnishings for the motel will cost an additional $700,000 and will require replacement every 5 years. Annual operating and maintenance costs for the motel are estimated to be $800,000. The average rental rate for a unit is anticipated to be $40/day. Value Lodges expects the motel to have a life of 15 years and a salvage value of $900,000 at the end of 15 years. This estimated salvage value assumes that the furnishings are not new. Furnishings have no salvage value at the end of each 5-year replacement interval. Assume average daily occupancy percentages of 50 percent, 60 percent, 70 percent, 80 percent for years 1 through 4, respectively, and 90 percent for the fifth through fifteenth years, *MARR* of 12 percent/year, 365 operating days/year, and ignoring the cost of land, should the motel be built? Base your decision on a future worth analysis.

62. Nu Things, Inc., is considering an investment in a business venture with the following anticipated cash flow results:

EOY	Cash Flow	EOY	Cash Flow	EOY	Cash Flow
0	−$70,000	7	14,000	14	7,000
1	20,000	8	13,000	15	6,000
2	19,000	9	12,000	16	5,000
3	18,000	10	11,000	17	4,000
4	17,000	11	10,000	18	3,000
5	16,000	12	9,000	19	2,000
6	15,000	13	8,000	20	1,000

Assume *MARR* is 20 percent per year. Based on a future worth analysis, (1) determine the investment's worth, (2) state whether or not your results indicate the investment should be undertaken, and (3) state the decision rule you used to arrive at this conclusion.

63. Reconsider the data from Problem 62.

   a. Plot a graph of FW versus *MARR*, where *MARR* varies from 0 percent to 50 percent by 1 percent increments. FW should be on the *y*-axis and *MARR* on the *x*-axis.

   b. Explain the significance of the *y*-axis intercept.

   c. Explain the significance of the *x*-axis intercept.

64. Packaging equipment for Xi Cling Wrap costs $60,000 and is expected to result in end-of-year net savings of $23,000 per year for 3 years. The equipment will have a market value of $10,000 after 3 years. The equipment can be leased for $21,000 per year, payable at the beginning of each year. Xi Cling's *MARR* is 10 percent/year. Based on a future worth analysis, determine if the packaging equipment should be purchased or leased.

Section 6.4

ILEY ⊕ 65. An investor has $100,000 to invest in a business venture, or she can earn 10 percent/year with a $100,000 certificate of deposit for 4 years. Three possible business ventures have been identified. Any money not invested in the business venture can be put into a bank account that earns 7 percent/year. Based on a future worth analysis, what should be done with the $100,000?

End of Year	BV01	BV02	BV03
0	−$35,000	−$80,000	−$60,000
1	$0	$10,000	$0
2	$0	$10,000	$40,000
3	$0	$10,000	$0
4	$50,000	$90,000	$40,000

66. Reconsider the data from Problem 57 (Orpheum Productions lighting enhancement). Assume that any money not invested in the lighting enhancements will be placed in an interest-bearing account earning *MARR* and will be used for future studio modernization projects.

   a. Use the total portfolio approach to examine the future worth of each alternative.

   b. Compare the future worth results from Problem 57 with your FW results for part (a). Explain your conclusions from this comparison.

Section 6.5

ILEY ⊕ 67. Octavia Bakery is planning to purchase one of two ovens. The expected cash flows for each oven are shown below. *MARR* is 8 percent/year.

	Model 127B	Model 334A
Initial Investment	$50,000	$80,000
Estimated Life	10	5
End of Life Salvage	$10,000	$0
Annual Income	$19,400	$26,000
Annual Expense	$10,000	$6,000

a. What is the future worth of each investment?

b. What is the decision rule for determining the preferred investment based on future worth ranking?

c. Which oven should Octavia purchase?

68. Reconsider Problem 67. Determine which oven should be purchased based on an incremental future worth analysis.

 69. Two storage structures, given code names Y and Z, are being considered for a military base located in Sontaga. The military uses a 5 percent/year expected rate of return and a 24-year life for decisions of this type. The relevant characteristics for each structure are shown below.

	Structure Y	Structure Z
First Cost	$4,500	$10,000
Estimated Life	12 years	24 years
Estimated Salvage Value	None	$1,800
Annual Maintenance Cost	$1,000	$720

a. What is the future worth of each machine?

b. What is the decision rule for determining the preferred machine based on future worth ranking?

c. Which structure should be recommended?

Chapter 7

ANNUAL WORTH

Harley-Davidson motorcycle powertrains are assembled at its manufacturing facility in Menomonee Falls, Wisconsin. (Courtesy of Harley-Davidson, Inc.)

Harley-Davidson

Harley-Davidson, Inc., headquartered in Milwaukee, Wisconsin, was founded in 1903 and incorporated in 1907. In 1981, Harley-Davidson purchased the motorcycle business from AMF Incorporated and in 1986, it became publicly held. As the only major American motorcycle manufacturer, Harley-Davidson has maintained the largest share of the U.S. heavyweight motorcycle market since 1986. During 2010, its share of the U.S. heavyweight (651 + cc) motorcycle market was 54.9 percent. From being ranked 6th in Europe in 2007, it rose to be ranked 2nd by the end of 2010.

Over 75 percent of Harley-Davidson's total net revenue comes from motorcycle sales, which in 2010 amounted to $4.2 billion. As of December 31, 2010, it employed approximately 6,300 people and spent $136.2 million on R&D.

Beginning in 2009, the company began a major transformation in its motorcycle manufacturing strategy, focusing on lean manufacturing, continuous improvement, flexible manufacturing, and rapid responses to customer demand. In its 2010 Annual Report, Matt Levatich, President & COO, observed, ''The motorcycle business is a seasonal business, and a manufacturing model like we've had until now—one that's built for constant, level production—can't respond well to changes in demand or customer needs.'' Karl Eberle, Sr. V.P., Manufacturing, added, ''And that's meant a change for us, across the board. You've got to remember that manufacturing processes in any business are designed to make the same thing every day, year-round. Doing that provides a certain level of productivity and predictability for us and our suppliers and employees who are skilled at certain things. But in today's world, that system is not nearly as agile in terms of dialing production up and down when we need to. And it's not an efficient way to support the sales channel and dealer network, either.'' Eberle noted, ''Bottom line, we need to be able to make any product on any line on any day. So we're structuring our capital investments to enable our manufacturing to be a lot more flexible—and making sure our employees. . .can perform a much wider range of functions.''

I n this third chapter on comparing alternatives, we address our final equivalent worth method—annual worth. Previously, we calculated present worth, capitalized worth, and future worth.

7-1   INTRODUCTION

Among the *DCF* ''worth'' methods of comparing investment alternatives, *annual worth* is more frequently used than *future worth* and *capitalized worth* but less frequently used than *present worth*. As the name implies, annual worth is used by those who wish to express economic equivalency in the form of a uniform annual series over the planning horizon.

Systematic Economic Analysis Technique

1.   Identify the investment alternatives
2.   Define the planning horizon
3.   Specify the discount rate
4.   Estimate the cash flows
5.   **Compare the alternatives**
6.   Perform supplementary analyses
7.   Select the preferred investment

Like the other worth methods, annual worth is a ranking method. Therefore, when choosing from among mutually exclusive alternatives on the basis of monetary considerations, the alternative with the greatest annual worth over the planning horizon is recommended for investment.

Several years ago, if asked which of the *DCF* methods we preferred, we would have chosen annual worth, because it more closely models the way returns occur during the planning horizon. With both present worth and future worth, the single sum, equivalent value for cash flows over a 10-year planning horizon can be such a large number that it is difficult for many to grasp. For example, with a 10 percent *TVOM*, an annual worth of $150,000 per year for a 10-year planning horizon has a present worth equivalent of nearly $1 million ($921,685.07, to be exact) and a future worth equivalent of almost $15 million ($14,689,286.24, to be exact). Since costs and savings occur almost uniformly throughout the planning horizon, for many, annual worth provides a more realistic picture of the fiscal impact of an investment.

However, if asked today which *DCF* method we prefer, we would choose present worth. Why did we change preferences? Two reasons: We found that our clients preferred present worth, and we found that when others performed annual worth calculations, they often did them incorrectly. Regarding the latter, the mistake people typically make concerns the planning horizon when alternatives have unequal lives. (We'll say more about this later in the chapter.)

In this chapter, we learn how to determine the uniform series equivalent for the cash flows that occur for an investment alternative during the planning horizon, and, when multiple mutually exclusive alternatives are available for investment, we learn how to choose the one that maximizes economic worth. We also learn how to use annual worth analysis to determine the point in time when an investment begins to "make money." In addition, we learn how to solve problems involving the least common multiple of lives assumption on a Fundamentals of Engineering examination. And, finally, we learn how to calculate the capital recovery cost for an investment.

7-2 ANNUAL WORTH: SINGLE ALTERNATIVE

WILEY
VIDEO LESSON

Recalling our work in Chapter 2, the annual worth of an investment can be expressed mathematically as follows:

$$AW = \left[\sum_{t=0}^{n} A_t (1 + MARR)^{n-t} \right] (A|F\ MARR\%,n) \tag{7.1}$$

Of course, the annual worth can also be calculated using Equation 5.2 to compute the present worth and multiplying the result by $(A|P\ MARR\%,n)$.

$$AW(i\%) = \left[\sum_{t=0}^{n} A_t (1 + i)^{-t} \right] \left[\frac{i(1 + i)^n}{(1 + i)^n - 1} \right]$$

$$AW(i\%) = PW(i\%)(A|P\ i\%,n)$$

As with present worth and future worth analyses, the decision to pursue an investment opportunity depends on $AW > 0$, assuming the do-nothing alternative is feasible and has a negligible net cost. If the annual worth is positive, then the investment will be recommended.

EXAMPLE 7.1 Annual Worth of the SMP Investment as a Function of the Planning Horizon

We continue to use the acquisition of the SMP machine as our example of a single alternative. Recall, it involved a $500,000 investment, with annual returns of $92,500 and a $50,000 salvage value at the end of the 10-year planning horizon.

The annual worth for the investment will be

$$AW = -\$500,000(A|P\ 10\%,10) + \$92,500 + \$50,000(A|F\ 10\%,10)$$

$$= -\$500,000(0.16275) + \$92,500 + \$50,000(0.06275) = \$14,262.50$$

or, using Excel®,

$$AW = \text{PMT}(10\%,10,500000,-50000)+92500 = \$14,264.57$$

Since the choice is either do nothing or invest in the SMP machine and obtain an annual worth of **$14,264.57** for the 10-year planning horizon, we choose to make the investment. Of course, the same choice would occur as long as $AW > \$0$.

As in the previous two chapters, we examine the annual worth for the SMP machine investment for various planning horizon durations and for salvage value decreasing geometrically and as a negative gradient series over the 10-year planning horizon.

EXAMPLE 7.2   Salvage Value Decreasing as Gradient and Geometric Series

As shown in Figure 7.1, annual worth is computed for the case of salvage value decreasing at a geometric rate of 20.6 percent per year, as well as decreasing by $45,000 per year over the 10-year planning horizon. In sharp contrast to the convex form of future worth, annual worth as a function of the planning horizon's length is concave, closely approximating the form of the curve obtained for present worth. (Notice, when salvage value decreases geometrically in

	A	B	C	D	E	F	G
			fx	$-$PMT($B$1,A9,-$B$3,-C9)+B9			
1	MARR =	10%					
2	Planning Horizon	CF	SV$_{geometric}$	AW$_{geometric}$	SV$_{gradient}$	AW$_{gradient}$	Excel Formula for AW$_{gradient}$
3	0	-$500,000	$500,000	n/a	$500,000	n/a	
4	1	$92,500	$397,000	-$60,500.00	$455,000	-$2,500.00	=PMT($B$1,A4,-$B$3,-E4)+B4
5	2	$92,500	$315,218	-$45,491.43	$410,000	-$357.14	=PMT($B$1,A5,-$B$3,-E5)+B5
6	3	$92,500	$250,283	-$32,943.17	$365,000	$1,714.50	=PMT($B$1,A6,-$B$3,-E6)+B6
7	4	$92,500	$198,725	-$22,416.01	$320,000	$3,715.26	=PMT($B$1,A7,-$B$3,-E7)+B7
8	5	$92,500	$157,787	-$13,553.55	$275,000	$5,645.57	=PMT($B$1,A8,-$B$3,-E8)+B8
9	6	$92,500	$125,283	-$6,066.06	$230,000	$7,506.01	=PMT($B$1,A9,-$B$3,-E9)+B9
10	7	$92,500	$99,475	$282.45	$185,000	$9,297.27	=PMT($B$1,A10,-$B$3,-E10)+B10
11	8	$92,500	$78,983	$5,684.59	$140,000	$11,020.15	=PMT($B$1,A11,-$B$3,-E11)+B11
12	9	$92,500	$62,713	$10,297.92	$95,000		
13	10	$137,500	$49,794	$14,251.63	$50,000		
14	AW =	$14,264.57	=PMT(B1,10,500000,-50000)+92500				

FIGURE 7.1

Annual Worth of the SMP Investment as a Function of the Planning Horizon.

D9 ▾ fx =PMT($B$1,A9,-$B$3,-C9)+B9

	A	B	C	D	E	F	G
1	MARR =	10%					
2	Planning Horizon	CF	SV$_{geometric}$	AW$_{geometric}$	SV$_{gradient}$	AW$_{gradient}$	
3	0	-$500,000	$500,000	n/a	$500,000	n/a	
4	1	$92,500	$397,000	-$60,500.00	$455,000	-$2,500.00	
5	2	$92,500	$315,218	-$45,491.43	$410,000	-$357.14	
6	3	$92,500	$250,283	-$32,943.17	$36...		
7	4	$92,500	$198,725	-$22,416.01	$32...		
8	5	$92,500	$157,787	-$13,553.55	$27...		
9	6	$92,500	$125,283	-$6,066.06	$23...		
10	7	$92,500	$99,475	$282.45	$18...		
11	8	$92,500	$78,983	$5,684.59	$14...		
12	9	$92,500	$62,713	$10,297.92	$9...		
13	10	$137,500	$49,794	$14,251.63	$8...		
14	AW =	$14,264.57	=PMT(B1,10,500000,-50000)...				
15		geometric	gradient				
16	n =	6.9518752	2.169974				
17	AW =	$0.00	$0.00	=PMT($B$1,C17,500000,-500000+45000*C17)+92500			
18			=PMT($B$1,B17,500000,-500000*(1-0.206)^B17)+92500				
19							

Solver Parameters

Set Target Cell: $B$17

Equal To: ◯ Max ◯ Min ◉ Value of: 0

By Changing Cells:

$B$16

Subject to the Constraints:

FIGURE 7.2

Annual Worth when Salvage Value Decreases as Gradient and Geometric Series.

value over time, the annual worth curve is more concave than when it decreases as a gradient series.)

Using the Excel® **SOLVER** tool, for the data in Example 7.1, we can determine the point in time when the annual worth equals 0 with the salvage value decreasing at a geometric rate and decreasing as a gradient series. As shown in Figure 7.2, when salvage value decreases geometrically, annual worth equals 0 after 6.95 years; similarly, when salvage value decreases as a gradient series, annual worth equals 0 after 2.17 years. (The latter assumes that salvage value decreases linearly during a year.)

In Chapters 5 and 6, we examined the impact of changes in the *MARR* on the economic worth of an investment. However, we only did so when we were considering multiple alternatives. There was no reason for not performing a similar analysis for a single alternative. But we chose to wait until now to do so.

EXAMPLE 7.3 Impact of Changes in the *MARR*

Let's examine the behavior of annual worth when the *MARR* changes values, ranging from 0 percent to 20 percent. The plot of annual worth for the 10-year planning horizon is provided in Figure 7.3. Also shown in the figure is the result of using the Excel® **SOLVER** tool to determine the value of the *MARR* that makes the annual worth equal 0; the value obtained is 13.80 percent. (In the next Chapter, we explore the *internal rate of return*, which is the *MARR* value that makes the annual worth, present worth, or future worth of an investment equal 0.)

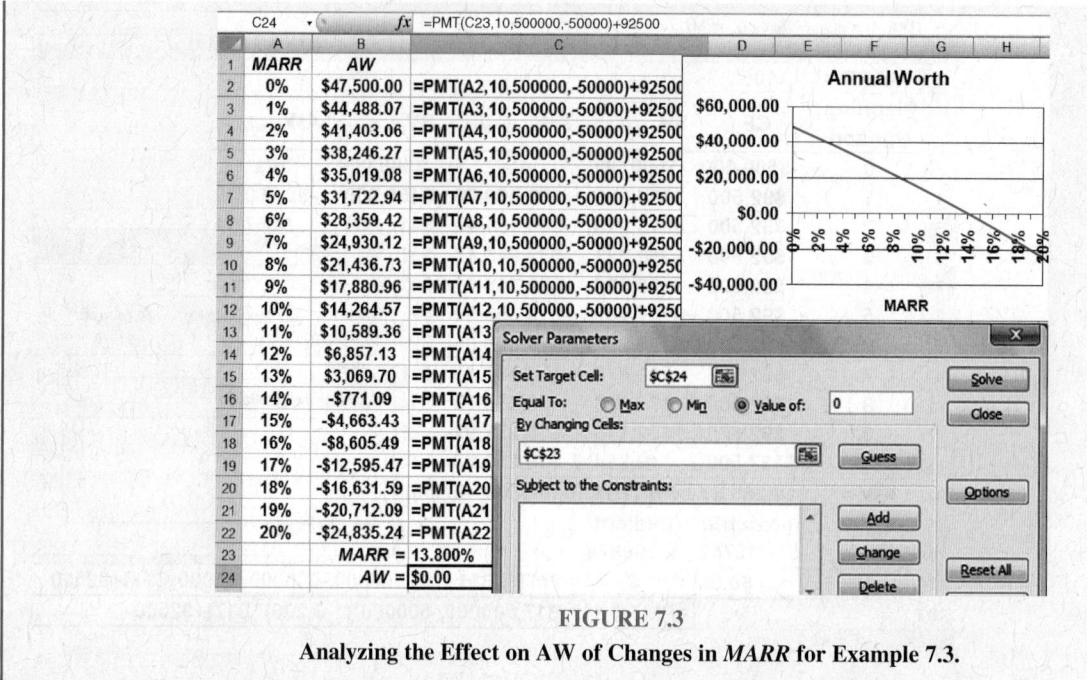

FIGURE 7.3
Analyzing the Effect on AW of Changes in *MARR* for Example 7.3.

7-3 ANNUAL WORTH: MULTIPLE ALTERNATIVES

Ranking Approach. When attempting to determine the preferred alternative from among multiple mutually exclusive alternatives and when using annual worth as the measure of economic worth, choose the alternative that maximizes annual worth over the planning horizon of *n* years. Mathematically, the objective can be stated as

$$\text{Maximize } AW_j = \left[\sum_{t=0}^{n} A_{tj}(1 + MARR)^{n-t} \right] (A|F\ MARR\%,n) \qquad (7.2)$$

$$\text{Maximize } AW_j(i\%) = \left[\sum_{t=0}^{n} A_{tj}(1 + i)^{-t} \right] \left[\frac{i(1 + i)^n}{(1 + i)^n - 1} \right]$$

EXAMPLE 7.4 Using Annual Worth to Choose Between Two Alternatives

In Chapters 5 and 6, we considered the installation of a new ride (the Scream Machine) at a theme park in Florida. Two alternative designs (A and B) were considered: Alternative A required a $300,000 investment, produced net annual after-tax revenues of $55,000, and had a negligible salvage value at the end of the 10-year planning horizon. Alternative B required a $450,000 investment, generated net annual after-tax revenues of $80,000, and also had a negligible salvage value at the end of the 10-year planning horizon. The do-nothing (DN) alternative was feasible and had an economic worth of $0. Based on a 10 percent *MARR* and using an annual worth measure, which design, if either, should be chosen?

$$AW_A = -\$300,000(A|P\ 10\%,10) + \$55,000$$
$$= -\$300,00(0.16275) + \$55,000$$
$$= \$6,175.00$$
$$= \text{PMT}(10\%,10,300000) + 55000 = \$6,176.38$$

Likewise,

$$AW_B = -\$450,000(A|P\ 10\%,10) + \$80,000$$
$$= -\$450,000(0.16275) + \$80,000$$
$$= \$6,762.50$$
$$= \text{PMT}(10\%,10,450000) + 80000 = \$6,764.57$$

Since $AW_B > AW_A > AW_{DN}$, Design B is recommended.

To determine how annual worth changes during the planning horizon, we use the same approach as in the previous chapters and estimate the salvage values of the two designs if used for *n* years, based on a terminal value of 0.1¢ after 10 years. The geometric rate for Alternative A is −85.80 percent; the geometric rate for Alternative B is −86.364 percent, as determined in Chapter 6. Figure 7.4 includes the salvage values for each alternative at the end of the planning horizon, the annual worth for each alternative, a plot of the annual worths, and the **SOLVER** solutions for the DPBP for each design alternative.

To gain a better understanding of the differences in economic performance of Designs A and B, Figure 7.5 depicts the annual worth for each design for various values of the *MARR*. Notice, for *MARR* < 10.56 percent, $AW(B) > AW(A)$; for *MARR* = 10.56 percent, $AW(B) = AW(A)$; and for *MARR* > 10.56 percent, $AW(B) < AW(A)$. (In Chapter 8, we show that $AW(B) = AW(A)$ for *MARR* = 10.56 percent, which is the *internal rate of return on the incremental investment*.)

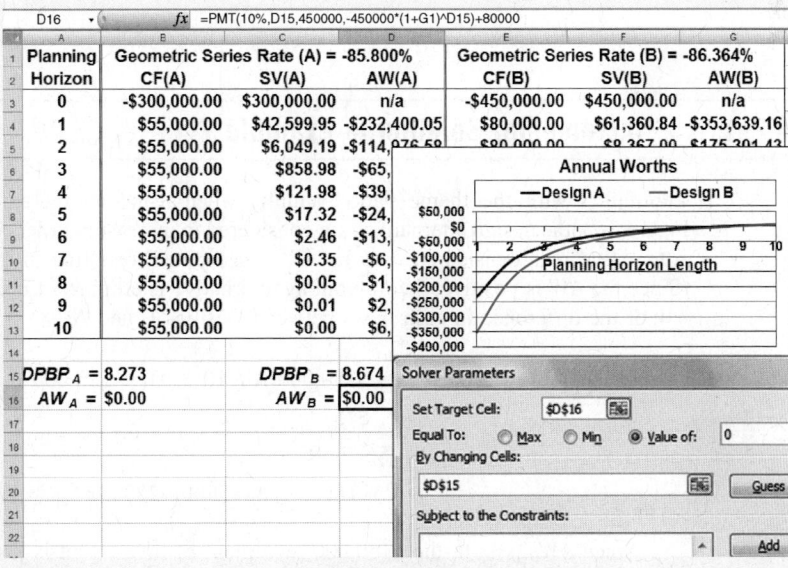

FIGURE 7.4

Analysis of the Impact of the Planning Horizon on Annual Worth with Geometrically Decreasing Salvage Values.

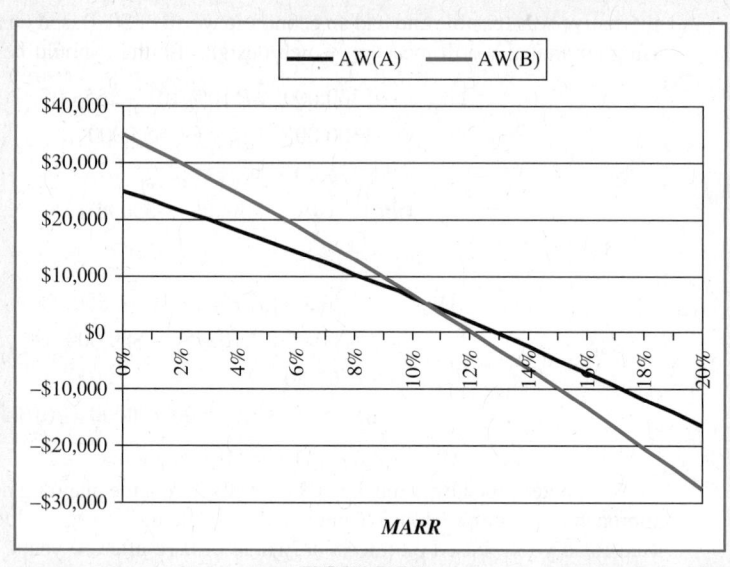

FIGURE 7.5
Impact of *MARR* on Annual Worth for Example 7.4.

Incremental Approach. As with present worth and future worth, annual worth can be applied using incremental analysis. But, as noted in Chapter 5, we do not know why anyone would choose to use incremental analysis, since a ranking approach is simpler to use. However, we will use incremental analysis in solving the previous example problem.

EXAMPLE 7.5 Incremental Solution to Example 7.4

Continuing with the theme park example, when using an incremental approach (see Figure 5.7), the design alternatives are considered in increasing order of investment. Hence, Alternative A is considered first. Its *AW* is computed, resulting in a value of $6,176.38. (Since the *AW* is positive, the do-nothing alternative is eliminated.) Next, we compute the *AW* of the difference in cash flows between Designs B and A:

$$AW_{B-A} = -\$150,000(A|P\ 10\%,10) + \$25,000$$
$$= -\$150,000(0.16275) + \$25,000$$
$$= \$587.50$$
$$= \text{PMT}(10\%,10,-15000)+25000 = \$588.19$$

Since $AW_{B-A} > 0$, the $150,000 increment of investment is justified economically. Hence, Design Alternative B is recommended. Using the results from Excel®, its overall annual worth is $AW_A + AW_{B-A} = \$6,176.38 + \$588.19 = \$6,764.57 = AW_B$.

7-4 LEAST COMMON MULTIPLE OF LIVES ASSUMPTION

When the economic worth of mutually exclusive investment alternatives having unequal lives is being determined using annual worth analysis, it is often recommended
that the alternative having the greatest annual worth over an individual life cycle be
chosen. The following example illustrates the approach recommended by many.

EXAMPLE 7.6 Revisiting Example 6.8 with Annual Worth Analysis

Recall, in Example 6.8, three mutually exclusive investment alternatives were considered. The
first alternative required an investment of $10,000, yielded returns of $5,000/year for 3 years,
and had a salvage value of $5,000 at the end of the third year; the second alternative required a
$14,500 investment, yielded annual returns of $5,000 for 6 years, and had a negligible salvage
value; and the third alternative required a $20,000 investment, yielded annual returns equal to
a $3,000 gradient series, and had a negligible salvage value. The investor's *MARR* was
12 percent. Let's apply annual worth analysis to determine the best alternative for the investor.

Table 7.1 provides the cash flow profiles for the three investments. We will consider
three investment scenarios: individual life cycles for each investment; a least common
multiple of lives planning horizon; and a 6-year planning horizon with the investments being
one-shot investments. In the latter scenario, no cash flows occur during years 4, 5, and 6 for
the first investment.

Scenario 1: Individual Life Cycles

$$AW_1 = -\$10,000(A|P\,12\%,3) + \$5,000 + \$5,000(A|F\,12\%,3)$$
$$= -\$10,000(0.41635) + \$5,000 + \$5,000(0.29635)$$
$$= \$2,318.25$$

or, using Excel®,

$$AW_1 = \text{PMT}(12\%,3,10000,-5000) + 5000 = \$2,318.26$$

Similarly, for Alternative 2,

$$AW_2 = -\$14,500(A|P\,12\%,6) + \$5,000$$
$$= -\$14,500(0.24323) + \$5,000$$
$$= \$1,473.17$$

TABLE 7.1			
Cash Flows for Scenario 1 in Example 7.6.			
EOY	CF(1)	CF(2)	CF(3)
0	−$10,000	−$14,500	−$20,000
1	$5,000	$5,000	$0
2	$5,000	$5,000	$3,000
3	$10,000	$5,000	$6,000
4		$5,000	$9,000
5		$5,000	$12,000
6		$5,000	$15,000

or, using Excel®,

$$AW_2 = \text{PMT}(12\%,6,14500)+5000 = \$1,473.23$$

Likewise, for Alternative 3,

$$AW_3 = -\$20,000(A|P\ 12\%,6) + \$3,000(A|G\ 12\%,6)$$
$$= -\$20,000(0.24323) + \$3,000(2.17205)$$
$$= \$1,651.55$$

or, using Excel®,

$$AW_3 = \text{PMT}(12\%,6,-1000*\text{NPV}(12\%,0,3,6,9,12,15)+20000) = \$1,651.63$$

Based on the annual worth analysis, the third investment is preferred; the first investment is least attractive financially.

Scenario 2: Least Common Multiple of Lives Planning Horizon

Now let's consider a planning horizon equal to the least common multiple of lives, 6 years. In doing so, we assume equally attractive investment opportunities will be available in 3 years when the first investment ends. By fully recovering the initial investment in the third year, funds will be available to repeat the investment, as shown in Table 7.2.

Clearly, the annual worths for the second and third investment will be unchanged from the first scenario. The annual worth for the repetition of Investment 1 will be

$$AW_1 = -\$10,000(A|P\ 12\%,6)$$
$$+ [\$5,000 - \$5,000(F|P\ 12\%,3)](A|F\ 12\%,6) + \$5,000$$
$$= -\$10,000(0.24323) + [\$5,000 - \$5,000(1.40493)](0.12323)$$
$$+ \$5,000 = \$2,318.26$$

or, using Excel®,

$$AW_1 = \text{PMT}(12\%,6,10000,-5000)+\text{PMT}(12\%,6,,\text{FV}(12\%,3,,-5000))+5000$$
$$= \$2,318.26$$

If the investment can be repeated in 3 years, then the first investment is preferred. If it cannot be repeated, then the third investment should be chosen.

TABLE 7.2
Cash Flows for Scenario 2 in Example 7.6.

EOY	CF(1')	CF(2)	CF(3)
0	−$10,000	−$14,500	−$20,000
1	$5,000	$5,000	$0
2	$5,000	$5,000	$3,000
3	$0	$5,000	$6,000
4	$5,000	$5,000	$9,000
5	$5,000	$5,000	$12,000
6	$10,000	$5,000	$15,000

	TABLE 7.3		
	Cash flows for Scenario 3 in Example 7.6		
EOY	CF(1)	CF(2)	CF(3)
0	−$10,000	−$14,500	−$20,000
1	$5,000	$5,000	$0
2	$5,000	$5,000	$3,000
3	$10,000	$5,000	$6,000
4	$0	$5,000	$9,000
5	$0	$5,000	$12,000
6	$0	$5,000	$15,000

Notice, the annual worth for the first investment when the planning horizon equals the least common multiple of lives is identical to that obtained when single life cycles are considered. Hence, when using annual worth analysis with a least common multiple of lives planning horizon, you only need to compute the annual worth for a single life cycle for each investment alternative.

Scenario 3: One-Shot Investments

Finally, we consider a 6-year planning horizon, without Investment 1 being repeated during the final 3 years of the planning horizon. The cash flows for this scenario are given in Table 7.3. As before, the annual worths for the second and third investment are unchanged.

$$AW_1 = \{-\$10,000 + [\$5,000(P|A\ 12\%,3) + \$5,000(P|F\ 12\%,3)]\}(A|P\ 12\%,6)$$
$$= \{-\$10,000 + [\$5,000(2.40183) + \$5,000(0.71178)]\}(0.24323)$$
$$= \$1,354.32$$

or, using Excel®,

$$AW_1 = \text{PMT}(12\%,6,10000\text{-PV}(12\%,3,-5000,-5000)) = \$1,354.29$$

As before, the third investment is the best and the first investment is the worst when a 6-year planning horizon is used and the first investment has no cash flows during years 4, 5, and 6.

What should the investor do? Is it reasonable to assume the first investment will be repeated, as assumed under the first and second scenarios? Recall, when the *MARR* of 12 percent was established, it was to reflect what the investor would do with money not invested in one of the three alternatives. The *MARR* reflects the opportunity for returns of comparable risk available to the investor. Hence, there is no reason to expect that an equally attractive investment will be available in 3 years. If there is reason to expect such opportunities, then the *MARR* was set too low.

To gain an increased understanding of how the three alternatives perform for various *MARR* values, see Figure 6.15. From the close-up of the region defined by the future worth between $9,800 and $11,800, it is obvious that the first investment is preferred if $MARR \geq 14.5$ percent. In such a case, the assumption of repeatability is not needed to justify the investment.

In the end, the choice comes down to what we believe the future holds. As for us, we fall back on the selection of the *MARR*. If it truly is 12 percent, then the third investment should be chosen; if the *MARR* is greater than 14.5 percent, then the first investment should be chosen. (As we stated in Chapter 4, the *MARR* value matters!)

EXAMPLE 7.7 Annual Worth Analysis with Unequal-Lived Alternatives

Three industrial mowers (small, medium, and large) are being evaluated by a company that provides lawn care service. At the end of its useful life, each mower will have a negligible salvage value. Determine the economic choice, based on the following cost and performance parameters:

	Small	**Medium**	**Large**
First cost:	$1,500	$2,000	$5,000
Operating cost/hour:	$35	$50	$76
Revenue/hour:	$55	$75	$100
Hours/year:	1,000	1,100	1,200
Useful life:	2 yrs	3 yrs	5 yrs

$$AW_{small} = -\$1,500(A|P\ 12\%,2) + \$20(1,000)$$
$$= \$19,112.45$$
$$=PMT(12\%,2,1500)+20*1000$$
$$=\$19,112.45$$

$$AW_{medium} = -\$2,000(A|P\ 12\%,3) + \$25(1,100)$$
$$= \$26,667.30$$
$$=PMT(12\%,3,2000)+25*1100$$
$$=\$26,667.30$$

$$AW_{large} = -\$5,000(A|P\ 12\%,5) + \$24(1,200)$$
$$= \$27,412.95$$
$$=PMT(12\%,5,5000)+24*1200$$
$$=\$27,412.95$$

Using the traditional least common multiple of lives assumption, the annual worth analysis indicates the large mower is the economic choice.

Did anything about the analysis bother you? The following two things bother us:

1. Implicit in the solution is an assumption that the lawn care service will continue to require mowers having cost profiles identical (or very similar) to those considered above.

2. It is also assumed that the service will be needed for at least 30 years (the least common multiple of 2, 3, and 5 years) or that the salvage values for any remaining useful lives of mowers or replacement mowers will be such that the calculated annual worth holds true.

In Chapter 6, we noted that an advantage of future worth analysis over annual worth analysis is the requirement to be explicit about what cash flows will occur between the end of an alternative's life cycle and the end of the planning horizon when the alternatives have unequal lives.

EXAMPLE 7.8   Impact of a 5-Year Planning Horizon

In Example 7.7, suppose a planning horizon of 5 years is to be used. Since the useful life for the large mower is 5 years, no additional analysis is needed for it. Its annual worth equals $27,412.95. What assumptions are needed regarding the small and medium-sized mowers for the annual worth results obtained above to hold true?

Consider first the small mower. We assume that identical mowers will be purchased after 2 years and after 4 years. Then, we calculate what the salvage value will have to be for a 1-year-old mower 5 years in the future in order to have an annual worth of $19,112.45.

$$SV_{small} = \$19,112.45(F|A\ 12\%,1) - \$20,000(F|A\ 12\%,1) + \$1,500(F|P\ 12\%,1)$$
$$= \$792.45$$
$$= FV(12\%,1,-19112.45) - FV(12\%,1,-20000,1500)$$
$$= \$792.45$$

We believe the mower is unlikely to have a salvage value greater than half its purchase price after 1 year if its salvage value is 0 after 2 years.

Next, consider the medium-sized mower. We assume an identical mower will be purchased after 3 years. Therefore, we must calculate what a 2-year-old mower's salvage value must be to have an annual worth of $26,667.30 five years in the future.

$$SV_{medium} = \$26,667.30(F|A\ 12\%,2) - \$27,500(F|A\ 12\%,2) + \$2,000(F|P\ 12\%,2)$$
$$= \$743.48$$
$$= FV(12\%,2,-26667.3) - FV(12\%,2,-27500,2000)$$
$$= \$743.48$$

How likely is it that the mower, after being used two-thirds of its useful life, will have a salvage value equal to 37.17 percent of its initial price, when its salvage value in another year will be negligible? Perhaps it is not an unreasonable assumption for the medium-sized mower to have a $743.48 salvage value after 2 years of use. However, we believe it is better to estimate the salvage value instead of assuming it will be whatever it takes to yield an annual worth equal to $26,667.30.

7-5   UNEQUAL LIVES REVISITED

As noted previously, one of the factors that made us prefer (indeed, to emphasize in teaching and consulting) present worth and future worth more than annual worth is the prevalent mistake people make in performing annual worth analyses when mutually exclusive investment alternatives have different lives. The issue is the choice of the planning horizon used. We have addressed the issue many times in this chapter and the previous three chapters.

We are not being repetitious because we doubt your ability to understand the issue. Rather, it is because faculty members differ in their choices of subject matter to teach, as well as the sequence of the material they present. (For example, some might choose to omit Chapters 4 and 6.) For that reason, we felt it necessary to touch on the subject in each of the "worth" chapters. (We will touch on it in several other chapters, too.)

And, frankly, another reason for emphasizing the challenges posed by having unequal-lived alternatives is that we believe some authors fail to point out the mistakes that can easily occur when using annual worth analysis to compare unequal-lived alternatives. The mistake occurs when students are encouraged to compute the annual worths of individual life cycles of alternatives with differing useful lives, and then very little attention is given to the implicit assumption that the planning horizon will be at least as long as a least common multiple of lives for the alternatives.

That is fine and good, but every economic justification we (and our associates) have performed over the past 40-plus years has involved planning horizons that are less than the least common multiple of lives. In the logistics, manufacturing, and military settings where we have worked, useful lives of alternatives range from 5 to 15 years. As a result, if the useful lives are unequal, then it is quite likely the least common multiples of lives will be at least 30 years (the least common multiple of 5 and 6 years). Commercial interests tend to make financial decisions based on planning horizons of 10 years or less.

We recall using 15-year planning horizons on a few occasions with clients, but that was many years ago. The speed with which new technologies are developed, the dynamics of the global business world, and investors' emphases on near-term profitability have caused planning horizons to be shorter today than they were 20 years ago.

It is also the case that one cannot be as definitive about the length of an investment alternative's useful life as some contend. For example, if a production machine, or an over-the-road tractor, or a chemical mixer, or a power generator is being considered and a useful life of 5 years is specified, then it is highly unlikely that the machine, tractor, mixer, or generator cannot be used for 6 or even 7 years if the need exists.

Can alternatives have unequal useful lives? Of course they can. As children, we learned that from the story "The Three Little Pigs." There was no doubt that the houses made of straw, sticks, and bricks would have had different lives even if the big bad wolf had not come for a visit. The choice of the materials used in a product often determines its useful life. In Chapter 5, that was the case in the capitalized cost example involving the choice of paving materials for a highway, as well as the capitalized cost example involving alternative methods of delivering water to an arid region of a developing country.

As the age of equipment is extended, annual operating and maintenance costs tend to increase. Therefore, when a 5-year useful life is specified, it could be that 5 years is the most economical life for the particular investment alternative. Extending its life will likely cause other costs to increase.

EXAMPLE 7.9   Extending the Useful Life of an Investment Alternative

In the previous example, suppose a planning horizon of 6 years had been used. Since 6 years is the least common multiple of the useful lives for the small and medium-sized mowers, the annual worths based on individual life cycles is accurate. Hence,

$$AW_{small} = \$19,112.45$$
$$AW_{medium} = \$26,667.30$$

What about the large mower? Since its useful life was estimated to be 5 years, we might consider keeping it another year. Doing so might cause the operating cost to increase in the sixth year by, say, 15 percent. If so, then

$$\text{AW}_{\text{large}} = -\$5,000(A|P\ 12\%,6) + \$24(1200) - 0.15(\$76)(1200)(A|F\ 12\%,6)$$
$$= \$25,898.06$$

=PMT(12%,6,5000,.15*76*1200)+24*1200
=$25,898.14

The medium-sized mower now becomes the economic choice.

Yet another possibility for filling in the gap between the end of an alternative's useful life and the end of the planning horizon is to lease equipment.

EXAMPLE 7.10   Leasing to "Fill the Gap"

In the previous example, which had a 6-year planning horizon, suppose a mower identical to the large mower can be leased for the sixth year at an annual *beginning-of-year* cost of $1,500. Also, suppose the leased mower has an *end-of-year* operating cost of $77, instead of the $76 annual operating cost of the purchased mower.

As before,

$$\text{AW}_{\text{small}} = \$19,112.45$$
$$\text{AW}_{\text{medium}} = \$26,667.30$$

The annual worth for the large mower will be

$$\text{AW}_{\text{large}} = -\$5,000(A|P\ 12\%,6) + \$24(1200)$$
$$- [\$1(1,200) + \$1,500(F|P\ 12\%,1)](A|F\ 12\%,6)$$
$$= \$27,228.95$$

=PMT(12%,6,5000,1200-FV(12%,1,1500)+24*1200 = $27,228.98)

Using a leased mower for the sixth year is the preferred alternative.

Fundamentals of Engineering Examination. Even though you might not encounter a situation in your professional practice that requires you to use the least common multiple of lives assumption, you will probably have problems of this type on the FE exam. Therefore, you need to be familiar with how to solve such problems. Specifically, unless instructions are given to do otherwise, calculate the annual worth for life cycles of each alternative and recommend the one that has the greatest annual worth.

> ### Fundamentals of Engineering Examination
>
> In taking the FE Exam, *unless instructions are given to do otherwise*, <u>calculate the annual worth for a life cycle of each alternative and recommend the one that has the greatest annual worth.</u>

$$CR = P(A|P\,i,n) - F(A|F\,i,n)$$
$$CR = (P - F)(A|F\,i,n) + Pi$$
$$CR = (P - F)(A|P\,i,n) + Fi$$
$$CR = \text{PMT}(i,n, -P,F)$$

7-6   CAPITAL RECOVERY COST

WILEY
VIDEO LESSON

In engineering economic analyses, it is common to refer to an asset's *capital recovery cost*. This is the uniform annual cost equivalent of the initial investment and terminal or salvage value for an asset. Specifically, if an investment of P is made in an asset and the asset is disposed of for a salvage value of F after n years, then, based on the firm's cost of capital of $i\%$, the capital recovery cost (CR) is defined as

$$CR = P(A|P\,i\%,n) - F(A|F\,i\%,n) \qquad (7.3)$$

where costs are shown as positive-valued and revenues are shown as negative-valued. The equivalency is shown in Figure 7.6 in the form of cash flow diagrams.

Recall the relationship between the *sinking fund factor* and the *capital recovery factor*,

$$(A|F\,i\%,n) = (A|P\,i\%,n) - i \qquad (7.4)$$

Substituting Equation 7.4 into Equation 7.3, we obtain two more capital recovery cost formulas:

$$CR = (P - F)(A|F\,i\%,n) + Pi \qquad (7.5)$$
$$CR = (P - F)(A|P\,i\%,n) + Fi \qquad (7.6)$$

Among the three formulas for computing capital recovery cost, Equation 7.6 was the most popular for years. In fact, its popularity led to the $(A|P\,i\%,n)$ factor being called the *capital recovery factor*.

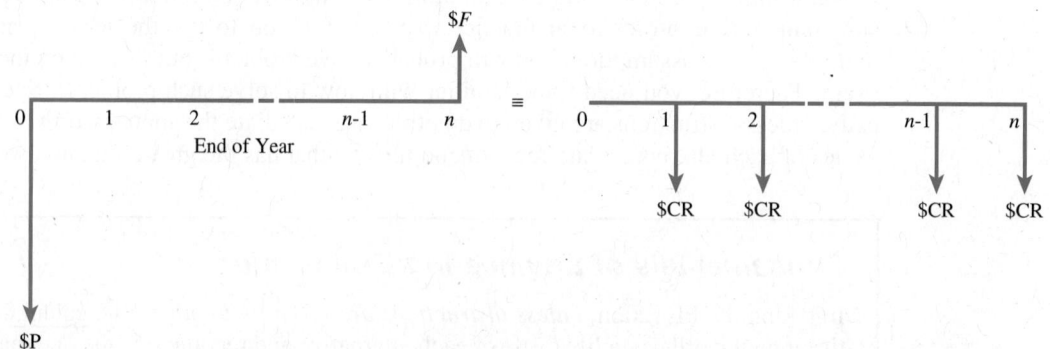

FIGURE 7.6

CFD for Capital Recovery Cost (CR).

Using Excel®, the capital recovery cost is easily obtained using the **PMT** worksheet function.

$$CR = \text{PMT}(i,n,-P,F) \tag{7.7}$$

The relationship between capital recovery cost and depreciation or cost recovery is discussed in Chapter 9. We will use the capital recovery cost in Chapter 11, when we discuss optimum replacement intervals for equipment.

In preparation for the discussion of optimum replacement intervals, we note that CR decreases with increasing values of n. The decreasing value of CR indicates that the longer one keeps an asset, the less its overall annual cost of ownership.

Since CR decreases with increasing n, why not keep equipment "forever" in order to minimize annual cost? Generally, as equipment ages, maintenance costs increase. In addition, new technologies are introduced that can cause aging equipment to be less competitive. Even if operating costs do not increase as the equipment ages, revenues may well decrease due to the use of less productive equipment.

EXAMPLE 7.11   Computing Capital Recovery Cost

Recall the SMP investment: $500,000 investment with a salvage value of $50,000 after 10 years. Using Equation 7.3, with a *MARR* of 10 percent, the capital recovery cost is

$$CR = \$500,000(A|P\,10\%,10) - \$50,000(A|F\,10\%,10)$$
$$= \$500,000(0.16275) - \$50,000(0.06275)$$
$$= \$78,237.50/\text{year}$$

Using Equation 7.5, with a 10 percent *MARR*,

$$CR = (\$500,000 - \$50,000)(A|F\,10\%,10) + \$500,000(0.10)$$
$$= \$450,000(0.06275) + \$50,000 = \$78,237.50/\text{year}$$

Using Equation 7.6, with a 10 percent cost of capital,

$$CR = (\$500,000 - \$50,000)(A|P\,10\%,10) + \$50,000(0.10)$$
$$= \$450,000(0.16275) + \$5,000 = \$78,237.50/\text{year}$$

Using Equation 7.7, with a 10 percent cost of capital,

$$CR = \text{PMT}(10\%,10,-500000,50000)$$
$$= \$78,235.43/\text{year}$$

(As usual, the difference in answers obtained using the compound interest tables in Appendix A and the Excel® financial functions is due to round-off error in the tables.)

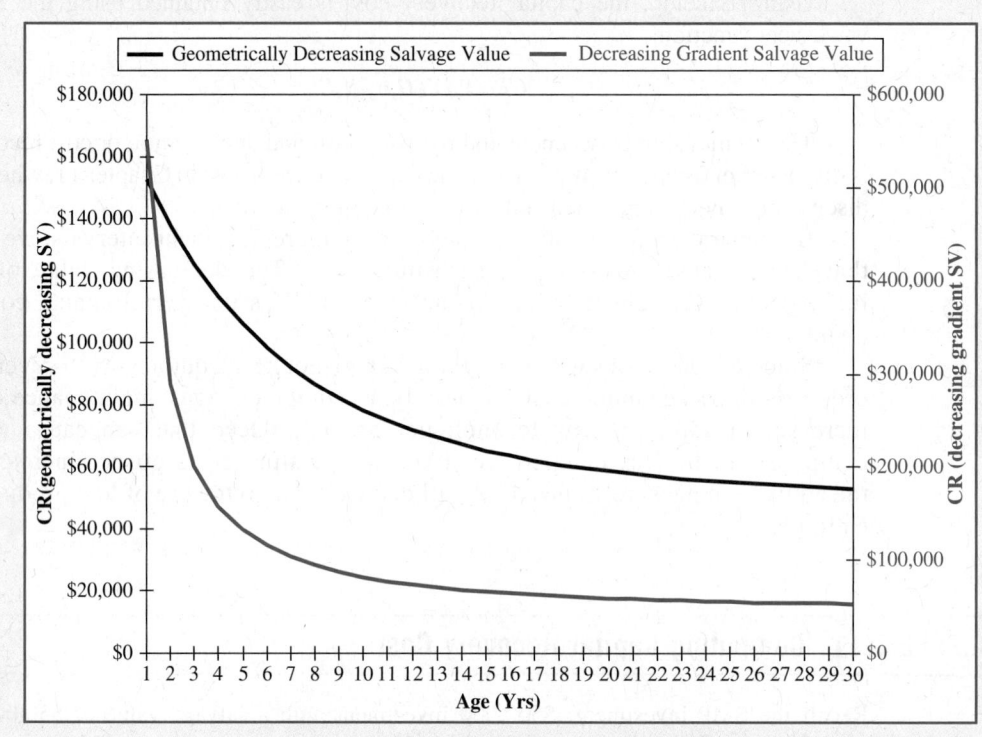

FIGURE 7.7

Impact of Age on Capital Recovery Cost for Example 7.10.

Depending on how salvage value decreases with age, different *CR* profiles result. In Figure 7.7, we assume salvage value decreases $45,000 annually for 10 years, and that salvage value decreases geometrically at a rate that causes salvage value to equal $50,000 after 10 years use.

Principle #8

Compare investment alternatives over a common period of time.

7-7 SUMMARY

Having completed the third chapter on measuring the worth of investments, we are in a position to evaluate the economic viability of one or more investments. From our study of annual worth, we learned

1. how to calculate the annual worth of a single investment;
2. how to choose, from among several mutually exclusive investment alternatives, the one that maximizes economic worth;

3. that the discounted payback period can be determined using annual worth calculations, giving the point in time when an investment begins to "make money";

4. how to solve problems involving the least common multiple of lives assumption on a Fundamentals of Engineering examination—*compute the annual worth of individual life cycles of the mutually exclusive investment alternatives*; and

5. how to calculate the capital recovery cost for an investment.

Pit Stop #7—No Time to Coast!

1. True or False: Annual worth analysis is the most popular *DCF* measure of economic worth.

2. True or False: Unless non-monetary considerations dictate otherwise, choose the mutually exclusive investment alternative that has the greatest annual worth over the planning horizon.

3. True or False: The capital recovery cost is the uniform annual cost of the investment less the uniform annual worth of the salvage value.

4. True or False: If $AW > 0$, then $PW > 0$, and $FW > 0$.

5. True or False: If $AW(A) > AW(B)$, then $PW(A) > PW(B)$.

6. True or False: If $AW(A) < AW(B)$, then $AW(B-A) > 0$.

7. True or False: If $AW(A) > AW(B)$, then $CW(A) > CW(B)$ and $DPBP(A) < DPBP(B)$.

8. True or False: AW can be applied as either a ranking method or as an incremental method.

9. True or False: To compute capital recovery cost using Excel, enter $= \text{PMT}(i\%,n,-P,F)$ in any cell in a spreadsheet.

10. True or False: When using annual worth analysis with mutually exclusive alternatives having unequal lives, always use a planning horizon equal to the least common multiple of lives.

 Tutoring problem available (at instructor's discretion) in *WileyPLUS*.

 Problem available (at instructor's discretion) in *WileyPLUS*.

 Worked Problem Video available in *WileyPLUS*.

FE-LIKE PROBLEMS

1. Consider a palletizer at a bottling plant that has a first cost of $150,000, operating and maintenance costs of $17,500 per year, and an estimated net salvage value of $25,000 at the end of 30 years. Assume an interest rate of 8 percent. What is the annual equivalent cost of the investment if the planning horizon is 30 years?

    a. $29,760   c. $31,980
    b. $30,600   d. $35,130

2. When using annual worth to evaluate the attractiveness of a single alternative, what value is the calculated AW compared to?
   a. PW
   b. FW
   c. 0.0
   d. *MARR*

3. The annual worth of an alternative is 0. Which of the following is (are) also true?
   (1) PW = 0
   (2) FW = 0
   a. (1) only
   b. (2) only
   c. Both (1) and (2)
   d. Neither (1) nor (2)

4. The overhead costs in a highly automated factory are expected to increase at an annual compound rate of 10 percent for the next 7 years. The overhead cost at the end of the first year is $200,000. What is the annual worth of the overhead costs for the 7-year period? The time value of money rate is 8 percent/year.
   a. $263,250
   b. $231,520
   c. $200,000
   d. $187,020

5. The operating and maintenance expenses for a mining machine are expected to be $11,000 in the first year and increase by $800 per year during the 15-year life of the machine. What uniform series of payments would cover these expenses over the life of the machine? Interest is 10 percent/year compounded annually.
   a. $11,000
   b. $4,223
   c. $13,423
   d. $15,223

6. A successful alumnus gives a state university $2 million to establish an endowed scholarship fund. If the university can invest at 5 percent/year and gives $100,000 in scholarships each year, for how many years will the endowment last?
   a. 37 years
   b. 20 years
   c. Forever
   d. Cannot be determined

7. Consider cash flows given below. With i = 8%, what is the annual worth of these costs?

End of Year	Cost
0	$1,000
1	$100
2	$200
3	$300
4	$400
5	$300

   a. $418
   b. $436
   c. $502
   d. $536

8. A grinding machine has a first cost of $24,000 with an expected useful life of 13 years. Salvage value at the end of its useful life is estimated to be $8,000. Annual maintenance expenses are $350. With i = 8%, what is the equivalent uniform annual cost (EUAC) of the grinding machine?
   a. $2,370
   b. $2,665
   c. $2,980
   d. $3,010

9. Reconsider the grinding machine from the previous question. What is the capital recovery cost of the grinding machine?
   a. $2,020
   b. $2,665
   c. $2,980
   d. $3,010

10. What is the equivalent uniform annual cost of the following cash flow profile? Assume an interest rate of 15 percent.

End of Year	Cost
0	$50,000
1	$100,000
2	$25,000
3	$37,500

   a. $45,130
   b. $53,125
   c. $62,100
   d. $79,050

PROBLEMS

Note to Instructors and Students

Many of the problems in this chapter are similar to problems in previous chapters. This similarity is intentional. It is designed to illustrate the use of different measures of merit on the same problem.

Section 7.1

1. What do you know about the mathematical value of the annual worth of a project under each of the following conditions?

   a. The present worth of the project is greater than 0.

   b. The present worth of the project is equal to 0.

   c. The present worth of the project is less than 0.

   d. The future worth of the project is greater than 0.

   e. The future worth of the project is equal to 0.

   f. The future worth of the project is less than 0.

2. Determine whether each of the following is true or false. In each case, assume P is located at $t = 0$ and F is located at $t = n$, and the As are spread uniformly over the planning horizon.

   a. $(A|P\,i\%,1) = (F|P\,i\%,1)$

   b. $(A|P\,i\%,n) = (F|P\,i\%,n)$; for $n > 1$

   c. $P(A|P\,i\%,n) = P(F|P\,i\%,n)(A|F\,i\%,n)$

   d. $F(A|F\,i\%,n) = F(P|F\,i\%,n)(A|P\,i\%,n)$

   e. $P(A|P\,i\%,n) = P(A|P\,i\%,n-3)+P(A|P\,i\%,3)$; for $n > 3$

   f. $P(A|P\,i\%,n) = P(A|P\,i\%,n-3)(A|P\,i\%,3)$; for $n > 3$

3. Reconsider Parts (a) through (f) of Problem 2. For each "true" statement, develop a mathematical proof based on the time value of money factor equations from Table 2.6 in Chapter 2.

Section 7.2

4. A project has been selected for implementation. The net cash flow (NCF) profile associated with the project is shown below. *MARR* is 10 percent/year.

EOY	0	1	2	3	4	5	6
NCF	−$70,000	$30,000	$30,000	$30,000	$30,000	$30,000	$30,000 + $2,000

   a. What is the annual worth of this investment?

   b. What is the decision rule for judging the attractiveness of investments based on annual worth?

   c. Is the project economically justified?

5. Reconsider the data from Problem 4. Management has expressed some concern over the life of the project and the impact of possible early termination. As a result, you have developed additional data based on three possible salvage value scenarios. In each case, the possible salvage values progress from $70,000 at EOY 0 to $2,000 at EOY 6. Case 1 is based on a schedule provided by the vendor as shown below. Case 2 is based on a gradient series decline. Case 3 is based on a geometric series decline.

EOY	0	1	2	3	4	5	6
NCF	−$70,000	$30,000	$30,000	$30,000	$30,000	$30,000	$30,000
Vendor SV	$70,000	$50,000	$30,000	$20,000	$10,000	$5,000	$2,000

a. Determine the salvage decline rate for the gradient case.

b. Determine the salvage value decline rate for the geometric case.

c. Determine the annual worth for each case for each planning horizon from 1 to 6 by 1.

d. Plot a graph similar to Figure 7.1 depicting your results from c.

6. Nu Things, Inc., is considering an investment in a business venture with the following anticipated cash flow results:

EOY	Cash Flow	EOY	Cash Flow	EOY	Cash Flow
0	−$70,000	7	$14,000	14	$7,000
1	$20,000	8	$13,000	15	$6,000
2	$19,000	9	$12,000	16	$5,000
3	$18,000	10	$11,000	17	$4,000
4	$17,000	11	$10,000	18	$3,000
5	$16,000	12	$9,000	19	$2,000
6	$15,000	13	$8,000	20	$1,000

Assume *MARR* is 20 percent per year. Based on an annual worth analysis, (1) determine the investment's worth; (2) state whether or not your results indicate the investment should be undertaken, and (3) state the decision rule you used to arrive at this conclusion.

7. Reconsider the data from Problem 6.

a. Plot a graph of AW versus *MARR*, where *MARR* varies from 0 percent to 50 percent by 1 percent increments. AW should be on the *y*-axis and *MARR* on the *x*-axis.

b. Explain the significance of the *y*-axis intercept.

c. Explain the significance of the *x*-axis intercept.

8. An investment has the following cash flow profile. *MARR* is 12 percent/year. What is the minimum value of X such that the investment is attractive based on an annual worth measure of merit?

End of Year	0	1	2	3	4
Cash Flow	−$30,000	$6,000	$13,500	$X	$13,500

9. The cash flows associated with a project are shown below. The interest rate varies from year to year as shown. Determine an equivalent uniform annual series of cash flows.

EOY	Cash Flow	Interest Period	Interest Rate
0	$0	EOY 0 to EOY 1	10%/yr
1	$200	EOY 1 to EOY 2	10%/yr
2	−$200	EOY 2 to EOY 3	8%/yr
3	$300	EOY 3 to EOY 4	8%/yr
4	$0	EOY 4 to EOY 5	12%/yr
5	$200		

10. Bailey, Inc., is considering buying a new gang punch that would allow them to produce circuit boards more efficiently. The punch has a first cost of $100,000 and a useful life of 15 years. At the end of its useful life, the punch has no salvage value. Labor costs would increase $2,000 per year using the gang punch, but raw material costs would decrease $12,000 per year. *MARR* is 5 percent/year.

a. What is the annual worth of this investment?

b. What is the decision rule for judging the attractiveness of investments based on annual worth?

c. Should Bailey buy the gang punch?

11. Carlisle Company has been cited and must invest in equipment to reduce stack emissions or face EPA fines of $18,500 per year. An emission reduction filter will cost $75,000 and have an expected life of 5 years. Carlisle's *MARR* is 10 percent/year.

a. What is the annual worth of this investment?

b. What is the decision rule for judging the attractiveness of investments based on annual worth?

c. Is the filter economically justified?

12. DuraTech Manufacturing is evaluating a process improvement project. The estimated receipts and disbursements associated with the project are shown below. *MARR* is 6 percent/year.

End of Year	Receipts	Disbursements
0	$0	$5,000
1	$0	$200
2	$2,000	$300
3	$4,000	$600
4	$3,000	$1,000
5	$1,600	$1,500

a. What is the annual worth of this investment?

b. What is the decision rule for judging the attractiveness of investments based on annual worth?

c. Should DuraTech implement the proposed process improvement?

13. Eddie's Precision Machine Shop is insured for $700,000. The present yearly insurance premium is $1.00 per $100 of coverage. A sprinkler system with an estimated life of 20 years and no salvage value can be installed for $20,000. Annual maintenance costs for the sprinkler system are $400. If the sprinkler system is installed, the system must be included in the shop's value for insurance purposes, but the insurance premium will reduce to $0.40 per $100 of coverage. Eddie uses a *MARR* of 15 percent/year.

a. What is the annual worth of this investment?

b. What is the decision rule for judging the attractiveness of investments based on annual worth?

c. Is the sprinkler system economically justified?

14. Fabco, Inc., is considering the purchase of flow valves that will reduce annual operating costs by $10,000 per year for the next 12 years. Fabco's *MARR* is 7 percent/year. Using an annual worth approach, determine the maximum amount Fabco should be willing to pay for the valves.

15. Galvanized Products is considering the purchase of a new computer system for their enterprise data management system. The vendor has quoted a purchase price of $100,000. Galvanized Products is planning to borrow one-fourth of the purchase price from a bank at 15 percent compounded annually. The loan is to be repaid using equal annual payments over a 3-year period. The computer system is expected to last 5 years and has a salvage value of $5,000 at that time. Over the 5-year period, Galvanized Products expects to pay a technician $25,000 per year to maintain the system but will save $55,000 per year through increased efficiencies. Galvanized Products uses a *MARR* of 18 percent/year to evaluate investments.

a. What is the annual worth of this investment?

b. What is the decision rule for judging the attractiveness of investments based on annual worth?

c. Should the new computer system be purchased?

16. Quilts R Us (QRU) is considering an investment in a new patterning attachment with the cash flow profile shown in the table below. QRU's *MARR* is 13.5 percent/year.

EOY	Cash Flow	EOY	Cash Flow
0	−$1,400	8	$600
1	$0	9	$700
2	$500	10	$800
3	$500	11	$900
4	$500	12	−$1,000
5	$500	13	−$2,000
6	$0	14	−$3,000
7	$500	15	$1,400

    a. What is the annual worth of this investment?

    b. What is the decision rule for judging the attractiveness of investments based on annual worth?

    c. Should QRU invest?

17. Imagineering, Inc., is considering an investment in CAD-CAM compatible design software with the cash flow profile shown in the table below. Imagineering's *MARR* is 18 percent/year.

EOY	0	1	2	3	4	5	6	7
Cash Flow (M$)	−$12	−$1	$5	$2	$5	$5	$2	$5

    a. What is the annual worth of this investment?

    b. What is the decision rule for judging the attractiveness of investments based on annual worth?

    c. Should Imagineering invest?

18. Jupiter's is considering investing time and administrative expense on an effort that promises one large payoff in the future, followed by additional expenses over a 10-year horizon. The cash flow profile is shown in the table below. Jupiter's *MARR* is 12 percent/year.

EOY	0	1	2	3	4	5	6	7	8	9	10
Cash Flow (K$)	−$2	−$10	−$12	−$14	−$16	−$18	$200	−$10	−$12	−$14	−$100

    a. What is the annual worth of this investment?

    b. What is the decision rule for judging the attractiveness of investments based on annual worth?

    c. Should Jupiter invest?

19. Aerotron Electronics is considering the purchase of a water filtration system to assist in circuit board manufacturing. The system costs $40,000. It has an expected life of 7 years at which time its salvage value will be $7,500. Operating and maintenance expenses are estimated to be $2,000 per year. If the filtration system is not purchased, Aerotron Electronics will have to pay Bay City $12,000 per year for water purification. If the system is purchased, no water purification from Bay City will be needed. Aerotron Electronics must borrow half of the purchase price, but they cannot start repaying the loan for 2 years. The bank has agreed to three equal annual payments, with the first payment due at the end of year 2. The loan interest rate is 8 percent compounded annually. Aerotron Electronics' *MARR* is 10 percent compounded annually.

    a. What is the annual worth of this investment?

    b. What is the decision rule for judging the attractiveness of investments based on annual worth?

    c. Should Aerotron Electronics buy the water filtration system?

20. Home Innovation is evaluating a new product design. The estimated receipts and disbursements associated with the new product are shown below. *MARR* is 10 percent/year.

End of Year	Receipts	Disbursements
0	$0	$1,000
1	$600	$300
2	$600	$300
3	$700	$300
4	$700	$300
5	$700	$300

    a. What is the annual worth of this investment?

    b. What is the decision rule for judging the attractiveness of investments based on annual worth?

    c. Should Home Innovations pursue this new product?

21. Mayberry, Inc., is considering a design change that will cost $6,000 and will result in an annual savings of $1,000 per year for the 6-year life of the project. A cost of $2,000 will be avoided at the end of the project as a result of the change. *MARR* is 8 percent/year.

    a. What is the annual worth of this investment?

    b. What is the decision rule for judging the attractiveness of investments based on annual worth?

    c. Should Mayberry implement the design change?

22. Nancy's Notions pays a delivery firm to distribute its products in the metro area. Delivery costs are $30,000 per year. Nancy can buy a used truck for $10,000 that will be adequate for the next 3 years. Operating and maintenance costs are estimated to be $25,000 per year. At the end of 3 years, the used truck will have an estimated salvage value of $3,000. Nancy's *MARR* is 24 percent/year.

    a. What is the annual worth of this investment?

    b. What is the decision rule for judging the attractiveness of investments based on annual worth?

    c. Should Nancy buy the truck?

Section 7.3

23. The engineering team at Manuel's Manufacturing, Inc., is planning to purchase an enterprise resource planning (ERP) system. The software and installation from Vendor A costs $380,000 initially and is expected to increase revenue $125,000 per year every year. The software and installation from Vendor B costs $280,000 and is expected to increase revenue $95,000 per year. Manuel's uses a 4-year planning horizon and a 10 percent per year *MARR*.

    a. What is the annual worth of each investment?

    b. What is the decision rule for determining the preferred investment based on annual worth ranking?

    c. Which ERP system should Manuel purchase?

24. Reconsider Problem 23. Determine which ERP system should be purchased based on an incremental annual worth analysis.

25. Nadine Chelesvig has patented her invention. She is offering a potential manufacturer two contracts for the exclusive right to manufacture and market her product. Plan A calls for an immediate single lump sum payment to her of $30,000. Plan B calls for an annual payment of $1,000 plus a royalty of $0.50 per unit sold. The remaining life of the patent is 10 years. Nadine uses a *MARR* of 10 percent/year. What must be the uniform annual sales volume of the product for Nadine to be indifferent between the contracts, based on an annual worth analysis?

26. Parker County Community College (PCCC) is trying to determine whether to use no insulation or to use insulation that is either 1 inch thick or 2 inches thick on its steam pipes. The heat loss from the pipes without insulation is expected to cost $1.50 per year per foot of pipe. A 1-inch thick insulated covering will eliminate 89 percent of the loss and will cost $0.40 per foot. A 2-inch thick insulated covering will eliminate 92 percent of the loss and will cost

$0.85 per foot. PCCC Physical Plant Services estimates that there are 250,000 feet of steam pipe on campus. The PCCC Accounting Office requires a 10 percent/year return to justify capital expenditures. The insulation has a life expectancy of 10 years. Determine which insulation (if any) should be purchased using a ranking annual worth analysis.

27. Reconsider Problem 26. Determine which insulation (if any) should be purchased based on an incremental annual worth analysis.

28. Quantum Logistics, Inc., a wholesale distributor, is considering the construction of a new warehouse to serve the southeastern geographic region near the Alabama–Georgia border. There are three cities being considered. After site visits and a budget analysis, the expected income and costs associated with locating in each of the cities have been determined. The life of the warehouse is expected to be 12 years, and *MARR* is 15 percent/year.

City	Initial Cost	Net Annual Income
Lagrange	$1,260,000	$480,000
Auburn	$1,000,000	$410,000
Anniston	$1,620,000	$520,000

a. What is the annual worth of each site?

b. What is the decision rule for determining the preferred site based on annual worth ranking?

c. Which city should be recommended?

29. Reconsider Problem 28. Determine which city should be recommended based on an incremental annual worth analysis.

30. DelRay Foods must purchase a new gumdrop machine. Two machines are available. Machine 7745 has a first cost of $10,000, an estimated life of 10 years, a salvage value of $1,000, and annual operating costs estimated at $0.01 per 1,000 gumdrops. Machine A37Y has a first cost of $8,000, a life of 10 years, and no salvage value. Its annual operating costs will be $300 regardless of the number of gumdrops produced. *MARR* is 6 percent/year, and 30 million gumdrops are produced each year.

a. What is the annual worth of each machine?

b. What is the decision rule for determining the preferred machine based on annual worth ranking?

c. Which machine should be recommended?

31. Reconsider Problem 30. Determine which machine should be recommended based on an incremental annual worth analysis.

32. Tempura, Inc., is considering two projects. Project A requires an investment of $50,000. Estimated annual receipts for 20 years are $20,000; estimated annual costs are $12,500. An alternative project, B, requires an investment of $75,000, has annual receipts for 20 years of $28,000, and has annual costs of $18,000. Assume both projects have zero salvage value and that *MARR* is 12 percent/year.

a. What is the annual worth of each project?

b. Which project should be recommended?

33. Final Finishing is considering three mutually exclusive alternatives for a new polisher. Each alternative has an expected life of 10 years and no salvage value. Polisher 1 requires an initial investment of $20,000 and provides annual benefits of $4,465. Polisher 2 requires an initial investment of $10,000 and provides annual benefits of $1,770. Polisher 3 requires an initial investment of $15,000 and provides annual benefits of $3,580. *MARR* is 15 percent/year.

a. What is the annual worth of each polisher?

b. Which polisher should be recommended?

34. Xanadu Mining is considering three mutually exclusive alternatives as shown in the table below. *MARR* is 10 percent/year.

EOY	A001	B002	C003
0	−$210	−$110	−$160
1	$80	$60	$80
2	$90	$60	$80
3	$100	$60	$80
4	$110	$70	$80

    a. What is the annual worth of each alternative?

    b. Which alternative should be recommended?

35. Yani has $12,000 for investment purposes. His bank has offered the following three choices:

    a. A special savings certificate that will pay $100 each month for 5 years and a lump sum payment at the end of 5 years of $13,000

    b. Buy a share of a racehorse for $12,000 that will be worth $20,000 in 5 years

    c. Put the money in a savings account that will have an interest rate of 12 percent per year compounded monthly

    Use an annual worth analysis to make a recommendation to Yani.

36. Two numerically controlled drill presses are being considered by the production department of Zunni's Manufacturing; one must be selected. Comparison data is shown in the table below. *MARR* is 10 percent/year.

	Drill Press T	Drill Press M
Initial Investment	$20,000	$30,000
Estimated Life	10 years	10 years
Estimated Salvage Value	$5,000	$7,000
Annual Operating Cost	$12,000	$6,000
Annual Maintenance Cost	$2,000	$4,000

    a. What is the annual worth of each drill press?

    b. Which drill press should be recommended?

37. Alpha Electronics can purchase a needed service for $90 per unit. The same service can be provided by equipment that costs $100,000 and that will have a salvage value of 0 at the end of 10 years. Annual operating costs for the equipment will be $7,000 per year plus $25 per unit produced. *MARR* is 12 percent/year.

    a. Based on an annual worth analysis, should the equipment be purchased if the expected production is 200 units/year?

    b. Based on an annual worth analysis, should the equipment be purchased if the expected demand is 500 units/year?

    c. Determine the breakeven value for annual production that will return *MARR* on the investment in the new equipment.

38. On-Site Testing Service has received four investment proposals for consideration. Two of the proposals, X1 and X2, are mutually exclusive. The other two proposals, Y1 and Y2 are also mutually exclusive. Proposal Y1 is contingent on X1 and Y2 is contingent on X2. Other than these restrictions, any combination of proposals (including null) is feasible. *MARR* is 10 percent/year. The expected cash flows for the proposals are shown below. An annual worth analysis is to be conducted.

End of Year	X1	X2	Y1	Y2
0	−$10,000	−$15,000	−$6,000	−$9,000
1 through 8	$1,600	$2,600	$2,500	$3,500

   a. List all the alternatives to be considered.

   b. Determine which (if any) proposals On-Site Testing should accept.

39. Dark Skies Observatory is considering several options to purchase a new deep-space telescope. Revenue would be generated from the telescope by selling "time and use" slots to various researchers around the world. Four possible telescopes have been identified in addition to the possibility of not buying a telescope if none are financially attractive. The table below details the characteristics of each telescope. An annual worth ranking analysis is to be performed.

	T1	T2	T3	T4
Useful Life	10 years	10 years	10 years	10 years
First Cost	$600,000	$800,000	$470,000	$540,000
Salvage Value	$70,000	$130,000	$65,000	$200,000
Annual Revenue	$400,000	$600,000	$260,000	$320,000
Annual Expenses	$130,000	$270,000	$70,000	$120,000

   a. Determine the preferred telescope if *MARR* is 25 percent/year.

   b. Determine the preferred telescope if *MARR* is 42 percent/year.

40. Delta Dawn's Bakery is considering purchasing a new van to deliver bread. The van will cost $18,000. Two-thirds ($12,000) of this cost will be borrowed. The loan is to be repaid with four equal annual payments (first payment at $t = 1$) based on an interest rate of 4 percent/year. It is anticipated that the van will be used for 6 years and then sold for a salvage value of $500. Annual operating and maintenance expenses for the van over the 6-year life are estimated to be $700 per year. If the van is purchased, Delta will realize a cost savings of $3,800 per year. Delta uses a *MARR* of 6 percent/year. Based on an annual worth analysis, is the purchase of the van economically attractive?

41. Several years ago, a man won $27 million in the state lottery. To pay off the winner, the state planned to make an initial $1 million payment immediately, followed by equal annual payments of $1.3 million at the end of each year for the next 20 years. Just before receiving any money, the man offered to sell the winning ticket back to the state for a one-time immediate payment of $14.4 million. If the state uses a 6 percent/year *MARR*, should it accept the man's offer? Use an annual worth analysis.

42. Allied Electronics must purchase a new automatic soldering machine to meet increased demand for its electronic goods. Of all the machines considered, management has narrowed the choices to the following three mutually exclusive machines:

	Machine 1	Machine 2	Machine 3
Initial Cost	$800,000	$650,000	$575,000
Annual Operating Cost	$50,000	$90,000	$105,000
Salvage Value	$40,000	$32,500	$28,750

Allied Electronics uses a 4-year planning horizon, and *MARR* is 12 percent/year. Based on an annual worth analysis, determine which machine should be purchased.

43. The management of Brawn Engineering is considering three alternatives to satisfy an OSHA requirement for safety gates in the machine shop. Each gate will completely satisfy the requirement, so no combinations need to be considered. The first costs, operating costs, and salvage values over a 5-year planning horizon are shown below. Using an annual worth analysis with a *MARR* of 20 percent/year, determine the preferred gate.

End of Year	Gate 1	Gate 2	Gate 3
0	−$15,000	−$19,000	−$24,000
1	−$6,500	−$5,600	−$4,000
2	−$6,500	−$5,600	−$4,000
3	−$6,500	−$5,600	−$4,000
4	−$6,500	−$5,600	−$4,000
5	−$6,500+$0	−$5,600+$2,000	−$4,000+$5,000

44. RealTurf is considering purchasing an automatic sprinkler system for its sod farm by borrowing the entire $30,000 purchase price. The loan would be repaid with four equal annual payments at an interest rate of 12 percent/year/year. It is anticipated that the sprinkler system would be used for 9 years and then sold for a salvage value of $2,000. Annual operating and maintenance expenses for the system over the 9-year life are estimated to be $9,000 per year. If the new system is purchased, cost savings of $15,000 per year will be realized over the present manual watering system. RealTurf uses a *MARR* of 15 percent/year for economic decision making. Based on an annual worth analysis, is the purchase of the new sprinkler system economically attractive?

45. Orpheum Productions in Nevada is considering three mutually exclusive alternatives for lighting enhancements to one of its recording studios. Each enhancement will increase revenues by attracting directors who prefer this lighting style. The cash flow details, in thousands of dollars, for these enhancements are shown in the chart below. *MARR* is 10 percent/year. Based on an annual worth analysis, which alternative (if any) should be implemented?

End of Year	Light Bar	Sliding Spots	Reflected Beam
0	−$6,000	−$14,000	−$20,000
1	$2,000	$3,500	$0
2	$2,000	$3,500	$2,300
3	$2,000	$3,500	$4,600
4	$2,000	$3,500	$6,900
5	$2,000	$3,500	$9,200
6	$2,000	$3,500	$11,500

46. Deep Seas Submarine must implement a new engine in its submarines to meet the needs of clients who desire quieter operation. Two designs, both technologically feasible, have been created, and Deep Seas wishes to know which one to pursue. Design 1 would require an up-front manufacturing cost of $15,000,000 and will cost $2,500,000 per year for 3 years to swap out the engines in all its current submarines. Design 2 will cost $20,000,000

up front, but due to a higher degree of compatibility will only require $1,500,000 per year to implement. *MARR* is 10 percent/year. Based on an annual worth analysis, determine which design should be chosen.

47. Calisto Launch Services is an independent space corporation and has been contracted to develop and launch one of two different satellites. Initial equipment will cost $750,000 for the first satellite and $850,000 for the second. Development will take 5 years at an expected cost of $150,000 per year for the first satellite, $120,000 per year for the second. The same launch vehicle can be used for either satellite and will cost $275,000 at the time of the launch 5 years from now. At the conclusion of the launch, the contracting company will pay Calisto $2,500,000 for either satellite.

Calisto is also considering launching both satellites. Because the company would have to upgrade its facilities to handle two concurrent projects, the initial costs would rise by $150,000 in addition to the first costs of each satellite. Calisto would need to hire additional engineers and workers, raising the yearly costs to a total of $400,000. An extra compartment would be added to the launch vehicle at an additional cost of $75,000. As an incentive to do both, the contracting company will pay for both launches plus a bonus of $1,000,000. Using an annual worth analysis with a *MARR* of 10 percent/year, what should Calisto Launch Services do?

48. Baon Chemicals Unlimited purchases a computer-controlled filter for $100,000. They borrow half the purchase price from a bank at 15 percent compounded annually. The loan is to be paid back with equal annual payments over a 5-year period. The filter is expected to last 10 years, at which time it will have a salvage value of $10,000. Over the 10-year period, the operating and maintenance costs are expected to equal $20,000 in year 1 and increase by $1,500/year each year thereafter. By making the investment, annual fines of $50,000 for pollution will be avoided. Baon expects to earn 12 percent compounded annually on its investments. Based on an annual worth analysis, determine whether purchasing the filter is economically justified.

49. Value Lodges owns an economy motel chain and is considering building a new 200-unit motel. The cost to build the motel is estimated at $8,000,000; Value Lodges estimates furnishings for the motel will cost an additional $700,000 and will require replacement every 5 years. Annual operating and maintenance costs for the motel are estimated to be $800,000. The average rental rate for a unit is anticipated to be $40/day. Value Lodges expects the motel to have a life of 15 years and a salvage value of $900,000 at the end of 15 years. This estimated salvage value assumes that the furnishings are not new. Furnishings have no salvage value at the end of each 5-year replacement interval. Assuming average daily occupancy percentages of 50 percent, 60 percent, 70 percent, and 80 percent for years 1 through 4, respectively, and 90 percent for the fifth through fifteenth years, a *MARR* of 12 percent/year, 365 operating days/year, and ignoring the cost of land, should the motel be built? Base your decision on an annual worth analysis.

50. Packaging equipment for Xi Cling Wrap costs $60,000 and is expected to result in end of year net savings of $23,000 per year for 3 years. The equipment will have a market value of $10,000 after 3 years. The equipment can be leased for $21,000 per year, payable at the beginning of each year. Xi Cling's *MARR* is 10 percent/year. Based on an annual worth analysis, determine if the packaging equipment should be purchased or leased.

Section 7.4

51. Alternatives 1, 2, and 3 have lives of 3, 4, and 6 years, respectively. Their net cash flow (NCF) and salvage value (SV) profiles are as follows:

EOY	Alternative 1		Alternative 2		Alternative 3	
	NCF1	SV1	NCF2	SV2	NCF3	SV3
0	−$20,000	—	−$40,000	$40,000	−$70,000	$70,000
1	$8,000	—	$20,000	$30,000	$30,000	$50,000
2	$8,000	—	$20,000	$20,000	$30,000	$30,000
3	$28,000	—	$20,000	$10,000	$30,000	$20,000
4			$20,000	$0	$30,000	$10,000
5					$30,000	$5,000
6					$30,000	$2,000

Additional explanation is necessary: The NCF profile of Alternative 1 that is shown above is the net result of a $20,000/year lease payment payable at the beginning of each year, plus an end of year net revenue of $28,000. This lease arrangement may be renewed in 3-year increments; however, premature cancellation of the lease results in a lease termination penalty (cost) of $10,000 at the time of cancellation. *MARR* is 8 percent.

a. What is the planning horizon for these alternatives if a least common multiple approach is used to determine the planning horizon?

b. Assume the NCFs of all alternatives are expected to repeat indefinitely as shown. If a least common multiple of lives approach is to be used, specify the complete set of cash flows for each alternative and the annual worth for each alternative.

c. Repeat Part b by determining the annual worth of each alternative based on its "natural" life (i.e., 3 years for Alt. 1, 4 years for Alt. 2, and 6 years for Alt. 3).

d. Compare your answers for Parts b and c. Explain how your results either confirm or dispute the claim that the AW measure of merit implicitly assumes a least common multiple planning horizon.

52. Consider the net cash flows (NCF) and salvage values (SV) shown below for each of the two feasible alternatives to be considered in an economic analysis. Alternatives 1 and 2 have lives of 3 and 5 years, respectively. Assume each alternative can be renewed indefinitely with the same NCF and SV profiles. The MARR is 10%.

EOY	Alternative 1		Alternative 2	
	NCF1	SV1	NCF2	SV2
0	−$50,000	$50,000	−$80,000	$80,000
1	$25,000	$25,000	$35,000	$50,000
2	$30,000	$10,000	$45,000	$20,000
3	$35,000	$0	$50,000	$10,000
4			$55,000	$0
5			$60,000	$0

a. What is the planning horizon for these alternatives if a least common multiple approach is used to determine the planning horizon?

b. Assume the NCFs of all alternatives are expected to repeat indefinitely as shown. If a least common multiple of lives approach is to be used, specify the complete set of cash flows for each alternative and the annual worth for each alternative.

c. Repeat Part b by determining the annual worth of each alternative based on its "natural" life (i.e., 3 years for Alt. 1 and 5 years for Alt. 2).

53. Consider the net cash flows and salvage values shown below. Assume the alternatives can be indefinitely renewed with the same cash flows and salvage values. Using a MARR of 8%, specify the planning horizon and complete set of cash flows for each alternative using each of the following:

EOY	Alternative 1		Alternative 2	
	NCF	SV	NCF	SV
0	−$100	$100	−$70	$70
1	$20	$40	$30	$50
2	$20	$20	$40	$30
3	$40		$50	
4	$60			

a. What is the planning horizon for these alternatives if a least common multiple approach is used to determine the planning horizon?

b. Assume the NCFs of all alternatives are expected to repeat indefinitely as shown. If a least common multiple of lives approach is to be used, specify the complete set of cash flows for each alternative and the annual worth for each alternative using a MARR of 8%.

c. Repeat Part b by determining the annual worth of each alternative based on its "natural" life (i.e., 4 years for Alt. 1 and 3 years for Alt. 2).

Section 7.5

54. A university pumps its water from wells located on campus. The falling water table has caused pumping costs to increase, the quantity of water available to decrease, and the quality of water to deteriorate. A public water company now has a large water main that runs within a few hundred yards of the university's pumping station. The university has decided to build a pipeline connecting to the company's water main and to purchase water for the school. Two alternative types of pipe are being considered to supply the needs for a 60-year period. The relevant data is shown below:

	Pipe A	Pipe B
Initial Investment in Pipe	$120,000	$80,000
Estimated Pipe Life	60 years	30 years
Initial Investment in Pumping Equipment	$15,000	$20,000
Estimated Life of Pumping Equipment	20 years	20 years
Annual Maintenance and Energy Costs	$3,000	$4,000

Using a 60-year study period, recommend a pipe alternative based on equivalent uniform annual cost. Since the university is tax exempt, it uses a *MARR* of 6 percent/year. Assume a zero net terminal salvage value for the pipe and the pumping equipment, and assume that renewal costs during the 60-year period will be the same as the initial costs.

55. Consider the two one-shot investment alternatives shown in the table below. Neither alternative is expected to be available again in the future, but it is expected that investment options returning *MARR* will always be available. *MARR* is 11 percent/year.

EOY	0	1	2	3	4	5	6	7
Alternative W	−$100,000	$20,000	$20,000	$50,000	$80,000	$110,000		
Alternative X	−$150,000	$40,000	$45,000	$50,000	$55,000	$60,000	$65,000	$70,000

Determine the following:

a. What is the length of the planning horizon?

b. Which alternative is preferred?

56. Octavia Bakery is planning to purchase one of two ovens. The expected cash flows for each oven are shown below. *MARR* is 8 percent/year.

	Model 127B	Model 334A
Initial Investment	$50,000	$80,000
Estimated Life	10	5
End of Life Salvage	$10,000	$0
Annual Income	$19,400	$26,000
Annual Expense	$10,000	$6,000

    a. What is the annual worth of each investment?

    b. What is the decision rule for determining the preferred investment based on annual worth ranking?

    c. Which oven should Octavia purchase?

57. Reconsider Problem 56. Determine which oven should be purchased based on an incremental annual worth analysis.

58. Two storage structures, given code names Y and Z, are being considered for a military base located in Sontaga. The military uses a 5 percent/year expected rate of return and a 24-year life for decisions of this type. The relevant characteristics for each structure are shown below.

	Structure Y	Structure Z
First Cost	$4,500	$10,000
Estimated Life	12 years	24 years
Estimated Salvage Value	None	$1,800
Annual Maintenance Cost	$1,000	$720

    a. What is the annual worth of each machine?

    b. What is the decision rule for determining the preferred machine based on annual worth ranking?

    c. Which structure should be recommended?

Section 7.6

59. Using only the factor formulas given in Table 2.6, derive Equation 7.5 starting with Equation 7.3.

60. An asset has the estimated salvage values for various lives, shown in the table below. For each possible life from 1 to 6 by 1, determine the capital recovery cost for *MARR* of 8 percent/year.

EOY	0	1	2	3	4	5	6
NCF	−$70,000	$30,000	$30,000	$30,000	$30,000	$30,000	$30,000
Estimated SV	$70,000	$50,000	$30,000	$20,000	$10,000	$5,000	$2,000

61. Using only the factor formulas given in Table 2.6, derive Equation 7.6 starting with Equation 7.3.

62. Reconsider the data from Problem 56. What is the capital recovery cost of Model 127B?

63. Reconsider the data from Problem 56. What is the capital recovery cost of Model 334A?

64. Reconsider the data from Problem 51. What is the capital recovery cost of Alternative 3 for a 6-year life?

65. Crush Autosmashers can purchase a new electromagnet for moving cars at a cost of $20,000. At the end of its useful life, the electromagnet will be worth $1,000. If Crush's *MARR* is 12 percent/year, how many years must the electromagnet last so that its capital recovery cost will be $3,000/year or less?

66. Reconsider Problem 65. Plot a graph of capital recovery cost versus useful life for lives 1 to 25 by 1.

67. Reconsider Problem 66.

   a. Extend your graph to include useful lives from 1 to 100 by 1.

   b. Estimate the asymptotic limit the capital recovery cost is approaching.

   c. Repeat Part b for a salvage value of $2,000.

   d. Repeat Part b for a salvage value of $0.

   e. Repeat Part b for a salvage value of $15,000.

   f. Starting with any of the capital recovery equations (Equation 7.3, 7.5, or 7.6), derive an equation for the asymptotic limit of capital recovery cost in terms of P, F, and i.

   g. Is your equation in Part f consistent with your results in Parts b, c, d, and e?

Chapter 8

RATE OF RETURN ANALYSIS

(a) A senior production manager inspects the placing head of a Fuji NXT surface mount placement machine while a programmer clears a feeder error. (Courtesy of Motorola, Inc.) (b) A process engineering manager reviews component placement integrity on a printed circuit board for a pilot run through a surface mount placement machine. (Courtesy of Motorola, Inc.)

Motorola

Motorola was founded in Illinois in 1928. From car radios to televisions to two-way radios, Motorola evolved into a communications company that today is designing, building, marketing, and selling products, services, and applications that enable telephony, data, and video to be experienced across multiple domains.

Although it offers a broad set of products in wireless, broadband, and automotive communications, Motorola is best known for its cellular telephones. However, Motorola is much more than a cellular telephone manufacturer. It also has a broad portfolio of products, including cable set-top boxes, iDEN handsets and network infrastructure, two-way radios, computer-aided dispatch systems, cable modems, WiFi, WiMax, and VoIP, among other hardware and software products.

During 2010, Motorola was organized in three business segments: Mobile Devices, Home and Networks Mobility, and Enterprise Mobility Solutions. At the end of 2010, Mobile Devices' major facilities were located in Brazil, China, Singapore, and the United States. Home and Networks Mobility had major facilities in China, England, India, Malaysia, Mexico, Taiwan, and the United States. Major facilities for Enterprise Mobility Solutions were located in China, the Czech Republic, England, Germany, Israel, Malaysia, Mexico, and the United States.

In 2010, sales totaled $19.3 billion. Capital expenditures in 2010 totaled $335 million. As of December 31, 2010, Motorola had 51,000 employees located around the world. In 2010, its R&D expenditures totaled $2.5 billion and involved over 21,000 engineers and scientists. At the end of 2010, it owned 10,117 U.S. patents and 13,732 foreign patents.

A technology company, Motorola is highly disciplined in managing its capital. Discounted cash flow methods are used throughout the company to ensure that shareholders receive attractive returns on their invested capital.

(On January 4, 2011, Motorola spun off Mobile Devices and Home to form an independent company, Motorola Mobility, Inc. The remaining business was renamed Motorola Solutions, Inc.)

Although this chapter does not have *worth* in its title, rates of return are also measures of economic worth. Instead of measuring economic worth in dollars, here we measure it in percentages.

8-1 INTRODUCTION

Among the *DCF* measures of economic worth, *rates of return* are probably the second most popular among corporations, ranked just behind *present worth*. However, for personal investment decision making, rates of return are used more frequently than present worth. No doubt its popularity is due to investors' familiarity with interest rates and the ease with which investment returns can be compared with costs of capital for investment.

Rates of return can be used in choosing the mutually exclusive investment alternative having the greatest economic worth. However, they tend to be used more frequently in industry as supplements to one of the traditional "worth" methods—present, future, or annual worth.

Unlike present, future, and annual worths, rates of return are *not* ranking methods. When used to choose from among mutually exclusive alternatives on the basis of monetary

---

Systematic Economic Analysis Technique

1. Identify the investment alternatives
2. Define the planning horizon
3. Specify the discount rate
4. Estimate the cash flows
5. Compare the alternatives
6. Perform supplementary analyses
7. Select the preferred investment

considerations, incremental analysis is required when using rates of return. However, when performed correctly, the incremental analysis will result in the same investment alternative being recommended as occurs when using one of the ranking methods.

Although many different rates of return exist, in this chapter we consider only three, all of which are discounted cash flow methods: *internal rate of return*, *external rate of return*, and, in Appendix 8.A, *modified internal rate of return*.

In this chapter, we learn how to compare mutually exclusive investment alternatives using rate of return methods. In the process, we learn that the rate of return methods can be used even when the individual investment alternatives do not have rates of return. In the case of the internal rate of return method, we learn that multiple solutions can occur, and we figure out how to deal with them.

8-2   INTERNAL RATE OF RETURN: SINGLE ALTERNATIVE

The internal rate of return is also referred to as the *discounted cash flow rate of return*, the *cash flow rate of return*, the *rate of return (ROR)*, the *return on investment (ROI)*, and the *true rate of return*. However, the more common name is *internal rate of return (IRR)*. Mathematically, investment j's internal rate of return, denoted i_j^*, satisfies the following equality:

$$0 = \sum_{t=0}^{n} A_{jt}(1 + i_j^*)^{n-t} \tag{8.1}$$

In words, the internal rate of return is the interest rate that makes the future worth of an investment equal 0. Likewise, it is the interest rate that equates the present worth and annual worth to 0. (Depending on the form of a particular cash flow profile, it might be more convenient to use a present worth or an annual worth formulation to determine the internal rate of return for an investment alternative.)

If the internal rate of return is at least equal to the *MARR*, the investment should be made.

EXAMPLE 8.1   The Surface-Mount Placement Machine Investment

Recall the manager of a Motorola electronics manufacturing plant who was asked to approve the purchase of a surface mount placement (SMP) machine having an initial cost of $500,000 in order to reduce annual operating and maintenance costs by $92,500 per year. At the end of the 10-year planning horizon, it was estimated that the SMP machine would be worth $50,000. Using a 10 percent *MARR* and internal rate of return analysis, should the investment be made?

Setting the future worth for the investment equal to 0 gives

$$0 = -\$500,000(F|P\,i^*\%,10) + \$92,500(F|A\,i^*\%,10) + \$50,000$$

Recalling the formulas used to compute capital recovery cost, the following annual worth formulation can be solved for the internal rate of return:

$$0 = (\$500,000 - \$50,000)(A|P\,i^*,10) + \$50,000i^* - \$92,500$$

For $i = 12\%$,

$$\$450,000(A|P\,12\%,10) + \$50,000(0.12) - \$92,500 = -\$6,850$$

For $i = 15\%$,

$$\$450,000(A|P\ 15\%,10) + \$50,000(0.15) - \$92,500 = \$4,685$$

Interpolating for i^* gives 13.78%.

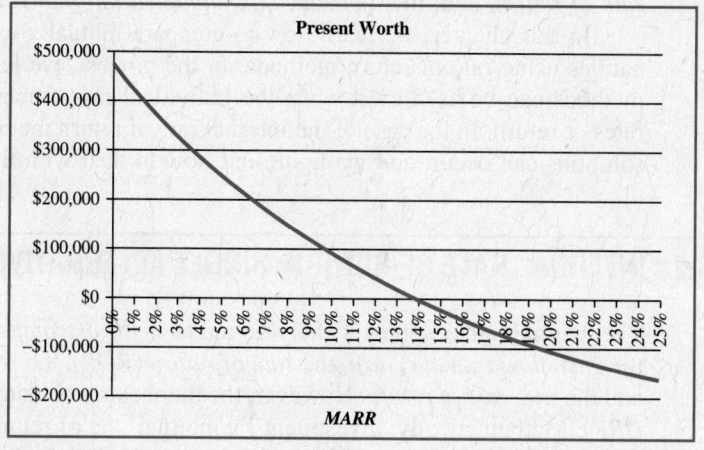

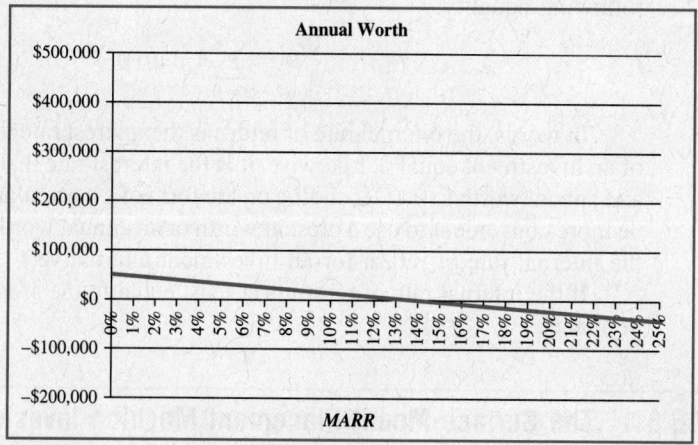

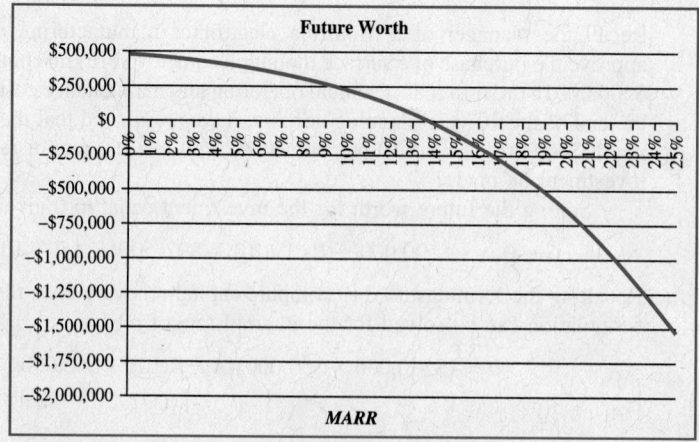

FIGURE 8.1

Plots of *AW*, *PW*, and *FW* for Example 8.1.

Solving for i^* is not a simple task. By trial and error and by interpolation, one can approximate the value of i^*. Alternately, one can use the Excel® **RATE** worksheet function to solve for i^* in this example:

$$i^* = \text{RATE}(10,92500,-500000,50000)$$
$$= 13.8\%$$

Since $i^* > 10$ percent, the investment is recommended.

Figure 8.1 portrays present worth, future worth, and annual worth as a function of the *MARR* for the example. As you can see, each equals 0 when the interest rate equals 13.8 percent.

The example illustrated one of the attractions of the IRR method. Which of the following statements do you find to be more informative?

1. Invest \$500,000 to obtain a present worth of \$87,649.62.
2. Invest \$500,000 to obtain a future worth in 10 years of \$227,340.55.
3. Invest \$500,000 to obtain an annual worth for 10 years of \$14,264.57.
4. Invest \$500,000 to obtain a 13.8 percent return on your investment.

For many, expressing the measure of economic worth as an annual compounding percentage is more informative than a dollar figure, whether expressed as a single sum or as a uniform annual series.

It is important to understand the definition of the internal rate of return inherent in Equation 8.1. In particular, the internal rate of return on an investment is defined as *the rate of interest earned on the unrecovered balance of an investment*. This concept was demonstrated in Chapter 3 in discussing the amount of a loan payment that was principal. It is illustrated again in Table 8.1, where \$10,000 is invested to obtain the receipts shown over a 6-year period. A_t denotes the cash flow at the *end* of period t, B_t represents the unrecovered balance at the *beginning* of period t, E_t is the unrecovered

TABLE 8.1
Data Illustrating the Meaning of the Internal Rate of Return.

t	A_t	B_t	I_t^a	E_t
0	−\$10,000			−\$10,000
1	\$2,525	−\$10,000	−\$2,000	−\$9,475
2	\$2,525	−\$9,475	−\$1,895	−\$8,845
3	\$2,525	−\$8,845	−\$1,769	−\$8,089
4	\$3,840	−\$8,089	−\$1,618	−\$5,867
5	\$3,840	−\$5,867	−\$1,173	−\$3,200
6	\$3,840	−\$3,200	−\$640	\$0

[a]Based on $i = 0.20$.

balance at the *end* of period t, and I_t is defined as the interest on the unrecovered balance *during* period t. The following relationships exist:

$$E_0 = A_0$$
$$B_t = E_{t-1} \qquad\qquad t = 1,\ldots,n$$
$$I_t = B_t i \qquad\qquad t = 1,\ldots,n$$
$$E_t = A_t + B_t + I_t \qquad t = 1,\ldots,n$$

If i is the internal rate of return, then E_n will equal 0. As indicated in Table 8.1, if i is 20 percent, E_n is approximately 0. Consequently, i^* is approximately 20 percent. The equivalence of E_n being 0 and the future worth being 0 is easily understood by recognizing that E_n is actually the future worth of the cash flow profile. To see why this is true, notice that

$$E_n = A_n + B_n + I_n$$

Employing the definition of I_n,

$$E_n = A_n + B_n(1 + i)$$

By the relationship between B_n and E_{n-1}, it is seen that

$$E_n = A_n + E_{n-1}(1 + i)$$

Since a similar relationship exists between E_{n-1} and E_{n-2}, we note that

$$E_n = A_n + A_{n-1}(1 + i) + E_{n-2}(1 + i)^2$$

Generalizing, the recursive relationship between E_t and E_{t-1} gives

$$E_n = A_n + A_{n-1}(1 + i) + A_{n-2}(1 + i)^2 + \cdots + A_0(1 + i)^n$$

Hence, as anticipated, we see that

$$E_n = \mathrm{FW}(i\%)$$

The above example illustrates that the *TVOM* operations involved in the IRR method are equivalent to assuming that all monies received are reinvested and earn interest at a rate equal to the internal rate of return. This can also be seen mathematically by letting

A_{jt} = net cash flow for investment j in period t

$$R_{jt} = \begin{cases} A_{jt}, & \text{if } A_{jt} \geq 0 \\ 0, & \text{otherwise} \end{cases}$$

$$C_{jt} = \begin{cases} -A_{jt}, & \text{if } A_{jt} \leq 0 \\ 0, & \text{otherwise} \end{cases}$$

r_t = reinvestment rate for positive-valued cash flows occurring in period t

i' = the rate of return for negative-valued cash flows

Then the following relationship can be defined.

$$\sum_{t=0}^{n} R_{jt}(1 + r_t)^{n-t} = \sum_{t=0}^{n} C_{jt}(1 + i')^{n-t} \tag{8.2}$$

Note that the future worth of reinvested monies received must equal the future worth of investments.

If r_t equals i', Equation 8.2 becomes

$$0 = \sum_{t=0}^{n} (R_{jt} - C_{jt})(1 + i')^{n-t} \tag{8.3}$$

Letting A_{jt} equal $R_{jt} - C_{jt}$ defines the IRR method given by Equation 8.1. Hence, we see that the rate of return obtained using the IRR method can be interpreted as the reinvestment rate for all recovered funds.

It should be noted that it is not essential that recovered funds be reinvested at the solving rate of return in order for the initial investment to have yielded the internal rate of return. For example, suppose an investment of $100,000 yields $10,000 annually for a 4-year period, and at the end of the fifth period the investment is terminated and $110,000 is recovered. Clearly, the investment yielded an internal rate of return of 10 percent, regardless of what was done with the annual recovery of $10,000. The recovered amounts could have been invested in, say, the stock market and resulted in positive or negative results. However, the original investment of $100,000 did, in fact, yield a 10 percent return.[1]

Since determining the rate of return involves solving Equation 8.1 for i_j^*, it is seen that (for a given investment j) it is necessary to determine the values of x that satisfy the n-degree polynomial

$$0 = A_{j,n} + A_{j,n-1}x + A_{j,n-2}x^2 + \cdots + A_{j,1}x^{n-1} + A_{j,0}x^n$$

where $x = (1 + i_j^*)$. In general, there can exist n distinct roots (values of x) for an n-degree polynomial; however, most cash flow profiles encountered in practice will have a unique root (internal rate of return).

Descartes' rule of signs indicates the n-degree polynomial will have a single positive real root if there is a single sign change in the sequence of cash flows, $A_0, A_1, \ldots, A_{n-1}, A_n$. If there are two sign changes, then there will be either two or no positive real roots; if there are three sign changes, there will be either three or one positive real roots; if there are four sign changes, there will be either four, two, or no positive real roots; if there are five sign changes, there will be either five, three, or one positive real roots; and so forth. Since the typical cash flow pattern begins with a negative cash flow followed by one or more positive cash flows, a unique root normally exists. [Note, since $x = (1 + i_j^*)$, a positive real root can occur even when i_j^* is negative—i.e., x will be positive when $i > -1$.]

EXAMPLE 8.2   Multiple Roots

To illustrate a cash flow profile having multiple roots, consider the data given in Table 8.2. The future worth of the cash flow series will be 0 using a 20, 40, or 50 percent interest rate.

$$FW_1(20\%) = -\$4,000(1.2)^3 + \$16,400(1.2)^2 - \$22,320(1.2) + \$10,080 = 0$$

$$FW_2(40\%) = -\$4,000(1.4)^3 + \$16,400(1.4)^2 - \$22,320(1.4) + \$10,080 = 0$$

$$FW_3(50\%) = -\$4,000(1.5)^3 + \$16,400(1.5)^2 - \$22,320(1.5) + \$10,080 = 0$$

[1]Lohmann, J. R., "The IRR, NPV and the Fallacy of the Reinvestment Rate Assumptions," *The Engineering Economist*, 33 (4), 1988, pp. 303–330.

TABLE 8.2	
Cash Flow Profile.	
EOY	CF
0	−$4,000
1	$16,400
2	−$22,320
3	$10,080

A plot of the future worth for this example is given in Figure 8.2. The future worth polynomial is a third degree, and there are three changes of sign in the ordered sequence of cash flows $(-, +, -, +)$. In this case, there are three unique positive real roots, corresponding to $i = 0.20$, $i = 0.40$, and $i = 0.50$. This is seen by factoring the future worth polynomial, which can be written as

$$FW_1(i\%) = \$4,000(1.2 - x)(1.4 - x)(1.5 - x)$$

where $x = (1 + i)$.

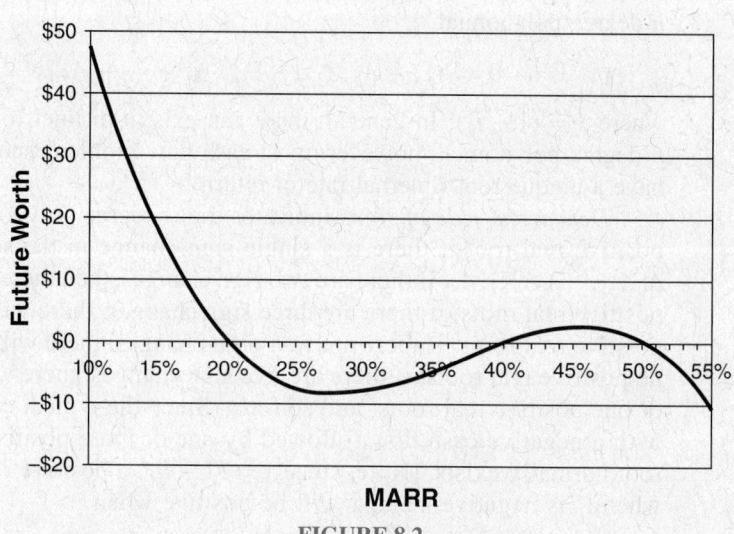

FIGURE 8.2

Plot of Future Worth for Example 8.2.

Multiple rates of return, as seen in Example 8.2, are difficult to interpret properly without other information, such as the future worth, present worth, or annual worth. For example, the pattern of cash flows shown in Table 8.2 is preferred to investing at the *MARR* if $0\% \le MARR < 20\%$ or $40\% < MARR < 50\%$. This is easily seen by looking at Figure 8.2 but is not immediately obvious from the three roots of the future worth equation.

The difficulty of interpreting the polynomial roots in complex cash flow profiles is a severe drawback to using the IRR approach. Unfortunately, the Excel® **IRR** worksheet function cannot resolve the difficulty; a single answer is provided—no indication is given of possible multiple solutions.

Recall, a parameter of the Excel® **IRR** worksheet function allows the user to guess the value of the IRR. As shown in Figure 8.3, the answer obtained for

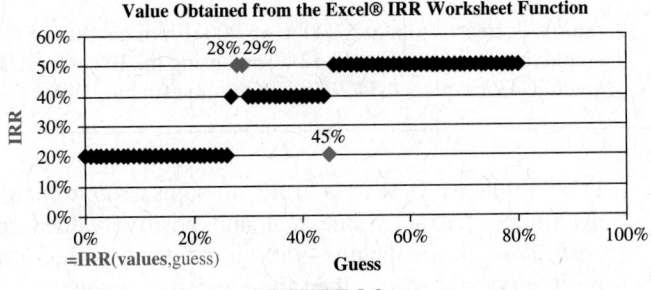

FIGURE 8.3

Results Obtained from the Excel® IRR Worksheet Function for Various Guesses.

Example 8.2 depends on the guess provided; if no guess is made, a value of 20 percent is obtained. Notice the three anomalies that occurred for guesses of 28 percent, 29 percent, and 45 percent.

As noted, even though multiple sign changes occur, it is not necessarily the case that multiple roots will exist.

EXAMPLE 8.3 An Example with Multiple Sign Changes and a Single Root

Julian Stewart invested $250,000 in a limited partnership to drill for natural gas. His investment yielded annual returns of $45,000 the first year, followed by annual increases of $10,000 until the sixth year, at which time an additional $150,000 had to be invested for deeper drilling. As shown in Figure 8.4, following the supplemental investment, the annual

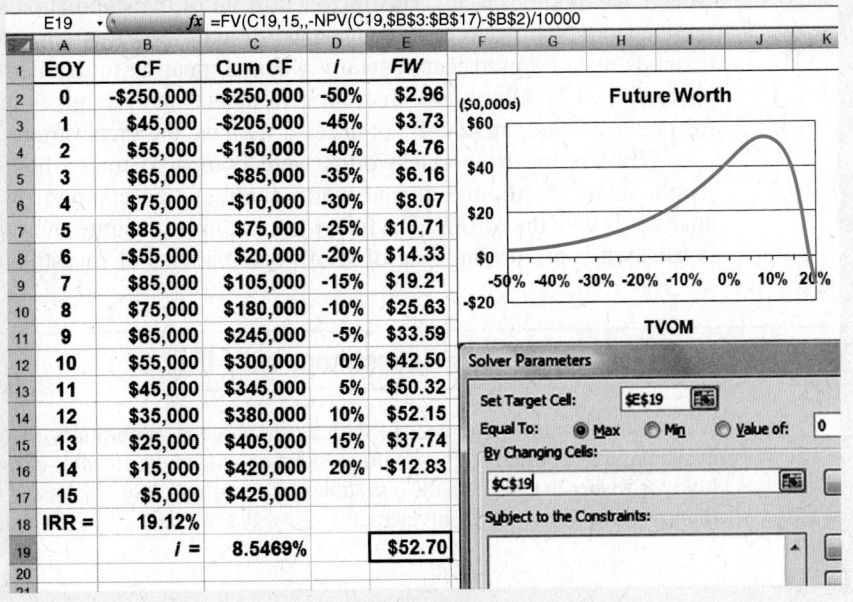

FIGURE 8.4

***IRR* for a Natural Gas Investment.**

returns decrease from \$85,000 to \$5,000. From the plot of future worth, it is evident that a single root exists, at $i^* = 19.12\%$, and using the Excel® **SOLVER** tool, FW is maximized when *MARR* equals **8.5469%**. For the investment, **IRR=19.12%**.

In addition to Descartes' rule of signs, *Norstrom's criterion* can be applied to determine if exactly one real and positive-valued root exists. If the *cumulative cash flow series* begins with a negative value and changes only once to a positive-valued series, then there exists a unique positive real root.[2] In Figure 8.4, notice that the cumulate cash flow series changes from negative to positive and remains positive; therefore, a unique positive real root exists. (Interestingly, if the interim investment is \$200,000 instead of \$150,000, Norstrom's criterion is not met, but a single positive root exists. Norstrom's criterion is a sufficient, not a necessary, condition for a single, real positive root to exist.)

8-3   INTERNAL RATE OF RETURN: MULTIPLE ALTERNATIVES

In computing the internal rate of return for each of several investments, we continue to search for the interest rate that equates the economic worth to 0. Mathematically, from Equation 8.1, the internal rate of return for alternative j, denoted i_j^*, satisfies the following equality:

$$0 = \sum_{t=0}^{n} A_{jt}(1 + i_j^*)^{n-t}$$

Notice, we did not place "Maximize" in front of the summation sign, as we did with present worth, future worth, and annual worth analyses. As noted previously, rate of return methods must be used incrementally when comparing mutually exclusive investment alternatives. (Recall the flow chart for incremental analyses given in Figure 5.4.) Hence, the preferred alternative will not necessarily have the greatest internal rate of return.

Whereas the economic worths were compared to 0 when performing present worth, future worth, and annual worth analyses, the comparison with rate of return analyses is with the *MARR*. The following example illustrates why incremental analysis is used when performing rate of return comparisons of investment alternatives.

EXAMPLE 8.4   Choosing the Best Investment with IRR

An investor has been approached with a very unique opportunity. Five investments are available; only one can be chosen. Regardless of which investment is chosen, at any time the investor wishes to terminate the investment, the original amount invested will be returned to the investor. The required investments, as well as the guaranteed annual returns and the

---

[2]See Bernhard, R. H., "Modified Rates of Return for Investment Project Evaluation—A Clarification of Their Assumptions," *Journal of Industrial Engineering*, 18 (1), 1962, pp. 19–27.

TABLE 8.3 Data for Example 8.4.					
Investment	1	2	3	4	5
Initial Investment	$15,000.00	$25,000.00	$40,000.00	$50,000.00	$70,000.00
Annual Return	$3,750.00	$5,000.00	$9,250.00	$11,250.00	$14,250.00
Salvage Value	$15,000.00	$25,000.00	$40,000.00	$50,000.00	$70,000.00
Internal Rate of Return	25.00%	20.00%	23.13%	22.50%	20.36%

guaranteed salvage values of 100 percent of the initial investment, are shown in Table 8.3. The investor's *MARR* is 18 percent.

To determine the internal rate of return, we use the capital recovery cost formulation to express the equivalent uniform annual cost of an investment. Setting the result equal to 0 gives

$$0 = (P - F)(A|P\, i^*, n) + Fi^* - A \tag{8.4}$$

where P denotes the initial investment, F denotes the salvage value, A denotes the annual return, and i^* denotes the internal rate of return. Since, for the example, $P = F$, Equation 8.4 reduces to

$$i^* = A/P \tag{8.5}$$

> When the salvage value equals the initial investment and annual returns are a uniform annual series, the internal rate of return equals the quotient of the annual return and the initial investment.

The internal rate of return for each investment alternative is shown in Table 8.4. Notice, every investment has an internal rate of return that is greater than the *MARR* of 18 percent. If ranking was used and the preferred alternative was designated as having the greatest IRR, then Alternative 1 would be chosen for investment—its IRR is 25 percent. The rank ordering of the internal rates of returns is 1, 3, 4, 5, 2.

However, if either of the economic worth methods (PW, FW, or AW) was used, which would be recommended? Arbitrarily choosing a planning horizon of 10 years and using a *MARR* of 18 percent, the present worths will be as shown in Table 8.4. On the basis of present worth, the rank-ordered preference is 4, 3, 5, 1, 2. Clearly, rank ordering IRR does not result in the same recommendation as occurs using PW, FW, or AW.

For the investor to consider investing in Alternative 5, $70,000 must have been available for investment. What happens to the balance of the $70,000 after an amount is invested in one of the five alternatives available? Based on the *MARR*, it earns a return of 18 percent.

TABLE 8.4 Present Worths for Example 8.4.					
Investment	1	2	3	4	5
Initial Investment	$15,000.00	$25,000.00	$40,000.00	$50,000.00	$70,000.00
Annual Return	$3,750.00	$5,000.00	$9,250.00	$11,250.00	$14,250.00
Salvage Value	$15,000.00	$25,000.00	$40,000.00	$50,000.00	$70,000.00
Present Worth	$4,718.79	$2,247.04	$9,212.88	$10,111.69	$7,415.24

Recalling our discussion of the investment portfolio in Section 6.4, let's compute the total annual return for each alternative.

Alternative 0: If the investor does not pursue either of the five investments, a total annual return of 18 percent times the $70,000 in the *reserve pool*, or $12,600, would result each year.

Alternative 1: The investor receives $3,750 annually, plus 18 percent times the $55,000 in the *reserve pool*, for a total annual return of $13,650. Since $13,650 > $12,600, Alternative 1 is preferred to the "do nothing" alternative.

Alternative 2: The investor receives $5,000 annually, plus 18 percent times the $45,000 in the *reserve pool*, for a total annual return of $13,100. Since $13,100 < $13,650, Alternative 1 is superior to Alternative 2.

Alternative 3: The investor receives $9,250 annually, plus 18 percent times the $30,000 in the *reserve pool*, for a total annual return of $14,650. Since $14,650 > $13,650, Alternative 3 is preferred to Alternative 1.

Alternative 4: The investor receives $11,250 annually, plus 18 percent times the $20,000 in the *reserve pool*, for a total annual return of $14,850. Since $14,850 > $14,650, Alternative 4 is better than Alternative 3.

Alternative 5: The investor receives $14,250 annually, which exhausts the *reserve pool* and represents the total annual return. Since $14,250 < $14,850, Alternative 4 is more desirable than Alternative 5 and would be recommended for investment.

Using the incremental approach given in Figure 5.4 yields the following results (summarized in Table 8.5):

1. The alternatives are ranked in increasing order of the initial investment. The internal rate of return is computed for the alternative having the smallest initial investment: $IRR_1 = 25\% > MARR = 18\%$. Therefore, Alternative 1 is preferred to "doing nothing" and is designated the defender.

2. The internal rate of return is computed for the increment of investment required to move from the current defender (Alternative 1) to the new challenger (Alternative 2). A $10,000 investment increment is required; it yields an incremental return of $1,250 annually. $IRR_{2-1} = \$1,250/\$10,000 = 12.5\% < MARR = 18\%$. Therefore, Alternative 2 is rejected; Alternative 1 remains the defender.

3. The internal rate of return is computed for the increment of investment required to move from the current defender (Alternative 1) to the new challenger (Alternative 3). A $25,000 investment increment is required; it yields an incremental return of $5,500 annually. $IRR_{3-1} = 22\% > MARR = 18\%$. Therefore, Alternative 1 is rejected; Alternative 3 becomes the defender.

TABLE 8.5
Incremental *IRR* Solution for Example 8.4.

Investment	1	2 − 1	3 − 1	4 − 3	5 − 4
Δ Investment	$15,000.00	$10,000.00	$25,000.00	$10,000.00	$20,000.00
Δ Annual Return	$3,750.00	$1,250.00	$5,500.00	$2,000.00	$3,000.00
Δ Salvage Value	$15,000.00	$10,000.00	$25,000.00	$10,000.00	$20,000.00
Δ IRR	25.00%	12.50%	22.00%	20.00%	15.00%
≥ MARR?	Yes	No	Yes	Yes	No
Defender	1	1	3	4	4

4. The internal rate of return is computed for the increment of investment required to move from the current defender (Alternative 3) to the new challenger (Alternative 4). A $10,000 investment increment is required; it will yield an incremental return of $2,000 annually. $IRR_{4-3} = 20\% > MARR = 18\%$. Therefore, Alternative 3 is rejected; Alternative 4 becomes the defender.

5. The internal rate of return is computed for the increment of investment required to move from the current defender (Alternative 4) to the new challenger (Alternative 5). A $20,000 investment increment is required; it yields an incremental return of $3,000 annually. $IRR_{5-4} = 15\% < MARR = 18\%$. Therefore, Alternative 5 is rejected; Alternative 4 remains the defender.

6. Since no challengers remain, Alternative 4 is chosen for investment. Its overall IRR of 22.5 percent consists of a 25 percent return on the first $15,000 invested, plus a 22 percent return on the next $25,000 invested, plus a 20 percent return on the next $10,000 invested. The weighted average return is

$$[\$15,000(0.25) + \$25,000(0.22) + \$10,000(0.20)]/\$50,000 = 0.225 \quad \text{or} \quad 22.5\%$$

The example illustrates Principle 6: *Continue to invest as long as each additional increment of investment yields a return that is greater than the investor's TVOM*. Examine the following modified version of Donaldson Brown's 1924 comment and notice how it fits this example perfectly: "The object of management is not necessarily the highest rate of return on capital, but...to assure profit with each increment of [capital] that will at least equal the economic cost of additional capital [or minimum attractive rate of return]."

Principle #6

Continue to invest as long as each additional increment of investment yields a return that is greater than the investor's *TVOM*.

EXAMPLE 8.5   IRR Analysis with Mutually Exclusive Alternatives

Recall the example of the theme park in Florida that is considering two designs for a new ride called the Scream Machine. The first design alternative (A) requires a $300,000 investment and will produce net annual after-tax revenue of $55,000 over the 10-year planning horizon; the second alternative (B) requires a $450,000 investment and will produce net annual after-tax revenue of $80,000 annually. Both alternatives are expected to have negligible salvage values after the 10-year planning horizon. Based on a 10 percent *MARR* and an IRR comparison, which design (if either) should be chosen?

First, we compute the IRR for Design A, since its initial investment is less than that for Design B.

$$i_A^* = \text{RATE}(10,-55000,300000)$$
$$= 12.87\% > MARR = 10\%$$

Since Design A is justified, the internal rate of return on the $150,000 incremental investment is computed:

$$i^*_{B-A} = \text{RATE}(10,-25000,150000)$$
$$= 10.56\% > MARR = 10\%$$

Since the internal rate of return is greater than the *MARR* (albeit only slightly), the increment of investment needed to acquire Design B is justified. The overall internal rate of return for Design B is

$$i^*_B = \text{RATE}(10,-80000,450000)$$
$$= 12.11\%$$

The return on the first $300,000 is **12.87%**, and the return on the last $150,000 is **10.56%** for an overall return of **12.11%**.

For reasons that will become clear later in the chapter, the following example introduces a situation in which multiple negative cash flows occur in the cash flow profile for each alternative.

EXAMPLE 8.6   IRR Analysis with Irregular Cash Flow Series

A batch chemical processing company is considering adding new technology that will allow it to enter a new market. The large, specially designed centrifuges and associated equipment being considered include state-of-the-art computer controls. The cash flows for the two new technology alternatives are given in Figure 8.5. Using a before-tax analysis, the firm requires a minimum attractive rate of return of 18.5 percent.

	A	B	C	D	E	F
	EOY	CF(A)	CF(B)	CF(B-A)		
1						
2	0	-$7,585,000.00	-$10,285,000.00	-$2,700,000.00		
3	1	-$1,237,500.00	-$1,575,500.00	-$338,000.00		
4	2	$1,695,500.00	$2,455,700.00	$760,200.00		
5	3	$2,002,800.00	$2,657,500.00	$654,700.00		=C5-B5
6	4	$2,345,700.00	$2,877,500.00	$531,800.00		
7	5	$2,450,500.00	$3,025,000.00	$574,500.00		
8	6	$2,575,600.00	$3,250,300.00	$674,700.00		
9	7	$2,735,000.00	$3,565,800.00	$830,800.00		
10	8	$3,005,300.00	$3,750,000.00	$744,700.00		
11	9	$3,857,500.00	$4,252,500.00	$395,000.00		
12	10	$5,285,000.00	$8,750,000.00	$3,465,000.00		
13	IRR =	19.39%	18.93%	17.61%		
15			IRR(D2:D12)			
17			=IRR(B2:B12)			

C13 · fx =IRR(C2:C12)

FIGURE 8.5
IRR **Analysis of a Batch Chemical Processing Investment.**

Since Alternative A requires the smallest initial investment, we compute its IRR. From Figure 8.5, we see that $IRR_A = 19.39\% > MARR = 18.5\%$; therefore, Alternative A is justified economically. Next, we compute the IRR for the $2.7 million incremental investment required to acquire Alternative B. From Figure 8.5, $IRR_{B-A} = 17.61\% < MARR = 18.5\%$. Since the incremental investment is not justified, Alternative A is recommended.

Notice, the multiple negative-valued cash flows did not create a problem, since the cumulative cash flow did not have more than one sign reversal.

When comparing mutually exclusive investment alternatives, each of which has well-behaved cash flows, it is quite likely that multiple roots will occur. The reason for this is, except for the initial step, incremental analyses are performed. When one well-behaved cash flow series is subtracted from another, there is no guarantee that the difference in the cash flow series will be well behaved, as the following example illustrates.

EXAMPLE 8.7   IRR Analysis with Regular Cash Flow Series

Three mutually exclusive investment alternatives are being considered. The *MARR* is 15 percent. The cash flow profiles for the alternatives are given in Table 8.6. Alternative 1 requires an initial investment of $100,000; it returns $20,000 annually for 5 years, at which time the initial investment is fully recovered; its IRR is 20 percent. Alternative 2 requires 2 years to complete the initial investment of $150,000, with $125,000 being spent during the current year and $25,000 being spent the next year; thereafter occur revenues equal to a $5,000 decreasing gradient series added to a $75,000 base, for an internal rate of return of 19.39%. Alternative 3 also requires 2 years to complete the investment, with $150,000 being spent initially and an additional $35,000 being spent the following year; revenues equal to a $75,000 uniform series occur for 4 years, plus a $20,000 salvage value; the internal rate of return is 18.01%.

First, the alternatives are ordered by increasing investment. Since Alternative 1 has the smallest initial investment, it is considered first; it is justified, since $IRR_1 = 20\% > MARR = 15\%$. Next considered is Alternative 2. The incremental investment required to move from Alternative 1 to Alternative 2 is $25,000 initially, followed by $45,000 the next year; three positive-valued cash flows of $55,000, $50,000, and $40,000 occur, followed by a negative-valued cash flow of $65,000. From Table 8.6 and Figures 8.6 and 8.7, it appears that a

TABLE 8.6
Data for Example 8.7.

EOY	CF(1)	CF(2)	CF(3)	CF(2-1)	CF(3-2)
0	−$100,000	−$125,000	−$150,000	−$25,000	−$25,000
1	$20,000	−$25,000	−$35,000	−$45,000	−$10,000
2	$20,000	$75,000	$75,000	$55,000	$0
3	$20,000	$70,000	$75,000	$50,000	$5,000
4	$20,000	$60,000	$75,000	$40,000	$15,000
5	$120,000	$55,000	$95,000	−$65,000	$40,000
IRR =	20.00%	19.39%	18.01%	16.41%	13.44%

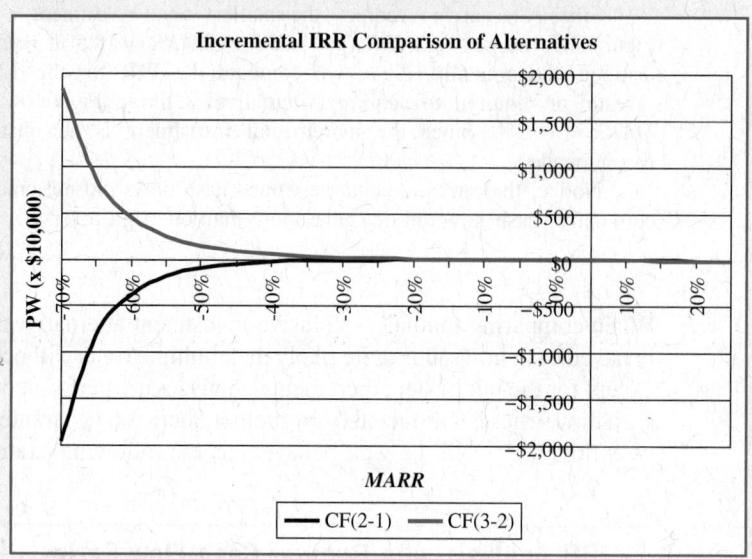

FIGURE 8.6
***IRR* Incremental Analysis with Three Investment Alternatives.**

single positive-valued root exists and $IRR_{2-1} = 16.41\% > MARR = 15\%$. Therefore, the incremental investment is justified; Alternative 1 is eliminated from further consideration. (Notice, Norstrom's criterion is satisfied, since the cumulative incremental cash flow begins with a negative sign and ends with a positive sign and does not switch signs more than once.)

Next, we compute the internal rate of return on the incremental investment required to move from Alternative 2 to Alternative 3. The incremental cash flow profile is quite irregular; expressed in $000s, it is {−$25, −$10, $0, $5, $15, $40}. Norstrom's criterion

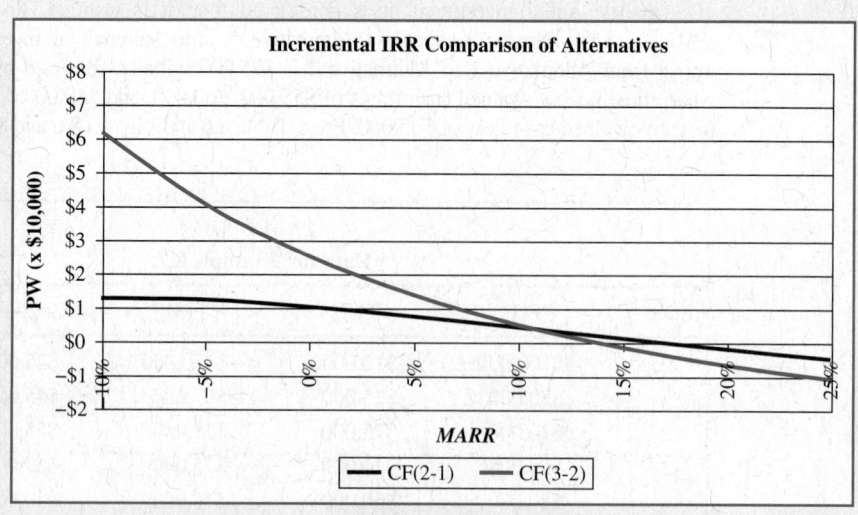

FIGURE 8.7
Close Up of Critical Region of Figure 8.6.

is satisfied, since the cumulative incremental cash flow begins with a negative sign and the cumulative incremental cash flow changes signs only once: $\{-\$25, -\$35, -\$35, -\$30, -\$15, \$25\}$. From Table 8.6 and Figures 8.6 and 8.7, a single positive-valued root exists and $IRR_{3-2} = 13.41\% < MARR = 15\%$. The incremental investment is not justified.

Based on IRR analysis, it is recommended that Alternative 2 be acquired, resulting in an IRR of 19.39%. (The present worths for the three alternatives are $16,760.78, $17,647.70, and $15,702.99; based on a present worth analysis, Alternative 2 is recommended.)

8-4 EXTERNAL RATE OF RETURN: SINGLE ALTERNATIVE

Because of the possibilities of multiple roots when using the internal rate of return method, in 1976 we developed an alternative approach, which we called the *external rate of return (ERR)* method.[3] Our approach was based on the following variation of Equation 8.2:

$$\sum_{t=0}^{n} R_t (1 + r)^{n-t} = \sum_{t=0}^{n} C_t (1 + i')^{n-t} \tag{8.6}$$

where R_t denotes the positive-valued cash flows in a cash flow series and C_t denotes the negative-valued cash flows in a cash flow series; r is the reinvestment rate, which we call the *MARR*, and i' is the external rate of return.

Our reasoning in creating the ERR went like this: Any funds remaining in the investment pool are assumed to earn returns equal to the *MARR*. Therefore, money recovered from an investment should also earn returns equal to the *MARR*. The interest rate that makes the future worth of negative-valued cash flows equal to the future worth of positive-valued cash flows that are reinvested at the *MARR* we called the *external rate of return*. We chose the word *external* because we wanted to make the point that recovered funds were not reinvested at a rate equal to the *internal rate of return*, and we wanted to point out that the return earned on recovered capital was external to the investment in question.

Two features of the ERR are important: There exists a unique solution (no multiple roots), and the ERR is always *between* the IRR and the *MARR*. Hence, if IRR > MARR, then IRR > ERR > MARR; likewise, if IRR < MARR, then IRR < ERR < MARR; and if IRR = MARR, then IRR = ERR = MARR.

- If $IRR < MARR$, then $IRR < ERR < MARR$
- If $IRR > MARR$, then $IRR > ERR > MARR$
- If $IRR = MARR$, then $IRR = ERR = MARR$

[3]White, J. A., K. E. Case, and M. H. Agee, "Rate of Return: An Explicit Reinvestment Rate Approach," *Proceedings of the 1976 AIIE Conference*, American Institute of Industrial Engineers, Norcross, GA, 1976.

EXAMPLE 8.8 Computing the External Rate of Return for the SMP Investment

The investment of $500,000 in a surface mount placement machine is expected to reduce manufacturing costs by $92,500 per year. At the end of the 10-year planning horizon, it is expected the SMP machine will be worth $50,000. Using a 10 percent *MARR* and an external rate of return analysis, should the investment be made?

The only negative-valued cash flow is the initial investment. Therefore, Equation 8.6 becomes

$$\$500,000(F|P\ i',10) = \$92,500(F|A\ 10\%,10) + \$50,000$$

$$(1 + i')^{10} = [\$92,500(15.93742) + \$50,000]/\$500,000 = 3.048423$$

$$i' = 11.79117\%$$

or

$$i' = \text{RATE}(10,,-500000,\text{FV}(10\%,10,-92500)+50000)$$

$$= 11.79118\%$$

Since $i' > MARR$, the machine is justified economically.

The ERR can also be obtained using the Excel® **MIRR** worksheet function. (We treat the *modified internal rate of return [MIRR]* as a measure of economic worth in Appendix 8.A.) The syntax for the Excel® **MIRR** worksheet function is **MIRR(values,finance_rate,reinvest_rate)**; for purposes of computing the ERR, the finance rate is ignored. As shown in Figure 8.8, using the **MIRR** worksheet function, we obtain the exact figure for the ERR: **11.79118%**. Also shown in Figure 8.8 is the relationship among the IRR, *MARR*, and ERR. Recall, for this example, IRR = **13.8%**.

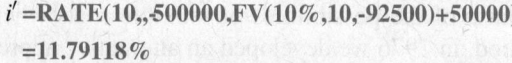

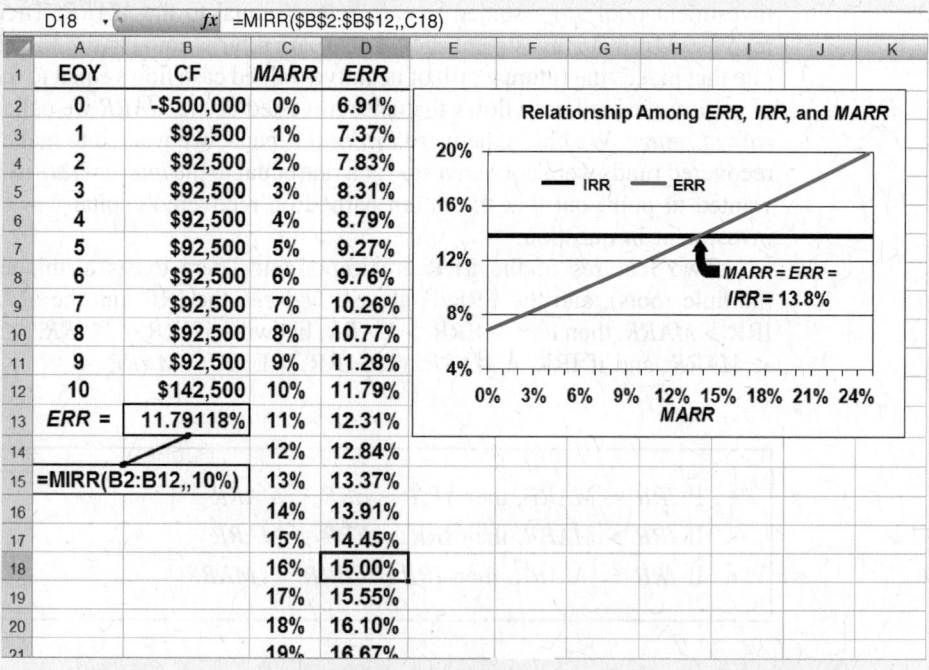

FIGURE 8.8

***ERR* Solution to Example 8.8.**

EXAMPLE 8.9   Using the ERR to Resolve a Multiple Root Problem

Recall the data in Example 8.2 that led to multiple solutions to the IRR formulation. The following four cash flows occurred at $t = 0, 1, 2,$ and 3: $-\$1{,}000, \$4{,}100, -\$5{,}580,$ and $\$2{,}520,$ respectively. Using a *MARR* of 12 percent, from Equation 8.6,

$$\$1{,}000(F|P\,i',3) + \$5{,}580(F|P\,i',1) = \$4{,}100(F|P\,12\%,2) + \$2{,}520$$

To determine the value of i' that satisfies the equality, trial-and-error methods can be used, followed by interpolation. Due to the multiple negative signs, the Excel® **MIRR** function cannot be used to obtain the ERR value. However, the Excel® **SOLVER** and **GOAL SEEK** tools can be used. Figure 8.9 provides the **SOLVER** setup and solution. Both **SOLVER** and **GOAL SEEK** yield a value of **12.0911%** for the ERR obtained.

Shown in Table 8.7 are ERR values for various values of the *MARR*. Notice, for *MARR* < 20%, ERR > *MARR*; for 20% < *MARR* < 40%, ERR < *MARR*; for 40% < *MARR* < 50%, ERR > *MARR*; and for *MARR* > 50%, ERR < *MARR*.

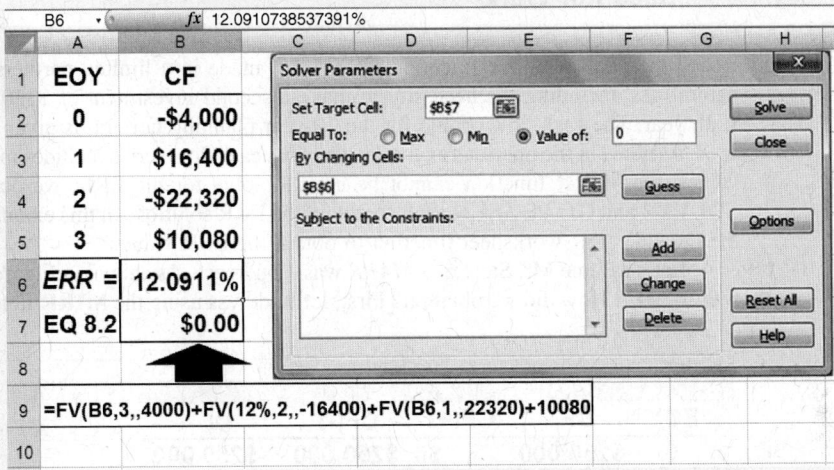

FIGURE 8.9
Excel® SOLVER Set Up and Solution to Example 8.9.

TABLE 8.7
ERR Solutions for Various *MARR* Values in Example 8.9.

MARR	ERR	MARR	ERR
0%	0.4654%	30%	29.9812%
2%	2.3768%	32%	31.9840%
4%	4.2999%	34%	33.9877%
6%	6.2338%	36%	35.9919%
8%	8.1775%	38%	37.9962%
10%	10.1302%	40%	40.0000%
12%	12.0911%	42%	42.0030%
14%	14.0592%	44%	44.0049%
16%	16.0339%	46%	46.0052%

(*Continued*)

TABLE 8.7
(Continued)

MARR	ERR	MARR	ERR
18%	18.0144%	48%	48.0037%
20%	20.0000%	50%	50.0000%
22%	21.9900%	52%	51.9939%
24%	23.9837%	54%	53.9850%
26%	25.9805%	56%	55.9732%
28%	27.9799%	58%	57.9581%

EXAMPLE 8.10 Solving for the ERR When the Excel® MIRR Function Does Not Work

Recall the $250,000 investment Julian Stewart made in a limited partnership to drill for natural gas, including the necessity to make a second investment of $150,000 during the sixth year. The cash flow profile for the 10-year planning horizon is given in Figure 8.10.

As noted in the previous example, when the cash flow series includes multiple negative values, the **MIRR** function cannot be used to solve for the ERR; we used the Excel® **SOLVER** and **GOAL SEEK** tools to obtain the ERR solution. In this example, we will use the Excel® **IRR** worksheet function to obtain the ERR value.

Let's assume Mr. Stewart's *MARR* was 15 percent. As shown in Figure 8.10, his ERR was **16.25%**. How did we obtain it? First, let's address using the **MIRR** function. If we had

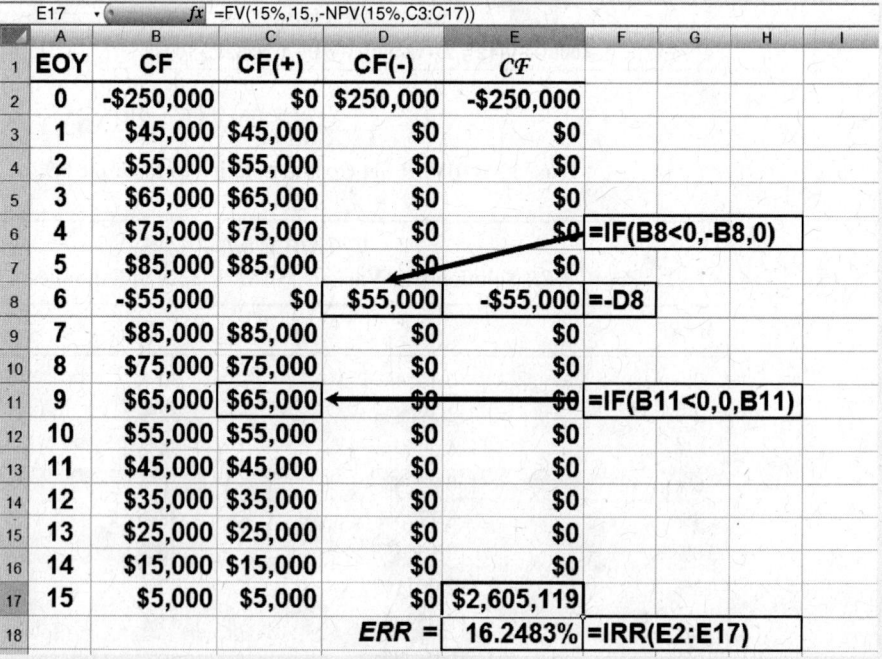

FIGURE 8.10
ERR for the Natural Gas Investment.

entered **=MIRR(B2:B17,,15%)** in any cell, we would have obtained the value 15.3724%. However, as we shall see, that is not a correct solution for the ERR.

To solve the problem, we took the following steps:

1. Because of the multiple negative cash flows, we defined two new cash flow series: $\mathscr{CF}(+)$ and $\mathscr{CF}(-)$. Using the Excel® **IF** function, we separated the original cash flow roots into two series: $\{R_t, t = 0, \ldots, 15\}$ and $\{C_t, t = 0, \ldots, 15\}$.

2. Next, we developed a new cash flow series $\{\mathscr{CF}_t, t = 0, \ldots, 15\}$, which, except for $t = 15$, is the negative of $\{C_t\}$.

3. Then we computed the future worth of the positive-valued cash flows and added it to the negative cash flow (although in this example none existed) in the last year of the planning horizon.

4. The resulting series (E2:E17) contains zeros, the negative-valued cash flows from the original cash flow series, and the future worth of all positive-valued cash flows; the latter (shown in cell E17) was obtained using the *MARR* of 15 percent.

5. Recalling the definition of the external rate of return (the interest rate that makes the absolute value of the future worth of the negative-valued cash flows equal to the future worth of the positive-valued cash flows, based on the *MARR*), we used the Excel® **IRR** worksheet function to solve for the ERR, as indicated in cell E18.

For the example, *ERR* = 16.2483%, not the 15.3724% that would have resulted if we had used the Excel® **MIRR** worksheet function.

8-5 EXTERNAL RATE OF RETURN: MULTIPLE ALTERNATIVES

When mutually exclusive investment alternatives exist, the external rate of return method can be used to select the most economic. However, like the internal rate of return method, it must be applied incrementally. Although there are multiple alternatives and each has its own external rate of return (i_j'), there is a common reinvestment rate (r). Mathematically, for alternative j, the following equality must hold:

$$\sum_{t=0}^{n} R_{jt}(1+r)^{n-t} = \sum_{t=0}^{n} C_{jt}(1+i_j')^{n-t} \tag{8.7}$$

where R_{jt} denotes the positive-valued cash flows and C_{jt} denotes the negative-valued cash flows in the cash flow series for alternative j.

EXAMPLE 8.11   Using ERR to Solve the Five-Investment Problem

Recall the five investments with 100 percent salvage values, considered in Example 8.4. Let's solve the problem using the ERR method. To do so, we assume a 10-year planning horizon. Recall, the investor's *MARR* is 18 percent.

In Table 8.8 are the data for the example, as well as the external rates of return for the five investments. Using an incremental analysis, the following steps are taken:

1. The alternatives are ranked in increasing order of the initial investment. The external rate of return is computed for the alternative having the smallest initial investment: $ERR_1 = 21.27\% > MARR = 18\%$. Therefore, Alternative 1 is preferred to "doing nothing" and is designated the defender.

TABLE 8.8					
Data for Example 8.10.					
Investment	1	2	3	4	5
Initial Investment	$15,000.00	$25,000.00	$40,000.00	$50,000.00	$70,000.00
Annual Return	$3,750.00	$5,000.00	$9,250.00	$11,250.00	$14,250.00
Salvage Value	$15,000.00	$25,000.00	$40,000.00	$50,000.00	$70,000.00
External Rate of Return	21.27%	19.02%	20.47%	20.19%	19.19%

2. The external rate of return is computed for the increment of investment required to move from the current defender (Alternative 1) to the new challenger (Alternative 2). A $10,000 investment increment is required; it yields an incremental return of $1,250 annually. $ERR_{2-1} = 14.7\% < MARR = 18\%$. Therefore, Alternative 2 is rejected; Alternative 1 remains the defender.

3. The external rate of return is computed for the increment of investment required to move from the current defender (Alternative 1) to the new challenger (Alternative 3). A $25,000 investment increment is required; it yields an incremental return of $5,500 annually. $ERR_{3-1} = 19.97\% > MARR = 18\%$. Therefore, Alternative 1 is rejected; Alternative 3 becomes the defender.

4. The external rate of return is computed for the increment of investment required to move from the current defender (Alternative 3) to the new challenger (Alternative 4). A $10,000 investment increment is required; it yields an incremental return of $2,000 annually. $ERR_{4-3} = 19.02\% > MARR = 18\%$. Therefore, Alternative 3 is rejected; Alternative 4 becomes the defender.

5. The external rate of return is computed for the increment of investment required to move from the current defender (Alternative 4) to the new challenger (Alternative 5). A $20,000 investment increment is required; it yields an incremental return of $3,000 annually. $ERR_{5-4} = 16.3\% < MARR = 18\%$. Therefore, Alternative 5 is rejected; Alternative 4 remains the defender.

6. Since no challengers remain, Alternative 4 is chosen for investment. Its overall ERR is 20.19 percent. Table 8.9 summarizes the solution procedure used.

 In contrast to the IRR, the ERR is not equal to the quotient of the annual return and the initial investment, nor is it obtained with a comparably simple calculation. However, the Excel® **MIRR** worksheet function can be used to obtain the ERR values for the example.

TABLE 8.9					
Incremental *ERR* Solution for Example 8.10.					
Investment	1	2 − 1	3 − 1	4 − 3	5 − 4
Δ Investment	$15,000.00	$10,000.00	$25,000.00	$10,000.00	$20,000.00
Δ Annual Return	$3,750.00	$1,250.00	$5,500.00	$2,000.00	$3,000.00
Δ Salvage Value	$15,000.00	$10,000.00	$25,000.00	$10,000.00	$20,000.00
Δ ERR	21.27%	14.70%	19.97%	19.02%	16.30%
≥MARR?	Yes	No	Yes	Yes	No
Defender	1	1	3	4	4

EXAMPLE 8.12   **Using the ERR to Compare Two Alternatives for the Scream Machine**

Recall the example involving two design alternatives for a new ride called the Scream Machine, the first of which requires an initial investment of $300,000 and yields net annual revenue of $55,000 over a 10-year planning period; the second requires an initial investment of $450,000 and yields a net annual revenue of $80,000 over a 10-year period.

Based on a 10 percent *MARR*, the following steps are taken to solve the problem:

1. Compute the ERR for Design Alternative A:

$$\$300,000(1 + i'_A)^{10} = \$55,000(F|A\ 10\%,10)$$
$$(1 + i'_A)^{10} = \$55,000(15.93742)/\$300,000$$
$$i'_A = 11.31814\% > MARR = 10\%$$

or

$$i'_A = \text{RATE}(10,,-300000,\text{FV}(10\%,10,-55000))$$
$$i'_A = 11.31814\% > MARR = 10\%$$

Design Alternative A is justified economically.

2. Compute the ERR for the $150,000 incremental investment to move from Design A to Design B:

$$\$150,000(1 + i'_{B-A})^{10} = \$25,000(F|A\ 10\%,10)$$
$$(1 + i'_{B-A})^{10} = \$25,000(15.9374)/\$150,000$$
$$i'_{B-A} = 10.26219\% > MARR = 10\%$$

or

$$i'_{B-A} = \text{RATE}(10,,-150000,\text{FV}(10\%,10,-25000))$$
$$= 10.26219\% > MARR = 10\%$$

The incremental investment required to acquire and install Design Alternative B is justified economically.

3. Design Alternative B is recommended for acquisition; it will have an overall external rate of return of

$$\$450,000(1 + i'_B)^{10} = \$80,000(F|A\ 10\%, 10)$$
$$(1 + i'_B)^{10} = \$80,000(15.9374)/\$450,000$$
$$i'_B = 10.97611\%$$

or

$$i'_B = \text{RATE}(10,,-450000,\text{FV}(10\%,10,-80000))$$
$$= 10.97611\%$$

EXAMPLE 8.13 ERR Analysis with Irregular Cash Flow Series

The batch processing chemical plant example can also be solved using ERR analysis. Recall, the cash flow profiles were as shown in Figure 8.11. Because of the multiple negative values in the cash flow series for Centrifuge A and the multiple negative values in the incremental cash flow series between Centrifuges B and A, we cannot use the **MIRR** worksheet function. However, we can employ the approach used in Example 8.9. Specifically, we can do the following:

1. Sort the alternatives in increasing order of investments: consider A first, then B.

2. Since $\{\mathscr{CF}(A)\}$ contains multiple negative-valued cash flows, create a new cash flow series $\{CF(A)\}$ by inserting only the negative-valued cash flows for Centrifuge A and the future worth of the positive-valued cash flows for Centrifuge A. As shown, the future worth equals **\$49,090,929.92**.

3. Use the Excel® **IRR** worksheet function to compute the ERR for Centrifuge A: **18.9938%**. Since $ERR_A > MARR = 18.5\%$, Alternative A is justified economically, eliminating the do-nothing alternative from consideration.

4. Create the incremental cash flow series $\{CF(B)-CF(A)\}$.

5. Create a new cash flow series $\{\mathscr{CF}(B - A)\}$ by inserting only the negative-valued cash flows from the incremental cash flow series and the future worth of the positive-valued incremental cash flows. As shown, the future worth of the positive-valued incremental cash flows equals **\$15,610,551.99**.

6. Use Excel's® **IRR** worksheet function to compute ERR_{B-A}: **17.9848%**. Since $ERR_{B-A} < MARR = 18.5\%$, Alternative B is not justified economically; eliminating it from consideration leaves Alternative A as the preferred choice.

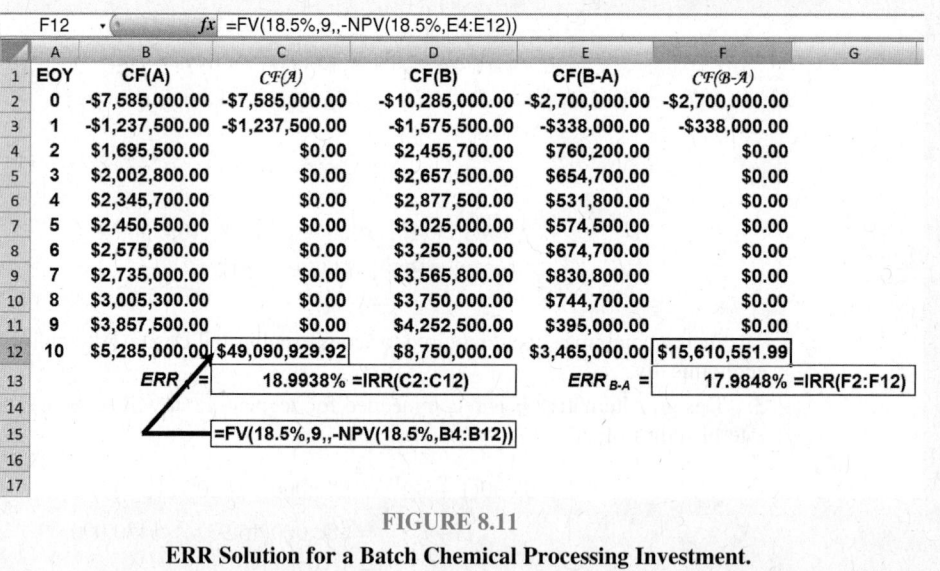

FIGURE 8.11
ERR Solution for a Batch Chemical Processing Investment.

EXAMPLE 8.14 ERR Analysis with Regular Cash Flow Series

Recall the three mutually exclusive investments considered in Example 8.6. We shall solve the example using ERR analysis.

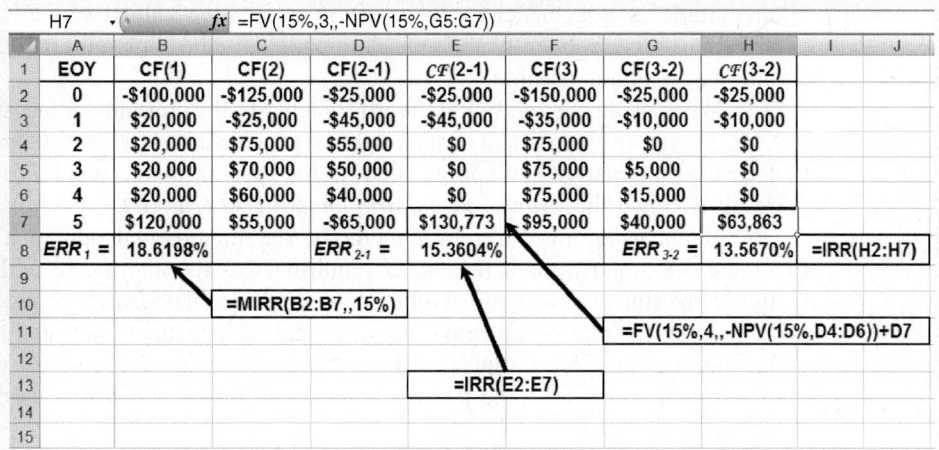

	A	B	C	D	E	F	G	H	I	J
	H7	▾	*fx*	=FV(15%,3,,-NPV(15%,G5:G7))						
1	EOY	CF(1)	CF(2)	CF(2-1)	C𝓕(2-1)	CF(3)	CF(3-2)	C𝓕(3-2)		
2	0	-$100,000	-$125,000	-$25,000	-$25,000	-$150,000	-$25,000	-$25,000		
3	1	$20,000	-$25,000	-$45,000	-$45,000	-$35,000	-$10,000	-$10,000		
4	2	$20,000	$75,000	$55,000	$0	$75,000	$0	$0		
5	3	$20,000	$70,000	$50,000	$0	$75,000	$5,000	$0		
6	4	$20,000	$60,000	$40,000	$0	$75,000	$15,000	$0		
7	5	$120,000	$55,000	-$65,000	$130,773	$95,000	$40,000	$63,863		
8	ERR₁ =	18.6198%		ERR₂₋₁ =	15.3604%		ERR₃₋₂ =	13.5670%	=IRR(H2:H7)	
9										
10			=MIRR(B2:B7,,15%)							
11							=FV(15%,4,,-NPV(15%,D4:D6))+D7			
12										
13				=IRR(E2:E7)						
14										
15										

FIGURE 8.12

***ERR* Incremental Analysis with Three Investment Alternatives.**

1. As indicated in Figure 8.12, Alternative 1 is considered first, because it has the smallest initial investment. Alternative 2 is then considered.

2. Compute ERR_1. Since {CF(1)} contains only one negative-valued cash flow, the Excel® **MIRR** function can be used. Since $ERR_1 = 18.62\% > MARR = 15\%$, Alternative 1 is justified economically and the do-nothing alternative need not be considered.

3. Create the incremental cash flow series {CF(2) − CF(1)}.

4. Create a new cash flow series $\{\mathscr{CF}(2-1)\}$ by inserting only the negative-valued cash flows from the incremental cash flow series {CF(2 − 1)} and add the future worth of the positive-valued incremental cash flows to the last entry in {CF(2 − 1)}, which is negative-valued. As shown, $130,773 is the sum of the future worth of the positive-valued incremental cash flows and the −$65,000 incremental cash flow at EOY = 5.

5. Use the Excel® **IRR** worksheet function to compute ERR_{2-1}. Since $ERR_{2-1} = 15.3604\% > MARR = 15\%$, Alternative 2 is justified economically, eliminating Alternative 1 from consideration.

6. Create the incremental cash flow series {CF(3) − CF(2)}.

7. Create a new cash flow series $\{\mathscr{CF}(3-2)\}$ by inserting only the negative-valued cash flows from the incremental cash flow series and the future worth of the positive-valued incremental cash flows. As shown, the future worth of the positive-valued incremental cash flows equals $63,863.

8. Use the Excel® **IRR** worksheet function to compute ERR_{3-2}. Since $ERR_{3-2} = 13.567\% < MARR = 15\%$, Alternative 3 is not justified economically; eliminating Alternative 3 from consideration leaves Alternative 2 as the preferred choice.

8-6   ANALYZING ALTERNATIVES WITH NO POSITIVE CASH FLOWS

The previous analysis of the economic viability of investment alternatives included positive-valued cash flows. Hence, it was possible for each investment to have an internal and external rate of return. But what if no positive cash flows exist, or their magnitude is not sufficient to result in a positive-valued rate of return? Such situations arise frequently and are accompanied by the constraint that the do-nothing alternative is not feasible.

When using the traditional "worth" methods, the present worth cost, future worth cost, annual worth cost, and capitalized cost are calculated for each alternative, and the least cost alternative is recommended. In the case of annual worth cost analysis, the result is called the *equivalent uniform annual cost (EUAC)*.

When using rate of return methods, the incremental approach portrayed in Figure 5.8 is performed. Instead of requiring that the alternative with the smallest initial investment have a rate of return at least equal to the *MARR*, the process begins by computing the rate of return on the increment of investment between the alternative having the smallest initial investment and that with the next-to-smallest initial investment. Thereafter, the process is identical to that which was used for positive-valued cash flows.

EXAMPLE 8.15 **Evaluating Mutually Exclusive Alternatives Having Only Negative Cash Flows**

A company has concluded that a new incinerator is required in order to comply with air-quality standards. Several choices are being considered, but three finalists meet the quality and performance specifications established by the company. The incinerators differ in the initial investment required and their operating and maintenance costs; all have negligible salvage values. Based on benchmark studies, the following cost estimates are available:

Alternative	Initial Investment	Annual Operating Cost	Annual Maintenance Cost
A	$250,000	$105,000	$42,000
B	$385,000	$78,000	$28,000
C	$475,000	$65,000	$18,000

Based on a *MARR* of 12 percent and a 7-year planning horizon, which of the incinerators should be pursued? Perform the analysis using PW, AW, IRR, and ERR analyses.

Present Worth Analysis (Costs Are Denoted with Positive Values)

$$PW_A = \$250,000 + \$147,000(P|A\ 12\%,7)$$
$$= \$250,000 + \$147,000(4.56376)$$
$$= \$920,872.72$$
$$= PV(12\%,7,-147000)+250000$$
$$= \$920,872.21$$

$$PW_B = \$385,000 + \$106,000(P|A\ 12\%,7)$$
$$= \$385,000 + \$106,000(4.56376)$$
$$= \$868,758.56$$
$$= PV(12\%,7,-106000)+385000$$
$$= \$868,758.19$$

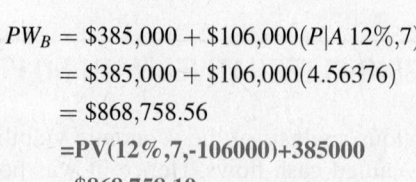

$$PW_C = \$475,000 + \$83,000(P|A\ 12\%,7)$$
$$= \$475,000 + \$83,000(4.56376)$$
$$= \$853,792.08$$
$$=PV(12\%,7,-83000)+475000$$
$$=\$853,791.79$$

Based on a present worth analysis, Alternative C should be chosen. Even though it has the largest initial investment, its annual operating and maintenance costs are substantially less than either of the other finalists.

Annual Worth Analysis (Denoted Equivalent Uniform Annual Cost, *or* EUAC*):*

$$EUAC_A = \$250,000(A|P\ 12\%,7) + \$147,000$$
$$= \$250,000(0.21912) + \$147,000$$
$$= \$201,780.00$$
$$=PMT(12\%,7,-250000)+147000$$
$$=\$201,779.43$$

$$EUAC_B = \$385,000(A|P\ 12\%,7) + \$106,000$$
$$= \$385,000(0.21912) + \$106,000$$
$$= \$190,361.20$$
$$=PMT(12\%,7,-385000)+106000$$
$$=\$190,360.33$$

$$EUAC_C = \$475,000(A|P\ 12\%,7) + \$83,000$$
$$= \$475,000(0.21912) + \$83,000$$
$$= \$187,082.00$$
$$=PMT(12\%,7,-475000)+83000$$
$$=\$187,080.92$$

Based on an equivalent uniform annual cost analysis, Alternative C is recommended.

Internal Rate of Return Analysis

Ranking the alternatives in increasing order of investment, consider them in the following sequence: A, B, and C. First, consider the incremental investment required to upgrade from A to B:

$$(\$385,000 - \$250,000)(A|P\ IRR_{B-A},7) = (\$147,000 - \$106,000)$$

or

$$IRR_{B-A} = RATE(7,41000,-135000)$$
$$=23.4\% > 12\%$$

Therefore, Alternative B is preferred to Alternative A.

Second, consider the incremental investment required to upgrade from B to C:

$$(\$475,000 - \$385,000)(A|P\ IRR_{C-B},7) = (\$106,000 - \$83,000)$$

or

$$IRR_{C-B} = RATE(7,23000,-90000)$$
$$=17.082\% > 12\%$$

Therefore, Alternative C is preferred to Alternative B and is recommended.

External Rate of Return Analysis

Consider the alternatives in the sequence A, B, and C. First, consider the $135,000 incremental investment required to upgrade from A to B and the resulting $41,000 in reduced incremental annual costs:

$$\$135,000(1 + ERR_{B-A})^7 = \$41,000(F|A\ 12\%, 7)$$

$$(1 + ERR_{B-A})^7 = [\$41,000(10.0890)]/\$135,000$$

$$ERR_{B-A} = 17.347\% > 12\%$$

$$=\text{RATE}(7,,,-135000,\text{FV}(12\%,7,-41000))$$

$$=17.347\% > 12\%$$

Therefore, Alternative B is preferred to Alternative A.

Second, consider the $90,000 incremental investment required to upgrade from B to C, which produces $23,000 in reduced annual costs:

$$\$90,000(1 + ERR_{C-B})^7 = \$23,000(F|A\ 12\%, 7)$$

$$(1 + ERR_{C-B})^7 = [\$23,000(10.0890)]/\$90,000$$

$$ERR_{C-B} = 14.489\% > 12\%$$

$$=\text{RATE}(7,,,-90000,\text{FV}(12\%,7,-23000))$$

$$=14.489\% > 12\%$$

Therefore, Alternative C is preferred to Alternative B and is recommended.

8-7 SUMMARY

We've achieved a milestone. Except for the benefit/cost ratio, we have covered all the methods of comparing economic alternatives that will be used in the rest of the text. The remaining material applies the methods described in the previous chapters.

In our study of rate of return methods, we learned

1. how to calculate the internal rate of return, the external rate of return, and, in Appendix 8.A, the modified internal rate of return when evaluating the economic merits of an individual investment;

2. how to perform incremental comparisons of mutually exclusive investment alternatives to determine the one that maximizes economic worth;

3. how to use the Excel® **IRR** and **MIRR** worksheet functions to obtain IRR, ERR, and MIRR values;

4. how to use the Excel® **SOLVER** and **GOAL SEEK** tools to obtain ERR values when multiple negative-valued cash flows occur;

5. how to apply Descartes' rule of signs and Norstrom's criterion to test for multiple roots when using the IRR method; and

6. how to solve problems using IRR and ERR methods when all the cash flows have negative values.

We have covered a tremendous amount of material in eight chapters. Along the way, we have applied almost all the principles of engineering economic analysis. However, in many ways, we have merely been laying the foundation for the more challenging aspects of comparing investment alternatives: consideration of income taxes, inflation, and risk and uncertainty. So, the fun is not over. More to come!

Pit Stop #8—Halfway Home! Miles to Go!

1. True or False: For personal investment decision making, rates of return are used more frequently than present worth.

2. True or False: Unless non-monetary considerations dictate otherwise, you should choose the mutually exclusive investment alternative having the greatest rate of return over the planning horizon.

3. True or False: If $ERR > MARR$, then $IRR > ERR > MARR$.

4. True or False: If $PW > 0$, then $IRR > MARR$.

5. True or False: If $ERR > MARR$, then $MIRR > MARR$.

6. True or False: If $IRR(A) > IRR(B)$, then $ERR(A) > ERR(B)$.

7. True or False: If $PW(A) > PW(B)$, then $FW(A) > FW(B)$, $AW(A) > AW(B)$, $CW(A) > CW(B)$, and $IRR(A) > IRR(B)$.

8. True or False: Multiple roots can exist when using IRR and $MIRR$ methods.

9. True or False: If MARR = 10% and IRR = 9%, then ERR < 10% and PW > \$0.

10. True or False: The following annual cash flows in years 1 thru 7, respectively, have a single real positive-valued root: $-\$100, +\$15, -\$25, +\$75, -\$10, +\$50, +\$50$.

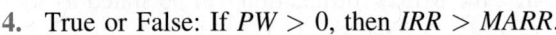

MODIFIED INTERNAL RATE OF RETURN

8.A-1 SINGLE ALTERNATIVE

The Excel® **Modified Internal Rate of Return** (**MIRR**) worksheet function is an extension of the external rate of return formulation. In addition to including re-investment of recovered capital using the minimum attractive rate of return, it also allows the negative-valued cash flows to be funded through borrowing.

Mathematically, the MIRR formulation can be stated as follows:

$$\sum_{t=0}^{n} R_t (1 + r)^{n-t} = \sum_{t=0}^{n} C_t (1 + f)^{-t}](1 + i_m)^n \tag{8.A.1}$$

where f is the finance rate paid for borrowed capital, and i_m is the *modified internal rate of return*.

Essentially, all negative-valued cash flows are brought back to the present using the finance rate. Then the present worth of the negative-valued cash flows (borrowed capital) is set equal to the future worth of the reinvested positive-valued cash flows. The interest rate that equates the future worth of the present worth of borrowed capital to the future worth of reinvested capital is the modified internal rate of return.

For the MIRR to differ from the ERR, multiple negative-valued cash flows must occur, or the single negative-valued cash flow must occur at a point in time other than the present. Hence, there is no reason to compute the MIRR for the $500,000 SMP investment; regardless of the finance rate used, the same answer occurs: MIRR = **11.791178%**.

EXAMPLE 8.A.1 Using the MIRR with the Natural Gas Example

Recall from Examples 8.3 and 8.10, Julian Stewart's investment in a natural gas well. An initial investment of $250,000 was made, followed by a $150,000 investment in the sixth year that created a second negative-valued cash flow. Recall, Mr. Stewart's *MARR* is 15 percent. Assume he borrowed the money to pay for the net negative-valued cash flows and paid a finance rate of 10 percent compounded annually. In the sixth year, since he received $95,000 from the natural gas well, we assume he borrowed $55,000, instead of $150,000.

The cash flows are shown in Figure 8.A.1. Notice, the original cash flows are divided into two streams: one for negative-valued cash flows and one for positive-valued cash flows. Next, the present worth of the negative-valued cash flows is calculated using the 10 percent finance rate. The present worth of the invested capital is −**$281,046**.

The future worth of the recovered capital is calculated using the 15 percent *MARR*. The future worth obtained is **$2,605,119**.

	B8	▾	*fx*	=95000-150000						
	A	B	C	D	E	F	G	H	I	J
1	EOY	CF	PW(-)	FW(+)						
2	0	-$250,000	-$250,000	$0						
3	1	$45,000	$0	$318,407						
4	2	$55,000	$0	$338,403						
5	3	$65,000	$0	$347,766						
6	4	$75,000	$0	$348,929						
7	5	$85,000	$0	$343,872	=IF(B8<0,PV(10%,A8,,-B8),0)					
8	6	-$55,000	-$31,046	$0						
9	7	$85,000	$0	$260,017	=IF(B9>0,B9*(1.15^(15-A9)),0)					
10	8	$75,000	$0	$199,501						
11	9	$65,000	$0	$150,349						
12	10	$55,000	$0	$110,625						
13	11	$45,000	$0	$78,705						
14	12	$35,000	$0	$53,231						
15	13	$25,000	$0	$33,063						
16	14	$15,000	$0	$17,250						
17	15	$5,000	$0	$5,000						
18			-$281,046	$2,605,119	=SUM(D2:D17)					
19	*MIRR* =	16.003%	=RATE(15,,C18,D18)							
20	*MIRR* =	16.003%	=MIRR(B2:B17,10%,15%)							

FIGURE 8.A.1

***MIRR* Solution for the Natural Gas Investment.**

Knowing the present value (−$281,046) of the invested capital and the future value ($2,605,119) of the recovered capital, we used the Excel® RATE worksheet function to determine what annual compound rate equates the present and future values. The rate obtained was 16.003%.

To verify that the solution procedure used is that which underlies the Excel® MIRR worksheet function, we applied it to the example. As shown in cell B20, the same result was obtained.

Although we can make claims regarding the value of ERR relative to the values of IRR and *MARR*, we cannot do so because of the finance rate included in the calculation of MIRR. Depending on the finance rate, an investment that is justified using IRR (and, thereby, ERR, PW, FW, and AW) might or might not be justified using MIRR. A revision to the previous example illustrates the difference in MIRR and the other measures of economic worth we have considered.

EXAMPLE 8.A.2   "Blowing Up" the Natural Gas Justification

In the previous example, suppose the finance rate decreases to 2 percent and the investment increases to $275,000. The IRR will be 16.756% > *MARR*, so the investment is justified economically. However, as shown in Figure 8.A.2, the MIRR will be 14.912% < *MARR*, and the investment is *not* justified economically.

Because the MIRR might not yield recommendations identical to those that result when using PW, FW, AW, IRR, and ERR methods, we do not consider it in later chapters.

	B8	▾	fx	=95000-150000					
	A	B	C	D	E	F	G	H	I	J
1	EOY	CF	PW(-)	FW(+)						
2	0	-$275,000	-$275,000	$0						
3	1	$45,000	$0	$318,407						
4	2	$55,000	$0	$338,403						
5	3	$65,000	$0	$347,766						
6	4	$75,000	$0	$348,929						
7	5	$85,000	$0	$343,872	=IF(B8<0,PV(2%,A8,,-B8),0)					
8	6	-$55,000	-$48,838	$0						
9	7	$85,000	$0	$260,017	=IF(B9>0,B9*(1.15^(15-A9)),0)					
10	8	$75,000	$0	$199,501						
11	9	$65,000	$0	$150,349						
12	10	$55,000	$0	$110,625						
13	11	$45,000	$0	$78,705						
14	12	$35,000	$0	$53,231						
15	13	$25,000	$0	$33,063						
16	14	$15,000	$0	$17,250						
17	15	$5,000	$0	$5,000						
18	IRR =	16.756%	-$323,838	$2,605,119	=SUM(D2:D17)					
19	MIRR =	14.912%	=RATE(15,,C18,D18)							
20	MIRR =	14.912%	=MIRR(B2:B17,2%,15%)							

FIGURE 8.A.2

MIRR **Solution to a Modification of the Natural Gas Investment.**

Based on the results from Examples 8.A.1 and 8.A.2, it is useful to examine the relationships among the MIRR, the finance rate used in the MIRR calculation, the ERR, and the IRR. Figure 8.A.3 depicts the relationships for the data in Example 8.A.1. Notice, *MIRR* < *ERR* < *IRR* for all finance rates.

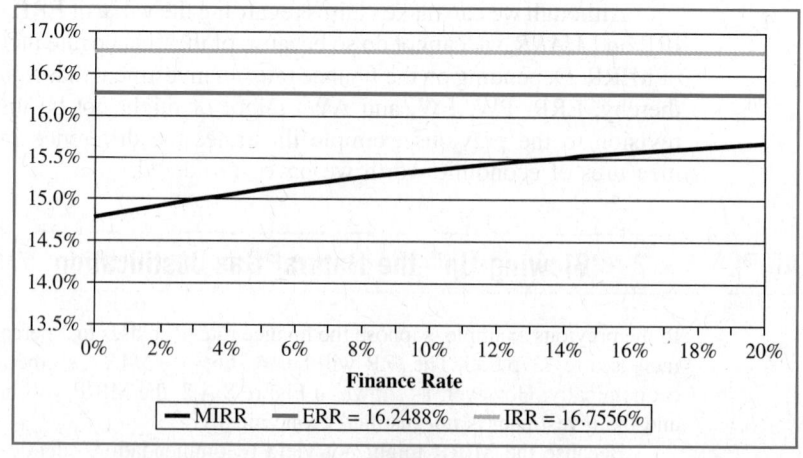

FIGURE 8.A.3

Relationships Among the Finance Rate, *MIRR*, *ERR*, and *IRR* in Example 8.A.2.

8.A-2 MULTIPLE ALTERNATIVES

As was the case with the internal rate of return and the external rate of return methods, when using the modified internal rate of return method to evaluate mutually exclusive investment alternatives, an incremental analysis is required. Mathematically, for alternative j, the MIRR is the value of $i_{m,j}$ for which

$$\sum_{t=0}^{n} R_{jt}(1+r)^{n-t} = \left[\sum_{t=0}^{n} C_{jt}(1+f)^{-t} \right] (1+i_{m,j})^{n} \qquad (8.A.2)$$

EXAMPLE 8.A.3 Solving the Batch Chemical Processing Problem with MIRR

We introduced the batch chemical processing example in this chapter to demonstrate calculating the MIRR with a finance rate. Recall, for the MIRR value to differ from the ERR value, an investment alternative must have multiple negative-valued cash flows.

The cash flows for the two alternatives under consideration are shown in Table 8.A.1. Alternative A has the smallest initial investment, so it is considered first. Using a finance rate of 12 percent and a reinvestment rate of 18.5 percent, the Excel® **MIRR** function yields a value of 18.9046 percent for Alternative A. Since $MIRR_A > MARR$, Alternative A is justified economically.

Next we consider the incremental cash flow between Alternatives A and B. As shown, the $MIRR$ for the difference in cash flows between Alternatives B and A equals **17.9244%**, which is less than the $MARR$ of 18.5 percent. Therefore, Alternative A is recommended.

TABLE 8.1
Incremental MIRR Solution for Example 8.A.3.

EOY	CF(A)	CF(B)	CF(B-A)
0	−$7,585,000.00	−$10,285,000.00	−$2,700,000.00
1	−$1,237,500.00	−$1,575,500.00	−$338,000.00
2	$1,695,500.00	$2,455,700.00	$760,200.00
3	$2,002,800.00	$2,657,500.00	$654,700.00
4	$2,345,700.00	$2,877,500.00	$531,800.00
5	$2,450,500.00	$3,025,000.00	$574,500.00
6	$2,575,600.00	$3,250,300.00	$674,700.00
7	$2,735,000.00	$3,565,800.00	$830,800.00
8	$3,005,300.00	$3,750,000.00	$744,700.00
9	$3,857,500.00	$4,252,500.00	$395,000.00
10	$5,285,000.00	$8,750,000.00	$3,465,000.00
	$MIRR_A = 18.9046\%$		$MIRR_{B-A} = 17.9244\%$

 Tutoring problem available (at instructor's discretion) in *WileyPLUS*.

 Problem available (at instructor's discretion) in *WileyPLUS*.

 Worked Problem Video available in *WileyPLUS*.

FE-LIKE PROBLEMS

1. Using an incremental internal rate of return (IRR) analysis, the decision to replace the "current best" by the "challenger" is based on what decision rule?

    a. The internal rate of return of the increment is greater than the external rate of return.

    b. The increment's internal rate of return is greater than the previous increment's internal rate of return.

    c. The increment's internal rate of return is greater than 0.

    d. The increment's internal rate of return is greater than *MARR*.

2. A company is considering two alternatives, one of which must be implemented. Of the two projects, A has the higher maintenance cost, but B has the higher investment cost. The appropriate (and properly calculated) incremental IRR is 17.6 percent. Which alternative is preferred if the minimum attractive rate of return is 20 percent?

    a. A

    b. B

    c. The company is indifferent between A and B

    d. Cannot be determined from the information given

3. Consider the calculation of an external rate of return (ERR). The positive cash flows in the cash flow profile are moved forward to $t = n$ using what value of i in the $(F|P\,i, n - t)$ factors?

    a. 0

    b. The unknown value of ERR (i')

    c. *MARR*

    d. IRR

4. If a well-behaved investment alternative's internal rate of return (IRR) is equal to *MARR*, which of the following statements about the other measures of worth for this alternative must be true?

    1. PW $= 0$

    2. AW $= 0$

    a. (1) only

    b. (2) only

    c. Neither (1) nor (2)

    d. Both (1) and (2)

5. An investment is guaranteed to have a unique value of IRR if which of the following is true?

    a. Alternating positive and negative cash flows

    b. An initial negative cash flow followed by all positive cash flows

    c. A unique value for ERR

    d. A positive PW at *MARR*

6. Consider the IRR and ERR measures of worth. If we define a *root* to mean a value for the measure that results in PW $= 0$, then which of the following statements is true?

    a. Both IRR and ERR can have multiple roots.

    b. IRR has only a single root, but ERR can have multiple roots.

    c. ERR has only a single root, but IRR can have multiple roots.

    d. Both IRR and ERR have only a single root.

7. When conducting an incremental analysis, what step must always be taken immediately prior to beginning the pairwise comparisons?

    a. Order the alternatives from highest to lowest initial investment

    b. Order the alternatives from lowest to highest present worth

    c. Order the alternatives from lowest to highest internal rate of return

    d. Order the alternatives from lowest to highest initial investment

The next two questions are based on the following "present worth versus interest rate" graph for a well-behaved investment.

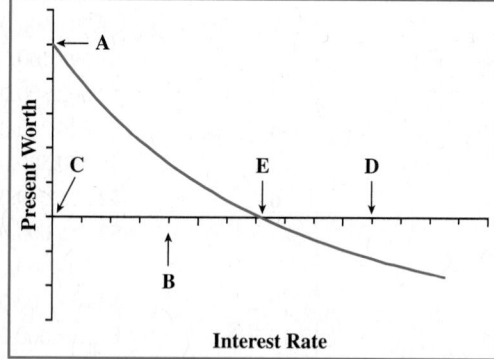

8. If the interest rate at B is 20 percent, then which of the following best describes the analysis of the investment?

    a. The IRR of the investment is less than 20 percent.

    b. The IRR of the investment is equal to 20 percent.

    c. The IRR of the investment is greater than 20 percent.

    d. None of the above are true.

9. The IRR of this investment is located at which point?

   a. A

   b. C

   c. D

   d. E

10. If the IRR of Alternative A is 18 percent, the IRR of Alternative B is 16 percent, and *MARR* is 12 percent, which of the following is correct?

   a. Alternative B is preferred over Alternative A.

   b. Alternative A is preferred over Alternative B.

   c. Not enough information is given to determine which alternative is preferred.

   d. Neither Alternative A nor Alternative B is acceptable.

11. Consider the following cash flow diagram. What is the value of X if the internal rate of return is 15 percent?

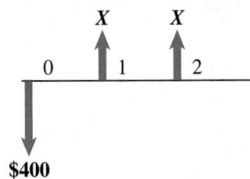

   a. $246

   b. $255

   c. $281

   d. $290

12. What is the internal rate of return of the following cash flow diagram?

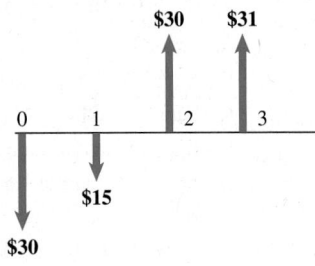

   a. 20 percent

   b. 18.2 percent

   c. 17.5 percent

   d. 15 percent

13. A snow-cone machine at an ice-cream shop costs $15,000. The machine is expected to generate profits of $2,500 each year of its 10-year useful life. At the end of the 10 years, the machine will have a salvage value of 0. Within what interest rate range does the IRR fall?

   a. Less than 10 percent

   b. 10 percent to 12 percent

   c. 12 percent to 14 percent

   d. Greater than 14 percent

PROBLEMS

Note to Instructors and Students

Many of the problems in this chapter are similar to problems in previous chapters. This similarity is intentional. It is designed to illustrate the use of different measures of merit on the same problem.

Section 8.1

1. Match the measures of worth in the first column with one (or more) of the analysis approaches that is (are) appropriate for that measure.

<table>
<tr><th>Measure of Worth</th><th>Analysis Approach</th></tr>
<tr><td>(a) Annual Worth</td><td>(1) Ranking Approach</td></tr>
<tr><td>(b) External Rate of Return</td><td>(2) Incremental Approach</td></tr>
<tr><td>(c) Future Worth</td><td></td></tr>
<tr><td>(d) Internal Rate of Return</td><td></td></tr>
<tr><td>(e) Modified Internal Rate of Return</td><td></td></tr>
<tr><td>(f) Present Worth</td><td></td></tr>
</table>

2. Match the measures of worth in the first column with the appropriate unit of measure that results from the analysis.

Measure of Worth	Resulting Units of Measure
(a) Annual Worth	(1) Dollars
(b) External Rate of Return	(2) Percentage
(c) Future Worth	
(d) Internal Rate of Return	
(e) Modified Internal Rate of Return	
(f) Present Worth	

Section 8.2

3. Consider the following cash flow profile, and assume *MARR* is 10 percent/year.

EOY	0	1	2	3	4	5	6
NCF	−$100	$15	$15	$15	$15	$15	$15

    a. What does Descartes' rule of signs tell us about the IRR(s) of this project?
    b. What does Norstrom's criterion tell us about the IRR(s) of this project?
    c. Determine the IRR(s) for this project.
    d. Is this project economically attractive?

4. Consider the following cash flow profile and assume *MARR* is 10 percent/year.

EOY	0	1	2	3	4	5	6
NCF	−$100	$25	$25	$25	$25	$25	$25

    a. What does Descartes' rule of signs tell us about the IRR(s) of this project?
    b. What does Norstrom's criterion tell us about the IRR9s) of this project?
    c. Determine the IRR(s) for this project.
    d. Is this project economically attractive?

5. Consider the following cash flow profile and assume *MARR* is 10 percent/year.

EOY	0	1	2	3	4	5	6
NCF	−$100	$25	$25	$60	−$30	$60	$25

    a. What does Descartes' rule of signs tell us about the IRR(s) of this project?
    b. What does Norstrom's criterion tell us about the IRR9s) of this project?
    c. Determine the IRR(s) for this project.
    d. Is this project economically attractive?

6. Consider the following cash flow profile and assume *MARR* is 10 percent/year.

EOY	0	1	2	3	4	5	6
NCF	−$100	$25	$200	−$100	$250	−$200	−$100

    a. What does Descartes' rule of signs tell us about the IRR(s) of this project?
    b. What does Norstrom's criterion tell us about the IRR(s) of this project?

    c. Determine the IRR(s) for this project.

    d. Is this project economically attractive?

7. Consider the following cash flow profile and assume *MARR* is 10 percent/year.

EOY	0	1	2	3	4	5	6
NCF	−$100	$800	−$750	$900	−$950	$700	−$800

    a. What does Descartes' rule of signs tell us about the IRR(s) of this project?

    b. What does Norstrom's criterion tell us about the IRR(s) of this project?

    c. Determine the IRR(s) for this project.

    d. Is this project economically attractive?

8. Consider the following cash flow profile and assume *MARR* is 10 percent/year.

EOY	0	1	2	3	4	5	6
NCF	−$101	$411	−$558	$253	$2	$8	−$14

    a. Determine the IRR(s) for this project.

    b. Is this project economically attractive?

9. An engineer prepares a report to evaluate a project using PW and IRR. Just before submitting the report, he spills coffee on it, making the first digit of the 2-digit IRR unreadable. The second digit is a 2. The PW is negative and *MARR* is 15 percent. He doesn't have time to redo the analysis. Can you help him figure out the IRR?

10. What do you know about the mathematical value of a project's internal rate of return under each of the following conditions?

    a. The present worth of the project is greater than 0.

    b. The present worth of the project is equal to 0.

    c. The present worth of the project is less than 0.

    d. The future worth of the project is greater than 0.

    e. The future worth of the project is equal to 0.

    f. The future worth of the project is less than 0.

    g. The annual worth of the project is greater than 0.

    h. The annual worth of the project is equal to 0.

    i. The annual worth of the project is less than 0.

11. Draw a cash flow diagram of any investment that exhibits both of the following properties:

    1. The investment has a 4-year life.

    2. The investment has a 10 percent/year internal rate of return.

12. A project has been selected for implementation. The net cash flow (NCF) profile associated with the project is shown below. *MARR* is 10 percent/year.

EOY	0	1	2	3	4	5	6
NCF	−$70,000	$30,000	$30,000	$30,000	$30,000	$30,000	$30,000 + $2,000

    a. What is the internal rate of return of this investment?

    b. What is the decision rule for judging the attractiveness of investments based on internal rate of return?

    c. Is the project economically justified?

13. Nu Things, Inc., is considering investing in a business venture with the following anticipated cash flow results: Assume *MARR* is 20 percent per year. Based on an internal rate of return analysis, (1) determine the investment's worth, (2) state whether or not your results indicate the investment should be undertaken, and (3) state the decision rule you used to arrive at this conclusion.

EOY	Cash Flow	EOY	Cash Flow	EOY	Cash Flow
0	−$70,000	7	$14,000	14	$7,000
1	$20,000	8	$13,000	15	$6,000
2	$19,000	9	$12,000	16	$5,000
3	$18,000	10	$11,000	17	$4,000
4	$17,000	11	$10,000	18	$3,000
5	$16,000	12	$9,000	19	$2,000
6	$15,000	13	$8,000	20	$1,000

14. An investment has the following cash flow profile. For each value of MARR below, what is the minimum value of X such that the investment is attractive based on an internal rate of return measure of merit?

End of Year	0	1	2	3	4
Cash Flow	−$30,000	$6,000	$13,500	$X	$13,500

   a. MARR is 12 percent/year
   b. MARR is 15 percent/year
   c. MARR is 24 percent/year
   d. MARR is 8 percent/year
   e. MARR is 0 percent/year

15. Bailey, Inc., is considering buying a new gang punch that would allow them to produce circuit boards more efficiently. The punch has a first cost of $100,000 and a useful life of 15 years. At the end of its useful life, the punch has no salvage value. Labor costs would increase $2,000 per year using the gang punch, but raw material costs would decrease $12,000 per year. MARR is 5 percent/year.

   a. What is the internal rate of return of this investment?
   b. What is the decision rule for judging the attractiveness of investments based on internal rate of return?
   c. Should Bailey buy the gang punch?

16. Carlisle Company has been cited and must invest in equipment to reduce stack emissions or face EPA fines of $18,500 per year. An emission reduction filter will cost $75,000 and will have an expected life of 5 years. Carlisle's MARR is 10 percent/year.

   a. What is the internal rate of return of this investment?
   b. What is the decision rule for judging the attractiveness of investments based on internal rate of return?
   c. Is the filter economically justified?

17. DuraTech Manufacturing is evaluating a process improvement project. The estimated receipts and disbursements associated with the project are shown below. MARR is 6 percent/year.

End of Year	0	1	2	3	4	5
Receipts	$0	$0	$2,000	$4,000	$3,000	$1,600
Disbursements	$5,000	$200	$300	$600	$1,000	$1,500

   a. What is the internal rate of return of this investment?
   b. What is the decision rule for judging the attractiveness of investments based on internal rate of return?
   c. Should DuraTech implement the proposed process improvement?

18. Eddie's Precision Machine Shop is insured for $700,000. The present yearly insurance premium is $1.00 per $100 of coverage. A sprinkler system with an estimated life of 20 years and no salvage value can be installed for $20,000. Annual maintenance costs for the sprinkler system are $400. If the sprinkler system is installed, the system must be

included in the shop's value for insurance purposes, but the insurance premium will reduce to $0.40 per $100 of coverage. Eddie uses a *MARR* of 15 percent/year.

a. What is the internal rate of return of this investment?

b. What is the decision rule for judging the attractiveness of investments based on internal rate of return?

c. Is the sprinkler system economically justified?

19. Fabco, Inc., is considering purchasing flow valves that will reduce annual operating costs by $10,000 per year for the next 12 years. Fabco's *MARR* is 7 percent/year. Using an internal rate of return approach, determine the maximum amount Fabco should be willing to pay for the valves.

20. Galvanized Products is considering purchasing a new computer system for their enterprise data management system. The vendor has quoted a purchase price of $100,000. Galvanized Products is planning to borrow one-fourth of the purchase price from a bank at 15 percent compounded annually. The loan is to be repaid using equal annual payments over a 3-year period. The computer system is expected to last 5 years and has a salvage value of $5,000 at that time. Over the 5-year period, Galvanized Products expects to pay a technician $25,000 per year to maintain the system but will save $55,000 per year through increased efficiencies. Galvanized Products uses a *MARR* of 18 percent/year to evaluate investments.

a. What is this investment's internal rate of return?

b. What is the decision rule for judging the attractiveness of investments based on internal rate of return?

c. Should the new computer system be purchased?

21. Quilts R Us (QRU) is considering investing in a new patterning attachment with the cash flow profile shown in the table below. QRU's *MARR* is 13.5 percent/year.

EOY	Cash Flow	EOY	Cash Flow
0	−$1,400	8	$600
1	$0	9	$700
2	$500	10	$800
3	$500	11	$900
4	$500	12	−$1,000
5	$500	13	−$2,000
6	$0	14	−$3,000
7	$500	15	$1,400

a. What is the internal rate of return of this investment?

b. What is the decision rule for judging the attractiveness of investments based on internal rate of return?

c. Should QRU invest?

22. Imagineering, Inc., is considering an investment in CAD-CAM compatible design software with the cash flow profile shown in the table below. Imagineering's *MARR* is 18 percent/year.

EOY	0	1	2	3	4	5	6	7
Cash Flow (M$)	−$12	−$1	$5	$2	$5	$5	$2	$5

a. What is this investment's internal rate of return?

b. What is the decision rule for judging the attractiveness of investments based on internal rate of return?

c. Should Imagineering invest?

23. Jupiter's is considering an investment in time and administrative expense on an effort that promises one large payoff in the future, followed by additional expenses over a 10-year horizon. The cash flow profile is shown in the table below. Jupiter's *MARR* is 12 percent/year.

EOY	0	1	2	3	4	5	6	7	8	9	10
Cash Flow (K$)	−$2	−$10	−$12	−$14	−$16	−$18	$200	−$10	−$12	−$14	−$100

   a. What is the internal rate of return of this investment?

   b. What is the decision rule for judging the attractiveness of investments based on internal rate of return?

   c. Should Jupiter invest?

24. Aerotron Electronics is considering purchasing a water filtration system to assist in circuit board manufacturing. The system costs $40,000. It has an expected life of 7 years, at which time its salvage value will be $7,500. Operating and maintenance expenses are estimated to be $2,000 per year. If the filtration system is not purchased, Aerotron Electronics will have to pay Bay City $12,000 per year for water purification. If the system is purchased, no water purification from Bay City will be needed. Aerotron Electronics must borrow half of the purchase price, but they cannot start repaying the loan for 2 years. The bank has agreed to three equal annual payments, with the first payment due at the end of year 2. The loan interest rate is 8 percent compounded annually. Aerotron Electronics' *MARR* is 10 percent compounded annually.

   a. What is this investment's internal rate of return?

   b. What is the decision rule for judging the attractiveness of investments based on internal rate of return?

   c. Should Aerotron Electronics buy the water filtration system?

25. Home Innovation is evaluating a new product design. The estimated receipts and disbursements associated with the new product are shown below. *MARR* is 10 percent/year.

End of Year	0	1	2	3	4	5
Receipts	$0	$600	$600	$700	$700	$700
Disbursements	$1,000	$300	$300	$300	$300	$300

   a. What is this investment's internal rate of return?

   b. What is the decision rule for judging the attractiveness of investments based on internal rate of return?

   c. Should Home Innovations pursue this new product?

26. A design change being considered by Mayberry, Inc., will cost $6,000 and will result in an annual savings of $1,000 per year for the 6-year life of the project. A cost of $2,000 will be avoided at the project's end as a result of the change. *MARR* is 8 percent/year.

   a. What is this investment's internal rate of return?

   b. What is the decision rule for judging the attractiveness of investments based on internal rate of return?

   c. Should Mayberry implement the design change?

27. Nancy's Notions pays a delivery firm to distribute its products in the metro area. Delivery costs are $30,000 per year. Nancy can buy a used truck for $10,000 that will be adequate for the next 3 years. Operating and maintenance costs are estimated to be $25,000 per year. At the end of 3 years, the used truck will have an estimated salvage value of $3,000. Nancy's *MARR* is 24 percent/year.

   a. What is this investment's internal rate of return?

   b. What is the decision rule for judging the attractiveness of investments based on internal rate of return?

   c. Should Nancy buy the truck?

28. Delta Dawn's Bakery is considering purchasing a new van to deliver bread. The van will cost $18,000. Two-thirds ($12,000) of this cost will be borrowed. The loan is to be repaid with four equal annual payments (first payment at $t = 1$) based on an interest rate of 4 percent/year. It is anticipated that the van will be used for 6 years and then sold for a salvage value of $500. Annual operating and maintenance expenses for the van over the 6-year life are estimated to be $700 per year. If the van is purchased, Delta will realize a cost savings of $3,800 per year. Delta uses a *MARR* of 6 percent/year. Based on an internal rate of return analysis, is purchasing the van economically attractive?

29. RealTurf is considering purchasing an automatic sprinkler system for its sod farm by borrowing the entire $30,000 purchase price. The loan would be repaid with four equal annual payments at an interest rate of 12 percent/year. It is anticipated that the sprinkler system would be used for 9 years and then sold for a salvage value of $2,000. Annual operating and maintenance expenses for the system over the 9-year life are estimated to be $9,000 per year. If the new system is purchased, cost savings of $15,000 per year will be realized over the present manual watering system. RealTurf uses a *MARR* of 15 percent/year for economic decision making. Based on an internal rate of return analysis, is the purchase of the new sprinkler system economically attractive?

30. Baon Chemicals Unlimited purchases a computer-controlled filter for $100,000. They borrow half the purchase price from a bank at 15 percent compounded annually. The loan is to be paid back with equal annual payments over a 5-year period. The filter is expected to last 10 years, at which time it will have a salvage value of $10,000. Over the 10-year period, the operating and maintenance costs are expected to equal $20,000 in year 1 and increase by $1,500/year each year thereafter. By making the investment, annual fines of $50,000 for pollution will be avoided. Baon expects to earn 12 percent compounded annually on its investments. Based on an internal rate of return analysis, determine whether purchasing the filter is economically justified.

31. Value Lodges owns an economy motel chain and is considering building a new 200-unit motel. The cost to build the motel is estimated at $8,000,000; Value Lodges estimates furnishings for the motel will cost an additional $700,000 and will require replacement every 5 years. Annual operating and maintenance costs for the motel are estimated to be $800,000. The average rental rate for a unit is anticipated to be $40/day. Value Lodges expects the motel to have a life of 15 years and a salvage value of $900,000 at the end of 15 years. This estimated salvage value assumes that the furnishings are not new. Furnishings have no salvage value at the end of each 5-year replacement interval. Assuming average daily occupancy percentages of 50 percent, 60 percent, 70 percent, and 80 percent for years 1 through 4, respectively, and 90 percent for the fifth through fifteenth years, a *MARR* of 12 percent/year, 365 operating days/year, and ignoring the cost of land, should the motel be built? Base your decision on an internal rate of return analysis.

Section 8.3

32. A large company has the opportunity to select one of seven projects—A, B, C, D, E, F, G—or choose the null (do-nothing) alternative. Each project requires a single initial investment as shown in the table below. Information on each alternative was fed into a computer program that calculated the IRR for each project and all the pertinent incremental IRRs as shown in the table below.

Project	Initial Investment	Incremental Rate of Return of "Row" – "Column"						
		Null	A	B	C	D	E	F
A	$10,000	10%						
B	$12,000	9%	7%					
C	$13,000	8%	2%	0.1%				
D	$15,000	7%	9%	5%	9%			
E	$16,000	6%	5%	1%	6%	3%		
F	$18,000	5%	8%	2%	5%	5%	5%	
G	$23,000	7%	3%	8%	7%	4%	3%	2%

For example, the IRR for Project A is 10 percent and the incremental IRR of Project C minus Project B (C – B) is 0.1 percent. For each value of *MARR* below, indicate which project is preferred and the evaluations you made to arrive at this conclusion.

a. *MARR* = 12 percent

b. *MARR* = 9.5 percent

c. *MARR* = 8 percent

d. *MARR* = 3.5 percent

e. *MARR* = 1.5 percent

33. ZeeZee's Construction Company has the opportunity to select one of four projects (A, B, C, or D) or choose the null (do-nothing) alternative. Each project requires a single initial investment and has an internal rate of return as shown in the first table below. The second table shows the incremental IRRs for pairwise comparisons between each project and all other projects with a smaller initial investment.

Investments and IRRs

Project	Initial Investment	IRR
Null	$0	0.0%
A	$600,000	44%
B	$800,000	40%
C	$470,000	39.2%
D	$540,000	36%

Incremental IRRs

Increment	Incremental IRR
B-A	28.3%
B-D	48.8%
B-C	41.4%
A-D	116.5%
A-C	61%
D-C	18.4%

For each of the values of *MARR* below, indicate which project is preferred based on an incremental IRR analysis.
   a. *MARR* = 50 percent
   b. *MARR* = 41 percent
   c. *MARR* = 25 percent

34. Five projects form the mutually exclusive, collectively exhaustive set under consideration. The cash flow profiles for the five projects are given in the table below.

	Null	A	B	C	D
Life	10 years	10 years	10 years	10 years	10 years
Initial Investment	$0	$600,000	$800,000	$470,000	$540,000
Salvage Value	$0	$70,000	$130,000	$65,000	$200,000
Annual Revenues	$0	$400,000	$600,000	$260,000	$320,000
Annual Expenses	$0	$130,000	$270,000	$70,000	$120,000

Information on each project was fed into a computer program that calculated the IRRs and incremental IRRs as shown in the table below. Unfortunately, when the table was printed, one of the cells was overprinted with Xs and was unreadable. As the resident expert on incremental IRR analysis, you have been asked to assist.

Project	Incremental Rate of Return of "Row" – "Column"			
	Null	C	D	A
C	39%			
D	36%	18%		
A	44%	XXXXX	117%	
B	40%	41%	49%	28%

a. Specify the incremental cash flow profile that must be analyzed to determine the value in the overprinted incremental IRR cell.

b. Determine the incremental IRR value that belongs in the overprinted cell.

c. If *MARR* is 37 percent/year, which project is preferred?

d. Based on the data in the table, if *MARR* is 40 percent, specify whether the present worth of each project would be positive, negative, or zero when evaluated at *MARR*?

35. The four alternatives described below are being evaluated:

Alternative	W	X	Y	Z
Initial Investment	$100,000	$75,000	$40,000	$200,000
IRR	16%	15%	29%	14%

The Incremental IRRs are:

$$IRR_{W\text{-}Y} = 7\% \qquad IRR_{W\text{-}X} = 20\%$$
$$IRR_{X\text{-}Y} = 1\% \qquad IRR_{Z\text{-}X} = 14\%$$
$$IRR_{Z\text{-}Y} = 10\% \qquad IRR_{Z\text{-}W} = 12\%$$

a. If the alternatives are independent, which one(s) should be selected if $MARR = 15.5$ percent/year?

b. If the alternatives are mutually exclusive, which one(s) should be selected if $MARR = 9.5$ percent/year?

36. The engineering team at Manuel's Manufacturing, Inc., is planning to purchase an enterprise resource planning (ERP) system. The software and installation from Vendor A costs $380,000 initially and is expected to increase revenue $125,000 per year every year. The software and installation from Vendor B costs $280,000 and is expected to increase revenue $95,000 per year. Manuel's uses a 4-year planning horizon and a 10 percent per year *MARR*. Based on an internal rate of return analysis, which ERP system should Manuel purchase?

37. Parker County Community College (PCCC) is trying to determine whether to use no insulation or to use insulation that is either 1 inch thick or 2 inches thick on its steam pipes. The heat loss from the pipes without insulation is expected to cost $1.50 per year per foot of pipe. A 1-inch thick insulated covering will eliminate 89 percent of the loss and will cost $0.40 per foot. A 2-sinch thick insulated covering will eliminate 92 percent of the loss and will cost $0.85 per foot. PCCC Physical Plant Services estimates that there are 250,000 feet of steam pipe on campus. The PCCC Accounting Office requires a 10 percent/year return to justify capital expenditures. The insulation has a life expectancy of 10 years. Determine which insulation (if any) should be purchased using an internal rate of return analysis.

38. Quantum Logistics, Inc., a wholesale distributor, is considering constructing a new warehouse to serve the southeastern geographic region near the Alabama–Georgia border. There are three cities being considered. After site visits and a budget analysis, the expected income and costs associated with locating in each of the cities have been determined. The life of the warehouse is expected to be 12 years, and *MARR* is 15 percent/year. Based on an internal rate of return analysis, which city should be recommended?

City	Initial Cost	Net Annual Income
Lagrange	$1,260,000	$480,000
Auburn	$1,000,000	$410,000
Anniston	$1,620,000	$520,000

39. DelRay Foods must purchase a new gumdrop machine. Two machines are available. Machine 7745 has a first cost of $10,000, an estimated life of 10 years, a salvage value of $1,000, and annual operating costs estimated at $0.01 per 1,000 gumdrops. Machine A37Y has a first cost of $8,000, a life of 10 years, and no salvage value. Its annual operating costs will be $300 regardless of the number of gumdrops produced. *MARR* is 6 percent/year, and 30 million gumdrops are produced each year. Based on an internal rate of return analysis, which machine should be recommended?

40. Tempura, Inc., is considering two projects. Project A requires an investment of $50,000. Estimated annual receipts for 20 years are $20,000; estimated annual costs are $12,500. An alternative project, B, requires an investment of $75,000, has annual receipts for 20 years of $28,000, and has annual costs of $18,000. Assume both projects have a 0 salvage value and that *MARR* is 12 percent/year. Based on an internal rate of return analysis, which project should be recommended?

41. Final Finishing is considering three mutually exclusive alternatives for a new polisher. Each alternative has an expected life of 10 years and no salvage value. Polisher 1 requires an initial investment of $20,000 and provides annual benefits of $4,465. Polisher 2 requires an initial investment of $10,000 and provides annual benefits of $1,770. Polisher 3 requires an initial investment of $15,000 and provides annual benefits of $3,580. *MARR* is 15 percent/year. Based on an internal rate of return analysis, which polisher should be recommended?

42. Xanadu Mining is considering three mutually exclusive alternatives as shown in the table below. *MARR* is 10 percent/year. Based on an internal rate of return analysis, which alternative should be recommended?

EOY	0	1	2	3	4
A001	−$210	$80	$90	$100	$110
B002	−$110	$60	$60	$60	$70
C003	−$160	$80	$80	$80	$80

43. Yani has $12,000 for investment purposes. His bank has offered the following three choices:

   1. A special savings certificate that will pay $100 each month for 5 years and a lump sum payment at the end of 5 years of $13,000
   2. Buy a share of a racehorse for $12,000 that will be worth $20,000 in 5 years
   3. Put the money in a savings account that will have an interest rate of 12 percent per year compounded monthly

   Use an internal rate of return analysis to make a recommendation to Yani.

44. On-Site Testing Service has received four investment proposals for consideration. Two of the proposals, X1 and X2, are mutually exclusive. The other two proposals, Y1 and Y2, are also mutually exclusive. Proposal Y1 is contingent on X1, and Y2 is contingent on X2. Other than these restrictions, any combination of proposals (including null) is feasible. *MARR* is 10 percent/year. The expected cash flows for the proposals are shown below. An internal rate of return analysis is to be conducted.

End of Year	X1	X2	Y1	Y2
0	−$10,000	−$15,000	−$6,000	−$9,000
1 through 8	$1,600	$2,600	$2,500	$3,500

a. List all the alternatives to be considered.

b. Determine which (if any) proposals On-Site Testing should accept.

45. Dark Skies Observatory is considering several options to purchase a new deep-space telescope. Revenue would be generated from the telescope by selling "time and use" slots to various researchers around the world. Four possible telescopes have been identified in addition to the possibility of not buying a telescope if none are financially attractive. The table below details the characteristics of each telescope. An internal rate of return analysis is to be performed.

	T1	**T2**	**T3**	**T4**
Useful Life	10 years	10 years	10 years	10 years
First Cost	$600,000	$800,000	$470,000	$540,000
Salvage Value	$70,000	$130,000	$65,000	$200,000
Annual Revenue	$400,000	$600,000	$260,000	$320,000
Annual Expenses	$130,000	$270,000	$70,000	$120,000

a. Determine the preferred telescope if *MARR* is 25 percent/year.

b. Determine the preferred telescope if *MARR* is 42 percent/year.

46. Several years ago, a man won $27 million in the state lottery. To pay off the winner, the state planned to make an initial $1 million payment immediately, followed by equal annual payments of $1.3 million at the end of each year for the next 20 years. Just before receiving any money, the man offered to sell the winning ticket back to the state for a one-time immediate payment of $14.4 million. If the state uses a 6 percent/year *MARR*, should it accept the man's offer? Use an internal rate of return analysis.

47. The management of Brawn Engineering is considering three alternatives to satisfy an OSHA requirement for safety gates in the machine shop. Each gate will completely satisfy the requirement, so no combinations need to be considered. The first costs, operating costs, and salvage values over a 5-year planning horizon are shown below. Using an internal rate of return analysis with a *MARR* of 20 percent/year, determine the preferred gate.

End of Year	0	1	2	3	4	5
Gate 1	−$15,000	−$6,500	−$6,500	−$6,500	−$6,500	−$6,500 + $0
Gate 2	−$19,000	−$5,600	−$5,600	−$5,600	−$5,600	−$5,600 + $2,000
Gate 3	−$24,000	−$4,000	−$4,000	−$4,000	−$4,000	−$4,000 + $5,000

48. Orpheum Productions in Nevada is considering three mutually exclusive alternatives for lighting enhancements to one of its recording studios. Each enhancement will increase revenues by attracting directors who prefer this lighting style. The cash flow details, in thousands of dollars, for these enhancements are shown in the chart below. *MARR* is 10 percent/year. Based on an internal rate of return analysis, which alternative (if any) should be implemented?

End of Year	0	1	2	3	4	5	6
Light Bar	−$6,000	$2,000	$2,000	$2,000	$2,000	$2,000	$2,000
Sliding Spots	−$14,000	$3,500	$3,500	$3,500	$3,500	$3,500	$3,500
Reflected Beam	−$20,000	$0	$2,300	$4,600	$6,900	$9,200	$11,500

49. Calisto Launch Services is an independent space corporation and has been contracted to develop and launch one of two different satellites. Initial equipment will cost $750,000 for the first satellite and $850,000 for the second. Development will take 5 years at an expected cost of $150,000 per year for the first satellite, $120,000 per year for the second. The same launch vehicle can be used for either satellite and will cost $275,000 at the time of the launch 5 years from now. At the conclusion of the launch, the contracting company will pay Calisto $2,500,000 for either satellite.

    Calisto is also considering launching both satellites. Because Calisto would have to upgrade its facilities to handle two concurrent projects, the initial costs would rise by $150,000 in addition to the first costs of each satellite. Calisto would need to hire additional engineers and workers, raising the yearly costs to a total of $400,000. An extra compartment would be added to the launch vehicle at an additional cost of $75,000. As an incentive to do both, the contracting company will pay for both launches plus a bonus of $1,000,000. Using an internal rate of return analysis with a *MARR* of 10 percent/year, what should Calisto Launch Services do?

50. Packaging equipment for Xi Cling Wrap costs $60,000 and is expected to result in end-of-year net savings of $23,000 per year for 3 years. The equipment will have a market value of $10,000 after 3 years. The equipment can be leased for $21,000 per year, payable at the beginning of each year. Xi Cling's *MARR* is 10 percent/year. Based on an internal rate of return analysis, determine if the packaging equipment should be purchased or leased.

Section 8.4

51. Consider the following cash flow profile and assume *MARR* is 10 percent/year.

EOY	0	1	2	3	4	5	6
NCF	−$100	$15	$15	$15	$15	$15	$15

    a. Determine the ERR for this project.

    b. Is this project economically attractive?

52. Consider the following cash flow profile and assume *MARR* is 10 percent/year.

EOY	0	1	2	3	4	5	6
NCF	−$100	$25	$25	$25	$25	$25	$25

    a. Determine the ERR for this project.

    b. Is this project economically attractive?

53. Consider the following cash flow profile and assume *MARR* is 10 percent/year.

EOY	0	1	2	3	4	5	6
NCF	−$100	$25	$25	$60	−$30	$60	$25

    a. Determine the ERR for this project.

    b. Is this project economically attractive?

54. Consider the following cash flow profile and assume *MARR* is 10 percent/year.

EOY	0	1	2	3	4	5	6
NCF	−$100	$25	$200	−$100	$250	−$200	−$100

    a. Determine the ERR for this project.

    b. Is this project economically attractive?

55. Consider the following cash flow profile and assume *MARR* is 10 percent/year.

EOY	0	1	2	3	4	5	6
NCF	−$100	$800	−$750	$900	−$950	$700	−$800

   a. Determine the ERR for this project.

   b. Is this project economically attractive?

56. Consider the following cash flow profile and assume *MARR* is 10 percent/year.

EOY	0	1	2	3	4	5	6
NCF	−$101	$411	−$558	$253	$2	$8	−$14

   a. Determine the ERR for this project.

   b. Is this project economically attractive?

57. Nu Things, Inc., is considering an investment in a business venture with the following anticipated cash flow results: Assume *MARR* is 20 percent per year. Based on an external rate of return analysis, (1) determine the investment's worth, (2) state whether or not your results indicate the investment should be undertaken, and (3) state the decision rule you used to arrive at this conclusion.

EOY	Cash Flow	EOY	Cash Flow	EOY	Cash Flow
0	−$70,000	7	14,000	14	7,000
1	20,000	8	13,000	15	6,000
2	19,000	9	12,000	16	5,000
3	18,000	10	11,000	17	4,000
4	17,000	11	10,000	18	3,000
5	16,000	12	9,000	19	2,000
6	15,000	13	8,000	20	1,000

58. DuraTech Manufacturing is evaluating a process improvement project. The estimated receipts and disbursements associated with the project are shown below. *MARR* is 6 percent/year.

End of Year	0	1	2	3	4	5
Receipts	$0	$0	$2,000	$4,000	$3,000	$1,600
Disbursements	$5,000	$200	$300	$600	$1,000	$1,500

   a. What is the external rate of return of this investment?

   b. What is the decision rule for judging the attractiveness of investments based on external rate of return?

   c. Should DuraTech implement the proposed process improvement?

59. Galvanized Products is considering purchasing a new computer system for their enterprise data management system. The vendor has quoted a purchase price of $100,000. Galvanized Products is planning to borrow one-fourth of the purchase price from a bank at 15 percent compounded annually. The loan is to be repaid using equal annual payments over a 3-year period. The computer system is expected to last 5 years and has a salvage value of $5,000 at that time. Over the 5-year period, Galvanized Products expects to pay a technician $25,000 per year to maintain the

system but will save $55,000 per year through increased efficiencies. Galvanized Products uses a *MARR* of 18 percent/year to evaluate investments.

a. What is the external rate of return of this investment?

b. What is the decision rule for judging the attractiveness of investments based on external rate of return?

c. Should the new computer system be purchased?

60. Quilts R Us (QRU) is considering investing in a new patterning attachment with the cash flow profile shown in the table below. QRU's *MARR* is 13.5 percent/year.

EOY	Cash Flow	EOY	Cash Flow
0	−$1,400	8	$600
1	$0	9	$700
2	$500	10	$800
3	$500	11	$900
4	$500	12	−$1,000
5	$500	13	−$2,000
6	$0	14	−$3,000
7	$500	15	$1,400

a. What is this investment's external rate of return?

b. What is the decision rule for judging the attractiveness of investments based on external rate of return?

c. Should QRU invest?

61. Aerotron Electronics is considering purchasing a water filtration system to assist in circuit board manufacturing. The system costs $40,000. It has an expected life of 7 years, at which time its salvage value will be $7,500. Operating and maintenance expenses are estimated to be $2,000 per year. If the filtration system is not purchased, Aerotron Electronics will have to pay Bay City $12,000 per year for water purification. If the system is purchased, no water purification from Bay City will be needed. Aerotron Electronics must borrow half of the purchase price, but they cannot start repaying the loan for 2 years. The bank has agreed to three equal annual payments, with the first payment due at the end of year 2. The loan interest rate is 8 percent compounded annually. Aerotron Electronics' *MARR* is 10 percent compounded annually.

a. What is this investment's external rate of return?

b. What is the decision rule for judging the attractiveness of investments based on external rate of return?

c. Should Aerotron Electronics buy the water filtration system?

62. Home Innovation is evaluating a new product design. The estimated receipts and disbursements associated with the new product are shown below. *MARR* is 10 percent/year.

End of Year	0	1	2	3	4	5
Receipts	$0	$600	$600	$700	$700	$700
Disbursements	$1,000	$300	$300	$300	$300	$300

a. What is this investment's external rate of return?

b. What is the decision rule for judging the attractiveness of investments based on external rate of return?

c. Should Home Innovations pursue this new product?

Section 8.5

63. The engineering team at Manuel's Manufacturing, Inc., is planning to purchase an enterprise resource planning (ERP) system. The software and installation from Vendor A costs $380,000 initially and is expected to increase revenue $125,000 per year every year. The software and installation from Vendor B costs $280,000 and is expected

to increase revenue $95,000 per year. Manuel's uses a 4-year planning horizon and a 10 percent per year *MARR*. Based on an external rate of return analysis, which ERP system should Manuel purchase?

64. Tempura, Inc., is considering two projects. Project A requires an investment of $50,000. Estimated annual receipts for 20 years are $20,000; estimated annual costs are $12,500. An alternative project, B, requires an investment of $75,000, has annual receipts for 20 years of $28,000, and has annual costs of $18,000. Assume both projects have zero salvage value and that *MARR* is 12 percent/year. Based on an external rate of return analysis, which project should be recommended?

65. Dark Skies Observatory is considering several options to purchase a new deep-space telescope. Revenue would be generated from the telescope by selling "time and use" slots to various researchers around the world. Four possible telescopes have been identified in addition to the possibility of not buying a telescope if none are financially attractive. The table below details the characteristics of each telescope. An external rate of return analysis is to be performed using a 25% MARR.

	T1	T2	T3	T4
Useful Life	10 years	10 years	10 years	10 years
First Cost	$600,000	$800,000	$470,000	$540,000
Salvage Value	$70,000	$130,000	$65,000	$200,000
Annual Revenue	$400,000	$600,000	$260,000	$320,000
Annual Expenses	$130,000	$270,000	$70,000	$120,000

66. The management of Brawn Engineering is considering three alternatives to satisfy an OSHA requirement for safety gates in the machine shop. Each gate will completely satisfy the requirement, so no combinations need to be considered. The first costs, operating costs, and salvage values over a 5-year planning horizon are shown below. Using an external rate of return analysis with a *MARR* of 20 percent/year, determine the preferred gate.

End of Year	Gate 1	Gate 2	Gate 3
0	−$15,000	−$19,000	−$24,000
1	−$6,500	−$5,600	−$4,000
2	−$6,500	−$5,600	−$4,000
3	−$6,500	−$5,600	−$4,000
4	−$6,500	−$5,600	−$4,000
5	−$6,500 + $0	−$5,600 + $2,000	−$4,000 + $5,000

67. Calisto Launch Services is an independent space corporation and has been contracted to develop and launch one of two different satellites. Initial equipment will cost $750,000 for the first satellite and $850,000 for the second. Development will take 5 years, at an expected cost of $150,000 per year for the first satellite, $120,000 per year for the second. The same launch vehicle can be used for either satellite and will cost $275,000 at the time of the launch 5 years from now. At the conclusion of the launch, the contracting company will pay Calisto $2,500,000 for either satellite.

Calisto is also considering launching both satellites. Because Calisto would have to upgrade its facilities to handle two concurrent projects, the initial costs would rise by $150,000 in addition to the first costs of each satellite. Calisto would need to hire additional engineers and workers, raising the yearly costs to a total of $400,000. An extra compartment would be added to the launch vehicle at an additional cost of $75,000. As an incentive to do both, the contracting company will pay for both launches plus a bonus of $1,000,000. Using an external rate of return analysis with a *MARR* of 10 percent/year, what should Calisto Launch Services do?

Section 8.6

68. Consider two alternatives, each of which will accomplish the same EPA-mandated pollution control. Using an incremental IRR analysis, determine the preferred alternative assuming *MARR* is 20 percent/year.

EOY	0	1	2	3	4
Alternative 1	−$5,000	−$2,200	−$2,200	−$2,200	−$2,200
Alternative 2	−$8,000	−$1,000	−$1,000	−$1,000	−$1,000

WILEY ⊕

69. The production department of Zunni's Manufacturing is considering two numerically controlled drill presses; one must be selected. Comparison data is shown in the table below. *MARR* is 10 percent/year. Based on an internal rate of return analysis, which drill press should be recommended?

	Drill Press T	Drill Press M
Initial Investment	$20,000	$30,000
Estimated Life	10 years	10 years
Estimated Salvage Value	$5,000	$7,000
Annual Operating Cost	$12,000	$6,000
Annual Maintenance Cost	$2,000	$4,000

70. Alpha Electronics can purchase a needed service for $90 per unit. The same service can be provided by equipment that costs $100,000 and that will have a salvage value of zero at the end of 10 years. Annual operating costs for the equipment will be $7,000 per year plus $25 per unit produced. *MARR* is 12 percent/year.

   a. Based on an internal rate of return analysis, should the equipment be purchased if the expected production is 200 units/year?

   b. Based on an internal rate of return analysis, should the equipment be purchased if the expected demand is 500 units/year?

WILEY ⊕

71. Allied Electronics must purchase a new automatic soldering machine to meet increased demand for its electronic goods. Of all the machines considered, management has narrowed the choices to the following three mutually exclusive machines:

	Machine 1	Machine 2	Machine 3
Initial Cost	$800,000	$650,000	$575,000
Annual Operating Cost	$50,000	$90,000	$105,000
Salvage Value	$40,000	$32,500	$28,750

Allied Electronics uses a 4-year planning horizon, and *MARR* is 12 percent/year. Based on an internal rate of return analysis, determine which machine should be purchased.

72. Deep Seas Submarine must implement a new engine in its submarines to meet the needs of clients who desire quieter operation. Two designs, both technologically feasible, have been created, and Deep Seas wishes to know which one to pursue. Design 1 would require an up-front manufacturing cost of $15,000,000 and will cost $2,500,000 per year for 3 years to swap out the engines in all its current submarines. Design 2 will cost $20,000,000 up front, but due to a higher degree of compatibility will only require $1,500,000 per year to implement. *MARR* is 10 percent/year. Based on an internal rate of return analysis, determine which design should be chosen.

73. A university pumps its water from wells located on campus. The falling water table has caused pumping costs to increase, the quantity of water available to decrease, and the quality of water to deteriorate. A public water company now has a large water main that runs within a few hundred yards of the university's pumping station. The university has decided to build a pipeline connecting to the company's water main and purchase water for the school. Two alternative types of pipe are being considered to supply the needs for a 60-year period. The relevant data is shown below:

	Pipe A	Pipe B
Initial Investment in Pipe	$120,000	$80,000
Estimated Pipe Life	60 years	30 years
Initial Investment in Pumping Equipment	$15,000	$20,000
Estimated Life of Pumping Equipment	20 years	20 years
Annual Maintenance and Energy Costs	$3,000	$4,000

Using a 60-year study period, recommend a pipe alternative based on an internal rate of return analysis. Since the university is tax exempt, it uses a MARR of 6 percent/year. Assume a zero net terminal salvage value for the pipe and the pumping equipment, and assume that renewal costs during the 60-year period will be the same as the initial costs.

74. Two storage structures, given code names Y and Z, are being considered for a military base located in Sontaga. The military uses a 5 percent/year expected rate of return and a 24-year life for decisions of this type. The relevant characteristics for each structure are shown below. Conduct an internal rate of return analysis to determine the preferred structure.

	Structure Y	Structure Z
First Cost	$4,500	$10,000
Estimated Life	12 years	24 years
Estimated Salvage Value	None	$1,800
Annual Maintenance Cost	$1,000	$720

Appendix

75. Consider the following cash flow profile and assume MARR is 10 percent/year and the finance rate is 4 percent/year.

EOY	0	1	2	3	4	5	6
NCF	−$100	$25	$200	−$100	$250	−$200	−$100

a. Determine the MIRR for this project.
b. Is this project economically attractive?

76. Consider the following cash flow profile, and assume MARR is 10 percent/year and the finance rate is 4 percent/year.

EOY	0	1	2	3	4	5	6
NCF	−$100	$25	$25	$60	−$30	$60	$25

a. Determine the MIRR for this project.
b. Is this project economically attractive?

77. Consider the following cash flow profile and assume MARR is 10 percent/year and the finance rate is 4 percent/year.

EOY	0	1	2	3	4	5	6
NCF	−$101	$411	−$558	$253	$2	$8	−$14

a. Determine the MIRR for this project.

b. Is this project economically attractive?

78. Consider the following cash flow profile and assume *MARR* is 10 percent/year and the finance rate is 4 percent/year.

EOY	0	1	2	3	4	5	6
NCF	−$100	$800	−$750	$900	−$950	$700	−$800

a. Determine the MIRR for this project.

b. Is this project economically attractive?

79. Orpheum Productions in Nevada is considering three mutually exclusive alternatives for lighting enhancements to one of its recording studios. Each enhancement will increase revenues by attracting directors who prefer this lighting style. The cash flow details, in thousands of dollars, for these enhancements are shown in the chart below. *MARR* is 10 percent/year, and the finance rate is 5 percent/year. Based on a modified internal rate of return analysis, which alternative (if any) should be implemented?

End of Year	Light Bar	Sliding Spots	Reflected Beam
0	−$6,000	−$14,000	−$20,000
1	$2,000	$3,500	$0
2	$2,000	$3,500	$2,300
3	$2,000	$3,500	$4,600
4	$2,000	$3,500	$6,900
5	$2,000	$3,500	$9,200
6	$2,000	$3,500	$11,500

80. Quilts R Us (QRU) is considering an investment in a new patterning attachment with the cash flow profile shown in the table below. QRU's *MARR* is 13.5 percent/year, and the finance rate is 6 percent/year.

EOY	Cash Flow	EOY	Cash Flow
0	−$1,400	8	$600
1	$0	9	$700
2	$500	10	$800
3	$500	11	$900
4	$500	12	−$1,000
5	$500	13	−$2,000
6	$0	14	−$3,000
7	$500	15	$1,400

a. What is this investment's modified internal rate of return?

b. What is the decision rule for judging the attractiveness of investments based on modified internal rate of return?

c. Should QRU invest?

81. Management is considering three alternatives to satisfy an urgent need. Each of the alternatives will completely satisfy the need, so no combinations have to be considered. The first costs, operating costs, and salvage values over a 5-year planning horizon are shown below. Using a modified internal rate of return analysis with a *MARR* of 20 percent/year and a finance rate of 10 percent/year, determine the preferred alternative.

End of Year	Alternative 1	Alternative 2	Alternative 3
0	−$15,000	−$19,000	−$24,000
1	$6,500	$7,600	$4,000
2	$6,500	$7,600	$6,000
3	$6,500	$7,600	$10,000
4	$6,500	$7,600	$15,000
5	$6,500 + $0	$5,600 + $2,000	$15,000 + $3,000

82. Calisto Launch Services is an independent space corporation and has been contracted to develop and launch one of two different satellites. Initial equipment will cost $750,000 for the first satellite and $850,000 for the second. Development will take 5 years at an expected cost of $150,000 per year for the first satellite, $120,000 per year for the second. The same launch vehicle can be used for either satellite and will cost $275,000 at the time of the launch 5 years from now. At the conclusion of the launch, the contracting company will pay Calisto $2,500,000 for either satellite.

Calisto is also considering launching both satellites. Because Calisto would have to upgrade its facilities to handle two concurrent projects, the initial costs would rise by $150,000 in addition to the first costs of each satellite. Calisto would need to hire additional engineers and workers, raising the yearly costs to a total of $400,000. An extra compartment would be added to the launch vehicle at an additional cost of $75,000. As an incentive to do both, the contracting company will pay for both launches plus a bonus of $1,000,000. Using a modified internal rate of return analysis with a *MARR* of 10 percent/year and a finance rate of 5 percent/year, what should Calisto Launch Services do?

Chapter 9

DEPRECIATION METHODS

(a) Schneider tractor being attached to a Schneider trailer. (Courtesy of Schneider National, Inc.) (b) Schneider trailer being loaded at a distribution center. (Courtesy of Schneider National, Inc.)

Schneider National

Based on 2010 revenues, Schneider National is a $3.1 billion privately held company in the transportation and logistics sector. Headquartered in Green Bay, Wisconsin, its customers include many of the global companies on Fortune magazine's list of top 100 companies. Schneider operates within North America and China, it employs 18,395 associates, and it is structured into three principle business units—truckload, intermodal, and logistics. The largest business unit, truckload, includes 10,100 company drivers and 1,685 owner-operators (independent drivers with their own tractors), operating 11,700 tractors and 33,300 trailers. Intermodal, a business that combines the geographic reach and delivery of trucking with the efficient long-haul transportation of railroads, is the second largest business unit: it employs 1,066 company drivers and 65 owner-operators, 12,000 containers to service customers in the intermodal market.

The smallest, but fastest growing business is Schneider Logistics; its 3,000 associates worldwide provide a variety of value-added services to customers, including Transportation Management (Brokerage), Port Logistics (Transloading and Distribution, Inland Logistics Management and China Solutions), and Supply Chain Management (Transportation Network Design, Supplier Management, Integrated Delivery Services (LTL and Cross-dock) and Schneider Consulting.

Each of Schneider's businesses has a different level of asset intensity. However, the entire portfolio results in $1 billion of invested capital showing on its balance sheet. As a result, it is critical that each increment of investment produce positive contributions to after-tax income, ensuring value creation for shareholders commensurate with its level of risk. Engineering economic analysis principles and tools are used by Schneider in allocating capital and human resources decisions.

Three recent examples of economic analyses performed include the design of a trailer fleet, the use of trailer-tracking devices, and a strategic acquisition.

- Economic analyses showed that increasing the purchase price of dura-plate 53-foot Wabash trailers by adding a 22-inch ''high rail'' aluminum strip at the bottom of the trailer's sides reduced a significant amount of damage from lift-truck forks and mishandling by trailer-pool hostlers. The analysis included reductions in maintenance expense, plus savings by reducing the number of trailers due to less repair time required.

- The incorporation of economic analysis at the project's beginning significantly influenced the ultimate design and functionality of a trailer-tracking device installed on all of Schneider's trailers. The initial results evidenced that knowing where trailers were at all times added significant value for Schneider and its customers.

- In pursuing a strategic acquisition, Schneider required that the investment produce a series of cash flows that meet or exceed its weighted average cost of capital, adjusted for risk. Because of the inevitability of future downside considerations, as well as the cyclical nature of the transportation market, the economic justifications were required to include well-demonstrated and documented scenario and risk-management plans showing how the returns on the target acquisitions would be impacted.

Since Schneider National is privately owned, it is not required to satisfy United States Securities and Exchange Commission rules that apply to publicly traded corporations. As a result, less pressure exists to meet or exceed estimates of quarterly earnings developed by financial analysts. Financial decisions at Schneider are based on after-tax returns on investment.

In contrast to Schneider, U.S. publicly traded corporations generally maintain two sets of books, or accounting records—and it is perfectly legal. Consequently, two different depreciation schedules are maintained: one for financial reporting and another for computing income taxes to be paid. We consider both in this chapter. In the following chapter, we address the tax consequences of various depreciation allowances.

When capital assets are distributed around the world, when income-tax laws vary from country to country, and when capital equipment is purchased, replaced, and modified frequently, it is a challenge to maintain accurate records regarding the value of assets owned by the shareholders.

9-1 INTRODUCTION

Most property decreases in value with use and time—that is, it *depreciates*. Depreciation is the subject of this chapter. We present it to ensure that you understand the implications of making investments in things that must (by U.S. tax law) be depreciated versus those that do not. Also, we want to ensure that you understand how a depreciation method can impact the profitability of an investment alternative.

Recall, in Chapter 1, we declared that we would use a *cash flow* approach throughout the book. For that reason, we seldom used the word *depreciation*,[1] because depreciation is not a cash flow. Typically, there are two cash flows associated with a capital asset: what you pay for it and what you get when you sell or trade it in for a replacement. Depreciation is an artifice that reflects the decrease in the asset's value over time or with usage.

A principal reason for developing the concept of depreciation is to allow a reasonably accurate report to the owners of a business regarding its value at any given point in time. Another reason is to allow reasonable estimates to be made concerning the cost of doing business; prices need to be set at levels that will recapture investments made in depreciable property—property that is used to produce the goods and services sold by the business.

A report to the owners of the business regarding its profitability, based strictly on cash flows, can be misleading. For example, suppose you own a business with annual revenues that exceed annual expenses by, say, $1 million. However, this year you spend $1.5 million on revenue-producing equipment that will be used for 5 years. If all you count is cash, then a cash flow calculation will indicate that you lost $0.5 million this year. On the other hand, if you spread the $1.5 million investment out over the 5-year period of its use, then your business will be accurately portrayed as being profitable.

To spread the investment costs over the useful life of the equipment purchased, there are various approaches you can use. We consider a number of them in this chapter.

Depreciation charges are a convenient mechanism for recovering the capital that is invested. As such, when the time comes to replace an asset, funds will be available to do so (unless prices have increased over the asset's life). Also, as mentioned, treating depreciation charges as expenses allows one to incorporate such charges in the cost of production and ensure that prices are sufficient to recover invested capital.

As good as the foregoing arguments are for considering depreciation, they are *not* the reason for including a treatment of depreciation in this book. We include it because U.S. income-tax law permits depreciation allowances to be deducted from taxable income; in other words, depreciation allowances can be treated as expenses *even though they are not cash flows*. As a result, depreciation affects income taxes, which are *cash flows*. Therefore, when comparing investment alternatives using an after-tax analysis, an accurate consideration of deprecation becomes important.

---

[1]Depreciation was mentioned once in Chapter 7, when referring to a subsequent discussion of capital recovery cost in this chapter. We mentioned *depreciate* once in Chapter 4 when pointing out that you have choices as to where you spend your money: on things that depreciate in value (cars and trucks) or on things that appreciate in value (college degree and investments).

> ## Systematic Economic Analysis Technique
>
> 1. Identify the investment alternatives
> 2. Define the planning horizon
> 3. Specify the discount rate
> 4. Estimate the cash flows
> 5. **Compare the alternatives**
> 6. Perform supplementary analyses
> 7. Select the preferred investment

In this chapter and its appendices, you will learn about the historical development of depreciation methods, as well as some terminology we will use in subsequent chapters. You will also learn how to calculate deprecation charges for several depreciation methods and how the various methods compare with one another. Finally, you will learn how to calculate *depletion* charges.

However, in addition to learning the mechanics of calculating depreciation charges, we want you to gain an understanding of why depreciation and the accompanying income-tax treatments are important in performing engineering economic analyses. Engineers make decisions in the process of designing products and processes that can have significant after-tax effects. For example, whether to design a production process that will be performed by people versus one that will be performed by robots is a typical choice made by mechanical and manufacturing engineers. But the after-tax consequences are quite different, depending on the choice made.

If people perform the work, labor costs are treated as expenses and are fully deducted from taxable income in the year in which they occur. However, if robots perform the work, only the robots' operating costs are treated as expenses. The acquisition cost for the robots must be depreciated. As such, the investment will be recovered over several years.

So, as you learn the material in the chapter, don't lose sight of WHY you are learning about depreciation. *Remember, you are learning about depreciation because your design decisions can affect the way investments and annual operating costs are treated from an income-tax perspective.*

> *Engineers need to learn about depreciation because their design decisions can affect the way investments and annual operating costs are treated from an income tax perspective.*

9-2   BACKGROUND ON DEPRECIATION ACCOUNTING

Business expenditures are either expensed or depreciated. Expensing an expenditure is akin to depreciating it fully in the year in which it occurs. Expenditures for labor, materials, and energy are examples of items that are fully deducted from taxable income. On the other hand, expenditures for production equipment, vehicles, and buildings cannot be fully deducted from taxable income in the year in which they occur; instead, they must be spread out or distributed over some allowable recovery period.

Technically speaking, U.S. tax law permits deduction from taxable income of a reasonable allowance for wear and tear, natural decay or decline, exhaustion, or obsolescence of property used in a trade or business or of property held for producing income. Specifically, the Internal Revenue Service requires that the following requirements be met for *depreciable* property:

1. It must be used in business or held for the production of income.
2. It must have a life that can be determined, and that life must be longer than a year.
3. It must be something that wears out, decays, gets used up, becomes obsolete, or loses value from natural causes.

Depreciable property may be *tangible* or *intangible*. *Tangible property* can be seen or touched and can be categorized as *personal* or *real*. *Personal property* is goods such as cars, trucks, machinery, furniture, equipment, and anything that is tangible except real property. *Real property* is land and generally anything that is erected on, growing on, or attached to it. Land, by itself, *does not qualify* for depreciation, but the buildings, structures, and equipment on it *do qualify*; land does not qualify because it does not pass the third requirement, given above. In contrast to tangible property, *intangible property* cannot be seen or touched but has value to the owner; it includes copyrights, brands, software, goodwill, formulas, designs, patents, trademarks, licenses, information bases, and franchises.

A term used synonymously with *depreciation* is *amortization*. Generally speaking, depreciation is associated with personal property and real property (other than land); whereas, amortization is associated with intangible property. The U.S. income-tax code defines amortization as "the recovery of certain capital expenditures, that are not ordinarily deductible, in a manner that is similar to straight-line depreciation."[2]

Intangible assets "acquired after August 10, 1993, and used in a trade or business or for the production of income are ratably amortized over a 15-year period generally beginning in the month of the acquisition. Intangibles amortizable under this provision are referred to as 'section 197 intangibles.'"[3]

Prior to World War II, far less attention was given to depreciation than has occurred since. In fact, some businesses actually established savings accounts in which uniform annual deposits were placed so that, at the end of its useful life, an asset could be replaced. If P denotes the *cost basis*[4] or the amount paid for an asset, F denotes the

---

[2]*2006 U.S. Master Tax Guide*, CCH Inc., Chicago, IL, 2005, p. 1287

[3]op. cit, p. 1288.

[4]In financial accounting, publicly traded corporations are allowed by the Securities Exchange Commission to include in the cost basis certain expenditures related to the acquisition and installation of depreciable property. However, for tax accounting purposes, corporations typically include in the cost basis *only* those expenditures so required by the Internal Revenue Service, preferring to *expense* expenditures related to the acquisition and installation of depreciable property. *Expensing* means deducting the expenditure from taxable income in the year in which it occurs. Expenditures that enhance or extend the capabilities of depreciable property are generally required to be included in the cost basis.

asset's *salvage value* at the end of the *useful life*, *recovery period*, or *depreciable life* of n years, and the "depreciation account" paid annual compound interest of $i\%$, then the annual deposit to the depreciation account is

$$d = (P - F)(A|F\ i\%, n)$$
$$=\text{PMT}(i\%,n,,-(P\text{-}F))$$

(9.1)

Recall, the $(A|F\ i\%, n)$ compound interest factor is called the *sinking fund factor*. It was used to determine the amount of money to be *sunk* or *paid* into a savings account or *fund* in order to have a future worth sufficient to replace the asset. Since a salvage value of F would be received at the end of n years, annual depreciation deposits of size d were required to accumulate $(P - F)$ dollars.

The depreciation method, based on Equation 9.1, is called *sinking fund depreciation* (SF). The actual depreciation charge for year (d_t) is the sum of the annual deposit and the accumulated interest for year t. Hence,

$$d_t = d(F|P\ i\%, t - 1)$$
$$=\text{FV}(i\%,t\text{-}1,,-\text{PMT}(i\%,n,,-(P\text{-}F)))$$

(9.2)

Finally, the undepreciated portion of an asset is called the *book value*. Also referred to as the *unrecovered investment*, the *adjusted cost basis*, and the *adjusted basis,* the book value (B_t) at the end of year t, based on sinking fund depreciation, is the *cost basis* less the *cumulative depreciation charge*, or

$$B_t = P - d(F|A\ i\%, t)$$
$$=P\text{-}\text{FV}(i\%,t,-\text{PMT}(i\%,n,,-(P\text{-}F)))$$

(9.3)

EXAMPLE 9.1 Sinking Fund Depreciation Applied

To illustrate the calculation of sinking fund depreciation charges, recall the $500,000 investment in a surface mount placement machine having a $50,000 salvage value after 10 years of use. If a 10 percent interest rate is used, the following holds for, say, year 5:

$$d = \$450,000(A|F\ 10\%, 10)$$
$$= \$450,000(0.6275)$$
$$= \$28,237.50$$
$$=\text{PMT}(10\%,10,,-450000)$$
$$= \$28,235.43$$

$$d_5 = \$28,237.50(F|P\ 10\%, 5 - 1)$$
$$= \$28,237.50(1.46410)$$
$$= \$41,342.52$$
$$=\text{FV}(10\%,4,,-\text{PMT}(10\%,10,,-450000))$$
$$= \$41,339.49$$

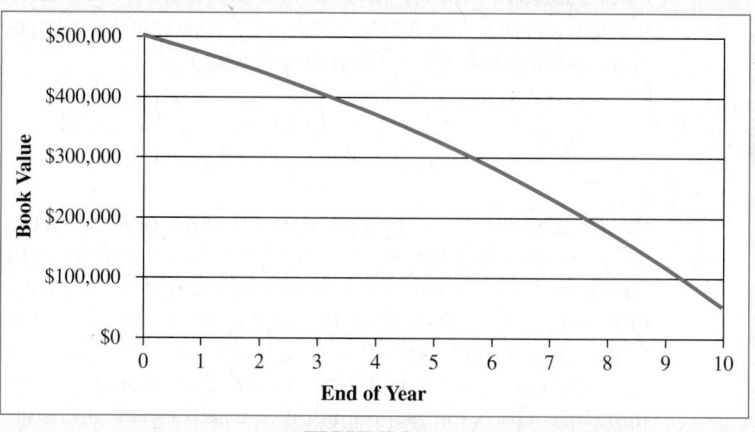

FIGURE 9.1

Book Value for Sinking Fund Depreciation Example.

$$B_5 = \$500,000.00 - \$28,237.50(F|A\ 10\%,5)$$
$$= \$500,000.00 - \$28,237.50(6.10510)$$
$$= \$327,607.24$$
$$= 500000 - FV(10\%,5,-PMT(10\%,10,,-450000))$$
$$= \$327,619.89$$

In Figure 9.1, a plot of B_t is provided for $t = 1, \ldots, 10$. (The values were obtained using Excel®.) Notice, book value is a concave function when sinking fund depreciation is used. The significance of the curve's shape will be treated later in the chapter and in Chapter 10.

Sinking fund depreciation was used by a number of firms prior to World War II. However, following the war, during the decade of the 1950s, U.S. corporate income-tax rates increased significantly. For example, from 1942 through 1945, corporate taxable income in excess of $50,000 was taxed at a rate of 40 percent. From 1946 through 1949, corporate taxable income was taxed at a rate of 38 percent. Then, in 1950, corporate taxable income in excess of $25,000 was taxed at a rate of 42 percent; in 1951, corporate taxable income in excess of $25,000 was taxed at a rate of 50.75 percent. From 1952 to 1963, corporate taxable income in excess of $25,000 was taxed at a rate of 52 percent; the highest corporate income-tax bracket was 53 percent. (To put things in perspective, today corporate taxable income in excess of $18,333,333 is taxed at a rate of 35 percent.)

As a result of the increased income-tax rates, a strong lobbying effort developed to allow the use of depreciation methods that *front-end loaded* or *accelerated* depreciation charges. Because of its compound interest feature, sinking fund depreciation *back-end loaded* depreciation charges and lost its appeal. By the end of the 1950s, few, if any, businesses used sinking fund depreciation. We present it purely for historical purposes.

During the 1950s, few U.S. manufacturing firms had the capital needed to retool and purchase new manufacturing equipment. As a result, the economy was quite sluggish. To stimulate corporate investments, Congress made sweeping changes to U.S. income-tax laws and approved the use of accelerated depreciation plans, such as *declining balance* and *sum-of-years' digits* depreciation methods.[5]

9-3 STRAIGHT-LINE DEPRECIATION (SLN)

Straight-line depreciation is the oldest of the depreciation methods in use today. As the name implies, annual depreciation charges form a uniform annual series. Hence, book value is a straight line. Depending on its application, the straight-line depreciation charge can be based on a salvage value. For purposes of financial reporting, a salvage value is often included; whereas, for purposes of computing income taxes, a salvage value is not included.

Using SLN, the annual depreciation charge for year t is

$$d_t = (P - F)/n$$
$$= \text{SLN}(P, F, n) \tag{9.4}$$

where **SLN** is the Excel® worksheet function for calculating the annual depreciation charge. The syntax for the **SLN** function, **SLN(cost,salvage,life)**, is self-explanatory.

The book value at the end of year t, is

$$B_t = P - td$$
$$= P - t(P - F)/n \tag{9.5}$$

Straight-Line Depreciation

$$d_t = (P - F)/n$$
$$= \text{SLN}(P, F, N)$$
$$B_t = P - td_t$$

Based on the time value of money, one might wonder why straight-line depreciation would ever be used to compute income tax liabilities. Three responses come to mind. First, SLN is required in some countries. Second, SLN is required in the United States when depreciating intangible property. Third, while it is doubtful that corporate

---

[5]During his graduate studies at Virginia Tech in the early 1960s, one of the coauthors (John A. White) learned that two Virginia Tech industrial engineering professors (Grant and Norton) played a role in persuading the U.S. Congress to approve the use of accelerated depreciation methods in computing taxable income; they testified before a congressional committee and, based on their extensive research on depreciation accounting, made recommendations for change, including the use of accelerated depreciation methods. White has not been able to verify the accuracy of what he was told, but he heard similar descriptions from others who were at Virginia Tech during the 1950s.

A book by Grant and Norton was widely cited during the 1950s and 1960s. (Grant, Eugene, and P. T. Norton, Jr., *Depreciation*, The Ronald Press Company, New York, NY, 1955.) Grant and Norton were both Virginia Tech professors; Norton was chair of the industrial engineering department.

income taxes will be based on straight-line depreciation, we know of companies that require the use of straight-line depreciation in engineering economic justifications. Why? We were given the following reasons:

1. Management does not want an investment's economic viability to be decided on the basis of the depreciation method used. Recognizing that cash flow estimates are just that, *estimates*, and they are likely to prove to be incorrect, management does not feel that it is justified to be so precise regarding depreciation when errors in the cash flow estimates can easily offset any gains made by using accelerated depreciation.

2. Management wishes to use a standardized approach and, because of its simplicity, chose to use SLN in all economic justifications.

We recall vividly a discussion with the CFO of a major multinational corporation who said he was beginning to have doubts concerning the value of having engineers use *DCF* methods because "the engineers will use whatever numbers they have to in order to justify the investments they want." A sad commentary, indeed, but it is something we must deal with. It is important for honesty and integrity to exist throughout the economic justification process.

EXAMPLE 9.2   Straight-Line Depreciation Applied to the SMP Machine

From the previous example involving a \$500,000 investment in an SMP machine having a \$50,000 salvage value after 10 years of use, the following values occur for $t = 5$, with SLN:

$$d_5 = (\$500,000 - \$50,000)/10$$
$$= \$45,000$$
$$= \text{SLN}(500000,50000,10)$$
$$= \$45,000$$
$$B_5 = \$500,000 - 5(\$45,000)$$
$$= \$275,000$$

9-4   DECLINING BALANCE AND DOUBLE DECLINING BALANCE DEPRECIATION (DB AND DDB)

Declining balance depreciation is an accelerated depreciation method. As such, it provides larger depreciation charges in the early years and smaller depreciation charges in the later years. Where SLN produced a uniform annual series of depreciation charges, DB produces a negative geometric series of depreciation charges. With DB, the depreciation charge in a given year is a fixed percentage of the book value at the beginning of the year. Letting p denote the DB percentage or depreciation rate used,

$$d_t = pB_{t-1}$$
$$= pP(1 - p)^{t-1} \tag{9.6}$$

and

$$B_t = P(1 - p)^t \qquad (9.7)$$

Notice, salvage value is not incorporated in the calculations for DB. As a result, the book value at the end of the cost recovery period is unlikely to equal the salvage value obtained for the asset. (We will discuss the income-tax implications of book values not equaling salvage values in Chapter 10.)

What depreciation rate or value of p should be used? Among the most often used values are 125 percent, 150 percent, and 200 percent of the straight-line rate, which is $1/n$. If it is desired to use a percentage such that the book value equals the salvage value after n years, then, from Equation 9.7,

$$F = P(1 - p)^n$$

solving for p gives

$$p = 1 - (F/P)^{1/n}$$
$$= \text{-RATE}(n,,-P,F) \qquad (9.8)$$

Notice the minus sign between the equal sign and the Excel® **RATE** worksheet function. Also, when $p = 2/n$, which is twice, or 200 percent, the straight-line rate, the DB plan is called *double declining balance* depreciation (DDB).

Declining Balance Depreciation

$$d_t = pP(1 - p)^{t-1}$$
$$= DB(P,F,n,t)$$
$$B_t = P(1 - p)^t$$

Excel® has three declining balance worksheet functions: **DB**, **DDB**, and **VDB**. The syntaxes for the three worksheet functions are

DB(**cost,salvage,life,period,**month);
DDB(**cost,salvage,life,**period,factor); and
VDB(**cost,salvage,life,start_period,end_period,**factor,no_switch)

where

cost = the cost basis of the asset

salvage = the salvage value of the asset

life = the cost recovery period of the asset

period = the time period for which the depreciation charge is desired

month = the number of months to be depreciated during the first year[6]

---

[6]If month is omitted, ''month'' is assumed to equal 12.

factor $=$ the depreciation rate (p) to use; in the case of *DDB*, if omitted, it is assumed to equal 2, the double-declining rate

start_period $=$ the starting period for which depreciation is calculated; must use the same units as life

end_period $=$ the ending period for which depreciation is calculated; must use the same units as life

no_switch $=$ a logical value specifying whether to switch to straight-line depreciation when depreciation is greater than the declining balance calculation

When the Excel® **DB** function is used, a depreciation rate is computed that yields a book value at the end of the cost recovery period equal to the salvage value. When the Excel® **DDB** function is used, a depreciation rate equal to $2/n$ is used. Finally, when using the Excel® **VDB** function, switching from declining balance to straight-line depreciation is an option; if the declining balance depreciation rate is not specified, it is assumed to equal $2/n$.

DB(cost,salvage,life,period,month);
DDB(cost,salvage,life,period,factor); and
VDB(cost,salvage,life,start_period,end_period,factor,no_switch)

We address the concept of switching depreciation methods in the next section. Since we have introduced the syntax for the Excel® **VDB** function, note that when **no_switch** is TRUE, Excel® does not switch to straight-line depreciation even when the depreciation is greater than the declining balance calculation; if **no_switch** is FALSE or omitted, Excel® switches to straight-line depreciation when depreciation is greater than the declining balance calculation. *Finally, all arguments except* **no_switch** *must be positive numbers*; therefore, the cost basis is not shown as a negative-valued cash flow.

EXAMPLE 9.3 Declining Balance Depreciation Applied to the SMP Machine

Let's use declining balance depreciation with the SMP machine. First, we compute the depreciation charge and book value for $t = 5$, using Equations 9.6 and 9.7. Before doing so, we use Equation 9.8 to determine the depreciation rate that equates the book value at the end of the recovery period to the salvage value.

Recall, a \$500,000 investment is made in the SMP machine; it has an estimated \$50,000 salvage value after 10 years of usage. Therefore,

$$p = 1 - (\$50,000/\$500,000)^{0.1}$$
$$= 20.5672\%$$
$$\text{=-RATE}(10,,-500000,50000)$$
$$= 20.5672\%$$

$$d_5 = 0.205672(\$500,000)(1.000000 - 0.205672)^4$$
$$= \$40,939.70$$

$$B_5 = \$500,000(0.794328)^5$$
$$= \$158,113.65$$

Using the Excel® **DB** worksheet function gives

$$d_5 = DB(500000,50000,10,5)$$
$$= \$40,937.30$$

(Notice, the answer obtained from the Excel® **DB** worksheet function differs from that obtained using $p = 20.5672$ percent. The **DB** function computes a value of p that is supposed to cause the asset to be fully depreciated at the end of the write-off period and then applies it. The value of p is not exact, as seen in Table 9.1, since $B_{10} = \$49,793.77$, instead of \$50,000.)

To obtain the book value using the Excel® **DB**, **DDB**, and **VDB** worksheet functions, it is necessary to compute the depreciation charges for all previous years and then subtract the cumulative depreciation charges from the cost basis.

Next, suppose the declining balance rate is to be twice the straight-line rate. Letting $p = 2/10$, from Equations 9.6 and 9.7,

$$d_5 = 0.20(\$500,000)(0.80)^4$$
$$= \$40,960.00$$

$$B_5 = \$500,000(0.80)^5$$
$$= \$163,840.00$$

Using the Excel® **DDB** worksheet function gives

$$d_5 = DDB(500000,50000,10,5)$$
$$= \$40,960.00$$

When using the Excel® **VDB** worksheet function, it is necessary to specify a beginning and ending year for the calculation of the depreciation charge. To compute the depreciation charge for $t = 5$,

$$d_5 = VDB(500000,50000,10,4,5,2)$$
$$= \$40,960.00$$

Table 9.1 provides the depreciation charges obtained and the associated book values for the \$500,000 SMP investment for $t = 1, \ldots, 10$ using the Excel® worksheet functions. Figure 9.2 contains a plot of B_t for SF, **SLN**, **DB**, **DDB**, and **VDB** over the recovery period. Notice that the final book value with **DDB** does not equal \$50,000. Also, notice that the depreciation charges are identical for **VDB** and **DDB** until year 9, at which time **VDB** switches from a declining balance rate to a straight-line rate.

If our objective is to maximize the present worth of depreciation charges, then **DB** is clearly the preferred depreciation method. However, the 20.5672 percent depreciation rate used by **DB**, which is 205.672 percent of the straight-line rate, is greater than the maximum rate allowed by the IRS. For many assets, the maximum allowable rate is twice the straight-line rate, or $2/n$—or, for the example, 200 percent, or DDB.

TABLE 9.1
Depreciation Allowances and Book Values for the SMP Investment.

t	SF d_t	SF B_t	SLN d_t	SLN B_t	DB d_t	DB B_t	DDB d_t	DDB B_t	VDB d_t	VDB B_t
0		$500,000.00		$500,000.00		$500,000.00		$500,000.00		$500,000.00
1	$28,235.43	$471,764.57	$45,000.00	$455,000.00	$103,000.00	$397,000.00	$100,000.00	$400,000.00	$100,000.00	$400,000.00
2	$31,058.97	$440,705.60	$45,000.00	$410,000.00	$81,782.00	$315,218.00	$80,000.00	$320,000.00	$80,000.00	$320,000.00
3	$34,164.87	$406,540.73	$45,000.00	$365,000.00	$64,934.91	$250,283.09	$64,000.00	$256,000.00	$64,000.00	$256,000.00
4	$37,581.35	$368,959.38	$45,000.00	$320,000.00	$51,558.32	$198,724.78	$51,200.00	$204,800.00	$51,200.00	$204,800.00
5	$41,339.49	$327,619.89	$45,000.00	$275,000.00	$40,937.30	$157,787.47	$40,960.00	$163,840.00	$40,960.00	$163,840.00
6	$45,473.44	$282,146.45	$45,000.00	$230,000.00	$32,504.22	$125,283.25	$32,768.00	$131,072.00	$32,768.00	$131,072.00
7	$50,020.78	$232,125.67	$45,000.00	$185,000.00	$25,808.35	$99,474.90	$26,214.40	$104,857.60	$26,214.40	$104,857.60
8	$55,022.86	$177,102.81	$45,000.00	$140,000.00	$20,491.83	$78,983.07	$20,971.52	$83,886.08	$20,971.52	$83,886.08
9	$60,525.15	$116,577.66	$45,000.00	$95,000.00	$16,270.51	$62,712.56	$16,777.22	$67,108.86	$16,943.04	$66,943.04
10	$66,577.66	$50,000.00	$45,000.00	$50,000.00	$12,918.79	$49,793.77	$13,421.77	$53,687.09	$16,943.04	$50,000.00

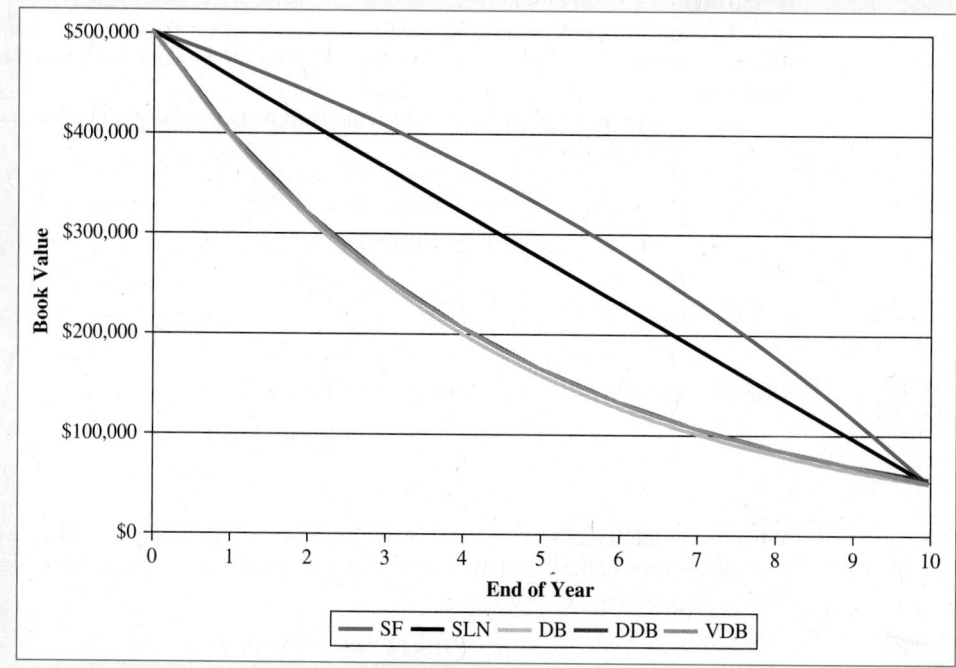

FIGURE 9.2
Comparison of Five Depreciation Methods.

9-5　SWITCHING FROM DDB TO SLN WITH THE EXCEL® VDB FUNCTION

As noted, the Excel® **VDB** worksheet function includes an optional feature: It can switch from using a specified declining balance rate to a straight-line rate when it is optimum to do so. But what criterion is used to define *optimum*?

Assuming a time value of money greater than 0, since depreciation charges can be deducted from taxable income, after-tax present worth is maximized when the present worth of depreciation charges is maximized. Just as one prefers to receive money sooner rather than later, due to the *TVOM*, so should one prefer to depreciate an asset sooner rather than later. Therefore, accelerated depreciation methods are preferred to straight-line depreciation but only up to a point, and **VDB** determines that point.

As shown in Figure 9.2, the declining balance methods *front-end load* depreciation charges. However, because declining balance methods compute depreciation charges using a constant percentage of the book value, toward the recovery period's latter stages, the amount of depreciation charged drops off precipitously with declining balance methods. And, as was the case with DDB in the previous example, the book value calculated with declining balance methods might not reach the salvage value during the recovery period.

The Excel® **VDB** function computes the depreciation charge that would result if declining balance continued to be used and compares it with the depreciation charge that would result if straight-line depreciation were used for the balance of the recovery period. The optimum time to switch is the first time the depreciation charge with straight-line depreciation is greater than would result if declining balance were continued. Hence, a switch to straight-line depreciation occurs at the first year for which

$$\frac{B_{t-1} - F}{n - (t - 1)} > pB_{t-1} \tag{9.9}$$

Notice, the estimated salvage value is used in determining the straight-line depreciation component, even though it is neglected in the **DDB** calculations. Switching to straight-line depreciation is never desirable if the estimated salvage value, F, exceeds B_n, the declining balance unrecovered investment for the last year of the recovery period.

Switch from DDB to SLN as soon as

$$\frac{B_{t-1} - F}{n - (t - 1)} > pB_{t-1}$$

EXAMPLE 9.4   Switching from DDB to SLN with the SMP Machine

From the previous example involving the purchase of a surface mount placement machine, we note that $P = \$500,000$, $F = \$50,000$, $n = 10$, and $p = 0.2$ for DDB.

When $t = 1$, the left-hand side (LHS) of Equation 9.9 is $(\$500,000 - \$50,000)/10 = \$45,000$; the right-hand side (RHS) of Equation 9.9 is $0.20(\$500,000) = \$100,000$. Since LHS < RHS, try $t = 2$.

When $t = 2$, the LHS of Equation 9.9 is $(\$400,000 - \$50,000)/9 = \$38,888.89$; the RHS of Equation 9.9 is $0.20(\$400,000) = \$80,000$. Since LHS < RHS, try $t = 3$.

When $t = 3$, the LHS of Equation 9.9 is $(\$320,000 - \$50,000)/8 = \$33,750$; the RHS of Equation 9.9 is $0.20(\$320,000) = \$64,000$. Since LHS < RHS, try $t = 4$.

When $t = 4$, the LHS of Equation 9.9 is ($256,000 − $50,000)/7 = $29,428.57$; the RHS of Equation 9.9 is $0.20($256,000) = $51,200$. Since LHS < RHS, try $t = 5$.

When $t = 5$, the LHS of Equation 9.9 is ($204,800 − $50,000)/6 = $25,800$; the RHS of Equation 9.9 is $0.20($204,800) = 40,960$. Since LHS < RHS, try $t = 6$.

When $t = 6$, the LHS of Equation 9.9 is ($163,840 − $50,000)/5 = $22,768$; the RHS of Equation 9.9 is $0.20($163,840) = $32,768$. Since LHS < RHS, try $t = 7$.

When $t = 7$, the LHS of Equation 9.9 is ($131,072 − $50,000)/4 = $20,268$; the RHS of Equation 9.9 is $0.20($131,072) = $26,214.40$. Since LHS < RHS, try $t = 8$.

When $t = 8$, the LHS of Equation 9.9 is ($104,857.60− $50,000)/3 = $18,285.87$; the RHS of Equation 9.9 is $0.20($104,857.60) = $20,971.52$. Since LHS < RHS, try $t = 9$.

When $t = 9$, the LHS of Equation 9.9 is ($83,886.08 − $50,000)/2 = $16,943.04$; the RHS of Equation 9.9 is $0.20($83,886.08) = $16,777.22$. Since LHS > RHS, switch to SLN for the ninth year. During years 9 and 10, the depreciation charge will be $16,943.04.

The calculations performed and the process used to determine the optimum time to switch from *DDB* to SLN are shown in Figure 9.3.

E5		fx =IF(C5>D5,"Yes","No")				
	A	B	C	D	E	F	G

	t	VDB B_t	$\mathcal{SLN}$ d_t	DDB d_t	$\mathcal{SLN}$ d_t > DDB d_t?	VDB d_t	
2	0	$500,000.00					
3	1	$400,000.00	$45,000.00	$100,000.00	No	$100,000.00	
4	2	$320,000.00	$38,888.89	$80,000.00	No	$80,000.00	
5	3	$256,000.00	$33,750.00	$64,000.00	No	$64,000.00	
6	4	$204,800.00	$29,428.57	$51,200.00	No	$51,200.00	=B5-B6
7	5	$163,840.00	$25,800.00	$40,960.00	No	$40,960.00	
8	6	$131,072.00	$22,768.00	$32,768.00	No	$32,768.00	
9	7	$104,857.60	$20,268.00	$26,214.40	No	$26,214.40	
10	8	$83,886.08	$18,285.87	$20,971.52	No	$20,971.52	
11	9	$66,943.04	$16,943.04	$16,777.22	Yes	$16,943.04	
12	10	$50,000.00				$16,943.04	
13						=DDB(500000,50000,10,A7)	
14			=(B5-50000)/(10-A5)				
15		=B8-VDB(500000,50000,10,A8,A9,2,FALSE)					
16							
17							
18							

FIGURE 9.3
Calculations for Switching from DOB to SLN.

As noted previously, it is not always necessary to incorporate salvage values in depreciation calculations. Indeed, the salvage value used in financial reporting is an estimate of the market value at the end of the asset's useful life. Such estimates can vary widely. In the previous example, what differences, if any, would occur if the depreciation charges were based on a negligible salvage value?

EXAMPLE 9.5   Basing DB Depreciation Charges on a Negligible Salvage Value

When the salvage value of the $500,000 SMP machine is estimated to be negligible, DB cannot be used, since a finite rate does not exist that will reduce the book value to 0 over the recovery period. Table 9.2 provides the results for the four remaining depreciation methods; Figure 9.4 shows graphically how the book values compare. As expected, the book value for DDB exceeds the salvage value. Notice, the switch to SLN occurred 2 years sooner with **VDB**, in year 7.

TABLE 9.2
Depreciation Allowances and Book Values for the SMP Investment with a Negligible Salvage Value

t	SF d_t	SF B_t	SLN d_t	SLN B_t	DDB d_t	DDB B_t	VDB d_t	VDB B_t
0		$500,000.00		$500,000.00		$500,000.00		$500,000.00
1	$31,372.70	$468,627.30	$50,000.00	$450,000.00	$100,000.00	$400,000.00	$100,000.00	$400,000.00
2	$34,509.97	$434,117.34	$50,000.00	$400,000.00	$80,000.00	$320,000.00	$80,000.00	$320,000.00
3	$37,960.96	$396,156.37	$50,000.00	$350,000.00	$64,000.00	$256,000.00	$64,000.00	$256,000.00
4	$41,757.06	$354,399.31	$50,000.00	$300,000.00	$51,200.00	$204,800.00	$51,200.00	$204,800.00
5	$45,932.77	$308,466.54	$50,000.00	$250,000.00	$40,960.00	$163,840.00	$40,960.00	$163,840.00
6	$50,526.04	$257,940.50	$50,000.00	$200,000.00	$32,768.00	$131,072.00	$32,768.00	$131,072.00
7	$55,578.65	$202,361.85	$50,000.00	$150,000.00	$26,214.40	$104,857.60	$32,768.00	$98,304.00
8	$61,136.51	$141,225.34	$50,000.00	$100,000.00	$20,971.52	$83,886.08	$32,768.00	$65,536.00
9	$67,250.16	$73,975.18	$50,000.00	$50,000.00	$16,777.22	$67,108.86	$32,768.00	$32,768.00
10	$73,975.18	$0.00	$50,000.00	$0.00	$13,421.77	$53,687.09	$32,768.00	$0.00

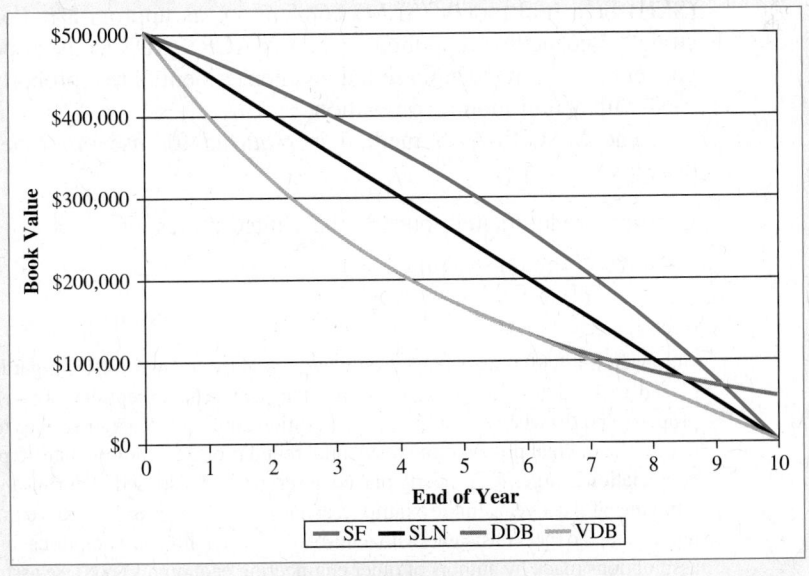

FIGURE 9.4
Comparison of Four Depreciation Methods, with a Negligible Salvage Value.

9-6   MODIFIED ACCELERATED COST RECOVERY SYSTEM (MACRS)

Although SLN is the most commonly used depreciation method in the United States for purposes of financial reporting, MACRS is the only depreciation method approved by the IRS for computing income-tax liability.

Most depreciable property placed in service after 1986 qualifies for MACRS. There are two variations of MACRS: the General Depreciation System (GDS) and the Alternative Depreciation System (ADS). For most applications of interest to us, GDS is based on double declining balance, switching to straight-line depreciation. (That is the reason we presented declining balance and straight-line depreciation methods before studying MACRS methods.) ADS is based on straight-line depreciation, with a longer recovery period than GDS. Both MACRS-GDS and MACRS-ADS have preestablished recovery periods for most property; in the case of MACRS-GDS, most property is assigned to eight property classes, which establish the number of years over which the cost basis is to be recovered.

Both MACRS-GDS and MACRS-ADS include a feature we have not used previously: *a half-year convention*. It is assumed that, on average, a property is used for half of the first year of service. Similarly, it is assumed that it is used for half of the last year of service.[7] *H* is used to designate the half-year convention. Hence, 200%DBSLH-GDS denotes double declining balance, switching to straight-line depreciation with the half-year convention applied to the first and last years of service over the GDS recovery period.

9.6.1   MACRS-ADS

Although MACRS-GDS is far more popular, taxpayers may elect to claim MACRS-ADS deductions instead of the regular allowances available with MACRS-GDS. The MACRS-ADS method is simply straight-line depreciation with either a half-year (SLH) or a mid-month (SLM) convention, as appropriate. For most property, the straight-line method is applied over the MACRS-ADS recovery period with a half-year convention. For residential rental and nonresidential real property, a 40-year period is used with a mid-month convention.

The MACRS-ADS method is *required* for use on some property, including property

1. used predominately outside the United States;
2. having any tax-exempt use;

---

[7]In general, a half-year depreciation charge is allowed by the IRS, regardless of when an asset is placed in service or disposed of during the year. The exceptions are (a) 27.5-year and 39-year property and (b) when a mid-quarter convention applies. The latter applies to all property, other than nonresidential real property and residential rental property, if more than 40 percent of the cumulative depreciation charges for property placed in service and disposed of during a year occur during the last 3 months of a tax year. In the examples and end-of-chapter problems, we assume exception (b) does not occur. To be consistent with end-of-year cash flow assumptions in previous chapters and assumptions made by authors of other engineering economics texts, we assume investments occur at the end of year 0 and the first half-year depreciation charge occurs at the end of year 1. We do so, realizing that in practice, the half-year depreciation charges and investments generally occur in the same tax year.

3. financed by tax-exempt bonds; or

4. imported and covered by executive order of the U.S. president.

Other than public sector applications, it is unlikely that a taxpayer would choose to use MACRS-ADS depreciation, because, in most cases, maximizing the present worth of depreciation charges will minimize the present worth of income taxes paid over the recovery period.

Certainly, accelerated depreciation is not guaranteed to minimize the present worth of income taxes paid, because U.S. income-tax rates increase with increasing taxable income; in essence, the more you make, the higher your income-tax rate. Therefore, for start-up businesses, income-tax rates will very likely increase during the recovery period. In fact, a start-up company might lose money the first few years; in such a situation, saving depreciation allowances for later years would be a reasonable tactic. However, such a situation occurs so infrequently that most financial people agree with choosing accelerated depreciation (MACRS-GDS) over uniform depreciation (MACRS-ADS). (Also, net operating losses [NOLs] can be carried forward and applied in future years to reduce income taxes.) Hence, we limit our consideration to MACRS-GDS.

9.6.2   MACRS-GDS

Depreciable tangible property may be assigned to one of the eight MACRS[8] classes, shown in Table 9.3. From the property class descriptions, it is obvious that determining the class to which a given property belongs is a complex task. For that reason, if there is any uncertainty regarding the appropriate class to use, we recommend you consult tax professionals or review publications available from the IRS, Department of the Treasury, U.S. Government.

TABLE 9.3 MACRS-GDS Property Classes.	
Property Class	Personal Property
3-Year Property	Qualifying property with a class life of *4 years or less*, including: tractor units for over-the-road use; special tools for manufacturing motor vehicles; special handling devices for manufacture of food and beverages; and special tools for manufacturing rubber, finished plastic, glass, and fabricated metal products
5-Year Property	Qualifying property with a class life of *more than 4 years but less than 10 years*, including: automobiles and light, general purpose trucks; certain research and experimentation equipment; alternative energy and biomass property; computers and peripheral equipment; satellite space segment property; data-handling equipment (typewriters, calculators, copiers, printers, facsimile machines, etc.); heavy, general-purpose trucks; timber cutting assets; offshore oil and gas well drilling assets; certain construction assets; computer-based telephone central office switching equipment; and many assets used for the manufacture of knitted goods, carpets, apparel, medical and dental supplies, chemicals, and electronic components

(Continued)

[8]Unless stated otherwise, when we refer to MACRS, we will be referring to MACRS-GDS.

TABLE 9.3

(Continued)

Property Class	Personal Property
7-Year Property	Qualifying property with a class life of *10 or more years but less than 16 years*, property without any class life and not included in the 27.5- and 39-year categories, including: office furniture, fixtures, and equipment; theme and amusement park assets; assets used in the exploration for and production of petroleum and natural gas deposits; most assets used for manufacturing such things as food products, spun yarn, wood products and furniture, pulp and paper, rubber products, finished plastic products, leather products, glass products, foundry products, fabricated metal products, motor vehicles, aerospace products, athletic goods, and jewelry
10-Year Property	Qualifying property with a class life of *16 or more years but less than 20 years*, including: vessels, tugs, and similar water transportation equipment; petroleum refining assets; assets used in the manufacture of grain, sugar, vegetable oil products, and substitute natural gas-coal gasification
15-Year Property	Qualifying property with a class life of *20 or more years but less than 25 years*, including: land improvements, such as sidewalks, roads, drainage facilities, sewers, bridges, fencing, and landscaping; cement manufacturing assets; some water and pipeline transportation assets; municipal wastewater treatment plants; telephone distribution plant assets; certain electric and gas utility property; and some liquified natural gas assets
20-Year Property	Qualifying property with a class life of *25 years or more, other than real property with a class life of 27.5 years or more*, plus municipal sewers, including such assets as: farm buildings; some railroad structures; some electric generating equipment, such as certain transmission lines, pole lines, buried cable, repeaters, and much other utility property
Property Class	Real Property
27.5-Year Property	*Residential rental property, including a rental home or structure for which 80% or more of the gross rental income for the tax year is rental income from dwelling units.* A dwelling unit is a house or an apartment used to provide living accommodations in a building or structure, but not a unit in a hotel, motel, inn, or other establishment in which more than one-half of the units are used on a transient basis
39-Year Property	*Nonresidential real property: depreciable property with a class life of 27.5 years or more and is not residential rental property*

Below, we show how to calculate the depreciation allowance for an asset, given its MACRS property class. However, it is much easier to use the values provided in Table 9.4 for 3-, 5-, 7-, 10-, 15-, and 20-year property. For 27.5- and 39-year property, use the percentages given in Table 9.5, which are based on the month in which the property was placed in service. For 3-, 5-, 7-, and 10-year property, the annual depreciation charge is based on 200%DBSLH-GDS; for 15- and 20-year property, the annual depreciation charge is based on 150%DBSLH-GDS; for 27.5- and 39-year property, the annual depreciation charge is based on SLM, or straight-line depreciation, mid-month convention.

TABLE 9.4

MACRS-GDS percentages for 3-, 5-, 7-, and 10-year property are 200% DBSLH and 15- and 20-year property are 150% DBSLH.

EOY	3-Year Property	5-Year Property	7-Year Property	10-Year Property	15-Year Property	20-Year Property
1	33.33	20.00	14.29	10.00	5.00	3.750
2	44.45	32.00	24.49	18.00	9.50	7.219
3	14.81	19.20	17.49	14.40	8.55	6.677
4	7.41	11.52	12.49	11.52	7.70	6.177
5		11.52	8.93	9.22	6.93	5.713
6		5.76	8.92	7.37	6.23	5.285
7			8.93	6.55	5.90	4.888
8			4.46	6.55	5.90	4.522
9				6.56	5.91	4.462
10				6.55	5.90	4.461
11				3.28	5.91	4.462
12					5.90	4.461
13					5.91	4.462
14					5.90	4.461
15					5.91	4.462
16					2.95	4.461
17						4.462
18						4.461
19						4.462
20						4.461
21						2.231

TABLE 9.5

a. MACRS-GDS percentages for 27.5-year residential rental property using mid-month convention.

Year	Month in Tax Year Property Placed in Service											
	1	2	3	4	5	6	7	8	9	10	11	12
1	3.485%	3.182%	2.879%	2.576%	2.273%	1.970%	1.667%	1.364%	1.061%	0.758%	0.455%	0.152%
2-9	3.636%	3.636%	3.636%	3.636%	3.636%	3.636%	3.636%	3.636%	3.636%	3.636%	3.636%	3.636%
10-26*	3.637%	3.637%	3.637%	3.637%	3.637%	3.637%	3.637%	3.637%	3.637%	3.637%	3.637%	3.637%
11-27**	3.636%	3.636%	3.636%	3.636%	3.636%	3.636%	3.636%	3.636%	3.636%	3.636%	3.636%	3.636%
28	1.970%	2.273%	2.258%	2.879%	3.182%	3.485%	3.636%	3.636%	3.636%	3.636%	3.636%	3.636%
29							0.152%	0.455%	0.758%	1.061%	1.364%	1.667%

(Continued)

TABLE 9.5

(Continued)

b. MACRS-GDS percentages for 39-year nonresidential real property using mid-month convention.

Year	\multicolumn{12}{c}{Month in Tax Year Property Placed in Service}

Year	1	2	3	4	5	6	7	8	9	10	11	12
1	2.461%	2.247%	2.033%	1.819%	1.605%	1.391%	1.177%	0.963%	0.749%	0.535%	0.321%	0.107%
2-39	2.564%	2.564%	2.564%	2.564%	2.564%	2.564%	2.564%	2.564%	2.564%	2.564%	2.564%	2.564%
40	0.107%	0.321%	0.535%	0.749%	0.963%	1.177%	1.391%	1.605%	1.819%	2.033%	2.247%	2.461%

*even-numbered year

**odd-numbered year

EXAMPLE 9.6 Calculating MACRS Depreciation Rates

The Excel® **VDB** worksheet function can be used to calculate the MACRS depreciation rates, shown in Table 9.4. We will demonstrate the **VDB** function's use by generating several of the values for the 5-year and 20-year classes.

Five-Year Property

Recall, **VDB(cost,salvage,life,start_period,end_period,factor,no_switch)**

Let **cost = 1**, **salvage = 0**, **life = 5**,, and factor = 2.

For **start_period = 0** and **end_period = 0.5**, =**VDB(1,0,5,0,0.5,2) = 20%**, which is the beginning half-year rate.

For **start_period = 0.5**, **end_period = 1.5**, =**VDB(1,0,5,0.5,1.5,2) = 32%**

For **start_period = 1.5**, **end_period = 2.5**, =**VDB(1,0,5,1.5,2.5,2) = 19.2%**

For **start_period = 2.5**, **end_period = 3.5**, =**VDB(1,0,5,2.5,3.5,2) = 11.52%**

For **start_period = 3.5**, **end_period = 4.5**, =**VDB(1,0,5,3.5,4.5,2) = 11.52%**

For **start_period = 4.5**, **end_period = 5**, =**VDB(1,0,5,4.5,5,2) = 5.76%** which is the final half-year rate.

Twenty-Year Property

Let **cost = 1**, **salvage = 0**, **life = 20**, and factor = **1.5**

For **start_period = 0** and **end_period = 0.5**, =**VDB(1,0,20,0,0.5,1.5) = 3.75%** which is the beginning half-year rate.

For **start_period = 0.5**, **end_period = 1.5**, =**VDB(1,0,20,0.5,1.5,1.5) = 7.219%**

For **start_period = 1.5**, **end_period = 2.5**, =**VDB(1,0,20,1.5,2.5,1.5) = 6.677%**

For **start_period = 2.5**, **end_period = 3.5**, =**VDB(1,0,20,2.5,3.5,1.5) = 6.177%**

For **start_period = 3.5**, **end_period = 4.5**, =**VDB(1,0,20,3.5,4.5,1.5) = 5.713%**

The process continues until, finally, the last half-year rate is calculated, with **start_period = 19.5**, **end_period = 20**, =**VDB(1,0,20,19.5,20,1.5) = 2.231%**.

For a given property class, the sum of the depreciation rates equals 100 percent. Therefore, the asset is fully depreciated over the recovery period. The depreciation allowance for a given year is the product of the cost basis and the depreciation rate taken from, as appropriate, Table 9.4 or 9.5.

Letting p_t denote the MACRS depreciation rate for year t, the depreciation charge for year t and the book value at the end of year t are given by

$$d_t = p_t P \tag{9.10}$$

and

$$B_t = P - \sum_{j=1}^{t} d_j = P\left(1 - \sum_{j=1}^{t} p_j\right) \tag{9.11}$$

EXAMPLE 9.7 Applying MACRS with the SMP Machine Investment

The IRS allows the $500,000 investment in a surface mount placement machine to qualify as 5-year property. Consequently, the depreciation charges and the book values for the SMP machine will be as shown below:

$d_1 = 0.20(\$500,000) = \$100,000$ $B_1 = \$500,000 - \$100,000 = \$400,000$

$d_2 = 0.32(\$500,000) = \$160,000$ $B_2 = \$400,000 - \$160,000 = \$240,000$

$d_3 = 0.192(\$500,000) = \$96,000$ $B_3 = \$240,000 - \$96,000 = \$144,000$

$d_4 = 0.1152(\$500,000) = \$57,600$ $B_4 = \$144,000 - \$57,600 = \$86,400$

$d_5 = 0.1152(\$500,000) = \$57,600$ $B_5 = \$86,400 - \$57,600 = \$28,800$

$d_6 = 0.0576(\$500,000) = \$28,800$ $B_6 = \$28,800 - \$28,800 = \$0$

Many variations exist in how depreciation charges are computed for the wide range of depreciable properties that exist. As noted at the chapter's beginning, our objective is to ensure that you understand the after-tax consequences of the design decisions that engineers make. Since depreciation affects income taxes, engineers must understand how depreciation allowances are determined.

9-7 COMPARISON OF DEPRECIATION METHODS

Previously, we compared SF, SLN, DB, DDB, and VDB depreciation methods. We did this to familiarize you with the difference in accelerated depreciation (DB, DDB, VDB) versus decelerated depreciation (SF) versus uniform depreciation (SLN) methods. Our comparisons were based on all five methods having the same recovery period. In our examples, the recovery period was 10 years.

With MACRS, the recovery period is stated. For each MACRS property class, a range of possible useful lives (typically called *asset depreciation range*, or ADR) exists for the same property class: for 3-year property, ADR ≤ 4; for 5-year property, $4 < \text{ADR} \leq 10$;

for 7-year property, $10 < \text{ADR} \leq 16$; for 10-year property, $16 < \text{ADR} \leq 20$; for 15-year property, $20 < \text{ADR} \leq 25$; and for 20-year property, ≥ 25 years.

In Example 9.7, the $500,000 investment in the surface mount placement machine was expected to have a useful life of 10 years. With an ADR of 10 years, it qualifies as 5-year property. (Note: a planning horizon greater than 10 years would not change the SMP classification. We have confirmed that an SMP machine of the type considered here does, indeed, qualify as 5-year property using MACRS-GDS depreciation.)

With a planning horizon of 10 years and the SMP machine qualifying for treatment as 5-year property, how should a comparison of depreciation methods be performed? Since MACRS uses a half-year convention, to make an apples-to-apples comparison, we will apply the half-year convention to SLN and DDB and consider all three over a 6-year period. (It does not serve any useful purpose to compare MACRS with SF, since SF has not been used for several decades; neither does it make sense to compare MACRS with VDB, since identical results would occur; and, finally, there is no reason to compare MACRS with DB, since the most favorable allowable version of DB is DDB.)

Finally, two measures of comparison will be considered: book value and present worth. As we have noted, the principal benefit of accelerated depreciation methods is the minimization of the present worth of income taxes paid. (Recall the proviso we offered regarding this point when concluding our treatment of MACRS-ADS.)

EXAMPLE 9.8 Comparing SLN, DDB, and MACRS Depreciation Methods with the SMP Machine Investment

For the $500,000 investment in the SMP machine, since no salvage value is included in MACRS and DDB calculations, we will ignore the salvage value in calculating SLN depreciation charges. Also, since we will depreciate the property using the half-year convention, depreciation allowances will be spread over a 6-year period, even though the equipment qualifies as 5-year property. Finally, for comparative purposes, we will include SLN and DDB without the half-year convention, recognizing they will benefit from a full-year allowance in the first year; to "stack the deck" even more in favor of DDB, we will also consider DDB with switching to SLN (which we denote DDB/SLN).

SLH method: Not surprisingly, the half-year depreciation allowances will be half of a full-year allowance. Hence, $d_1 = d_6 = \$500,000/12 = \$41,666.67$, and $d_t = \$500,000/6 = \$83,333.33$ for $2 \leq t \leq 5$.

200%DBH method: Because of our desire to adopt the half-year convention, DDB allowances will be obtained using the Excel® VDB function. The only difference in DDB and MACRS will be that the latter switches to SLN when optimum to do so.

Table 9.6 provides the depreciation allowances, the book values, and the present worths for the depreciation allowances. The latter is based on a 10 percent *MARR*. Figure 9.5 illustrates the differences in book values over the recovery period. Not surprising, the present worth of the depreciation allowances is greatest using DDB/SLN, because a full-year allowance was taken in the first year, thus surpassing MACRS in the "present worth competition." However, we recognize that we gave DDB/SLN every advantage that MACRS has, plus one. In practice, MACRS maximizes the present worth of depreciation allowances.

TABLE 9.6
Depreciation Allowances for Example 9.8.

EOY	SLH d	200%DBH d	MACRS d	SLN d	DDB d	DDB/SLN d
0						
1	$50,000.00	$100,000.00	$100,000.00	$100,000.00	$200,000.00	$200,000.00
2	$100,000.00	$160,000.00	$160,000.00	$100,000.00	$120,000.00	$120,000.00
3	$100,000.00	$96,000.00	$96,000.00	$100,000.00	$72,000.00	$72,000.00
4	$100,000.00	$57,600.00	$57,600.00	$100,000.00	$43,200.00	$54,000.00
5	$100,000.00	$34,560.00	$57,600.00	$100,000.00	$25,920.00	$54,000.00
6	$50,000.00	$12,960.00	$28,800.00	$0.00	$0.00	$0.00
PW =	$361,847.83	$363,382.91	$386,630.21	$379,078.68	$380,686.86	$405,498.88

EOY	B	B	B	B	B	B
0	$500,000.00	$500,000.00	$500,000.00	$500,000.00	$500,000.00	$500,000.00
1	$450,000.00	$400,000.00	$400,000.00	$400,000.00	$300,000.00	$300,000.00
2	$350,000.00	$240,000.00	$240,000.00	$300,000.00	$180,000.00	$180,000.00
3	$250,000.00	$144,000.00	$144,000.00	$200,000.00	$108,000.00	$108,000.00
4	$150,000.00	$86,400.00	$86,400.00	$100,000.00	$64,800.00	$54,000.00
5	$50,000.00	$51,840.00	$28,800.00	$0.00	$38,880.00	$0.00
6	$0.00	$38,880.00	$0.00	$0.00	$38,880.00	$0.00

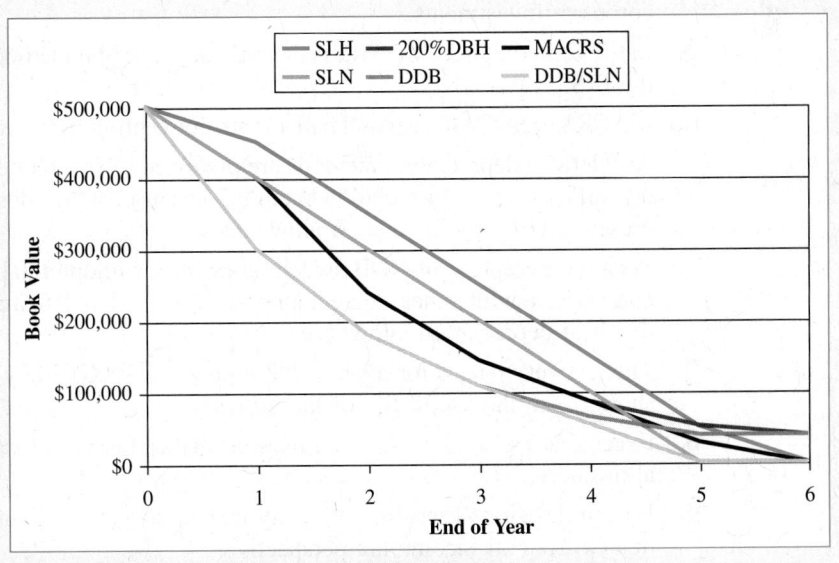

FIGURE 9.5
Comparison of Depreciation Methods.

Before concluding our treatment of depreciation methods, note that the computation of the annual deposit into a sinking fund, Equation 9.1, and the computation of the declining balance rate, Equation 9.8, assume implicitly that an asset is placed in service at the end of year 0, followed by n end-of-year deprecation charges. With MACRS-GDS, regardless of when an asset is placed in service, a half-year depreciation charge is taken. In practice, the depreciation charge is often taken in the same year in which the asset is acquired. The convention within engineering economics circles is to show the expenditure at the end of year 0 and show the first year's depreciation charge at the end of year 1. We follow that convention throughout the text, recognizing the expenditure and the first year's depreciation charge frequently occur in the same year.

In preceding chapters, we let any particular point in time be arbitrarily designated as the present. When income taxes are incorporated in an engineering economic analysis, depreciation charges are for given tax years, which is a calendar year for many corporations. Hence, the timing during the year when an asset is placed in service can affect whether the cash flow, known as the *cost basis* (*P*), occurs in the same tax year as the first depreciation charge taken. We address this further in Chapters 10 and 11.

9-8 SUMMARY

In this chapter, we discussed several depreciation methods, and several others are considered in this chapter's appendices, including a brief treatment of depletion. Through our study of depreciation, we provided the following important messages:

1. The depreciation method used can significantly impact the present worth of depreciation allowances and thereby can significantly impact the income taxes a business pays.

2. Depreciation laws vary among countries and change frequently, often to stimulate corporate investments.

3. In the United States, MACRS is the only depreciation method approved for use by the IRS.

4. MACRS uses a half-year and half-month convention for various types of property.

5. Accelerated depreciation methods are preferred to decelerated depreciation methods and uniform depreciation methods because of the desire to maximize the present worth of depreciation allowances.

6. With the exception of DDB switching to SLN without a half-year convention, in comparison with other depreciation methods, MACRS maximizes the present worth of depreciation allowances.

7. The recovery period for depreciable property is specified by the IRS; usually it is shorter than the useful life of the property.

8. Excel® has several worksheet functions that can be used to calculate depreciation allowances.

9. Design decisions can affect the way investments and annual operating costs are treated from an income-tax perspective.

10. Corporations keep two depreciation schedules: one for income-tax purposes, based on MACRS; and another for financial reporting, usually based on straight-line depreciation. And there is nothing wrong with them doing so!

Remember, the only reason we introduced the subject of depreciation was to establish a foundation for considering income taxes in engineering economic analyses; therefore, this chapter is simply a prelude to our treatment of income taxes in the following chapter.

Pit Stop #9—Avoid the Pot Holes!

1. True or False: Straight-line depreciation is the most popular depreciation method used in financial reporting.

2. True or False: The Modified Accelerated Cost Recovery System is the most popular depreciation method used in computing corporate income tax liabilities.

3. True or False: Based on maximizing the present worth of depreciation allowances, MACRS is preferred to SLN for recovery periods greater than 5 years.

4. True or False: Accelerated depreciation plans were adopted after World War II to stimulate capital investment.

5. True or False: Engineers seldom have an opportunity to influence the recovery period for expenditures.

6. True or False: MACRS is equivalent to DDB, switching to SLN, with a mid-year convention.

7. True or False: The most popular variation of MACRS is MACRS-ADS.

8. True or False: Sum-of-Years'-Digits depreciation is a popular depreciation method and is most often used to compute income tax liabilities.

9. True or False: When given a choice of depreciation methods to use, choose the one that maximizes the present worth of book value.

10. True or False: Sinking fund depreciation is the only depreciation method described in the book that is based on the time value of money.

SUM-OF-YEARS'-DIGITS DEPRECIATION (SYD)

In addition to declining balance methods, one of the early accelerated depreciation methods was sum-of-years'-digits depreciation. The name *sum-of-years'-digits* comes from the fact that the sum

$$1 + 2 + \cdots + (n - 1) + n = n(n + 1)/2$$

is used directly in the calculation of allowable depreciation. The depreciation deduction during any year t is expressed as

$$d_t = \frac{n - (t - 1)}{n(n + 1)/2}(P - F) \tag{9.A.1}$$

The unrecovered investment or book value at the end of each year t is given by

$$B_t = P - \sum_{j=1}^{t} \frac{n - (j - 1)}{n(n + 1)/2}(P - F) \tag{9.A.2}$$

which reduces to

$$B_t = (P - F)\frac{(n - t)(n - t + 1)}{n(n + 1)} + F \tag{9.A.3}$$

The Excel® **SYD** worksheet function can be used to calculate SYD depreciation allowances. The syntax for the **SYD** function is **SYD(cost,salvage,life,per)**.

SYD was a popular depreciation method, prior to the introduction of the accelerated cost recovery system in 1981. Several limited partnerships were formed to fund the construction of office buildings, with the primary purpose being to provide tax shelters for individuals who had extraordinary incomes and who could use the depreciation deductions to minimize their taxable income.

With SYD, if a building was being depreciated over a 20-year period, nearly 43 percent of the depreciation occurred during the first 5 years. As a result, buildings were traded back and forth between partnerships every 5 to 7 years, since each time the ownership changed, a new cost basis was obtained for the depreciation schedule. The IRS soon stopped such practices for passive investors seeking tax shelters.

EXAMPLE 9.A.1 Sum-of-Years'-Digits Depreciation Applied

Recall the $500,000 investment in an SMP machine, with a $50,000 salvage value at the end of a 10-year recovery period. Using SYD, the annual depreciation allowances and end-of-year book values are given in Table 9.A.1. Notice, book value is a decreasing gradient series. The size of the gradient step is $2(P - F)/[n(n + 1)]$ or, for the example, $450,000/55 = 8,181.82$.

TABLE 9.A.1

SYD Depreciation Allowances and Book Values for the SMP Investment

t	SYD	
	d_t	B_t
0		$500,000.00
1	$81,818.18	$418,181.82
2	$73,636.36	$344,545.45
3	$65,454.55	$279,090.91
4	$57,272.73	$221,818.18
5	$49,090.91	$172,727.27
6	$40,909.09	$131,818.18
7	$32,727.27	$99,090.91
8	$24,545.45	$74,545.45
9	$16,363.64	$58,181.82
10	$8,181.82	$50,000.00

OTHER DEPRECIATION METHODS

Most depreciation methods are tied to the passage of time. Occasionally, however, recovery of cost over time would have little relation to an asset's use or its production of income. That is why the IRS may allow taxpayers to utilize other consistent methods of depreciation. Some recognized methods are briefly presented below. Assets that we elect to depreciate in any of these ways may require IRS approval and are specifically excluded from the definition of property when the MACRS applies.

9.B.1 Units of Production Method

This procedure allows equal depreciation per each unit of output, regardless of the lapse of time involved. The allowance for year t is equal to the total depreciation amount $(P - F)$ times the ratio of units produced during the year (U_t) to the total units that are expected to be produced during the useful life of the asset (U)-that is,

$$D_t = (P - F)(U_t/U) \tag{9.B.1}$$

This method has proven suitable for depreciating equipment used in exploring resources such as mines, wells, and so on. It has also been used as the basis for depreciating printing presses, based on the number of pages printed.

9.B.2 Operating Day (Hour) Method

This is similar to the previous method, in that year t depreciation is based on the ratio of days (hours) used during the year (Q_t) to total days (hours) expected in a useful life (Q). Depreciation is expressed as

$$D_t = (P - F)(Q_t/Q) \tag{9.B.2}$$

9.B.3 Income Forecast Method

This method is applicable to depreciate the cost of rental property such as videotapes, sound recordings, and motion pictures. The ratio of year t rental income (R_t) to the total useful life income (R) is multiplied by the total lifetime depreciation, or

$$D_t = (P - F)(R_t/R) \tag{9.B.3}$$

DEPLETION

Depletion is a gradual reduction of minerals, gas and oil, timber, and natural deposits. In a sense, depletion is closely akin to depreciation. The difference is that while a depleting asset is losing value by actually being removed and sold, a depreciable asset is losing value through wear, tear, and obsolescence in the manufacture of goods to be sold. Money recovered through the depletion allowance is likely to be used in the exploration and development of depletable assets, just as depreciation reserves are reinvested for new equipment. As in most tax-related matters, laws relating to lessors, lessees, royalties, and sales are complex and will probably require expert assistance. If you are faced with a situation in which depletion is appropriate, consult the IRS Web site: www.irs.gov/publications/p535/ch09.html#d0e6766, among others.

Two alternative methods can determine the depletion allowance to use: *cost depletion* and *percentage depletion*. They are described briefly below and are illustrated with an example.

Cost depletion is the basic method of computing the depletion deduction. First, for any given year, the number of units (tons, barrels, board feet, cubic feet, etc.) remaining in the property must be estimated. Then, the adjusted cost basis (first cost less depletion deductions taken previously) is divided by the number of units remaining. This quotient, multiplied by the number of units sold during the year, determines the depletion allowance. It is expressed as

$$\text{Cost depletion deduction} = \frac{\text{Adjusted cost basis (number of units sold)}}{\text{Number of units remaining in property}}$$

This calculated deduction may or may not be used, depending on whether or not the percentage depletion allowance provides a larger deduction.

TABLE 9.C.1
Depletion Percentage for Some Minerals and Similar Resources

Type	Depletion Percentage
Oil and gas (percentage depletion is not allowed, except for certain gas and oil production)	
a. Oil and gas – independent producers and royalty owners, with some limitations	15
b. Natural gas – regulated natural gas and gas sold under a fixed contract, with some limitations	22
Sulphur and uranium; and, if from U.S. deposits, asbestos, bauxite, chromite, graphite, mica, quartz crystals, cadmium, cobalt, lead, mercury, nickel, tin, zinc, and certain other ores and minerals	22
Gold, silver, oil shale, copper, and iron ore if from U.S. deposits	15
Numerous other minerals such as diatomaceous earth, granite, limestone, marble, and so forth	14
Coal, lignite, perlite, and sodium chloride	10
Clay and shale used for sewer pipe and brick	7.5
Clay (for roofing tile, flower pots, etc.), gravel, peat, pumice, sand, and stone	5

Percentage depletion provides an allowance equal to a percentage of the gross income from the mineral property. (Timber cannot be depleted using the percentage depletion method.) The applicable percentage depends on the type of property depleted. Table 9.C.1 gives some depletion percentages. For a complete listing, consult Section 613(b) of the Internal Revenue Code.

The percentage depletion deduction may not exceed 50 percent of the taxable income *before* allowance for depletion. The total of allowances under percentage depletion is in no way limited by the adjusted basis of the property. Thus, even though the basis of depleted property may be reduced to $0.00, percentage depletion is still allowed. Cost depletion, however, stops when the adjusted basis reaches $0.00. Whichever of the two depletion methods results in the higher allowance in a given year *must be used*.

EXAMPLE 9.C.1   Determining Depletion Allowances for an Oil Well

A small independent oil company has purchased the rights, drilled, and developed a 48,000-barrel oil well on NW/4 35/19N/1W, Payne County, Oklahoma, for $140,000. Operating expenses, based on past experience, are equal to $5 + 43(t - 1)$/barrel, where t is the year in which the oil is removed and sold. This increase in cost per barrel over time indicates the increased difficulty of recovering the oil as the field is depleted. A geological consultant estimates the field will last 6 years, yielding 15,000, 13,000, 10,000, 6,000, 3,000, and 1,000 barrels of oil over that time. Each barrel will be worth $20 to the company. The cash flow calculations are given in Table 9.C.2.

Using the cost method, ($140,000/48,000 barrels)(15,000 barrels) = $43,750 is the depletion allowance during year 1. From Table 9.C.1, the depletion percentage is 15 percent. This results in a $300,000(0.15) = $45,000 deduction in year 1. Since the depletion percentage ($45,000) > the cost depletion ($43,750), the depletion allowance in year 1 will be $45,000.

Therefore, the adjusted cost basis for year 2 is ($140,000 − $45,000) = $95,000, which is "spread" over (48,000 − 15,000) = 33,000 barrels. Since 13,000 barrels are sold in year 2, $95,000(13,000/33,000) = $37,424 is the cost depletion for year 2. Finally, since the percentage depletion ($39,000) > the cost depletion ($37,424), the depletion allowance in year 2 will be $39,000.

The adjusted cost basis for year 3 is ($95,000 − $39,000) = $56,000, which is to be spread over (33,000 − 13,000) = 20,000 barrels. Since 10,000 barrels are sold in year 3,

---

TABLE 9.C.2
Depletion Allowance Calculation for Example 9.C.1

EOY A	Barrels Sold B	Gross Income C	Operating Cost D	Taxable Income Before Depletion E = C−D	50% of Taxable Income Before Depletion F = 0.5D	Percentage Depletion G = 0.15C	Cost Depletion H	Depletion Allowance Used I
0		−$140,000		−$140,000	−$70,000			
1	15,000	$300,000	$75,000	$225,000	$112,500	$45,000	$43,750	$45,000
2	13,000	$260,000	$104,000	$156,000	$78,000	$39,000	$37,424	$39,000
3	10,000	$200,000	$110,000	$90,000	$45,000	$30,000	$28,000	$30,000
4	6,000	$120,000	$84,000	$36,000	$18,000	$18,000	$15,600	$18,000
5	3,000	$60,000	$51,000	$9,000	$4,500	$9,000	$6,000	$6,000
6	1,000	$20,000	$20,000	$0	$0	$3,000	$2,000	$2,000

$56,000(10,000/20,000) = \$28,000$ is the cost depletion for year 3. Since the percentage depletion ($30,000) > the cost depletion ($28,000), the depletion allowance in year 3 will be $30,000.

The adjusted cost basis for year 4 is ($56,000 − $30,000) = $26,000, which is to be spread over (20,000 − 10,000) = 10,000 barrels. Since 6,000 barrels are sold in year 4, $26,000(6,000)/(10,000) = \$15,600$ is the cost depletion for year 4. However, since the percentage depletion ($18,000) > the cost depletion ($15,600), the depletion allowance in year 4 will be $18,000.

The adjusted cost basis for year 5 is ($26,000 − $18,000) = $8,000, which is to be spread over (10,000 − 6,000) = 4,000 barrels. Since 3,000 barrels are sold in year 5, $8,000(3,000/4,000) = \$6,000$ is the cost depletion for year 5. Since the percentage depletion is limited to no more than 50 percent of taxable income before depletion, the percentage depletion allowance for the fifth year is limited to $4,500. Since the cost depletion ($6,000) > the percentage depletion ($4,500), the depletion allowance in year 5 will be $6,000.

Finally, the adjusted cost basis for year 6 is $2,000, which is to be spread over 1,000 barrels. Since 1,000 barrels are sold in year 6, the cost depletion for year 6 is $2,000. Since the percentage depletion is the smaller of $0 and $3,000, which, of course, is $0. Hence, the depletion allowance in year 6 will be the cost depletion of $2,000.

Tutoring problem available (at instructor's discretion) in *WileyPLUS*.

Problem available (at instructor's discretion) in *WileyPLUS*.

Worked Problem Video available in *WileyPLUS*.

FE-LIKE PROBLEMS

1. A lumber company purchases and installs a wood chipper for $200,000. The chipper is classified as MACRS 7-year property. Its useful life is 10 years. The estimated salvage value at the end of 10 years is $25,000. Using MACRS depreciation, compute the first-year depreciation.
   a. $17,500
   b. $20,000
   c. $25,007.50
   d. $28,580

2. A lumber company purchases and installs a wood chipper for $200,000. The chipper is classified as MACRS 7-year property. Its useful life is 10 years. The estimated salvage value at the end of 10 years is $25,000. Using straight-line depreciation, compute the first-year depreciation.
   a. $28,571.43
   b. $20,000
   c. $17,500
   d. $25,000

3. The concept similar to depreciation that is applied to natural resources is called what?
   a. Depletion
   b. Declining balance
   c. Amortization
   d. MACRS

4. An X-ray machine at a dental office is MACRS 5-year property. It costs $6,000 and has an expected useful life of 8 years. The salvage value at the end of 8 years is expected to be $500. Assuming MACRS depreciation, what is the book value at the end of the third year?
   a. $1,584
   b. $1,728
   c. $3,916
   d. $4,272

5. Which of the following is not a requirement for an asset to be depreciable?
   a. It must have a life longer than 1 year.
   b. It must have a basis (initial purchase plus installation cost) greater than $1,000.

c. It must be held with the intent to produce income.

d. It must wear out or get used up.

6. MACRS-GDS deductions are a combination of which other methods of depreciation?

a. Sum-of-years'-digits and straight line

b. Sum-of-years'-digits and declining balance

c. Double declining balance and 150 percent declining balance

d. Double declining balance and straight line

7. Production equipment used in the bottling of soft drinks (MACRS-GDS, 10-year property) is purchased and installed for $630,000. What is the depreciation deduction in the fourth year under MACRS-GDS?

a. $90,720

b. $78,687

c. $72,576

d. $48,510

8. Which of the following is (are) required to calculate MACRS-GDS depreciation deductions?

1. Property class

2. Salvage value

3. First cost

4. Annual maintenance costs

a. 1 and 3 only

b. 2 and 3 only

c. 1, 2, and 3

d. 1, 2, 3, and 4

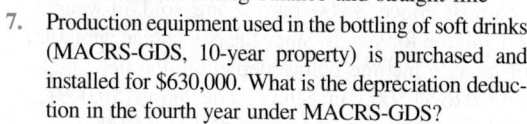

9. The depreciation deduction for year 11 of a 15-year property with a 20-year class life is $4,000. If the asset's salvage value is estimated to be $5,000 and MACRS-GDS is used to calculate the depreciation deduction for year 11, what was the asset's initial cost?

a. $42,105

b. $67,682

c. $72,682

d. $80,000

10. The depreciation deduction for year 11 of an asset with a 20-year useful life is $4,000. If the asset's salvage value was estimated to be zero and straight-line depreciation was used to calculate the depreciation deduction for year 11, what was the asset's initial cost?

a. $42,105

b. $67,682

c. $72,682

d. $80,000

11. Which of the following is *not* true about depreciation?

a. Depreciation is not a cash flow.

b. To be depreciable, an asset must have a life longer than 1 year.

c. A 5-year property will generate a regular MACRS-GDS depreciation deduction in 6 fiscal years.

d. For MACRS-GDS, an estimate of the salvage values is required.

12. The depreciation allowance for a $100,000 MACRS-GDS asset was $8,550 after its third year. What was the depreciation allowance after its second year?

a. $8,550

b. $9,500

c. $18,000

d. Cannot be determined with the information given

PROBLEMS

Section 9.1

1. SteelTubes had sales of $300 million this year. Expenses were $250 million. Aside from these figures, the company also invested in new mills for carbon steel tubing, complete with peripheral loading, straightening, and coiling equipment plus facility reconfiguration totaling $14 million. SteelTubes believes the usable life of the mill will be only 7 years, owing to technological advances. There were no other financial considerations.

a. Looking strictly at cash flows, what will be reported as the financial gain or loss? Is this a fair representation of financial performance?

b. If, for internal financial reporting, the manufacturer writes off equal amounts of the capital investment over the usable life, beginning this year, what will be the reported financial gain or loss?

2. Taxes are paid each year on some measure of financial gain. We typically think of financial gain as ''cash inflows minus cash outflows,'' and yet simply subtracting outflows due to capital investments in plant and equipment that will be used over multiple years is not allowed.

a. Why are these outflows not allowed to just be subtracted?

b. Where do depreciation allowances fit into the tax picture, especially since they are not cash flows?

3. Michelin is considering going "lights-out" in the mixing area of the business that operates 24/7. Currently, personnel with a loaded cost of $600,000 per year are used to manually weigh real rubber, synthetic rubber, carbon black, oils, and other components prior to manual insertion in a Banbary mixer that provides a homogeneous blend of rubber for making tires. New technology is available that has the reliability and consistency desired to equal or exceed the quality of blend now achieved manually. It requires an investment of $3.75 million, with $80,000 per year operational costs, and will replace all the manual effort described above.

   a. How are the current manual expenditures handled for tax purposes?

   b. How would the new technology expenditures be handled for tax purposes?

Section 9.2

4. For each of the following assets, state whether the asset is tangible/intangible property, personal/real property, and depreciable/nondepreciable property.

   a. A melt-indexer used in a company research lab

   b. A computer used for personal e-mail, blogging, and hobbies

   c. A plot of land for the production of income

   d. A file cabinet in your business office

   e. A restaurant franchise

   f. A commercial delivery truck

   g. An amateur radio tower attached to land with multiple antennas on it

   h. An office complex for business

   i. Fencing and landscaping around an office complex

5. For each of the following assets, state whether the asset is tangible/intangible property, personal/real property, and depreciable/nondepreciable property. (9.2)

   a. A cell phone tower

   b. A tractor (part of tractor-trailer rig, an 18-wheeler)

   c. A plot of land for your personal use

   d. A copyright

   e. A computer used in your job

   f. An all-in-one copier, scanner, fax machine used in your business

   g. A Mooney viscometer used in a polymers lab

   h. A rental home for the purpose of generating rental income

   i. An electric generator purchased by a public utility

6. At the beginning of the fiscal year, Remington purchased a mold for manufacturing powdered metal firearm parts for $120,000. The estimated salvage value after 8 years is $10,000. Suppose they wish to make end-of-year deposits into an account earning 9 percent over the life of the mold in order to have enough money to purchase another $120,000 mold in 8 years.

   a. What is the equal annual deposit to the fund?

   b. Counting both the deposit and the interest earned, what will be the increase in the account value in year 6?

   c. The answer to Part b is also known as the allowance in year 6 using what kind of depreciation?

   d. What will be the total value of the account at the end of 8 years?

7. Determine the sinking fund depreciation allowance and the book value at the end of each year for a computerized truck tire balancer costing $18,000 and having a market value of $2,000 after a useful life of 5 years. Interest is 12 percent.

8. Calculate the sinking fund depreciation allowance for a company-owned executive car having a cost basis of $60,000. The company will keep it for 3 years, and it can be sold at $25,000 at that time. Interest is 10 percent.

   a. Determine the sinking fund depreciation for each of the 3 years.

   b. Why is this depreciation method considered to be back-end loaded?

   c. Why is sinking fund out of favor as a depreciation strategy?

Sections 9.3, 9.4, 9.5, 9.A

9. A small truck is purchased for $17,000. It is expected to be of use to the company for 6 years, after which it will be sold for $3,500. Determine the depreciation deduction and the resulting unrecovered investment during each year of the asset's life.

   a. Use straight-line depreciation (9.3)

   b. Use declining balance depreciation, with a rate that ensures the book value equals the salvage value (9.4)

   c. Use double declining balance depreciation (9.4)

   d. Use double declining balance, switching to straight-line depreciation (9.5)

   e. Use sum-of-years'-digits depreciation. (9.A)

10. A surface mount PCB placement/soldering line is to be installed for $1.6 million. It will have a salvage value of $100,000 after 5 years. Determine the depreciation deduction and the resulting unrecovered investment during each year of the asset's life.

    a. Use straight-line depreciation(9.3)

    b. Use declining-balance depreciation, with a rate that ensures the book value equals the salvage value (9.4)

    c. Use double declining balance depreciation (9.4)

    d. Use double declining balance, switching to straight-line depreciation (9.5)

    e. Use sum-of-years'-digits depreciation (9.A)

11. A tractor for over-the-road hauling is purchased for $90,000. It is expected to be of use to the company for 6 years, after which it will be salvaged for $4,000. Calculate the depreciation deduction and the unrecovered investment during each year of the tractor's life.

    a. Use straight-line depreciation (9.3)

    b. Use declining-balance depreciation, with a rate that ensures the book value equals the salvage value (9.4)

    c. Use double declining balance depreciation (9.4)

    d. Use double declining balance, switching to straight-line depreciation (9.5)

    e. Use sum-of-years'-digits depreciation (9.A)

12. WindPower Inc. designs and commissions the manufacture of a wind-powered inverter-based constant voltage generator for research and experimentation with low-rated, highly variable wind fields as a form of alternative energy. The unit cost $35,000 plus $3,000 for shipping and installation. After 3 years, WindPower had no further use for the experimental unit and was able to sell it for $2,000, less $500 for removal. WindPower had depreciated the generator cost over the 3 years with an estimated life of 5 years and a terminal book value of $1,000. All of the following parts relate to financial reporting, not computing income taxes.

    a. What is the total investment cost (basis) for this generator?

    b. What is the net market value actually received after 3 years?

    c. By what amount did the book value differ from the net market value at the end of 3 years if the following depreciation method was used?

       (i) Straight-line depreciation (9.3)

       (ii) Declining-balance depreciation using a rate that ensures the book value equals the salvage value (9.4)

       (iii) Double declining balance depreciation (9.4)

       (iv) Double declining balance, switching to straight-line depreciation (9.5)

       (v) Sum-of-years'-digits depreciation. (9.A)

13. A high-precision programmable router for shaping furniture components is purchased by Henredon for $190,000. It is expected to last 12 years and have a salvage value of $5,000. Calculate the depreciation deduction and book value for each year.

    a. Use straight-line depreciation (9.3)

    b. Use declining-balance depreciation, with a rate that ensures the book value equals the salvage value (9.4)

    c. Use double declining balance depreciation (9.4)

    d. Use double declining balance, switching to straight-line depreciation (9.5)

    e. Use sum-of-years'-digits depreciation (9.A)

14. A land grant university has upgraded its course management system (CMS), integrating the system throughout all of its main campus and branch campuses around the state. It has purchased a set of 15 servers and peripherals for needs associated with the CMS. The total cost basis is $120,000 and expected use will be 5 years, after which they will have no projected value. Calculate the depreciation deduction and book value for each year.

    a. Use straight-line depreciation (9.3)

    b. Use declining balance depreciation, with a rate that ensures the book value equals the salvage value (9.4)

    c. Use double declining balance depreciation (9.4)

    d. Use double declining balance, switching to straight-line depreciation (9.5)

    e. Use sum-of-years'-digits depreciation (9.A)

Section 9.6

15. MACRS-ADS depreciation is only considered in Section 9.6.1, and no tables are provided in this text. Suppose you have an injection molding machine for plastic products costing $220,000, and for whatever reason, you decide to depreciate it using MACRS-ADS. It is considered to be in a 7-year property class and yet is depreciated over 11 years if MACRS-ADS is elected. Determine the depreciation percentages to two places after the decimal (e.g., 9.62 percent) and the depreciation allowance for each year. Hint: Don't forget the half-year convention!

16. MACRS-ADS depreciation is only considered in Section 9.6.1, and no tables are provided in this text. A 27.5-year residential rental property is purchased in April by a calendar-year taxpayer for $88,000. Determine the first, fifth, and forty-first year's depreciation percentage to two places after the decimal (e.g., 4.28 percent) and the depreciation allowance using MACRS-ADS with a midmonth convention. Remember, a 40-year period is used. Hint: There are 8.5 months left in the first year for an asset purchased in mid-April.

17. Pretend that you have misplaced your MACRS tables. Develop the MACRS depreciation table for a property class of 3 years, assuming 200 percent DB depreciation switching to straight line; a half-year convention; and a salvage value equal to $0. Your table should match the one for MACRS-GDS 3-year property.

18. Pretend that you have misplaced your MACRS tables. Develop the MACRS depreciation table for a property class of 5 years, assuming 200 percent DB depreciation switching to straight line; a half-year convention; and a salvage value equal to $0. Your table should match the one for MACRS-GDS 5-year property.

19. Suppose the IRS has instituted a new MACRS-GDS property class of only 2 years. It will follow the usual depreciation conventions, determined in the same way as 3-, 5-, 7-, and 10-year property. Determine the yearly MACRS-GDS percentages for each year.

20. Suppose the IRS has instituted a new MACRS-GDS property class of 4 years. It will follow the usual depreciation conventions, determined in the same way as 3-, 5-, 7-, and 10-year property. Determine the yearly MACRS-GDS percentages for each year.

21. For each of the assets named in Problem 9.4 (a–g), state both the MACRS-GDS property class, if applicable, and the specific depreciation method to be used. (e.g., 15-year Property; 150 percent DBSLH)

22. For each of the assets named in problem 9.5 (a–g), state both the MACRS-GDS property class, if applicable, and the specific depreciation method to be used (e.g., 15-year property; 150 percent DBSLH).

23. Englehard purchases a slurry-based separator for the mining of clay that costs $700,000 and has an estimated useful life of 10 years, a MACRS-GDS property class of 7 years, and an estimated salvage value of $75,000 after 10 years. It was financed using a $200,000 down payment and a loan of $500,000 over a period of 5 years with interest at 10 percent. Loan payments are made in equal annual amounts (principal plus interest) over the 5 years.

    a. What is the amount of the MACRS-GDS depreciation taken in the third year?

    b. What is the book value at the end of the third year?

    c. Returning to the original situation, what is the amount of the MACRS-GDS depreciation taken in the third year if the separator is also sold during the third year?

24. Bell's Amusements purchased an expensive ride for their theme and amusement park situated within a city-owned expo center. Bell's had a multiyear contract with the expo center. The ride cost $1.2 million. Bells anticipated that the ride would have a useful life of 12 years, after which the net salvage value would be $0. After 4 years, the city and Bell's were unable to come to an agreement regarding an extended contract. In order to expedite Bell's departure, the expo center agreed to purchase the ride and leave it in place. Right at the end of the fourth fiscal year,

the expo center paid Bell's the unrecovered investment (remember the half-year convention for MACRS-GDS). Determine the amount paid, assuming

    a. straight-line depreciation used for valuation purposes was agreed upon. (9.3)

    b. MACRS-GDS depreciation used for tax purposes (state the property class) was agreed upon. (9.6.2)

25. A manufacturing system for fabricated metal products is purchased for $800,000 in the middle of the fiscal year. The estimated salvage value after 10 years is $130,000.

    a. What is the MACRS-GDS property class?

    b. Determine the depreciation deduction during each year of the asset's 10-year life.

    c. Determine the unrecovered investment at the end of each of the 10 years.

26. Milliken uses a digitally controlled ''dyer'' for placing intricate and integrated patterns on manufactured carpet squares for home and commercial use. It is purchased on April 1 for $350,000. It is expected to last 8 years and have a salvage value of $30,000.

    a. What is the MACRS-GDS property class?

    b. Determine the depreciation deduction during each year of the asset's 8-year life.

    c. Determine the unrecovered investment at the end of each of the 8 years.

27. At the beginning of the fiscal year, Remington purchases a mold for manufacturing powdered metal firearm parts for $120,000. The estimated salvage value after 8 years is $10,000. Calculate the depreciation deduction and the book value for each year using MACRS-GDS allowances.

    a. What is the MACRS-GDS property class?

    b. Assume the complete depreciation schedule is used.

    c. Assume the asset is sold during the sixth year of use.

28. A tractor for over-the-road hauling is purchased for $90,000. It is expected to be of use to the company for 6 years, after which it will be salvaged for $4,000. Calculate the depreciation deduction and the unrecovered investment during each year of the tractor's life using MACRS-GDS allowances.

    a. What is the MACRS-GDS property class?

    b. Assume the tractor is used for the full 6 years.

    c. Assume the tractor is sold during the fourth year of use.

    d. Assume the tractor is sold during the third year of use.

WILEY   29. A virtual mold apparatus for producing dental crowns permits an infinite number of shapes to be custom constructed based upon mold imprints taken by dentists. It costs $28,500 and is purchased at the beginning of the tax year. It is expected to last 9 years with no salvage value at that time. The dental supplier depreciates assets using MACRS but values assets of the company using straight-line depreciation. Determine the depreciation allowance and the unrecovered investment for each year using each of the following:

    a. For tax purposes (be sure to identify the MACRS-GDS property class) (9.6.2)

    b. For company valuation purposes (9.3)

WILEY   30. A surface mount PCB placement/soldering line for the manufacture of electronic components is to be installed for
VS $1.6 million with an expected life of 6 years. Determine the depreciation deduction and the resulting unrecovered investment during each year of the asset's life using MACRS-GDS allowances.

    a. What is the MACRS-GDS property class?

    b. Assume the line equipment will be sold shortly after the fifth year.

    c. Assume the line equipment is sold during the third year of use.

WILEY   31. A high-precision programmable router for shaping furniture components is purchased by Henredon for $190,000. It
GO   is expected to last 12 years. Calculate the depreciation deduction and book value for each year using MACRS-GDS allowances.

    a. What is the MACRS-GDS property class?

    b. Assume the complete allowable depreciation schedule is used.

    c. Assume the asset is sold during the fifth year of use.

32. A portable concrete test instrument used in construction for evaluating and profiling concrete surfaces (MACRS-GDS 5-year property class) is purchased in December by a calendar-year taxpayer for $22,000. The instrument will be used for 6 years and will be worth $2,000 at that time.

   a. Calculate the depreciation deduction for years 1, 3, and 6.

   b. If the instrument is sold in year 4, determine the depreciation deduction for years 1, 3, and 4.

33. A three-in-one grain conveyor used in the manufacture of grain for transporting, filling, or emptying is purchased and installed for $75,000. It is placed in service during the middle of the tax year.

   a. What is the MACRS-GDS property class?

   b. If it is removed just before the end of the tax year approximately 4.5 years from the date placed in service, determine the depreciation deduction during each of the tax years involved.

   c. If it is removed just after the end of the tax year approximately 4.5 years from the date placed in service, determine the depreciation deduction during each of the tax years involved.

34. Material handling equipment used in the manufacture of sugar is purchased and installed for $250,000. It is placed in service in the middle of the tax year and removed from service 5.5 years later.

   a. What is the MACRS-GDS property class?

   b. Determine the MACRS-GDS depreciation deduction during each of the tax years involved if the equipment is removed one day before the end of the tax year.

   c. Determine the MACRS-GDS depreciation deduction during each of the tax years involved if the equipment is removed one day after the end of the tax year.

35. Electric generating and transmission equipment is placed in service at a cost of $3,000,000. It is expected to last 30 years with a salvage value of $250,000.

   a. What is the MACRS-GDS property class?

   b. Determine the depreciation deduction and the unrecovered investment during each of the first 4 tax years.

36. A hydroprocessing reactor, an asset used in petroleum refining, is placed into service at a cost of $2.7 million. It is thought to have a useful life, with turnarounds and proper maintenance, of 18 years and will have a salvage value of nothing at that time.

   a. What is the MACRS-GDS property class?

   b. Determine the depreciation deduction and the unrecovered investment over the depreciable life of the reactor.

37. A public utility purchases a gas-powered electric generator as part of an expansion program. It is expected to be useful, with proper maintenance, for an estimated 30 years. The cost is $17 million, installed. The salvage value at the end of 30 years is expected to be 10 percent of the original cost.

   a. What is the MACRS-GDS property class?

   b. Determine the depreciation deduction and the unrecovered investment for years 1, 5, and the last depreciable year of the generator.

38. A building with business offices, a reception area, and numerous small diagnosis rooms is placed in service by a group of three orthopedic surgeons on January 4 for $650,000.

   a. What is the MACRS-GDS property class?

   b. Calculate the depreciation deduction for years 1, 4, and 7 if it is kept longer than 7 years.

   c. Calculate the depreciation deduction for years 1, 4, and 7 if it is sold on July 1 in the seventh calendar year.

   d. Why is it highly unlikely the building will ever be completely depreciated?

39. A nonresidential business building is placed in service by a calendar-year taxpayer on March 3 for $300,000.

   a. What is the MACRS-GDS property class?

   b. Calculate the depreciation deduction for years 1, 4, and 8 if it is kept longer than 8 years.

   c. Calculate the depreciation deduction for years 1, 4, and 8 if it is sold on August 12 in the eighth calendar year.

   d. Why is it highly unlikely the building will ever be completely depreciated?

40. A residential rental apartment complex is placed in service by a calendar-year taxpayer on February 27 for $530,000. The apartments are kept for slightly more than 6 years and are sold on March 6.

   a. What is the MACRS-GDS property class?

   b. Determine the depreciation deduction during each of the 7 years involved.

   c. Determine the unrecovered investment during each of the 7 years involved.

41. A permanent steel building used for the overhaul of dewatering systems (engines, pumps, and wellpoints) is placed in service on July 10 by a calendar-year taxpayer for $240,000. It is sold almost 5 years later on May 15.

    a. What is the MACRS-GDS property class?

    b. Determine the depreciation deduction during each of the years involved.

    c. Determine the unrecovered investment during each of the years involved.

42. Now that you are making the big bucks, your spouse has decided to venture into the rental property business. He purchases a rental house, and after making some improvements, it has a basis of $85,000. He places it in service as a calendar-year taxpayer during May and sells it in September, just over 4 years later.

    a. What is the MACRS-GDS property class?

    b. Determine the depreciation deduction during each of the years involved.

    c. Determine the unrecovered investment during each of the years involved.

Section 9.7

43. Computer-based central office electronic switching for telephone and data use has an installed cost of $300,000. It is in the MACRS-GDS 5-year property class. Upon disposal, the equipment will be given away in return for dismantling and moving it, resulting in a net $0 salvage. Compare MACRS to traditional depreciation methods by calculating yearly depreciation allowances, present worth of the depreciation allowances, and book value for each year using each of the following (*MARR* is 10 percent): (9.7)

    a. MACRS-GDS as is proper over 6 years (9.6.2)

    b. 200 percent DBH with deductions in years 1 through 6 (9.6.2)

    c. DDB taking a full deduction in the first year, with the last deduction in year 5 (9.4)

    d. DDB switching to straight line, taking a full deduction in the first year, with the last deduction in year 5 (9.5)

    e. SLN taking a full deduction in the first year, with the last deduction in year 5 (9.3)

    f. SLH with deductions in years 1 through 6 (9.6.1)

    g. SYD with the last deduction in year 5 (9.A)

44. Ultra-clean special handling devices used in the filling process for baby-food manufacture are placed into use at a cost of $850,000. These devices are expected to be useful for 4 years with a salvage value of nothing at that time. Compare MACRS to traditional depreciation methods by calculating yearly depreciation allowances, present worth of the depreciation allowances, and book value for each year using each of the following (*MARR* is 11 percent): (9.7)

    a. MACRS-GDS as is proper over its property class depreciation life (9.6.2)

    b. 200 percent DBH with deductions in years 1 through 4 (9.6.2)

    c. DDB taking a full deduction in the first year, with the last deduction in year 3 (9.4)

    d. DDB switching to straight line, taking a full deduction in the first year, with the last deduction in year 3 (9.5)

    e. SLN taking a full deduction in the first year, with the last deduction in year 3 (9.3)

    f. SLH with deductions in years 1 through 4 (9.6.1)

    g. SYD with the last deduction in year 3 (9.A)

45. Equipment for manufacturing vegetable oil products is purchased from Alfa. Items such as oil expellers, filter presses, and a steam generator are purchased for $1.2 million. These devices are expected to be used for 11 years with no salvage value at that time. Compare MACRS to traditional depreciation methods by calculating yearly depreciation allowances, present worth of the depreciation allowances, and book value for each year using each of the following (*MARR* is 9 percent): (9.7)

    a. MACRS-GDS as is proper over its property class depreciation life (9.6.2)

    b. 200 percent DBH with deductions in years 1 through 11 (9.6.2)

    c. DDB taking a full deduction in the first year, with the last deduction in year 10 (9.4)

    d. DDB switching to straight line, taking a full deduction in the first year, with the last deduction in year 10 (9.5)

    e. SLN taking a full deduction in the first year, with the last deduction in year 10 (9.3)

    f. SLH with deductions in years 1 through 11 (9.6.1)

    g. SYD with the last deduction in year 10 (9.A)

Section 9.B

46. A supplier of plastic and resin parts has demands for thousands of different part configurations from hundreds of small customers. Many of these parts are similar, and rather than mold each different one, a common molded blank may be used and machined to insert holes, grooves, fins, threads, and so on. Some of these parts may be called for in large amounts one year and almost disregarded the next year. Consider a spiral groover costing $16,000 with a life of approximately 24,000 machined parts and a salvage value of $2,000. Depreciation allowances taken over 4 years based upon the units of production method are (1) $933.33, (2) $5,454.17, (3) $4,433.33, and (4) $694.17. (9.B.1)
    a. How many parts were machined each year?
    b. How many, if any, parts can still be machined with this spiral groover?

47. The Eimac tubes in a linear amplifier for radio transmission are estimated to provide 18,000 hours of operation before requiring replacement. A pair of tubes costs $20,000 and has no salvage value. Their use, expressed in hours over a 4-year period, is (1) 2,500, (2) 4,500, (3) 3,000, and (4) 3,900. Determine the current book value based upon the operating hour method of depreciation. (9.B.2)

48. A robotic precision spot welder is purchased for $380,000. The installation cost is $45,000, which will be expensed. It will have a useful life of 24,000 hours of operation, after which it will have a salvage value of $60,000. It takes 6 minutes to weld a part, and approximately 24,000 units are expected to be welded in the first year, increasing by 24,000 units each year thereafter. (9.B.2)
    a. What is the cost basis?
    b. What is the salvage value?
    c. How many years of useful life are expected?
    d. What is the depreciation each year, using the operating hour method of depreciation?

49. A tractor with a front-end loader and a backhoe costs $20,000 and is rented by the hour, day, or week. It is expected to depreciate to $2,000 when it has been rented out until the total rental income equals $72,000. Annual incomes for the tractor are expected to be $24,000, $18,000, $16,000, and $10,000 per year over the next 4 years. (9.B.3)
    a. What are the depreciation charges for each year, using the income forecast method?
    b. How much additional income is expected from the tractor?

Section 9.C

50. Rights to mine copper from a tract of land are purchased for $1,200,000. It is estimated that there are 1,800,000 pounds of copper in the reservoir to be mined. The copper can be sold for $3.30 per pound, on average, although the cost to mine it is $2.20 per pound. If 300,000 pounds of copper are produced this year, determine the depletion allowance using (9.C)
    a. cost depletion.
    b. percentage depletion.

51. A Central Appalachia 12,500 Btu, 1.2 SO_2 coal has an average price of $60 per ton. A mine having 7 million tons of coal has a first cost of $42 million. The cost of mining is $45 per ton. If, during the first 3 years of operation, the mine yields 300,000, 600,000, and 500,000 tons, respectively, determine the depletion allowance using the better method of depletion for each year. (9.C)

52. Mineral rights on a gold-producing property are purchased for $2,300,000. A total of 27,000 of gold is expected to be mined and can be sold for $450/ounce. It will cost $250/ounce to mine and process it for sale. If 3,000 ounces are produced and sold this year, determine the depletion allowance using (9.C)
    a. cost depletion.
    b. percentage depletion.

Chapter 10

AFTER-TAX ECONOMIC ANALYSIS

An Intel manufacturing technician, shown here, uses a scanner to start the very first 45 nm production lot of 300 mm wafers inside Fab 32, Intel's first high-volume 45 nm chip factory, located in Chandler, Arizona. The factory produces millions of Intel's new 45 nm high-k metal gate microprocessors. (Courtesy of Intel)

Intel

With revenue of $43.6 billion in 2010, Intel is the world's largest semiconductor chip maker. The chances are great that your computer includes one or more of Intel's products: chips, printed circuit boards, and other semiconductor components. More specifically, Intel's products include microprocessors, chipsets, motherboards, flash memory, wired and wireless connectivity products, communications infrastructure components (including network processors), application and cellular baseband processors, and products for networked storage. Intel's products appear in computers, as well as in servers and networking and communications products.

As of December 25, 2010, 61 percent of Intel's wafer fabrication was conducted in the United States. The wafer-fabrication facilities located outside the U.S. are in China, Ireland, and Israel. Assembly and test facilities are in Malaysia, China, Costa Rica, and Vietnam. As of December 25, 2010, Intel employed 82,500 people worldwide, with approximately 55 percent of those employees located in the U.S. A substantial number of Intel's employees are engineers or computer scientists. Approximately 30 percent of its employees are engaged in R&D activities, which totaled $6.6 billion in 2010.

According to its 2010 Annual Report, Intel plans to make $9 billion of capital investments in 2011 to "build and equip our 22nm process technology manufacturing capacity, which will increase our leading-edge facilities to four." Semiconductor manufacturing is very expensive. Many of Intel's competitors do not own manufacturing, assembly, and test facilities. Instead, they contract with third parties to perform those functions. Intel considers its ownership of fabrication facilities to be one of its most significant strategic advantages.

Given the multiplicity of tax laws, depreciation and depletion allowances, and special regulations facing multinational companies, determining income tax effects on capital investment is not a simple matter. But similar challenges face all multinational firms.

There are few certainties in this world, but most agree that two things cannot be avoided: death and taxes! To those two, we can add tax laws changing. Although they have not changed significantly in several years, incremental changes occur frequently, and major changes often accompany changes in the political party currently controlling the U.S. Congress and in the state of the nation's overall economy.

Consequently, we focus on *three main messages* in this chapter, rather than on details concerning U.S. tax law. (What are the three main messages? Read on! Those who are impatient can skip to the Summary.) To ensure that they are not missed, we call them out as we present them. We do our best to avoid discussing minute details of tax law. Rather, our objective in this chapter is to communicate the major aspects of corporate tax treatment so that you can perform economic analyses on an after-tax basis and can recognize when you need help. Particularly regarding income taxes, we encourage you to seek assistance from corporate tax personnel when performing after-tax economic justifications.

10-1 INTRODUCTION

From our discussion of depreciation methods, we know that income taxes can significantly impact the economic viability of a capital investment. Tax dollars *are* cash flows, and therefore it is necessary to consider them explicitly, just as costs of wages, equipment, material, and energy are considered. One of the major factors affecting income taxes is depreciation. Although depreciation allowances are not cash flows, their magnitudes and timing affect income taxes. Therefore, proper knowledge and application of tax laws can make the economic difference between accepting or rejecting an investment alternative, as well as between profit or loss on the corporate bottom line.

While the Omnibus Reconciliation Act of 1993 rewrote the tax rates, the Tax Reform Act of 1986 virtually rewrote the book on the method of calculating depreciation and income taxes. This followed the major revisions of the Economic Recovery Act of 1981, which vastly changed the pre-1981 depreciation and tax laws.

In this chapter, we begin with basic concepts of income taxes. Except for one example, the chapter focuses on corporate, not personal, investments. Next, we consider the impact of depreciation allowances on after-tax cash flows and demonstrate the after-tax effects of accelerated depreciation methods. Then we expand our consideration of after-tax consequences to the use of borrowed capital, since interest paid by businesses is deductible from taxable income.

In presenting the material, we revisit several *before-tax* examples from previous chapters to demonstrate the impact income taxes can have on the economic viability of investment alternatives. Examples considered previously in before-tax comparisons are also used to demonstrate that changes can occur in the preferred alternative because of income-tax effects.

Systematic Economic Analysis Technique

1. Identify the investment alternatives
2. Define the planning horizon
3. Specify the discount rate
4. Estimate the cash flows
5. **Compare the alternatives**
6. Perform supplementary analyses
7. Select the preferred investment

10-2 TAX CONCEPTS

WILEY
VIDEO LESSON

The taxes a corporation pays represent a real cost of doing business and, consequently, affect the cash flow profile. For this reason, it is wise to perform economic analyses on an *after-tax* basis. After-tax analysis procedures are identical to before-tax procedures; however, cash flows are adjusted for taxes paid or saved.

Corporations typically pay a variety of taxes, including *ad valorem* (property), *sales*, *excise* (a tax on the manufacture, sale, or consumption of a commodity), and *income taxes*. Among the various types of taxes paid, corporate income taxes tend to be the most significant when performing an economic analysis, because most of the other taxes are not affected by the kinds of investments generally included in an engineering economic analysis. Income taxes are assessed on gross income less certain allowable deductions and on gains resulting from the disposal of property.

Federal and state income tax regulations are detailed, intricate, and subject to change over time. Also, as pointed out in Chapter 9, there is a tendency to change tax laws in an attempt to affect and improve the nation's economy. Hence, only general concepts and procedures for calculating after-tax cash flow profiles and performing after-tax analyses are emphasized here. Furthermore, due to the diversity of state laws, only federal income taxes are considered.

The first of our three main messages is *perform after-tax, not before-tax, analyses, except in unusual situations*. Income taxes matter! Consideration of income taxes in engineering economic analyses is not difficult, particularly at the 10,000 foot level we maintain in the chapter. Generally, it is worth including income-tax considerations in engineering economic analyses.

Main Message #1

Perform after-tax analyses, not before-tax analyses, except in unusual situations.

10-3   CORPORATE INCOME TAXES

WILEY
VIDEO LESSON

For income-tax purposes, a corporation includes associations, business trusts, joint stock companies, insurance firms, and trusts and partnerships that actually operate as associations or corporations. Corporate income tax, however, is not limited to traditional business organizations. Engineers, doctors, lawyers, and other professional people may be treated as corporations if they have formally organized under state professional association acts.

Ordinary federal income-tax rates imposed on corporations are given in Table 10.1. The tax rates shown are current for 2007; in fact, they have not changed since 1993. (The fourth edition of this book is the only one thus far that was not impacted by changes in federal tax rates. However, it is likely that the 2008 elections will result in changes to corporate income tax rates. Therefore, we recommend you consult the Web site for the Internal Revenue Service before performing after-tax analyses.)

Since income tax laws may differ from those described in the text, consult the U.S. Internal Revenue Service web site (**http://www.irs.gov**) for up-to-date information on U.S. tax laws

---

In Chapter 9, we noted how much the corporate income-tax rates changed. They have changed for corporations and for individuals. For example, the highest marginal U.S. income tax rates for married individuals filing jointly were 7 percent in 1913, 73 percent in 1920, 25 percent in 1930, 63 percent in 1935, 81.1 percent in 1940, 94 percent in 1945, 91 percent from 1954 through 1963, 70 percent from 1971 through 1980, 50 percent from 1982 through 1986, 39.6 percent from 1993 through 2000, and 35 percent from 2003 through 2011. For corporations, the highest marginal rates were 1 percent in 1913, 10 percent in 1920, 12 percent in 1930, 13.75 percent in 1935, 38.30

TABLE 10.1
Corporate Income Tax Rates for Tax Years Beginning January 1, 1993 and Beyond.

Taxable Income (TI), in $	Tax Rate (t)	Income Tax (T)
$0 < \text{TI} \leq 50{,}000$	0.15	$0.15(\text{TI})$
$50{,}000 < \text{TI} \leq 75{,}000$	0.25	$7500 + 0.25(\text{TI} - 50{,}000)$
$75{,}000 < \text{TI} \leq 100{,}000$	0.34	$13{,}750 + 0.34(\text{TI} - 75{,}000)$
$100{,}000 < \text{TI} \leq 335{,}000$	$0.39(0.34 + 0.05)$	$22{,}250 + 0.39(\text{TI} - 100{,}000)$
$335{,}000 < \text{TI} \leq 10{,}000{,}000$	0.34	$113{,}900 + 0.34(\text{TI} - 335{,}000)$
$10{,}000{,}000 < \text{TI} \leq 15{,}000{,}000$	0.35	$3{,}400{,}000 + 0.35(\text{TI} - 10{,}000{,}000)$
$15{,}000{,}000 < \text{TI} \leq 18{,}333{,}333$	$0.38(0.35 + 0.03)$	$5{,}150{,}000 + 0.38(\text{TI} - 15{,}000{,}000)$
$18{,}333{,}333 < \text{TI}$	0.35	$0.35(\text{TI})$

percent in 1940, 40 percent in 1945, 52 percent from 1952 through 1963, 46 percent from 1979 through 1986, and 35 percent from 1993 through 2011.[1]

As illustrated in Table 10.1, small businesses with taxable incomes less than $50,000 are subject to a 15 percent tax rate. Note the 39 percent and 38 percent rates for some certain taxable incomes. The 39 percent rate over a taxable income range from $100,000 to $335,000 effectively eliminates the benefit of graduated rates for midsized corporations with taxable incomes of at least $335,000; they will, in effect, pay a flat rate of 34 percent on every dollar of taxable income up to $10,000,000. The 38 percent rate over a taxable income range from $15,000,000 to $18,333,333 has the same effect on large corporations with taxable income of at least $18,333,333; they will, in effect, pay a flat rate of 35 percent on every dollar of taxable income.

EXAMPLE 10.1 Computing Income Taxes for Corporations

To illustrate the computation of corporate income taxes, suppose a small company is currently forecasting a taxable income of $50,000 for the year. The company's owner is considering an investment that will increase taxable income by $45,000. If the investment is pursued and the anticipated return occurs, what will be the magnitude of the increase in income taxes caused by the new investment? What will it be if the company forecasts a taxable income of $400,000 for the year?

With a "base" taxable income of $50,000, the federal income tax will be 0.15($50,000), or $7,500. The income tax for a taxable income of $95,000 will be $13,750 + 0.34($20,000) = $20,550.

With a "base" taxable income of $400,000, the federal income tax will be $113,900 + 0.34($65,000) = $136,000, or 34 percent of $400,000. Because every dollar of the additional $45,000 in taxable income will be taxed at 34 percent, the increase in taxable income will be 0.34($45,000) = $15,300, for a total tax of $151,300.

From the example, we can define three tax rates for the corporation:

1. The *effective tax rate,* or *average tax rate,* which equals the income tax divided by the taxable income

2. The *incremental tax rate,* which is the average rate charged to the incremental investment

3. The *marginal tax rate,* which is the tax rate that will apply to the last dollar included in taxable income

> - *effective tax rate* = income tax divided by taxable income;
> - *incremental tax rate* = average rate charged to incremental investment; and
> - *marginal tax rate* = tax rate that applies to the last dollar included in taxable income.

[1]See www.taxpolicycenter.org/taxfacts/displayafact.cfm?Docid=213 for top individual tax rates; see www.taxpolicycenter.org/taxfacts/displayafact.cfm?Docid=658&Topic2id=70 for top corporate rates from 1909 through 2009.

The effective tax rate is more correctly defined as the sum of taxes on ongoing operations and tax on unusual and extraordinary items divided by the sum of pretax income for ongoing operations and pretax income for unusual and extraordinary items. In the absence of unusual and extraordinary items, the effective tax rate is as defined above.

Effective income tax rates vary greatly, depending on deferred taxes, tax reserves released, tax exemptions in certain countries, and so forth. For example, in 2010, ABB's effective tax rate was 27 percent, Abbott Laboratories' was 19 percent, Coca-Cola's was 16 percent, ConocoPhillips's was 42 percent, Eli Lilly's was 22 percent, FedEx's was 38 percent, Hewlettt-Packard's was 20 percent, Home Depot's was 37 percent, Pepsi's was 23 percent, UPS's was 37 percent, and Wal-Mart's was 32 percent.

According to a February 1, 2011, column by David Leonhart of *The New York Times*, 115 of the 500 companies in Standard & Poor's stock index (known as the S&P 500) had an effective income tax rate of less than 20 percent over the previous five years. 39 had a rate less than 10 percent. The 5-year average rate for the S&P 500 was 32.8 percent. Among those paying more than the average over the 5 years were Exxon Mobil, FedEx, Starbucks, and Wal-Mart. While the U.S. corporate tax rate is one of the highest in the world, firms have found ways to minimize their income tax liabilities.

EXAMPLE 10.2   Computing Effective and Incremental Income Tax Rates

In the previous example, what were the effective, incremental, and marginal tax rates when the base taxable income was $50,000?

When the base taxable income was $50,000, the corporation had an effective tax rate of 15 percent: $7,500/$50,000. With the addition of $45,000 in taxable income, the new effective tax rate became $20,550/$95,000 = 21.63 percent.

The $45,000 increase in taxable income caused taxes to increase from $7,500 to $20,550. Therefore, $13,050/$45,000, or 29 percent, is the incremental tax rate.

The marginal tax rate was 34 percent, since taxable income of $95,000 is in the 34 percent tax bracket. Therefore, the last $1 added to taxable income contributed 34¢ to the company's income taxes.

Conservatively, when performing economic justifications, an investment alternative's after-tax economic worth should be computed using the *marginal tax rate*.

In performing engineering economic analyses, use the *marginal tax rate*.

Taxable income must first be determined before any tax rate can be applied. Taxable income is gross income less allowable deductions. Gross income is income in a general sense less any monies specifically exempt from tax liability. Corporate deductions are subtracted from gross income and commonly include items such as salaries, wages, repairs, rent, bad debts, taxes (other than income), charitable contributions, casualty losses, interest, and depreciation. Interest and depreciation are of

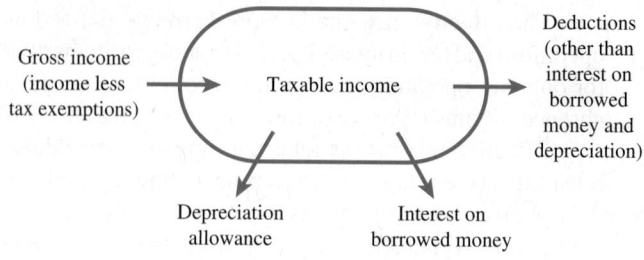

FIGURE 10.1

Pictorial Representation of Taxable Income.

particular importance, because we can control them to some extent through financing arrangements and accounting procedures.

Taxable income is represented pictorially in Figure 10.1, which shows that taxable income for any year is what is left after deductions—including interest on borrowed money and depreciation allowance—are subtracted from gross income. These components are not all cash flows, since the depreciation allowance is simply treated as an expense in determining taxable income.

10-4 AFTER-TAX CASH FLOW WITHOUT BORROWING

We have now looked at the base elements needed to calculate after-tax cash flow (ATCF). These elements are summarized in Figure 10.2, which shows that the ATCF is the amount remaining after income taxes and deductions-including interest but excluding depreciation allowance-are subtracted from gross income.

In many of the following tables and spreadsheets, we simplify our terminology by speaking of *before-tax cash flow (BTCF)*. This term is used when no borrowed money is involved and when it equals gross income less deductions, not including depreciation. The term *before-tax-and-loan cash flow (BT&LCF)* is used when borrowed money is involved and when it equals gross income less deductions, not including either depreciation or principal or interest on the loan.

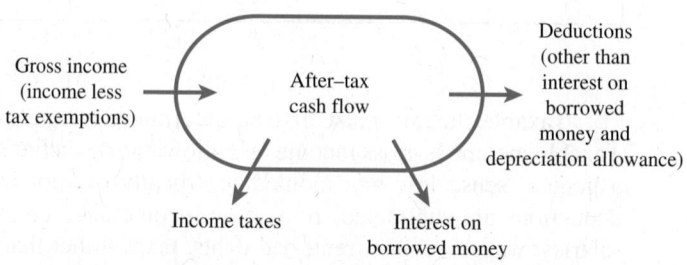

FIGURE 10.2

Pictorial Representation of After-Tax Cash Flow (ATCF).

The following notation will be used for after-tax analysis of an investment alternative's economic worth, without borrowed capital:

$BTCF$ = before-tax cash flow

DWO = depreciation write-off, allowance or charge

TI = taxable income

itr = income tax rate

T = income tax

$ATCF$ = after-tax cash flow

The following equation holds for investments in depreciable property:

$$ATCF = BTCF - T \qquad (10.1)$$

where

$$T = itr(TI) \qquad (10.2)$$

where

$$TI = BTCF - DWO \qquad (10.3)$$

Therefore,

$$ATCF = BTCF(1 - itr) + itr(DWO) \qquad (10.4)$$

As indicated in Equation 10.1, ATCF is obtained by subtracting from BTCF the cash flows required to pay income taxes. From Equation 10.2, the income-tax cash flow is obtained by multiplying taxable income by the income-tax rate. Taxable income, as indicated in Equation 10.3, is obtained by subtracting from BTCF the depreciation allowance. Finally, by combining equations, Equation 10.1 can be expressed as Equation 10.4. From Equation 10.4, notice that every dollar of depreciation contributes *itr* cents of positive ATCF.

$$\boxed{ATCF = BTCF(1 - itr) + itr(DWO)}$$

Since state income taxes are generally deductible expenses when computing federal income taxes, the overall income-tax rate should equal

$$itr = str + ftr(1 - str) \qquad (10.5)$$

where

str = state income-tax rate, and

ftr = federal income-tax rate.

In the text, a value of 40 percent will be used for the combined income-tax rate in most examples and end-of-chapter problems. The 40 percent rate is obtained using a 7 percent state income-tax rate and a 35 percent federal income-tax rate. From Equation 10.5,

$$0.07 + 0.35(1 - 0.07) = 0.3955 \text{ or } 39.55\%$$

Depending on the particular state (and country) in which the investment is made, a different *marginal income tax rate* might be more appropriate. For example, many states have income-tax rates that are greater than the 7 percent used here; other states have income-tax rates that are significantly less than 7 percent.

EXAMPLE 10.3   After-Tax Analysis with SLN Depreciation

Recall the $500,000 investment in the surface mount placement (SMP) machine in an electronics manufacturing plant. It produced $92,500 in net revenue for 10 years, plus a $50,000 salvage value at the end of the 10-year period. Now, to determine the after-tax economic worth of the investment, we will use a 40 percent income-tax rate and will perform an after-tax analysis using a 10 percent after-tax *MARR*.

In the previous chapters, the $92,500 net revenue was given to be an after-tax figure. Although we did not specify the depreciation method used to generate the ATCF amount of $92,500, it was based on straight-line depreciation over a 10-year recovery period. As shown in Table 10.2, a BTCF of $124,166.67 results in an ATCF of $92,500 when straight-line depreciation is used with a $50,000 salvage value.

The computation of ATCF is as shown in Table 10.2. In the tenth year, notice how the salvage value is handled. The $500,000 investment is not fully recovered through depreciation allowances. Straight-line depreciation allowances of $45,000 over a 10-year period reduce the book value to $50,000 at the end of the 10-year planning horizon. Since the book value exactly equals the salvage value, there is no income tax associated with the sale of the

TABLE 10.2
Before-Tax and After-Tax Analysis of the SMP Investment with SLN Depreciation.

EOY	BTCF	DWO	TI	T	ATCF
0	−$500,000.00				−$500,000.00
1	$124,166.67	$45,000.00	$79,166.67	$31,666.67	$92,500.00
2	$124,166.67	$45,000.00	$79,166.67	$31,666.67	$92,500.00
3	$124,166.67	$45,000.00	$79,166.67	$31,666.67	$92,500.00
4	$124,166.67	$45,000.00	$79,166.67	$31,666.67	$92,500.00
5	$124,166.67	$45,000.00	$79,166.67	$31,666.67	$92,500.00
6	$124,166.67	$45,000.00	$79,166.67	$31,666.67	$92,500.00
7	$124,166.67	$45,000.00	$79,166.67	$31,666.67	$92,500.00
8	$124,166.67	$45,000.00	$79,166.67	$31,666.67	$92,500.00
9	$124,166.67	$45,000.00	$79,166.67	$31,666.67	$92,500.00
10	$174,166.67	$45,000.00	$79,166.67	$31,666.67	$142,500.00
$MARR_{BT} =$	16.667%			$MARR_{AT} =$	10%
$PW_{BT} =$	$96,229.49			$PW_{AT} =$	$87,649.62
$FW_{BT} =$	$449,547.99			$FW_{AT} =$	$227,340.55
$AW_{BT} =$	$20,406.41			$AW_{AT} =$	$14,264.57
$IRR_{BT} =$	21.64%			$IRR_{AT} =$	13.80%
$ERR_{BT} =$	18.74%			$ERR_{AT} =$	11.79%

SMP machine for $50,000. Therefore, the taxable income in year 10 is identical to that in each of the nine previous years.

Table 10.2 provides values for the various *DCF*-based measures of economic worth treated in previous chapters. As expected, the ATCF values and the after-tax measures of economic worth shown in Table 10.2 are identical to those obtained in Chapters 5 through 8.

If, in the previous chapters, BTCF was used and a before-tax analysis was performed, then a before-tax minimum attractive rate of return (BTMARR) must be used. An estimate of the BTMARR is obtained by dividing the after-tax minimum attractive rate of return (ATMARR) by 1 minus the income-tax rate. Hence, with a 40 percent tax rate and a 10 percent ATMARR, a BTMARR of 16.667 percent would be used.

As shown in Table 10.2, the before-tax measures of economic worth overstate the profitability of the investment. As an exercise, you can use the Excel® SOLVER tool to determine what BTMARR values yield before-tax values for PW, FW, and AW that are identical to the after-tax values for PW, FW, and AW obtained using a 10 percent ATMARR. In doing so, you will find that the ATMARR must be 17.055 percent for the PW_{BT} and PW_{AT} values to be the same, 19.479 percent for the FW_{BT} and FW_{AT} values to be the same, and 18.190 percent for the AW_{BT} and AW_{AT} values to be the same.

(Recall, we previously approximated after-tax results by multiplying before-tax results by 1 minus the income-tax rate. In this case, before-tax results would have been multiplied by 0.60 to obtain after-tax approximations. As shown, the approximation is not very accurate. It is less accurate when accelerated depreciation is used. Hence, we recommend that after-tax, rather than before-tax, analyses be performed.)

EXAMPLE 10.4   After-Tax Analysis with MACRS Depreciation

As noted in Chapter 9, the SMP machine purchased for $500,000 qualifies as 5-year property for MACRS depreciation. What is the after-tax effect on the measures of economic worth if MACRS is used instead of SLN?

Table 10.3 provides the results of the after-tax analysis. Notice, since MACRS fully recovers the investment, the book value at the end of year 10 is 0. If the equipment is sold for $50,000, then the full amount of the salvage value is taxable income. (When a depreciable asset is sold for more than its book value, the gain is called *depreciation recapture* and is taxed as ordinary income under current tax law[2].)

As pointed out in Chapter 9, since depreciation is deducted from taxable income, accelerated depreciation yields a greater economic worth than occurs using straight-line depreciation. This is the second of our three main messages.

---

[2]This is an instance of us omitting details regarding disposal of depreciable property. Much of the law regarding disposition refers to Section 1231 property, named after the section that provides details on what is to be done. Section 1231 property includes property used in a trade or business or held for the production of rents or royalties and held for more than 1 year. As such, nearly any property in an engineering economic analysis is Section 1231 property. Another detail omitted is the special case of an asset being sold for more than its cost basis, creating a capital gain. We omit it because it rarely occurs, and although the capital gains mechanism exists, such gains for corporations are currently taxed as ordinary income.

TABLE 10.3
After-Tax Analysis of the SMP Investment with *MACRS* Depreciation.

EOY	BTCF	DWO	TI	T	ATCF
0	−$500,000.00				−$500,000.00
1	$124,166.67	$100,000.00	$24,166.67	$9,666.67	$114,500.00
2	$124,166.67	$160,000.00	−$35,833.33	−$14,333.33	$138,500.00
3	$124,166.67	$96,000.00	$28,166.67	$11,266.67	$112,900.00
4	$124,166.67	$57,600.00	$66,566.67	$26,626.67	$97,540.00
5	$124,166.67	$57,600.00	$66,566.67	$26,626.67	$97,540.00
6	$124,166.67	$28,800.00	$95,366.67	$38,146.67	$86,020.00
7	$124,166.67	$0.00	$124,166.67	$49,666.67	$74,500.00
8	$124,166.67	$0.00	$124,166.67	$49,666.67	$74,500.00
9	$124,166.67	$0.00	$124,166.67	$49,666.67	$74,500.00
10	$174,166.67	$0.00	$174,166.67	$69,666.67	$104,500.00
				$PW_{AT} =$	$123,988.64
				$FW_{AT} =$	$321,594.61
				$AW_{AT} =$	$20,178.58
				$IRR_{AT} =$	16.12%
				$ERR_{AT} =$	12.46%

What impact did the depreciation method have? For the example, the following values were obtained for the measures of economic worth:

Measure of Economic Worth	With SLN	With MACRS
PW_{AT}	$87,649.62	$123,988.64
FW_{AT}	$227,340.55	$321,594.61
AW_{AT}	$14,264.57	$20,178.58
IRR_{AT}	13.80%	16.12%
ERR_{AT}	11.79%	12.46%

Main Message #2

In general, the faster an investment is depreciated, the greater its after-tax present worth.

We have considered an example in which salvage value equals book value at the planning horizon's end, as well as an example in which salvage value is greater than book value at the planning horizon's end. What about the case where salvage value is less than book value?

For our purposes, when a depreciable asset is sold for less than its book value, the difference is termed a *book loss* and is deducted from taxable income. Although there are carry-forward and carry-back rules, for purposes of the text, we will not present the details; instead, we encourage you to consult income-tax guides or tax experts if you encounter such a situation.

In general, we recommend that the following relationships be used to compute taxable income in the year of property disposal. Specifically, if disposal occurs at the end of year n at a salvage value of F_n,

$$TI_n = BTCF_n(incl\ F_n) - DWO_n - B_n \qquad (10.6)$$

In words, taxable income in the year of a depreciable asset's disposal equals the before-tax cash flow, including the salvage value, less the depreciation allowance, less the book value at the time of disposal.

If depreciable property is disposed of before the end of the recovery period, when using MACRS depreciation, a half-year allowance (in the case of personal property) or midmonth allowance (in the case of real property) is permitted in the year of disposal. For example, if an asset is sold at the end of the sixth tax year and it is 7-year property, then the MACRS depreciation allowance percentages are 14.29 percent, 24.49 percent, 17.49 percent, 12.49 percent, 8.93 percent, and 4.46 percent; normally, the depreciation percentage for the sixth year would be 8.92 percent.

EXAMPLE 10.5   After-Tax Analysis with DDB Depreciation

Suppose DDB depreciation is used to depreciate the SMP machine over the 10-year planning horizon. The book value at the end of the 10-year planning horizon is $53,687.09, which is greater than the salvage value of $50,000. As shown in Table 10.4, $TI_{10} = \$174,166.67 - \$13,421.77 - \$53,687.09 = \$107,057.81$.

TABLE 10.4
After-Tax Analysis of the SMP Investment with *DDB* Depreciation.

EOY	BTCF	DWO	TI	T	ATCF
0	−$500,000.00				−$500,000.00
1	$124,166.67	$100,000.00	$24,166.67	$9,666.67	$114,500.00
2	$124,166.67	$80,000.00	$44,166.67	$17,666.67	$106,500.00
3	$124,166.67	$64,000.00	$60,166.67	$24,066.67	$100,100.00
4	$124,166.67	$51,200.00	$72,966.67	$29,186.67	$94,980.00
5	$124,166.67	$40,960.00	$83,206.67	$33,282.67	$90,884.00
6	$124,166.67	$32,768.00	$91,398.67	$36,559.47	$87,607.20

(Continued)

TABLE 10.4
(Continued)

EOY	BTCF	DWO	TI	T	ATCF
7	$124,166.67	$26,214.40	$97,952.27	$39,180.91	$84,985.76
8	$124,166.67	$20,971.52	$103,195.15	$41,278.06	$82,888.61
9	$124,166.67	$16,777.22	$107,389.45	$42,955.78	$81,210.89
10	$174,166.67	$13,421.77	$107,057.81	$42,823.12	$131,343.55
	$B_{10} =$	$53,687.09		$PW_{AT} =$	$105,429.72
				$FW_{AT} =$	$273,457.54
				$AW_{AT} =$	$17,158.20
				$IRR_{AT} =$	14.88%
				$ERR_{AT} =$	12.12%

Notice, even though DDB included a full allowance in the first year, because depreciation was extended over the 10-year period, the values for the measures of economic worth are less than those obtained using MACRS depreciation.

Not all expenditures are to acquire depreciable property. Consider, for example, an expenditure on a consulting study to identify cost-saving opportunities. Another example of alternatives with different tax consequences is leasing versus purchasing equipment. Likewise, let's not forget expenditures on advertising to generate increased revenue. For tax purposes, these types of expenditures are "expensed" or "written off" in the year in which they occur. Other expenditures that can be expensed include software and most R&D expenses.[3]

The following example shows the after-tax effects of expenditures that can be expensed versus those that must be capitalized and depreciated.

EXAMPLE 10.6 After-Tax Analysis with Nondepreciable Expenditures

In the previous examples, $500,000 was invested in depreciable property to obtain before-tax annual revenues of $124,166.67 each of the following 9 years and $174,166.67 the tenth year. Now suppose the expenditure is on a consulting study that identifies cost-saving opportunities that will produce the same BTCF. With a 40 percent income-tax rate and an after-tax *MARR* of 10 percent, what will be the after-tax measures of economic worth for the investment?

Table 10.5 provides the results of the after-tax analysis. Notice, the investment reduces taxable income by $500,000 in the year in which it occurs. As a result, ATCF is equal to the product of BTCF and $(1 - itr)$, or 60 percent. Hence, $IRR_{AT} = IRR_{BT}$.

[3]Recall, in Chapter 9 we noted that publicly traded corporations frequently have different cost bases for financial reporting purposes than for income-tax purposes. Even though the SEC allows companies to include in the cost basis certain expenditures related to the acquisition and installation of depreciable property, companies tend to expense such expenditures unless specifically required by the IRS to include them in the cost basis.

TABLE 10.5
After-Tax Analysis of a $500,000 Investment in a Consulting Study.

EOY	BTCF	TI	T	ATCF
0	−$500,000.00	−$500,000.00	−$200,000.00	−$300,000.00
1	$124,166.67	$124,166.67	$49,666.67	$74,500.00
2	$124,166.67	$124,166.67	$49,666.67	$74,500.00
3	$124,166.67	$124,166.67	$49,666.67	$74,500.00
4	$124,166.67	$124,166.67	$49,666.67	$74,500.00
5	$124,166.67	$124,166.67	$49,666.67	$74,500.00
6	$124,166.67	$124,166.67	$49,666.67	$74,500.00
7	$124,166.67	$124,166.67	$49,666.67	$74,500.00
8	$124,166.67	$124,166.67	$49,666.67	$74,500.00
9	$124,166.67	$124,166.67	$49,666.67	$74,500.00
10	$174,166.67	$174,166.67	$69,666.67	$104,500.00
			$PW_{AT} =$	$169,336.56
			$FW_{AT} =$	$439,215.43
			$AW_{AT} =$	$27,558.75
			$IRR_{AT} =$	21.64%
			$ERR_{AT} =$	15.03%

Notice the difference in the values of the measures of economic worth when the investment can be *expensed*, instead of *capitalized* and depreciated using MACRS.

Measure of Economic Worth	Expensed	Capitalized
PW_{AT}	$169,336.56	$123,988.64
FW_{AT}	$439,215.43	$321,594.61
AW_{AT}	$27,558.75	$20,178.58
IRR_{AT}	21.64%	16.12%
ERR_{AT}	15.03%	12.46%

10-5   AFTER-TAX COMPARISON OF ALTERNATIVES

An after-tax comparison of investment alternatives follows the procedures described in previous chapters. The only changes are that the comparison is based on ATCF instead of BTCF, and the comparison uses an ATMARR instead of a BTMARR.

Depending on the alternatives being considered, different depreciation allowances might apply to the alternatives. For example, if investment capital is limited and a decision is being made between investing in equipment and investing in labor, there will be obvious differences in the write-offs for the investments. Likewise, the choice might be between two types of equipment, one of which qualifies as 5-year property and the other qualifies as 7-year property.

EXAMPLE 10.7   After-Tax Comparison of Alternatives

Recall the two design alternatives for a new ride (the Scream Machine) at a theme park considered in Chapters 5 through 8. Design A requires a $300,000 investment and produces net annual after-tax revenue of $55,000, based on straight-line depreciation over a 10-year planning horizon; Design B requires a $450,000 investment and produces net annual after-tax revenue of $80,000, based on straight-line depreciation over the 10-year planning horizon. The straight-line depreciation was used for accounting purposes. As shown in Table 10.6,

TABLE 10.6
Accounting-based treatment of investment alternatives.

EOY	BTCF(A)	DWO(A)	TI(A)	T(A)	ATCF(A)
0	−$300,000.00				−$300,000.00
1	$71,666.67	$30,000.00	$41,666.67	$16,666.67	$55,000.00
2	$71,666.67	$30,000.00	$41,666.67	$16,666.67	$55,000.00
3	$71,666.67	$30,000.00	$41,666.67	$16,666.67	$55,000.00
4	$71,666.67	$30,000.00	$41,666.67	$16,666.67	$55,000.00
5	$71,666.67	$30,000.00	$41,666.67	$16,666.67	$55,000.00
6	$71,666.67	$30,000.00	$41,666.67	$16,666.67	$55,000.00
7	$71,666.67	$30,000.00	$41,666.67	$16,666.67	$55,000.00
8	$71,666.67	$30,000.00	$41,666.67	$16,666.67	$55,000.00
9	$71,666.67	$30,000.00	$41,666.67	$16,666.67	$55,000.00
10	$71,666.67	$30,000.00	$41,666.67	$16,666.67	$55,000.00
BTPW(A) =	$37,954.92			ATPW(A) =	$37,951.19
EOY	BTCF(B)	DWO(B)	TI(B)	T(B)	ATCF(B)
0	−$450,000.00				−$450,000.00
1	$103,333.33	$45,000.00	$58,333.33	$23,333.33	$80,000.00
2	$103,333.33	$45,000.00	$58,333.33	$23,333.33	$80,000.00
3	$103,333.33	$45,000.00	$58,333.33	$23,333.33	$80,000.00
4	$103,333.33	$45,000.00	$58,333.33	$23,333.33	$80,000.00
5	$103,333.33	$45,000.00	$58,333.33	$23,333.33	$80,000.00
6	$103,333.33	$45,000.00	$58,333.33	$23,333.33	$80,000.00
7	$103,333.33	$45,000.00	$58,333.33	$23,333.33	$80,000.00

8	$103,333.33	$45,000.00	$58,333.33	$23,333.33	$80,000.00
9	$103,333.33	$45,000.00	$58,333.33	$23,333.33	$80,000.00
10	$103,333.33	$45,000.00	$58,333.33	$23,333.33	$80,000.00
$BTPW(B) =$	$37,283.84			$ATPW(B) =$	$41,565.37

based on a 40 percent income-tax rate, the accounting-based before-tax annual savings for the two design alternatives are $71,666.67 and $103,333.33, respectively. Notice, Design A is preferred on a before-tax basis and Design B is preferred on an after-tax basis using SLN depreciation.

For income-tax purposes, as noted in Table 9.3, the theme park equipment qualifies as 7-year property, and MACRS depreciation is used to compute the after-tax cash flows. An after-tax *MARR* of 10 percent applies. Which alternative will be preferred, based on an after-tax analysis?

As shown in Table 10.7, Design A is preferred on a before-tax basis and Design B is preferred on an after-tax basis using MACRS depreciation. The ATPW for Alternative A is $50,790.36 and for Alternative B is $60,824.10. As evidenced by this solution, it is not necessarily the case that an after-tax analysis will produce the same recommendation as a before-tax analysis.

TABLE 10.7
After-Tax Comparison of Investment Alternatives.

EOY	BTCF(A)	DWO(A)	TI(A)	T(A)	ATCF(A)
0	−$300,000.00				−$300,000.00
1	$71,666.67	$42,870.00	$28,796.67	$11,518.67	$60,148.00
2	$71,666.67	$73,470.00	−$1,803.33	−$721.33	$72,388.00
3	$71,666.67	$52,470.00	$19,196.67	$7,678.67	$63,988.00
4	$71,666.67	$37,470.00	$34,196.67	$13,678.67	$57,988.00
5	$71,666.67	$26,790.00	$44,876.67	$17,950.67	$53,716.00
6	$71,666.67	$26,760.00	$44,906.67	$17,962.67	$53,704.00
7	$71,666.67	$26,790.00	$44,876.67	$17,950.67	$53,716.00
8	$71,666.67	$13,380.00	$58,286.67	$23,314.67	$48,352.00
9	$71,666.67	$0.00	$71,666.67	$28,666.67	$43,000.00
10	$71,666.67	$0.00	$71,666.67	$28,666.67	$43,000.00
$BTPW(A) =$	$37,954.94			$ATPW(A) =$	$50,790.36
EOY	BTCF(B)	DWO(B)	TI(B)	T(B)	ATCF(B)
0	−$450,000.00				−$450,000.00
1	$103,333.33	$64,305.00	$39,028.33	$15,611.33	$87,722.00
2	$103,333.33	$110,205.00	−$6,871.67	−$2,748.67	$106,082.00
3	$103,333.33	$78,705.00	$24,628.33	$9,851.33	$93,482.00

(*Continued*)

TABLE 10.7
(Continued)

EOY	BTCF(B)	DWO(B)	TI(B)	T(B)	ATCF(B)
4	$103,333.33	$56,205.00	$47,128.33	$18,851.33	$84,482.00
5	$103,333.33	$40,185.00	$63,148.33	$25,259.33	$78,074.00
6	$103,333.33	$40,140.00	$63,193.33	$25,277.33	$78,056.00
7	$103,333.33	$40,185.00	$63,148.33	$25,259.33	$78,074.00
8	$103,333.33	$20,070.00	$83,263.33	$33,305.33	$70,028.00
9	$103,333.33	$0.00	$103,333.33	$41,333.33	$62,000.00
10	$103,333.33	$0.00	$103,333.33	$41,333.33	$62,000.00
BTPW(B) =	$37,283.83			ATPW(B) =	$60,824.10

EXAMPLE 10.8 **After-Tax Comparison of Alternatives with Different Property Classes**

Using the cash flow data from the previous example, suppose different investments are being considered, investments that qualify for different property classes. In particular, suppose Alternative A is for specialized tools that qualify as 3-year property, and Alternative B is for production equipment that qualifies as 7-year property. As shown in Table 10.8, Alternative A is preferred on both a before-tax and an after-tax basis, with an after-tax present worth of $64,084.76. (If Alternative A had been an investment in something that could be expensed, the after-tax present worth would have been $84,216.40.)

TABLE 10.8
After-Tax Comparison of Investment Alternatives with Different Property Classes.

EOY	BTCF(A)	DWO(A)	TI(A)	T(A)	ATCF(A)
0	−$300,000.00				−$300,000.00
1	$71,666.67	$99,990.00	−$28,323.33	−$11,329.33	$82,996.00
2	$71,666.67	$133,350.00	−$61,683.33	−$24,673.33	$96,340.00
3	$71,666.67	$44,430.00	$27,236.67	$10,894.67	$60,772.00
4	$71,666.67	$22,230.00	$49,436.67	$19,774.67	$51,892.00
5	$71,666.67	$0.00	$71,666.67	$28,666.67	$43,000.00
6	$71,666.67	$0.00	$71,666.67	$28,666.67	$43,000.00
7	$71,666.67	$0.00	$71,666.67	$28,666.67	$43,000.00
8	$71,666.67	$0.00	$71,666.67	$28,666.67	$43,000.00
9	$71,666.67	$0.00	$71,666.67	$28,666.67	$43,000.00
10	$71,666.67	$0.00	$71,666.67	$28,666.67	$43,000.00
BTPW(A) =	$37,954.94			ATPW(A) =	$64,084.76

EOY	BTCF(B)	DWO(B)	TI(B)	T(B)	ATCF(B)
0	−$450,000.00				−$450,000.00
1	$103,333.33	$64,305.00	$39,028.33	$15,611.33	$87,722.00
2	$103,333.33	$110,205.00	−$6,871.67	−$2,748.67	$106,082.00
3	$103,333.33	$78,705.00	$24,628.33	$9,851.33	$93,482.00
4	$103,333.33	$56,205.00	$47,128.33	$18,851.33	$84,482.00
5	$103,333.33	$40,185.00	$63,148.33	$25,259.33	$78,074.00
6	$103,333.33	$40,140.00	$63,193.33	$25,277.33	$78,056.00
7	$103,333.33	$40,185.00	$63,148.33	$25,259.33	$78,074.00
8	$103,333.33	$20,070.00	$83,263.33	$33,305.33	$70,028.00
9	$103,333.33	$0.00	$103,333.33	$41,333.33	$62,000.00
10	$103,333.33	$0.00	$103,333.33	$41,333.33	$62,000.00
BTPW(B) =	$37,283.83			ATPW(B) =	$60,824.10

EXAMPLE 10.9 After-Tax Comparison of Manual versus Automated Solutions

In a distribution center, loads to be shipped have been palletized manually. A proposal has been made to use a robot to perform the palletizing operation. Since cartons to be palletized are not dimensionally uniform, a vision system coupled with optimization software will be required with the robot.

Currently, two people perform palletizing. The labor cost for this is $50,000 per year. A fully equipped robot to perform the task will cost $125,000 and will have annual operating costs of $500. The robot qualifies as 3-year property. If a tax rate of 40 percent and a *MARR* of 10 percent are used, should the robot be purchased? Use a 5-year planning horizon and perform an after-tax annual worth analysis; assume a salvage value of $25,000 for the robot after 5 years of use.

Manual palletizing: Since the labor cost can be expensed in the year in which it occurs, the after-tax equivalent uniform annual cost of manually palletizing equals $50,000(0.60), or $30,000.

TABLE 10.9
After-Tax Comparison of Manual versus Robotic Palletizing.

EOY	BTCF	DWO	TI	T	ATCF
0	−$125,000.00				−$125,000.00
1	−$500.00	$41,662.50	−$42,162.50	−$16,865.00	$16,365.00
2	−$500.00	$55,562.50	−$56,062.50	−$22,425.00	$21,925.00
3	−$500.00	$18,512.50	−$19,012.50	−$7,605.00	$7,105.00
4	−$500.00	$9,262.50	−$9,762.50	−$3,905.00	$3,405.00
5	$24,500.00	$0.00	$24,500.00	$9,800.00	$14,700.00
$EUAC_{BT}$ =	$29,379.75			$EUAC_{AT}$ =	$19,840.63

Robotic palletizing: As shown in Table 10.9, the equivalent uniform annual cost of robotic palletizing equals $19,840.63. Therefore, the robot is justified economically.

EXAMPLE 10.10   After-Tax Comparison of Leasing versus Purchasing

The Acme Brick Company is considering adding five lift trucks to its fleet. Both purchasing and leasing were discussed with the fork-truck supplier. If the lift trucks are purchased, they will have a first cost of $18,000; annual operating and maintenance costs are estimated to be $3,750 per truck. At the end of the 5-year planning horizon, the lift trucks are estimated to have salvage values of $3,000 each. The lift trucks qualify as MACRS 3-year property.

If the lift trucks are leased, beginning-of-year lease payments will be $5,900 per truck. The supplier includes maintenance in the lease price. However, the company must pay annual operating costs of $1,800 per truck. Lease payments can be expensed for tax purposes.

Using an after-tax *MARR* of 12 percent and an income-tax rate of 40 percent, should the company lease the lift trucks?

As shown in Table 10.10, an after-tax analysis indicates the lift trucks should be leased. The present worth cost of purchasing is $96,486.74, whereas the present worth cost of

TABLE 10.10
After-Tax Comparison of Purchasing versus Leasing Lift Trucks.

EOY	BTCF(P)	DWO(P)	TI(P)	T(P)	ATCF(P)
0	−$90,000.00				−$90,000.00
1	−$18,750.00	$29,997.00	−$48,747.00	−$19,498.80	$748.80
2	−$18,750.00	$40,005.00	−$58,755.00	−$23,502.00	$4,752.00
3	−$18,750.00	$13,329.00	−$32,079.00	−$12,831.60	−$5,918.40
4	−$18,750.00	$6,669.00	−$25,419.00	−$10,167.60	−$8,582.40
5	−$3,750.00	$0.00	−$3,750.00	−$1,500.00	−$2,250.00
$PW_{BT}(P) =$	−$140,045.81			$PW_{AT}(P) =$	−$96,486.74

EOY	BTCF(L)	DWO(L)	TI(L)	T(L)	ATCF(L)
0	−$29,500.00		−$29,500.00	−$11,800.00	−$17,700.00
1	−$38,500.00	$0.00	−$38,500.00	−$15,400.00	−$23,100.00
2	−$38,500.00	$0.00	−$38,500.00	−$15,400.00	−$23,100.00
3	−$38,500.00	$0.00	−$38,500.00	−$15,400.00	−$23,100.00
4	−$38,500.00	$0.00	−$38,500.00	−$15,400.00	−$23,100.00
5	−$9,000.00	$0.00	−$9,000.00	−$3,600.00	−$5,400.00
$PW_{BT}(L) =$	−$132,783.18			$PW_{AT}(L) =$	−$90,926.87

leasing is $90,926.87. The $5,559.87 difference in present worth costs is probably great enough for the company to lease the lift trucks.

Interestingly, as shown in Table 10.10, if the decision had been made using a before-tax *MARR* of 0.12/(1 − 0.4), or 20 percent, the before-tax present worth cost of purchasing is $140,045.81, and the present worth cost of leasing is $132,783.18. Again, the $7,262.63 difference in the present worths is probably great enough for the company to decide to lease the lift trucks.

10-6 AFTER-TAX CASH FLOW WITH BORROWING

The previous after-tax analysis assumed the investments were paid for using retained earnings. However, depreciable property is frequently purchased using borrowed funds. Since interest is deductible from taxable income, it is useful to consider how an after-tax analysis is performed when using borrowed funds.

When borrowed funds are used, additional notation is needed. Let

$PPMT$ = principal payment

$IPMT$ = interest payment

LCF = loan cash flow $= PPMT + IPMT$

The following formulas apply when borrowed funds are used:

$$ATCF = BT\&LCF - LCF - T \tag{10.7}$$

After-tax cash flow equals before-tax-and-loan cash flow, less the loan payment, less the income tax. As before,

$$T = itr(TI)$$

but, now,

$$TI = BT\&LCF - IPMT - DWO \tag{10.8}$$

Taxable income equals before-tax-and-loan cash flow, less the interest paid, less the depreciation allowance. Therefore,

$$ATCF = BT\&LCF(1 - itr) - LCF + itr(DWO + IPMT) \tag{10.9}$$

After-tax cash flow equals before-tax-and-loan cash flow times 1 minus the income-tax rate, less the loan cash flow, plus the income-tax rate times the sum of the depreciation allowance and the interest payment.

$$ATCF = BT\&LCF(1 - itr) - LCF + itr(DWO + IPMT)$$

Notice, every dollar of interest paid after-taxes costs $(1 - itr)$ cents. Hence, for a 40 percent tax rate, each dollar spent on interest costs 60¢ after taxes.

Finally, in the year of the depreciable property's disposal,

$$TI_n = BT\&LCF_n(incl\ F_n) - IPMT_n - DWO_n - B_n \qquad (10.10)$$

Recall, in Chapter 3, we considered four loan payment plans: (1) pay the accumulated interest at the end of each interest period and repay the principal at the end of the loan period; (2) make equal principal payments, plus interest on the unpaid balance at the end of the period; (3) make equal end-of-period payments; and (4) make a single payment of principal and interest at the end of the loan period.

Because interest can be deducted from taxable income, the effective after-tax interest rate paid on borrowed funds is

$$i_{\text{eff}} = i(1 - itr) \qquad (10.11)$$

In comparison with the interest rate on borrowed funds, the BTMARR is given by $ATMARR/(1 - itr)$. Hence, if the interest rate is 12 percent, the income-tax rate is 40 percent, and the ATMARR is 10 percent, then the BTMARR is 0.10/0.60, or 16.667 percent. When the interest rate is less than the BTMARR, one should borrow as much as possible and delay repaying the loan as long as possible; when the interest rate is greater than the BTMARR, one should borrow as little as possible and repay the principal as quickly as possible. (Of course, other factors must be considered, including maintaining a reasonable debt-to-equity ratio. However, within limits, the above holds, as the examples demonstrate.)

EXAMPLE 10.11 After-Tax Effects of Borrowed Funds

Now, let's examine the four payment plans as they are used to secure $300,000 financing for the $500,000 SMP machine acquisition considered in earlier examples. Figure 10.3 depicts the after-tax analysis for Plan 1, in which only the interest is paid each year; at the end of year 10, the $300,000 principal is repaid.

As shown, the after-tax present worth (ATPW), based on a 12 percent interest rate on the $300,000 loan and a 10 percent ATMARR, is $175,603.01. When no borrowed funds were used, the ATPW was $123,988.64. Borrowing the $300,000 at 12 percent compound annual interest increased ATPW, because interest is deducted from taxable income.

Notice, because of the single payment of principal in year 10, the ATCF is negative. Hence, there are two negative values in the ATCF column. Descartes' rule of signs indicates either two or zero roots exist; the two roots occur at −18.62 percent and at 41.54 percent. Since multiple negative values exist, the Excel® MIRR worksheet function cannot be used to compute the ERR; however, as shown, the ERR can be calculated and equals 17.16 percent.

Table 10.11 provides the after-tax analysis for Plan 2, in which equal annual principal payments are made, plus interest on the unpaid loan balance. As shown, the ATPW is $156,374.28. Plan 2 is not as attractive as Plan 1. Why? Since the after-tax interest rate is less than the *MARR*, it is better to delay repaying principal.

Table 10.12 contains the results for Plan 3, in which equal annual payments are made over the 10-year period. For Plan 3, the ATPW is $160,734.89. As expected, since principal payments increase over time, Plan 3 performs better than Plan 2 but not as well as Plan 1, where no principal payments are made until the end of the loan period.

Figure 10.4 provides the results for Plan 4, in which no payment is made until the end of the loan period. Notice, with an ATPW worth of $162,184.44, Plan 4 ranks second to Plan 1 in maximizing ATPW.

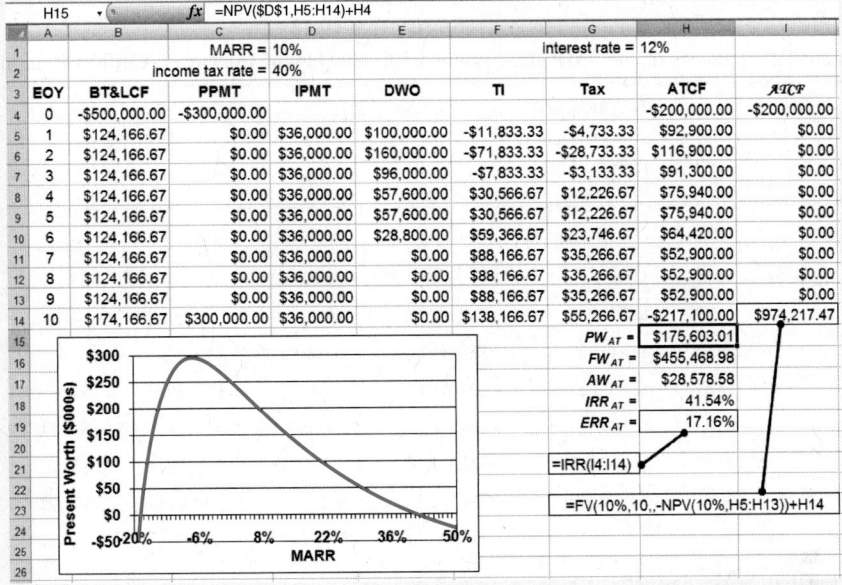

FIGURE 10.3

After-Tax Analysis of the SMP Investment with $300,000 of Borrowed Capital Repaid Using Plan 1.

TABLE 10.11

After-Tax Analysis of the SMP Investment with $300,000 of Borrowed Capital Repaid Using Plan 2.

EOY	BT&LCF	ATMARR = 10% income tax rate = 40% PPMT	IPMT	DWO	TI	interest rate = 12% Tax	ATCF
0	−$500,000.00	−$300,000.00					−$200,000.00
1	$124,166.67	$30,000.00	$36,000.00	$100,000.00	−$11,833.33	−$4,733.33	$62,900.00
2	$124,166.67	$30,000.00	$32,400.00	$160,000.00	−$68,233.33	−$27,293.33	$89,060.00
3	$124,166.67	$30,000.00	$28,800.00	$96,000.00	−$633.33	−$253.33	$65,620.00
4	$124,166.67	$30,000.00	$25,200.00	$57,600.00	$41,366.67	$16,546.67	$52,420.00
5	$124,166.67	$30,000.00	$21,600.00	$57,600.00	$44,966.67	$17,986.67	$54,580.00
6	$124,166.67	$30,000.00	$18,000.00	$28,800.00	$77,366.67	$30,946.67	$45,220.00
7	$124,166.67	$30,000.00	$14,400.00	$0.00	$109,766.67	$43,906.67	$35,860.00
8	$124,166.67	$30,000.00	$10,800.00	$0.00	$113,366.67	$45,346.67	$38,020.00
9	$124,166.67	$30,000.00	$7,200.00	$0.00	$116,966.67	$46,786.67	$40,180.00
10	$174,166.67	$30,000.00	$3,600.00	$0.00	$170,566.67	$68,226.67	$72,340.00
						$PW_{AT} =$	$156,374.28
						$FW_{AT} =$	$405,594.61
						$AW_{AT} =$	$25,449.19
						$IRR_{AT} =$	28.51%
						$ERR_{AT} =$	16.54%

TABLE 10.12
After-Tax Analysis of the SMP Investment with $300,000 of Borrowed Capital Repaid Using Plan 3.

		ATMARR = 10% income tax rate = 40%			interest rate = 12%		
EOY	BT&LCF	PPMT	IPMT	DWO	TI	Tax	ATCF
0	−$500,000.00	−$300,000.00					−$200,000.00
1	$124,166.67	$17,095.25	$36,000.00	$100,000.00	−$11,833.33	−$4,733.33	$75,804.75
2	$124,166.67	$19,146.68	$33,948.57	$160,000.00	−$69,781.90	−$27,912.76	$98,984.18
3	$124,166.67	$21,444.28	$31,650.97	$96,000.00	−$3,484.30	−$1,393.72	$72,465.14
4	$124,166.67	$24,017.59	$29,077.65	$57,600.00	$37,489.02	$14,995.61	$56,075.81
5	$124,166.67	$26,899.71	$26,195.54	$57,600.00	$40,371.13	$16,148.45	$54,922.97
6	$124,166.67	$30,127.67	$22,967.58	$28,800.00	$72,399.09	$28,959.64	$42,111.78
7	$124,166.67	$33,742.99	$19,352.26	$0.00	$104,814.41	$41,925.76	$29,145.66
8	$124,166.67	$37,792.15	$15,303.10	$0.00	$108,863.57	$43,545.43	$27,525.99
9	$124,166.67	$42,327.21	$10,768.04	$0.00	$113,398.63	$45,359.45	$25,711.97
10	$174,166.67	$47,406.47	$5,688.78	$0.00	$168,477.89	$67,391.16	$53,680.26
						$PW_{AT} =$	$160,734.89
						$FW_{AT} =$	$416,904.92
						$AW_{AT} =$	$26,158.86
						$IRR_{AT} =$	31.65%
						$ERR_{AT} =$	16.68%

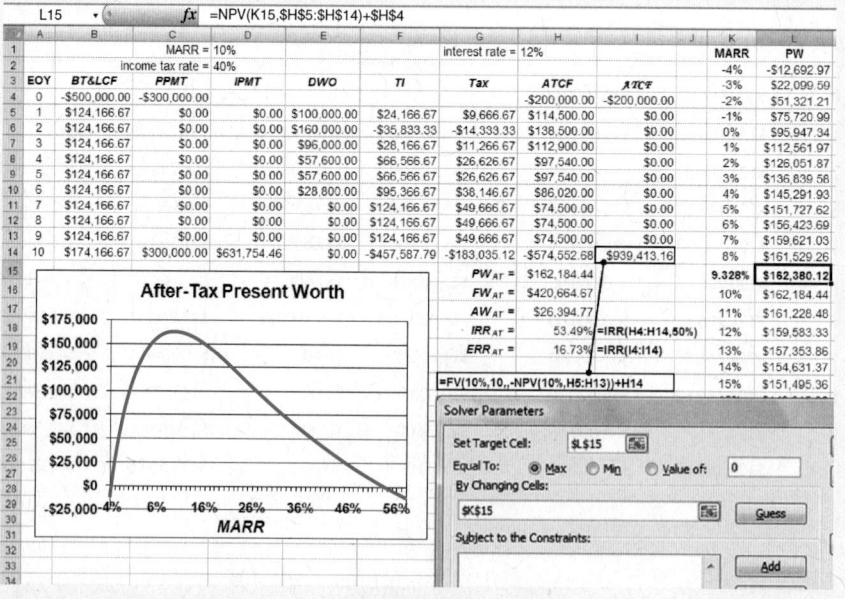

FIGURE 10.4
After-Tax Analysis of SMP Investment with $300,000 of Borrowed Capital Repaid Using Plan 4.

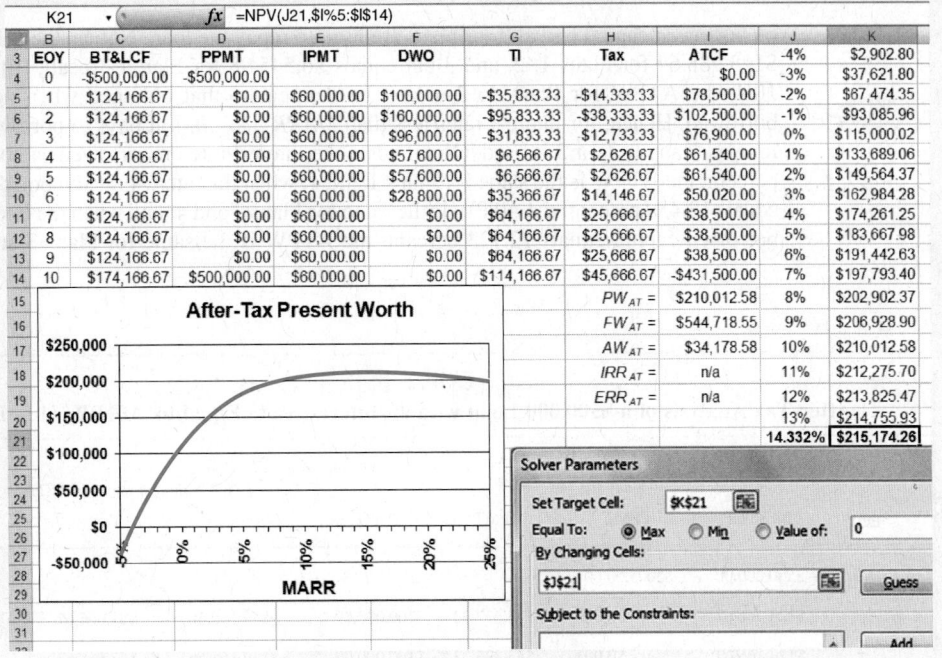

	K21	▾	*fx*	=NPV(J21,$I$5:$I$14)						
	B	C	D	E	F	G	H	I	J	K
3	EOY	BT&LCF	PPMT	IPMT	DWO	TI	Tax	ATCF	-4%	$2,902.80
4	0	-$500,000.00	-$500,000.00					$0.00	-3%	$37,621.80
5	1	$124,166.67	$0.00	$60,000.00	$100,000.00	-$35,833.33	-$14,333.33	$78,500.00	-2%	$67,474.35
6	2	$124,166.67	$0.00	$60,000.00	$160,000.00	-$95,833.33	-$38,333.33	$102,500.00	-1%	$93,085.96
7	3	$124,166.67	$0.00	$60,000.00	$96,000.00	-$31,833.33	$12,733.33	$76,900.00	0%	$115,000.02
8	4	$124,166.67	$0.00	$60,000.00	$57,600.00	$6,566.67	$2,626.67	$61,540.00	1%	$133,689.06
9	5	$124,166.67	$0.00	$60,000.00	$57,600.00	$6,566.67	$2,626.67	$61,540.00	2%	$149,564.37
10	6	$124,166.67	$0.00	$60,000.00	$28,800.00	$35,366.67	$14,146.67	$50,020.00	3%	$162,984.28
11	7	$124,166.67	$0.00	$60,000.00	$0.00	$64,166.67	$25,666.67	$38,500.00	4%	$174,261.25
12	8	$124,166.67	$0.00	$60,000.00	$0.00	$64,166.67	$25,666.67	$38,500.00	5%	$183,667.98
13	9	$124,166.67	$0.00	$60,000.00	$0.00	$64,166.67	$25,666.67	$38,500.00	6%	$191,442.63
14	10	$174,166.67	$500,000.00	$60,000.00	$0.00	$114,166.67	$45,666.67	-$431,500.00	7%	$197,793.40
15						PW_{AT} =	$210,012.58		8%	$202,902.37
16						FW_{AT} =	$544,718.55		9%	$206,928.90
17						AW_{AT} =	$34,178.58		10%	$210,012.58
18						IRR_{AT} =	n/a		11%	$212,275.70
19						ERR_{AT} =	n/a		12%	$213,825.47
20									13%	$214,755.93
21									14.332%	$215,174.26

FIGURE 10.5

**After-Tax Analysis of $500,000 Investment with 100% Borrowed Capital Repaid
Using Plan 1.**

With Plan 4, no payment is made until year 10. Hence, the most negative cash flow occurs at that time. Descartes' rule of signs indicates either two or zero roots exist; as shown in Figure 10.4, the two roots occur at −3.65 percent and at 53.49 percent. Since multiple negative values exist, the Excel® **MIRR** worksheet function cannot be used to compute the ERR; however, as shown, the ERR can be calculated and equals 16.73 percent. Notice, ATPW is maximized when ATMARR equals 9.328 percent. (We used the Excel® **SOLVER** tool to obtain the ATMARR value that maximized ATPW.)

Given the results obtained for the four payment plans, it is anticipated that ATPW will increase as the amount borrowed increases. Figure 10.5 presents the results for Plan 1 if the investment is entirely paid for using borrowed funds. As expected, the ATPW of $210,012.58 is greater than the ATPW of $175,603.01 that occurred when only $300,000 was borrowed.

When 100 percent of investment capital is obtained by borrowing, no initial investment occurs at the beginning of the ATCF series. As shown in Figure 10.5, the only negative-valued cash flow occurs at the end of year 10. As such, increases in the *MARR* will increase ATPW. This is just the opposite of what we observed previously. Because there are no negative-valued cash flows prior to the planning horizon's end, the IRR and the ERR are not defined. (Notice, ATPW is maximized when *MARR* = 14.332 percent.)

How much can the interest rate increase and have it still be profitable to borrow money? It depends on the payment plan used. With a *MARR* of 10 percent, as long as the interest rate paid on borrowed capital is less than 10 percent/(1 − 0.40), or 16.667 percent, there is a payment plan for which it is economical to borrow investment capital. Table 10.13 provides the after-tax results when a 16.667 percent interest rate is paid on borrowed capital and all four plans are used to repay the loan. Notice, the ATPW equals $123,988.64 for Plans 1, 2, and 3 but equals $6,545.98 for Plan 4. Recall, from Example 10.4, the ATPW for Plans 1, 2, and 3 is identical to that obtained when no money is borrowed. Hence, for interest rates less than $MARR/(1 - itr)$, it pays to borrow money, as long as Plans 1, 2, or 3 is used. (Note: when the interest rate on borrowed capital equals 10 percent, the ATPW is the same for Plans 1 and 4; when the interest rate on borrowed capital equals 12.459 percent, the ATPW is the same for Plans 2 and 4; and when the interest rate on borrowed capital equals 12.123 percent, the ATPW is the same for Plans 3 and 4.)

TABLE 10.13
After-Tax Analysis of a $500,000 Loan with an Interest Rate Equal to $MARR/(1 - itr)$.

	EOY	BT&LCF	PPMT	IPMT	DWO	TI	Tax	ATCF
		ATMARR = 10% income tax rate = 40%				interest rate = 16.667%		
	0	−$500,000.00	−$500,000.00					$0.00
	1	$124,166.67	$0.00	$83,333.33	$100,000.00	−$59,166.66	−$23,666.67	$64,500.00
	2	$124,166.67	$0.00	$83,333.33	$160,000.00	−$119,166.66	−$47,666.67	$88,500.00
	3	$124,166.67	$0.00	$83,333.33	$96,000.00	−$55,166.66	−$22,066.67	$62,900.00
	4	$124,166.67	$0.00	$83,333.33	$57,600.00	−$16,766.66	−$6,706.67	$47,540.00
Plan 1	5	$124,166.67	$0.00	$83,333.33	$57,600.00	−$16,766.66	−$6,706.67	$47,540.00
	6	$124,166.67	$0.00	$83,333.33	$28,800.00	$12,033.34	$4,813.33	$36,020.00
	7	$124,166.67	$0.00	$83,333.33	$0.00	$40,833.34	$16,333.33	$24,500.00
	8	$124,166.67	$0.00	$83,333.33	$0.00	$40,833.34	$16,333.33	$24,500.00
	9	$124,166.67	$0.00	$83,333.33	$0.00	$40,833.34	$16,333.33	$24,500.00
	10	$174,166.67	$500,000.00	$83,333.33	$0.00	$90,833.34	$36,333.33	−$445,500.00
							PW_{AT} =	$123,988.64
	0	−$500,000.00	−$500,000.00					$0.00
	1	$124,166.67	$50,000.00	$83,333.33	$100,000.00	−$59,166.66	−$23,666.67	$14,500.00
	2	$124,166.67	$50,000.00	$75,000.00	$160,000.00	−$110,833.33	−$44,333.33	$43,500.00
	3	$124,166.67	$50,000.00	$66,666.67	$96,000.00	−$38,500.00	−$15,400.00	$22,900.00
	4	$124,166.67	$50,000.00	$58,333.33	$57,600.00	$8,233.34	$3,293.33	$12,540.00
Plan 2	5	$124,166.67	$50,000.00	$50,000.00	$57,600.00	$16,566.67	$6,626.67	$17,540.00
	6	$124,166.67	$50,000.00	$41,666.67	$28,800.00	$53,700.00	$21,480.00	$11,020.00
	7	$124,166.67	$50,000.00	$33,333.33	$0.00	$90,833.34	$36,333.33	$4,500.00
	8	$124,166.67	$50,000.00	$25,000.00	$0.00	$99,166.67	$39,666.67	$9,500.00
	9	$124,166.67	$50,000.00	$16,666.67	$0.00	$107,500.00	$43,000.00	$14,500.00
	10	$174,166.67	$50,000.00	$8,333.33	$0.00	$165,833.34	$66,333.33	$49,500.00
							PW_{AT} =	$123,988.64

0	−$500,000.00	−$500,000.00					$0.00
1	$124,166.67	$22,696.59	$83,333.33	$100,000.00	−$59,166.66	−$23,666.67	$41,803.42
2	$124,166.67	$26,479.35	$79,550.57	$160,000.00	−$115,383.90	−$46,153.56	$64,290.31
3	$124,166.67	$30,892.58	$75,137.34	$96,000.00	−$46,970.67	−$18,788.27	$36,925.02
4	$124,166.67	$36,041.34	$69,988.58	$57,600.00	−$3,421.91	−$1,368.76	$19,505.52
5	$124,166.67	$42,048.23	$63,981.69	$57,600.00	$2,584.98	$1,033.99	$17,102.76
6	$124,166.67	$49,056.27	$56,973.65	$28,800.00	$38,393.02	$15,357.21	$2,779.54
7	$124,166.67	$57,232.31	$48,797.61	$0.00	$75,369.06	$30,147.62	−$12,010.87
8	$124,166.67	$66,771.03	$39,258.89	$0.00	$84,907.78	$33,963.11	−$15,826.36
9	$124,166.67	$77,899.53	$28,130.39	$0.00	$96,036.28	$38,414.51	−$20,277.76
10	$174,166.67	$90,882.79	$15,147.13	$0.00	$159,019.54	$63,607.82	$4,528.94
						$PW_{AT} =$	$123,988.64

(Plan 3)

0	−$500,000.00	−$500,000.00					$0.00
1	$124,166.67	$0.00	$0.00	$100,000.00	$24,166.67	$9,666.67	$114,500.00
2	$124,166.67	$0.00	$0.00	$160,000.00	−$35,833.33	−$14,333.33	$138,500.00
3	$124,166.67	$0.00	$0.00	$96,000.00	$28,166.67	$11,266.67	$112,900.00
4	$124,166.67	$0.00	$0.00	$57,600.00	$66,566.67	$26,626.67	$97,540.00
5	$124,166.67	$0.00	$0.00	$57,600.00	$66,566.67	$26,626.67	$97,540.00
6	$124,166.67	$0.00	$0.00	$28,800.00	$95,366.67	$38,146.67	$86,020.00
7	$124,166.67	$0.00	$0.00	$0.00	$124,166.67	$49,666.67	$74,500.00
8	$124,166.67	$0.00	$0.00	$0.00	$124,166.67	$49,666.67	$74,500.00
9	$124,166.67	$0.00	$0.00	$0.00	$124,166.67	$49,666.67	$74,500.00
10	$174,166.67	$500,000.00	$1,835,812.08	$0.00	−$1,661,645.41	−$664,658.17	−$1,496,987.25
						$PW_{AT} =$	$6,545.98

(Plan 4)

EXAMPLE 10.12   An After-Tax Extension to Example 3.1

Recall, in Example 3.1, an individual borrowed $10,000 at 15 percent compounded annually and repaid the loan over a 5-year period. Here, we consider a small business borrowing $100,000 at 15 percent compounded annually and repaying the loan over a 5-year period. Since it is a business, the interest paid is deductible from taxable income. We continue to use an income-tax rate of 40 percent. The same four plans are available for repaying the loan, and we consider them, as before; initially, we consider a 10 percent *MARR* for the borrower. As shown in Table 10.14, Plan 1 is best.

TABLE 10.14
After-Tax Analysis of Four Plans of Repaying a $100,000 Loan.

	EOY	PPMT	IPMT	TI	T	ATCF
Plan 1	0	−$100,000.00				$100,000.00
	1	$0.00	$15,000.00	−$15,000.00	−$6,000.00	−$9,000.00
	2	$0.00	$15,000.00	−$15,000.00	−$6,000.00	−$9,000.00
	3	$0.00	$15,000.00	−$15,000.00	−$6,000.00	−$9,000.00
	4	$0.00	$15,000.00	−$15,000.00	−$6,000.00	−$9,000.00
	5	$100,000.00	$15,000.00	−$15,000.00	−$6,000.00	−$109,000.00
					$PW_{AT} =$	$3,790.79
Plan 2	0	−$100,000.00				$100,000.00
	1	$20,000.00	$15,000.00	−$15,000.00	−$6,000.00	−$29,000.00
	2	$20,000.00	$12,000.00	−$12,000.00	−$4,800.00	−$27,200.00
	3	$20,000.00	$9,000.00	−$9,000.00	−$3,600.00	−$25,400.00
	4	$20,000.00	$6,000.00	−$6,000.00	−$2,400.00	−$23,600.00
	5	$20,000.00	$3,000.00	−$3,000.00	−$1,200.00	−$21,800.00
					$PW_{AT} =$	$2,418.43
Plan 3	0	$100,000.00				$100,000.00
	1	$14,831.56	$15,000.00	−$15,000.00	−$6,000.00	−$23,831.56
	2	$17,056.29	$12,775.27	−$12,775.27	−$5,110.11	−$24,721.45
	3	$19,614.73	$10,216.82	−$10,216.82	−$4,086.73	−$25,744.83
	4	$22,556.94	$7,274.61	−$7,274.61	−$2,909.85	−$26,921.71
	5	$25,940.48	$3,891.07	−$3,891.07	−$1,556.43	−$28,275.13
					$PW_{AT} =$	$2,617.01
Plan 4	0	$100,000.00				$100,000.00
	1	$0.00	$0.00	$0.00	$0.00	$0.00
	2	$0.00	$0.00	$0.00	$0.00	$0.00
	3	$0.00	$0.00	$0.00	$0.00	$0.00
	4	$0.00	$0.00	$0.00	$0.00	$0.00
	5	$100,000.00	$101,135.72	−$101,135.72	−$40,454.29	−$160,681.43
					$PW_{AT} =$	$229.47

Figure 10.6 shows ATPW results for the four payment plans for interest rates from 0 percent to 20 percent. Plan 4 is the best payment plan for interest rates less than the ATMARR; for interest rates greater than the ATMARR but less than ATMARR/$(1 − itr)$, Plan 1 is best; thereafter, if borrowing is required, Plan 2 is best.

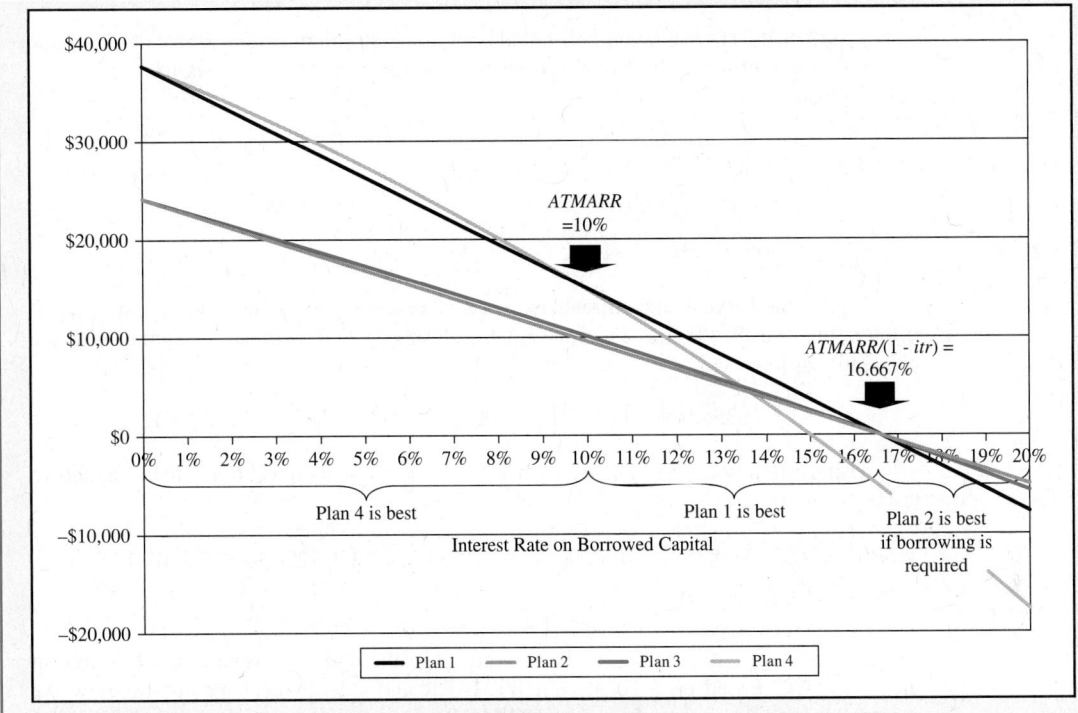

FIGURE 10.6

After-Tax Present Worth on $100,000 Loan for Each of Four Payment Plans.

EXAMPLE 10.13   An After-Tax Examination of Example 3.8—Selecting a Mortgage Plan

Although we have focused on corporate, rather than personal, income taxes, we will provide one example of after-tax analysis for personal investments. Recall, Example 3.8 examined three alternative methods of financing the purchase of a house: a 30-year interest-only, or balloon, loan; a 30-year adjustable rate mortgage; and a 30-year conventional loan. Due to risks and uncertainties regarding future interest rates, the ARM was eliminated from consideration.

Because interest paid on one's principal residence can be deducted from taxable income, income-tax considerations should be incorporated in the comparison of the 30-year balloon loan and the 30-year conventional loan. The analysis is relatively simple for the 30-year balloon loan, since no principal payments are made. Hence, if the professional couple files a joint marital return and if they are in, say, a 35 percent income tax bracket, then every dollar of interest paid costs them 65¢ after taxes.

Recall, $350,000 was borrowed. The 5-year interest-only loan had a 6.1 percent annual nominal interest rate and 1.753 points, plus $7,500 in additional loan-related closing costs. The monthly payment with this loan was obtained as follows:

$$A = (0.061/12)[\$350,000(1.01753) + \$7,500] = \$1,848.48$$

Based on a 10 percent nominal annual before-tax minimum attractive rate of return, the before-tax present worth of the loan cash flow was expressed as follows for the 30-year balloon loan:

$$BTPW = -\$1,848.48(P|A\ 10/12\%,60) - [\$350,000(1.01753) + \$7,500]$$
$$\times\ (P|F\ 10/12\%,60)$$
$$= -\$308,012.92$$

Recall, the 30-year conventional loan had a 7 percent nominal annual rate and included 0.157 points, plus \$1,000 for other loan-related closing costs. The monthly payment with the conventional loan was

$$A = [\$350,000(1.00157) + \$1,000](A|P\ 7/12\%,360) = \$2,338.87.$$

Using a 10 percent BTMARR, the BTPW for the 30-year conventional loan was shown to be

$$BTPW = -\$2,338.87(P|A\ 10/12\%,60) - \$2,338.87(P|A\ 7/12\%,300)(P|F\ 10/12\%,60)$$
$$= -\$311,208.54.$$

To perform an after-tax analysis of the two mortgage alternatives, it is necessary to establish the ATMARR. Based on a 10 percent BTMARR and a 33 percent income-tax rate, the professional couple used a 6.5 percent ATMARR to compare the two mortgage alternatives.

Due to the deductibility of interest and since the monthly payment of \$1,848.48 is solely interest, the after-tax present worth for the interest-only loan is obtained as follows:

$$ATPW = -\$1,848.48(0.65)(P|A\ 6.5/12\%,60) - [\$350,000(1.01753) + \$7,500]$$
$$\times\ (P|F\ 6.5/12\%,60)$$
$$=PV(0.065/12,60,0.65*1848.48)+PV(0.065/12,60,,350000*1.01753$$
$$+7500)$$
$$= -\$324,374.82$$

The after-tax analysis of the 30-year conventional loan requires a separation of the 60 monthly payments into principal versus interest components. The results of the analysis are given in Table 10.15. The after-tax present worth of the payments and balance owed after 5 years is −\$323,302.93.

TABLE 10.15
After-Tax Analysis of 30-Year Conventional Loan in Example 10.11.

Month	BTLCF	IPMT	TI	T	ATLCF	Month	BTLCF	IPMT	TI	T	ATLCF
1	−\$2,338.87	\$2,039.04	−\$2,039.04	−\$713.66	−\$1,625.20	31	−\$2,338.87	\$1,984.42	−\$1,984.42	−\$694.55	−\$1,644.32
2	−\$2,338.87	\$2,037.37	−\$2,037.37	−\$713.08	−\$1,625.79	32	−\$2,338.87	\$1,982.43	−\$1,982.43	−\$693.85	−\$1,645.02
3	−\$2,338.87	\$2,035.69	−\$2,035.69	−\$712.49	−\$1,626.38	33	−\$2,338.87	\$1,980.42	−\$1,980.42	−\$693.15	−\$1,645.72
4	−\$2,338.87	\$2,034.00	−\$2,034.00	−\$711.90	−\$1,626.97	34	−\$2,338.87	\$1,978.41	−\$1,978.41	−\$692.44	−\$1,646.42
5	−\$2,338.87	\$2,032.29	−\$2,032.29	−\$711.30	−\$1,627.56	35	−\$2,338.87	\$1,976.39	−\$1,976.39	−\$691.74	−\$1,647.13

6	−$2,338.87	$2,030.58	−$2,030.58	−$710.70	−$1,628.16	36	−$2,338.87	$1,974.35	−$1,974.35	−$691.02	−$1,647.85
7	−$2,338.87	$2,028.86	−$2,028.86	−$710.10	−$1,628.77	37	−$2,338.87	$1,972.30	−$1,972.30	−$690.31	−$1,648.56
8	−$2,338.87	$2,027.13	−$2,027.13	−$709.50	−$1,629.37	38	−$2,338.87	$1,970.24	−$1,970.24	−$689.58	−$1,649.28
9	−$2,338.87	$2,025.39	−$2,025.39	−$708.89	−$1,629.98	39	−$2,338.87	$1,968.17	−$1,968.17	−$688.86	−$1,650.01
10	−$2,338.87	$2,023.64	−$2,023.64	−$708.27	−$1,630.59	40	−$2,338.87	$1,966.08	−$1,966.08	−$688.13	−$1,650.74
11	−$2,338.87	$2,021.88	−$2,021.88	−$707.66	−$1,631.21	41	−$2,338.87	$1,963.99	−$1,963.99	−$687.39	−$1,651.47
12	−$2,338.87	$2,020.11	−$2,020.11	−$707.04	−$1,631.83	42	−$2,338.87	$1,961.88	−$1,961.88	−$686.66	−$1,652.21
13	−$2,338.87	$2,018.33	−$2,018.33	−$706.41	−$1,632.45	43	−$2,338.87	$1,959.75	−$1,959.75	−$685.91	−$1,652.95
14	−$2,338.87	$2,016.53	−$2,016.53	−$705.79	−$1,633.08	44	−$2,338.87	$1,957.62	−$1,957.62	−$685.17	−$1,653.70
15	−$2,338.87	$2,014.73	−$2,014.73	−$705.16	−$1,633.71	45	−$2,338.87	$1,955.47	−$1,955.47	−$684.42	−$1,654.45
16	−$2,338.87	$2,012.92	−$2,012.92	−$704.52	−$1,634.35	46	−$2,338.87	$1,953.32	−$1,953.32	−$683.66	−$1,655.21
17	−$2,338.87	$2,011.09	−$2,011.09	−$703.88	−$1,634.98	47	−$2,338.87	$1,951.14	−$1,951.14	−$682.90	−$1,655.97
18	−$2,338.87	$2,009.26	−$2,009.26	−$703.24	−$1,635.63	48	−$2,338.87	$1,948.96	−$1,948.96	−$682.14	−$1,656.73
19	−$2,338.87	$2,007.41	−$2,007.41	−$702.60	−$1,636.27	49	−$2,338.87	$1,946.76	−$1,946.76	−$681.37	−$1,657.50
20	−$2,338.87	$2,005.56	−$2,005.56	−$701.95	−$1,636.92	50	−$2,338.87	$1,944.55	−$1,944.55	−$680.59	−$1,658.27
21	−$2,338.87	$2,003.69	−$2,003.69	−$701.29	−$1,637.58	51	−$2,338.87	$1,942.33	−$1,942.33	−$679.82	−$1,659.05
22	−$2,338.87	$2,001.81	−$2,001.81	−$700.64	−$1,638.23	52	−$2,338.87	$1,940.10	−$1,940.10	−$679.03	−$1,659.83
23	−$2,338.87	$1,999.93	−$1,999.93	−$699.97	−$1,638.89	53	−$2,338.87	$1,937.85	−$1,937.85	−$678.25	−$1,660.62
24	−$2,338.87	$1,998.03	−$1,998.03	−$699.31	−$1,639.56	54	−$2,338.87	$1,935.59	−$1,935.59	−$677.45	−$1,661.41
25	−$2,338.87	$1,996.12	−$1,996.12	−$698.64	−$1,640.23	55	−$2,338.87	$1,933.31	−$1,933.31	−$676.66	−$1,662.21
26	−$2,338.87	$1,994.19	−$1,994.19	−$697.97	−$1,640.90	56	−$2,338.87	$1,931.02	−$1,931.02	−$675.86	−$1,663.01
27	−$2,338.87	$1,992.26	−$1,992.26	−$697.29	−$1,641.58	57	−$2,338.87	$1,928.72	−$1,928.72	−$675.05	−$1,663.82
28	−$2,338.87	$1,990.32	−$1,990.32	−$696.61	−$1,642.26	58	−$2,338.87	$1,926.41	−$1,926.41	−$674.24	−$1,664.63
29	−$2,338.87	$1,988.36	−$1,988.36	−$695.93	−$1,642.94	59	−$2,338.87	$1,924.08	−$1,924.08	−$673.43	−$1,665.44
30	−$2,338.87	$1,986.39	−$1,986.39	−$695.24	−$1,643.63	60	−$333,258.00	$1,921.74	−$1,921.74	−$672.61	−$332,585.39
			BTPW =	−$311,208.54					*ATPW* =	−$323,302.93	

In the before-tax analysis, the 5-year interest-only loan was preferred by $3,185.94; now, the 30-year conventional loan is preferred by $1,071.89. Tax deductibility of interest made a difference! It reversed the decision.

10-7 HOW MUCH MONEY SHOULD A COMPANY BORROW?

In Chapter 3 and again in this chapter, when we analyzed the four repayment methods, we observed that *money should be borrowed as long as the cost of borrowed capital was less than the minimum attractive rate of return.* We also noted that there are limitations to how much is borrowed. Certainly, money should not be borrowed that cannot be repaid. But, beyond that, there are limitations.

Independent rating agencies, also known as "nationally recognized statistical rating organizations," or "NRSROs," assign ratings to a company's short-term and long-term debt. Currently, there are five NRSROs—A.M. Best Company, Inc.; Dominion Bond Rating Service Ltd.; Fitch, Inc.; Moody's Investors Service; and the Standard & Poor's Division of the McGraw-Hill Companies, Inc. All five are recognized by the Securities and Exchange Commission (SEC). Their ratings directly affect the cost of debt capital for the firm.

For a company's debt ratings to be considered "investment grade," the company's senior long-term debt must be rated no lower than "BBB-" by S&P or Fitch and no lower than "Baa3" by Moody's. Falling below those thresholds moves a company into junk-bond status, and the costs of debt increase dramatically.

When a firm's debt-to-equity ratio gets too high, investors become skeptical of buying the firm's stock. What constitutes "too high" varies from industry to industry, but unlimited borrowing will not be viewed positively by shareholders, current or prospective.

A consensus view does not exist regarding the best debt-to-equity ratio for a company to maintain. It would be nice to claim that the lower the debt-to-equity ratio, the lower the cost of capital, but research does not support the claim. In 1958, two Nobel–prize winning economists, Franco Modigliani and Merton Miller, published "The Cost of Capital, Corporate Finance and the Theory of Investment," in *American Economic Review*. The paper argued that there is no right ratio; instead of worrying about the debt-to-equity ratio, the objective should be to minimize tax liability and maximize corporate net wealth. Our approach to the subject is consistent with the Modigliani-Miller theorem, which forms the basis for modern thinking on the capital structure of a corporation. According to Wikipedia, "The basic theorem states that, in the absence of taxes, bankruptcy costs, and asymmetric information and in an efficient market, the value of a firm is unaffected by how the firm is financed. It does not matter if the firm's capital is raised by issuing stock or selling debt. It does not matter what the firm's dividend policy is."[4]

For the Modigliani-Miller theorem to hold, several assumptions must be met: The cost of the firm borrowing money is the same as for those who are buying its stock, no taxes exist, and no transaction costs exist. Few, if any, of these assumptions will be met in the real world. However, the theorem's basic premise is worth remembering: *maximize corporate wealth by minimizing income taxes paid.*

We are reminded of Roberto C. Goizueta, a chemical engineering immigrant from Cuba, who became chairman and CEO of the Coca-Cola Company in 1980 and who served in that capacity until his death in 1997. During his tenure as CEO, he created more shareholder wealth than any other CEO in history. His success is marked by his emphasis on marketing and globalism. However, another significant change occurred during his tenure as CEO. Prior to Goizueta taking over the reins, the company prided itself in having no debt. He argued that debt capital was far less expensive than equity capital and began to secure debt capital, which he used to expand the business around the world. The results were obvious. In fact, it was through our work with the Coca-Cola Company that we began to appreciate more fully the wisdom of using borrowed funds.

Finally, one possible objection to our use of after-tax present worth in determining the amount of investment capital to be borrowed is that the *ATMARR*, which is based on the cost of capital, incorporates the cost of borrowing. Hence, using the *ATMARR*

---

[4]See http://en.wikipedia.org/wiki/Modigliani-Millertheorem.

while also deducting the cost of borrowed funds from taxable income in essence deducts interest twice.

It is true that the *ATMARR* reflects the cost of capital for the firm, which includes the cost of debt. However, the *ATMARR* also reflects the opportunity cost for the money being invested. If one can borrow money at a lower after-tax cost than what one can earn after taxes, no theoretical arguments to the contrary can make that an unwise action—;assuming the borrowed money can be repaid. Further, on an incremental basis, the amount borrowed is unlikely to change the overall cost of capital for the firm.

Our position remains the same as before—using borrowed funds can be a wise investment strategy for businesses and individuals. But, as with most good things, it should be done in moderation. Hence, the third of our three main messages: It is profitable to borrow investment capital as long as the interest rate is less than the *ATMARR* divided by 1 minus the income-tax rate.

Main Message #3

It is profitable to borrow investment capital as long as the interest rate is less than the *ATMARR* divided by one minus the income tax rate.

10-8 ADDITIONAL TAX CONSIDERATIONS

Two additional tax topics merit our attention: investment tax credit and Section 179 expense deduction.

10.8.1 Investment Tax Credit

Previously we mentioned the use of incentives to stimulate capital investment when the economy is weak. The *investment tax credit* (*ITC*) is one incentive that has been used over the years. It provides reduced taxation in the year in which an asset is placed in service. The ITC has had a turbulent history, dating back to 1962. It has been on-again, off-again during that time, with varying rules, percentages, and so forth. The ITC was repealed for property placed in service after 1985. It was argued that with the lowering of the maximum tax rate from 46 percent to 34 percent, at that time, a further tax break such as the ITC should be discontinued. However, it could be reinstated if economic conditions justify it (and if legislators believe it is in the economic interest of the United States, and/or their reelection efforts).

To introduce the concept of the ITC, we present a brief explanation and one example. The introduction will be kept simple, but beware! The rules governing the ITC were somewhat complex. For a more thorough treatment of the ITC, see earlier editions of this text or pre-1986 tax law.

The ITC permitted taxpayers to claim a credit, not just a deduction, against income taxes for qualified investment in certain new or used depreciable property. The regular credit allowable was 10 percent of the eligible investment. If the full ITC was taken, the asset's cost basis had to be reduced by an amount equal to half the ITC, thereby lessening the allowable cost recovery through depreciation. For example, if the 10 percent ITC was claimed, the asset's cost basis was to be reduced immediately by 5 percent.

EXAMPLE 10.14 Applying the Investment Tax Credit

If the ITC was reinstated exactly as when it was last in effect, for the SMP investment of $500,000, a 10 percent tax credit of $50,000, would be taken in the first year, and the cost basis would be reduced by (0.05)($500,000), or $25,000. Hence, MACRS allowances would be based on a cost basis of $475,000, as shown in Table 10.16. With a 10% ATMAR, the after-tax present worth increases from $123,988.64 to $161,710.59, due entirely to the ITC.

TABLE 10.16
Applying the Investment Tax Credit to the SMP Investment.

EOY	BTCF	DWO	TI	T	ITC	ATCF
0	−$500,000.00					−$500,000.00
1	$124,166.67	$95,000.00	$29,166.67	$11,666.67	$50,000.00	$162,500.00
2	$124,166.67	$152,000.00	−$27,833.33	−$11,133.33	$0.00	$135,300.00
3	$124,166.67	$91,200.00	$32,966.67	$13,186.67	$0.00	$110,980.00
4	$124,166.67	$54,720.00	$69,446.67	$27,778.67	$0.00	$96,388.00
5	$124,166.67	$54,720.00	$69,446.67	$27,778.67	$0.00	$96,388.00
6	$124,166.67	$27,360.00	$96,806.67	$38,722.67	$0.00	$85,444.00
7	$124,166.67	$0.00	$124,166.67	$49,666.67	$0.00	$74,500.00
8	$124,166.67	$0.00	$124,166.67	$49,666.67	$0.00	$74,500.00
9	$124,166.67	$0.00	$124,166.67	$49,666.67	$0.00	$74,500.00
10	$174,166.67	$0.00	$174,166.67	$69,666.67	$0.00	$104,500.00

$$PW_{AT} = \$161,710.59$$
$$FW_{AT} = \$419,435.61$$
$$AW_{AT} = \$26,317.65$$
$$IRR_{AT} = 18.39\%$$
$$ERR_{AT} = 13.13\%$$

=0.95*500000*0.32

Obviously, the ITC can be a major economic factor for companies of any size. As such, pressure may be exerted on Congress to reinstate the ITC in the future.

10.8.2 Section 179 Expense Deduction

The Section 179 expense deduction is designed to stimulate investment, primarily by smaller firms, by providing reduced taxation in the first year of an asset's life. Taxpayers may elect to treat the cost of certain property as an expense rather than as a capital expenditure. This property, called Section 179 property, is depreciable. It includes most tangible property, other than buildings, that would be of interest in an engineering economic analysis.

The election to expense must take place in the year the property is placed in service. The expense deduction is limited to a certain amount for qualifying property;

the limit changes from year to year. (Consult the IRS Web site for up-to-date information on its use: www.irs.gov. For more information on Section 179 expense deduction, see IRS Publication 946, *How to Depreciate Property*.)

The Small Business Jobs Act of 2010 increased Section 179 deduction limits to $500,000 for businesses with total asset purchases of $2,000,000 or less for tax years beginning in 2010 and 2011. The 2010 Tax Relief Act sets the maximum Sec. 179 expense for 2012 at $125,000 for companies purchasing up to $500,000 in eligible assets. (Note: in 1998, the maximum deduction was $17,500 and the limit was $200,000; in 2006, the maximum deduction was $108,000 and the limit was $430,000. In 2008, the maximum deduction was $250,000 and the limit was $800,000. Extensions are made periodically. However, unless Congress acts, the maximum deduction will be $25,000 and the limit will be $200,000 after 2012. This is an example of income-tax law that changes frequently. Consequently, check the IRS Web site to see what changes occur.)

The deduction limits apply to each taxpayer, not to each investment. Hence, if more than one item of qualifying property is acquired and placed in service during the year, the Section 179 deduction can be allocated among the items, as long as the total deduction is not more than $500,000. The amount eligible to be expensed for any tax year is reduced, dollar for dollar, by the amount of the aggregate cost of qualifying property that exceeds $2,000,000.

To determine the amount that can be expensed, let $K denote the aggregate cost of qualifying property in a given tax year. If $K < $500,000, then $K can be expensed, if $500,000 < $K < $2,000,000, then $500,000 can be expensed, if $2,000,000 < $K < $2,500,000, then $2,500,000 - $K can be expensed, and if $K > $2,500,000, then nothing can be expensed. Hence, if the amount of eligible property placed in service during a tax year is a) $400,000, b) $1,000,000, c) $2,200,000, or d) $2,800,000, then the maximum amount that may be expensed is a) $400,000, b) $500,000, c) $300,000, or d) $0, respectively.

In summary, the amount that can be expensed is given by Equation 10.12.

$$\text{Amount Expensed} = \max(\$0, (\min(\$500,000, \$K) - \max(\$0, (\$K - \$2,000,000)))) \tag{10.12}$$

The amount eligible to be expensed cannot exceed the taxable income derived from the trade or business in which the property is used. Also, when a Section 179 expense deduction is taken, *the cost basis is reduced by the amount deducted.*

EXAMPLE 10.15 Applying the Section 179 Expense Deduction

To illustrate the application of a Section 179 expense deduction using the $500,000 investment in SMP equipment, we assume three identical SMP machines are purchased and placed in service during the 2011 tax year. We also assume no other qualifying equipment is purchased during the year. The annual BTCF equals $372,500 and the salvage value equals $150,000.

Since the $1,500,000 investment does not exceed $2,000,000, a $500,000 expense deduction is allowed and the cost basis is reduced to $1,000,000, due to the Section 179 deduction of $500,000. As shown in Table 10.17, the ATPW is $399,131.99. Hence, the ATPW per SMP machine is $133,044.00, compared to the $123,988.64 ATPW in Example 10.4 for one SMP machine without a Section 179 expense deduction.

When multiple qualifying properties are acquired during a year, the $250,000 expense deduction can be allocated among them, as the taxpayer prefers.

TABLE 10.17
Applying the Section 179 Expense Deduction to the SMP Investment.

EOY	BTCF	Section 179 Deduction	DWO	TI	T	ATCF
0	-$1,500,000.00					-$1,500,000.00
1	$372,500.00	$500,000.00	$200,000.00	-$327,500.00	-$131,000.00	$503,500.00
2	$372,500.00	$0.00	$320,000.00	$52,500.00	$21,000.00	$351,500.00
3	$372,500.00	$0.00	$192,000.00	$180,500.00	$72,200.00	$300,300.00
4	$372,500.00	$0.00	$115,200.00	$257,300.00	$102,920.00	$269,580.00
5	$372,500.00	$0.00	$115,200.00	$257,300.00	$102,920.00	$269,580.00
6	$372,500.00	$0.00	$57,600.00	$314,900.00	$125,960.00	$246,540.00
7	$372,500.00	$0.00	$0.00	$372,500.00	$149,000.00	$223,500.00
8	$372,500.00	$0.00	$0.00	$372,500.00	$149,000.00	$223,500.00
9	$372,500.00	$0.00	$0.00	$372,500.00	$149,000.00	$223,500.00
10	$522,500.00	$0.00	$0.00	$522,500.00	$209,000.00	$313,500.00
					PW =	$399,131.99
					FW =	$1,035,245.60
			=(1500000-500000)*0.32		AW =	$64,956.89
					IRR =	16.90%
					ERR =	12.63%

10.8.3   Bonus Depreciation

The 2008 Economic Stimulus Act created a provision to spur investment by allowing businesses to rapidly recover capital expenditure costs by providing an additional first-year depreciation, called "bonus depreciation." For assets placed in service after December 31, 2007 and before January 1, 2011, for most property, and before January 1, 2012, for certain property, taxpayers are allowed to claim 50 percent of an asset's basis in the year the asset is placed in service. Taxpayers may then claim the regular depreciation amount on the remaining 50 percent of the asset's basis.

The 2010 Tax Relief Act extended bonus depreciation through 2012. For new property placed in service after September 9, 2010 and before January 1, 2011, the Act increased bonus depreciation to 100 percent. Whereas Section 179 deductions are limited to "small businesses," bonus depreciation applies to businesses of any size. (Since the continuation of bonus depreciation is unlikely, ignore it when working the problems.)

EXAMPLE 10.16   **Applying Bonus Depreciation in Purchasing the SMP Machine**

To illustrate the impact of bonus depreciation on ATPW, recall Example 10.4, in which an SMP machine was purchased and depreciated using MACRS 5-year depreciation. As shown in Table 10.18, if the equipment is placed in service during 2011 and 100 percent bonus depreciation applies, the ATPW increases from $123,988.64 without bonus depreciation to $151,154.74 with 100 percent bonus depreciation. If the equipment is placed in service during 2012 and qualifies for "only" 50 percent bonus depreciation, the ATPW is $137,571.69.

TABLE 10.18
Applying Bonus Depreciation to the SMP Investment.

Bonus Depreciation = 100%

EOY	BTCF	DWO	TI	T	ATCF
0	−$500,000.00				−$500,000.00
1	$124,166.67	$500,000.00	−$375,833.33	−$150,333.33	$274,500.00
2	$124,166.67	$0.00	$124,166.67	$49,666.67	$74,500.00
3	$124,166.67	$0.00	$124,166.67	$49,666.67	$74,500.00
4	$124,166.67	$0.00	$124,166.67	$49,666.67	$74,500.00
5	$124,166.67	$0.00	$124,166.67	$49,666.67	$74,500.00
6	$124,166.67	$0.00	$124,166.67	$49,666.67	$74,500.00
7	$124,166.67	$0.00	$124,166.67	$49,666.67	$74,500.00
8	$124,166.67	$0.00	$124,166.67	$49,666.67	$74,500.00
9	$124,166.67	$0.00	$124,166.67	$49,666.67	$74,500.00
10	$174,166.67	$0.00	$174,166.67	$69,666.67	$104,500.00
				PW =	$151,154.74

Bonus Depreciation = 50%

EOY	BTCF	DWO	TI	T	ATCF
0	−$500,000.00				−$500,000.00
1	$124,166.67	$300,000.00	−$175,833.33	−$70,333.33	$194,500.00
2	$124,166.67	$80,000.00	$44,166.67	$17,666.67	$106,500.00
3	$124,166.67	$48,000.00	$76,166.67	$30,466.67	$93,700.00
4	$124,166.67	$28,800.00	$95,366.67	$38,146.67	$86,020.00
5	$124,166.67	$28,800.00	$95,366.67	$38,146.67	$86,020.00
6	$124,166.67	$14,400.00	$109,766.67	$43,906.67	$80,260.00
7	$124,166.67	$0.00	$124,166.67	$49,666.67	$74,500.00
8	$124,166.67	$0.00	$124,166.67	$49,666.67	$74,500.00
9	$124,166.67	$0.00	$124,166.67	$49,666.67	$74,500.00
10	$174,166.67	$0.00	$174,166.67	$69,666.67	$104,500.00
				PW =	$137,571.69

10-9 TIMING OF INVESTMENT VERSUS FIRST YEAR'S DEPRECIATION CHARGE

At the end of Chapter 9, we noted that the first year's depreciation charge often occurs in the same year as the investment in tangible property. In all of the examples in this chapter, the investment was shown to occur at EOY = 0, and the first DWO was shown to occur at EOY = 1. If the first DWO occurs at EOY = 0, how will that impact the results?

EXAMPLE 10.17 Returning to the Theme Park Investment

Recall the alternative designs for the Scream Machine in a theme park in Florida. Design A required an initial investment of $300,000, produced before-tax cash flows of $71,666.67 annually for 10 years, and qualified as MACRS-GDS 7-year property. Design B required an initial investment of $450,000, produced before-tax cash flows of $103,333.33 annually for 10 years, and also qualified as MACRS-GDS 7-year property. An ATMARR of 10 percent applies. Now consider the effect of the first year's DWO occurring at the EOY = 0.

Table 10.19 provides the results of the after-tax analysis. Recall that we obtained the following in Example 10.7: ATPW(A) = $37,951.19 and ATPW(B) = $41,565.37, for an incremental difference of $3,614.18. Shifting the depreciation charges forward in time by 1 year produced a $14,362.43 difference in after-tax present worths. The preferred design remains Alternative B.

TABLE 10.19
Depreciation Write-Off Occurring in the Year of Acquisition.

EOY	BTCF(A)	DWO(A)	TI(A)	T(A)	ATCF(A)
0	−$300,000.00	$42,870.00	−$42,870.00	−$17,148.00	−$282,852.00
1	$71,666.67	$73,470.00	−$1,803.33	−$721.33	$72,388.00
2	$71,666.67	$52,470.00	$19,196.67	$7,678.67	$63,988.00
3	$71,666.67	$37,470.00	$34,196.67	$13,678.67	$57,988.00
4	$71,666.67	$26,790.00	$44,876.67	$17,950.67	$53,716.00
5	$71,666.67	$26,760.00	$44,906.67	$17,962.67	$53,704.00
6	$71,666.67	$26,790.00	$44,876.67	$17,950.67	$53,716.00
7	$71,666.67	$13,380.00	$58,286.67	$23,314.67	$48,352.00
8	$71,666.67	$0.00	$71,666.67	$28,666.67	$43,000.00
9	$71,666.67	$0.00	$71,666.67	$28,666.67	$43,000.00
10	$71,666.67	$0.00	$71,666.67	$28,666.67	$43,000.00
				PW(A) =	$59,447.76

EOY	BTCF(B)	DWO(B)	TI(B)	T(B)	ATCF(B)
0	−$450,000.00	$64,305.00	−$64,305.00	−$25,722.00	−$424,278.00
1	$103,333.33	$110,205.00	−$6,871.67	−$2,748.67	$106,082.00
2	$103,333.33	$78,705.00	$24,628.33	$9,851.33	$93,482.00
3	$103,333.33	$56,205.00	$47,128.33	$18,851.33	$84,482.00
4	$103,333.33	$40,185.00	$63,148.33	$25,259.33	$78,074.00
5	$103,333.33	$40,140.00	$63,193.33	$25,277.33	$78,056.00
6	$103,333.33	$40,185.00	$63,148.33	$25,259.33	$78,074.00
7	$103,333.33	$20,070.00	$83,263.33	$33,305.33	$70,028.00
8	$103,333.33	$0.00	$103,333.33	$41,333.33	$62,000.00
9	$103,333.33	$0.00	$103,333.33	$41,333.33	$62,000.00
10	$103,333.33	$0.00	$103,333.33	$41,333.33	$62,000.00
				PW(B) =	$73,810.19

10-10 SUMMARY

Our treatment of income taxes skimmed the surface. We did not go into great detail about tax law. Instead, we delivered *three main messages*:

1. Perform after-tax, not before-tax, analyses, except in unusual situations.
2. In general, the faster an investment is depreciated or amortized, the greater its after-tax present worth.
3. If investment capital can be borrowed at rates less than the minimum attractive rate of return divided by 1 minus the income tax rate, it is economic to do so.

In addition to learning the benefits of after-tax analyses and accelerated depreciation, and using someone else's money to make even more money for ourselves, we learned the following:

1. Income-tax rates and regulations change rapidly.
2. The difference in the *effective income-tax rate*, the *incremental income-tax rate*, and the *marginal income-tax rate*
3. Marginal income tax rates should be used in performing engineering economic analyses.
4. An expert in income taxes should be consulted if income taxes will play a major role in determining the economic viability of an investment.
5. Straight-line depreciation is the most commonly used depreciation method in financial reporting.
6. The modified accelerated cost recovery system (MACRS) is *the* depreciation method allowed by the IRS in performing income-tax calculations.
7. If an investment can be expensed, the after-tax cost equals the product of the investment and 1 minus the income tax rate.
8. If borrowed capital is used to fund an investment, each dollar of interest paid costs 60 cents after taxes if the income tax rate is 40 percent.
9. Every dollar of depreciation increases ATCF by the product of the income-tax rate and the depreciation allowance (see Equation 10.4).
10. When borrowing investment capital at interest rates less than the minimum attractive rate of return, delay repaying principal and interest as long as possible (i.e., use Plan 4).
11. When borrowing investment capital at an interest rate greater than the minimum attractive rate of return but less than the minimum attractive rate of return divided by 1 minus the income-tax rate, delay paying principal as long as possible (i.e., use Plan 1).
12. When the interest rate is greater than the minimum attractive rate of return divided by 1 minus the income-tax rate, avoid borrowing investment capital; if borrowed capital is required, then repay as much of the principal as possible as quickly as possible (i.e., Plan 2).
13. Income-tax considerations can change the recommendation regarding the investment to be made.
14. Research has shown that a firm's cost of capital is not significantly influenced by its debt-to-equity ratio.

15. Nobel Prizes in economics were awarded to two researchers who developed a theorem that states that corporate wealth is maximized by minimizing income taxes paid.

Pit Stop #10—A Taxing Experience!

1. True or False: If an investment cannot be justified economically using a before-tax analysis, it cannot be justified using an after-tax analysis.

2. True or False: After-tax present worth will be greater when using MACRS than it will be when using *SLN*.

3. True or False: The faster an asset is depreciated, the greater will be its after-tax present worth.

4. True or False: If money can be borrowed for 20% compounded annually and the marginal income tax rate is 40%, then it will be profitable to borrow the investment capital if your after-tax *MARR* is greater than 12%.

5. True or False: If the same amount of money is invested in something that can be expensed as in something that must be depreciated (and both provide the same annual returns) then you should choose the investment that can be depreciated.

6. True or False: If investment capital is borrowed, the income tax rate equals 40%, the after-tax *MARR* is 12%, and the loan rate is 15%, then it is best to repay the loan using Plan 1.

7. True or False: If investment capital is borrowed, the income tax rate equals 40%, the after-tax *MARR* is 12%, and the loan rate is 10%, then it is best to repay the loan using Plan 4.

8. True or False: If investment capital is borrowed, the income tax rate equals 40%, the after-tax *MARR* is 9%, and the loan rate is 18%, then it is best to repay the loan using Plan 2.

9. True or False: The investment tax credit is not in force, currently.

10. True or False: Section 179 Expense Deduction is not in force, currently.

FE-LIKE PROBLEMS

1. The correctly calculated taxes due on a corporate taxable income of $13,000,000 are closest to which of the following? (Table 10.1 or similar is required for this question.)
   a. $3,400,000
   b. $4,420,000
   c. $4,450,000
   d. $4,550,000

2. When a business calculates taxable income from gross income, which of the following is true?
   a. Depreciation, interest, and principal are all subtracted.
   b. Depreciation and interest are subtracted; principal is not.
   c. Depreciation is subtracted; interest and principal are not.

d. Interest and principal are subtracted; depreciation is not.

3. Consider the following data extracted from an after-tax cash flow calculation:

Before Tax Cash Flow = $22,500
Loan Principal Payment = $5,926
Loan Interest Payment = $2,400
MACRS Depreciation Deduction = $16,665

Which of the following is closest to the taxable income?

a. −$2,491
b. −$91
c. $3,435
d. $14,174

4. Consider the following data extracted from an after-tax cash flow calculation:

Before Tax Cash Flow = 22,500
Loan Principal Payment = 7,434
Loan Interest Payment = 892
MACRS Depreciation Deduction = 7,405
Taxes Due = 5,397

Which of the following is closest to the after-tax cash flow?

a. $1,372
b. $8,777
c. $8,806
d. $16,211

5. The marginal tax rate on a corporate income of $87,000 is closest to which of the following? (Table 10.1 or similar is required for this question.)

a. 15 percent
b. 20.5 percent
c. 25 percent
d. 34 percent

6. The average tax rate on a corporate income of $87,000 is closest to which of the following? (Table 10.1 or similar is required for this question.)

a. 15 percent
b. 20.5 percent
c. 25 percent
d. 34 percent

7. When considering the use of debt capital to finance a project, the upper limit for the interest rate on an attractive loan can be determined by which of the following?

a. MARR
b. MARR * (1 + tax rate)
c. MARR/(1 − tax rate)
d. MARR * (1 − tax rate)

8. Consider the following data for 2007 from an after-tax cash flow analysis. What is the after-tax cash flow for 2007?

Before − Tax Cash Flow = $23,000
Loan Principal Payment = $3,203
Loan Interest Payment = $3,877
Depreciation Deduction = $12,490
Taxable Income = $6,633
Taxes Due = $2,255

a. $20,744
b. $13,665
c. $3,430
d. $1,175

9. Consider the following data for 2007 from an after-tax cash flow analysis. What is the taxable income for 2007?

Before − Tax Cash Flow = $23,000
Loan Principal Payment = $3,203
Loan Interest Payment = $3,877
Depreciation Deduction = $12,490
Taxes Due = $2,255
After − Tax Cash Flow = $21,530

a. $40,000
b. $35,540
c. $6,633
d. $28,460

10. Consider the following data for 2007 from an after-tax cash flow analysis. What is the loan interest payment for 2007?

Before − Tax Cash Flow = $20,000
Loan Principal Payment = $4,018
Depreciation Deduction = $8,920
Taxable Income = $8,018
Taxes Due = $2,726
After − Tax Cash Flow = $10,194

a. $1,274
b. $3,062
c. $7,062
d. $11,080

PROBLEMS

Section 10.1

1. For each statement in Parts a through d, give a short answer or indicate True or False.
    a. Which of the following is a cash flow: (1) depreciation, (2) loan interest paid, and/or (3) income tax?
    b. We know that depreciation law has changed dramatically since 1950; however, tax law has not changed. (T or F)
    c. Depreciation method affects taxes owed. (T or F)
    d. In an alternative evaluation, the inclusion of taxes will change the amount of the measures of merit (e.g., PW or AW) but will not change which alternative is selected as most desirable. (T or F)

2. What are the three main messages from this chapter (you should know where to find them)?

Section 10.2

3. What are the various taxes that corporations pay in the United States? Which has the most significant impact upon economic analyses?

4. Income taxes are calculated based on gross income less certain allowable deductions. They are also assessed on gains resulting from the disposal of property. In 10 words or less, define (appropriate for a corporation) each of the following factors, based on Wikipedia:
    a. Gross income
    b. Expenses
    c. Depreciation
    d. Interest
    e. Property (e.g., equipment) disposition

Section 10.3

5. Calculate the corporate income tax for each of the following corporate taxable incomes. For each, determine the effective (average) tax rate and the marginal tax rate.
    a. $15,000
    b. $88,000
    c. $180,000
    d. $400,000
    e. $16,700,000

6. Calculate the corporate income tax for each of the following corporate taxable incomes. For each, determine the effective (average) tax rate and the marginal tax rate.
    a. $12,000
    b. $65,000
    c. $220,000
    d. $1,000,000
    e. $19,300,000

7. Calculate the corporate income tax for each of the following corporate taxable incomes. For each, determine the effective (average) tax rate and the marginal tax rate.
    a. $22,000
    b. $93,000

c. $225,000

d. $3,400,000

e. $36,555,000

8. Determine the *smallest* taxable income on which

   a. the very *last* dollar is taxed at 35 percent or more.

   b. the effective tax rate is 34 percent or more.

   c. the effective tax rate is 35 percent or more.

9. Determine the *smallest* taxable income on which

   a. the very *last* dollar is taxed at 25 percent or more.

   b. the effective tax rate is 20 percent or more.

   c. the effective tax rate is 25 percent or more.

10. An engineer named Don maintains a small incorporated civil engineering consulting practice. Last year, Don's firm's taxable income was $41,000. During that year, he spent a great deal of nonbillable time developing computerized tools for analyzing changes in water runoff due to new highway, building, and parking lot construction. Given his expertise and his ability to sign off as a licensed professional engineer (he took the FE exam in college), this year his company has been given the opportunity to take on two projects that will increase taxable income by $175,000.

    a. Determine the effective (average) tax rate on all of last year's taxable income.

    b. Determine the effective (average) tax rate on all of this year's taxable income.

    c. Determine the incremental tax rate.

    d. Determine the marginal tax rate this year.

11. Noise Sniffers Inc. (NSI) is a contractor to public utilities providing electrical service to homes and businesses. Most small- and midsized municipal utilities do not have the expertise or the equipment to go out and "sniff" noise caused by foreign objects on power lines, poor grounding on poles, cracked or carbonized lightning arrestors, and so on. Success means reduction in energy loss to the utility and reduction in static to those using radios nearby. Early on, ham radio operator K5KC suggested NSI personnel get training from the American Radio Relay League and purchase the right detection equipment. NSI now travels throughout the state to help utilities in need. Taxable income last year was only about $30,000 for this sporadic part-time work. This year, NSI is adding a larger adjoining state as a customer and will enjoy an increase of about $40,000 in taxable income.

    a. Determine the effective (average) tax rate on all of last year's taxable income.

    b. Determine the effective (average) tax rate on all of this year's taxable income.

    c. Determine the incremental tax rate.

    d. Determine the marginal tax rate this year.

12. Matrix Service Company is an industrial service contractor with a strong reputation in refining, power, petrochemicals, gas/LNG, and related areas. Their base taxable income is $19.2 million on sales of $490 million. They have landed two large aboveground storage tank projects and expect taxable income to increase to $25.7 million on sales of $540 million next year.

    a. Determine the effective (average) tax rate on all of last year's taxable income.

    b. Determine the effective (average) tax rate on all of this year's taxable income.

    c. Determine the incremental tax rate.

    d. Determine the marginal tax rate for next year.

13. TenTec in Sevierville, Tennessee, makes commercial and amateur radio equipment, including receivers, transceivers, antenna tuners, linear amplifiers, and so on. Their taxable income last year was $720,000. They have established a new line of electronic equipment that is on sale this year and that is expected to add another $140,000 to taxable income.

    a. Determine the effective (average) tax rate on all of last year's taxable income.

    b. Determine the effective (average) tax rate on all of this year's taxable income.

c. Determine the incremental tax rate.

d. Determine the marginal tax rate this year.

Section 10.4

14. Westwood Specialties had an increase in taxable income of $5,000,000 this year. Their increase in taxes was exactly $1,720,000.

    a. What was their taxable income last year?

    b. What was their total income tax this year?

15. West Mountain Radio, an electronics firm specializing in equipment interfaces, had been in a marginal tax bracket of 39 percent and then this year had an increase in taxable income of $150,000. Their increase in taxes was exactly $54,750. For each of the following, determine the smallest amount that meets the conditions given above.

    a. What was their taxable income last year?

    b. What was their total income tax this year?

16. Pneumatics, a start-up firm of four persons, had an increase in taxable income of $20,000 this year. Their increase in taxes was exactly $6,350.

    a. What was their taxable income last year?

    b. What was their total income tax this year?

17. Acme Universal is a micro-cap that had a $3,000,000 drop in taxable income this year. Their drop in taxes was $1,030,000. For each of the following, determine the largest amount that meets the conditions given above.

    a. What was their taxable income last year?

    b. What was their total income tax this year?

18. Raytheon wishes to use an automated environmental chamber in the manufacture of electronic components. The chamber is to be used for rigorous reliability testing and burn-in. It is installed for $1.4 million and will have a salvage value of $200,000 after 8 years. Its use will create an opportunity to increase sales by $650,000 per year and will have operating expenses of $250,000 per year. Corporate income taxes are 40 percent. Develop tables using a spreadsheet to determine the ATCF for each year and the after-tax PW, AW, IRR, and ERR if the chamber is kept for 8 years. After-tax *MARR* is 10 percent.

    a. Use straight-line depreciation (no half-year convention).

    b. Use MACRS-GDS and state the appropriate property class.

    c. Use double declining balance depreciation (no half-year convention, no switching).

19. A subsidiary of AEP places in service electric generating and transmission equipment at a cost of $3,000,000. The equipment is expected to last 30 years with a salvage value of $250,000. The equipment will increase net income by $500,000 in the first year, increasing by 2.4 percent each year thereafter. The subsidiary's tax rate is 40 percent, and the after-tax *MARR* is 9 percent. There is some concern that the need for this equipment will last only 10 years and must be sold off for $550,000 at that time. Develop tables using a spreadsheet to determine the ATCF for each year and the after-tax PW, AW, IRR, and ERR after only 10 years to see if the venture would be worthwhile economically.

    a. Use straight-line depreciation (no half-year convention).

    b. Use MACRS-GDS and state the appropriate property class.

    c. Use double declining balance depreciation (no half-year convention, no switching).

20. Bell's Amusements purchased an expensive ride for their theme and amusement park situated within a city-owned expo center. Bell's had a multiyear contract with the expo center. The ride cost $1.35 million, installed. Gross income from the ride was $420,000 per year, with operating expenses of $120,000. Bell's anticipated that the ride would have a useful life of 12 years, after which the net salvage value would be $0. After 4 years, the city and Bell's were unable to reach an agreement regarding an extended contract. In order to expedite Bell's departure, the expo center agreed to purchase the ride and leave it in place. Right at the end of the fourth

fiscal year, the expo center paid to Bell's the $900,000 unrecovered investment based on using straight-line depreciation. Corporate income taxes are 40 percent, and the after-tax *MARR* is 9 percent. Develop tables using a spreadsheet to determine the ATCF for each year and the after-tax PW, AW, IRR, and ERR after 4 years.

   a. Use straight-line depreciation (no half-year convention).

   b. Use MACRS-GDS and state the appropriate property class.

   c. Use double declining balance depreciation (no half-year convention, no switching).

21. Milliken uses a digitally controlled dyer for placing intricate and integrated patterns on manufactured carpet squares for home and commercial use. It is purchased for $400,000. It is expected to last 8 years and have a salvage value of $30,000. Increased net income due to this dyer is $95,000 per year. Milliken's tax rate is 40 percent, and the after-tax *MARR* is 12 percent. Develop tables using a spreadsheet to determine the ATCF for each year and the after-tax PW, AW, IRR, and ERR after 8 years.

   a. Use straight-line depreciation (no half-year convention).

   b. Use MACRS-GDS and state the appropriate property class.

   c. Use double declining balance depreciation (no half-year convention, no switching).

22. Suppose Milliken has an opportunity with similar cash flows to those in problem 21 for a digitally controlled dyer, although there are no depreciable items. They can invest in a marketing study by a blue-ribbon consultancy costing $400,000. Expected net returns are $95,000 per year over 7 years and $125,000 during the eighth year. Milliken's tax rate is 40 percent, and the after-tax *MARR* is 12 percent.

   a. Develop tables using a spreadsheet to determine the ATCF for each year and the after-tax PW, AW, IRR, and ERR after 8 years.

   b. Compare the results of Part a with those of Problem 21b, where MACRS-GDS is used. Explain the differences.

23. AgriGrow is to purchase a tractor for over-the-road hauling for $90,000. It is expected to be of use to the company for 6 years, after which it will be salvaged for $4,000. Transportation cost savings are expected to be $170,000 per year; however, the cost of drivers is expected to be $70,000 per year, and operating expenses are expected to be $63,000 per year, including fuel, maintenance, insurance, and the like. The company's marginal tax rate is 40 percent, and *MARR* is 10 percent on after-tax cash flows. Suppose that, to AgriGrow's surprise, they actually dispose of the tractor at the end of the fourth tax year for $6,000. Develop tables using a spreadsheet to determine the ATCF for each year and the after-tax PW, AW, IRR, and ERR after only 4 years.

   a. Use straight-line depreciation (no half-year convention).

   b. Use MACRS-GDS and state the appropriate property class.

   c. Use double declining balance depreciation (no half-year convention, no switching).

24. AgriGrow can invest in a 100-day short-term project with similar cash flows to those in problem 23 costing $90,000 to improve customer service. They believe the return on the project will be a net increase in sales of $37,000 per year over 3 years and of $43,000 in the fourth year. AgriGrow's marginal tax rate is 40 percent, and *MARR* is 10 percent on the after-tax cash flows.

   a. Develop tables using a spreadsheet to determine the ATCF for each year and the after-tax PW, AW, IRR, and ERR after 4 years.

   b. Compare the results of Part a with those of Problem 23b, where MACRS-GDS is used. Explain the differences.

25. Henredon purchases a high-precision programmable router for shaping furniture components for $190,000. It is expected to last 12 years and have a salvage value of $5,000. It will produce $45,000 in net revenue each year during its life. Corporate income taxes are 40 percent, and the after-tax *MARR* is 10 percent. Develop tables using a spreadsheet to determine the ATCF for each year and the after-tax PW, AW, IRR, and ERR if the router is kept for 12 years.

   a. Use straight-line depreciation (no half-year convention).

   b. Use MACRS-GDS and state the appropriate property class.

   c. Use double declining balance depreciation (no half-year convention, no switching).

26. Henredon can spend $190,000 now, similar to the investment in problem 25, for a design portfolio with a different furniture look inspired by some of the ultramodern culture in the metropolitan areas of Dubai. While some consider this a gamble, it is generally conceded that such a new line can result in increased net revenues of $45,000 per year for 11 years, plus $50,000 in the twelfth year. Henredon's marginal tax rate is 40 percent, and *MARR* is 10 percent on the after-tax cash flows.

    a. Develop tables using a spreadsheet to determine the ATCF for each year and the after-tax PW, AW, IRR, and ERR after 12 years.

    b. Compare the results of Part a with those of Problem 25b, where MACRS-GDS is used. Explain the differences.

Section 10.5

27. A portable concrete test instrument used in construction for evaluating and profiling concrete surfaces (MACRS-GDS 5-year property class) is under consideration by a construction firm for $22,000. The instrument will be used for 6 years and be worth $2,000 at that time. The annual cost of use and maintenance will be $9,500. Alternatively, a more automated instrument (same property class) available from the manufacturer costs $29,000, with use and maintenance costs of only $7,500 and salvage value after 6 years of $3,000. The marginal tax rate is 40 percent, and *MARR* is an after-tax 12 percent. Determine which alternative is less costly, based upon comparison of after-tax annual worth.

28. A virtual mold apparatus for producing dental crowns permits an infinite number of shapes to be custom constructed based upon mold imprints taken by dentists. Two models are available. One costs $58,500 and is expected to last 9 years with no salvage value at that time. Costs of use are $30 per crown, and 5,000 crowns per year are produced. The other mold apparatus costs $87,500, lasts 9 years, has no salvage value, and is less costly to use at $25 per crown. The dental supplier depreciates assets using MACRS but values the company's assets using straight-line depreciation. The marginal tax rate is 40 percent, and *MARR* is an after-tax 10 percent.

    a. Based upon the use of MACRS-GDS depreciation (be sure to state the property class), compare the after-tax AW of each alternative to determine which should be selected.

    b. Based upon the use of straight-line (no half-year) depreciation, compare the after-tax AW of each alternative to determine which should be selected.

29. A granary has two options for a conveyor used in the manufacture of grain for transporting, filling, or emptying. One conveyor can be purchased and installed for $70,000 with $3,000 salvage value after 16 years. The other can be purchased and installed for $110,000 with $4,000 salvage value after 16 years Operation and maintenance for each is expected to be $18,000 and $14,000 per year, respectively. The granary uses MACRS-GDS depreciation, has a marginal tax rate of 40 percent, and has a *MARR* of 9 percent after taxes.

    a. Determine which alternative is less costly, based upon comparison of after-tax annual worth.

    b. What must the cost of the second (more expensive) conveyor be for there to be no economic advantage between the two?

30. Two concrete test instrument investment alternatives qualify for different property classes. Investment A has a cost of $22,000, a useful life of 6 years with a salvage value of $2,000 at that time, and an annual cost of use and maintenance of $9,500. Also, suppose it is eligible for a 3-year property class. Investment B has a cost of $29,000, a useful life of 6 years with a salvage value of $3,000 at that time, and an annual cost of use and maintenance of $7,500. It is in the 5-year property class. The marginal tax rate is 40 percent, and *MARR* is an after-tax 12 percent. Determine which investment is less costly, based upon comparison of after-tax annual worth.

31. Two investments involving a virtual mold apparatus for producing dental crowns qualify for different property classes. Investment A has a cost of $58,500, lasts 9 years with no salvage value, and costs $150,000 per year in operating expenses. It is in the 3-year property class. Investment B has a cost of $87,500, lasts

9 years with no salvage value, and costs $125,000 per year. Investment B, however, is in the 7-year property class. The company marginal tax rate is 40 percent, and *MARR* is an after-tax 10 percent.

a. Based upon the use of MACRS-GDS depreciation, compare the AW of each alternative to determine which should be selected.

b. What must be Investment B's cost of operating expenses for these two investments to be equivalent?

32. Two investments involving a granary qualify for different property classes. Investment A costs $70,000 with $3,000 salvage value after 16 years and is depreciated as MACRS-GDS in the 10-year property class. Investment B costs $110,000 with a $4,000 salvage value after 16 years and is in the MACRS-GDS 5-year property class. Operation and maintenance for each is expected to be $18,000 and $14,000 per year, respectively. The marginal tax rate is 40 percent, and *MARR* is 9 percent after taxes.

a. Determine which alternative is less costly, based upon comparison of after-tax annual worth.

b. What must the cost of the second (more expensive) investment be for there to be no economic advantage between the two?

33. Ben Alexander, an enterprising young engineering graduate who worked part-time as a machinist during college, decided to establish his own mechanical design and specialty manufacturing business after graduating. His workload is increasing due to a few good contracts, and he is spending longer hours on hands-on machining tasks producing fabricated metal products. Ben is considering the purchase of a bed-type milling machine with automatic table feed and other features. The cost of the machine is $21,000 with an expected life of 12 years. He would keep it for only 5 years, however, and be able to sell it for $5,000 at that time. Ben has a time limitation of only 500 hours per year that he can devote to milling operations, even though he can sell everything he produces. If he buys the mill, he will be able to complete parts in 4 minutes each. If he does not purchase the mill, he will continue producing with current equipment at a rate of 12 minutes each. Each part he turns out provides a net income before taxes of $2. A third alternative, in addition to buying or not, includes leasing the milling machine for $4,000 paid annually at the beginning of the year. Marginal taxes are 40 percent, and the after-tax *MARR* is 9 percent.

a. Determine the annual worth associated with buying the milling machine. Be sure to give the appropriate MACRS-GDS property class.

b. Determine the annual worth of continuing with current equipment.

c. Determine the annual worth of leasing.

d. Determine the annual lease cost that makes Ben indifferent between purchasing and leasing the new milling machine.

34. Griffin Dewatering is considering three alternatives. The first is the purchase of a permanent steel building to house their existing equipment for the overhaul of dewatering systems (engines, pumps, and well points). The building can be put into service for $240,000 in early January of this year. The planning horizon for this is 10 years, at which time the building can be sold for $120,000 in late December. Maintenance and upkeep of the equipment, plus labor and materials for overhaul, costs $130,000 per year. A second alternative is to lease a building for $15,000 per year at the beginning of each year, in which case all operating costs are identical except for an additional $4,000 per year cost due to the inconvenient location of the lease property. Third, they could simply contract out the overhaul work for $170,000 per end-of-year, with an immediate credit through salvage of their present equipment for $45,000. Marginal taxes are 40 percent, and the after-tax *MARR* is 12 percent.

a. Determine the annual worth associated with buying the building. Be sure to give the appropriate MACRS-GDS property class.

b. Determine the annual worth of leasing.

c. Determine the annual worth of contracting out the work.

d. Determine the annual contract price that makes contracting and leasing economically equivalent.

35. Michelin is considering going "lights-out" in the mixing area of the business that operates 24/7. Currently, personnel with a loaded cost of $600,000 per year are used to manually weigh real rubber, synthetic rubber, carbon black, oils, and other components prior to manual insertion in a Banbary mixer that provides a homogeneous blend of rubber for making tires (rubber products). New technology is available that has the reliability and consistency

desired to equal or exceed the quality of blend now achieved manually. It requires an investment of $2.5 million, with $110,000 per year operational costs and will replace all the manual effort described above. The planning horizon is 8 years, and there will be a $300,000 salvage value at that time for the new technology. Marginal taxes are 40 percent, and the after-tax *MARR* is 10 percent.

a. Determine the annual cost of purchasing the new technology.

b. Determine the annual cost of continuing with the manual mixing.

c. Determine the amount of the investment in new technology that would make the two alternatives equivalent.

Section 10.6

36. What is the difference or distinction being made when we speak of *before-tax cash flows* and *before-tax and loan cash flows*. Be precise in your answer.

37. Abbott placed into service a flexible manufacturing cell costing $850,000 early this year for production of their analytical testing equipment. Gross income due to the cell is expected to be $750,000 with deductible expenses of $475,000. Depreciation is based on MACRS-GDS, and the cell is in the 7-year property class, calling for a depreciation percentage of 14.29 percent, or $121,465, in the first year. Half of the cell cost is financed at 11 percent with principal paid back in equal amounts over 5 years. The first year's interest is therefore $46,750, while the principal payment is $85,000.

a. Determine the taxable income for the first year.

b. Determine the tax paid due to the cell during the first year using a 40 percent marginal tax rate.

c. Determine the after-tax cash flow for the first year.

38. Hyundai USA has numerous robotic welders and checkers with vision. One underbody robotic welder was installed and is increasing productivity by 2.5 percent in one area. The result is a savings of $500,000 per year. Deductible expenses other than depreciation and interest associated with the installed robotic welder are only $120,000. Depreciation is $171,480 this year. Interest on borrowed money is $60,500, and no principal is paid back this year.

a. Determine the taxable income for the year.

b. Determine the income tax for the year assuming a marginal tax rate of 40 percent.

c. Determine the after-tax cash flow for the year.

39. Chevron Phillips (CP) has put into place new laboratory equipment for the production of chemicals; the cost is $1,800,000 installed. CP borrows 45 percent of all capital needed, and the borrowing rate is 12.5 percent. In the first year, 25 percent of the principal borrowed will be paid back. The throughput rate for in-process test samples has increased the capacity of the lab, saving a net of $X per year. In this first year, depreciation is $360,000 and taxable income is $328,000.

a. What is the gross income or annual savings X?

b. Determine the income tax for the first year assuming a marginal tax rate of 40 percent.

c. What is the after-tax cash flow for the first year?

40. A Boeing contractor responsible for producing a portion of the landing gear for huge airliners experienced a storm-related power glitch during the multi-axis milling, to tolerances less than 0.001 inch, of a large and complex part. The value already in the part, plus the equipment damage, was $300,000. Risk analysis indicates that a similar event might occur once per year on average if nothing is done. PolyPhaser, a leader in lightning and surge protection, was commissioned to do a turnkey installation to protect this critical portion of the process. The first cost is $480,000 installed. A total of $275,000 is borrowed at a rate of 12 percent per year, and no principal is repaid in the first year. Deductible annual costs are Y, and depreciation is MACRS-GDS in the 7-year property class, or 14.29 percent, in the first year. The taxable income is $15,000.

a. What is the value of the deductions, or Y, in the first year?

b. What is the income tax paid in the first year, assuming a marginal tax rate of 40 percent?

c. What is the after-tax cash flow for the first year?

41. Abbott placed into service a flexible manufacturing cell costing $850,000 early this year. They financed $425,000 of it at 11 percent per year over 5 years. Gross income due to the cell is expected to be $750,000 with deductible expenses of $475,000. Depreciation is based on MACRS-GDS, and the cell is in the 7-year property class. Abbott's marginal tax rate is 40 percent, *MARR* is 10 percent after taxes, and they expect to keep the cell for 8 years. Determine the PW, FW, AW, IRR, and ERR for the investment if

   a. the loan is paid back using Method 1 (interest only at the end of each year of the loan, plus principal at the end of the last year).

   b. the loan is paid back using Method 2 (equal annual principal payments plus interest on the unpaid loan balance).

   c. the loan is paid back using Method 3 (equal annual principal plus interest payments during each year of the loan).

   d. the loan is paid back using Method 4 (principal plus interest is paid at the end of the loan period).

42. Hyundai USA has numerous robotic welders and checkers with vision. One underbody robotic welder costing $1,200,000 (7-year property class) was installed and is increasing productivity by 2.5 percent in one area. The result is a savings of $500,000 per year. Deductible expenses other than depreciation and interest associated with the installed robotic welder are only $120,000. Hyundai borrowed $550,000 at 11 percent for 5 years. They plan to keep the welder for 8 years. Hyundai's marginal tax rate is 40 percent, and their *MARR* is 9 percent after taxes. Determine the PW, FW, AW, IRR, and ERR for the investment if

   a. the loan is paid back using Method 1 (interest only at the end of each year of the loan, plus principal at the end of the last year).

   b. the loan is paid back using Method 2 (equal annual principal payments plus interest on the unpaid loan balance).

   c. the loan is paid back using Method 3 (equal annual principal plus interest payments during each year of the loan).

   d. the loan is paid back using Method 4 (principal plus interest is paid at the end of the loan period).

43. Chevron Phillips has put into place new laboratory equipment for the production of chemicals; the first cost is $1,800,000 installed. Chevron Phillips borrows 45 percent of all capital needed, and the borrowing rate is 12.5 percent over 4 years. The throughput rate for in-process test samples has increased the capacity of the lab, with a net savings of $X per year. Depreciation follows MACRS-GDS, *ATMARR* is 11 percent, and the planning horizon is 6 years with a salvage value of $250,000 at that time. Based on a 40% marginal tax rate, use Goal Seek or Solver in Excel® to determine the value of X such that *ATMARR* is exactly achieved, no more and no less, if

   a. the loan is paid back using Method 1 (interest only at the end of each year of the loan, plus principal at the end of the last year).

   b. the loan is paid back using Method 2 (equal annual principal payments plus interest on the unpaid loan balance).

   c. the loan is paid back using Method 3 (equal annual principal plus interest payments during each year of the loan).

   d. the loan is paid back using Method 4 (principal plus interest is paid at the end of the loan period).

44. A Boeing contractor responsible for producing a portion of the landing gear for huge airliners experienced a storm-related power glitch during the multi-axis milling, to tolerances less than 0.001 inch, of a large and complex part. The value already in the part, plus the equipment damage, was $300,000. Risk analysis indicated that a similar cost might occur once per year on average if nothing is done. PolyPhaser, a leader in lightning and surge protection, was commissioned to do a turnkey installation to protect the process from similar yearly losses. The first cost is $480,000 installed. A total of $275,000 is borrowed at a rate of 12 percent per year for the entire 10-year planning horizon. Deductible annual operating and maintenance costs are $Y, and depreciation is MACRS-GDS in the 7-year property class. The marginal tax rate is 40 percent, *ATMARR* is 10 percent, and the expected life of the PolyPhaser equipment is 10 years. There is no salvage value. Use Goal Seek or Solver in Excel® to determine the value of Y such that *ATMARR* is exactly achieved, no more and no less, if

   a. the loan is paid back using Method 1 (interest only at the end of each year of the loan, plus principal at the end of the last year).

   b. the loan is paid back using Method 2 (equal annual principal payments plus interest on the unpaid loan balance).

   c. the loan is paid back using Method 3 (equal annual principal plus interest payments during each year of the loan).

   d. the loan is paid back using Method 4 (principal plus interest is paid at the end of the loan period).

45. Raytheon wishes to use an automated environmental chamber in the manufacture of electronic components. The chamber is to be used for rigorous reliability testing and burn-in. It is installed for $1.4 million, $600,000 of which is borrowed at 11 percent for 5 years, and will have a salvage value of $200,000 after 8 years. Its use will create an opportunity to increase sales by $650,000 per year and will have operating expenses of $250,000 per year. Corporate income taxes are 40 percent. Develop tables using a spreadsheet to determine the ATCF for each year and the after-tax PW, AW, IRR, and ERR if the chamber is kept for 8 years. After-tax *MARR* is 10 percent. Determine for each year the ATCF and the PW, FW, AW, IRR, and ERR for the investment if

   a. straight-line depreciation is used over 8 years with no half-year convention and the loan is paid back using Method 1 (interest only at the end of each year of the loan, plus principal at the end of the last year).

   b. straight-line depreciation is used over 8 years with no half-year convention and the loan is paid back using Method 2 (equal annual principal payments plus interest on the unpaid loan balance).

   c. straight-line depreciation is used over 8 years with no half-year convention and the loan is paid back using Method 3 (equal annual principal plus interest payments during each year of the loan).

   d. MACRS-GDS depreciation is used with the appropriate property class and the loan is paid back using Method 1 (interest only at the end of each year of the loan, plus principal at the end of the last year).

   e. MACRS-GDS depreciation is used with the appropriate property class and the loan is paid back using Method 2 (equal annual principal payments plus interest on the unpaid loan balance).

   f. MACRS-GDS depreciation is used with the appropriate property class and the loan is paid back using Method 3 (equal annual principal plus interest payments during each year of the loan).

46. A subsidiary of AEP places in service electric generating and transmission line equipment at a cost of $3,000,000 with half of it borrowed at 11 percent over 8 years. It is expected to last 30 years with a salvage value of $250,000. The equipment will increase net income by $500,000 in the first year, increasing by 2.4 percent each year thereafter. The subsidiary's tax rate is 40 percent, and the after-tax *MARR* is 9 percent. There is some concern that the need for this equipment will last only 10 years and need to be sold off for $550,000 at that time. Develop tables using a spreadsheet to determine the ATCF for each year and the after-tax PW, AW, IRR, and ERR after only 10 years to see if the venture would be worthwhile economically if

   a. straight-line depreciation is used with no half-year convention and the loan is paid back using Method 1 (interest only at the end of each year of the loan, plus principal at the end of the last year).

   b. straight-line depreciation is used with no half-year convention and the loan is paid back using Method 2 (equal annual principal payments plus interest on the unpaid loan balance).

   c. straight-line depreciation is used with no half-year convention and the loan is paid back using Method 3 (equal annual principal plus interest payments during each year of the loan).

   d. MACRS-GDS depreciation is used with the appropriate property class and the loan is paid back using Method 1 (interest only at the end of each year of the loan, plus principal at the end of the last year).

   e. MACRS-GDS depreciation is used with the appropriate property class and the loan is paid back using Method 2 (equal annual principal payments plus interest on the unpaid loan balance).

   f. MACRS-GDS depreciation is used with the appropriate property class and the loan is paid back using Method 3 (equal annual principal plus interest payments during each year of the loan).

47. A project has a first cost of $180,000, an estimated salvage value of $20,000 after 6 years, and other economic attributes as detailed in the table below. Unfortunately, as the end of year 4 neared, the project had to be abandoned, and the asset's market value at that time was different from the original estimated salvage value. There was a loan to help finance the project. It was being paid back in equal annual installments (the yearly principal plus interest payment was the same). The remaining principal had to be paid at the end of year 4 when the project was stopped. Following is the table (Note: The shaded cells would normally have something in them but have been erased for this exercise):

EOY	BTLCF +IN; -OUT	LOAN PRINC +IN; -OUT	LOAN PRINC REMAIN	LOAN INT +IN; -OUT	DEPR	BK VALUE	TI	TAX +IN; -OUT	ATCF +IN; -OUT	PWATCF
0	−$180,000	$70,000	$70,000			$180,000			−$110,000	−$110,000.00
1	$40,000	−$9,785.71	$60,214.29	−$4,900.00	$36,000	$144,000			$25,638.29	$22,891.33
2	$40,000		$49,743.59	−$4,215.00				$7,853.40		
3	$40,000						$1,957.95	−$704.62	$24,609.43	
4		−$38,539.93		−$2,697.80	$10,368	$41,472	$15,462.20			

a.   Fill in all of the blanks with BOLD BORDERS.

b.   What is the value of *MARR*?

c.   What is the loan interest rate?

d.   What is the MACRS property class?

e.   What is the tax rate?

48.   An asset is purchased for $90,000 with the intention of keeping it for 10 years but is sold at the end of year 3. A total of $30,000 was borrowed money that was to be repaid over 3 years in **equal annual payments,** including principal and interest. The depreciation is correct for the appropriate MACRS recovery period.

EOY	BTLCF	LOAN	LOAN INT	LOAN PRINC	DEPR	BK VALUE	TI	TAX	ATCF	PWATCF
	+ RCVD	+ RCVD	+ RCVD	+ RCVD				+ RCVD	+ RCVD	
	− PAID	− PAID	− PAID	− PAID				− PAID	− PAID	
0	−$90,000	$30,000				$90,000			−$60,000	−$60,000
1	$35,000		−$4,500	−$8,639.31	$12,861	$77,139	$17,639	−$7,408.38	$14,452.31	$12,903.85
2	$35,000		−$3,204.10					$9,754.90	−$4,097.06	$17,763.63	$14,161.06
3	$40,000				$7,870.50	$47,227.50				

a.   What is the property class of the asset?

b.   What is the value of *MARR*?

c.   What is the salvage value received at the end of year 3?

d.   What is the loan interest rate?

e.   Determine the value of the entries in the BOLD BORDERED cells.

Section 10.7

49.   Perform a Web search on "Modigliani-Miller Theorem" and write (copy), in one or two sentences, the essence of their theory. This may best be done by looking at the Wikipedia summary.

50.   Determine the long-term debt to total stockholder equity for the following organizations. One approach is to do a search on "XXX financials," where "XXX" is the company name. There will likely be many search results. Look for something that gives you the balance sheet in the company's financials area.

a.   Coca-Cola

b.   Motorola

    c. American Electric Power (AEP)

    d. Microsoft

    e. Company of interest to you or your instructor.

Section 10.8

51. A granary is considering a conveyor used in the manufacture of grain for transporting, filling, or emptying. It can be purchased and installed for $70,000 with $3,000 salvage value after 16 years. Operation and maintenance is expected to be $18,000 per year. The granary uses MACRS-GDS depreciation, has a marginal tax rate of 40 percent, and a *MARR* of 9 percent after taxes. If this conveyor is put into service, it will be the only capital investment for the year.

    a. Determine the after-tax annual worth assuming the investment tax credit has been reinstated at the 10 percent level.

    b. Determine the after-tax annual worth, assuming the Section 179 expense deduction is used.

52. A Boeing contractor responsible for producing a portion of the landing gear for huge airliners experienced a storm-related power glitch that did considerable damage. Risk analysis indicated that a cost of approximately $600,000/year might be expected if nothing is done. PolyPhaser was commissioned to do a turnkey installation, costing $960,000 installed, to protect the process from these yearly losses. This will be the company's only capital expenditure during 2011. A total of $550,000 is borrowed at a rate of 12 percent per year for the entire 10-year planning horizon. Deductible annual operating and maintenance costs are Y, and depreciation is MACRS-GDS in the 7-year property class. The marginal tax rate is 40 percent, the after-tax *MARR* is 10 percent, and the expected life of the PolyPhaser equipment is 10 years. The loan is paid back using Method 1 (interest only at the end of each year of the loan, plus principal at the end of the last year). There is no salvage value. Use Goal Seek or Solver in Excel® to determine the value of Y such that the *ATMARR* is exactly achieved, no more and no less, if

    a. the investment tax credit has been reinstated at the 10 percent level.

    b. the Section 179 expense deduction is used.

Chapter 11

REPLACEMENT ANALYSIS

A load of 60 52-foot J.B. Hunt containers is being shipped to the United States from China for use in intermodel transport. (Courtesy of J.B. Hunt Transport Services, Inc.).

J. B. Hunt Transport Services

J. B. Hunt Transport Services Inc. (JBHT) is one of the largest surface transportation companies in North America. A full truckload transportation firm that delivers goods all over the United States, its more than 10,000 drivers make short- and long-haul deliveries. In 2010, JBHT's consolidated revenue was $3.8 billion, spread across its four business segments: intermodal (JBI), dedicated contract services (DCS), truck (JBT), and integrated capacity solutions (ICS). Intermodal is a partnership between JBHT and most major North American rail carriers to deliver freight throughout the continental United States, Canada, and Mexico; full containers are delivered by JBI between customers and railroads. In 2010, JBI generated 56 percent of the company's total revenue. Dedicated contract services involve partnerships with major corporations such as Home Depot, Wal-Mart, Procter & Gamble, and Coca-Cola; DCS provides logistics services for its partners, often driving trucks and trailers showing the customers' logos rather than JBHT's logo; in 2010, DCS accounted for 24 percent of total revenue. The truck segment, consisting of truckload dry-van shipping, is the most visible, with its JBHT trucks regularly traveling U.S. interstates and highways; in 2010, JBT represented 12 percent of total revenue. The newest segment, integrated capacity solutions, provides transportation solutions to customers by utilizing third-party carriers, as well as JBHT-owned equipment. In a sense, ICS serves as a freight broker; it purchases transportation services on behalf of its customers and bills its customers for services provided. ICS services include flatbed, refrigerated, less-than-truckload (LTL), and a variety of dry-van and intermodal solutions. In 2010, ICS generated 8 percent of total revenue.

With more than 8,500 company-owned tractors and 66,500 trailers and containers used to ship more than 3 million loads in 2010, JBHT is constantly faced with decisions regarding the acquisition and replacement of tractors and trailers. Also, using its own fleet versus contracting with independent truckers and purchasing versus leasing over-the-road equipment are examples of decisions the company must make on a regular basis.

In a typical year, JBHT purchases hundreds of new over-the-road tractors, each of which has a retail price of approximately $100,000. In addition, JBHT annually purchases a large quantity of trailers and vans at an average cost of approximately $25,000. Also, JBHT annually purchases several hundred intermodal containers for approximately $15,000 each, plus the chassis to haul the containers (each chassis costs approximately $13,000).

Tractors tend to be replaced after driving approximately 600,000 miles; during the life of a tractor, it incurs annual repair and maintenance expenses in excess of $7,000. Trade-in values on used tractors vary depending on use, but it is typical for JBHT to receive approximately $25,000 for a used tractor and $10,000 for a used trailer or van. Clearly, with hundreds of millions of dollars being spent annually on tractors and trailers, determining the most economic time to replace its moving equipment is a key to JBHT's economic performance.

Airlines, railroads, and other transportation companies are faced with replacement decisions that involve hundreds of thousands, even millions, of dollars. And they are not alone. Automotive, chemical, construction, electronic, furniture, metal processing, paper processing, plastics processing, printing, lumber, telecommunications, theme parks, and a host of other businesses also face decisions of when to replace existing equipment. This chapter addresses decisions regarding the replacement of tangible property.

11-1 INTRODUCTION

In Chapters 5 through 10, comparisons have been made of various investment alternatives. Two situations were considered: a single alternative (where the decision was between investing and not investing) and a set of mutually exclusive investment alternatives (where we recommended the alternative having the greatest economic worth). Both situations could have involved a replacement of an existing asset.

In the case of the single alternative, a decision not to invest in a new asset could involve continuing to use a current asset; likewise, a decision to invest could involve replacing a current asset. The same holds for a set of mutually exclusive investment alternatives, since one of the choices could be the continued usage of an existing asset.

Because decisions to replace versus continue to use an asset occur so frequently, a body of literature has evolved on this subject. We use the term *replacement analysis* when referring to the comparison of investment alternatives that involve replacing an asset.

Replacement decisions occur all around us. You might have recently faced one regarding a camera, a car, a cell phone, a computer, a printer, a sound system, or a television. If so, then your decision might have been influenced by economics, capacity, quality of service provided, changing requirements, prestige, fads, or a host of other reasons.

Although replacement decisions occur for a variety of reasons, the following are typical:

1. The current asset, which we call the *defender*, has developed several deficiencies, including high setup cost, excessive maintenance expense, declining productivity, high energy cost, limited capability, and physical impairment.

2. Potential replacement assets, which we call the *challengers*, are available and have a number of advantages over the defender, including new technology that is quicker to set up and easier to use, along with having lower labor cost, lower maintenance expense, lower energy cost, higher productivity, and additional capabilities.

3. A changing external environment, including

    a. changing user and customer preferences and expectations;

    b. changing requirements;

    c. new, alternative ways of obtaining the functionality provided by the defender, including the availability of leased equipment and third-party suppliers; and

    d. increased demand that cannot be met with the current equipment—either supplementary or replacement equipment is required to meet demand.

Obsolescence is a frequently cited reason for replacing an asset. Various types of obsolescence can occur, including,

1. *functional obsolescence*, which can result from physical deterioration of the defender, increased demand that exceeds the defender's capacity, or new requirements that the defender cannot meet;

2. *technological obsolescence*, which occurs through the introduction of new technology, such that challengers possess capabilities not present in the defender;

3. *economic obsolescence*, which occurs when the economic worth of one or more challengers exceeds the defender's economic worth.

Replacement analyses are basically just another type of alternative comparison. As such, the same systematic seven-step approach described in Chapter 1 can be used. Likewise, the consistent measures of economic worth described previously can be used. Yet, replacement decisions seem to pose unique difficulties. Why? Perhaps it is because an ''emotional'' attachment to present equipment can occur. Also, perhaps it is due to the presence of *sunk costs*. Recall, sunk costs are past costs that have no bearing on current decisions. (A long history of maintenance and repair can cause owners to be reluctant to replace equipment—doing so might appear as an admission that mistakes were made in the past by keeping the equipment longer than it should have been.)

Systematic Economic Analysis Technique

1. Identify the investment alternatives
2. Define the planning horizon
3. Specify the discount rate
4. Estimate the cash flows
5. **Compare the alternatives**
6. Perform supplementary analyses
7. Select the preferred investment

Based on a *DCF* comparison, many companies use equipment long after replacements would be justified economically. Why? Several reasons come to mind:

1. The firm is currently making a profit, so there is no compelling reason to invest in new technology.

2. The current equipment still works and produces a product of acceptable quality—an "if it isn't broken, don't replace it" attitude prevails.

3. There are risks and uncertainties associated with change—replacing the "tried and true" proven defender with an unproven challenger is viewed as too risky (we recall the cartoon character Pogo saying, "Change is good! You go first!").

4. A decision to replace existing technology is a stronger commitment, for a period of time into the future, than continuing to use the defender—given the rapidly changing world and the growth of outsourcing and offshoring, some managers are reluctant to invest new capital in domestic operations.

5. Due to limitations on investment capital, replacements are given secondary consideration over investments that expand operations or add new capabilities (even though the replacement might have a greater economic worth).

6. Uncertainty regarding the future—the defender has a track record insofar as annual costs are concerned, the challenger is unproven, estimates of future demand might not materialize, and annual costs estimates for the challenger could be incorrect.

7. The psychological impact of sunk costs—it is very hard for some people to ignore what was spent in the past; as a result, they continue to waste money by supporting equipment they should replace.

8. The technological improvement trap—because technological improvements occur so frequently, some are reluctant to replace the defender with this year's challenger, because next year's challenger will be less expensive and will have greater capability than this year's.

9. Some companies prefer to be "technology followers" instead of "technology leaders"—they want others to debug the new generation of technology, and since new technology is being introduced so rapidly, they can never bring themselves to make the replacement decision.

10. Management is concerned about taking a hit on the quarterly financial statement by writing off an asset that is not fully depreciated, regardless of the *DCF* analysis.

In performing replacement analyses, two equivalent but slightly different approaches are used. The first is called the *cash flow approach* or *insider viewpoint approach*, where actual cash flows associated with keeping, purchasing, or leasing an asset are used directly. The second is called the *opportunity cost approach* or *outsider viewpoint approach*, which takes the view of an objective person outside the organization. As we shall see, the primary difference in the two viewpoints involves the treatment of the defender's value at the time of replacement.

Two Replacement Analysis Approaches

- Cash Flow Approach (Insider Viewpoint)
- Opportunity Cost Approach (Outsider Viewpoint)

As noted, the approaches are equivalent; therefore, regardless of which viewpoint is taken, when performed correctly, the same recommendation will result. While the choice of which approach to use is a matter of preference, we have found the *cash flow approach* to be the most straightforward and recommend it, unless there are compelling reasons to do otherwise.

In this chapter, we present both the *cash flow approach* and the *opportunity cost approach* in performing replacement analyses. For each, we give before-tax and after-tax examples to illustrate the equivalence of the two approaches and to illustrate how income taxes can impact replacement decisions. In addition, we consider a special section of the U.S. income-tax code, Section 1031, that allows realized gains to be deferred when qualified property is replaced with like-kind property. Finally, we consider the optimum replacement frequency for equipment that will be used year in and year out and is referred to as *optimum replacement interval analysis*.

11-2 CASH FLOW APPROACH

Recall, when we considered single alternatives, the decision of whether to invest or not was based on the magnitude of the measure of economic worth. If PW, CW, FW, or AW were positive-valued or if IRR or ERR were greater than the *MARR*, then it was recommended that the investment be made. In such evaluations, the alternative of *not investing* was considered to have negligible incremental economic impact. In essence, the do-nothing alternative was considered to have zero incremental cost.

In the case of replacement analyses involving a single challenger, doing nothing won't necessarily have negligible economic consequences. For example, operating and maintenance costs will continue to occur, perhaps increasing in magnitude. Also, do not forget the second principle of engineering economic analysis: *make investments that are economically justified*. No doubt, Henry Ford had a replacement decision in mind when he stated, "If you need a new machine and don't buy it, you pay for it without ever getting it." A challenger's economic viability often hinges on the difference in its annual operating and maintenance costs versus those of the defender;

hence, it is important to consider explicitly the costs of the defender if it is continued in service.

Principle #2

Make investments that are economically justified *"If you need a new machine and don't buy it, you pay for it without ever getting it."*

Henry Ford

In developing the cash flow profiles for the defender and the challenger(s), answer the following question: How much money will be spent, and how much will be received if this particular challenger replaces the defender? As noted above, past costs should be viewed from the proper perspective; unrecoverable past costs are sunk costs and are not to be included in economy studies that deal with the future, unless they will affect income taxes if a present asset is replaced.

The planning horizon to be used is at the decision maker's discretion. As in any alternative evaluation, the current asset and its challengers must be evaluated over a common planning horizon, with cash flows extending throughout, but not beyond, the horizon for each alternative. Since the defender's remaining life is usually shorter than the challenger's, the *shortest life among the alternatives* is often chosen as the duration of the planning horizon.

11.2.1 Before-Tax Analysis

In performing a before-tax analysis of a replacement decision, we will use a before-tax *MARR* equal to the after-tax *MARR* divided by 1 minus the income-tax rate. Hence, if the ATMARR equals 9 percent and the income-tax rate equals 40 percent, then the BTMARR equals 15 percent.

EXAMPLE 11.1 Before-Tax Analysis of a Surface-Mount Placement Machine Replacement Opportunity

Recall, previously we considered the acquisition of a surface-mount placement machine for a new cellular phone assembly line. Here, we consider an identical SMP machine as a candidate for replacing an existing machine, which was acquired 10 years ago for $300,000. The used SMP machine (defender) can be kept for a maximum of 5 more years, at which time it will have a negligible salvage value. Based on the defender's remaining useful life, a 5-year planning horizon is used. Annual operating and maintenance (O&M) costs for the defender have been increasing by $5,000 a year since its acquisition. Next year, the O&M costs will total $120,000.

If a new SMP machine (challenger) is acquired, the defender will have a market value of $50,000. The new SMP machine will cost $500,000 and will have annual operating and maintenance costs of $10,000 the first year, increasing by $5,000 a year thereafter. After 5 years, the challenger will have a market value of $200,000.

Based on a before-tax minimum attractive rate of return of 16.67 percent and a 5-year planning horizon, should the defender be replaced?

TABLE 11.1
Before-Tax Cash Flows for Example 11.1.

EOY	CF(1)	CF(2)	CF(2) − CF(1)
0	$0.00	−$450,000.00	−$450,000.00
1	−$120,000.00	−$10,000.00	$110,000.00
2	−$125,000.00	−$15,000.00	$110,000.00
3	−$130,000.00	−$20,000.00	$110,000.00
4	−$135,000.00	−$25,000.00	$110,000.00
5	−$140,000.00	$170,000.00	$310,000.00

Table 11.1 provides the cash flows for the two alternatives: keep the defender (Alternative 1) and replace the defender with the challenger (Alternative 2). Also shown are the incremental cash flows.

Notice, using the cash flow approach, for EOY = 0, no investment is required to continue using the defender, whereas, for the challenger, the net cash flow of $450,000 is the difference in the $500,000 purchase price for the challenger and the $50,000 market value for the defender.

An incremental equivalent uniform annual cost analysis is performed.

$$BTEUAC_{2-1}(16.67\%) = \$450,000(A|P\,16.67\%,5) - \$200,000(A|F\,16.67\%,5) - \$110,000$$
$$= \$890.00$$

or, using the Excel® PMT function,

$$BTEUAC_{2-1}(16.67\%) = \text{PMT}(16.67\%,5,-450000,200000)-110000$$
$$= \$889.06$$

Since the incremental *BTEUAC* is positive, the annual worth is negative and the incremental investment required to replace the defender is not justified economically. Based on a before-tax study, the old SMP machine should be used until a more attractive challenger is available.

EXAMPLE 11.2 Before-Tax Analysis of a Filter Press Replacement

A chemical plant bought a filter press 3 years ago for $30,000. In the financial records, its book value is $21,000. Actual operating and maintenance (*O&M*) expenses (excluding labor) for the press have been $4,000, $5,000, and $6,000 each of the past 3 years, as depicted in Table 11.2. It is anticipated that the filter press can be used for 5 more years and, at that time, be salvaged for $2,000. If it is replaced, its current market value is $9,000.

Technological developments the past 3 years have resulted in the introduction of several new filter presses on the market. One that is being considered as a replacement for the current filter press (defender) can be purchased for $36,000. It has an anticipated life of 10 years and is expected to have *O&M* costs consisting of a $1,000 gradient series. Based on historical data concerning salvage values of filter presses, estimated salvage values (S_t) for the new press (challenger) for various useful lives are also given in Table 11.2.

TABLE 11.2
Data for a Filter Press Replacement Analysis.

EOY (t)	O&$M_{1,t}$	O&$M_{2,t}$	$S_{2,t}$
-3	—	—	
-2	$4,000	—	
-1	5,000	—	
0	6,000	—	$36,000
1	7,000	—	30,000
2	8,000	$1,000	24,600
3	9,000	2,000	19,800
4	10,000	3,000	15,600
5	11,000	4,000	12,000
6		5,000	9,000
7		6,000	6,600
8		7,000	4,800
9		8,000	3,600
10		9,000	3,000

Alternative 1 supports keeping the defender. Alternative 2 supports replacing the defender with the challenger.

Since the defender can be used for only 5 more years, a planning horizon of 5 years is specified; the salvage value for the challenger is estimated to be $12,000 in 5 years. Cash flows for each alternative are given in Table 11.3. Note that the defender's $9,000 market value is applied as a positive cash flow for the challenger, since the defender will be sold if the challenger is purchased. Again, an incremental analysis is performed. Here, though, we compute the incremental before-tax equivalent uniform annual cost (*BTEUAC*) using a before-tax *MARR* of 15 percent:

$$BTEUAC_{2-1}(15\%) = \$27,000(A|P\ 15\%,5) - \$10,000(A|F\ 15\%,5) - \$7,000$$
$$= \$27,000(0.29832) - \$10,000(0.14832) - \$7,000$$
$$= -\$428.56$$

TABLE 11.3
Cash Flows for a Filter Press Replacement Analysis.

EOY	CF(1)	CF(2)	CF(2) − CF(1)
0	$0.00	−$27,000.00	−$27,000.00
1	−$7,000.00	$0.00	$7,000.00
2	−$8,000.00	−$1,000.00	$7,000.00
3	−$9,000.00	−$2,000.00	$7,000.00
4	−$10,000.00	−$3,000.00	$7,000.00
5	−$9,000.00	$8,000.00	$17,000.00

or, using the Excel® **PMT** function,

$$BTEUAC_{2-1}(15\%) = PMT(15\%,5,-27000,10000)-7000$$
$$= -\$428.64$$

Based on the negative-valued incremental *BTEUAC* (which means the incremental annual worth is positive), it is recommended that the new filter press (challenger) be purchased for $36,000 and the old press (defender) be sold for $9,000.

In listing the cash flows for each alternative in Table 11.3, we ignored the *O&M* costs that will occur after the fifth year if the challenger is purchased. We did so because of the specification of a 5-year planning horizon, which was based on the defender's maximum useful life. If the defender is retained, then it will have to be replaced in 5 years (if not before, due to possible development of attractive replacement alternatives in the future). Consequently, in 5 years, we might have an alternative available that will yield even greater *O&M* savings than the challenger currently being considered. Once the planning horizon has been established, it is not fair to include cash flows that might occur later for one alternative without including similar estimates for the other alternative(s).

The above interpretation defines the planning horizon as a window through which only the cash flows that occur during the planning horizon can be seen. This window should *include a terminal (salvage) value for any alternative having a life longer than the planning horizon*, even though the alternative might not be physically replaced at that time. The end of the planning horizon defines a point in time at which another replacement study is planned. At that time, the future savings and costs will be compared against other available replacement candidates.

It should also be noted that neither the $30,000 first cost for the defender nor the $21,000 book value appears in the calculation of economic worth. The $30,000 is a past cost that is now irrelevant (except as it affects taxes, as noted in Chapter 10); the $12,000 difference between the value on our accounting books ($21,000) and the market value ($9,000) is a sunk cost that analysts are often tempted to add to the challenger's first cost in an attempt to recover it. To do so is absolutely incorrect and biases the decision maker against the proposed replacement. For example, if we burdened Alternative 2 by adding a sunk cost of $12,000 to its first cost, the incremental *EUAC* would be decreased by $12,000(A|P 15%,5) = 12,000(0.2983) = 3,579.60/year; hence, the incremental *EUAC* would be $428.90 − $3579.60 = −$3150.70 < $0. On this basis, we would mistakenly recommend Alternative 1 and continue to operate an economically inferior filter press.

EXAMPLE 11.3 Before-Tax Analysis with a 10-Year Planning Horizon

If, in Example 11.2, a 10-year planning horizon is desired, we recommend that replacing the "old" filter press in 5 years be considered. Based on a forecast of the growth of filter press technology, suppose we anticipate that at the end of 5 years, a filter press will be available at a cost of $31,000. Net *O&M* costs and a salvage value of $15,000 are anticipated to be as depicted in Table 11.4. Recall that the challenger's salvage value after 10 years is $3,000.

TABLE 11.4

Cash Flows for a Replacement Analysis with a 10-Year Planning Horizon.

EOY	CF(1)	CF(2)
0	$0.00	–$27,000.00
1	–$7,000.00	$0.00
2	–$8,000.00	–$1,000.00
3	–$9,000.00	–$2,000.00
4	–$10,000.00	–$3,000.00
5	–$40,000.00	–$4,000.00
6	$0.00	–$5,000.00
7	–$1,000.00	–$6,000.00
8	–$2,000.00	–$7,000.00
9	–$3,000.00	–$8,000.00
10	$11,000.00	–$6,000.00

=–4000+15000

=–11000–31000+2000

Calculating the *BTEUAC* for the two alternatives (''keep'' versus ''replace'') with a 15% BTMARR gives

$$BTEUAC_1(15\%) = [\$7,000(P|A\ 15\%,5) + \$1,000(P|G\ 15\%,5) + \$29,000(P|F\ 15\%,5)$$
$$+ \$1,000(P|G\ 15\%,5)(P|F\ 15\%,5) - \$15,000(P|F\ 15\%,10)](A|P\ 15\%,10)$$
$$= [\$7,000(3.35216) + \$1,000(5.77514) + \$29,000(0.49718)$$
$$+ \$1,000(5.77514)(0.49718) - \$15,000(0.24718)](0.19925)$$
$$= \$8,532.30/year$$

$$BTEUAC_2(15\%) = \$27,000(A|P\ 15\%,10) + \$1,000(A|G\ 15\%,\ 10) - \$3,000(A|F\ 15\%,\ 10)$$
$$= \$27,000(0.19925) + \$1000(3.38320) - \$3,000(0.04925)$$
$$= \$8,615.20/year$$

These computations establish that the spread (difference) in the *BTEUAC* values for the two alternatives is $82.90/year, with Alternative 1 being preferred. Thus, on the basis of technological forecasts of filter press alternatives that will be available in 5 years, it would appear to be advantageous to postpone the replacement. However, the degree of uncertainty in the forecast of the cash flows for a projected future replacement candidate might cause us to question the merits of postponing the replacement when the difference in annual worths is ''only'' $82.90/year. (Using Excel®, $BTEUAC_1(15\%) = \$8532.34$, $BTEUAC_2(15\%) = \$8615.25$, and $BTEUAC_{2-1}(15\%) = \$82.90$.)

Often, different trade-in allowances are available if several potential replacement assets are being considered. Further, trade-in allowances can have little relationship to the true market value that can be realized if the defender is sold separately. In this case, when using the cash flow approach, the appropriate question to ask is still, ''How much money will be spent or received if I pursue this alternative?''

EXAMPLE 11.4 Before-Tax Analysis with Four Replacement Alternatives

In Example 11.2, Alternative 1 was keep the old filter press, which had a market value of $9,000 and a $2,000 salvage value after 5 years; Alternative 2 was replace the defender with a new press that has an initial cost of $36,000 and a salvage value of $12,000 after 5 years. Suppose the equipment supplier offers to allow a $10,000 trade-in for the old press. Also, suppose two additional alternatives have emerged. Alternative 3 is a new filter press that costs $40,000, has a $13,000 salvage value in 5 years, has annual *O&M* costs as given in Table 11.5, and includes a trade-in allowance of $12,000 for the old press. Alternative 4 is to lease a press for $7,500/year, payable at the beginning of each year during the 5-year planning horizon; in addition to the lease payments, end-of-year *O&M* costs given by an $800 gradient series will be incurred (if the lease is taken, it is assumed the existing press will be sold on the used-equipment market for $9,000). The cash flow profiles for the alternatives are given in Table 11.5.

$$BTEUAC_1(15\%) = \$7,000 + \$1,000(A|G\,15\%,5) - \$2,000(A|F\,15\%,5)$$
$$= \$7,000 + \$1,000(1.72281) - \$2,000(0.14832)$$
$$= \$8,426.17/\text{year}(\mathbf{\$8426.18}\text{ with Excel\textregistered})$$

$$BTEUAC_2(15\%) = \$26,000(A|P\,15\%,5) + \$1,000(A|G\,15\%,5) - \$12,000(A|F\,15\%,5)$$
$$= \$26,000(0.29832) + \$1,000(1.72281) - \$12,000(0.14832)$$
$$= \$7,699.29/\text{year}(\mathbf{\$7699.23}\text{ with Excel\textregistered})$$

$$BTEUAC_3(15\%) = \$28,000(A|P\,15\%,5) + \$500 + \$500(A|G\,15\%,5) - \$13,000(A|F\,15\%,5)$$
$$= \$28,000(0.29832) + \$500 + \$500(1.72281) - \$13,000(0.14832)$$
$$= \$7,786.21/\text{year}(\mathbf{\$7786.14}\text{ with Excel\textregistered})$$

$$BTEUAC_4(15\%) = \$7,500(F|P\,15\%,1) + \$800(A|G\,15\%,5) - \$9,000(A|P\,15\%,5)$$
$$= \$7,500(1.1500) + \$800(1.72281) - \$9,000(0.29832)$$
$$= \$7,318.37/\text{year}(\mathbf{\$7318.41}\text{ with Excel\textregistered})$$

Based on the *BTEUAC* results, leasing (Alternative 4) a new filter press and selling the old one on the used-equipment market appear to be most favorable economically. The rank ordering of alternatives, based on *EUAC*, is $4 > 2 > 3 > 1$.

TABLE 11.5
Cash Flows for a Replacement Alternatives.

EOY	CF(1)	CF(2)	CF(3)	CF(4)
0	$0.00	-$26,000.00	-$28,000.00	$1,500.00
1	-$7,000.00	$0.00	-$500.00	-$7,500.00
2	-$8,000.00	-$1,000.00	-$1,000.00	-$8,300.00
3	-$9,000.00	-$2,000.00	-$1,500.00	-$9,100.00 [=-7500-1600]
4	-$10,000.00	-$3,000.00	-$2,000.00	-$9,900.00
5	-$9,000.00	$8,000.00	$10,500.00	-$3,200.00

=-2500+13000

=-36000+10000

=-40000+12000

11.2.2 After-Tax Analysis

Since book values are not cash flows, they can be ignored in before-tax analyses. In after-tax analyses, however, it is important to compare the defender's book value with its trade-in value. From Chapter 10, if the book value is greater than what is received, then a *book loss* occurs and a tax savings results; if the book value is less than what is received, then a *book gain* occurs and income tax is paid on the difference.

As noted in Chapter 9, two book values are usually available on an asset: the book value for tax purposes and the book value for financial reporting purposes. It is important for the book value for tax purposes to be used in after-tax analyses. Since MACRS is the only depreciation method allowed in the United States for tax purposes, the book value used must come from MACRS depreciation in after-tax analyses.

Also, as noted in Chapter 9, MACRS includes a half-year convention: Half of a full year allowance is taken the first and last year of the recovery period. Recall from Chapter 10, when property is disposed of before the recovery period's end, the MACRS half-year convention allows only 50 percent of a full year's depreciation in the year of disposal. Attention must be given to this when performing after-tax replacement analyses.

Because considerable negotiation can occur when replacing an asset, several different *market values* can be assigned to the defender. Further, the equipment vendor can either reduce the sales price on the challenger or increase the trade-in allowance for the defender. We will examine the after-tax consequences of each way of pricing the challenger and the defender's trade-in allowance.

Before illustrating how after-tax replacement analyses are conducted in the following examples, we must agree on the timing of the initial investment, the initial depreciation charge on the investment, the receipt of the defender's salvage value, and the tax or tax savings that results from replacing the defender. Recall, in Chapter 10, we showed the initial investment occurring at $EOY = 0$ and the first depreciation charge occurring at $EOY = 1$. We did so because that is the standard convention in engineering economics; as noted in Chapter 9, in practice, the first depreciation charge is often taken immediately upon acquisition and placement in service of the equipment in question. (Some argue that the investment occurs at the beginning of year 1, which is the same as the end of year 0.)

What about tax consequences of the defender being disposed of at a value different from its book value? When do they occur? We adopt the convention of showing the tax on realized gains (or tax savings on realized losses) at $EOY = 1$. (We recognize that we show the tax consequences in the same year the salvage value occurs when salvage value differs from book value at the planning horizon's end.)

To summarize,

1. the initial investment of the challenger is shown at $EOY = 0$;
2. the initial depreciation charge for the challenger is shown at $EOY = 1$;
3. the tax or tax savings resulting from replacing the defender is shown at $EOY = 1$;

The following convention is adopted:

1. the initial investment of the *challenger* is shown at $EOY = 0$,
2. the initial depreciation charge for the *challenger* is shown at $EOY = 1$,
3. the tax or tax savings resulting from the replacement of the *defender* is shown at $EOY = 1$,
4. the salvage value for the *challenger* at the end of the planning horizon is shown at $EOY = n$, and
5. the tax or tax savings resulting from the salvage value for the *challenger* is shown at $EOY = n$.

4. the challenger's salvage value at the end of the planning horizon is shown at EOY $= n$; and

5. the tax or tax savings resulting from the challenger's salvage value is shown at EOY $= n$.

EXAMPLE 11.5 After-Tax Analysis of the SMP Machine Replacement

Now, let's examine the effect of income taxes on the replacement of the SMP machine. Recall from Example 11.1, the defender was purchased 10 years ago. Since SMP machines qualify as 5-year property, the defender is fully depreciated (i.e., its book value is 0). If the defender is replaced, it will have a market value of $50,000. If it is retained for another 5 years, it will have a negligible salvage value. Operating and maintenance costs for the defender can be represented by a $5,000 gradient series added to a uniform series of $120,000.

The challenger has a cost basis of $500,000. O&M costs for the challenger can be represented by a $5,000 gradient series added to a uniform series of $10,000. At the end of the 5-year planning horizon, the challenger will have a salvage value of $200,000.

Based on a 40 percent income tax rate, MACRS-GDS 5-year property for both the defender and the challenger, and a 10 percent after-tax *MARR*, use an after-tax equivalent uniform annual cost analysis to determine if the defender should be replaced.

Table 11.6 contains the cash flows for the defender and the challenger. Notice, from a cash flow perspective, there are no tax consequences for the defender if it is sold for $50,000. Since the sale of the defender will not occur unless it is replaced, no cash flows are shown for it for EOY $= 0$. However, for the challenger, the $50,000 is taxable income; based on our convention, it is shown at EOY $= 1$. Further, since the challenger is not fully depreciated at the end of the planning horizon, a portion of the $200,000 salvage value is included in taxable income. Based on Equation 10.6, taxable income for the challenger at the end of the planning horizon equals $170,000 less the sum of the half-year depreciation allowance of $28,800 and the book value of $57,600, or $83,600.

As shown in Table 11.6, ATEUAC(1) = $77,430.38 and ATEUAC(2) = $74,311.49. The incremental *ATEUAC* is $-$3,118.89. Therefore, the challenger is preferred to the

---

TABLE 11.6
After-Tax Replacement Analysis for the SMP Machine.

EOY	BTCF(1)	DW(1)	TI(1)	T(1)	ATCF(1)
0	$0.00	$0.00	$0.00	$0.00	$0.00
1	−$120,000.00	$0.00	−$120,000.00	−$48,000.00	−$72,000.00
2	−$125,000.00	$0.00	−$125,000.00	−$50,000.00	−$75,000.00
3	−$130,000.00	$0.00	−$130,000.00	−$52,000.00	−$78,000.00
4	−$135,000.00	$0.00	−$135,000.00	−$54,000.00	−$81,000.00
5	−$140,000.00	$0.00	−$140,000.00	−$56,000.00	−$84,000.00
				ATEUAC(1) =	$77,430.38

EOY	BTCF(2)	DW(2)	TI(2)	T(2)	ATCF(2)
0	−$450,000.00	$0.00	$0.00	$0.00	−$450,000.00
1	−$10,000.00	$100,000.00	−$60,000.00	−$24,000.00	$14,000.00
2	−$15,000.00	$160,000.00	−$175,000.00	−$70,000.00	$55,000.00
3	−$20,000.00	$96,000.00	−$116,000.00	−$46,400.00	$26,400.00
4	−$25,000.00	$57,600.00	−$82,600.00	−$33,040.00	$8,040.00
5	$170,000.00	$28,800.00	$83,600.00	$33,440.00	$136,560.00
				ATEUAC(2) =	$74,311.49

=−10000−100000+50000

=170000−28800−57600

$B(2)_5 = \$500,000(0.1152) = \$57,600$

defender! Based on a before-tax analysis, the defender was preferred. Hence, a reversal of recommendations occurred, based on income-tax considerations.

EXAMPLE 11.6 After-Tax Analysis of a Filter Press Replacement

Recall Example 11.2, in which a filter press was purchased 3 years ago for $30,000. Its book value is shown in the financial records to be $21,000. *O&M* costs for the next 5 years can be represented by a $1,000 gradient series added to a $7,000 uniform series. At the end of the 5-year planning horizon, the defender's salvage value is $2,000.

The challenger has a cost basis of $36,000. If the challenger is purchased, the defender will be sold for $9,000. *O&M* costs for the challenger are represented by a $1,000 gradient series. At the end of the 5-year planning horizon, the challenger will have a salvage value of $12,000.

Based on an after-tax analysis, with a 9 percent ATMARR, should the filter press be replaced?

Filter presses qualify as 3-year property. Recalling Principle 7 and considering only the differences in cash flows for the alternatives, notice that if the defender is continued in service, depreciation charges of $30,000(0.1481) = $4,443 and $30,000(0.0741) = $2,223 will occur at EOY = 0 and EOY = 1, respectively.

It is important to note that if the defender has a book value greater than 0 when replacement occurs, a half-year depreciation charge for both the defender and the challenger will occur in the same year—the year in which replacement occurs.

Based on the convention cited above, we show the cash flows associated with disposal of the defender and acquisition of the challenger occurring at the end of year 0. If the defender is replaced and is not fully depreciated, we show its half-year depreciation at the end of year 1, along with a half-year depreciation for the challenger.

For the example, we assume the defender is sold at the end of year 3, which we call the present and denote as end-of-year 0. We also assume the defender is taken out of service during the first year. Likewise, we assume the challenger is purchased at the end of year 0 and is placed in service during the first year. Finally, we assume that any income-tax consequences of the disposal of the defender and acquisition of the challenger occur during the first year of the 5-year planning horizon.

Since the defender is 3-year property, a full year of depreciation ($30,000(0.1481) = $4,443) is taken during year 0 regardless of whether it is continued in service or replaced. If retained, a final half-year depreciation charge will be taken during the first year; if replaced, a half-year depreciation charge will be taken during the first year. Coincidentally, a half-year depreciation charge will be taken during year 1, whether the defender is retained or replaced. Therefore, its book value at trade-in will be 0. Based on Principle 7, the $4,443 depreciation charge in year 0 is not shown for either alternative.

In Table 11.7, we include the $2,223 depreciation charge for both alternatives, because the depreciation charge in year 1 often will not be the same for both alternatives. For example, had the old filter press been purchased 2 years ago instead of 3, the depreciation charges in years 0 and 1 would have been $13,335 and $4,443, respectively, if the defender is retained; if the defender is traded, its depreciation charges would have been $13,335 and $2,221.50, since only a half-year depreciation charge can be taken in the year of disposal.

Hence, with $9,000 received for the defender's trade-in, $3,600 in incomes taxes are owed, based on the difference in $9,000 and the $0 book value. As shown in Table 11.7, for Alternative 2 (replace), the depreciation charge for year 1 equals the sum of $2,223 and $36,000(0.3333), or $14,221.80.

From Table 11.7, based on a 9 percent after-tax *MARR*, the after-tax *EUAC* for the defender (Alternative 1) is $4,886.68; for the challenger it is $4,339.91. Hence, the filter press should be replaced. The difference in the defender's and the challenger's *EUAC* (or "spread") is $546.77. (Recall, the before-tax incremental *EUAC* was $428.64.)

TABLE 11.7
After-Tax Analysis for Example 11.6.

EOY	BTCF(1)	DWO(1)	TI(1)	T(1)	ATCF(1)
0	$0.00	$0.00	$0.00	$0.00	$0.00
1	–$7,000.00	$2,223.00	–$9,223.00	–$3,689.20	–$3,310.80
2	–$8,000.00	$0.00	–$8,000.00	–$3,200.00	–$4,800.00
3	–$9,000.00	$0.00	–$9,000.00	–$3,600.00	–$5,400.00
4	–$10,000.00	$0.00	–$10,000.00	–$4,000.00	–$6,000.00
5	–$9,000.00	$0.00	–$9,000.00	–$3,600.00	–$5,400.00
				ATEUAC(1) =	$4,886.68
	=–11000+2000	=–36000+9000	=2223.00+11998.80		

EOY	BTCF(2)	DWO(2)	TI(2)	T(2)	ATCF(2)
0	–$27,000.00	$0.00	$0.00	$0.00	–$27,000.00
1	$0.00	$14,221.80	–$5,221.80	–$2,088.72	$2,088.72
2	–$1,000.00	$16,002.00	–$17,002.00	–$6,800.80	$5,800.80
3	–$2,000.00	$5,331.60	–$7,331.60	–$2,932.64	$932.64
4	–$3,000.00	$2,667.60	–$5,667.60	–$2,267.04	–$732.96
5	$8,000.00	$0.00	$8,000.00	$3,200.00	$4,800.00
				ATEUAC(2) =	$4,339.91
	=–4000+12000				

Now, suppose the equipment vendor says the old filter press is worth nothing, but the new filter press will be discounted $9,000. Thus, instead of a realized gain of $9,000, there is neither a book loss nor a book gain associated with the defender's disposal. Now, the cost basis for the challenger is reduced to $27,000.

From Table 11.8, the defender's after-tax *EUAC* is unchanged. However, the challenger's after-tax *EUAC* is reduced to $4,274.50. The spread between the defender's and the challenger's *EUAC* is $612.17. As before, replacement of the filter press is recommended.

TABLE 11.8
After-Tax Analysis with Reduced Trade-In and Reduced Sales Price.

EOY	BTCF(1)	DWO(1)	TI(1)	T(1)	ATCF(1)
0	$0.00	$0.00	$0.00	$0.00	$0.00
1	–$7,000.00	$2,223.00	–$9,223.00	–$3,689.20	–$3,310.80
2	–$8,000.00	$0.00	–$8,000.00	–$3,200.00	–$4,800.00
3	–$9,000.00	$0.00	–$9,000.00	–$3,600.00	–$5,400.00
4	–$10,000.00	$0.00	–$10,000.00	–$4,000.00	–$6,000.00
5	–$9,000.00	$0.00	–$9,000.00	–$3,600.00	–$5,400.00
	=–11000+2000			ATEUAC(1) =	$4,886.68

EOY	BTCF(2)	DWO(2)	TI(2)	T(2)	ATCF(2)
0	–$27,000.00	$0.00	$0.00	$0.00	–$27,000.00
1	$0.00	$11,222.10	–$11,222.10	–$4,488.84	$4,488.84
2	–$1,000.00	$12,001.50	–$13,001.50	–$5,200.60	$4,200.60
3	–$2,000.00	$3,998.70	–$5,998.70	–$2,399.48	$399.48
4	–$3,000.00	$2,000.70	–$5,000.70	–$2,000.28	–$999.72
5	$8,000.00	$0.00	$8,000.00	$3,200.00	$4,800.00
	=–4000+12000			ATEUAC(2) =	$4,274.50

EXAMPLE 11.7 After-Tax Analysis of Example 11.3

Recall, Example 11.3 and Table 11.4 involved a 10-year horizon for the filter press replacement. Assumptions were made regarding the defender's successor after its remaining 5-year life. Technological improvements in filter presses were forecast, including net operating and maintenance costs and salvage value at the planning horizon's end.

The after-tax analysis of Example 11.3 is quite straightforward. Again, MACRS (3-year property) is used to determine the book value for the defender if replaced, the book value for the defender at the planning horizon's end, and the book value for the challenger at the planning horizon's end.

From Table 11.9, with a 9 percent *ATMARR*, the defender's *ATEUAC* is \$3,519.49; the challenger's is \$4,854.88. Thus, the filter press should *not* be replaced; the reversal in the recommendation is due to the forecast of technology that will be available in 5 years.

The before-tax analysis resulted in a spread in the *ATEUAC* values of only \$82.90. However, the after-tax spread is much greater—\$1,335.39. Again, depending on one's confidence in the forecast of expenditures from 5 to 10 years in the future, the old filter press might be retained.

TABLE 11.9

After-Tax Analysis with a 10-Year Planning Horizon.

EOY	BTCF(1)	DWO(1)	TI(1)	T(1)	ATCF(1)
0	\$0.00	\$0.00	\$0.00	\$0.00	\$0.00
1	–\$7,000.00	\$2,223.00	–\$9,223.00	–\$3,689.20	–\$3,310.80
2	–\$8,000.00	\$0.00	–\$8,000.00	–\$3,200.00	–\$4,800.00
3	–\$9,000.00	\$0.00	–\$9,000.00	–\$3,600.00	–\$5,400.00
4	–\$10,000.00	\$0.00	–\$10,000.00	–\$4,000.00	–\$6,000.00
5	–\$40,000.00	\$0.00	–\$40,000.00	–\$16,000.00	–\$24,000.00
6	\$0.00	\$10,332.30	–\$10,332.30	–\$4,132.92	\$4,132.92
7	\$1,000.00	\$13,779.50	–\$12,779.50	–\$5,111.80	\$6,111.80
8	–\$2,000.00	\$4,591.10	–\$6,591.10	–\$2,636.44	\$636.44
9	–\$3,000.00	\$2,297.10	–\$5,297.10	–\$2,118.84	–\$881.16
10	\$11,000.00	\$0.00	\$11,000.00	\$4,400.00	\$6,600.00
				EUAC(1) =	\$3,519.49

=–11000–31000+2000   =–7000–2223

=–14221.80+9000

EOY	BTCF(2)	DWO(2)	TI(2)	T(2)	ATCF(2)
0	–\$27,000.00	\$0.00	\$0.00	\$0.00	–\$27,000.00
1	\$0.00	\$14,221.80	–\$5,221.80	–\$2,088.72	\$2,088.72
2	–\$1,000.00	\$16,002.00	–\$17,002.00	–\$6,800.80	\$5,800.80
3	–\$2,000.00	\$5,331.60	–\$7,331.60	–\$2,932.64	\$932.64
4	–\$3,000.00	\$2,667.60	–\$5,667.60	–\$2,267.04	–\$732.96
5	–\$4,000.00	\$0.00	–\$4,000.00	–\$1,600.00	–\$2,400.00
6	–\$5,000.00	\$0.00	–\$5,000.00	–\$2,000.00	–\$3,000.00
7	–\$6,000.00	\$0.00	–\$6,000.00	–\$2,400.00	–\$3,600.00
8	–\$7,000.00	\$0.00	–\$7,000.00	–\$2,800.00	–\$4,200.00
9	–\$8,000.00	\$0.00	–\$8,000.00	–\$3,200.00	–\$4,800.00
10	–\$6,000.00	\$0.00	–\$6,000.00	–\$2,400.00	–\$3,600.00
				EUAC(2) =	\$4,854.88

EXAMPLE 11.8 After-Tax Analysis of Example 11.4

Recall, Example 11.4 introduced two additional challengers to the filter press currently in use (defender). One of the new challengers is another filter press for purchase; the second new challenger is a lease alternative. (Recall, leases are expensed, not depreciated in after-tax analyses.)

The defender was purchased 3 years ago for $30,000 and has a current market value of $9,000. The original challenger (Alternative 2) has a first cost of $36,000 with a $10,000 trade-in for the current filter press, instead of the $9,000 market value. The new challenger, Alternative 3, has a first cost of $40,000 with a $12,000 trade-in allowance for the defender. The final challenger (Alternative 4) includes selling the defender for its true market value of $9,000.

Recall, there are tax consequences when salvage value differs from book value. Hence, in this example, with multiple trade-in allowances for the defender, we will assign a $9,000 "true" market value to the defender and discount sales prices for the challengers. In this way, the book gain will be the same for all challengers, at $9,000.[1]

As shown in Table 11.10, an after-tax *EUAC* of $4,169.90 is obtained for Alternative 2, based on a cost basis of $35,000 and a 9 percent *ATMARR*. For Alternative 3, an after-tax *EUAC* of $4,161.21 is obtained, using a cost basis of $37,000. (Recall, Alternative 2 included a $10,000 trade-in allowance, and Alternative 3 included a $12,000 trade-in allowance for the defender.) For Alternative 4, in EOY = 0, $9,000 is received by selling the defender in the used-equipment market, and $7,500 is paid to lease the filter press for the first year; an after-tax *EUAC* of $4,108.08 results.

TABLE 11.10
After-Tax Analysis of Four Replacement Alternative.

EOY	BTCF(1)	DWO(1)	TI(1)	T(1)	ATCF(1)
0	$0.00	$0.00	$0.00	$0.00	$0.00
1	−$7,000.00	$2,223.00	−$9,223.00	−$3,689.20	−$3,310.80
2	−$8,000.00	$0.00	−$8,000.00	−$3,200.00	−$4,800.00
3	−$9,000.00	$0.00	−$9,000.00	−$3,600.00	−$5,400.00
4	−$10,000.00	$0.00	−$10,000.00	−$4,000.00	−$6,000.00
5	−$9,000.00	$0.00	−$9,000.00	−$3,600.00	−$5,400.00
				ATEUAC(1) =	$4,886.68

EOY	BTCF(2)	DWO(2)	TI(2)	T(2)	ATCF(2)	
0	−$26,000.00	$0.00	$0.00	$0.00	−$26,000.00	=35000*0.3333+2223
1	$0.00	$13,888.50	−$4,888.50	−$1,955.40	$1,955.40	
2	−$1,000.00	$15,557.50	−$16,557.50	−$6,623.00	$5,623.00	=−13888.50+9000
3	−$2,000.00	$5,183.50	−$7,183.50	−$2,873.40	$873.40	
4	−$3,000.00	$2,593.50	−$5,593.50	−$2,237.40	−$762.60	
5	$8,000.00	$0.00	$8,000.00	$3,200.00	$4,800.00	
				ATEUAC(2) =	$4,169.90	

(Continued)

[1]Using the *cash flow* or *insider viewpoint* approach, it is not necessary that the true market value be established and applied to all alternatives. We do so in order to simplify the *opportunity cost* or *outsider viewpoint* approach to solving this example later in the chapter.

TABLE 11.10
(Continued)

EOY	BTCF(3)	DWO(3)	TI(3)	T(3)	ATCF(3)	=37000*0.3333+2223
0	-$28,000.00	$0.00	$0.00	$0.00	-$28,000.00	
1	-$500.00	$14,555.10	-$6,055.10	-$2,422.04	$1,922.04	
2	-$1,000.00	$16,446.50	-$17,446.50	-$6,978.60	$5,978.60	=-500-14555.10+9000
3	-$1,500.00	$5,479.70	-$6,979.70	-$2,791.88	$1,291.88	
4	-$2,000.00	$2,741.70	-$4,741.70	-$1,896.68	-$103.32	
5	$10,500.00	$0.00	$10,500.00	$4,200.00	$6,300.00	
				ATEUAC(3) =	$4,161.21	

EOY	BTCF(4)	DWO(4)	TI(4)	T(4)	ATCF(4)	=-7500+9000
0	$1,500.00	$0.00	-$7,500.00	-$3,000.00	$4,500.00	
1	-$7,500.00	$2,223.00	-$723.00	-$289.20	-$7,210.80	
2	-$8,300.00	$0.00	-$8,300.00	-$3,320.00	-$4,980.00	=-7500+9000-2223
3	-$9,100.00	$0.00	-$9,100.00	-$3,640.00	-$5,460.00	
4	-$9,900.00	$0.00	-$9,900.00	-$3,960.00	-$5,940.00	
5	-$3,200.00	$0.00	-$3,200.00	-$1,280.00	-$1,920.00	
				ATEUAC(4) =	$4,108.08	

=30000*0.0741

Based on the after-tax analysis, the lease alternative yields the smallest *ATEUAC*, with a value of $4,108.08. The second best choice is Alternative 3, with an *ATEUAC* of $4,161.21. Alternative 2 ranks next to last, with an *ATEUAC* of $4,169.90. (The rank order is not the same as obtained using a before-tax analysis, where it is $4 > 2 > 3 > 1$; with an after-tax analysis, the rank ordering is $4 > 3 > 2 > 1$.)

From the example, how trade-in allowances are handled in after-tax analyses can make a significant difference in the rank ordering for replacement alternatives.

The three preceding examples avoided a subject that we intentionally have not discussed previously: decisions influenced by financial reporting requirements for public corporations versus decisions influenced by discounted cash flow analysis. (Recall, this was the tenth reason given for why some managers fail to replace assets at the point in time when *DCF* analysis indicates they should.)

If the objective is to maximize after-tax present worth, then the approach we used in the examples is the correct one. However, if the objective is to maximize earnings for the next quarter, replacing an asset with a value of $21,000 on the financial books is not necessarily the correct decision.

As soon as the filter press is replaced, a charge must be taken equal to the difference in the asset's book value and market value. For this reason, a manager might decide to retain the defender or, if the defender is replaced, choose a very different combination of trade-in allowance and sales-price reduction for the challenger than would occur if one were attempting to maximize after-tax present worth. More will be said in Chapter 16 about decisions influenced by financial reporting.

11-3 OPPORTUNITY COST APPROACH[2]

Many prefer the opportunity cost or outsider viewpoint approach, because it forces the decision maker to view both the defender and its challengers from an objective, or outsider, point of view—that is, the outsider is assumed to have no existing asset. The outsider is then free to choose either a used asset (the defender) available for its market value price or any of the challengers.

In essence, the outsider viewpoint approach considers the salvage value of the existing asset to be its investment cost if it is retained in service. Such an approach is consistent with the opportunity cost concept discussed previously. Since retaining the defender is equivalent to forgoing the receipt of its salvage value, then an opportunity cost is assigned to the defender.

Although it is convenient to employ an outsider's viewpoint, the approach does not truly mimic what an outsider would do, particularly when income taxes are considered.

The analogy of an outsider purchasing the defender on a used-equipment market is likely to break down with respect to assumptions made regarding the planning horizon, depreciation allowances, and income-tax rate used. If an outsider purchases the defender, is it reasonable to assume that the same planning horizon will be used? Likewise, is it reasonable to assume the new owner will use the depreciation allowances available to the previous owner, instead of starting anew and taking full depreciation allowances for the equipment? Finally, is it reasonable to assume that the new owner's tax bracket is the same as that of the previous owner? For these reasons, we prefer to call this approach the *opportunity cost approach*.

11.3.1 Before-Tax Analysis

If the defender remains in service, the opportunity to sell or trade it and receive its market value is forgone. Therefore, the defender is "held accountable" for the amount forgone by treating the market value as an investment in the defender.

As we consider the previous examples, using an opportunity cost approach, notice that the difference in economic worths remains the same among the alternatives.

EXAMPLE 11.9 Opportunity Cost Analysis of the SMP Replacement Opportunity

Recall, an SMP machine is a candidate for replacement with an improved model. The defender was purchased 10 years ago for $300,000; today, its market value is $50,000. The defender's O&M costs can be represented by a $5,000 gradient series added to a uniform series of $120,000. At the end of the 5-year planning horizon, the defender will have a salvage value of $0.

The challenger has a cost basis of $500,000. The challenger's O&M costs can be represented by a $5,000 gradient series added to a uniform series of $10,000. At the end of the 5-year planning horizon, the challenger will have a salvage value of $200,000.

Based on a 16.67 percent BTMARR, use an opportunity cost or outsider viewpoint approach to determine if the SMP defender should be replaced.

---

[2]This section can be skipped if the cash flow or insider viewpoint is preferred to the opportunity cost or outsider viewpoint.

TABLE 11.11
Opportunity Cost Analysis of the SMP Machine Replacement.

EOY	CF(1)	CF(2)	CF(2) − CF(1)
0	−$50,000.00	−$500,000.00	−$450,000.00
1	−$120,000.00	−$10,000.00	$110,000.00
2	−$125,000.00	−$15,000.00	$110,000.00
3	−$130,000.00	−$20,000.00	$110,000.00
4	−$135,000.00	−$25,000.00	$110,000.00
5	−$140,000.00	$170,000.00	$310,000.00

In this example, the only difference between the *cash flow* or *insider viewpoint* approach and the *opportunity cost* or *outsider viewpoint* approach is the treatment of the defender's current market value. In Table 11.11, the defender's $50,000 market value is shown as an investment for Alternative 1: keep the defender.

The incremental cash flows are identical to those obtained using a cash flow approach. As expected, the incremental *BTEUAC* is identical to that obtained previously, in Example 11.1.

$$BTEUAC_{2-1}(16.67\%) = \$450,000(A|P\ 16.67\%,5) - \$200,000(A|F\ 16.67\%,5) - \$110,000$$

$$= \$890.00$$

or, using the Excel® **PMT** function,

$$BTEUAC_{2-1}(16.67\%) = \textbf{PMT(16.67\%,5,-450000,200000)-110000}$$

$$= \textbf{\$889.06}$$

Since the incremental equivalent uniform annual cost is positive, the incremental investment required to replace the defender is *not* justified economically. The old SMP machine should remain in use until a more attractive challenger is available.

EXAMPLE 11.10   Opportunity Cost Analysis of a Filter Press Replacement Alternative

Let us again consider Example 11.2, but this time using an opportunity cost analysis. Recall, the defender has a market value of $9,000, a remaining life of 5 years, and a salvage value of $2,000. The challenger has a first cost of $36,000, a life of 10 years, and estimated salvage values (S_t) at any point in time, as given in Table 11.2. Given the defender's limited useful life, a 5-year planning horizon is to be used, with a before-tax *MARR* of 15 percent. Cash flows from the outsider's point of view are given in Table 11.12.

Comparing Tables 11.3 and 11.12, we see that the differences in cash flows between alternatives are identical; therefore, the cash flow approach and the opportunity cost approach are equivalent. As further verification, we can calculate the incremental *BTEUAC* for the filter presses:

$$BTEUAC_{2-1} = \$27,000(A|P\ 15\%,5) - \$10,000(A|F\ 15\%,5) - \$7,000$$

$$= \$27,000(0.29832) - \$10,000(0.14832) - \$7,000$$

$$= -\$428.56/\text{year}$$

TABLE 11.12

Cash Flows for a Replacement Alternative.

EOY	CF(1)	CF(2)	CF(2)– CF(1)
0	−$9,000.00	−$36,000.00	−$27,000.00
1	−$7,000.00	$0.00	$7,000.00
2	−$8,000.00	−$1,000.00	$7,000.00
3	−$9,000.00	−$2,000.00	$7,000.00
4	−$10,000.00	−$3,000.00	$7,000.00
5	−$9,000.00	$8,000.00	$17,000.00

Since the incremental *BTEUAC* is negative, the incremental annual worth is positive, and the challenger is preferred. This is the identical conclusion reached in Example 11.2. (Using Excel®, the incremental *BTEUAC* is -$428.64.)

In using the opportunity cost approach, we must be careful to use "rational" first costs for each alternative. Example 11.3 showed that the trade-in allowances may differ among alternatives and that there may be little correspondence between the trade-in value and an asset's true market value.

If you have ever traded an automobile, you are well aware of the different trade-in values and selling prices quoted by various dealers. Some will increase the trade-in value on your old car, while others will reduce the price of the new car. And, occasionally, one will hold firmly to both the quoted trade-in value for the old automobile and the quoted sales price on the new vehicle.

A high trade-in value might indicate that an artificially high selling price has been placed on the new automobile. If so, then the artificially high sales price will likely be decreased if a straight purchase with no trade-in is offered. Therefore, for before-tax analysis purposes, when using the opportunity cost approach, *we will decrease the artificially high sales price for the challenger by the difference between the trade-in value and the asset's true market value.* Presumably, no adjustment is necessary if the trade-in allowance is less than the market value, since we would simply choose to sell the defender separately at the market value price.

EXAMPLE 11.11 An Opportunity Cost Analysis of Four Replacement Alternatives

Now, let us consider Example 11.4 from an opportunity cost approach. Recall that four investment alternatives exist: (1) retain the old filter press (defender) having a current market value of $9,000 and a salvage value of $2,000 after 5 years; (2) replace the filter press with a new press costing $36,000, having a salvage value of $12,000 after 5 years, and providing a $10,000 trade-in for the old press (Challenger 1); (3) replace the filter press with a new press costing $40,000, having a salvage value of $13,000 after 5 years, and providing a $12,000 trade-in for the old press (Challenger 2); and (4) leasing a new filter press and selling the old press for $9,000 on the used-equipment market (Challenger 3). Since the trade-in allowances for Challengers 2 and 3 are greater than the $9,000 market value by $1,000 and $3,000, respectively, the first costs for Alternatives 2 and 3 are reduced to $35,000 and $37,000,

TABLE 11.13

Cash Flows for Four Replacement Alternatives.

EOY	CF(1)	CF(2)	CF(3)	CF(4)
0	−$9,000.00	−$35,000.00	−$37,000.00	−$7,500.00
1	−$7,000.00	$0.00	−$500.00	−$7,500.00
2	−$8,000.00	−$1,000.00	−$1,000.00	−$8,300.00
3	−$9,000.00	−$2,000.00	−$1,500.00	−$9,100.00
4	−$10,000.00	−$3,000.00	−$2,000.00	−$9,900.00
5	−$9,000.00	$8,000.00	$10,500.00	−$3,200.00

respectively. A 5-year planning horizon and a before-tax *MARR* of 15 percent are still in effect. Table 11.13 presents the cash flow profiles from the outsider's point of view. Calculating the *BTEUAC* for each alternative results in

$$BTEUAC_1(15\%) = \$9,000(A|P\ 15\%,5) + \$7,000 + \$1,000(A|G\ 15\%,5) - \$2,000(A|F\ 15\%,5)$$
$$= \$9,000(0.29832) + \$7,000 + \$1,000(1.72281) - \$2,000(0.14832)$$
$$= \$11,111.05/\text{year}(\textbf{\$11,111.02}\text{ with Excel ®})$$

$$BTEUAC_2(15\%) = \$35,000(A|P\ 15\%,5) + \$1,000(A|G\ 15\%,5) - \$12,000(A|F\ 15\%,5)$$
$$= \$35,000(0.29832) + \$1,000(1.72281) - \$12,000(0.14832)$$
$$= \$10,384.17/\text{year}(\textbf{\$10,384.07}\text{ with Excel ®})$$

$$BTEUAC_3(15\%) = \$37,000(A|P\ 15\%,5) + \$500 + \$500(A|G\ 15\%,5) - \$13,000(A|F\ 15\%,5)$$
$$= \$37,000(0.29832) + \$500 + \$500(1.72281) - \$13,000(0.14832)$$
$$= \$10,471.19/\text{year}(\textbf{\$10,470.98}\text{ with Excel ®})$$

$$BTEUAC_4(15\%) = \$7,500(F|P\ 15\%,1) + \$800(A|G\ 15\%,5)$$
$$= \$7,500(1.1500) + \$800(1.72281)$$
$$= \$10,003.25/\text{year}(\textbf{\$10,003.25}\text{ with Excel ®})$$

Again, the lease alternative is preferred, based upon *BTEUAC* calculations. Note that the *BTEUAC* spreads between alternatives are identical to those obtained using the cash flow approach. This further substantiates the equivalence of the two approaches.

11.3.2 After-Tax Analysis

As with the before-tax opportunity cost analysis, we will revisit the examples used to demonstrate how an after-tax opportunity cost replacement analysis is performed.

EXAMPLE 11.12   After-Tax Opportunity Cost Analysis of Example 11.1

Recall, an SMP machine is a candidate for replacement with an improved model. The defender was purchased 10 years ago for $300,000; today, its market value is $50,000. The defender's *O&M* costs can be represented by a $5,000 gradient series added to a uniform series of $120,000. The SMP machine qualifies as 5-year property with MACRS-GDS

TABLE 11.14
After-Tax Analysis for Example 11.12.

EOY	BTCF(1)	DW(1)	TI(1)	T(1)	ATCF(1)
0	−$50,000.00	$0.00	$0.00	$0.00	−$50,000.00
1	−$120,000.00	$0.00	−$170,000.00	−$68,000.00	−$52,000.00
2	−$125,000.00	$0.00	−$125,000.00	−$50,000.00	−$75,000.00
3	−$130,000.00	$0.00	−$130,000.00	−$52,000.00	−$78,000.00
4	−$135,000.00	$0.00	−$135,000.00	−$54,000.00	−$81,000.00
5	−$140,000.00	$0.00	−$140,000.00	−$56,000.00	−$84,000.00
				ATEUAC(1) =	$85,823.93

EOY	BTCF(2)	DW(2)	TI(2)	T(2)	ATCF(2)
0	−$500,000.00	$0.00	$0.00	$0.00	−$500,000.00
1	−$10,000.00	$100,000.00	−$110,000.00	−$44,000.00	$34,000.00
2	−$15,000.00	$160,000.00	−$175,000.00	−$70,000.00	$55,000.00
3	−$20,000.00	$96,000.00	−$116,000.00	−$46,400.00	$26,400.00
4	−$25,000.00	$57,600.00	−$82,600.00	−$33,040.00	$8,040.00
5	$170,000.00	$28,800.00	$83,600.00	$33,440.00	$136,560.00
				ATEUAC(2) =	$82,705.05

depreciation. As such, the defender is fully depreciated. Hence, if $50,000 is received as trade-in for the defender, it will be taxed as ordinary income.

The challenger has a cost basis of $500,000. Its *O&M* costs can be represented by a $5,000 gradient series added to a uniform series of $10,000. At the end of the 5-year planning horizon, the challenger will have a salvage value of $200,000.

Based on a 10 percent ATMARR, we will use an opportunity cost approach to determine if the SMP defender should be replaced.

As before, the only difference between the cash flow and opportunity cost approaches is the treatment of the defender's market value. As demonstrated in Table 11.14, the defender's $50,000 market value is shown as an investment for Alternative 1: keep the defender. Similarly, by keeping the defender, taxable income of $50,000 is avoided during year 0; hence, based on our convention of showing the tax consequence of replacing the defender, a negative taxable income and negative tax are entered in the EOY = 1 row of Table 11.14 for the defender.

The incremental after-tax cash flows are identical to those obtained using a cash flow approach. The incremental ATEUAC, −$3,118.88, is identical to that obtained in Example 11.5.

Since the incremental after-tax equivalent uniform annual cost is negative, the incremental investment required to replace the defender is justified economically. The old SMP machine should be replaced.

EXAMPLE 11.13 After-Tax Opportunity Cost Analysis of Example 11.6

Recall Example 11.6, in which a filter press was purchased 3 years ago for $30,000. Its book value is shown in the financial records to be $21,000. *O&M* costs for the next 5 years can be represented by a $1,000 gradient series added to a $7,000 uniform series. At the end of the 5-year planning horizon, the defender's salvage value is $2,000.

TABLE 11.15
After-Tax Analysis for Example 11.13.

EOY	BTCF(1)	DWO(1)	TI(1)	T(1)	ATCF(1)
0	−$9,000.00	$0.00	$0.00	$0.00	−$9,000.00
1	−$7,000.00	$2,223.00	−$18,223.00	−$7,289.20	$289.20
2	−$8,000.00	$0.00	−$8,000.00	−$3,200.00	−$4,800.00
3	−$9,000.00	$0.00	−$9,000.00	−$3,600.00	−$5,400.00
4	−$10,000.00	$0.00	−$10,000.00	−$4,000.00	−$6,000.00
5	−$9,000.00	$0.00	−$9,000.00	−$3,600.00	−$5,400.00
				EUAC(1) =	$6,351.40
			=−7000−2223−9000		

EOY	BTCF(2)	DWO(2)	TI(2)	T(2)	ATCF(2)
0	−$36,000.00	$0.00	$0.00	$0.00	−$36,000.00
1	$0.00	$14,221.80	−$14,221.80	−$5,688.72	$5,688.72
2	−$1,000.00	$16,002.00	−$17,002.00	−$6,800.80	$5,800.80
3	−$2,000.00	$5,331.60	−$7,331.60	−$2,932.64	$932.64
4	−$3,000.00	$2,667.60	−$5,667.60	−$2,267.04	−$732.96
5	$8,000.00	$0.00	$8,000.00	$3,200.00	$4,800.00
				EUAC(2) =	$5,804.63
		=2223+11998.80			

A new filter press, the challenger, can be purchased for $36,000 and the defender sold for $9,000. The challenger's $O\&M$ costs are represented by a $1,000 gradient series. At the end of the 5-year planning horizon, the challenger will have a salvage value of $12,000.

Using an opportunity cost approach, most of the cost data are retained from Example 11.6. The difference is in the treatment of the defender's $9,000 market value.

From Table 11.15, an investment of $9,000 is shown for Alternative 1 (retain the defender), since the opportunity was passed up to receive $9,000 in trade-in. By keeping the old filter press, the "opportunity" to obtain a realized gain of $9,000 was forgone. Hence, the taxable income in year 1 of −$18,223 is obtained by subtracting the $2,223 depreciation charge and the forgone $9,000 realized gain from the −$7,000 before-tax cash flow.

For Alternative 2 (replace the defender with the challenger), a half-year depreciation charge of $2,223 resulting from the defender's disposal and a half-year depreciation charge of $11,998.80 resulting from acquiring the challenger are taken in year 1.

Based on a 9 percent ATMARR, the after-tax EUAC for Alternative 1 is $6,351.40; for Alternative 2, it is $5,804.63. The incremental ATEUAC of $546.77 is identical to that obtained using an after-tax cash flow analysis; the same recommendation results: replace the filter press.

Recall, in Example 11.6, we also considered the consequences of the equipment supplier taking the old machine from the chemical company, paying nothing for it, and discounting the new filter press by $9,000. Since the difference in the cash flow and opportunity cost approaches is how the defender's market value is treated, the market value under this scenario is 0, and the defender's book value at the end of year 1 is 0, so there will be no difference in results for the two approaches.

EXAMPLE 11.14   After-Tax Opportunity Cost Analysis of Examples 11.3 and 11.7

In Examples 11.3 and 11.7 with Tables 11.4 and 11.9, respectively, a 10-year planning horizon was used for the filter press replacement analysis. Since the defender can be used for only 5 more years, a decision was required regarding its replacement at the end of its useful life. Based on a forecast of investment and annual operating and maintenance costs, a before-tax analysis was performed. Here, we perform an after-tax analysis using an opportunity cost approach.

Table 11.16 presents the results of the after-tax, opportunity cost analysis. As before, the $9,000 trade-in allowance is shown as an investment for Alternative 1 (retain the filter press); likewise, the $3,600 tax consequence of passing up the opportunity to receive $9,000 in trade-in is assigned to Alternative 1.

Using a 9 percent *MARR*, the after-tax *EUAC* for Alternative 1 is $4,407.24; for Alternative 2, it is $5,742.62; the spread is identical to that obtained using a cash flow analysis, $1,335.38; and the decision is the same: retain the filter press.

TABLE 11.16
After-Tax Analysis for Example 11.14.

EOY	BTCF(1)	DWO(1)	TI(1)	T(1)	ATCF(1)
0	–$9,000.00	$0.00	$0.00	$0.00	–$9,000.00
1	–$7,000.00	$2,223.00	–$18,223.00	–$7,289.20	$289.20
2	–$8,000.00	$0.00	–$8,000.00	–$3,200.00	–$4,800.00
3	–$9,000.00	$0.00	–$9,000.00	–$3,600.00	–$5,400.00
4	–$10,000.00	$0.00	–$10,000.00	–$4,000.00	–$6,000.00
5	–$40,000.00	$0.00	–$40,000.00	–$16,000.00	–$24,000.00
6	$0.00	$10,332.30	–$10,332.30	–$4,132.92	$4,132.92
7	$1,000.00	$13,779.50	–$12,779.50	–$5,111.80	$6,111.80
8	–$2,000.00	$4,591.10	–$6,591.10	–$2,636.44	$636.44
9	–$3,000.00	$2,297.10	–$5,297.10	–$2,118.84	–$881.16
10	$11,000.00	$0.00	$11,000.00	$4,400.00	$6,600.00
				ATEUAC(1) =	$4,407.24
			=-7000-2223-9000		

EOY	BTCF(2)	DWO(2)	TI(2)	T(2)	ATCF(2)
0	–$36,000.00	$0.00	$0.00	$0.00	–$36,000.00
1	$0.00	$14,221.80	–$14,221.80	–$5,688.72	$5,688.72
2	–$1,000.00	$16,002.00	–$17,002.00	–$6,800.80	$5,800.80
3	–$2,000.00	$5,331.60	–$7,331.60	–$2,932.64	$932.64
4	–$3,000.00	$2,667.60	–$5,667.60	–$2,267.04	–$732.96
5	–$4,000.00	$0.00	–$4,000.00	–$1,600.00	–$2,400.00
6	–$5,000.00	$0.00	–$5,000.00	–$2,000.00	–$3,000.00
7	–$6,000.00	$0.00	–$6,000.00	–$2,400.00	–$3,600.00
8	–$7,000.00	$0.00	–$7,000.00	–$2,800.00	–$4,200.00
9	–$8,000.00	$0.00	–$8,000.00	–$3,200.00	–$4,800.00
10	–$6,000.00	$0.00	–$6,000.00	–$2,400.00	–$3,600.00
				ATEUAC(2) =	$5,742.62
			=0–14221.80		

EXAMPLE 11.15 After-Tax Opportunity Cost Analysis of Examples 11.4 and 11.8

Recall, in Examples 11.4 and 11.8 and Tables 11.5 and 11.10, respectively, two new filter press replacement alternatives were introduced: a purchase alternative (Challenger 2) and a lease alternative (Challenger 3). Also, different trade-in allowances accompanied the challengers. The *true market value* for the defender was determined to be $9,000. However, Alternative 2 included a trade-in allowance of $10,000 for the defender; Alternative 3 included a trade-in allowance of $12,000 for the defender; and Alternative 4 required that the defender be sold at market value.

TABLE 11.17
After-Tax Analysis with Section 1031 Property Exchange.

EOY	BTCF(1)	DWO(1)	TI(1)	T(1)	ATCF(1)	
0	−$9,000.00	$0.00	$0.00	$0.00	−$9,000.00	
1	−$7,000.00	$2,223.00	−$18,223.00	−$7,289.20	$289.20	
2	−$8,000.00	$0.00	−$8,000.00	−$3,200.00	−$4,800.00	=−7000-2223-9000
3	−$9,000.00	$0.00	−$9,000.00	−$3,600.00	−$5,400.00	
4	−$10,000.00	$0.00	−$10,000.00	−$4,000.00	−$6,000.00	
5	−$9,000.00	$0.00	−$9,000.00	−$3,600.00	−$5,400.00	
				ATEUAC(1) =	$6,351.40	

EOY	BTCF(2)	DWO(2)	TI(2)	T(2)	ATCF(2)	
0	−$35,000.00	$0.00	$0.00	$0.00	−$35,000.00	=35000*0.3333+2223
1	$0.00	$13,888.50	−$13,888.50	−$5,555.40	$5,555.40	
2	−$1,000.00	$15,557.50	−$16,557.50	−$6,623.00	$5,623.00	=−13888.50+0
3	−$2,000.00	$5,183.50	−$7,183.50	−$2,873.40	$873.40	
4	−$3,000.00	$2,593.50	−$5,593.50	−$2,237.40	−$762.60	
5	$8,000.00	$0.00	$8,000.00	$3,200.00	$4,800.00	
				ATEUAC(2) =	$5,634.61	

EOY	BTCF(3)	DWO(3)	TI(3)	T(3)	ATCF(3)	
0	−$37,000.00	$0.00	$0.00	$0.00	−$37,000.00	=37000*0.3333+2223
1	−$500.00	$14,555.10	−$15,055.10	−$6,022.04	$5,522.04	
2	−$1,000.00	$16,446.50	−$17,446.50	−$6,978.60	$5,978.60	=−500-14555.10
3	−$1,500.00	$5,479.70	−$6,979.70	−$2,791.88	$1,291.88	
4	−$2,000.00	$2,741.70	−$4,741.70	−$1,896.68	−$103.32	
5	$10,500.00	$0.00	$10,500.00	$4,200.00	$6,300.00	
				ATEUAC(3) =	$5,625.93	

EOY	BTCF(4)	DWO(4)	TI(4)	T(4)	ATCF(4)	
0	−$7,500.00	$0.00	−$7,500.00	−$3,000.00	−$4,500.00	
1	−$7,500.00	$2,223.00	−$9,723.00	−$3,889.20	−$3,610.80	
2	−$8,300.00	$0.00	−$8,300.00	−$3,320.00	−$4,980.00	=−7500-2223
3	−$9,100.00	$0.00	−$9,100.00	−$3,640.00	−$5,460.00	
4	−$9,900.00	$0.00	−$9,900.00	−$3,960.00	−$5,940.00	
5	−$3,200.00	$0.00	−$3,200.00	−$1,280.00	−$1,920.00	
				ATEUAC(4) =	$5,572.80	

In performing the cash flow analysis, we assigned a $9,000 trade-in allowance to each alternative and reduced the challenger's sales price by the difference in its trade-in allowance and the defender's true market value.[3] Table 11.17 contains the results of the after-tax analysis. As before, a $9,000 investment is shown for Alternative 1, along with the $3,600 tax consequence of passing up receiving $9,000 for the defender; the after-tax *EUAC* is $6,351.40. Again, a 9 percent after-tax *MARR* is used.

The cost basis for Alternative 2 is shown as $35,000, not $36,000. The $1,000 difference is due to $10,000 being offered in trade-in for the defender. The after-tax *EUAC* is $5,634.61, which is $716.78 less than the *ATEUAC* for the defender.

The cost basis for Alternative 3 is $37,000, not $40,000. The $3,000 difference is due to $12,000 being offered in trade-in for the defender. The after-tax *EUAC* is $5,625.93, which is $725.47 less than the *ATEUAC* for the defender.

Since Alternative 4 is a lease alternative, every dollar spent on lease payments costs 60¢ after taxes. The after-tax *EUAC* is $5,572.80, which is $778.59 less than the *ATEUAC* for the defender.

Based on an after-tax, opportunity cost analysis, the filter press should be sold on the used-equipment market, and a new filter press should be leased.

Often, major repairs are made to existing equipment in order to extend an asset's useful life, return it to productive use, add capacity, or extend its capability. In such cases, when performing after-tax replacement analyses, the expenditure is depreciated, not expensed. The amount expended in repairing or rebuilding the current asset becomes the cost basis for what is treated, essentially, as a new, separate asset having the same property class as the initial asset.

As an example, suppose an asset qualifying as 7-year property for MACRS-GDS depreciation has 3 years of depreciation remaining at the time it is repaired or rebuilt at a cost of, say, $150,000. The $150,000 will be depreciated as 7-year property; in addition, the current asset will be depreciated for the 3 remaining years. Even though the repaired or rebuilt asset is not restored to ''like new'' condition with a life expectancy equal to that of the original asset, the IRS requires that the expenditure be depreciated using the same property class as the original asset.

11-4   SECTION 1031 EXCHANGES

From the foregoing analysis, it is clear that how the defender's trade-in value is determined can significantly impact the challenger's after-tax economic worth. Therefore, one might anticipate that ''games'' would be played by firms in negotiating trade-in values and price reductions when equipment is replaced. To the contrary, because the IRS allows for the deferral of taxes on gains realized in

---

[3]Our reason for doing so is the challenge of doing otherwise when performing an opportunity cost analysis; it is quite easy to accommodate the different trade-in allowances when using a cash flow approach. For example, the ''sticker price'' can be used as the cost basis for the challengers, and the tax consequences of the different book gains for the challengers can be computed. However, determining the offsetting dollar transfers from challengers to the defender is not as straightforward using the opportunity cost approach.

like-property exchanges, businesses defer the taxes using what is called a Section 1031 exchange.

When property is replaced with like-kind property, the IRS provides a mechanism to allow taxes on realized gains to be deferred. The rules and regulations governing the tax-deferral exchange are found in Section 1031 of the IRS code.

When applying Section 1031, taxes on gains are not charged when a property is sold *if the money received from the sale is used to purchase another property of like kind*.[4] The payment of the tax is deferred until the property is sold and there is no reinvestment of the monies received in property of like kind.

To illustrate like-kind exchanges, in its 2006 publication 544, the IRS provided the following example: "You used your car in your business for 2 years. Its adjusted basis is $3,500 and its trade-in value is $4,500. You are interested in a new car that costs $20,000. Ordinarily, you would trade your old car for the new one and pay the dealer $15,500. Your basis for depreciation of the new car would then be $19,000 ($15,500 plus $3,500 adjusted basis of the old car).

"You want your new car to have a larger basis for depreciation, so you arrange to sell your old car to the dealer for $4,500. You then buy the new one for $20,000 from the same dealer. However, you are treated as having exchanged your old car for the new one because the sale and purchase are reciprocal and mutually dependent. Your basis for depreciation for the new car is $19,000, the same as if you traded the old car."

A Section 1031 exchange is available for like-kind properties that are used for business or investment purposes. Although best known for its use in the exchange of real property, Section 1031 also applies to personal property of like kind.

What does *like-kind property* mean? IRC 1031(a) defines it as properties that are of the same nature or character, even if they differ in grade or quality. The types of properties we consider in engineering economic analyses generally qualify, since they provide the same service. If they are from the same MACRS property class, then they qualify. However, you cannot replace equipment in the United States with property outside the United States.

IRS publication 544(2006) includes the following: "There must be an exchange of like-kind property. Like-kind properties are properties of the same nature or character, even if they differ in grade or quality. The exchange of real estate for real estate and the exchange of personal property for similar personal property are exchanges of like-kind property. For example, the trade of land improved with an apartment house for land improved with a store building, or a panel truck for a pickup truck, is a like-kind exchange.

"An exchange of personal property for real property does not qualify as a like-kind exchange. For example, an exchange of a piece of machinery for a store building does not qualify. Also, the exchange of livestock of different sexes does not qualify."

Other examples of like-kind exchanges include exchanging an apartment building for a farm or ranch, exchanging an office building for a hotel, exchanging raw land for retail space, exchanging unimproved property for commercial property, exchanging a tractor for a tractor, and exchanging a filter press for a filter press. According to the IRS, primary residences, stocks, bonds, notes, inventories, developed lots held primarily for sale, property that is to be resold immediately after initial purchase or completion of improvements, and, as noted above, livestock of different sexes do not qualify as like-kind properties.

---

[4]When owned equipment is replaced with leased equipment, a Section 1031 tax deferment cannot be taken. The replacement equipment must be purchased, not leased.

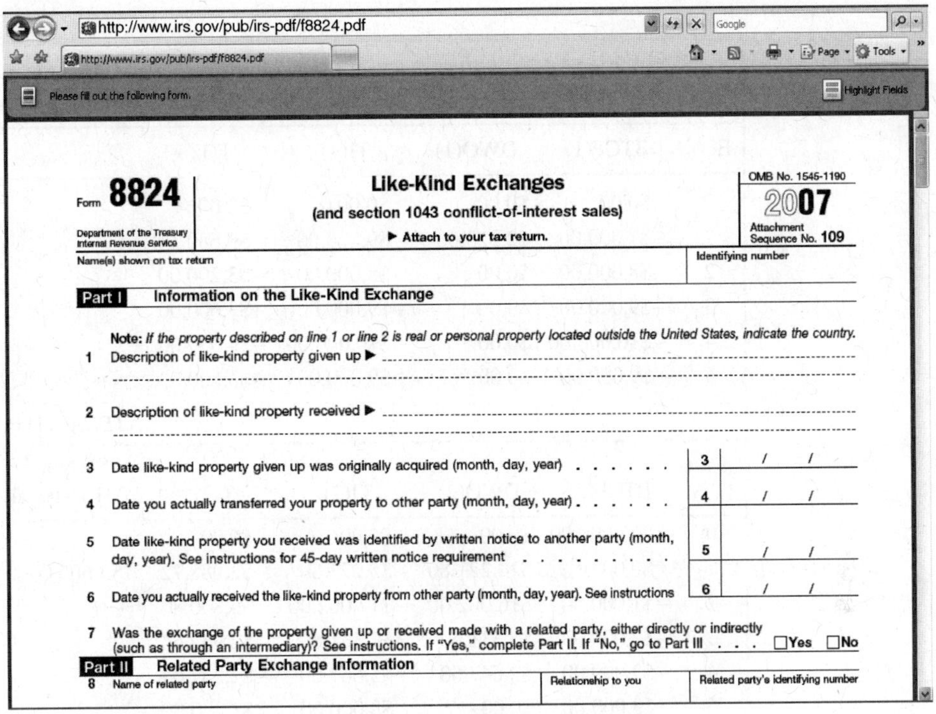

http://www.irs.gov/pub/irs-pdf/f8824.pdf

Please fill out the following form.

Form **8824** Department of the Treasury Internal Revenue Service

Like-Kind Exchanges

(and section 1043 conflict-of-interest sales)

▶ Attach to your tax return.

OMB No. 1545-1190 **2007** Attachment Sequence No. 109

Name(s) shown on tax return | Identifying number

Part I **Information on the Like-Kind Exchange**

Note: *If the property described on line 1 or line 2 is real or personal property located outside the United States, indicate the country.*

1 Description of like-kind property given up ▶

2 Description of like-kind property received ▶

3 Date like-kind property given up was originally acquired (month, day, year) . . . . . . 3 / /

4 Date you actually transferred your property to other party (month, day, year) . . . . . . 4 / /

5 Date like-kind property you received was identified by written notice to another party (month, day, year). See instructions for 45-day written notice requirement . . . . 5 / /

6 Date you actually received the like-kind property from other party (month, day, year). See instructions 6 / /

7 Was the exchange of the property given up or received made with a related party, either directly or indirectly (such as through an intermediary)? See instructions. If "Yes," complete Part II. If "No," go to Part III . . . ☐Yes ☐No

Part II **Related Party Exchange Information**

8 Name of related party | Relationship to you | Related party's identifying number

FIGURE 11.1

IRS Form for Use in a Section 1031 Exchange of Property.

To effect a Section 1031 exchange, a qualified intermediary must be involved to avoid ''sweetheart'' exchanges. In the examples we consider, an outside equipment supplier, with whom negotiations occur regarding trade-in allowances and new equipment prices, qualifies as an intermediary.

Interestingly, Section 1031 was first enacted in 1954. However, a similar provision was adopted in 1921, called Section 202 and was changed to Section 112(b)(1) in 1928. Various modifications to Section 1031 have occurred over the years. Therefore, it is advised that a tax authority or the IRS Web site be consulted before attempting to apply Section 1031.

Since taxes on book gains can be deferred when replacing equipment with like-kind equipment, the after-tax analysis is affected. However, how long is the tax deferred? For a company like J. B. Hunt Transport Services, Inc., which regularly replaces tractors and adds new tractors to its fleet, basically, the tax will be deferred as long as the company exists. As the company remains in business longer and longer, the present worth of the deferred tax approaches zero in value. Annually, JBHT's federal income statement includes millions of dollars in Section 1031 deferred gains. To examine the Section 1031 form that must be filed with the IRS, consult its Web site (see Figure 11.1).

EXAMPLE 11.16 Using a Section 1031 Exchange with Example 11.2

Recall Example 11.2, in which a 3-year-old filter press with a $21,000 financial book value is a candidate for replacement by a new filter press costing $36,000. A $9,000 trade-in allowance is offered for the existing filter press.

TABLE 11.18

After-Tax Analysis with Section 1031 Like-Kind Property Exchange.

EOY	BTCF(1)	DWO(1)	TI(1)	T(1)		ATCF(1)
0	$0.00	$0.00	$0.00	$0.00		$0.00
1	−$7,000.00	$2,223.00	−$9,223.00	−$3,689.20		−$3,310.80
2	−$8,000.00	$0.00	−$8,000.00	−$3,200.00		−$4,800.00
3	−$9,000.00	$0.00	−$9,000.00	−$3,600.00		−$5,400.00
4	−$10,000.00	$0.00	−$10,000.00	−$4,000.00		−$6,000.00
5	−$9,000.00	$0.00	−$9,000.00	−$3,600.00		−$5,400.00
					ATEUAC(1) =	$4,886.68

EOY	BTCF(2)	DWO(2)	TI(2)	T(2)	Section 1031 Deferral	ATCF(2)
0	−$27,000.00	$0.00	$0.00	$0.00		−$27,000.00
1	$0.00	$14,221.80	−$5,221.80	−$2,088.72	$3,600.00	$5,688.72
2	−$1,000.00	$16,002.00	−$17,002.00	−$6,800.80		$5,800.80
3	−$2,000.00	$5,331.60	−$7,331.60	−$2,932.64		$932.64
4	−$3,000.00	$2,667.60	−$5,667.60	−$2,267.04		−$732.96
5	$8,000.00	$0.00	$8,000.00	$3,200.00		$4,800.00
					ATEUAC(2) =	$3,490.80

Assuming the $3,600 tax on the realized gain can be deferred indefinitely, the after-tax analysis is as shown in Table 11.18. Notice, Table 11.18 is identical to Table 11.7, with the exception of an additional entry for a Section 1031 tax deferral for Alternative 2; the tax deferral offsets the income tax that otherwise would be paid on the $9,000 realized gain. Using an after-tax *MARR* of 9 percent, the *EUAC* for Alternative 2 is $3,490.80, which is $1,395.88 less than the *ATEUAC* for Alternative 1.

If indefinite deferral is not realistic, then the present worth of the $3,600 tax deferral should be computed, based on the anticipated time when the tax will be paid, and included appropriately in Table 11.18.

EXAMPLE 11.17   Using a Section 1031 Exchange with Example 11.8

Recall Example 11.8, in which there are three challengers to replace the current filter press. Previously, we used $9,000 as the defender's true market value and offset the challenger's purchase price and cost basis by the difference in trade-in value and true market value. Now, with a Section 1031 exchange, it is desired to maximize the tax on the realized gain (which will be deferred) and, thereby, maximize the cost basis.

As shown in Table 11.19, Alternative 3 has the smallest *ATEUAC*, $2,128.44; it is based on a $40,000 cost basis and full deferral of $4,800 in taxes on the $12,000 realized gain: the difference in the $12,000 trade-in allowance and the 0 book value. Next is Alternative 2, with an *ATEUAC* of $2,376.16, which includes a $36,000 cost basis and full deferral of $4,000 in taxes on the $10,000 realized gain: the difference in the $10,000 trade-in allowance and the 0 book value. The lease option (Alternative 4) has an *ATEUAC* of $3,468.70; it

TABLE 11.19
Section 1031 Property Exchange with Four Replacement Alternatives.

EOY	BTCF(1)	DWO(1)	TI(1)	T(1)		ATCF(1)
0	$0.00	$0.00	$0.00	$0.00		$0.00
1	−$7,000.00	$2,223.00	−$9,223.00	−$3,689.20		−$3,310.80
2	−$8,000.00	$0.00	−$8,000.00	−$3,200.00		−$4,800.00
3	−$9,000.00	$0.00	−$9,000.00	−$3,600.00		−$5,400.00
4	−$10,000.00	$0.00	−$10,000.00	−$4,000.00		−$6,000.00
5	−$9,000.00	$0.00	−$9,000.00	−$3,600.00		−$5,400.00
					$ATEUAC(1) =$	$4,886.68

EOY	BTCF(2)	DWO(2)	TI(2)	T(2)	Section 1031 Deferral	ATCF(2)
0	−$26,000.00	$0.00	$0.00	$0.00		−$26,000.00
1	$0.00	$14,221.80	−$13,321.80	−$5,328.72	$4,000.00	$9,328.72
2	−$1,000.00	$16,002.00	−$17,002.00	−$6,800.80		$5,800.80
3	−$2,000.00	$5,331.60	−$7,331.60	−$2,932.64		$932.64
4	−$3,000.00	$2,667.60	−$5,667.60	−$2,267.04		−$732.96
5	$8,000.00	$0.00	$8,000.00	$3,200.00		$4,800.00
					$ATEUAC(2) =$	$2,375.16

EOY	BTCF(3)	DWO(3)	TI(3)	T(3)	Section 1031 Deferral	ATCF(3)
0	−$28,000.00	$0.00	$0.00	$0.00		−$28,000.00
1	−$500.00	$13,332.00	−$13,832.00	−$5,532.80	$4,800.00	$9,832.80
2	−$1,000.00	$17,780.00	−$18,780.00	−$7,512.00		$6,512.00
3	−$1,500.00	$5,924.00	−$7,424.00	−$2,969.60		$1,469.60
4	−$2,000.00	$2,964.00	−$4,964.00	−$1,985.60		−$14.40
5	$10,500.00	$0.00	$10,500.00	$4,200.00		$6,300.00
					$ATEUAC(3) =$	$2,128.44

EOY	BTCF(4)	DWO(4)	TI(4)	T(4)	Section 1031 Deferral	ATCF(4)
0	$1,500.00	$0.00	−$7,500.00	−$3,000.00		$4,500.00
1	−$7,500.00	$0.00	−$7,500.00	−$3,000.00		−$4,500.00
2	−$8,300.00	$0.00	−$8,300.00	−$3,320.00		−$4,980.00
3	−$9,100.00	$0.00	−$9,100.00	−$3,640.00		−$5,460.00
4	−$9,900.00	$0.00	−$9,900.00	−$3,960.00		−$5,940.00
5	−$3,200.00	$0.00	−$3,200.00	−$1,280.00		−$1,920.00
					$ATEUAC(4) =$	$3,468.70

does not benefit from the deferral of $3,600 in taxes on the $9,000 realized gain (the difference in the $9,000 true market value and the 0 book value) since the equipment is leased, not purchased. Alternative 1 is unaffected by the Section 1031 exchange; its *ATEUAC* is $4,886.68.

> Based on an after-tax analysis with taxes on gains deferred through a Section 1031 like-kind property exchange, the recommendation is for the filter press to be replaced with a $40,000 filter press. A trade-in allowance of $12,000 will be received for the old filter press.
>
> As in the previous example, if it is not reasonable to assume that the present worth of the deferred tax gain is negligible, then an estimate of the gain's present worth should be used in the after-tax cash flow calculations. Given the magnitude of typical after-tax minimum attractive rates of return, if it is reasonable to expect it will be at least 50 years before the firm will pay the deferred tax, then it is reasonable to expect its present worth to be approximately 0.

11-5 OPTIMUM REPLACEMENT INTERVAL

As equipment ages, operating and maintenance (*O&M*) costs tend to increase. At the same time, the *capital recovery cost* decreases with prolonged use of the equipment. The combination of decreasing capital recovery costs and increasing annual *O&M* costs results in the *EUAC* taking on a form similar to that depicted in Figure 11.2. Notice, in particular, that *EUAC* is portrayed as a convex function of the equipment's life.

By forecasting the *O&M* costs for each year of service, as well as the anticipated salvage values for ages of equipment, the optimum replacement interval can be determined for the equipment in question.

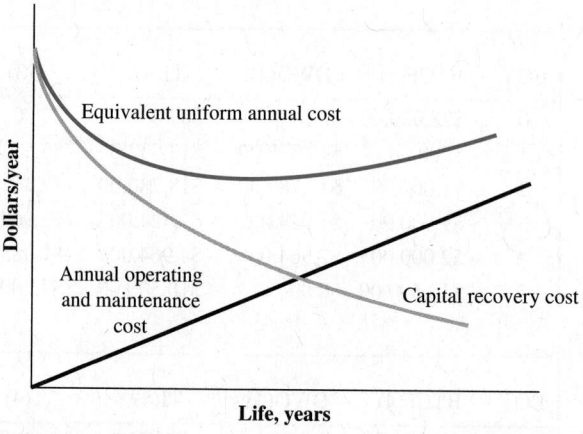

FIGURE 11.2

***EUAC* Components Used to Determine the Optimum Replacement Interval.**

EXAMPLE 11.18 Optimum Replacement Interval for a Compressor

Determine the optimum replacement interval for a medium-sized industrial-grade compressor, given the following parameters:

a. First cost = $10,000

Salvage value (*SV*) = $0, regardless of the replacement interval

O&M cost = $2,500 the first year and increasing $1,500 per year thereafter

BTMARR = 15 percent

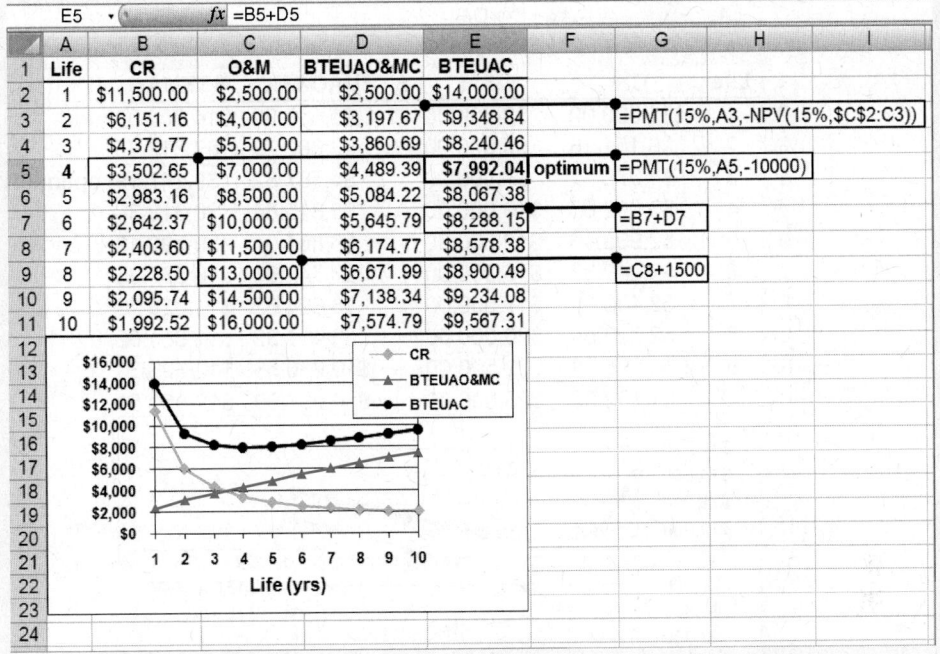

| E5 | ▾ | *fx* | =B5+D5 | | | | | |

	A	B	C	D	E	F	G	H	I
1	Life	CR	O&M	BTEUAO&MC	BTEUAC				
2	1	$11,500.00	$2,500.00	$2,500.00	$14,000.00				
3	2	$6,151.16	$4,000.00	$3,197.67	$9,348.84		=PMT(15%,A3,-NPV(15%,$C$2:C3))		
4	3	$4,379.77	$5,500.00	$3,860.69	$8,240.46				
5	4	$3,502.65	$7,000.00	$4,489.39	$7,992.04	optimum	=PMT(15%,A5,-10000)		
6	5	$2,983.16	$8,500.00	$5,084.22	$8,067.38				
7	6	$2,642.37	$10,000.00	$5,645.79	$8,288.15		=B7+D7		
8	7	$2,403.60	$11,500.00	$6,174.77	$8,578.38				
9	8	$2,228.50	$13,000.00	$6,671.99	$8,900.49		=C8+1500		
10	9	$2,095.74	$14,500.00	$7,138.34	$9,234.08				
11	10	$1,992.52	$16,000.00	$7,574.79	$9,567.31				

FIGURE 11.3

Optimum Replacement Interval for Example 11.18a: $1500 *O&M* Gradient Step.

The *BTEUAC* is given by

$$BTEUAC(15\%) = \$10,000(A|P\ 15\%,n) + \$2,500 + \$1,500(A|G\ 15\%,n)$$

As shown in Figure 11.3, the *BTEUAC* is the sum of the capital recovery cost (CR) and the before-tax equivalent uniform annual operating and maintenance cost (*BTEUAO&MC*). The minimum *BTEUAC* of $7,992.04 occurs when the compressor is kept for 4 years. Hence, the optimum replacement interval is 4 years. Notice, the region near the optimum is quite flat. Therefore, replacing sooner or later than the optimum time will not result in a significant increase in the uniform annual cost. Also shown in the figure are Excel® formulas that were used to compute CR, *O&M*, *BTEUAO&MC*, and *BTEUAC* values.

b. First cost = $10,000

SV = $0, regardless of the replacement interval

O&M cost = $2,500 the first year and increasing **$2,500 per year** thereafter

BTMARR = 15 percent

The *BTEUAC* is given by

$$BTEUAC(15\%) = \$10,000(A|P\ 15\%,n) + \$2,500 + \$2,500(A|G\ 15\%,n)$$

As shown in Figure 11.4, the minimum *BTEUAC* of $9,147.59 occurs when *n* is 3 years. Comparing the optimum replacement interval of 3 years with that obtained in the base case, we note that the optimum replacement interval tends to decrease as the rate of increase in *O&M* costs increases.

c. First cost = **$20,000**

SV = $0, regardless of the replacement interval

O&M cost = $2,500 the first year and increasing $2,500 per year thereafter

BTMARR = 15 percent

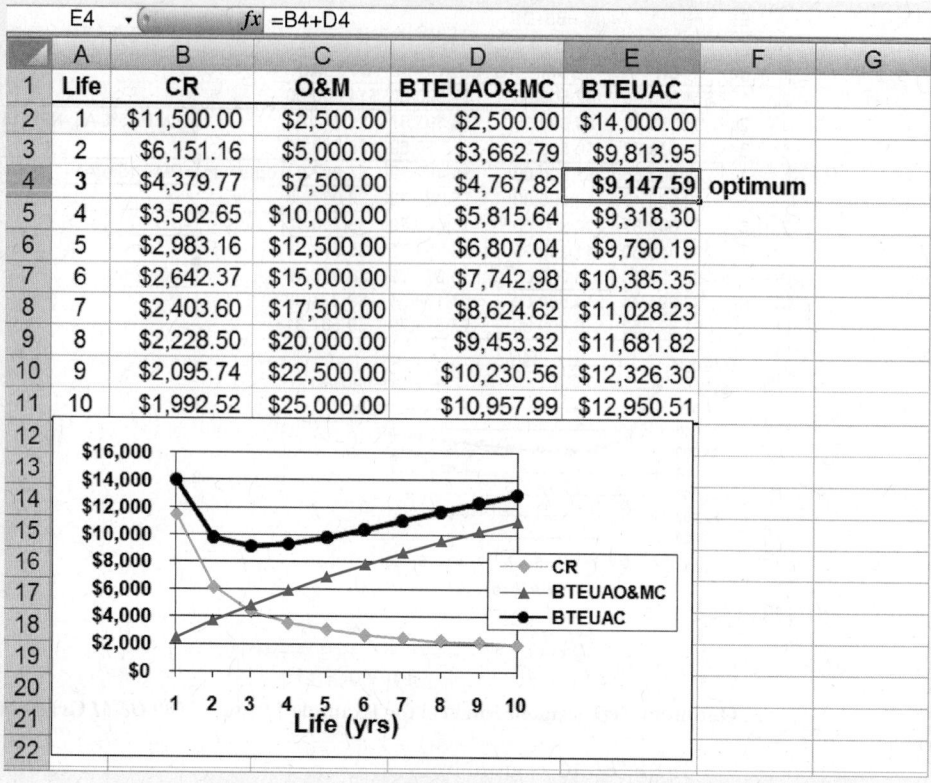

	A	B	C	D	E	F	G
1	Life	CR	O&M	BTEUAO&MC	BTEUAC		
2	1	$11,500.00	$2,500.00	$2,500.00	$14,000.00		
3	2	$6,151.16	$5,000.00	$3,662.79	$9,813.95		
4	3	$4,379.77	$7,500.00	$4,767.82	$9,147.59	optimum	
5	4	$3,502.65	$10,000.00	$5,815.64	$9,318.30		
6	5	$2,983.16	$12,500.00	$6,807.04	$9,790.19		
7	6	$2,642.37	$15,000.00	$7,742.98	$10,385.35		
8	7	$2,403.60	$17,500.00	$8,624.62	$11,028.23		
9	8	$2,228.50	$20,000.00	$9,453.32	$11,681.82		
10	9	$2,095.74	$22,500.00	$10,230.56	$12,326.30		
11	10	$1,992.52	$25,000.00	$10,957.99	$12,950.51		

FIGURE 11.4

Optimum Replacement Interval for Example 11.18b: $2500 *O&M* Gradient Step.

The *BTEUAC* is given by

$$BTEUAC(15\%) = \$20,000(A|P\,15\%,n) + \$2,500 + \$2,500(A|G\,15\%,n)$$

As shown in Figure 11.5, the optimum replacement interval is 5 years, with a *BTEUAC* of $12,773.35. Comparing this result with that in Part b, we note that the optimum replacement interval tends to increase as the initial investment increases.

d. First cost = $20,000

SV = $0, regardless of the replacement interval

O&M cost = $2,500 the first year and increasing $2,500 per year thereafter

BTMARR = **1.5 percent**

The *BTEUAC* is given by

$$BTEUAC(1.5\%) = \$20,000(A|P\,1.5\%,n) + \$2,500 + \$2,500(A|G\,1.5\%,n)$$

As shown in Figure 11.6, the optimum replacement interval is 4 years, with a *BTEUAC* of $11,392.37. Comparing this result with that in Part c, we note that the optimum replacement interval tends to decrease as the before-tax minimum attractive rate of return decreases.

e. First cost = $10,000

SV = **$10,000(0.8ⁿ)** (salvage value decreases 20 percent annually)

O&M cost = $2,500 the first year and increasing 10 percent per year thereafter

BTMARR = 15 percent

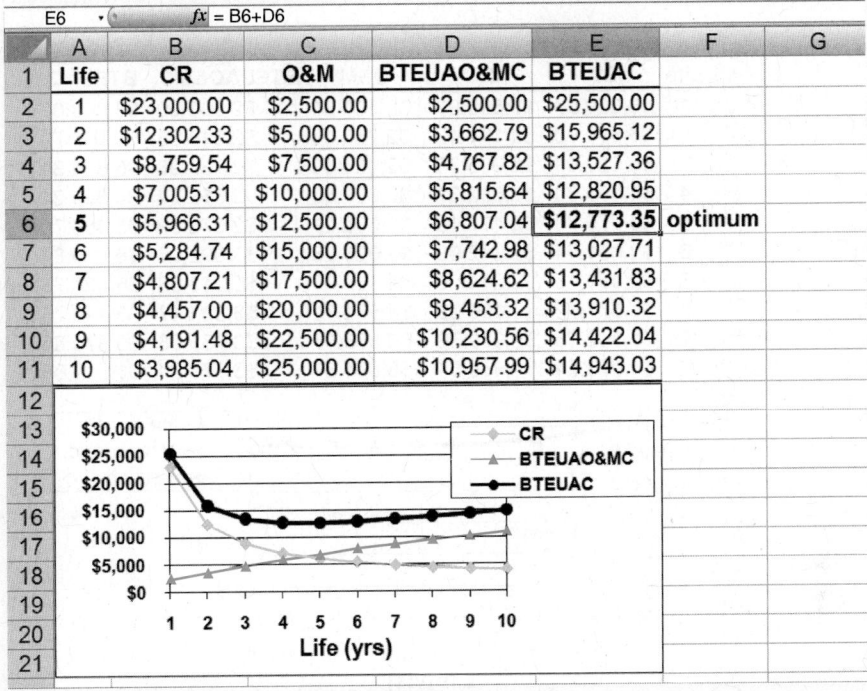

FIGURE 11.5

Optimum Replacement Interval for Example 11.18c: $20,000 Investment; $2500 *O&M*
Gradient Step.

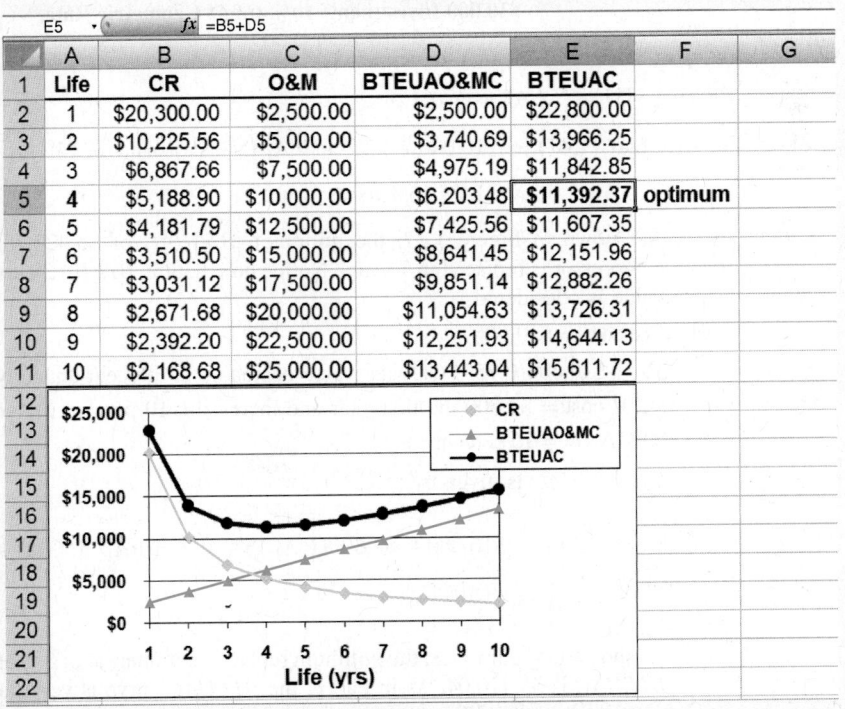

FIGURE 11.6

Optimum Replacement Interval for Example 11.18d: 1.5% *MARR*; $20,000 Investment;
$2500 *O&M* Gradient Step.

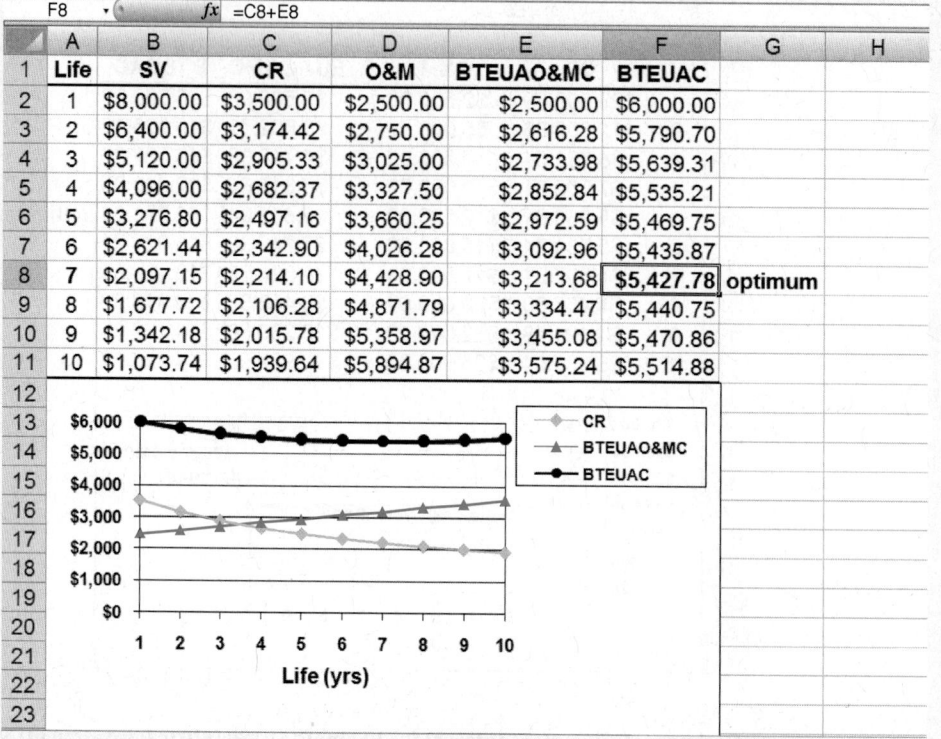

	A	B	C	D	E	F	G	H
					fx	=C8+E8		
1	Life	SV	CR	O&M	BTEUAO&MC	BTEUAC		
2	1	$8,000.00	$3,500.00	$2,500.00	$2,500.00	$6,000.00		
3	2	$6,400.00	$3,174.42	$2,750.00	$2,616.28	$5,790.70		
4	3	$5,120.00	$2,905.33	$3,025.00	$2,733.98	$5,639.31		
5	4	$4,096.00	$2,682.37	$3,327.50	$2,852.84	$5,535.21		
6	5	$3,276.80	$2,497.16	$3,660.25	$2,972.59	$5,469.75		
7	6	$2,621.44	$2,342.90	$4,026.28	$3,092.96	$5,435.87		
8	7	$2,097.15	$2,214.10	$4,428.90	$3,213.68	$5,427.78	optimum	
9	8	$1,677.72	$2,106.28	$4,871.79	$3,334.47	$5,440.75		
10	9	$1,342.18	$2,015.78	$5,358.97	$3,455.08	$5,470.86		
11	10	$1,073.74	$1,939.64	$5,894.87	$3,575.24	$5,514.88		

FIGURE 11.7

Optimum Replacement Interval for Example 11.18e: 20% Decrease in Salvage Value; $10,000 Investment; 10% O&M Geometric Rate.

The *BTEUAC* is given by

$$BTEUAC(15\%) = [\$10,000 + \$2,500(P|A_1\ 15\%,10\%,n)](A|P\ 15\%,n) - \$10,000(0.8^n)$$
$$\times (A|F\ 15\%,n)$$

As shown in Figure 11.7, the minimum *BTEUAC* of $5,427.78 occurs when the compressor is replaced in 7 years. Notice how flat the *BTEUAC* curve is when salvage value is considered.

f. First cost = $10,000

SV = **$10,000(0.75^n)** (salvage value decreases 25 percent annually)

O&M cost = $2,500 the first year and increasing 10 percent per year thereafter

BTMARR = 15 percent

The *BTEUAC* is given by

$$BTEUAC(15\%) = [\$10,000 + \$2,500(P|A_1\ 15\%,10\%,n)](A|P\ 15\%,n) - \$10,000(0.75^n)$$
$$\times (A|F\ 15\%,n)$$

As shown in Figure 11.8, the optimum replacement interval of 8 years occurs when the *BTEUAC* is $5,490.04. As in Part e, the *BTEUAC* curve is very flat. Comparing this result with that in Part e, we note that the optimum replacement interval tends to increase as the rate of decrease in salvage value increases.

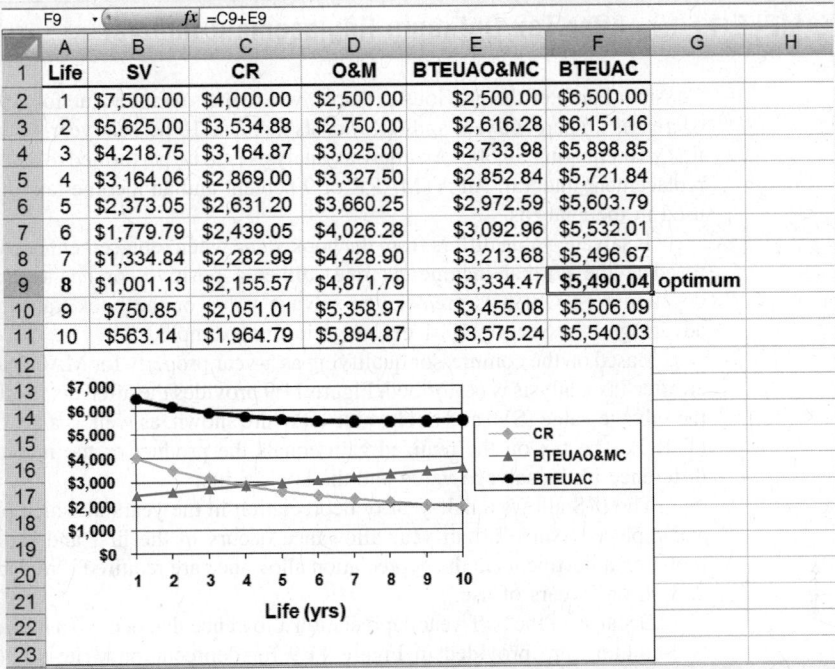

	A	B	C	D	E	F	G	H
F9		fx =C9+E9						
1	Life	SV	CR	O&M	BTEUAO&MC	BTEUAC		
2	1	$7,500.00	$4,000.00	$2,500.00	$2,500.00	$6,500.00		
3	2	$5,625.00	$3,534.88	$2,750.00	$2,616.28	$6,151.16		
4	3	$4,218.75	$3,164.87	$3,025.00	$2,733.98	$5,898.85		
5	4	$3,164.06	$2,869.00	$3,327.50	$2,852.84	$5,721.84		
6	5	$2,373.05	$2,631.20	$3,660.25	$2,972.59	$5,603.79		
7	6	$1,779.79	$2,439.05	$4,026.28	$3,092.96	$5,532.01		
8	7	$1,334.84	$2,282.99	$4,428.90	$3,213.68	$5,496.67		
9	8	$1,001.13	$2,155.57	$4,871.79	$3,334.47	$5,490.04	optimum	
10	9	$750.85	$2,051.01	$5,358.97	$3,455.08	$5,506.09		
11	10	$563.14	$1,964.79	$5,894.87	$3,575.24	$5,540.03		

FIGURE 11.8

Optimum Replacement Interval for Example 11.18f: 25% Decrease in Salvage Value; $10,000 Investment; 10% O&M Geometric Rate.

Let's summarize the general findings from Example 11.14 regarding the sensitivity of the optimum replacement interval to changes in the rate of change in *O&M* costs, initial investment, *BTMARR*, and salvage value. Specifically,

1. increasing (decreasing) the rate of increase in annual operating and maintenance costs tends to decrease (increase) the optimum replacement interval;

2. increasing (decreasing) the magnitude of the initial investment tends to increase (decrease) the optimum replacement interval;

3. increasing (decreasing) the minimum attractive rate of return tends to increase (decrease) the optimum replacement interval; and

4. increasing (decreasing) the rate of decrease in salvage value tends to increase (decrease) the optimum replacement interval.

Optimum Replacement Interval Sensitivity

- Increasing the rate of increase in *O&M* costs tends to decrease the optimum replacement interval
- Increasing the magnitude of the initial investment tends to increase the optimum replacement interval
- Increasing the *MARR* tends to increase the optimum replacement interval
- Increasing the rate of decrease in salvage value tends to increase the optimum replacement interval

EXAMPLE 11.19 After-Tax Optimum Replacement Interval

Consider Part e of the previous example, where the salvage value for a $10,000 compressor decreases 20 percent/year and O&M costs increase 10 percent/year, with the O&M cost the first year equaling $2,500. An after-tax analysis is to be performed to determine the optimum replacement interval. An ATMARR of 9 percent and an income-tax rate of 40 percent are used in the analysis.

If salvage value differs from the book value when replacement occurs, the difference is taxed at the normal income-tax rate. Either a positive- or negative-valued tax results, depending on which is greater, the salvage value or the book value. (We will not take advantage of a Section 1031 exchange in this example.)

Based on the compressor qualifying as 5-year property for MACRS-EDS depreciation, an after-tax analysis is performed. Figure 11.9 provides the after-tax results. Notice that both the salvage value (SV) and book value (BV) are shown, as well as a tax on the realized gain (ToRG). The tax on the realized gain equals the product of the income-tax rate and the difference in the salvage value and the book value.

The IRS allows a half-year of depreciation in the years in which property is acquired and replaced. Since a half-year allowance occurs in the first and sixth years for 5-year property, adjustments in the depreciation allowance are required if replacement occurs after 2, 3, 4, or 5 years of use.

Because of the half-year depreciation allowance that occurs in the year of replacement, two columns are provided in Figure 11.9 for depreciation write-off, (DWO) as well as taxable income (TI) and income tax (T). Column D provides the depreciation allowance for years in which a replacement does not occur; Column E provides half-year depreciation allowances, assuming replacement occurs in each year shown; Column F provides the

	C21	▾	fx	2000								
	A	B	C	D	E	F	G	H	I	J	K	L
1	Life	SV	O&M	DWO[1]	DWO[2]	TI[1]	TI[2]	T[1,3]	T[2,3]	BV[2]	ToRG[2,4]	ATEUAC
2	1	$8,000.00	-$2,500.00	$2,000.00	$2,000.00	-$4,500.00	-$4,500.00	-$1,800.00	-$1,800.00	$8,000.00	$0.00	$3,600.00
3	2	$6,400.00	-$2,750.00	$3,200.00	$1,600.00	-$5,950.00	-$4,350.00	-$2,380.00	-$1,740.00	$6,400.00	$0.00	$3,470.81
4	3	$5,120.00	-$3,025.00	$1,920.00	$960.00	-$4,945.00	-$3,985.00	-$1,978.00	-$1,594.00	$3,840.00	$512.00	$3,358.12
5	4	$4,096.00	-$3,327.50	$1,152.00	$576.00	-$4,479.50	-$3,903.50	-$1,791.80	-$1,561.40	$2,304.00	$716.80	$3,277.86
6	5	$3,276.80	-$3,660.25	$1,152.00	$576.00	-$4,812.25	-$4,236.25	-$1,924.90	-$1,694.50	$1,152.00	$849.92	$3,226.59
7	6	$2,621.44	-$4,026.28	$576.00	$576.00	-$4,602.28	-$4,602.28	-$1,840.91	-$1,840.91	$0.00	$1,048.58	$3,197.36
8	7	$2,097.15	-$4,428.90	$0.00	$0.00	-$4,428.90	-$4,428.90	-$1,771.56	-$1,771.56	$0.00	$838.86	**$3,188.24**
9	8	$1,677.72	-$4,871.79	$0.00	$0.00	-$4,871.79	-$4,871.79	-$1,948.72	-$1,948.72	$0.00	$671.09	$3,197.29
10	9	$1,342.18	-$5,358.97	$0.00	$0.00	-$5,358.97	-$5,358.97	-$2,143.59	-$2,143.59	$0.00	$536.87	$3,221.10
11	10	$1,073.74	-$5,894.87	$0.00	$0.00	-$5,894.87	-$5,894.87	-$2,357.95	-$2,357.95	$0.00	$429.50	$3,257.26
12	[1]assumes replacement occurs in a later year											
13	[2]assumes replacement occurs in current year					geometric rate of decrease in SV =		20%				
14	[3]does not include salvage value or realized gain (loss) from replacement					geometric rate of increase in O&M =		10%				
15	[4]includes tax on realized gain (loss)											
16						=-.PMT(9%,A6,-(-10000+NPV(9%,$C$2:C6)-NPV(9%,$H$2:H5)+PV(9%,A6,,I6)+PV(9%,A6,,K6)),-B6)							
17												
18	Replace after 1 Year						Replace after 7 Years					
19	EOY	CFBT	DWO	TI	T	ATCF	EOY	CFBT	DWO	TI	T	ATCF
20	0	-$10,000.00				-$10,000.00	0	-$10,000.00				-$10,000.00
21	1	$5,500.00	$2,000.00	-$4,500.00	-$1,800.00	$7,300.00	1	-$2,500.00	$2,000.00	-$4,500.00	-$1,800.00	-$700.00
22					ATPW =	-$3,302.75	2	-$2,750.00	$3,200.00	-$5,950.00	-$2,380.00	-$370.00
23					ATEUAC =	$3,600.00	3	-$3,025.00	$1,920.00	-$4,945.00	-$1,978.00	-$1,047.00
24	Replace after 2 Years						4	-$3,327.50	$1,152.00	-$4,479.50	-$1,791.80	-$1,535.70
25	EOY	CFBT	DWO	TI	T	ATCF	5	-$3,660.25	$1,152.00	-$4,812.25	-$1,924.90	-$1,735.35
26	0	-$10,000.00				-$10,000.00	6	-$4,026.28	$576.00	-$4,602.28	-$1,840.91	-$2,185.37
27	1	-$2,500.00	$2,000.00	-$4,500.00	-$1,800.00	-$700.00	7	-$2,331.75	$0.00	-$2,331.75	-$932.70	-$1,399.05
28	2	$3,650.00	$1,600.00	-$4,350.00	-$1,740.00	$5,390.00					ATPW =	-$16,046.28
29					ATPW =	-$6,105.55					ATEUAC =	$3,188.24
30					ATEUAC =	$3,470.81	Replace after 8 Years					
31	Replace after 3 Years						EOY	CFBT	DWO	TI	T	ATCF
32	EOY	CFBT	DWO	TI	T	ATCF	0	-$10,000.00				-$10,000.00

FIGURE 11.9

After-Tax Optimum Replacement Interval with 20% Decrease in Salvage Value and 10% O&M Increases.

taxable income for years in which a replacement does not occur; Column G provides taxable incomes for years in which a replacement occurs; Column H is the product of the income-tax rate and Column F; Column I is the product of the income-tax rate and Column G; Column J provides the book value, assuming replacement occurs in the year shown (hence, values from Column D are summed over previous years and then added to the value from Column E for the year in question). The tax on realized gain, shown in Column K, is obtained by multiplying the income-tax rate times the difference in the salvage value (Column B) and the book value (Column J). Finally, the after-tax equivalent uniform annual cost is obtained by converting to a uniform annual series the present worth of the after-tax cash flows for all years leading up to and including the year of replacement.

For years in which a replacement does not occur,

$$\text{ATCF} = 0.6(O\&M) + 0.4(\text{DWO})$$

For the year in which replacement occurs,

$$\text{ATCF} = 0.6(O\&M + \text{SV}) + 0.4(\text{DWO} + \text{BV})$$

For the example, suppose the compressor is replaced after 4 years of use; in the fourth year, taxable income equals the sum of the $O\&M$ cost (−$327.50) and the salvage value ($4,096), less the sum of a half-year's depreciation ($576) and the book value ($2,304) for a total of −$2,111.50. Likewise, the income tax in the fourth year will be 0.4(−$2,111.50), or −$844.60. Subtracting the income tax from the sum of the $O\&M$ cost and the salvage value gives the after-tax cash flow ($1,613.10).

	F69	▾	fx								
	A	B	C	D	E	F	G	H	I	J	K	L
1	Life	SV	O&M	DWO¹	DWO²	Π¹	Π²	T¹,³	T²,³	BV²	ToRG²,⁴	ATEUAC
2	1	$7,500.00	-$2,500.00	$2,000.00	$2,000.00	-$4,500.00	-$4,500.00	-$1,800.00	-$1,800.00	$8,000.00	-$200.00	$3,900.00
3	2	$5,625.00	-$3,125.00	$3,200.00	$1,600.00	-$6,325.00	-$4,725.00	-$2,530.00	-$1,890.00	$6,400.00	-$310.00	$3,800.96
4	3	$4,218.75	-$3,906.25	$1,920.00	$960.00	-$5,826.25	-$4,866.25	-$2,330.50	-$1,946.50	$3,840.00	$151.50	$3,759.19
5	4	$3,164.06	-$4,882.81	$1,152.00	$576.00	-$6,034.81	-$5,458.81	-$2,413.93	-$2,183.53	$2,304.00	$344.03	$3,788.67
6	5	$2,373.05	-$6,103.52	$1,152.00	$576.00	-$7,255.52	-$6,679.52	-$2,902.21	-$2,671.81	$1,152.00	$488.42	$3,885.77
7	6	$1,779.79	-$7,629.39	$576.00	$576.00	-$8,205.39	-$8,205.39	-$3,282.16	-$3,282.16	$0.00	$711.91	$4,044.84
8	7	$1,334.84	-$9,536.74	$0.00	$0.00	-$9,536.74	-$9,536.74	-$3,814.70	-$3,814.70	$0.00	$533.94	$4,266.60
9	8	$1,001.13	-$11,920.93	$0.00	$0.00	-$11,920.93	-$11,920.93	-$4,768.37	-$4,768.37	$0.00	$400.45	$4,552.97
10	9	$750.85	-$14,901.16	$0.00	$0.00	-$14,901.16	-$14,901.16	-$5,960.46	-$5,960.46	$0.00	$300.34	$4,905.63
11	10	$563.14	-$18,626.45	$0.00	$0.00	-$18,626.45	-$18,626.45	-$7,450.58	-$7,450.58	$0.00	$225.25	$5,328.42

12	¹assumes replacement occurs in a later year			
13	²assumes replacement occurs in current year		geometric rate of decrease in SV = 25%
14	³does not include salvage value or realized gain (loss) from replacement	geometric rate of increase in O&M = 25%
15	⁴includes tax on realized gain (loss)	
16		=-PMT(9%,A6,-(-10000+NPV(9%,$C$4:C6)-NPV(9%,$H$4:H5)+PV(9%,A6,,I6)+PV(9%,A6,,K6))),-B6)

	Replace after 1 Year					Replace after 7 Years				
18	Replace after 1 Year					Replace after 7 Years				
19	EOY	CFBT	DWO	TI	T	ATCF	EOY	CFBT	DWO	TI	T	ATCF
20	0	-$10,000.00				-$10,000.00	0	-$10,000.00				-$10,000.00
21	1	$5,000.00	$2,000.00	-$5,000.00	-$2,000.00	$7,000.00	1	-$2,500.00	$2,000.00	-$4,500.00	-$1,800.00	-$700.00
22					ATPW =	-$3,577.98	2	-$3,125.00	$3,200.00	-$6,325.00	-$2,530.00	-$595.00
23					ATEUAC =	$3,900.00	3	-$3,906.25	$1,920.00	-$5,826.25	-$2,330.50	-$1,575.75
24	Replace after 2 Years					4	-$4,882.81	$1,152.00	-$6,034.81	-$2,413.93	-$2,468.89
25	EOY	CFBT	DWO	TI	T	ATCF	5	-$6,103.52	$1,152.00	-$7,255.52	-$2,902.21	-$3,201.31
26	0	-$10,000.00				-$10,000.00	6	-$7,629.39	$576.00	-$8,205.39	-$3,282.16	-$4,347.24
27	1	-$2,500.00	$2,000.00	-$4,500.00	-$1,800.00	-$700.00	7	-$8,201.90	$0.00	-$8,201.90	-$3,280.76	-$4,921.14
28	2	$2,500.00	$1,600.00	-$5,500.00	-$2,200.00	$4,700.00					ATPW =	-$21,473.57
29					ATPW =	-$6,686.31					ATEUAC =	$4,266.60
30					ATEUAC =	$3,800.96	Replace after 8 Years				
31	Replace after 3 Years						EOY	CFBT	DWO	TI	T	ATCF
32	EOY	CFBT	DWO	TI	T	ATCF	0	-$10,000.00				-$10,000.00
33	0	-$10,000.00				-$10,000.00	1	-$2,500.00	$2,000.00	-$4,500.00	-$1,800.00	-$700.00
34	1	-$2,500.00	$2,000.00	-$4,500.00	-$1,800.00	-$700.00	2	-$3,125.00	$3,200.00	-$6,325.00	-$2,530.00	-$595.00
35	2	-$3,125.00	$3,200.00	-$6,325.00	-$2,530.00	-$595.00	3	-$3,906.25	$1,920.00	-$5,826.25	-$2,330.50	-$1,575.75
36	3	$312.50	$960.00	-$4,487.50	-$1,795.00	$2,107.50	4	-$4,882.81	$1,152.00	-$6,034.81	-$2,413.93	-$2,468.89
37					ATPW =	-$9,515.62	5	-$6,103.52	$1,152.00	-$7,255.52	-$2,902.21	-$3,201.31
38					ATEUAC =	$3,759.19	6	-$7,629.39	$576.00	-$8,205.39	-$3,282.16	-$4,347.24

FIGURE 11.10

After-Tax Optimum Replacement Interval with 25% Decrease in Salvage Value and 25% O&M Increases.

To obtain the same result, using the data shown in Table 11.12, the income tax (T) shown in Column I (−$1,561.40) is added to the tax on realized gain (ToRG) in Column K ($716.80), for a total of −$844.60. The tax on realized gain is obtained by multiplying the income-tax rate (40 percent) and the difference in salvage value ($4,096) and book value at the time of disposal ($2,304); book value at disposal equals the cost basis ($10,000) less accumulated depreciation ($2,000 + $3,200 + $1,920 + $576). Notice that the book value calculation was based on values from Column D for years 1, 2, and 3 and a value from Column E for year 4, since that is when the replacement occurred.

The Excel® formula used to compute the after-tax equivalent uniform annual cost (ATEUAC) is given in Figure 11.9. As shown, the optimum replacement interval is 7 years.

Figure 11.10 contains the after-tax analysis when the salvage value decreases at a geometric rate of 25 percent and O&M costs increase at a geometric rate of 25 percent. In this case, the optimum replacement interval is 3 years.

Two observations come to mind regarding optimum replacement intervals:

1. Implicit in the solution procedure we used to obtain the "optimum replacement interval" is an assumption that the planning horizon equals an integer multiple of the interval obtained.

2. If the integer multiple is greater than 1, then subsequent replacements must have cash flow profiles that are identical to their predecessors.

In the previous examples, the optimum replacement interval was determined without considering the planning horizon's length. In fact, it was implicitly assumed that the planning horizon equaled an integer multiple of the optimum replacement interval obtained. This gives rise to a third observation regarding the computation of optimum replacement intervals: *for the replacement interval to be truly optimum, it must minimize after-tax present worth over the planning horizon.*

Observations

1. Implicit in the solution for the optimum replacement interval is an assumption that the planning horizon equals an integer multiple of the interval obtained.

2. If the integer multiple is greater than one, then subsequent replacements must have identical cash flow profiles.

3. For the replacement interval to be optimum, it must minimize after-tax present worth over the planning horizon.

Suppose the planning horizon is fixed and greater than the optimum replacement interval. How might one determine the optimum time to replace the asset? The following example addresses this scenario.

EXAMPLE 11.20 Optimum Replacement Timing with a Given Planning Horizon

Recall Part a of Example 11.18, involving the replacement of the compressor. Assuming the compressor requires a $10,000 initial investment, has annual O&M costs that are represented by a 20 percent geometric series, has a first-year cost of $2,500, and has a before-tax MARR

TABLE 11.20
Optimum Replacement Interval for Example 11.20.

Life	CR	O&M	BTEUAO&MC	BTEUAC
1	$11,500.00	$2,500.00	$2,500.00	$14,000.00
2	$6,151.16	$3,000.00	$2,732.56	$8,883.72
3	$4,379.77	$3,600.00	$2,982.36	$7,362.13
4	$3,502.65	$4,320.00	$3,250.24	$6,752.90
5	$2,983.16	$5,184.00	$3,537.05	$6,520.21
6	$2,642.37	$6,220.80	$3,843.63	$6,486.00
7	$2,403.60	$7,464.96	$4,170.86	$6,574.46
8	$2,228.50	$8,957.95	$4,519.60	$6,748.10
9	$2,095.74	$10,749.54	$4,890.74	$6,986.48
10	$1,992.52	$12,899.45	$5,285.19	$7,277.71

of 15 percent, the *BTEUAC* for various replacement intervals is shown in Figure 11.3 and repeated in Table 11.20. The optimum replacement interval is 6 years.

Suppose a 10-year planning horizon is to be used, rather than some multiple of 6 years. Assuming replacements have identical cash flow profiles to their successor, several possibilities exist. For example, one could use the first compressor for 6 years and then use its successor for 4 years; alternatively, since the region around the optimum is quite flat (as illustrated in Figure 11.3), perhaps two 5-year replacement cycles is better.

We will compute the before-tax present worth for the following life sequences: {5,5}, {6,4}, {7,3}.

{5,5}

$$BTPW = \$6,520.21(P|A\ 15\%,10)$$
$$= \$6,520.21(5.01877)$$
$$= \$32,723.43$$

{6,4}

$$BTPW = \$6,846(P|A\ 15\%,6) + \$6,752.90(P|A\ 15\%,4)(P|F\ 15\%,6)$$
$$= \$6,486(3.78448) + \$6,752.90(2.85498)(0.43233)$$
$$= \$32,881.20$$

{7,3}

$$BTPW = \$6,574.46(P|A\ 15\%,7) + \$7,362.13(P|A\ 15\%,3)(P|F\ 15\%,7)$$
$$= \$6,574.46(4.16042) + \$7,362.13(2.28323)(0.37594)$$
$$= \$33,671.85$$

How did we know that we did not have to consider {4,6} and {3,7}? Based on the time value of money, the cycle time with the lesser of the two *BTEUAC* values should occur first. As shown by the *CFD* in Figure 11.11, since $BTEUAC(n = 7) < BTEUAC(n = 3)$, the sequence {7,3} will have a smaller present worth cost than the sequence {3,7}; a similar argument holds for the sequence {6,4} compared to the sequence {4,6}. Similar comparisons can be used to eliminate the remaining sequences: {10}, {9,1}, {8,2}, {2,8}, and {1,9}.

Based on the analysis, it is best to use a compressor for 5 years, then replace it with an identical compressor for the 5 remaining years in the planning horizon. The before-tax present worth cost is $32,723.61.

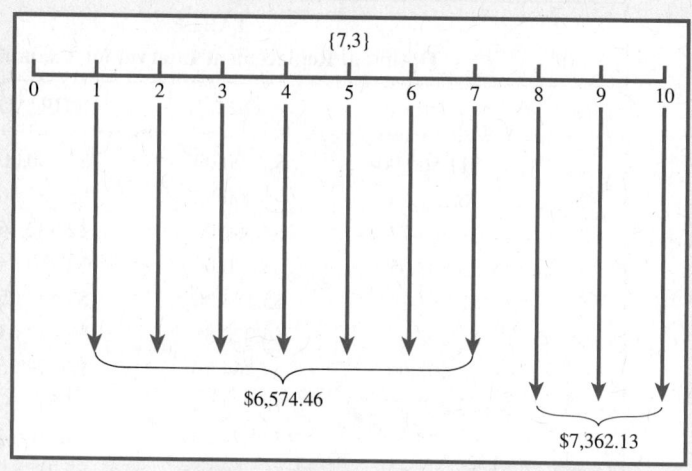

FIGURE 11.11
Cash Flow Diagram for Example 11.20.

For the previous examples, failure to replace the equipment at precisely the optimum time will not result in a significantly greater *BTEUAC*. This is often the case with many replacement situations; the resulting measure of economic worth is relatively insensitive to deviations from the optimum strategy. And, because of the *BTEUAC* function's shape, keeping the defender longer than its optimum life tends to be more economic than replacing the defender too soon.

However, it is advisable that companies establish operating policies of reviewing actual *O&M* costs for equipment "in the neighborhood" of the optimum replacement interval to verify that costs have been as anticipated and to review replacement options. With the rapid development of new and improved technology, stronger and stronger challengers will tend to emerge between the time a replacement analysis is performed and the apparent "optimum" time to replace an asset.

A number of variations on the previous examples can be explored, including successors with technological improvements that result in smaller *O&M* costs and smaller initial investments. A rich body of literature is available, addressing aspects of replacement analysis. Our goal is to expose you to the subject and encourage you to consult the research literature for further exploration of various replacement models.

11-6 SUMMARY

Our consideration of replacement analysis included both before-tax and after-tax analyses. Among the "take away" messages from the chapter are the following:

1. Two approaches can be used in performing a replacement analysis: the cash flow approach and the opportunity cost approach.

2. Income-tax considerations can change the recommendation made regarding replacement of an asset.

3. Section 1031 property exchanges can be used to defer taxes on realized gains when a property is replaced with like-kind property.

4. The optimum replacement interval can be sensitive to changes in the *MARR*, the magnitude of the initial investment, the rate at which *O&M* costs increase over time, and the rate at which the salvage value decreases over time.

Pit Stop #11—Pick Up the Pace! Don't Get Replaced!

1. True or False: In performing engineering economic analyses of replacement alternatives, it is best to perform before-tax analyses, since incorporating income tax considerations in the analysis is difficult, due to the treatment of trade-in values not equaling book values.

2. True or False: The two approaches used in performing replacement analyses are the cash flow approach and the insider viewpoint approach.

3. True or False: In determining the optimum replacement interval, it is necessary to assume negligible salvage values.

4. True or False: Before-tax replacement analyses and after-tax replacement analyses seldom yield the same recommendation.

5. True or False: Section 1031 exchanges of property can be performed for any real or personal property.

6. True or False: If the optimum replacement interval for an over-the-road tractor is 4 years and the initial cost of the tractor is increased by 20% then the optimum replacement interval for the next tractor might be less than 4 years.

7. True or False: If the optimum replacement interval for an over-the-road tractor is 4 years and the salvage value for used tractors is suddenly cut in half, then the optimum replacement interval for the next tractor might be greater than 4 years.

8. True or False: If the optimum replacement interval for an over-the-road tractor is 4 years and the after-tax *MARR* is increased from 9% to 12%, then the optimum replacement interval for the next tractor might be less than 4 years.

9. True or False: If the optimum replacement interval for an over-the-road tractor is 4 years and the rate of increase in *O&M* costs doubles, then the optimum replacement interval for the next tractor might be less than 4 years.

10. True or False: Section 1031 Property Exchanges are no longer permitted by the U.S. Internal Revenue Service.

Tutoring problem available (at instructor's discretion) in *WileyPLUS*.

Problem available (at instructor's discretion) in *WileyPLUS*.

Worked Problem Video available in *WileyPLUS*.

FE-LIKE PROBLEMS

1. A company owns a 6-year-old gear hobber that has a book value of $60,000. The present market value of the hobber is $80,000. A new gear hobber can be purchased for $450,000. Using an insider's point of view, what is the net first cost of purchasing the new gear hobber?

    a. $310,000
    b. $370,000
    c. $390,000
    d. $450,000

2. A company owns a 6-year-old gear hobber that has a book value of $60,000. The present market value of the hobber is $80,000. A new gear hobber can be purchased for $450,000. Using an outsider's point of view, what is the net first cost of purchasing the new gear hobber?

   a. $310,000
   b. $370,000
   c. $390,000
   d. $450,000

3. In evaluating a piece of equipment for its optimal replacement interval, the following table of equivalent uniform annual costs is obtained. What is the optimal replacement interval for the equipment?

n	EUAC(n)
1	1,582
2	1,550
3	1,575
4	1,580

   a. 1 year
   b. 2 years
   c. 3 years
   d. 4 years

4. A radiology clinic is considering buying a new $700,000 X-ray machine that will have no salvage value after installation, since the cost of removal will be approximately equal to its sales value. Maintenance is estimated at $24,000 per year as long as the machine is owned. After 10 years, the X-ray source will be depleted and the machine must be scrapped. Which of the following represents the most economic life of this X-ray machine?

   a. One year, since it will have no salvage after installation
   b. Five years, since the maintenance costs are constant
   c. Ten years, because maintenance costs don't increase
   d. Cannot be determined from the information given

5. Which of the following is not an approach to replacement analysis?

   a. Cash flow approach
   b. Insider viewpoint
   c. Outsider viewpoint
   d. Supply chain approach

6. The most common approach to determining the planning horizon for replacement analysis is which of the following?

   a. Shortest life
   b. Median Life
   c. Longest life
   d. Least common multiple

7. A company owns a 5-year-old turret lathe that has a book value of $20,000. The present market value of the lathe is $16,000. A new turret lathe can be purchased for $45,000. Using a before-tax analysis and an outsider's point of view, what is the first cost of keeping the old lathe?

   a. $29,000
   b. $45,000
   c. $20,000
   d. $16,000

8. A company owns a 5-year-old turret lathe that has a book value of $20,000. The present market value of the lathe is $16,000. A new turret lathe can be purchased for $45,000. Using a before-tax analysis and an insider's point of view, what is the first cost of the new lathe?

   a. $29,000
   b. $45,000
   c. $25,000
   d. $16,000

9. What two cost categories form the trade-off that leads to an optimal replacement interval?

   a. Direct costs and indirect costs
   b. Insider costs and outsider costs
   c. Operating and maintenance costs and capital recovery costs
   d. Sunk costs and opportunity costs

10. Increasing the magnitude of the initial investment tends to _____ the optimum replacement interval.

    a. decrease
    b. increase
    c. reverse
    d. not affect

PROBLEMS

Section 11.1

1. Identify something you own, perhaps even something you still use regularly.

   a. Give a list of at least six reasons why you might consider replacing the identified item.

   b. Identify at least two "challengers" that you might consider replacing the item with, and for each challenger, explain the main reason you would consider it.

2. Give two examples each of (1) functional obsolescence, (2) technological obsolescence, and (3) economic obsolescence for items that you or your family own.

3. Ten reasons why companies use equipment long after replacements would be justified economically are given in the text. In many cases, these reasons do not apply just to companies; rather, they apply to us as individuals. Give specific examples of at least 3 of the 10 reasons that apply to things owned by you or your family.

Sections 11.2.1 and 11.3.1

4. The Container Corporation of America is considering replacing an automatic painting machine purchased 9 years ago for $700,000. It has a market value today of $40,000. The unit costs $350,000 annually to operate and maintain. A new unit can be purchased for $800,000 and will have annual O&M costs of $120,000. If the old unit is retained, it will have no salvage value at the end of its remaining life of 10 years. The new unit, if purchased, will have a salvage value of $100,000 in 10 years. Using an *EUAC* measure and a *MARR* of 20 percent, perform a before-tax analysis to see if the automatic painting machine should be replaced if it is taken as a trade-in for its market value of $40,000.

   a. Use the cash flow approach (insider's viewpoint approach). (11.2.1)

   b. Use the opportunity cost approach (outsider's viewpoint approach). (11.3.1)

5. A specialty concrete mixer used in construction was purchased for $300,000 7 years ago. Its annual O&M costs are $105,000. At the end of the 8-year planning horizon, the mixer will have a salvage value of $5,000. If the mixer is replaced, a new mixer will require an initial investment of $375,000. At the end of the 8-year planning horizon, it will have a salvage value of $45,000. Its annual O&M cost will be only $40,000 due to newer technology. Analyze this using an *EUAC* measure and a *MARR* of 15 percent to see if the concrete mixer should be replaced if the old mixer is sold for its market value of $65,000.

   a. Use the cash flow approach (insider's viewpoint approach). (11.2.1)

   b. Use the opportunity cost approach (outsider's viewpoint approach). (11.3.1)

6. Online Educators (OE), a not-for-profit firm exempt from taxes, is considering replacing some electronic equipment associated with its distance learning (DL) facility. They spent $100,000 on the equipment 3 years ago and have depreciated it to a current book value of $40,000. Its end-of-year O&M costs are $9,000 per year. Today's newer technology, including high-definition digital TV, has a price tag of $125,000, and after some haggling, OE negotiates a price of either (1) $108,000 in cash or (2) $91,000 in cash plus the current equipment as a trade-in. OE checked around and determined it could do no better by selling the soon-to-be-obsolete equipment to someone else. OE will use a 5-year planning horizon. If the newer equipment is purchased, it will have end-of-year O&M costs of $8,000 and a salvage value of $20,000 at that time. If the old equipment is retained, it will have to be supplemented in years 3, 4, and 5 by leasing a hi-def add-on unit costing $30,000 per year payable at the beginning of the year with additional end-of-year O&M costs of $7,000. The old equipment will also have no salvage value at the end of the planning horizon. *MARR* is 10 percent.

   a. What is the market value of the old equipment using the cash flow approach (insider's viewpoint approach) ? (11.2.1)

   b. Use the cash flow approach (insider's viewpoint approach) to determine whether to keep or replace the current equipment. (11.2.1)

c. What is the market value of the old equipment using the opportunity cost approach (outsider's viewpoint approach)? (11.3.1)

d. Use the opportunity cost approach (outsider's viewpoint approach) to determine whether to keep or replace the current equipment. (11.3.1)

7. A currently owned shredder used in a refuse-powered electrical generating plant has a present net realizable value of $210,000 and is expected to have a market value of $10,000 after 4 years. Operating and maintenance disbursements are $100,000 per year. An equivalent shredder can be leased for $200 per day plus $80 per hour of actual use as determined by an hour meter, with both components assumed to be paid at year-end. Actual use is expected to be 1,500 hours and 250 days per year. Using a 4-year planning horizon, a before-tax analysis, and a *MARR* of 15 percent, determine the preferred alternative using the annual cost criterion.

a. Consider only the above information and use the cash flow approach (insider's viewpoint approach). (11.2.1)

b. Consider the addition of a third alternative, to operate without any shredder at all, at an annual cost of $190,000. Use the cash flow approach (insider's viewpoint approach). (11.2.1)

c. Consider only the above information and use the opportunity cost approach (outsider's viewpoint approach). (11.3.1)

d. Consider the addition of a third alternative, to operate without any shredder at all, at an annual cost of $190,000. Use the opportunity cost approach (outsider's viewpoint approach). (11.3.1)

8. Dell is considering replacing one of its material handling systems. It has an annual *O&M* cost of $48,000, a remaining operational life of 8 years, and an estimated salvage value of $6,000 at that time. A new system can be purchased for $175,000. It will be worth $50,000 in 8 years, and it will have annual *O&M* costs of only $17,000 per year due to new technology. If the new system is purchased, the old system will be traded in for $55,000, even though the old system can be sold for only $45,000 on the open market. Leasing a new system will cost $31,000 per year, payable at the beginning of the year, plus operating costs of $15,000 per year payable at year-end. If the new system is leased, the existing material handling system will be sold for its market value of $45,000. Use an 8-year planning horizon, an annual worth analysis, and *MARR* of 15 percent to decide which material handling system to recommend: (1) keep existing, (2) trade in existing and purchase new, or (3) sell existing and lease. Use the cash flow approach (insider's viewpoint approach). (11.2.1)

9. Allen Construction purchased a crane 6 years ago for $130,000. They need a crane of this capacity for the next 5 years. Normal operation costs $35,000 per year. The current crane will have no salvage value at the end of 5 more years. Allen can trade in the current crane for its market value of $40,000 toward the purchase of a new one, which costs $150,000. The new crane will cost only $8,000 per year under normal operating conditions and will have a salvage value of $55,000 after 5 years. If *MARR* is 20 percent, determine which option is preferred.

a. Use the cash flow approach (insider's viewpoint approach). (11.2.1)

b. Use the opportunity cost approach (outsider's viewpoint approach). (11.3.1)

10. A division of Raytheon owns a 5-year old turret lathe that has a non-tax book value of $24,000. It has a current market value of $18,000. The expected decline in market value is $3,000 per year from this point forward to a minimum of $3,000. *O&M* costs are $8,000 per year. Additional capability is needed. If the old lathe is kept, that new capability will be contracted out for $13,000, assumed payable at the end of each year. A new turret lathe has the increased capability to fulfill all needs, replacing the existing turret lathe and requiring no outside contracting. It can be purchased for $65,000 and will have an expected life of 8 years. Its market value is expected to be $65,000(0.7^t) at the end of year t. Annual *O&M* costs are expected to equal $10,000. *MARR* is 15 percent, and the planning horizon is 8 years.

a. Clearly show the cash flow profile for each alternative using a cash flow approach (insider's viewpoint approach). (11.2.1)

b. Using an *EUAC* and a cash flow approach (insider's viewpoint approach), decide which is the more favorable alternative. (11.2.1)

c. Clearly show the cash flow profile for each alternative using an opportunity cost approach (outsider's viewpoint approach). (11.3.1.)

d. Using an *EUAC* comparison and an opportunity cost approach (outsider's viewpoint approach), decide which is the more favorable alternative. (11.3.1)

11. Five years ago, a multi-axis NC machine was purchased for the express purpose of machining large, complex parts used in commercial and military aircraft worldwide. It cost $350,000, had an estimated life of 15 years, and O&M costs of $50,000 per year. It was originally thought to have a salvage value of $20,000 at the end of 15 years but is now believed to have a remaining life of 5 years with no salvage value at that time. With business booming, the existing machine is no longer sufficient to meet production needs. It can be kept and supplemented by purchasing a new, smaller Machine S for $210,000 that will cost $37,000 per year for O&M, have a life of 10 years, and a salvage value of $210,000(0.8^t) after t years. As an alternative, a larger, faster, and more capable Machine L can be used alone to replace the current machine. It has a cash price without trade-in of $450,000, O&M costs of $74,000 per year, a salvage value of $450,000(0.8^t) after t years, and a 15-year life. The present machine can be sold on the open market for a maximum of $70,000. MARR is 20 percent, and the planning horizon is 5 years.

   a. Clearly show the cash flow profile for each alternative using a cash flow approach (insider's viewpoint approach). (11.2.1)

   b. Using an EUAC and a cash flow approach (insider's viewpoint approach), decide which is the more favorable alternative. (11.2.1)

   c. Clearly show the cash flow profile for each alternative using an opportunity cost approach (outsider's viewpoint approach). (11.3.1)

   d. Using an EUAC comparison and an opportunity cost approach (outsider's viewpoint approach), decide which is the more favorable alternative. (11.3.1)

12. Five years ago, ARCHON, a regional architecture/contractor firm, purchased an HVAC unit for $25,000 that was expected to last 15 years. It will have a salvage value of $0 in 10 more years. The annual operating cost of this unit started at $2,000 in the first year and has increased steadily at $250 per year ever since; last year the cost was $3,000. Its book value is now $13,000. ARCHON has been phenomenally successful due to their reputation for highly functional, high-quality, cost-effective designs and construction. They are building a new wing at their regional headquarters to accommodate a much larger computer design emphasis requiring larger, faster computers, architectural printers, e-storage for a construction repository of previous designs, and an increased human heat load. They can buy an additional unit to air-condition the new wing for $18,000. It will have a service life of 15 years, a net salvage of $0 at that time, and a $3,000 market value after 10 years. It will have annual operating costs of $1,800 in the first year, increasing at $100 per year. As an alternative, ARCHON can buy a new unit to heat and cool the entire building for $35,000. It will last for 15 years and have a net salvage of $0 at that time; however, it will have a market value of $8,500 after 10 years. It will have first-year operating costs of $3,700/year, increasing at $200 per year. The present unit can be sold now for $7,000. MARR is 20 percent, and the planning horizon is 10 years.

   a. Clearly show the cash flow profile for each alternative using a cash flow approach (insider's viewpoint approach). (11.2.1)

   b. Using a PW analysis and a cash flow approach (insider's viewpoint approach), decide which is the more favorable alternative. (11.2.1)

   c. Clearly show the cash flow profile for each alternative using an opportunity cost approach (outsider's viewpoint approach). (11.3.1.)

   d. Using a PW analysis and an opportunity cost approach (outsider's viewpoint approach), decide which is the more favorable alternative. (11.3.1)

13. Clear Water Company has a down-hole well auger that was purchased 3 years ago for $30,000. O&M costs are $13,000 per year. Alternative A is to keep the existing auger, which has a current market value of $12,000. It will have a $0 salvage value after 7 more years. Alternative B is to buy a new auger that will cost $54,000 and will have a $14,000 salvage value after 7 years. O&M costs are $6,000 for the new auger. Clear Water can trade in the existing auger on the new one for $15,000. Alternative C is to trade in the existing auger on a "treated auger" that requires vastly less O&M cost at only $3,000 per year. It costs $68,000, and the trade-in allowance for the existing auger is $17,000. The "treated auger" will have an $18,000 salvage value after 7 years. Alternative D is to sell the existing auger on the open market and to contract with a current competitor to use their equipment and services to perform the drilling that would normally be done with the existing auger. The competitor requires a beginning-of-year retainer payment of $10,000. End-of-year O&M cost would be $6,000. MARR is 15 percent, and the planning horizon is 7 years.

a. Clearly show the cash flow profile for each alternative using a cash flow approach (insider's viewpoint approach). (11.2.1)

b. Using an *EUAC* and a cash flow approach (insider's viewpoint approach), decide which is the more favorable alternative. (11.2.1)

c. Clearly show the cash flow profile for each alternative using an opportunity cost approach (outsider's viewpoint approach). (11.3.1)

d. Using an *EUAC* comparison and an opportunity cost approach (outsider's viewpoint approach), decide which is the more favorable alternative. (11.3.1)

Sections 11.2.2, 11.3.2, and 11.4

14. The Container Corporation of America is considering replacing an automatic painting machine purchased 9 years ago for $700,000. It was depreciated as an asset for manufacturing fabricated metal products as MACRS-GDS 7-year property. It has a market value today of $40,000. The unit costs $350,000 annually to operate and maintain. A new unit, also MACRS-GDS 7-year property, can be purchased for $800,000 and will have annual *O&M* costs of $120,000. If the old unit is retained, it will have no salvage value at the end of the 10-year planning horizon. The new unit, if purchased, will have a salvage value of $100,000 in 10 years. Use an *EUAC* measure, a tax rate of 40 percent, and an after-tax *MARR* of 12 percent to perform an after-tax analysis to see if the automatic painting machine should be replaced if the old automatic painting machine is taken in as a trade-in for its market value of $40,000.

a. Use the cash flow approach (insider's viewpoint approach). (11.2.2)

b. Use the opportunity cost approach (outsider's viewpoint approach). (11.3.2)

c. Use the cash flow approach (insider's viewpoint approach), except note that a Section 1031 like-kind property exchange is to be used. The equipment replaced will continue to be replaced by like-kind investments in the United States indefinitely. (11.4)

15. A specialty concrete mixer used in construction was purchased for $300,000 7 years ago. It is MACRS-GDS 5-year property. Its annual *O&M* costs are $105,000. At the end of an 8-year planning horizon, the mixer will have a salvage value of $5,000. If the mixer is replaced, a new mixer will require an initial investment of $375,000, and at the end of the 8-year planning horizon, the new mixer will have a salvage value of $45,000. Its annual *O&M* cost will be only $40,000 due to newer technology. Use an *EUAC* measure, a tax rate of 40 percent, and an after-tax *MARR* of 9 percent to perform an after-tax analysis to see if the concrete mixer should be replaced if the old mixer is sold for its market value of $65,000.

a. Use the cash flow approach (insider's viewpoint approach). (11.2.2)

b. Use the opportunity cost approach (outsider's viewpoint approach). (11.3.2)

16. A currently owned shredder originally costing $800,000 was purchased 6 years ago for use in a refuse-powered electrical generating plant. It was depreciated as MACRS-GDS 5-year property due to its status as an alternative energy item. It has a present net realizable value of $210,000 and is expected to have a market value of $10,000 after 4 more years. Operating and maintenance disbursements are $100,000 per year. An equivalent shredder can be leased for $200 per day plus $80 per hour of actual use as determined by an hour meter, with both components assumed to be paid at year-end. Actual use is expected to be 1,500 hours and 250 days per year. Use the cash flow approach (insider's approach), a 4-year planning horizon, a tax rate of 40 percent, and an after-tax *MARR* of 9 percent to perform an after-tax analysis to determine the preferred alternative using the annual cost criterion.

a. Use only the above information. (11.2.2)

b. Consider the addition of a third alternative, to operate without any shredder, at an annual cost of $190,000. (11.2.2)

17. Dell is considering replacing one of its material handling systems. The old system was purchased 7 years ago for $130,000 and was depreciated as MACRS-GDS 5-year property since the system is used in the manufacture of electronic components. It has an annual *O&M* cost of $48,000, a remaining operational life of 8 years, and an estimated salvage value of $6,000 at that time. A new system can be purchased for $175,000. It will be worth $50,000 in 8 years, and it will have annual *O&M* costs of only $17,000 per year due to new technology. If the new system is purchased, the old system will be traded in for $55,000, even though the old system can be sold

for only $45,000 on the open market. Leasing a new system will cost $31,000 per year, payable at the beginning of the year, plus operating costs of $15,000 per year payable at year-end. If the new system is leased, the existing material handling system will be sold for its market value of $45,000. Use an 8-year planning horizon, an annual worth analysis, a tax rate of 40 percent, and an after-tax *MARR* of 9 percent to decide which material handling system to recommend: keep existing, trade in existing and purchase new, or sell existing and lease.

a. Use the cash flow approach (insider's viewpoint approach). (11.2.2)

b. Use the cash flow approach (insider's viewpoint approach), except note that a Section 1031 like-kind property exchange is to be used. The equipment replaced will continue to be replaced by like-kind investments in the United States indefinitely. Recall that a Section 1031 like-kind property exchange does not apply to leases. (11.4)

18. Allen Construction purchased a crane 6 years ago for $130,000 and depreciated it as MACRS-GDS 5-year property. They need a crane of this capacity for the next 5 years. Normal operation costs $35,000 per year. The current crane will have no salvage value at the end of 5 more years. Allen can trade in the current crane for its market value of $40,000 toward the purchase of a new one that costs $150,000. The new crane will cost only $8,000 per year under normal operating conditions and will have a salvage value of $55,000 after 5 years. If the after-tax *MARR* is 12 percent, the tax rate is 40 percent, and the planning horizon is 5 years, determine whether to keep the existing crane or buy the new crane.

a. Use the cash flow approach (insider's viewpoint approach). (11.2.2)

b. Use the opportunity cost approach (outsider's viewpoint approach). (11.3.2)

c. Use the cash flow approach (insider's viewpoint approach), except note that a Section 1031 like-kind property exchange is to be used. The equipment replaced will continue to be replaced by like-kind investments in the United States indefinitely. (11.4)

19. A division of Raytheon owns a 5-year-old turret lathe used to manufacture fabricated metal products that was purchased for $96,000 and now has a financial reporting (non-tax) book value of $24,000. It has been depreciated for tax purposes as MACRS-GDS 7-year property. It has a current market value of $18,000. The expected decline in market value is $3,000 per year from this point forward to a minimum of $3,000. *O&M* costs are $8,000 per year. Additional capability is needed. If the old lathe is kept, that new capability will be contracted out for $13,000, assumed payable at the end of each year. A new turret lathe has the increased capability to fulfill all needs, replacing the existing turret lathe and requiring no outside contracting. It can be purchased for $65,000 and will have an expected life of 8 years. Its market value is expected to be $65,000(0.7^t) at the end of year *t*. Annual *O&M* costs are expected to equal $10,000. If the after-tax *MARR* is 9 percent, the tax rate is 40 percent, and the planning horizon is 8 years, determine whether to keep and use a contractor or to sell and buy new.

a. Clearly show the cash flow profile for each alternative using the cash flow approach (insider's viewpoint approach). (11.2.2)

b. Using an *EUAC* comparison and a cash flow approach (insider's viewpoint approach), decide which is the more favorable alternative. (11.2.2)

20. Five years ago, a multi-axis NC machine was purchased for the express purpose of machining large, complex parts used in commercial and military aircraft worldwide. It cost $350,000, had an estimated life of 15 years, and *O&M* costs of $50,000 per year. The 5 years have been depreciated for tax purposes as MACRS-GDS 7-year property. The NC machine was originally thought to have a salvage value of $20,000 at the end of 15 years but is now believed to have a remaining life of only 5 years with no salvage value at that time. With business booming, the existing machine is no longer sufficient to meet production needs. It can be kept and supplemented by purchasing a new, smaller Machine S for $210,000 that will cost $37,000 per year for *O&M*, have a life of 10 years, and have a salvage value of $210,000(0.8^t) after *t* years. As an alternative, a larger, faster, and more capable Machine L can be used alone to replace the current machine. It has a cash price without trade-in of $450,000, *O&M* costs of $74,000 per year, and a 15-year life. The existing NC machine can be sold on the open market for a maximum of $70,000. The salvage value of Machine L is expected to be $450,000(0.8^t) after *t* years. The after-tax *MARR* is 12 percent, the tax rate is 40 percent, and the planning horizon is 5 years.

a. Clearly show the cash flow profile for each alternative using a cash flow approach (insider's viewpoint approach). (11.2.2)

b. Using an *EUAC* and a cash flow approach (insider's viewpoint approach), decide which is the more favorable alternative. (11.2.2)

c. Using an *EUAC* and a cash flow approach (insider's viewpoint approach), decide which is the more favorable alternative, except note that a Section 1031 like-kind property exchange is to be used. The equipment replaced will continue to be replaced by like-kind investments in the United States indefinitely. (11.4)

21. Five years ago, ARCHON, a regional architecture/contractor firm, purchased an HVAC unit for $25,000. It is expected to last 10 more years with a net salvage value of $0 at the end of that time. Depreciation over the 5 years has been as MACRS-GDS 7-year property. The annual operating cost of this unit started at $2,000 in the first year and has increased steadily at $250 per year ever since; last year the cost was $3,000. ARCHON has been phenomenally successful due to their reputation for highly functional, high-quality, cost-effective designs and construction. They are building a new wing at their regional headquarters to accommodate a much larger computer design emphasis requiring larger, faster computers, architectural printers, e-storage for a construction repository of previous designs, and an increased human heat load. They can buy an additional unit to air-condition the new wing for $18,000. It will have a service life of 15 years, a net salvage of $0 at that time, and a $3,000 market value after 10 years. It will have annual operating costs of $1,800 in the first year, increasing at $100 per year. As an alternative, ARCHON can buy a new replacement unit to heat and cool the entire building for $35,000. It will last for 15 years and have a net salvage of $0 at that time; however, it will have a market value of $8,500 after 10 years. It will have first-year operating costs of $3,700/year, increasing at $200 per year. The present unit can be sold now for $7,000. The after-tax *MARR* is 12 percent, the tax rate is 40 percent, and the planning horizon is 10 years.

a. Clearly show the cash flow profile for each alternative using a cash flow approach (insider's viewpoint approach). (11.2.2)

b. Using a PW analysis and a cash flow approach (insider's viewpoint approach), decide which is the more favorable alternative. (11.2.2)

c. Using a PW analysis and a cash flow approach (insider's viewpoint approach), decide which is the more favorable alternative, except note that a Section 1031 like-kind property exchange is to be used. The equipment replaced will continue to be replaced by like-kind investments in the United States indefinitely. (11.4)

22. Clear Water Company has a down-hole well auger that was purchased 3 years ago for $30,000. It has been depreciated over the 3 years as MACRS-GDS 5-year property. It has an estimated remaining life of 7 years. *O&M* costs are $13,000 per year. Alternative A is to keep the existing auger. It has a current market value of $12,000, and it will have a $0 salvage value after 7 more years. Alternative B is to buy a new auger that will cost $54,000 and will have a $14,000 salvage value after 7 years. *O&M* costs are $6,000 for the new auger. Clear Water can trade in the existing auger on the new one for $15,000. Alternative C is to trade in the existing auger on a "treated auger" that requires vastly less *O&M* cost at only $3,000 per year. It costs $68,000, and the trade-in allowance for the existing auger is $17,000. The "treated auger" will have an $18,000 salvage value after 7 years. Alternative D is to sell the existing auger for its market value of $12,000 and to contract with a current competitor to use their equipment and services to perform the drilling that would normally be done with the existing auger. The competitor requires a beginning-of-year retainer payment of $10,000. End-of-year *O&M* cost would be $6,000. The after-tax *MARR* is 9 percent, the tax rate is 40 percent, and the planning horizon is 7 years.

a. Clearly show the after-tax cash flow profile for each alternative using a cash flow approach (insider's viewpoint approach). (11.2.2)

b. Using an *EUAC* comparison and a cash flow approach (insider's viewpoint approach), decide which is the more favorable alternative. (11.2.2)

Section 11.5

23. You plan to purchase a car for $28,000. Its market value will decrease by 20 percent per year. You have determined that the IRS-allowed mileage reimbursement rate for business travel is about right for fuel and maintenance at $0.505 per mile in the first year. You anticipate that it will go up at a rate of 10 percent each year, with the price of oil rising, influencing gasoline, oils, greases, tires, and so on. You normally drive 15,000 miles per year. What is the optimum replacement interval for the car? Your *MARR* is 9 percent.

24. Griffin Dewatering purchases a wellpoint pump connected to a skid-mounted diesel engine for $14,000. Its market value for salvage purposes decrease by 30 percent each year. When installed on a construction job, a wellpoint system operates virtually 24/7, and operating and maintenance costs will be $3,500 the first year, increasing by $600 each year thereafter. What is the optimum replacement interval if $MARR = 15$ percent?

25. Polaris Industries wishes to purchase a multiple-use in-plant "road test" simulator that can be used for ATVs, motorcycles, and snowmobiles. It takes digital data from relatively short drives on a desired surface—from smooth to exceptionally harsh—and simulates the ride over and over while the vehicle is mounted to a test stand under load. It can run continuously if desired and provides opportunities to redesign areas of poor reliability. It costs $128,000, and its market value decreases by 30 percent each year. Operating costs are modest; however, maintenance costs can be significant due to the rugged use. $O\&M$ in the first year is expected to be $10,000, increasing by 25 percent each subsequent year. $MARR$ is 15 percent. What is the optimum replacement interval?

26. A granary purchases a conveyor used in the manufacture of grain for transporting, filling, or emptying. It is purchased and installed for $70,000 with a market value for salvage purposes that decreases at a rate of 20 percent per year with a minimum of $3,000. Operation and maintenance is expected to cost $14,000 in the first year, increasing by $1,000 per year thereafter. The granary uses a $MARR$ of 15 percent. What is the optimum replacement interval for the conveyor?

27. Milliken uses a digitally controlled dyer for placing intricate and integrated patterns on manufactured carpet squares for home and commercial use. It is purchased for $400,000. Its market value will be $310,000 at the end of the first year and drop by $40,000 per year thereafter to a minimum of $30,000. Operating costs are $20,000 the first year, increasing by 8 percent per year. Maintenance costs are only $8,000 the first year but will increase by 35 percent each year thereafter. Milliken's $MARR$ is 20 percent. Determine the optimum replacement interval for the dyer.

28. Griffin Dewatering purchases a wellpoint pump connected to a skid-mounted diesel engine for $14,000. These are considered "construction assets" and are classified as MACRS-GDS 5-year property (remember the half-year convention). Its market value for salvage purposes decreases by 30 percent each year. When installed on a construction job, a wellpoint system operates virtually 24/7, and operating and maintenance costs will be $3,500 the first year, increasing by $600 each year thereafter. Griffin is in the 40 percent tax bracket, and their after-tax $MARR$ is 9 percent. Determine the after-tax optimum replacement interval. Do not consider a Section 1031 exchange. If the salvage value differs from the book value when replacement occurs, the difference is taxed at the normal income tax rate.

29. Polaris Industries wishes to purchase a multiple-use in-plant "road test" simulator that can be used for ATVs, motorcycles, and snowmobiles. This is for research and experimentation and is considered MACRS-GDS 5-year property (remember the half-year convention). The simulator takes digital data from relatively short drives on a desired surface—from smooth to exceptionally harsh—and simulates the ride over and over while the vehicle is mounted to a test stand under load. It can run continuously if desired and provides opportunities to redesign areas of poor reliability. It costs $128,000, and its market value decreases by 30 percent each year. Operating costs are modest; however, maintenance costs can be significant due to the rugged use. $O\&M$ in the first year is expected to be $10,000, increasing by 25 percent each subsequent year. Polaris Industries is in the 40 percent tax bracket, and their after-tax $MARR$ is 9 percent. Determine the after-tax optimum replacement interval. Do not consider a Section 1031 exchange. If the salvage value differs from the book value when replacement occurs, the difference is taxed at the normal income tax rate.

30. A granary purchases a conveyor used in the manufacture of grain for transporting, filling, or emptying. The conveyor is considered MACRS-GDS 10-year property (remember the half-year convention). It is purchased and installed for $70,000 with a market value for salvage purposes that decreases at a rate of 20 percent per year with a minimum of $3,000. Operation and maintenance is expected to cost $14,000 in the first year, increasing by $1,000 per year thereafter. The granary is in the 40 percent tax bracket, and their after-tax $MARR$ is 9 percent. Determine the after-tax optimum replacement interval. Do not consider a Section 1031 exchange. If the salvage value differs from the book value when replacement occurs, the difference is taxed at the normal income tax rate.

31. Milliken uses a digitally controlled dyer for placing intricate and integrated patterns on manufactured carpet squares for home and commercial use. The dyer is classified as MACRS-GDS 5-year property (remember the

half-year convention). It is purchased for $400,000. Its market value will be $310,000 at the end of the first year and will drop by $40,000 per year thereafter to a minimum of $30,000. Operating costs are $20,000 the first year, increasing by 8 percent per year. Maintenance costs are only $8,000 the first year but will increase by 35 percent each year thereafter. Milliken is in the 40 percent tax bracket, and their after-tax *MARR* is 12 percent. Determine the after-tax optimum replacement interval. Do not consider a Section 1031 exchange. If the salvage value differs from the book value when replacement occurs, the difference is taxed at the normal income tax rate.

Chapter 12

INFLATION EFFECTS

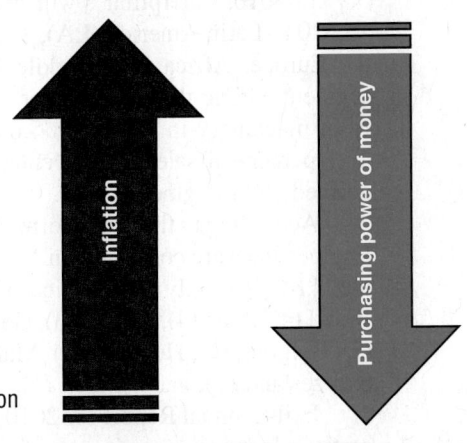

Inflation decreases the purchasing power of money. Multinational corporations, such as Caterpillar, experience different levels of inflation in the countries where they do business. Hence, inflation can also influence where a company chooses to make its investments.

The Effects of Inflation

Caterpillar

In 1890, two individuals, Benjamin Holt and Daniel Best, competed to see who could produce the best steam-powered tractor for use in farming. By 1925, they had merged their companies, forming the Caterpillar Tractor Company. Headquartered in Peoria, Illinois, Caterpillar is the world's leading manufacturer of construction and mining equipment, diesel and natural gas engines, and industrial gas turbines.

Caterpillar's new chairman and CEO, Douglas R. Oberhelman, stated in the 2010 Annual Report, "We have to think like our customers. That's what has to drive our decisions every day because we know that when our customers win, our company wins – and that includes our stockholders and our people." In support of its 2020 Vision, he rolled out a new Enterprise Strategy that included the strategic goals of superior results, global leadership, and having the best team to compete globally. The strategy supports the company's values of integrity, excellence, teamwork, and commitment.

In 2010, the company had sales and revenues totaling $42.6 billion, an increase of 31 percent from 2009. Sixty-eight percent of sales and revenue in 2010 occurred outside the U.S. With profits of $3.96 billion, compared with $0.58 billion in 2009, Caterpillar's stock performance was the best among the companies comprising the Dow Jones Industrial Average in 2010. Capital expenditures totaled $1.58 billion. R&D expenditures in 2010 were $1.9 billion, representing 4.5 percent of sales.

Caterpillar reports financial results for three business segments: machinery, engines, and financial products. In 2010, machinery accounted for 65.2 percent of sales and revenue, engines accounted for 28.4 percent, and financial services accounted for 6.4 percent.

In 2010, Caterpillar's worldwide employment was 104,490: 48,540 in the U.S., 15,220 in Latin America (LA), 17,753 in the Asia/Pacific (A/P) region, and 22,977 in the Europe, Africa, and Middle East (EAME) region. Sales and revenue vary by segment among the regions. For example, 72.5 percent of sales and revenue derived from machinery in A/P and 55.6 percent derived from machinery in EAME, while 40.1 percent of sales and revenue derived from engines in EAME and 23.4 percent derived from engines in A/P.

According to the 2010 Form 10-K, manufacturing activities of the Machinery and Engines lines are conducted in 178 plants around the world, including in the U.S. (94), the U.K. (16), Italy (9), Mexico (9), China (8), Canada (6), France (5), Australia (4), Brazil (4), India (4), Poland (3), Germany (2), Indonesia (2), Japan (2), the Netherlands (2), Belgium (1), Hungary (1), Malaysia (1), Nigeria (1), Russia (1), South Korea (1), Switzerland (1), and Tunisia (1).

In its Annual Report for 2010, the company stated, "Caterpillar's success is built on the talent and commitment of more than 104,000 employees in countries spanning the globe. Guided by *Our Values in Action* and leveraging the Caterpillar Production System and 6 Sigma principles, Caterpillar people demonstrate a passion for innovation and customer service."

Even though inflation might not be a significant factor in the "home country" of a multinational corporation such as Caterpillar, it is quite likely that inflation rates will be significant in one or more countries in which it operates and invests. ABB, BMW, BP, Canon, Coca-Cola, ExxonMobil, GE, IBM, Intel, Procter & Gamble, Microsoft, Motorola, Philips, Siemens, Sony, Toyota, and a host of other multinational firms have significant investments around the world. Inflation rates differ markedly from one economy to another, as do income-tax laws.

In this chapter, we examine the before-tax and after-tax effects of inflation on investments when capital is borrowed and when it comes from retained earnings. We show that inflation can significantly impact the economic viability of a capital investment. For that reason, when comparing investment alternatives in an inflationary economy, it is important to give explicit consideration to inflation.

Systematic Economic Analysis Technique

1. Identify the investment alternatives
2. Define the planning horizon
3. Specify the discount rate
4. Estimate the cash flows
5. **Compare the alternatives**
6. Perform supplementary analyses
7. Select the preferred investment

12-1 INTRODUCTION

Previously, we have said little about inflation and its effect on engineering economic justifications. In Chapter 1, we stated, *"Money has time value in the absence of inflation."* Now, however, we are equipped to consider the effects of inflation on various measures of economic worth.

What is inflation? While some would define it as *the erosion in the purchasing power of money*, that is an effect of inflation. Investopedia.com defines inflation ''as a sustained increase in the general level of prices for goods and services. It is measured as an annual percentage increase. As inflation rises, every dollar you own buys a smaller percentage of a good or service.''

Wikipedia defines inflation as ''a rise in the general level of prices, as measured against some baseline of purchasing power.''

InflationData.com points out that dictionaries do not agree on the definition of *inflation*; it also notes that the definition has changed over time. First, it presents the definition of inflation in *Webster's New Universal Unabridged Dictionary* published in 1983: ''An increase in the amount of currency in circulation, resulting in a relatively sharp and sudden fall in its value and rise in prices; it may be caused by an increase in the volume of paper money issued or of gold mined, or a relative increase in expenditures as when the supply of goods fails to meet the demand.'' Next, it provides the definition in Houghton Mifflin's fourth edition of *The American Heritage Dictionary of the English Language*: ''A persistent increase in the level of consumer prices or a persistent decline in the purchasing power of money, caused by an increase in available currency and credit beyond the proportion of available goods and services.'' Then, InflationData.com concludes, ''So between 1983 and 2000 the definition appears to have shifted from the cause to the result. Also, note that the cause could be either an increase in money supply or a decrease in available goods and services.''

Although general agreement regarding the definition of inflation does not exist, consumers understand the impact of inflation on their ability to purchase goods and services. As the value of a dollar diminishes over time, the effects of inflation are manifested.

In summary, inflation is characterized by a decrease in the purchasing power of money that is caused by an increase in general price levels of goods and services without an accompanying increase in the value of the goods and services. As noted above, inflationary pressure is created when more dollars are put into an economy without an accompanying increase in goods and services. In other words, printing more money without an increase in economic output generates inflation.

> Inflation decreases the purchasing power of money

Inflation can have such a significant impact on an investment's economic worth that it should be considered when comparing investment alternatives. Although it is important to consider the impact of inflation on investments made within one country, it is especially important to do so in multinational investment situations. The inflation rates in Argentina, Australia, Brazil, Canada, China, Egypt, France, Great Britain, Iceland, India, Italy, Japan, Malaysia, Mexico, Sweden, Thailand, Turkey, the United States, and Venezuela, for example, can be dramatically different. Hence, a firm that is faced with making decisions concerning investments of capital in various nations must give strong consideration to the inflationary conditions in the countries in question.

As noted, inflation adversely affects the purchasing power of money. To illustrate what we mean by the *purchasing power of money*, suppose a firm purchases 1 million pounds of a particular material each year, and the price of the material increases by 3 percent per year. The quantity of material the firm can purchase with a fixed amount of money—that is, the purchasing power of the firm's money—decreases over time. The only way the firm can afford to continue purchasing the material is to decrease its usage rate or to increase its source of funds. In the latter case, the firm might increase the price of the products it sells; if so, then the purchasing power of its customers' money will be decreased. In these situations, the continuing spiral of price increases does not contribute *real* increases to the firm's profits; instead, it results in an inflated representation of the firm's profits. The overall process of price increases without accompanying increases in the quality or value of the goods or services is referred to as *inflation*.

Since the early 1980s, annual price increases in the United States have occurred at both single-digit and double-digit rates; some countries have even experienced triple-digit rates. (We recall a student from a country with very high inflation saying that people rode buses instead of taxis because they paid when they got on the bus, but they paid when they got out of the taxi and their money was worth less. Although we think he was kidding, tuition increases occurred every academic quarter or semester, and salary increases were awarded multiple times during the year, due to inflation in his country.)

It has become widely accepted to associate price increases with inflation and price decreases with *deflation*. Deflation, which seldom occurs in developed countries, produces an increase in the purchasing power of money. (Under deflationary conditions, the deflation rate can be incorporated in economic analyses as a negative inflation rate.)

When inflation is incorporated in engineering economic analyses, it is often done so incorrectly. In this chapter, we demonstrate how to consider inflation in economic analyses, both before tax and after tax.

The material on inflation is covered in the following sequence:

1. We review background material on inflation, including the use of indexes to measure the year-to-year changes in inflation.
2. We show how to perform a before-tax analysis in inflationary conditions.
3. We examine the before-tax impact of inflation on the four loan repayment methods introduced in Chapter 3 and revisited in Chapter 10.
4. We show how to perform an after-tax analysis in inflationary conditions.
5. We examine the after-tax impact of inflation on the four loan repayment methods.

CPI Market Basket Categories

- Food and beverages
- Housing
- Apparel
- Transportation
- Medical care
- Recreation
- Education and communication
- Other goods and services

12-2 USING INDEXES TO MEASURE INFLATION

How is the inflation rate determined? The approach varies, depending on what rate is desired. For example, the most commonly used way of estimating the inflation rate for consumers in the United States is the consumer price index, developed by the U.S. Department of Labor's Bureau of Labor Statistics. Published monthly, the consumer price index (CPI) measures the price changes that occur from one month to the next for a specified set of products. Also called the retail price index, it is the index most often referred to by the U.S. media when referring to inflation rates.

The CPI is a *market basket rate*, in that it is based on 80,000 prices that are recorded in 87 urban areas. The so-called market basket is purchased each month and reflects what consumers buy for their day-to-day living. (To gain a better understanding of how the Bureau of Labor Statistics measures changes in consumer prices, see www.bls.gov/cpi/cpifact2htm.)

According to the Bureau of Labor Statistics (www.bls.gov/cpi/cpifaq.htm), the market basket includes more than 200 categories of expenditures, arranged in the following eight major groups:

1. Food and beverages (breakfast cereal, milk, coffee, chicken, wine, service meals and snacks)

2. Housing (rent of primary residence, owners' equivalent rent, fuel oil, bedroom furniture)

3. Apparel (men's shirts and sweaters, women's dresses, jewelry)

4. Transportation (new vehicles, airline fares, gasoline, motor vehicle insurance)

5. Medical care (prescription drugs and medical supplies, physicians' services, eyeglasses and eye care, hospital services)

6. Recreation (televisions, pets and pet products, sports equipment, admissions)

7. Education and communication (college tuition, postage, telephone services, computer software and accessories)

8. Other goods and services (tobacco and smoking products, haircuts and other personal services, funeral expenses)

The Bureau of Labor Statistics has collected data since 1913. The CPI has been "centered" several times. Also, major changes in definitions and methodology have occurred over the years. Three recent major changes occurred in 1967, 1984, and 2007. In 1984, the Bureau of Labor Statistics added semiannual averages to its CPI reports; prior to that time, it published monthly and annual averages. In 2007, it began publishing its monthly CPI, rounded to three decimal places, although the semiannual and annual averages continued to be expressed to one decimal place.

The CPI reflects spending patterns, not costs of living, for two population groups in the United States: all urban consumers and urban wage earners and clerical workers. Excluded from the CPI are spending patterns for people who live in rural non-metropolitan areas, farm families, Armed Forces personnel, and those who are in prisons and mental hospitals.

Two indexes measure the price change experience for the all-urban consumer group: the traditional CPI for all urban consumers (CPI-U) and the newer chained CPI for all urban consumers (C-CPI-U). Another index, CPI-W, is based on the expenditures of households in the CPI-U definition that also meet two requirements: more than one-half of household income comes from clerical or wage occupations, and at least one of the household's earners must have been employed for at least 37 weeks during the previous year. CPI-U is the index most often cited by the media and is the one that tends to be used to measure general inflation.

> The CPI-U is the index most often cited in the U.S. and tends to be used to measure general inflation

Figure 12.1 and Table 12.1 provide CPI values from 1961 through 2010, centered on 1983. The annual percentage changes in the CPI are, in fact, the estimates of inflation used by many businesses and financial institutions. As shown, double-digit inflation occurred in 1974, 1979, 1980, and 1981. From 2000 to 2010, inflation varied between −0.4 percent in 2009 and 3.8 percent in 2008.

Many countries publish their own version of the CPI. Although not all are defined the same way, there is general agreement in the methodology used among the statistical bodies that publish monthly reports in the various countries.

Not all businesses will experience inflation, as reflected by the market basket used to measure the CPI. For example, businesses that are heavily dependent on oil will be more affected by the price of oil than by the CPI. Likewise, producers deal with different pricing dynamics than retailers.

The producers price index (PPI) is a family of over 10,000 indexes published monthly by the Bureau of Labor Statistics. For practically any business, there is an index published by the Bureau of Labor Statistics. The indexes measure the average change over time in the selling prices of domestic producers of goods and services. Whereas the CPI measures price changes from the purchaser's perspective, the PPI

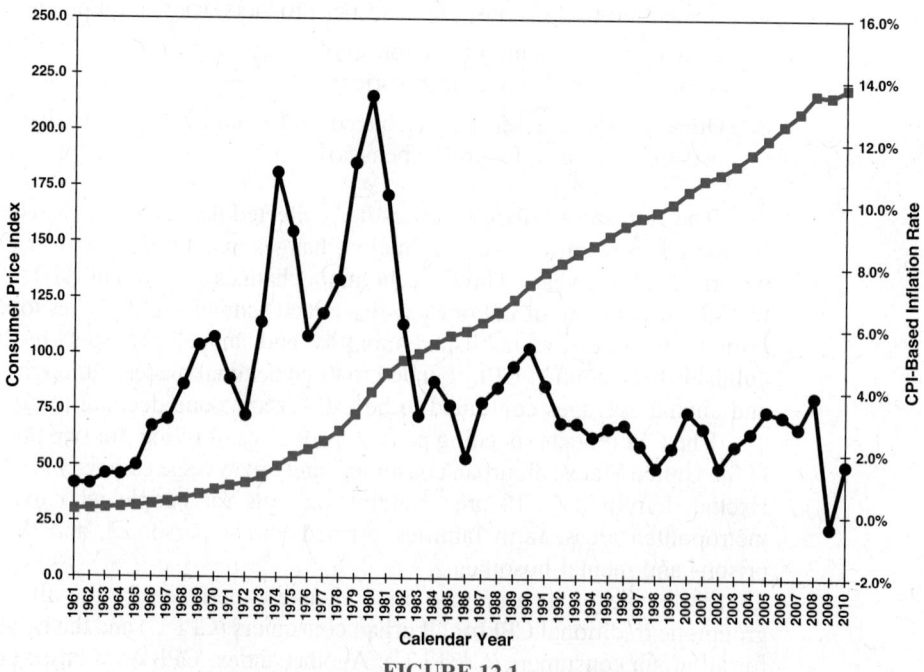

FIGURE 12.1

CPI and CPI Percent Increases (1961–2010).

TABLE 12.1

CPI and CPI Percent Increases, 1961 to 2010.

Year	CPI	1983 = 100.0	CPI %	Year	CPI	1983 = 100.0	CPI %
1961	29.9	30.0	1.0	1986	109.6	110.0	1.9
1962	30.2	30.3	1.0	1987	113.6	114.1	3.6
1963	30.6	30.7	1.3	1988	118.3	118.8	4.1
1964	31.0	31.1	1.3	1989	124.0	124.5	4.8
1965	31.5	31.6	1.6	1990	130.7	131.2	5.4
1966	32.4	32.5	2.9	1991	136.2	136.7	4.2
1967	33.4	33.5	3.1	1992	140.3	140.9	3.0
1968	34.8	34.9	4.2	1993	144.5	145.1	3.0
1969	36.7	36.8	5.5	1994	148.2	148.8	2.6
1970	38.8	39.0	5.7	1995	152.4	153.0	2.8
1971	40.5	40.7	4.4	1996	156.9	157.5	3.0
1972	41.8	42.0	3.2	1997	160.5	161.1	2.3
1973	44.4	44.6	6.2	1998	163.0	163.7	1.6
1974	49.3	49.5	11.0	1999	166.6	167.3	2.2
1975	53.8	54.0	9.1	2000	172.2	172.9	3.4
1976	56.9	57.1	5.8	2001	177.1	177.8	2.8
1977	60.6	60.8	6.5	2002	179.9	180.6	1.6
1978	65.2	65.5	7.6	2003	184.0	184.7	2.3
1979	72.6	72.9	11.3	2004	188.9	189.7	2.7
1980	82.4	82.7	13.5	2005	195.3	196.1	3.4
1981	90.9	91.3	10.3	2006	201.6	202.4	3.2
1982	96.5	96.9	6.2	2007	207.3	208.2	2.8
1983	99.6	100.0	3.2	2008	215.3	216.2	3.8
1984	103.9	104.3	4.3	2009	214.5	215.4	−0.4
1985	107.6	108.0	3.6	2010	218.1	218.9	1.6

Source: U.S. Department of Labor, Bureau of Labor Statistics

measures price changes from the seller's perspective. Formerly called the wholesale price index, the PPI may well provide a better measurement of the inflation effects for a particular business or for the purchase of particular equipment.

> The Higher Education Price Index (HEPI) reflects higher education inflation. It is less volatile than CPI, but its percent increases tend to be greater than those of CPI.

Not only are there different indexes for producers and consumers, but there is also an index for higher education, called the higher education price index (HEPI). According to the Commonfund Institute, HEPI "... is an inflation index designed specifically to track the main cost drivers in higher education. It is an essential planning tool for educational managers, enabling schools to project the future budget and funding increases required to maintain real purchasing power and investment. HEPI is issued annually by Commonfund Institute and is distributed free of charge to educational institutions.

''HEPI is a more accurate indicator of changes in costs for colleges and universities than the more familiar Consumer Price Index. It measures the average relative level of prices in a fixed basket of goods and services purchased by colleges and universities each year through current fund educational and general expenditures, excluding research.

''HEPI is compiled from data reported and published by government and economic agencies. The eight categories cover current operational costs of colleges and universities. These include salaries for faculty, administrative employees, clerical employees, and service employees, fringe benefits, utilities, supplies and materials, and miscellaneous services.''

The Web page goes on to note, ''HEPI has been calculated every year since 1983 and includes inflation data going back to 1961.''

To match academic calendars and fiscal years, HEPI is based on economic data from July 1 thru June 30. Table 12.2 and Figure 12.2 provide HEPI values and percent changes in HEPI since 1961.[1] How are HEPI and CPI related? CPI includes college tuition in one of its categories. However, CPI views the cost of higher education from the student's perspective. HEPI views the cost of higher education from the college's or university's perspective. Due to rapid increases in expenditures for library holdings, Internet upgrades, wireless connectivity, computing and laboratory equipment, health

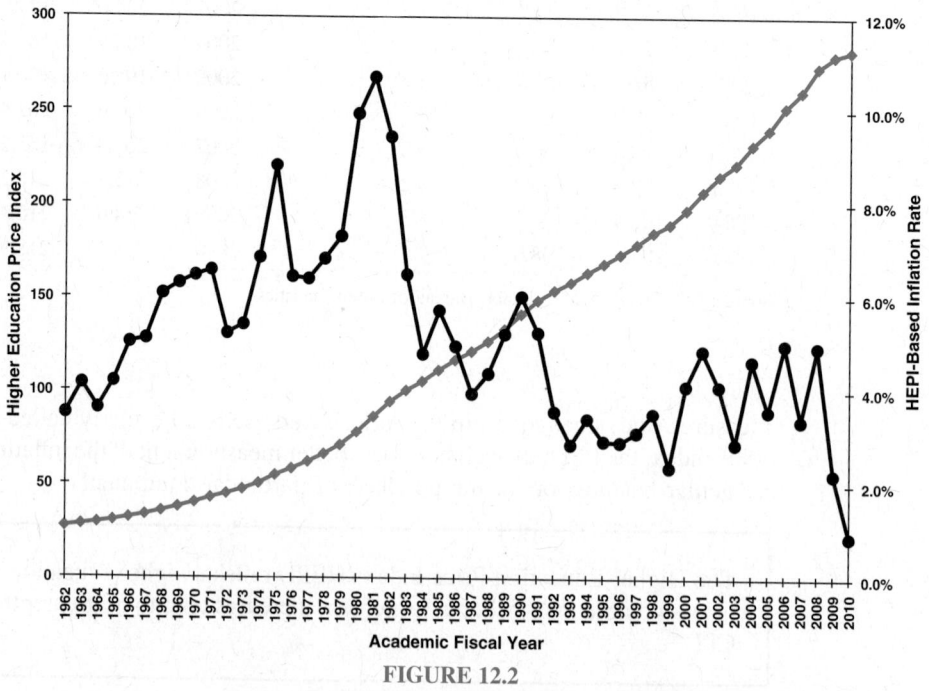

FIGURE 12.2

HEPI and HEPI Percent Increases (1962–2010).

[1]The source of the HEPI data is the Commonfund Institute. HEPI data are available at www .commonfund.org/Commonfund/

TABLE 12.2
HEPI and HEPI Percent Increases, 1961 to 2010.

Fiscal Year	1983 = 100 HEPI	% Change	Fiscal Year	1983 = 100 HEPI	% Change
1961	25.6		1986	116.3	5.0%
1962	26.5	3.5%	1987	120.9	4.0%
1963	27.6	4.2%	1988	126.2	4.4%
1964	28.6	3.6%	1989	132.8	5.2%
1965	29.8	4.2%	1990	140.8	6.0%
1966	31.3	5.0%	1991	148.2	5.3%
1967	32.9	5.1%	1992	153.5	3.6%
1968	34.9	6.1%	1993	157.9	2.9%
1969	37.1	6.3%	1994	163.3	3.4%
1970	39.5	6.5%	1995	168.1	2.9%
1971	42.1	6.6%	1996	173.0	2.9%
1972	44.3	5.2%	1997	178.4	3.1%
1973	46.7	5.4%	1998	184.7	3.5%
1974	49.9	6.9%	1999	189.1	2.4%
1975	54.3	8.8%	2000	196.9	4.1%
1976	57.8	6.4%	2001	206.5	4.9%
1977	61.5	6.4%	2002	215.0	4.1%
1978	65.7	6.8%	2003	221.2	2.9%
1979	70.5	7.3%	2004	231.5	4.7%
1980	77.5	9.9%	2005	239.8	3.6%
1981	85.8	10.7%	2006	251.8	5.0%
1982	93.9	9.4%	2007	260.3	3.4%
1983	100.0	6.5%	2008	273.2	5.0%
1984	104.8	4.8%	2009	279.3	2.2%
1985	110.8	5.7%	2010	281.8	0.9%

Source: Commonfund Institute

insurance, utilities, and faculty salaries in some key academic disciplines, in general, HEPI increases faster than CPI.

To compare CPI and HEPI, using monthly data provided by the U.S. Bureau of Labor Statistics, we computed the average CPI for academic fiscal years (July 1 thru June 30) from 1961 thru 2008 centered on 1983, Figures 12.3 and 12.4 show how CPI and HEPI have differed between FY 1962 and FY 2008. Figure 12.3 provides the values of indexes; Figure 12.4 provides year-to-year percentage increases over the same period.

Notice, from Figure 12.3, that HEPI tends to be less volatile than CPI. Howerver, its percent increases tend to be greater than those of CPI, for the reasons stated above.

> Price increases in one segment of the economy are generally felt in all segments of the economy

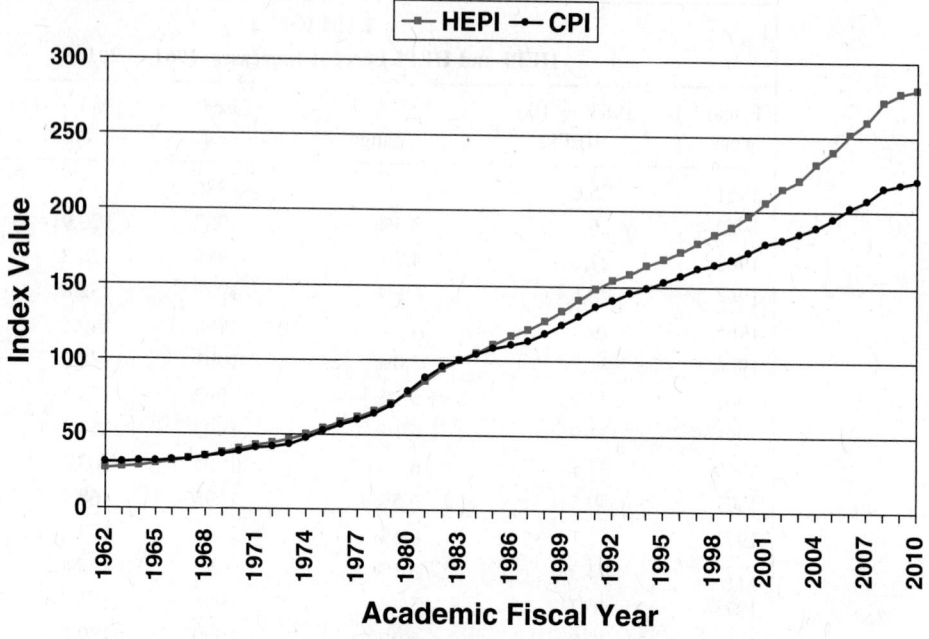

FIGURE 12.3

CPI and HEPI values, with 1983 = 100.

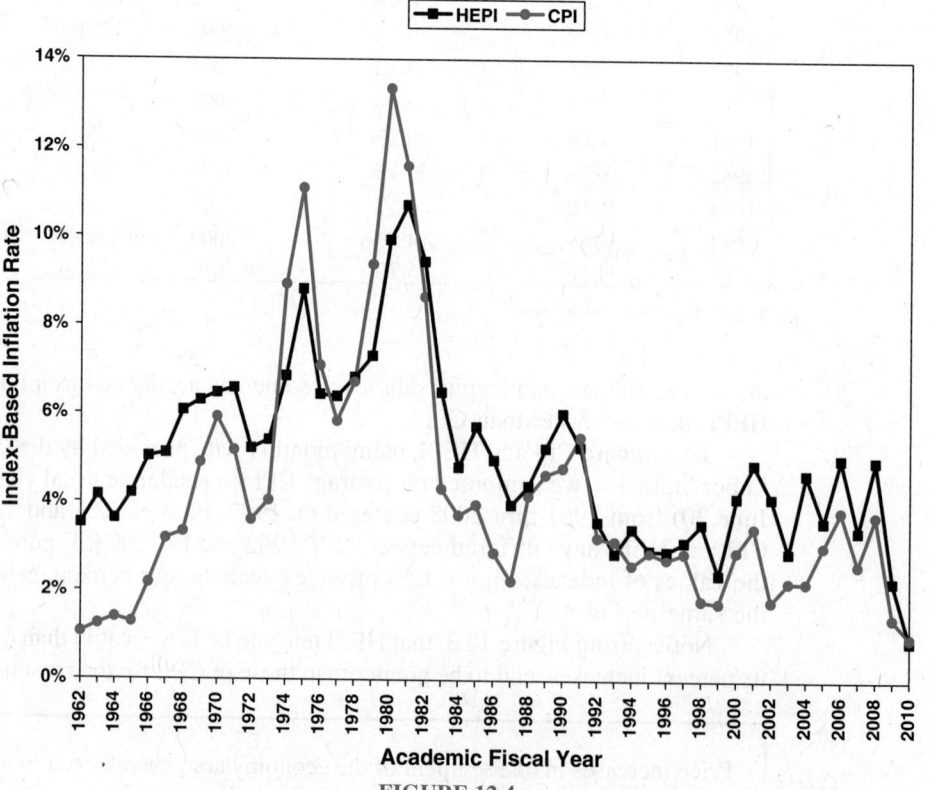

FIGURE 12.4

CPI and HEPI Percent Increases (1962–2010).

Some people contend that the CPI does not measure correctly the inflation they experience, because they do not purchase everything included in the CPI market basket calculation. As an example, if they do not intend to buy or sell a house, they argue that the changes in house prices have no influence on them. Further, if they are vegetarians, they argue that the change of prices for beef, pork, and chicken does not affect them. Similar arguments are made for a large number of the items in the market basket the Bureau of Labor Statistics uses to calculate the CPI.

While it is true that few, if any, people purchase all of the items included in the CPI market basket, it is incorrect to conclude that such price increases do not impact everyone. Today's economy is very interconnected. Consider vegetarians. How can their household budgets be impacted by increases in meat prices? If owners of stores where vegetarians shop eat meat and increase the prices in their stores because of price increases for meat, then vegetarians are impacted indirectly by increases in meat prices. In general, if store owners increase prices in reaction to price increases for items in the CPI market basket they purchase, then all of their customers are indirectly affected by the price increases in the CPI market basket. This phenomenon causes all of us to be impacted by price increases in things we do not purchase.

The same occurs in business. A soft-drink manufacturer that purchases large quantities of sugar but very little oil is still impacted when oil prices increase. Oil is consumed in manufacturing the plastic bottles and aluminum cans the soft-drink manufacturer uses; also, price increases for oil impact the cost of fuel to heat and air-condition the offices and production areas. Price increases in one segment of the economy are generally felt in all segments of the economy.

12-3   BEFORE-TAX ANALYSIS IN INFLATIONARY CONDITIONS

When incorporating inflation effects in economic analyses, *it is essential for the discount rate and cash flows to be consistent.* Recall, in Chapter 2, we emphasized the importance of the compounding frequency coinciding with the cash flow frequency. Here, we emphasize the importance of the discount rate and the cash flows being on the same basis.

Specifically, if inflation is to be incorporated explicitly, then inflationary effects must be incorporated in both the cash flows and in the discount rate. Likewise, if inflation is not to be incorporated in the analysis, then both the cash flows and the discount rate must exclude inflation or be *inflation-free*. Otherwise, the analysis will be flawed.

To facilitate a consideration of inflation in economic analyses, it is useful to define two terms: *constant dollars* and *then-current dollars*. Constant dollars are free of inflation; they are also called *real dollars, today's dollars, inflation-free dollars, constant purchasing power dollars, constant-value dollars*, and *constant-worth dollars*. Then-current dollars include inflation; they are also called *future dollars, nominal dollars, actual dollars*, and *inflated dollars*.

It is also useful to define three rates: the *real interest rate*, the *inflation rate*, and the *combined rate*. The real interest rate does not include inflation; it is a *pure discount rate*—one that expresses the real desired return on investment. The inflation rate is expressed as a percent and represents the loss of a dollar's purchasing power in 1 year. The combined rate, also called the *market rate* and the *inflation-adjusted interest rate*, includes both the real required return on investment and the inflation rate.

> Two equivalent approaches can be used to consider explicitly inflation in an economic justification—a *constant dollar* approach and a *then-current dollar* approach.
>
> The *constant dollar* approach uses cash flows and a discount rate, both of which are inflation-free.
>
> The *then-current* approach uses cash flows and a discount rate, both of which include inflation components.

Letting i_r denote the real interest rate, f denote the inflation rate, and i_c denote the combined rate, the following relationship exists among the three rates:

$$(1 + i_c) = (1 + i_r)(1 + f) \tag{12.1}$$

which reduces to

$$i_c = i_r + f + i_r(f) \tag{12.2}$$

The same relationships exist among the *real minimum attractive rate of return* ($MARR_r$), the inflation rate, and the *combined minimum attractive rate of return* ($MARR_c$):

$$MARR_c = MARR_r + f + MARR_r(f) \tag{12.3}$$

> $$i_c = i_r + f + i_r(f)$$
>
> The combined minimum attractive rate of return ($MARR_c$) equals the sum of the real minimum attractive rate of return ($MARR_r$), the inflation rate (f), and the product of the real minimum attractive rate of return ($MARR_r$) and the inflation rate (f).

EXAMPLE 12.1 Calculating the Combined *MARR*

If inflation averages 3 percent per year and you require a real return of 8 percent on your investments, what inflation adjusted minimum attractive rate of return should you use in performing economic justifications?

From Equation 12.3,

$$MARR_c = 0.03 + 0.08 + 0.03(0.08) = 0.1124, \quad \text{or} \quad 11.24\%$$

When given i_c and f, the value of i_r can be obtained from Equation 12.02. Specifically,

$$i_r = (i_c - f)/(1 + f) \tag{12.4}$$

Likewise,

$$MARR_r = (MARR_c - f)/(1 + f) \tag{12.5}$$

$$i_r = (i_c - f)/(1 + f)$$

The real minimum attractive rate of return ($MARR_r$) equals the difference in the combined minimum attractive rate of return ($MARR_c$) and the inflation rate (f), divided by one plus the inflation rate (f)

EXAMPLE 12.2 Calculating the Real Interest Rate

If inflation averages 4 percent per year and your return on an investment, based on then-current dollars, is 10 percent, what is your real return on investment?

From Equation 12.4,

$$i_r = (0.10 - 0.04)/(1 + 0.04) = 0.057692, \quad \text{or} \quad 5.7692\%$$

EXAMPLE 12.3 The Impact of Inflation on Buying Groceries

For the next 4 years, measured in today's dollars, a family anticipates buying $5,000 worth of groceries each year. If inflation is expected to be 3 percent/year, what will be the then-current cash flows required to purchase the groceries? (For purposes of the example, we assume that end-of-year expenditures are made for the groceries and that, like the CPI market basket, the same items are purchased in the same quantities each year.)

To purchase the groceries, the family must have the following amount of money available:

Year 1: dollars required = $5,000.00(1.03) = $5,150
Year 2: dollars required = $5,150.00(1.03) = $5,304.50
Year 3: dollars required = $5,304.50(1.03) = $5,463.64
Year 4: dollars required = $5,463.64(1.03) = $5,627.55

The amounts shown above are then-current dollars. In constant, or today's, dollars, the expenditures would be $5,000 each of the 4 years.

From the example, it is obvious that inflation, like interest, compounds over time. Hence, if $\$T_k$ denotes then-current dollars at end of year k, $\$C_k$ denotes constant dollars at the end of year k, and f denotes the annual inflation rate, then the following relationship holds:

$$\$T_k = \$C_k(1 + f)^k \tag{12.6}$$

or

$$\$T_k = \$C_k(F|P\ f\%, k) \tag{12.7}$$

Likewise,

$$\$C_k = \$T_k(1 + f)^{-k} \tag{12.8}$$

or

$$\$C_k = \$T_k(P|F\ f\%,k) \tag{12.9}$$

$$\$T_k = \$C_k(1+f)^k$$
$$\$T_k = \$C_k(F|P\ f\%,k)$$
$$\$C_k = \$T_k(1+f)^{-k}$$
$$\$C_k = \$T_k(P|F\ f\%,k)$$

EXAMPLE 12.4 Computing the Present Worth of the Expenditures for Groceries

In the previous example, if the family wanted to invest money today to cover the cost of groceries over the next 4 years, how much would they need to invest if they earn 6 percent compounded annually on their investment?

The 6 percent compounded annually is what will actually be earned, so it is a combined rate. Hence, $i_c = 6$ percent. Further, since the 6 percent interest rate includes an inflation component, the cash flows must include an inflation component; therefore, then-current dollars must be used with the 6 percent interest rate.

$$P = \$5{,}150.000(P|F\ 6\%,1) + \$5{,}304.50(P|F\ 6\%,2) + \$5{,}463.64(P|F\ 6\%,3)$$
$$+ \$5{,}627.55(P|F\ 6\%,4)$$
$$= \$18{,}624.42$$

Alternately, an inflation-free interest rate can be used with constant dollars to obtain the present worth. With inflation of 3 percent/year and a 6 percent market rate, the real interest rate will be

$$i_r = (0.06 - 0.03)/(1 + 0.03) = 0.03/1.03 = 0.029126, \quad \text{or} \quad 2.9126\%$$

Therefore, the family's real return on its investment is 2.9126 percent. Stripping out inflation's effects provides the discount rate that should be used with the $5,000 constant dollar estimates of future expenditures for groceries. The present worth, based on constant dollars, is

$$P = \$5{,}000(P|A\ 2.9126\%,4)$$
$$= \$5{,}000[(1.029126)^4 - 1]/[0.029126(1.029126)^4]$$
$$= \$18{,}624.40$$

(The 2¢ difference is due to round-off error in the tables for the $[(P|F\ 6\%,n)]$ factors.)

Excel® can be used to perform the calculations. Based on $\$T$, the following can be used to determine the present worth:

P=NPV(6%,FV(3%,1,,-5000),FV(3%,2,,-5000),FV(3%,3,,-5000),FV(3%,4,,-5000))

=$18,624.39

In the case of $\$C$, the following can be used to determine the present worth:

P=PV((0.06-0.03)/1.03,4,-5000)

=$18,624.39

As evidenced by the PPI and the HEPI, not all goods and services experience the same inflation rate. While it is important that forecasts of future expenditures be accurate, when incorporating inflation in *TVOM* calculations, it is equally important for the inflation rate to be the rate that impacts the decision maker.

Hence, if performing an economic justification for a chemical manufacturer, an inflation rate that applies to chemical manufacturers should be used in the analysis. Likewise, if performing an economic justification for a retailer, then an inflation rate that is accurate for retailers should be used. We must not let the multitude of inflation rates that exist confuse us. Instead, we must use the inflation rate that applies most directly to the situation at hand.

Importantly, not all cash flow increases are due entirely to inflation. Maintenance costs, for example, increase as a result of wear and tear on equipment. Labor costs increase because of increased skills of the workforce. Material costs increase because of increased demand for material. Utility costs increase because of more energy-consuming office equipment being used. Therefore, it is important to separate increases due to inflation from increases that will occur in the absence of inflation.

EXAMPLE 12.5   The Impact of Inflation on Maintenance Expenses

In a small manufacturing company, a stamping machine requires maintenance at an increasing rate. This year, the maintenance cost was $2,500. Each of the next 5 years, it is expected the machine will require maintenance 8 percent more times than the previous year. In addition, the cost of the labor and parts required to maintain the stamping machine are expected to increase, due to inflation, at a rate of 4 percent/year. The company has a real required return on investment of 9 percent/year. It is desired to determine the present worth of the maintenance costs over the next 5 years.

Here we have an example of the cost of maintenance increasing because of increased frequency of maintenance (8 percent/year) and inflation (4 percent/year). Therefore, constant maintenance costs will increase at a rate of 8 percent; then-current maintenance costs will increase at a combined rate of 8 percent + 4 percent + 8 percent(4 percent), or 12.32 percent.

In T, maintenance costs increase like a geometric series with a geometric rate of 12.32 percent. In C, maintenance costs increase like a geometric series with a geometric rate of 8 percent.

The real minimum attractive rate of return is 9 percent/year. The combined minimum attractive rate of return is 9 percent + 4 percent + 9 percent(4 percent), or 13.36 percent.

To determine the present worth of the maintenance costs, we can use either C and a $MARR_r$ of 9 percent or T and a $MARR_c$ of 13.36 percent. We will use both approaches, to illustrate that the same answer results *when the analysis is performed correctly*.

Constant dollar approach: $A_1 = \$2,500(1.08) = \$2,700$

$$P = \$2,700.00(P|A_1\ 9\%,8\%,5)$$
$$= \$2,700.00[1 - (1.08)^5(1.09)^{-5}]/(0.09 - 0.08)$$
$$= \$12,160.14$$

Then-current dollar approach: $A_1 = \$2,500(1.08)(1.04) = \$2,808$

$$P = \$2,808.00(P|A_1\ 13.36\%,12.32\%,5)$$
$$= \$2,808.00[1 - (1.1232)^5(1.1336)^{-5}]/(0.1336 - 0.1232)$$
$$= \$12,160.14$$

Table 12.3 provides the $C and $T values for the example. Table 12.4 summarizes the two approaches that can be used in performing economic justifications in inflationary conditions.

	TABLE 12.3	
Present Worth of Constant Dollar Cash Flows and Present Worth of Then-Current Dollar Cash Flows for Example 12.5.*		
EOY	$C	$T
0	$2,500.00	$2,500.00
1	$2,700.00	$2,808.00
2	$2,916.00	$3,153.95
3	$3,149.28	$3,542.51
4	$3,401.22	$3,978.95
5	$3,673.32	$4,469.16
$P =$	$12,160.14	$12,160.14

*Note: Present worth does not include cash flows at EOY = 0; only years 1 thru 5 are included

	TABLE 12.4	
Approaches to Economic Justification in Inflationary Conditions.		
	Then-Currrent Dollar ($T) Analysis	Constant Dollar ($C) Analysis
Cash Flows	Cash flows are then-current dollars; therefore, include inflation effects	Cash flows are constant dollars; therefore, inflation-free
Discount rate used in *TVOM* calculations	Use a combined interest rate, i_c	Use a real interest rate, i_r

---

EXAMPLE 12.6   Impact of Inflation on Four Loan Payment Plans

Recall, in Chapter 3, we considered four plans of repaying a $10,000 loan over a 5-year period, with interest being charged at an annual compound rate of 15 percent. The four annual payment plans were

1. pay the accumulated interest at the end of each year and repay the principal at the end of the fifth year;

2. make equal annual principal payments, plus interest on the unpaid balance at the end of the year;

3. make equal annual payments; and

4. make a single payment of principal and interest at the end of 5 years.

Based on our analysis, in the absence of inflation, we concluded that the borrower should choose Plan 2 when the borrower's *TVOM* is less than the 15 percent interest rate charged by the lender; we also concluded that Plan 4 should be chosen when the borrower's *TVOM* is greater than the 15 percent interest rate. Finally, if the borrower's *TVOM* equals the lender's interest rate, the four plans are equally preferred.

What impact will inflation have on the borrower's preference? To examine the effects of inflation, we assume the 15 percent interest rate is fixed and does not increase with inflation. (Recall the house mortgage example in Chapter 3, where fixed-rate and adjustable rate mortgages were considered.)

Table 12.5 presents the cash flow profiles for the four payment plans. From Chapter 3, we have the following expressions for computing the loan transaction's present worth, depending on which payment plan is used:

TABLE 12.5
Cash Flows for Four Loan Payment Plans.

Payment Plan	End of Year	Interest Accrued During Year	Total Money Owed Before Yearly Payment	Interest Payment	Principal Payment	Total Payment	Total Money Owed After Yearly Payment
1	0						$10,000.00
	1	$1,500.00	$11,500.00	$1,500.00	$0.00	$1,500.00	$10,000.00
	2	$1,500.00	$11,500.00	$1,500.00	$0.00	$1,500.00	$10,000.00
	3	$1,500.00	$11,500.00	$1,500.00	$0.00	$1,500.00	$10,000.00
	4	$1,500.00	$11,500.00	$1,500.00	$0.00	$1,500.00	$10,000.00
	5	$1,500.00	$11,500.00	$1,500.00	$10,000.00	$11,500.00	$0.00
2	0						$10,000.00
	1	$1,500.00	$11,500.00	$1,500.00	$2,000.00	$3,500.00	$8,000.00
	2	$1,200.00	$9,200.00	$1,200.00	$2,000.00	$3,200.00	$6,000.00
	3	$900.00	$6,900.00	$900.00	$2,000.00	$2,900.00	$4,000.00
	4	$600.00	$4,600.00	$600.00	$2,000.00	$2,600.00	$2,000.00
	5	$300.00	$2,300.00	$300.00	$2,000.00	$2,300.00	$0.00
3	0						$10,000.00
	1	$1,500.00	$11,500.00	$1,500.00	$1,483.16	$2,983.16	$8,516.84
	2	$1,277.53	$9,794.37	$1,277.53	$1,705.63	$2,983.16	$6,811.22
	3	$1,021.68	$7,832.90	$1,021.68	$1,961.47	$2,983.16	$4,849.74
	4	$727.46	$5,577.20	$727.46	$2,255.69	$2,983.16	$2,594.05
	5	$389.11	$2,983.16	$389.11	$2,594.05	$2,983.16	$0.00
4	0						$10,000.00
	1	$1,500.00	$11,500.00	$0.00	$0.00	$0.00	$11,500.00
	2	$1,725.00	$13,225.00	$0.00	$0.00	$0.00	$13,225.00
	3	$1,983.75	$15,208.75	$0.00	$0.00	$0.00	$15,208.75
	4	$2,281.31	$17,490.06	$0.00	$0.00	$0.00	$17,490.06
	5	$2,623.51	$20,113.57	$10,113.57	$10,000.00	$20,113.57	$0.00

$$PW_1(i\%) = \$1,500(P|A\ i\%,5) + \$10,000(P|F\ i\%,5)$$
$$PW_2(i\%) = \$3,500(P|A\ i\%,5) - \$300(P|G\ i\%,5)$$
$$PW_3(i\%) = \$2,983.16(P|A\ i\%,5)$$
$$PW_4(i\%) = \$20,113.57(P|F\ i\%,5)$$

Since the loan payments are in then-current dollars, the present worth calculation requires the use of a combined interest rate. In this case, we need to know the value of the borrower's real time value of money or real minimum attractive rate of return ($MARR_r$). Suppose, for example, that inflation is 4 percent/year and the borrower's $MARR_r$ is (a) 8 percent, (b) 10 percent, and (c) 12 percent. Which plan is best?

If $MARR_r = 8$ percent and $f = 4$ percent, then $MARR_c = 12.32$ percent. Likewise, if $MARR_r = 10$ percent and $f = 4$ percent, then $MARR_c = 14.4$ percent. Similarly, if $MARR_r = 12$ percent and $f = 4$ percent, then $MARR_c = 16.48$ percent.

As shown in Table 12.6, the same selection rule holds: choose Plan 2 for $MARR_r = 8$ percent and $MARR_r = 10$ percent, since in both cases $MARR_c < 15$ percent; choose Plan 4 for $MARR_r = 12$ percent, since $MARR_c > 15$ percent.

TABLE 12.6
Present Worth of Loan Payments in Inflationary Conditions.

End of Year	Plan 1 Payment	Plan 2 Payment	Plan 3 Payment	Plan 4 Payment
1	$1,500.00	$3,500.00	$2,983.16	$0.00
2	$1,500.00	$3,200.00	$2,983.16	$0.00
3	$1,500.00	$2,900.00	$2,983.16	$0.00
4	$1,500.00	$2,600.00	$2,983.16	$0.00
5	$11,500.00	$2,300.00	$2,983.16	$20,113.57
PW(12.32%)	$10,958.47	$10,619.37	$10,668.90	$11,251.33
PW(14.40%)	$10,204.02	$10,133.31	$10,143.72	$10,265.00
PW(16.48%)	$9,520.78	$9,683.52	$9,659.35	$9,380.64

Therefore, in before-tax analyses, if the borrower's combined *TVOM* is less than the lender's interest rate, use Plan 2; if the borrower's combined *TVOM* is greater than the lender's interest rate, use Plan 4; and if the borrower's combined *TVOM* equals the lender's interest rate, use either payment plan.

In before-tax analyses, if the borrower's combined time value of money is less than the lender's interest rate, use payment plan 2; if the borrower's combined time value of money is greater than the lender's interest rate, use payment plan 4; and if the borrower's combined time value of money equals the lender's interest rate, the payment plans are equivalent.

12-4 AFTER-TAX ANALYSIS IN INFLATIONARY CONDITIONS

In previous chapters, one of two assumptions was made: Our before-tax analysis was based on cash flows and interest rates either that were inflation-free or that included inflation effects. When cash flows are expressed in constant dollars and the minimum attractive rate of return is a real required return, nothing special needs to be done to accommodate inflation. Unfortunately, that is not true for after-tax analyses!

Why the difference? Because, in the United States, depreciation allowances are not permitted to increase with inflation. Depreciation allowances are expressed in then-current dollars, not constant dollars. Therefore, either the effects of inflation must be "stripped out" of the depreciation allowances in order to express them in constant dollars, or all other cash flows must be expressed in then-current dollars.

> In the United States, depreciation allowances are not allowed to increase with inflation; hence, depreciation allowances are in then-current dollars.

EXAMPLE 12.7 Considering the Impact of Inflation on the SMP Investment

Recall the $500,000 investment in a surface-mount placement machine that produces net annual savings, before-taxes, of $124,166.67 for 10 years, plus a $50,000 salvage value at the end of the 10-year period. The estimates were in constant dollars. The SMP machine qualified as 5-year property for MACRS-GDS depreciation. A 40 percent income tax rate and a $MARR_r$ of 10 percent were used to perform an after-tax analysis. To illustrate the effect of inflation in after-tax analyses, suppose annual inflation equals 4 percent.

As shown in Figure 12.5, then-current, before-tax cash flows ($TBTCF) are obtained by increasing constant dollar, before-tax cash flows ($CBTCF) at an annual compound rate of 4

B9		fx =1.04^A9*124166.67			
	A	B	C	D	E	F
1	EOY	$TBTCF	$TDWO	$TTI	$TT	$TATCF
2	0	-$500,000.00				-$500,000.00
3	1	$129,133.34	$100,000.00	$29,133.34	$11,653.33	$117,480.00
4	2	$134,298.67	$160,000.00	-$25,701.33	-$10,280.53	$144,579.20
5	3	$139,670.62	$96,000.00	$43,670.62	$17,468.25	$122,202.37
6	4	$145,257.44	$57,600.00	$87,657.44	$35,062.98	$110,194.47
7	5	$151,067.74	$57,600.00	$93,467.74	$37,387.10	$113,680.64
8	6	$157,110.45	$28,800.00	$128,310.45	$51,324.18	$105,786.27
9	7	$163,394.87	$0.00	$163,394.87	$65,357.95	$98,036.92
10	8	$169,930.66	$0.00	$169,930.66	$67,972.26	$101,958.40
11	9	$176,727.89	$0.00	$176,727.89	$70,691.16	$106,036.73
12	10	$257,809.22	$0.00	$257,809.22	$103,123.69	$154,685.53
13					PW_{ST} =	$109,201.18 =NPV(14.4%,F3:F12)+F2
14			=1.04^A7*124166.67		FW_{ST} =	$419,264.00 =FV(14.4%,10,,-F13)
15					AW_{ST} =	$21,263.15 =PMT(14.4%,10,-F13)
16		=1.04^A12*(50000+124166.67)			IRR_c =	19.99% =IRR(F2:F12)
17					ERR_c =	16.68% =MIRR(F2:F12,,14.4%)
18						
19						

FIGURE 12.5

After-Tax, Then-Current Dollar Analysis of the SMP Investment with 4% Inflation.

percent; depreciation allowances are in then-current dollars. The resulting then-current, after-tax present worth is \$109,201.18, compared to \$123,988.64 if inflation is negligible. Likewise, when inflation is negligible, the after-tax internal rate of return is 16.12 percent. With 4 percent inflation, the combined after-tax internal rate of return is 19.99 percent; therefore, the real after-tax internal rate of return is

$$IRR_r = (0.1999 - 0.04)/(1.04) = 0.1538, \text{ or } 15.38\%.$$

An alternative approach is to convert the depreciation allowances to constant dollars using Equation 12.8 or 12.9. As shown in Figure 12.6, the constant dollar, after-tax present worth is \$109,201.18, which is identical to the then-current result. The real after-tax internal rate of return is 15.38 percent.

	C4		fx =500000*0.32/1.04^2					
	A	B	C	D	E	F	G	H	I
1	**EOY**	**\$CBTCF**	**\$CDWO**	**\$CTI**	**\$CT**	**\$CATCF**			
2	0	-\$500,000.00				-\$500,000.00			
3	1	\$124,166.67	\$96,153.85	\$28,012.82	\$11,205.13	\$112,961.54			
4	2	\$124,166.67	\$147,928.99	-\$23,762.32	-\$9,504.93	\$133,671.60			
5	3	\$124,166.67	\$85,343.65	\$38,823.02	\$15,529.21	\$108,637.46			
6	4	\$124,166.67	\$49,236.72	\$74,929.95	\$29,971.98	\$94,194.69			
7	5	\$124,166.67	\$47,343.00	\$76,823.67	\$30,729.47	\$93,437.20			
8	6	\$124,166.67	\$22,761.06	\$101,405.61	\$40,562.24	\$83,604.43			
9	7	\$124,166.67	\$0.00	\$124,166.67	\$49,666.67	\$74,500.00			
10	8	\$124,166.67	\$0.00	\$124,166.67	\$49,666.67	\$74,500.00			
11	9	\$124,166.67	\$0.00	\$124,166.67	\$49,666.67	\$74,500.00			
12	10	\$174,166.67	\$0.00	\$174,166.67	\$69,666.67	\$104,500.00			
13					$PW_{\$C}$ =	\$109,201.18	=NPV(10%,F3:F12)+F2		
14					$FW_{\$C}$ =	\$283,239.74	=FV(10%,10,,-F13)		
15			=500000*0.1152*1.04^-5		$AW_{\$C}$ =	\$17,771.99	=PMT(10%,10,-F13)		
16					IRR_r =	15.38%	=IRR(F2:F12)		
17					ERR_r =	12.19%	=MIRR(F2:F12,,10%)		
18									

FIGURE 12.6

After-Tax, Constant Dollar Analysis of the SMP Investment with 4% Inflation.

12-5 AFTER-TAX ANALYSIS WITH INFLATION AND BORROWED CAPITAL

When money is borrowed at fixed rates, the loan payments (principal and interest) are then-current cash flows. Since depreciation allowances are also then-current cash flows, it is more convenient to perform after-tax analyses using a then-current approach when both inflation and borrowed funds are present. However, if one wishes to use a constant dollar approach, then the principal payments, interest payments, and depreciation allowances must be converted to constant dollar amounts. As noted above, Equation 12.8 or 12.9 can be used to perform the conversion.

EXAMPLE 12.8 Considering the Impact of Inflation on the SMP Investment When Money Is Borrowed

Suppose $300,000 is borrowed at a 12 percent annual compound interest rate and is repaid over a 10-year period using one of the four payment plans. Also, suppose inflation is 4 percent/year. Which of the payment plans should be used if the $MARR_r$ equals 10 percent? (As before, a 40 percent income tax rate is used. We do not include a Section 1031 deferment of realized gains, because the SMP machine is not expected to be replaced with like-kind property in 10 years.)

Figure 12.7 presents the results for Plan 1, where only interest payments are made until the end of the loan period. Tables 12.7 through 12.9 provide the after-tax results for Plans 2, 3, and 4, respectively.

Plan 1 yields an after-tax present worth of $220,132.29; Plan 2 yields an after-tax present worth of $182,165.68; Plan 3 yields an after-tax present worth of $191,157.40; and Plan 4 yields an after-tax present worth of $232,335.64. On this basis, Plan 4 should be used to repay the $300,000 loan over a 10-year period. (Similar conclusions are reached using either FW or AW then-current comparisons.)

In Chapter 10, the ATPW was $175,603.01 for Plan 1; $156,374.28 for Plan 2; $160,734.89 for Plan 3; and $162,184.44 for Plan 4. A comparison of the results indicates ATPW differences varied significantly among the repayment methods. However, with borrowed funds, inflation produced a greater ATPW for each plan.

Plan	ATPW(0% inflation)	ATPW(4% inflation)	Difference
1	$175,603.01	$220,132.29	$44,529.28
2	$156,374.28	$182,165.68	$25,791.40
3	$160,734.89	$191,157.40	$30,422.51
4	$162,184.44	$232,335.64	$70,151.20

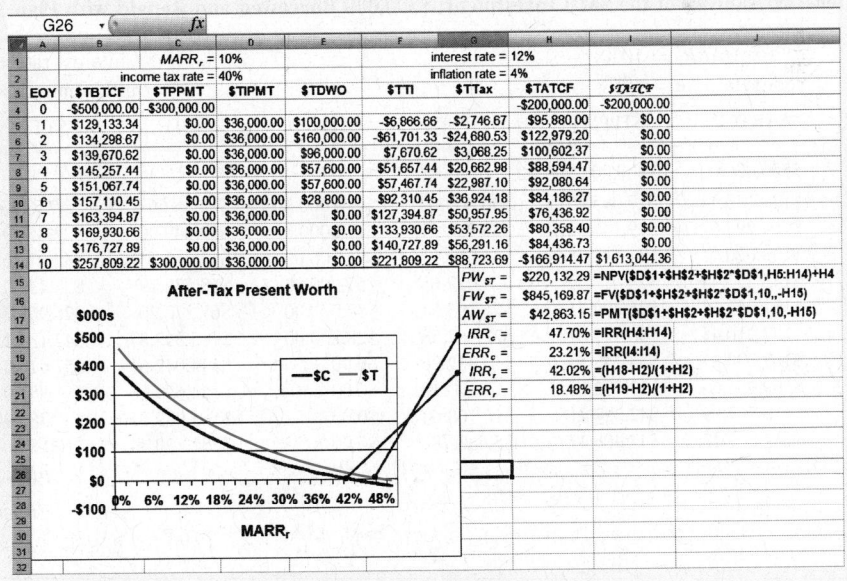

FIGURE 12.7

After-Tax Analysis of the SMP Investment with $300,000 Borrowed, Repaid with Plan 1, and 4% Inflation.

TABLE 12.7
After-Tax Analysis of the SMP Investment; $300,000 Borrowed and Repaid with Plan 2; 4% Inflation.

| | $MARR_r = 10\%$ | | | | interest rate = 12% | | |
| | income tax rate = 40% | | | | inflation rate = 4% | | |
EOY	$TBTCF	$TPPMT	$TIPMT	$TDWO	$TTI	$TTax	$TATCF
0	−$500,000.00	−$300,000.00					−$200,000.00
1	$129,133.34	$30,000.00	$36,000.00	$100,000.00	−$6,866.66	−$2,746.67	$65,880.00
2	$134,298.67	$30,000.00	$32,400.00	$160,000.00	−$58,101.33	−$23,240.53	$95,139.20
3	$139,670.62	$30,000.00	$28,800.00	$96,000.00	$14,870.62	$5,948.25	$74,922.37
4	$145,257.44	$30,000.00	$25,200.00	$57,600.00	$62,457.44	$24,982.98	$65,074.47
5	$151,067.74	$30,000.00	$21,600.00	$57,600.00	$71,867.74	$28,747.10	$70,720.64
6	$157,110.45	$30,000.00	$18,000.00	$28,800.00	$110,310.45	$44,124.18	$64,986.27
7	$163,394.87	$30,000.00	$14,400.00	$0.00	$148,994.87	$59,597.95	$59,396.92
8	$169,930.66	$30,000.00	$10,800.00	$0.00	$159,130.66	$63,652.26	$65,478.40
9	$176,727.89	$30,000.00	$7,200.00	$0.00	$169,527.89	$67,811.16	$71,716.73
10	$257,809.22	$30,000.00	$3,600.00	$0.00	$254,209.22	$101,683.69	$122,525.53

$PW_{ST} =$ $182,165.68
$FW_{ST} =$ $699,401.91
$AW_{ST} =$ $35,470.47
$IRR_c =$ 35.34%
$ERR_c =$ 22.05%
$IRR_r =$ 30.13%
$ERR_r =$ 17.36%

TABLE 12.8
After-Tax Analysis of the SMP Investment; $300,000 Borrowed and Repaid with Plan 3; 4% Inflation.

| | $MARR_r = 10\%$ | | | | interest rate = 12% | | |
| | income tax rate = 40% | | | | inflation rate = 4% | | |
EOY	$TBTCF	$TPPMT	$TIPMT	$TDWO	$TTI	$TTax	$TATCF
0	−$500,000.00	−$300,000.00					−$200,000.00
1	$129,133.34	$17,095.25	$36,000.00	$100,000.00	−$6,866.66	−$2,746.67	$78,784.75
2	$134,298.67	$19,146.68	$33,948.57	$160,000.00	−$59,649.90	−$23,859.96	$105,063.38
3	$139,670.62	$21,444.28	$31,650.97	$96,000.00	$12,019.65	$4,807.86	$81,767.51
4	$145,257.44	$24,017.59	$29,077.65	$57,600.00	$58,579.79	$23,431.91	$68,730.28
5	$151,067.74	$26,899.71	$26,195.54	$57,600.00	$67,272.20	$26,908.88	$71,063.61
6	$157,110.45	$30,127.67	$22,967.58	$28,800.00	$105,342.87	$42,137.15	$61,878.05
7	$163,394.87	$33,742.99	$19,352.26	$0.00	$144,042.61	$57,617.04	$52,682.57
8	$169,930.66	$37,792.15	$15,303.10	$0.00	$154,627.56	$61,851.02	$54,984.39
9	$176,727.89	$42,327.21	$10,768.04	$0.00	$165,959.85	$66,383.94	$57,248.70
10	$257,809.22	$47,406.47	$5,688.78	$0.00	$252,120.44	$100,848.18	$103,865.79

$PW_{ST} =$ $191,157.40
$FW_{ST} =$ $733,924.46
$AW_{ST} =$ $37,221.30
$IRR_c =$ 38.58%
$ERR_c =$ 22.34%
$IRR_r =$ 33.25%
$ERR_r =$ 17.63%

TABLE 12.9

After-Tax Analysis of the SMP Investment; $300,000 Borrowed and Repaid with Plan 4; 4% Inflation.

	$MARR_r = 10\%$ income tax rate = 40%					interest rate = 12% inflation rate = 4%			
EOY	$TBTCF	$TPPMT	$TIPMT	$TDWO	$TTI	$TTax	$TATCF	$\mathcal{S}TATCF$
0	−$500,000.00	−$300,000.00					−$200,000.00	−$200,000.00
1	$129,133.34	$0.00	$0.00	$100,000.00	$29,133.34	$11,653.33	$117,480.00	$0.00
2	$134,298.67	$0.00	$0.00	$160,000.00	−$25,701.33	−$10,280.53	$144,579.20	$0.00
3	$139,670.62	$0.00	$0.00	$96,000.00	$43,670.62	$17,468.25	$122,202.37	$0.00
4	$145,257.44	$0.00	$0.00	$57,600.00	$87,657.44	$35,062.98	$110,194.47	$0.00
5	$151,067.74	$0.00	$0.00	$57,600.00	$93,467.74	$37,387.10	$113,680.64	$0.00
6	$157,110.45	$0.00	$0.00	$28,800.00	$128,310.45	$51,324.18	$105,786.27	$0.00
7	$163,394.87	$0.00	$0.00	$0.00	$163,394.87	$65,357.95	$98,036.92	$0.00
8	$169,930.66	$0.00	$0.00	$0.00	$169,930.66	$67,972.26	$101,958.40	$0.00
9	$176,727.89	$0.00	$0.00	$0.00	$176,727.89	$70,691.16	$106,036.73	$0.00
10	$257,809.22	$300,000.00	$631,754.46	$0.00	−$373,945.24	−$149,578.10	−$524,367.15	$1,659,897.55

$PW_{ST} =$	$232,335.64
$FW_{ST} =$	$892,023.06
$AW_{ST} =$	$45,239.33
$IRR_c =$	58.76%
$ERR_c =$	23.57%
$IRR_r =$	52.66%
$ERR_r =$	18.82%

Notice the impact of inflation on the preferred plan. With no inflation, Plan 1 is preferred; with 4 percent inflation, Plan 4 is preferred.

EXAMPLE 12.9 **Analyzing the Impact of Borrowed Funds and Interest Rates on After-Tax Present Worth**

From our analysis in Chapter 10, where $100,000 was borrowed, it appears that the amount of investment capital borrowed can significantly impact after-tax present worth. Let's examine the impact of borrowing "only" 20 percent, or $100,000, in the purchase of the SMP machine.

As shown in Figures 12.8 through 12.11, the after-tax present worth decreases significantly as the amount of money borrowed decreases. Instead of an ATPW of $220,132.29 when $300,000 is borrowed, an ATPW of $146,178.22 occurs when $100,000 is borrowed and repaid using Plan 1.

When $100,000 of investment capital is borrowed, ATPW = $133,522.68 for Plan 2; ATPW = $136,519.92 for Plan 3; and ATPW = $150,246 for Plan 4. The preferred method is still Plan 4.

When 100 percent of investment capital is borrowed, how sensitive is after-tax present worth to an increase in the borrower's interest rate? Tables 12.10 through 12.13 present the after-tax results for a lender's interest rate of 24 percent. At that rate, Plans 1, 2, and 3 are equally preferred; Plan 4 is no longer attractive. Why is 24 percent a key interest rate? Because it equals the borrower's combined minimum attractive rate of return (14.4 percent) divided by 1 minus the income-tax rate (0.60).

			H14	▼	fx	=B14-C14-D14-G14		

	A	B	C	D	E	F	G	H
1			$MARR_r$ = 10%				interest rate = 12%	
2		income tax rate = 40%					inflation rate = 4%	
3	EOY	$TBTCF	$TPPMT	$TIPMT	$TDWO	$TTI	$TTax	$TATCF
4	0	-$500,000.00	-$100,000.00					-$400,000.00
5	1	$129,133.34	$0.00	$12,000.00	$100,000.00	$17,133.34	$6,853.33	$110,280.00
6	2	$134,298.67	$0.00	$12,000.00	$160,000.00	-$37,701.33	-$15,080.53	$137,379.20
7	3	$139,670.62	$0.00	$12,000.00	$96,000.00	$31,670.62	$12,668.25	$115,002.37
8	4	$145,257.44	$0.00	$12,000.00	$57,600.00	$75,657.44	$30,262.98	$102,994.47
9	5	$151,067.74	$0.00	$12,000.00	$57,600.00	$81,467.74	$32,587.10	$106,480.64
10	6	$157,110.45	$0.00	$12,000.00	$28,800.00	$116,310.45	$46,524.18	$98,586.27
11	7	$163,394.87	$0.00	$12,000.00	$0.00	$151,394.87	$60,557.95	$90,836.92
12	8	$169,930.66	$0.00	$12,000.00	$0.00	$157,930.66	$63,172.26	$94,758.40
13	9	$176,727.89	$0.00	$12,000.00	$0.00	$164,727.89	$65,891.16	$98,836.73
14	10	$257,809.22	$100,000.00	$12,000.00	$0.00	$245,809.22	$98,323.69	$47,485.53
15		PW_{ST} =	$146,178.22	=NPV($D$1+$H$2+$H$2*$D$1,H5:H14)+H4				
16		FW_{ST} =	$561,232.62	=FV($D$1+$H$2+$H$2*$D$1,10,,-C15)				
17		AW_{ST} =	$28,463.15	=PMT($D$1+$H$2+$H$2*$D$1,10,-C15)				
18		IRR_r =	19.44%	=(IRR(H4:H14)-H2)/(1+H2)				
19		ERR_r =	13.48%	=(MIRR(H4:H14,,H2+D1+D1*H2)-H2)/(1+H2)				
20								

FIGURE 12.8

Borrowing $100,000 to Finance the SMP Acquisition; Payment Plan 1; 4% Inflation.

			H14	▼	fx	=B14–C14–D14–G14		

	A	B	C	D	E	F	G	H
1			$MARR_r$ = 10%				interest rate = 12%	
2		income tax rate = 40%					inflation rate = 4%	
3	EOY	$TBTCF	$TPPMT	$TIPMT	$TDWO	$TTI	$TTax	$TATCF
4	0	-$500,000.00	-$100,000.00					-$400,000.00
5	1	$129,133.34	$10,000.00	$12,000.00	$100,000.00	$17,133.34	$6,853.33	$100,280.00
6	2	$134,298.67	$10,000.00	$10,800.00	$160,000.00	-$36,501.33	-$14,600.53	$128,099.20
7	3	$139,670.62	$10,000.00	$9,600.00	$96,000.00	$34,070.62	$13,628.25	$106,442.37
8	4	$145,257.44	$10,000.00	$8,400.00	$57,600.00	$79,257.44	$31,702.98	$95,154.47
9	5	$151,067.74	$10,000.00	$7,200.00	$57,600.00	$86,267.74	$34,507.10	$99,360.64
10	6	$157,110.45	$10,000.00	$6,000.00	$28,800.00	$122,310.45	$48,924.18	$92,186.27
11	7	$163,394.87	$10,000.00	$4,800.00	$0.00	$158,594.87	$63,437.95	$85,156.92
12	8	$169,930.66	$10,000.00	$3,600.00	$0.00	$166,330.66	$66,532.26	$89,798.40
13	9	$176,727.89	$10,000.00	$2,400.00	$0.00	$174,327.89	$69,731.16	$94,596.73
14	10	$257,809.22	$10,000.00	$1,200.00	$0.00	$256,609.22	$102,643.69	$143,965.53
15		PW_{ST} =	$133,522.68	=NPV($D$1+$H$2+$H$2*$D$1,H5:H14)+H4				
16		FW_{ST} =	$512,643.30	=FV($D$1+$H$2+$H$2*$D$1,10,,-C15)				
17		AW_{ST} =	$25,998.93	=PMT($D$1+$H$2+$H$2*$D$1,10,-C15)				
18		IRR_r =	18.03%	=(IRR(H4:H14)-H2)/(1+H2)				
19		ERR_r =	13.21%	=(MIRR(H4:H14,,H2+D1+D1*H2)-H2)/(1+H2)				
20								

FIGURE 12.9

Borrowing $100,000 to Finance the SMP Acquisition; Payment Plan 2; 4% Inflation.

	H14	▾	fx	=B14–C14–D14–G14			

	A	B	C	D	E	F	G	H
1		MARR_r = 10%					interest rate = 12%	
2		income tax rate = 40%					inflation rate = 4%	
3	EOY	$TBTCF	$TPPMT	$TIPMT	$TDWO	$TTI	$TTax	$TATCF
4	0	-$500,000.00	-$100,000.00					-$400,000.00
5	1	$129,133.34	$5,698.42	$12,000.00	$100,000.00	$17,133.34	$6,853.33	$104,581.59
6	2	$134,298.67	$6,382.23	$11,316.19	$160,000.00	-$37,017.52	-$14,807.01	$131,407.26
7	3	$139,670.62	$7,148.09	$10,550.32	$96,000.00	$33,120.29	$13,248.12	$108,724.08
8	4	$145,257.44	$8,005.86	$9,692.55	$57,600.00	$77,964.89	$31,185.96	$96,373.07
9	5	$151,067.74	$8,966.57	$8,731.85	$57,600.00	$84,735.89	$33,894.36	$99,474.97
10	6	$157,110.45	$10,042.56	$7,655.86	$28,800.00	$120,654.59	$48,261.84	$91,150.20
11	7	$163,394.87	$11,247.66	$6,450.75	$0.00	$156,944.11	$62,777.65	$82,918.80
12	8	$169,930.66	$12,597.38	$5,101.03	$0.00	$164,829.63	$65,931.85	$86,300.39
13	9	$176,727.89	$14,109.07	$3,589.35	$0.00	$173,138.54	$69,255.42	$89,774.06
14	10	$257,809.22	$15,802.16	$1,896.26	$0.00	$255,912.96	$102,365.18	$137,745.62
15	PW_ST =	$136,519.92	=NPV($D$1+$H$2+$H$2*$D$1,H5:H14)+H4					
16	FW_ST =	$524,150.82	=FV($D$1+$H$2+$H$2*$D$1,10,,-C15)					
17	AW_ST =	$26,582.54	=PMT($D$1+$H$2+$H$2*$D$1,10,-C15)					
18	IRR_r =	18.37%	=(IRR(H4:H14)-H2)/(1+H2)					
19	ERR_r =	13.28%	=(MIRR(H4:H14,,H2+D1+D1*H2)-H2)/(1+H2)					
20								

FIGURE 12.10

Borrowing $100,000 to Finance the SMP Acquisition; Payment Plan 3; 4% Inflation.

Not only is 24 percent the interest rate that makes Plans 1, 2, and 3 equivalent, but it is also the rate at which borrowing is no longer attractive financially. For interest rates less than 24 percent, it is more profitable to borrow investment capital than it is to use retained earnings to fund the investment. For interest rates greater than 24 percent, if borrowing is required, then Plan 2 should be used to repay the loan; if Plan 2 is not available and borrowing is required, then Plan 3 is the preferred repayment method.

	C19	▾	fx	=(IRR(I4:I14)–H2)/(1+H2)				

	A	B	C	D	E	F	G	H	I
1		MARR_r = 10%					interest rate = 12%		
2		income tax rate = 40%					inflation rate = 4%		
3	EOY	$TBTCF	$TPPMT	$TIPMT	$TDWO	$TTI	$TTax	$TATCF	$TATCF
4	0	-$500,000.00	-$100,000.00					-$400,000.00	-$400,000.00
5	1	$129,133.34	$0.00	$0.00	$100,000.00	$29,133.34	$11,653.33	$117,480.00	$0.00
6	2	$134,298.67	$0.00	$0.00	$160,000.00	-$25,701.33	-$10,280.53	$144,579.20	$0.00
7	3	$139,670.62	$0.00	$0.00	$96,000.00	$43,670.62	$17,468.25	$122,202.37	$0.00
8	4	$145,257.44	$0.00	$0.00	$57,600.00	$87,657.44	$35,062.98	$110,194.47	$0.00
9	5	$151,067.74	$0.00	$0.00	$57,600.00	$93,467.74	$37,387.10	$113,680.64	$0.00
10	6	$157,110.45	$0.00	$0.00	$28,800.00	$128,310.45	$51,324.18	$105,786.27	$0.00
11	7	$163,394.87	$0.00	$0.00	$0.00	$163,394.87	$65,357.95	$98,036.92	$0.00
12	8	$169,930.66	$0.00	$0.00	$0.00	$169,930.66	$67,972.26	$101,958.40	$0.00
13	9	$176,727.89	$0.00	$0.00	$0.00	$176,727.89	$70,691.16	$106,036.73	$0.00
14	10	$257,809.22	$100,000.00	$210,584.82	$0.00	$47,224.40	$18,889.76	-$71,665.36	$2,112,599.34
15	PW_ST =	$150,246.00	=NPV($D$1+$H$2+$H$2*$D$1,H5:H14)+H4						
16	FW_ST =	$576,850.35	=FV($D$1+$H$2+$H$2*$D$1,10,,-C15)						
17	AW_ST =	$29,255.21	=PMT($D$1+$H$2+$H$2*$D$1,10,-C15)						
18	IRR_r =	20.50%	=(IRR(H4:H14)-H2)/(1+H2)						
19	ERR_r =	13.56%	=(IRR(I4:I14)-H2)/(1+H2)						
20									
21								=FV(14.4%,10,,-NPV(14.4%,H5:H13))+H14	
22									

FIGURE 12.11

Borrowing $100,000 to Finance the SMP Acquisition; Payment Plan 4; 4% Inflation.

TABLE 12.10

Borrowing 100% of the Capital Needed for the SMP Acquisition; Paying with Plan 1; 4% Inflation; 24% Interest Rate.

$MARR_r = 10\%$
income tax rate = 40%

interest rate = 24%
inflation rate = 4%

EOY	$TBTCF	$TPPMT	$TIPMT	$TDWO	$TTI	$TTax	$TATCF
0	−$500,000.00	−$500,000.00					$0.00
1	$129,133.34	$0.00	$120,000.00	$100,000.00	−$90,866.66	−$36,346.67	$45,480.00
2	$134,298.67	$0.00	$120,000.00	$160,000.00	−$145,701.33	−$58,280.53	$72,579.20
3	$139,670.62	$0.00	$120,000.00	$96,000.00	−$76,329.38	−$30,531.75	$50,202.37
4	$145,257.44	$0.00	$120,000.00	$57,600.00	−$32,342.56	−$12,937.02	$38,194.47
5	$151,067.74	$0.00	$120,000.00	$57,600.00	−$26,532.26	−$10,612.90	$41,680.64
6	$157,110.45	$0.00	$120,000.00	$28,800.00	$8,310.45	$3,324.18	$33,786.27
7	$163,394.87	$0.00	$120,000.00	$0.00	$43,394.87	$17,357.95	$26,036.92
8	$169,930.66	$0.00	$120,000.00	$0.00	$49,930.66	$19,972.26	$29,958.40
9	$176,727.89	$0.00	$120,000.00	$0.00	$56,727.89	$22,691.16	$34,036.73
10	$257,809.22	$500,000.00	$120,000.00	$0.00	$137,809.22	$55,123.69	−$417,314.47

$PW_{ST} =$ $109,201.18
$FW_{ST} =$ $419,264.00
$AW_{ST} =$ $21,263.15

TABLE 12.11

Borrowing 100% of the Capital Needed for the SMP Acquisition; Paying with Plan 2; 4% Inflation; 24% Interest Rate.

$MARR_r = 10\%$
income tax rate = 40%

interest rate = 24%
inflation rate = 4%

EOY	$TBTCF	$TPPMT	$TIPMT	$TDWO	$TTI	$TTax	$TATCF
0	−$500,000.00	−$500,000.00					$0.00
1	$129,133.34	$50,000.00	$120,000.00	$100,000.00	−$90,866.66	−$36,346.67	−$4,520.00
2	$134,298.67	$50,000.00	$108,000.00	$160,000.00	−$133,701.33	−$53,480.53	$29,779.20
3	$139,670.62	$50,000.00	$96,000.00	$96,000.00	−$52,329.38	−$20,931.75	$14,602.37
4	$145,257.44	$50,000.00	$84,000.00	$57,600.00	$3,657.44	$1,462.98	$9,794.47
5	$151,067.74	$50,000.00	$72,000.00	$57,600.00	$21,467.74	$8,587.10	$20,480.64
6	$157,110.45	$50,000.00	$60,000.00	$28,800.00	$68,310.45	$27,324.18	$19,786.27
7	$163,394.87	$50,000.00	$48,000.00	$0.00	$115,394.87	$46,157.95	$19,236.92
8	$169,930.66	$50,000.00	$36,000.00	$0.00	$133,930.66	$53,572.26	$30,358.40
9	$176,727.89	$50,000.00	$24,000.00	$0.00	$152,727.89	$61,091.16	$41,636.73
10	$257,809.22	$50,000.00	$12,000.00	$0.00	$245,809.22	$98,323.69	$97,485.53

$PW_{ST} =$ $109,201.18
$FW_{ST} =$ $419,264.00
$AW_{ST} =$ $21,263.15

TABLE 12.12

Borrowing 100% of the Capital Needed for the SMP Acquisition; Paying with Plan 3; 4% Inflation; 24% Interest Rate.

	$MARR_r = 10\%$ income tax rate $= 40\%$				interest rate $= 24\%$ inflation rate $= 4\%$		
EOY	$TBTCF	$TPPMT	$TIPMT	$TDWO	$TTI	$TTax	$TATCF
0	−$500,000.00	−$500,000.00					$0.00
1	$129,133.34	$15,801.06	$120,000.00	$100,000.00	−$90,866.66	−$36,346.67	$29,678.94
2	$134,298.67	$19,593.32	$116,207.74	$160,000.00	−$141,909.07	−$56,763.63	$55,261.24
3	$139,670.62	$24,295.72	$111,505.35	$96,000.00	−$67,834.73	−$27,133.89	$31,003.45
4	$145,257.44	$30,126.69	$105,674.38	$57,600.00	−$18,016.93	−$7,206.77	$16,663.15
5	$151,067.74	$37,357.09	$98,443.97	$57,600.00	−$4,976.23	−$1,990.49	$17,257.17
6	$157,110.45	$46,322.79	$89,478.27	$28,800.00	$38,832.18	$15,532.87	$5,776.51
7	$163,394.87	$57,440.26	$78,360.80	$0.00	$85,034.07	$34,013.63	−$6,419.82
8	$169,930.66	$71,225.93	$64,575.14	$0.00	$105,355.53	$42,142.21	−$8,012.61
9	$176,727.89	$88,320.15	$47,480.91	$0.00	$129,246.98	$51,698.79	−$10,771.97
10	$257,809.22	$109,516.99	$26,284.08	$0.00	$231,525.14	$92,610.06	$29,398.10
						$PW_{ST} =$	$109,201.18
						$FW_{ST} =$	$419,264.00
						$AW_{ST} =$	$21,263.15

Figure 12.12 illustrates the effect on ATPW of interest rates ranging from 0 percent to 30 percent on the preferences among the Payment plans. Clearly, the value of the lender's interest rate is important, particularly as it relates to the borrower's combined minimum attractive rate of return and the ratio of the borrower's combined minimum attractive rate of return and 1 minus the income-tax rate.

TABLE 12.13

Borrowing 100% of the Capital Needed for the SMP Acquisition; Paying with Plan 4; 4% Inflation; 24% Interest Rate.

	$MARR_r = 10\%$ income tax rate $= 40\%$				interest rate $= 24\%$ inflation rate $= 4\%$		
EOY	$TBTCF	$TPPMT	$TIPMT	$TDWO	$TTI	$TTax	$TATCF
0	−$500,000.00	−$500,000.00					$0.00
1	$129,133.34	$0.00	$0.00	$100,000.00	$29,133.34	$11,653.33	$117,480.00
2	$134,298.67	$0.00	$0.00	$160,000.00	−$25,701.33	−$10,280.53	$144,579.20
3	$139,670.62	$0.00	$0.00	$96,000.00	$43,670.62	$17,468.25	$122,202.37
4	$145,257.44	$0.00	$0.00	$57,600.00	$87,657.44	$35,062.98	$110,194.47
5	$151,067.74	$0.00	$0.00	$57,600.00	$93,467.74	$37,387.10	$113,680.64
6	$157,110.45	$0.00	$0.00	$28,800.00	$128,310.45	$51,324.18	$105,786.27
7	$163,394.87	$0.00	$0.00	$0.00	$163,394.87	$65,357.95	$98,036.92
8	$169,930.66	$0.00	$0.00	$0.00	$169,930.66	$67,972.26	$101,958.40
9	$176,727.89	$0.00	$0.00	$0.00	$176,727.89	$70,691.16	$106,036.73
10	$257,809.22	$500,000.00	$3,797,212.75	$0.00	−$3,539,403.54	−$1,415,761.41	−$2,623,642.12
						$PW_{ST} =$	−$114,439.91
						$FW_{ST} =$	−$439,377.42
						$AW_{ST} =$	−$22,283.22

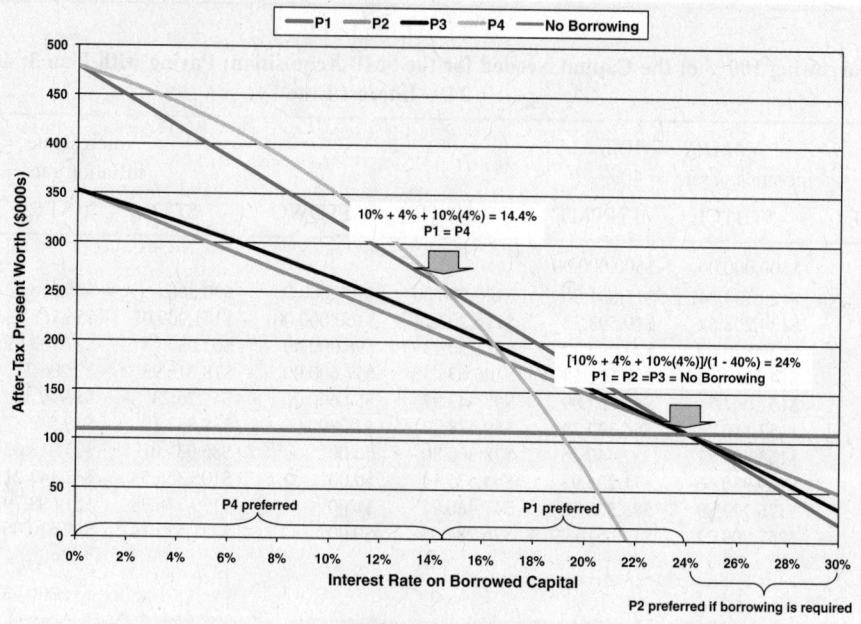

FIGURE 12.12

Impact on ATPW of the Interest Rate and Payment Plan for the SMP Investment.

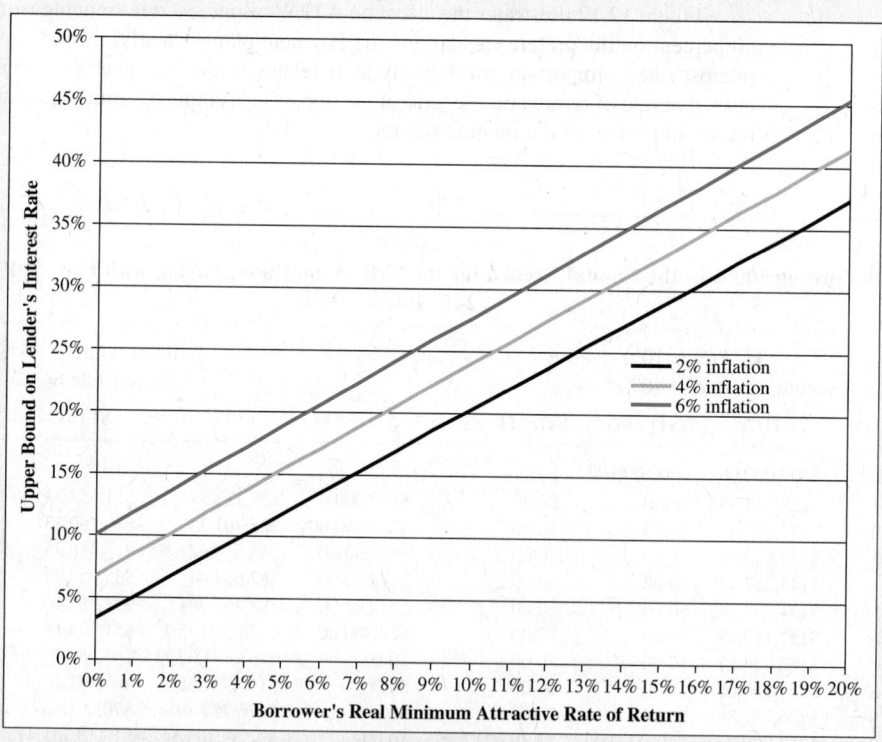

FIGURE 12.13

Limits on Lender's Interest Rate for it to Be Economically Attractive to Borrow Investment Capital.

Why is it profitable to borrow money at interest rates considerably greater than the borrower's $MARR_r$ of 10 percent? Two things are at work that benefit the borrower: interest paid and inflation! The deductibility of interest and the benefit of having a fixed-rate loan in inflationary conditions work to the borrower's benefit until the interest rate exceeds $MARR_c/(1 - itr)$; thereafter, the borrower should decline borrowing investment capital, unless extenuating circumstances necessitate it.

Figure 12.13 provides limits on the lender's interest rate for it to be economical to borrow investment capital. Three inflation levels are considered: 2 percent, 4 percent, and 6 percent. An income-tax rate of 40 percent is assumed. As shown, if the borrower's $MARR_r$ is 12 percent, then capital should be borrowed so long as the lender's interest rate is less than 23.73 percent when inflation equals 2 percent, less than 27.47 percent when inflation equals 4 percent, and less than 31.2 percent when inflation equals 6 percent.

From the previous example and after analyzing a large number of similar situations, we have concluded that Plan 4 is the preferred payment plan when the *lender's interest rate* is less than the $MARR_c$. Similarly, for $MARR_c$ < lender's interest rate < $MARR_c/(1 - itr)$, Plan 1 is preferred. For a lender's interest rate > $MARR_c/(1 - itr)$, it is best to not borrow investment capital; if borrowing is necessary, then Plan 2 is the preferred repayment plan.

After solving hundreds of examples involving numerous combinations of inflation rates, interest rates, and percentages of investment capital borrowed, we have drawn the following additional conclusions:

1. In the absence of borrowed funds, inflation has a negative impact on ATPW, because depreciation allowances do not increase with inflation.

2. For small percentages of investment capital being borrowed, increases in inflation will have a negative impact on ATPW.

3. As the amount of investment capital borrowed increases, increases in inflation will have a positive impact on ATPW, because interest charges do not increase with inflation and the larger the inflation rate (given a fixed interest rate on borrowed capital), the smaller the ATPW of interest charges. At some point, the disadvantage of depreciation not increasing with inflation is countered by the advantage of having a fixed interest rate as inflation increases.

4. Locking in an interest rate before the effects of inflation materialize can result in inflation working to an investor's benefit.

5. Although Plan 3 is the most common way to repay loans, it is never superior to all three of the remaining payment plans; however, there are times when it is superior to two of the remaining three payment plans.

If lender's interest rate < $MARR_c$ use Plan 4
If $MARR_c$ < *lender's interest rate* < $MARR_c/(1 - itr)$ use Plan 1
If lender's interest rate > $MARR_c/(1 - itr)$ do not borrow
(if borrowing is necessary, use Plan 2)

12-6 SUMMARY

Our consideration of inflation's effects on economic justifications included both before-tax and after-tax analyses. A dozen "take away" messages were emphasized:

1. Inflation erodes the purchasing power of money, but in the right situation it can work to an investor's benefit.

2. In an inflationary economy, explicit consideration of inflation should occur in engineering economic analyses.

3. Two approaches can be used to explicitly consider inflation in an economic justification—a constant dollar approach and a then-current dollar approach.

4. The constant dollar approach uses cash flows and a discount rate, both of which are inflation-free.

5. The then-current approach uses cash flows and a discount rate, both of which include inflation components.

6. When performed correctly, the constant dollar approach and the then-current dollar approach yield identical present worths.

7. Because the IRS treats depreciation allowances as then-current allowances, it is often simplest to take a then-current approach when performing after-tax analyses.

8. When performing after-tax analyses involving borrowed capital, a then-current analysis is often best, since interest payments and principal payments are then-current cash flows.

9. Unless borrowed capital is used, inflation reduces the after-tax present worth of an investment in capital equipment.

10. Depending on how much capital is borrowed, inflation can increase the after-tax present worth of an investment in capital equipment when using borrowed capital.

11. When borrowed capital is used and it is desired to maximize after-tax present worth, Plan 4 should be used to repay the loan when the lender's interest rate is less than the borrower's combined minimum attractive rate of return; Plan 1 should be used to repay the loan when the lender's interest rate is greater than the borrower's combined minimum attractive rate of return but less than the borrower's combined minimum attractive rate of return divided by 1 minus the income-tax rate; and, if borrowing is required, Plan 2 should be used to repay the loan when the lender's interest rate is greater than the borrower's combined minimum attractive rate of return divided by 1 minus the income-tax rate.

---

1. In the absence of borrowed funds, inflation has a negative impact on *ATPW*

2. For small percentages of borrowed capital, increases in inflation have a negative impact on *ATPW*

3. As the amount of investment capital borrowed increases, increases in inflation will have a positive impact on *ATPW*

4. "Fixed-interest-rate" loans benefit the borrower in inflationary times

5. Payment Plan 3 is never superior to *all* other payment plans considered

12. In the latter case (lender's interest rate $> MARR_c/(1 - itr)$), it is best to use one's own capital, since the after-tax present worth is greater than that which results when using borrowed capital.

Pit Stop #12—Check Your Tires for Proper Inflation!

1. True or False: Inflation decreases the purchasing power of money.
2. True or False: The most commonly used measure of inflation is the relative change in the Consumer Price Index.
3. True or False: The Consumer Price Index typically increases faster than the Higher Education Price Index.
4. True or False: In performing engineering economic analyses in inflationary conditions, the after-tax present worth will always be less than it would be if inflation were negligible.
5. True or False: The two approaches used in considering inflation are the constant dollar and the then-current dollar approaches.
6. True or False: If the real minimum attractive rate of return is 8%, inflation is 4%, and the tax rate is 40%, then money should not be borrowed if the interest rate on the loan is greater than 18%.
7. True or False: if the real minimum attractive rate of return is 8%, inflation is 4%, the tax rate is 40%, and money can be borrowed at 16% annual compound interest, then the loan should be repaid using Plan 4, i.e., don't pay anything until the end of the loan period.
8. True or False: If the real minimum attractive rate of return is 8%, inflation is 4%, the tax rate is 40%, and money can be borrowed at 12% annual compound interest, then the loan should be repaid using Plan 1, i.e., pay interest annually and pay principal at the end of the loan period.
9. True or False: If the combined minimum attractive rate of return is 12% and inflation is 4%, then the real minimum attractive rate of return is approximately 7.7%.
10. True or False: When investing in capital equipment, inflation reduces the after-tax present worth because depreciation does not increase with inflation.

Tutoring problem available (at instructor's discretion) in *WileyPLUS*.

Problem available (at instructor's discretion) in *WileyPLUS*.

Worked Problem Video available in *WileyPLUS*.

FE-LIKE PROBLEMS

1. Logan is conducting an economic evaluation under inflation using the then-current approach. If the inflation rate is j and the real time value of money rate is d, which of the following is the

interest rate he should use for discounting the cash flows?

a. j

b. d

c. $j + d$

d. $j + d + dj$

2. Mike's Veneer Shop owns a vacuum press that requires annual maintenance. Mike has a contract to cover the maintenance expenses for the next 5 years. The contract calls for an annual payment of $600 with adjustment each year for inflation. Inflation is expected to hold constant at 6 percent/year over this period. The then-current cash flow pattern for this expense is best described by which of the following?

a. Uniform series

b. Gradient series

c. Geometric series

d. Continuous series

3. Mike's Veneer Shop owns a vacuum press that requires annual maintenance. Mike has a contract to cover the maintenance expenses for the next 5 years. The contract calls for an annual payment of $600 with adjustment each year for inflation. Inflation is expected to hold constant at 6 percent/year over this period. The constant dollar cash flow pattern for this expense is best described by which of the following?

a. Uniform series

b. Gradient series

c. Geometric series

d. Continuous series

4. An economist has predicted that there will be a 7 percent per year inflation of prices during the next 10 years. If this prediction proves to be correct, an item that presently sells for $10 will sell for what price in 10 years?

a. $5.08

b. $10.70

c. $17.00

d. $19.67

5. If the real discount rate is 7 percent and the inflation rate is 10 percent, which of the following interest rates will be used to find the present worth of a series of cash flows that are in then-current dollars?

a. 10 percent

b. 17.7 percent

c. 7 percent

d. 10.7 percent

6. If the real discount rate is 7 percent and the inflation rate is 10 percent, which of the following interest rates will be used to find the present worth of a series of cash flows that are in constant-worth dollars?

a. 10 percent

b. 17.7 percent

c. 7 percent

d. 10.7 percent

7. When done correctly, what is the relationship between the present worth of an alternative calculated using a then-current approach and the present worth of the alternative calculated using a constant-worth approach?

a. They are equal.

b. Then-current PW is higher because it uses inflated dollars.

c. Constant-worth PW is higher because it uses a lower discount rate.

d. Cannot be determined without knowing the cash flows and inflation rate

8. A government agency has reported the quarterly inflation rates shown below for the previous four quarters. What was the effective annual inflation rate?

Quarter	Quarterly Inflation Rate
1	3%
2	2%
3	4%
4	2%

a. 2 percent

b. 2.75 percent

c. 11 percent

d. 11.45 percent

9. As reported by the Bureau of Labor Statistics, the CPI for 2005 was 585.0 (using a base year of $1967 = 100$). The CPI for 2006 was 603.9. Based on this data, what was the inflation rate for 2006?

a. 3.23 percent

b. 5.85 percent

c. 6.04 percent

d. 18.9 percent

10. Ten years ago, Jennifer bought an investment property for $100,000. Over the 10-year period, inflation has held consistently at 3 percent annually. If Jennifer expects a 13 percent/year real rate of return, what would she sell the property for today?

a. $116,000

b. $134,400

c. $339,500

d. $456,200

PROBLEMS

Section 12.1

1. What is a good working definition of *inflation* in 10 words or less?
2. Give four examples of goods or services that have exhibited inflation in recent years.
3. What is the relationship between "inflation" and "deflation"? Give an example of deflation experienced in your everyday life.
4. Give two examples of goods or services that you have seen inflate and deflate dramatically over the past few years.

Section 12.2

5. What is meant by a "market basket rate"?
. 6. What are the differences between the consumer price index (CPI) and the producers price index (PPI)?
7. What is the higher education price index (HEPI), where does it fit in with the CPI and the PPI, and how is the HEPI related to the CPI?
8. Suppose a friend argues that the CPI does not represent them because they do not purchase some of the things, including big-ticket items, in the market basket. Can they conclude that the CPI is irrelevant to them? Explain your reasoning.
9. The CPI-U (U.S. city average, all items) has the following annual averages:

Year	2006	2007	2008	2009	2010
Index	201.600	207.342	215.303	214.537	218.056

   a. For each year from 2007 to 2010, determine the annual inflation rate in percent to three decimal places.
   b. Since inflation, like interest, is compounded from period to period (e.g., year to year), estimate the overall annual inflation rate per year from 2006 to 2010. Suggestion: Do not simply average the rates of Part a.

10. The seasonally adjusted rate increases for gasoline, unleaded regular, during early 2011 are as follows:

Month	February	March	April
Rate %	2.215%	11.867%	7.629%

   a. Assuming the index value in January 2011 was 278.404, determine the index for each year from February to April 2011 to three places after the decimal.
   b. Since inflation, like interest, is compounded from period to period (e.g., month to month), estimate the monthly inflation rate per month from January 2011 to April 2011. Suggestion: Do not simply average the rates given above.

11. The United States manufacturing output per hour index is given as follows for years 2005 to 2009:

Year	2005	2006	2007	2008	2009
Index	122.8	127.2	135.2	135.7	146.2

   a. For each year from 2006 to 2009, determine the rate of increase in U.S. manufacturing output per hour in percent to two decimal places.

b. Since this index, like inflation, is compounded from period to period (e.g., year to year), estimate the overall annual rate of increase in U.S. manufacturing output per hour from 2005 to 2009. Suggestion: Do not simply average the rates of Part a.

12. The Korean hourly compensation percentage rates of increase, based on U.S. dollars, are presented as follows:

Year	2005	2006	2007	2008	2009
Rate %	18.853%	15.995%	10.665%	−16.220%	−12.723%

a. Assuming the Korean compensation index in U.S. dollar was $12.73 in 2004, determine the compensation rate in U.S. dollars for each of 2005 to 2009.

b. Since these rate, like inflation, are compounded from period to period (e.g., year to year), estimate the overall annual percentage rate of increase per year from 2004 to 2009. Suggestion: Do not simply average the rates given above.

Section 12.3

13. You are earning 5.2 percent on a certificate of deposit. Inflation is running 3.5 percent. What is the real rate of return on your investment?

14. You are considering a bond that pays annually at 6.2 percent. Inflation is projected to be running 4 percent. What will be your real interest rate?

15. Array Solutions requires a 14 percent return on their projects. Analysis shows that even though they have been earning the desired 14 percent, their real return appears to be only 10 percent when they look at what they can buy with their returns.

a. Explain why there is this discrepancy.

b. Determine the inflation rate.

16. ChevronPhillips requires a real return of 14.2 percent. If inflation is running 3.8 percent, what must be their *MARR*, or "hurdle rate," on capital investments when using then-current dollars in analyses?

17. Suppose you want to earn a real interest rate of 5 percent. For inflation rates of 0.0, 1.0, 2.0, . . . , 9.0, 10.0, 15.0, 20.0, and 50.0 percent, determine the combined rate of interest you must earn.

18. How much must you invest exactly 5 years from now to have $500,000 in today's buying power 20 years from now? You can invest your money at 10 percent per year, and inflation runs 4 percent.

19. A software company's labor requirements currently cost $350,000/year. The labor-hour requirements are expected to increase by 10 percent per year over the next 5 years. If inflation is 4 percent, determine the labor costs after 5 years using

a. then-current dollars.

b. constant-worth dollars.

20. You invested $10,000 on January 1, 2014, at 7 percent interest compounded annually. You have not touched the investment since that date. You are planning to take your money and close out the investment on January 1, 2024.

a. If average inflation is 3.7 percent, what has been your "real" annual interest rate?

b. At the time you originally invested, there was a boat you admired costing $8,000. Over the years, boats are inflating at a rate of 7 percent. You were also interested in a marine navigation system costing $4,000; similar systems are dropping in price at a 2 percent rate. If you decide to buy one of each when you close out the account, how much will the purchases cost you?

c. How much money will you have left over (or be short) after your purchases?

21. Your department is budgeting miscellaneous expenses for the next 5 years. Your best guess at the annual inflation rate is 3.9 percent, and the combined *MARR* is 15 percent. Expenses currently run $14,500 per year. Assume that expenses are end-of-year payments.

a. Determine the then-current dollar amounts for years 1, 2, 3, 4, and 5.

b. Determine the constant dollar amount for years 1, 2, 3, 4, and 5.

    c. Determine the PW of the then-current dollar amounts.

    d. Determine the PW of the constant dollar amounts.

22. Shea is pricing materials (wood, wire, pipe, etc.) for new home construction on a "per unit" basis. Inflation on materials has been running at 16 percent for the past 3 years and is expected to remain at that rate for the next 10 years. The actual dollars paid for expenses right now for a "unit" are $55,000.

    a. What did the same set of materials cost 3 years ago?

    b. If the trend continues, what will they cost 10 years from now?

23. Global steel prices have a year-over-year inflationary rate increase of 12.4 percent. Tube Fab purchased $700,000 of a particular carbon steel during the year just ended right now, and they intend to purchase the same quantity at the end of each of the next 5 years. Tube Fab earns a real rate of 16 percent on their money.

    a. Determine the then-current amounts they will pay for steel at the end of each of the next 5 years.

    b. Determine the constant value amounts they will pay for steel at the end of each of the next 5 years.

    c. Determine Tube Fab's PW of expenditures over the next 5 years using then-current dollars.

    d. Determine Tube Fab's PW of expenditures over the next 5 years using constant-value dollars.

24. Global steel prices have a year-over-year inflationary rate increase of 12.4 percent. Tube Fab purchased $700,000 of a particular carbon steel during the year just ended right now. Their business has been increasing, and they intend to purchase 20 percent more steel each year, over the previous year's purchase, for the next 5 years. Tube Fab earns a real rate of 16 percent on their money.

    a. Determine the then-current amounts they will pay for steel at the end of each of the next 5 years.

    b. Determine the constant value amounts they will pay for steel at the end of each of the next 5 years.

    c. Determine Tube Fab's PW of expenditures over the next 5 years using then-current dollars.

    d. Determine Tube Fab's PW of expenditures over the next 5 years using constant-value dollars.

25. Padayappa has now retired after 40 years of employment. He just made an annual deposit to his investment portfolio and realized he has $2 million (not counting home, cars, furniture, etc.). His money has been earning 7 percent per year, and inflation has been running 4 percent per year over the past 40 years.

    a. What equal amount of money did he put into his investment at the end of each year?

    b. What is the buying power of his $2 million in terms of a base 40 years ago?

    c. If he could buy a TV 40 years ago for $400, what would a comparable one cost today if the consumer electronics inflation rate is −3 percent?

26. A 24-year-old December 2012 graduate wants the equivalent of $2,500,000 in January 1, 2013, buying power to be available exactly 40 years later on January 1, 2053. He plans to make his first investment of $Z on January 1, 2014, and every year thereafter, with the last payment of $Z on January 1, 2053. He can earn 8 percent on his money and expects inflation to run 5 percent.

    a. How many actual dollars will there be in his account immediately after his last deposit?

    b. What is $Z?

27. An investment of $8,000 is made at time 0 with returns of $3,500 at the end of each of years 1 through 4, with all monetary amounts being in real dollars. Inflation is running 7 percent per year over that time. Also, the real *TVOM* is 15 percent per year. Determine the investment's present worth using both real dollars and then-current dollars.

28. The winner of a lottery is given a choice of $1,000,000 cash today or $2,000,000 paid out as follows: $100,000 cash per year for 20 years with the first payment today and 19 subsequent annual payments thereafter. The inflation rate is expected to be constant at 4 percent/year over the award period, and the winner's *TVOM* (real interest rate) is 3.5 percent/year.

    a. Which choice is better for the winner? Neglect the effect of taxes, life span, and uncertainty.

    b. At what value of inflation are the two choices economically equivalent?

    c. What would you do if you do NOT neglect the effect of life span and uncertainty?

29. Annual energy costs are rising at 20 percent/year, while general inflation is running 3.9 percent. Allied Energy offers an energy-saving device that would have saved $1,000 last year, with savings proportional to energy costs. What will be the present worth of the total energy savings if the estimated life of this device is the next 10 years and money has a combined time value (considering general inflation and real return) of 12 percent?

30. A landfill has a first cost of $270,000. Annual operating and maintenance costs for the first year will be $40,000. These costs will increase at 11 percent annually. Income for dumping rights at the landfill will be held fixed at $120,000 per year. The landfill will be operating for 10 years. Inflation will average 4.5 percent, and a real return of 3.6 percent is desired. What is the present worth of this project using

   a. a then-current analysis?

   b. a constant-worth analysis?

31. A family wishes to provide for their child's college education. Being a bit risk averse, they plan to invest in stable yet unspectacular opportunities yielding a 6 percent return. Their best guess at inflation is 4 percent for the foreseeable future. They plan to make investments on the child's birthday (U.S. style dictates first birthday is 1 year after date of birth), every year from age 1 through 18. They envision their child needing $100,000 at the beginning of the first year of college, with inflated amounts to follow for 3 more years. The first $100,000 will be needed right at the end of the eighteenth birthday's investment—right at the beginning of the nineteenth year.

   a. What equal amount of money must they invest at the end of each year?

   b. If the parents decide that their earning power will increase, and each year they will invest 10 percent more, how much must they invest in the first year?

   c. If a grandparent offers to put up the entire sum of money needed, on the date of the child's birth, what sum must they put up?

32. A ham radio operator wishes to borrow $160,000 to construct a world-class antenna system, transceiver, and amplifier at an electrically quiet location that can be accessed remotely and controlled via the Internet. Microphone, Morse code, radio teletype, slow-scan TV, and a host of other modes may be used for contesting, amassing DX awards, and chatting from anywhere in the world. She borrows the money at 8.5 percent. Inflation is running 3.8 percent. Her combined *MARR* is 9 percent. The loan is to be paid back over 5 years. What is the amount to be paid at each year-end and the PW (using both then-current and constant-dollar approaches) if repayment follows

   a. Method 1 (pay accumulated interest each year and principal at the end of the last year)?

   b. Method 2 (make equal annual principal payments each year, plus interest on the unpaid balance)?

   c. Method 3 (make equal annual payments)?

   d. Method 4 (make a single payment of principal and interest at the end of the last year)?

33. For the situation stated in Problem 32, let the interest on borrowed money go from 5 percent to 15 percent in 1 percent increments. For each borrowing rate, which repayment method is preferred? Do your answers match what is predicted in the text?

34. Steinway R&D is pursuing the development of an attachment that can easily clean the inside of grand pianos. This innovation will require a loan of $500,000 for fabrication and testing of several units. Inflation is 3.9 percent, and the loan is available to them at a rate of 10 percent. Their combined *MARR* is 17 percent. The loan is to be paid back over 4 years. What is the amount to be paid at the end of each year and the PW (using both then-current and constant-dollar approaches) if repayment follows

   a. Method 1 (pay accumulated interest each year and principal at the end of the last year)?

   b. Method 2 (make equal annual principal payments each year, plus interest on the unpaid balance)?

   c. Method 3 (make equal annual payments)?

   d. Method 4 (make a single payment of principal and interest at the end of the last year)?

35. For the situation stated in Problem 34, let the interest on borrowed money go from 7 percent to 20 percent in 1 percent increments. For each borrowing rate, which repayment method is preferred? Do your answers match what is predicted in the text?

Section 12.4

36. An economic analysis is being performed in real (not actual) dollars. The company's combined *MARR* is 10 percent, and the inflation rate is 4 percent. The asset has a first cost of $10,000. It will be depreciated as MACRS 3-year property using rates of 33.33 percent, 44.45 percent, 14.81 percent, and 7.41 percent. What depreciation amount will be shown in year 3 of the analysis?

37. Electronic Games is moving very quickly to introduce a new interrelated set of video games. The initial investment for equipment to produce the necessary electronic components is $9 million. The salvage value after 6 years is $700,000. Anticipated net contribution to income is $6 million the first year, decreasing by $1 million each year for 6 years, with all dollar amounts expressed in real dollars. Depreciation follows MACRS 5-year property, taxes are 40 percent, the real *MARR* is 18 percent, and inflation is 4 percent.

   a. Determine the actual after-tax cash flows for each year.

   b. Determine the PW of the after-tax cash flows.

   c. Determine the AW of the after-tax cash flows.

   d. Determine the FW of the after-tax cash flows.

   e. Determine the combined IRR of the after-tax cash flows.

   f. Determine the combined ERR of the after-tax cash flows.

   g. Determine the real IRR of the after-tax cash flows.

   h. Determine the real ERR of the after-tax cash flows.

38. Reconsider Problem 37 exactly as written.

   a. Determine the real after-tax cash flows for each year.

   b. Determine the PW of the after-tax cash flows.

   c. Determine the AW of the after-tax cash flows.

   d. Determine the FW of the after-tax cash flows.

   e. Determine the real IRR of the after-tax cash flows.

   f. Determine the real ERR of the after-tax cash flows.

   g. Determine the combined IRR of the after-tax cash flows.

   h. Determine the combined ERR of the after-tax cash flows.

39. Henredon purchases a high-precision programmable router for shaping furniture components for $190,000. It is expected to last 12 years and have a salvage value of $5,000. It will produce $45,000 in net revenue each year during its life. All dollar amounts are expressed in real dollars. Depreciation follows MACRS 7-year property, taxes are 40 percent, the real after-tax *MARR* is 10 percent, and inflation is 3.9 percent.

   a. Determine the actual after-tax cash flows for each year.

   b. Determine the PW of the after-tax cash flows.

   c. Determine the AW of the after-tax cash flows.

   d. Determine the FW of the after-tax cash flows.

   e. Determine the combined IRR of the after-tax cash flows.

   f. Determine the combined ERR of the after-tax cash flows.

   g. Determine the real IRR of the after-tax cash flows.

   h. Determine the real ERR of the after-tax cash flows.

40. Reconsider Problem 39 exactly as written.

   a. Determine the real after-tax cash flows for each year.

   b. Determine the PW of the after-tax cash flows.

   c. Determine the AW of the after-tax cash flows.

   d. Determine the FW of the after-tax cash flows.

   e. Determine the real IRR of the after-tax cash flows.

   f. Determine the real ERR of the after-tax cash flows.

   g. Determine the combined IRR of the after-tax cash flows.

   h. Determine the combined ERR of the after-tax cash flows.

41. Raytheon wishes to use an automated environmental chamber in the manufacture of electronic components. The chamber is to be used for rigorous reliability testing and burn-in. It is installed for $1.4 million and will have a salvage value of $200,000 after 8 years. Its use will create an opportunity to increase sales by $650,000 per year and will have operating expenses of $250,000 per year. All dollar amounts are expressed in real dollars.

Depreciation follows MACRS 5-year property, taxes are 40 percent, the real after-tax *MARR* is 10 percent, and inflation is 4.2 percent.

a. Determine the actual after-tax cash flows for each year.

b. Determine the PW of the after-tax cash flows.

c. Determine the AW of the after-tax cash flows.

d. Determine the FW of the after-tax cash flows.

e. Determine the combined IRR of the after-tax cash flows.

f. Determine the combined ERR of the after-tax cash flows.

g. Determine the real IRR of the after-tax cash flows.

h. Determine the real ERR of the after-tax cash flows.

42. Reconsider Problem 41 exactly as written.

a. Determine the real after-tax cash flows for each year.

b. Determine the PW of the after-tax cash flows.

c. Determine the AW of the after-tax cash flows.

d. Determine the FW of the after-tax cash flows.

e. Determine the real IRR of the after-tax cash flows.

f. Determine the real ERR of the after-tax cash flows.

g. Determine the combined IRR of the after-tax cash flows.

h. Determine the combined ERR of the after-tax cash flows.

43. Electronic Games is moving very quickly to introduce a new interrelated set of video games. The initial investment for equipment to produce the necessary electronic components is $9 million. The salvage value after 6 years is $700,000. Anticipated net production savings are $6 million the first year, decreasing by $1 million each year for 6 years, with all dollar amounts expressed in *actual* dollars. Depreciation follows MACRS 5-year property, taxes are 40 percent, the actual after-tax *MARR* is 22.72 percent, and inflation is 4 percent.

a. Determine the real after-tax cash flows for each year.

b. Determine the PW of the after-tax cash flows.

c. Determine the AW of the after-tax cash flows.

d. Determine the FW of the after-tax cash flows.

e. Determine the real IRR of the after-tax cash flows.

f. Determine the real ERR of the after-tax cash flows.

g. Determine the combined IRR of the after-tax cash flows.

h. Determine the combined ERR of the after-tax cash flows.

44. Reconsider Problem 43 exactly as written.

a. Determine the actual after-tax cash flows for each year.

b. Determine the PW of the after-tax cash flows.

c. Determine the AW of the after-tax cash flows.

d. Determine the FW of the after-tax cash flows.

e. Determine the combined IRR of the after-tax cash flows.

f. Determine the combined ERR of the after-tax cash flows.

g. Determine the real IRR of the after-tax cash flows.

h. Determine the real ERR of the after-tax cash flows.

45. Henredon purchases a high-precision programmable router for shaping furniture components for $190,000. It is expected to last 12 years and have a salvage value of $5,000. It will produce $45,000 in net revenue each year during its life. All dollar amounts are expressed in *actual* dollars. Depreciation follows MACRS 7-year property, taxes are 40 percent, the actual after-tax *MARR* is 14.62 percent, and inflation is 4.2 percent.

a. Determine the real after-tax cash flows for each year.

b. Determine the PW of the after-tax cash flows.

c. Determine the AW of the after-tax cash flows.

d. Determine the FW of the after-tax cash flows.

e. Determine the real IRR of the after-tax cash flows.

f. Determine the real ERR of the after-tax cash flows.

g. Determine the combined IRR of the after-tax cash flows.

h. Determine the combined ERR of the after-tax cash flows.

46. Reconsider Problem 45 exactly as written.

a. Determine the actual after-tax cash flows for each year.

b. Determine the PW of the after-tax cash flows.

c. Determine the AW of the after-tax cash flows.

d. Determine the FW of the after-tax cash flows.

e. Determine the combined IRR of the after-tax cash flows.

f. Determine the combined ERR of the after-tax cash flows.

g. Determine the real IRR of the after-tax cash flows.

h. Determine the real ERR of the after-tax cash flows.

47. Electronic Games is moving very quickly to introduce a new interrelated set of video games. The initial investment for equipment to produce the necessary electronic components is $9 million, with $4 million borrowed at 12 percent over 6 years and paying only the interest each year and the entire principal in the last year. The salvage value after 6 years is $700,000. Anticipated net contribution to income is $6 million the first year, decreasing by $1 million each year for 6 years, with all dollar amounts expressed in real dollars. Depreciation follows MACRS 5-year property, taxes are 40 percent, the real *MARR* is 18 percent, and inflation is 4 percent.

a. Determine the actual after-tax cash flows for each year.

b. Determine the PW of the after-tax cash flows.

c. Determine the AW of the after-tax cash flows.

d. Determine the FW of the after-tax cash flows.

e. Determine the combined IRR of the after-tax cash flows.

f. Determine the combined ERR of the after-tax cash flows.

g. Determine the real IRR of the after-tax cash flows.

h. Determine the real ERR of the after-tax cash flows.

48. Reconsider Problem 47 exactly as written.

a. Determine the real after-tax cash flows for each year.

b. Determine the PW of the after-tax cash flows.

c. Determine the AW of the after-tax cash flows.

d. Determine the FW of the after-tax cash flows.

e. Determine the real IRR of the after-tax cash flows.

f. Determine the real ERR of the after-tax cash flows.

g. Determine the combined IRR of the after-tax cash flows.

h. Determine the combined ERR of the after-tax cash flows.

49. Henredon purchases a high-precision programmable router for shaping furniture components for $190,000. It is expected to last 12 years and have a salvage value of $5,000. Henredon will borrow $100,000 at 13 percent over 6 years, paying only interest each year and paying all the principal in the sixth year. It will produce $45,000 in net revenue each year during its life. All dollar amounts are expressed in real dollars. Depreciation follows MACRS 7-year property, taxes are 40 percent, the real after-tax *MARR* is 10 percent, and inflation is 3.9 percent.

a. Determine the actual after-tax cash flows for each year.

b. Determine the PW of the after-tax cash flows.

c. Determine the AW of the after-tax cash flows.

d. Determine the FW of the after-tax cash flows.

    e. Determine the combined IRR of the after-tax cash flows.

    f. Determine the combined ERR of the after-tax cash flows.

    g. Determine the real IRR of the after-tax cash flows.

    h. Determine the real ERR of the after-tax cash flows.

50. Reconsider Problem 49 exactly as written.

    a. Determine the real after-tax cash flows for each year.

    b. Determine the PW of the after-tax cash flows.

    c. Determine the AW of the after-tax cash flows.

    d. Determine the FW of the after-tax cash flows.

    e. Determine the real IRR of the after-tax cash flows.

    f. Determine the real ERR of the after-tax cash flows.

    g. Determine the combined IRR of the after-tax cash flows.

    h. Determine the combined ERR of the after-tax cash flows.

51. Raytheon wishes to use an automated environmental chamber in the manufacture of electronic components. The chamber is to be used for rigorous reliability testing and burn-in. It is installed for $1.4 million and will have a salvage value of $200,000 after 8 years. Raytheon will borrow $800,000 at 12 percent to be paid back over 8 years. The environmental chamber will create an opportunity to increase sales by $650,000 per year and will have operating expenses of $250,000 per year. All dollar amounts are expressed in real dollars. Depreciation follows MACRS 5-year property, taxes are 40 percent, the real after-tax *MARR* is 10 percent, and inflation is 4.2 percent. Determine the actual after-tax cash flows for each year and the PW, FW, AW, IRR_c, ERR_c, IRR_r, and ERR_r for each of the following loan payment plans:

    a. Plan 1

    b. Plan 2

    c. Plan 3

    d. Plan 4

    e. Which is the preferred plan for Raytheon?

52. Electronic Games is moving very quickly to introduce a new interrelated set of video games. The initial investment for equipment to produce the necessary electronic components is $9 million, with $4 million borrowed at 12 percent over 6 years. The salvage value after 6 years is $700,000. Anticipated net contribution to income is $6 million the first year, decreasing by $1 million each year for 6 years, with all dollar amounts expressed in real dollars. Depreciation follows MACRS 5-year property, taxes are 40 percent, the real *MARR* is 18 percent, and inflation is 4 percent. Determine the actual after-tax cash flows for each year and the PW, FW, AW, IRR_c, ERR_c, IRR_r, and ERR_r for each of the following loan payment plans:

    a. Plan 1

    b. Plan 2

    c. Plan 3

    d. Plan 4

    e. Which is the preferred plan for Electronic Games?

Chapter 13

SUPPLEMENTARY ANALYSIS

BP's Texas City refinery, located in Texas City, Texas, processes many kinds of crude oil into a variety of fuels, chemical feedstock and other refined petroleum products for customers in the United States. (© BP p.l.c. Reprinted courtesy of BP p.l.c.)

BP

2010 was a difficult year for BP, one of the world's largest oil and gas companies. The Gulf of Mexico oil spill in April claimed eleven lives, injured multiple people, affected the incomes of thousands, and damaged the environment immeasurably. Carl-Henric Svanberg, BP's Chairman, wrote in the 2010 Annual Report, "In the days after the accident in the Gulf of Mexico the company faced a complex and fast-changing crisis. With oil escaping into the ocean, uncertainty grew around our ability to seal the well and restore the areas affected. This was an intense period, with the situation worsening almost daily. Our meeting with President Obama on 16 June 2010 provided reassurance to the U.S. government that BP would do the right thing in the Gulf, and this marked a turning point. Through diligence and invention, our teams stopped the flow of oil in July and completed relief-well operations in September." The accident reminds us of Machiavelli's claim in *The Prince*, ". . . not to extinguish our free will, I hold it to be true that Fortune is the arbiter of one-half of our actions, but that she still leaves us to direct the other half, or perhaps a little less."

As successful as BP had been until April of 2010, it cannot accurately predict what the future holds for it and its product portfolio. The uncertainty is due mainly to a host of exogenous factors, such as political instability in the Middle East, weather, earthquakes, the overall economy, and environmental concerns, among others. BP is not alone in this regard. No business or government is immune to the impact of unknown and unknowable factors on economic outcomes of capital investments. In fact, the Form10-K filings for publicly traded companies include extensive lists of risks that can significantly affect the profitability of the companies.

Unexpected things, such as natural disasters like earthquakes, tornadoes, and tsunamis, occur and have global impacts on businesses. In addition, disasters occur because of the actions or inaction of people, as in the subprime mortgage crisis in 2009 and 2010, the 2010 Gulf of Mexico oil spill, a series of explosions at BP's Texas City refinery in 2005, the U.S. terrorist attacks on September 11, 2001, the Exxon Valdez oil spill in Prince William Sound, Alaska, in 1989, and the release of 40 tons of methyl isocyanate gas from a Union Carbide pesticide plant in Bhopal, India, in 1984, causing more than 10,000 deaths. Each event impacted many lives and companies. But for every major event, there are thousands of smaller events that do not produce headlines, but still affect the financial outcomes of capital investments. Among the events that can have a significant ripple effect is a change in the price of a barrel of oil. Changes in oil prices have global economic impacts. The changes in retail gasoline prices have become more unpredictable than a ride on the Scream Machine.

In this chapter, we examine several techniques that are used to increase the confidence level of managers making capital investment decisions in the face of uncertain futures. As noted in Chapter 1, this chapter addresses the sixth step in the systematic economic analysis technique: *perform supplementary analyses*.

Systematic Economic Analysis Technique

1. Identify the investment alternatives
2. Define the planning horizon
3. Specify the discount rate
4. Estimate the cash flows
5. Compare the alternatives
6. Perform supplementary analyses
7. Select the preferred investment

13-1 INTRODUCTION

In performing engineering economic analyses, estimates of future cash flows are used. Since one seldom (if ever) knows with certainty what the future holds, it is advisable to examine the impact on an investment's economic worth for a range of values for the cash flows. Similarly, interest rates on borrowed funds, returns on invested capital, inflation rates, the duration of an investment, and the values for other economic analysis parameters either change during the planning horizon or are not known with certainty. Finally, some parameters are not easily quantified. In each of these situations, it is helpful to determine the answers to a number of "what if" questions.

This chapter begins by addressing situations where we want to know what single value for a particular parameter will make someone indifferent as to whether or not to make an investment. Such analyses are termed *break-even analyses,* and the *indifference value* is called the *break-even value* or *break-even point.*

The second type of supplementary analysis we consider is *sensitivity analysis.* In performing such analyses, we are interested in learning how sensitive the economic worth for one or more investments is to various values of one or more parameters.

The third type of supplementary analysis considered is *risk analysis.* In contrast to sensitivity analysis, probabilities are assigned to various values of one or more parameters, and a probabilistic statement is made regarding the economic worth for one or more investments. Typically, the probabilistic statement takes the form of "the probability of the investment having a positive-valued present worth is . . ." or "the probability of the internal rate of return for the investment being greater than the minimum attractive rate of return is . . ." or "the investment alternative having the greatest probability of having a positive-valued present worth is . . ."

Our consideration of risk analysis includes both analytical and simulation solutions. The analytical approaches to risk analysis require a familiarity with and an understanding of probability theory; the material on simulation can be understood without the same level of understanding. Both Monte Carlo and Latin hypercube simulation, manual and computer-based, are considered. (Finally, in an appendix, we describe the use of decision trees in coping with risk and uncertainty.)

After completing the material in this chapter, you should feel comfortable using various supplementary analysis methods when performing an engineering economic analysis. Further, because of their applicability to personal investing, the techniques we present can prove useful beyond engineering applications. Numerous examples and illustrations from simulation outputs are provided to facilitate understanding and to demonstrate the breadth of application of supplementary analyses. Depending on the objectives of the course, certain sections can be omitted and studied later, individually.

13-2   BREAK-EVEN ANALYSIS

Break-even analysis is normally used when an accurate estimate of a parameter's value cannot be provided, but intelligent judgments can be made as to whether or not the value is less than or greater than some break-even value. In performing a break-even analysis, we are seeking to determine the value of a parameter that equates to 0 the measure of economic worth being used (PW, FW, AW).

> In performing a break-even analysis, we are seeking to determine the value of a parameter that equates to zero the measure of economic worth being used (*PW, FW, AW*).

In an engineering economic analysis, break-even analysis is often used to determine the level of annual savings required to justify a particular capital investment. In a replacement study, break-even analysis is often performed on the purchase price or salvage value of the replacement alternatives. Likewise, break-even analysis might be used to determine how long annual savings must occur in order to economically justify a particular investment.

Although we did not label it as such, in Chapter 2 we performed several break-even analyses and referred to the process as *equivalence*. In particular, we posed a situation in which we determined the value of a particular parameter in order for two cash flow profiles to be equivalent. Another way of stating the problem could have been, "Determine the value of X that will yield a break-even situation between two alternatives." In this case, X denotes the parameter whose value is to be determined. Additionally, when the cash flow profiles for two alternatives are equivalent, a break-even situation can be said to exist between two alternatives.

The internal rate of return itself is a break-even value, since it is the interest rate that equates to 0 the economic worth of an investment. In other words, it is the interest rate that equates the present worth of the positive-valued cash flows to the present worth of the negative-valued cash flows. Stated another way, the internal rate of return is the break-even value for the reinvestment rate, since such a reinvestment rate will yield a future worth of 0 for either an individual alternative or the differences in cash flows for two alternatives. (Similarly, the external rate of return is a break-even value, since it is the interest rate that equates the future worth of negative-valued cash flows to the future worth of positive-valued cash flows when the positive-valued cash flows are reinvested and earn interest equal to the minimum attractive rate of return.)

Recall, in Chapters 5, 6, and 7, we introduced another example of break-even analysis. Specifically, we determined how long it would take to recover the initial investment, which is termed (a) the *payback period,* when the *TVOM* is negligible, and (b) the *discounted payback period,* when the *TVOM* is greater than 0. (Also, recall we used the Excel® **NPER** financial function to determine how long uniform annual savings had to occur in order to fully recover an initial investment, given a desired return on investment.)

Break-even analysis is certainly not an unfamiliar concept. Furthermore, the information obtained from it can be of considerable aid to anyone faced with an investment alternative involving a degree of uncertainty concerning some parameter's value. The term *break-even* is derived from the desire to determine the value of a given parameter that will result in neither a profit nor a loss.

EXAMPLE 13.1 Determining the Break-Even Sales Level

The Gizmo Manufacturing Company is considering making and selling a new product. The following data have been provided to management:

Sales price	$17.50/unit
Equipment cost	$250,000
Incremental overhead cost	$50,000/year
Sales and marketing cost	$150,000/year
Operating and maintenance cost	$25/operating hour
Production time/1,000 units	100 hours
Packaging and shipping cost	$0.50/unit
Planning horizon	5 years
Minimum attractive rate of return	15 percent

Some managers are reluctant to launch the new product because of the uncertainty of future sales. To provide management with information that might make it easier to draw the correct conclusion, a break-even analysis will be performed for annual sales required to economically justify introducing the new product.

Assuming a negligible salvage value for all equipment at the end of the 5-year planning horizon and letting X denote the annual sales for the product, the annual worth for the investment alternative can be determined as follows:

$$AW(15\%) = -\$250,000(A|P\,15\%,5) - \$50,000 - \$150,000 - 0.1(\$25)X - \$0.50X$$
$$+ \$17.50X$$
$$= -\$274,578.89 + \$14.50X$$

Setting the annual worth equal to 0 and solving for the break-even value gives a value of X equal to 18,936.475 units. Suppose there is certainty that annual sales will be between 20,000 and 30,000 units per year. In this case, obviously, the product should be launched. Clearly, it is not necessary to know precisely what the annual sales volume will be; instead, we need to know if it will be greater than or less than the break-even value.

The break-even value will not always fall outside the range of what are judged to be realistic values of a parameter. For example, if annual sales will be between 15,000 and 20,000 units per year, it is not obvious what decision should be made.

A graphical representation of the example is given in Figure 13.1. The chart is referred to as a *break-even chart,* since one can determine graphically the *break-even point* by observing the value of X when annual revenue equals annual cost.

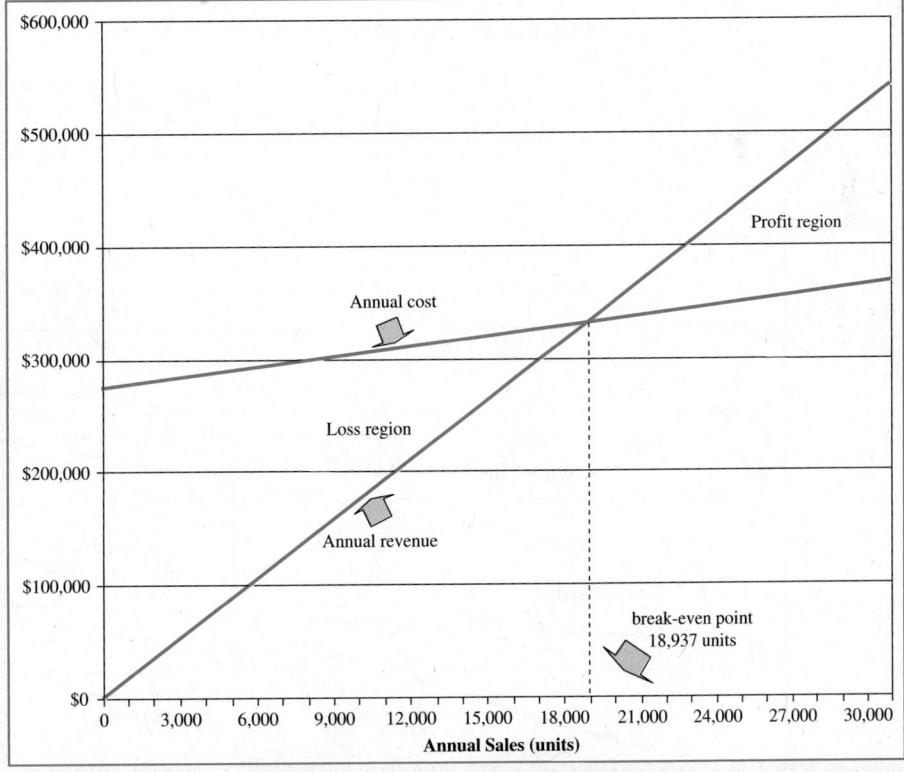

FIGURE 13.1

Break-Even Analysis for the Annual Sales of a New Product.

$42 \cdot)(+ 525000 \, AP + 50000 + 250000 + 45$

EXAMPLE 13.2 Determining the Break-Even Sales Volume for Two Products

Suppose Gizmo Manufacturing Company is considering making and selling a more sophisticated and more expensive version of the product, instead of the product considered in the previous example. Specifically, suppose the following data holds for Product 2:

Sales price	$42/unit
Equipment cost	$525,000
Incremental overhead cost	$50,000/year
Sales and marketing cost	$250,000/year
Operating and maintenance cost	$45/operating hour
Production time/1,000 units	215 hours
Packaging and shipping cost	$0.75/unit
Planning horizon	5 years
Minimum attractive rate of return	15 percent

Assuming a negligible salvage value for all equipment at the end of the 5-year planning horizon and letting Y denote the annual sales for Product 2, the annual worth for the investment alternative can be determined as follows:

$$AW_2(15\%) = -\$525,000(A|P\ 15\%,5) - \$50,000 - \$250,000 - 0.215(\$45)Y - \$0.75Y$$

$$+ \$41.25Y$$

$$= -\$456,615.67 + \$30.825Y$$

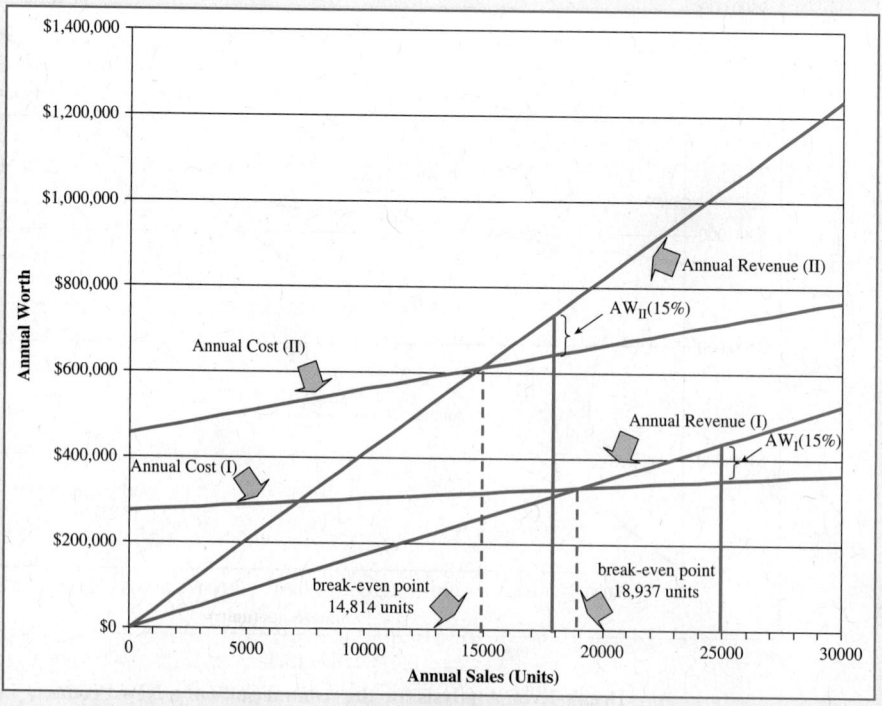

FIGURE 13.2
Break-Even Analysis for the Annual Sales of Two Competing Products.

Setting the annual worth equal to 0 and solving for the break-even value for the annual sales of Product 2 gives 14,813.16 units. To choose between the two products, a decision must be made concerning the likelihood of selling 18,937 units of the less sophisticated and less expensive Product 1 versus selling 14,814 units of the more sophisticated and more expensive Product 2. Since the two products would be competing in the same market, management recognizes it is not feasible to launch both.

Figure 13.2 provides a graphical representation of the choice Gizmo Manufacturing faces. From the charts, if management feels confident that Product 1 will achieve annual sales of 25,000 units and Product 2 will achieve annual sales of 18,000 units, which one should they manufacture and sell?

Since

$$AW_1(15\%) = -\$274{,}578.89 + \$14.50(25{,}000) = \$87{,}921.11$$

and

$$AW_2(15\%) = -\$456{,}615.67 + \$30.825(18{,}000) = \$98{,}234.33,$$

the more expensive product (2) should be launched.

EXAMPLE 13.3 Determining the Break-Even Value for Compressor Demand

Consider a small contracting business that utilizes compressors in its work. The contractor experiences a seasonal pattern of activity for compressors. When too few compressors are available, additional ones are rented from an equipment-rental firm. The business owns eight compressors, but based on recent demand, the owner is contemplating purchasing an additional one for use during heavy demand periods.

A local equipment-rental firm charges \$50/day for a compressor of the capacity the contracting business requires. The same compressor can be purchased for \$6,000. The operating and maintenance cost for compressors depends on annual usage and is estimated to be \$7.50/hour for owned compressors and \$2.50/hour for rentals.

Letting X denote the number of days a year that more than eight compressors are required, the following break-even analysis is performed. A 5-year planning horizon, a 0 salvage value, and a 15 percent minimum attractive rate of return are assumed. Also, it is assumed that compressors are operated 8 hours per day, if used at all. (P denotes the purchase alternative, and R denotes the rental alternative.)

$$EUAC_P(15\%) = \$6{,}000(A|P15\%, 5) + \$7.50(8)X$$
$$= \$1{,}789.80 + \$60X$$
$$EUAC_R(15\%) = \$50X + \$2.50(8)X$$
$$= \$70X$$

Setting the equivalent uniform annual cost equal for the two alternatives yields a break-even value of $X = 178.98$, or 179 days/year. Hence, if the contractor anticipates that a demand for more than eight compressors will occur 179 days or more during the year, then an additional compressor should be purchased.

EXAMPLE 13.4 Break-Even Analysis for the SMP Investment

Recall the $500,000 investment in a surface-mount placement machine, treated in previous chapters. Based on a 10-year planning horizon, a $50,000 salvage value, and a 10 percent *MARR*, what annual savings are required for the investment to *break even*?

Letting X denote the break-even value for annual savings, the following annual worth relationship must hold:

$$\$500{,}000(A|P\,10\%,10) = X + \$50{,}000(A|F\,10\%,10)$$

or

$$X = \$500{,}000(A|P\,10\%,10) - \$50{,}000(A|F\,10\%,10).$$

Using the Excel® **PMT** function,

$$X = \text{PMT}(10\%,10,-500000,50000)$$
$$= \$78{,}235.43$$

Similarly, suppose $92,500 is an accurate estimate of the annual savings that will result from the SMP investment, but it is not clear how long the machine will be used. To determine the break-even value for the investment's duration, an assumption is needed regarding the salvage value for the SMP machine if it is not used for 10 years.

First, suppose salvage value decreases linearly from $500,000 to $50,000 over a 10-year period. With salvage value decreasing at a rate of $45,000 per year, setting the EUAC of purchasing the SMP machine equal to the annual worth of the annual savings and salvage value gives

$$\$500{,}000(A|P\,10\%,n) = \$92{,}500 + (\$500{,}000 - \$45{,}000n)(A|F\,10\%,n).$$

What value of n is required for the equality to hold? As shown in Figure 13.3, using the Excel® **SOLVER** tool yields a value of 2.17 years for the break-even value of n.

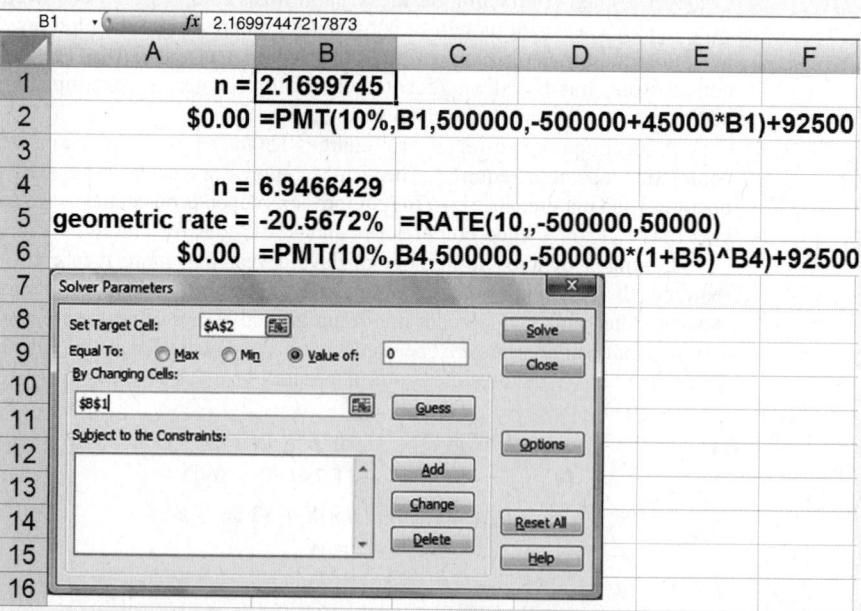

FIGURE 13.3

Using the Excel® SOLVER Tool to Determine the Break-Even Value for the Planning Horizon.

Second, suppose salvage value decreases geometrically from $500,000 to $50,000 over a 10-year period. Using the Excel® RATE function, the geometric rate is

$$j = \text{RATE}(10,,-500000,50000)$$
$$= -20.5672\%$$

Therefore,

$$\$500,000(A|P\ 10\%,n) = \$92,500 + \$500,000(0.794328^n)(A|F\ 10\%,n)$$

As shown in Figure 13.3, using the Excel® SOLVER tool yields a value of 6.95 years for the break-even value of n.

If we assume the salvage value is not a function of n and remains $50,000 regardless of the investment's duration, then the Excel® NPER function can be used to determine the break-even value of n:

$$n = \text{NPER}(92500,-500000,50000)$$
$$= 7.57668 \text{ years}$$

Likewise, if the salvage value is negligible, regardless of investment duration, the break-even value of n is given by

$$n = \text{NPER}(92500,-500000)$$
$$= 8.15972 \text{ years.}$$

EXAMPLE 13.5   Break-Even Analysis for a Snowblower Investment

A shopping center is considering paying $15,000 for a snowplow and blower, which will have a 5-year life, a negligible salvage value, and daily O&M expenses of $150. The firm can contract to have the snow removed at a cost of $450/day. With a *MARR* of 10 percent, how many days per year must the snowblower be used in order to justify the purchase?

Setting the equivalent uniform annual cost of the investment equal to 0 and solving for N, the number of days the snowplow and blower is used each year, gives

$$\$15,000(A|P\ 10\%, 5) + \$150N = \$450N$$

or

$$N = 50(A|P\ 10\%, 5) = 50(0.2638)$$
$$= 13.19 \text{ days/year}$$

Using the Excel® PMT function,

$$N = \text{PMT}(10\%,5,-50)$$
$$= 13.19 \text{ days/year}$$

We revisit break-even analysis in Chapter 16, where we consider fixed and variable costs. Now, we turn to the second supplementary analysis technique, sensitivity analysis.

13-3 SENSITIVITY ANALYSIS

Sensitivity analyses are performed to determine the impact on the measure of economic worth when values of one or more parameters vary over specified ranges. If modest changes of parameter values adversely affect an investment's economic worth, then it is said to be sensitive to changes in the particular parameters. On the other hand, if the economic choice is not affected by significant changes in the values of one or more parameters, then the decision is said to be insensitive to changes in the parameter values.

> Sensitivity analysis is performed to determine the impact on the measure of economic worth when values of one or more parameters vary over specified ranges.

We performed sensitivity analyses in several previous chapters, although we did not always refer to them as such. For example, in Chapters 5, 6, 7, and 8, we examined the impact on economic worth of the investment duration and minimum attractive rate of return. In Chapter 3, we examine the sensitivity of the preferred loan repayment method to changes in the borrower's *TVOM*. In Chapter 10, we examine the sensitivity of after-tax present worth to changes in the depreciation method, to changes in the amount of money borrowed, and to the interest rate on a loan. In Chapter 11, we examine the sensitivity of the optimum replacement interval to changes in the initial investment, the salvage value, the rate of increase in annual operating and management costs, and the minimum attractive rate of return. In Chapter 12, we examine the sensitivity of after-tax present worth to changes in the inflation rate; we also examine the impact of inflation on the preferred loan repayment method. In Chapter 15, we examine the sensitivity of the optimum investment portfolio to changes in the level of investment capital available and the minimum attractive rate of return.

A derisive term occasionally used to describe analytical models is *GIGO*—"garbage-in, garbage-out." In other words, what you get out of the model is no better than what you put into it. While one cannot always trust the results obtained from models of reality, perfect information is not often required to produce perfect or correct decisions. Sensitivity analysis can be used to determine if, in fact, less-than-perfect estimates of the parameter values will result in the best decision being made.

Among parameters that are most difficult to quantify in an engineering economic analysis are the intangible benefits that result from a particular investment. As an example, consider a material handling system that is to be installed in a distribution center. Among the benefits claimed for the new system are improved employee morale and increased flexibility. How might one go about quantifying morale and flexibility? Because they are not easily measured, some choose to ignore them.

When we encounter someone who is reluctant to consider intangible benefits, we think of Harvard accounting professor Robert Kaplan's comment in a *Harvard Business Review* article:[1] "Although intangible benefits are difficult to quantify, there is no reason to value them at zero in a capital expenditure analysis. Zero is,

---

[1] Kaplan, Robert S., "Must CIM Be Justified By Faith Alone?" *Harvard Business Review,* 64 (2), March–April 1986, pp. 87–95.

after all, no less arbitrary than any other number. Conservative accountants, who assign zero values to many intangible benefits, prefer being precisely wrong to being vaguely right. Managers need not follow their example.'' (We add, neither do engineers!)

For the material handling system in question, one might consider wide ranges of dollar values for the benefits of improved employee morale and of increased flexibility. Assigning modest values to intangible benefits may well prove to be the "tipping point" and cause a particular investment to be preferred over other alternatives. To ignore intangible benefits, as Kaplan noted, assigns them values of 0. If intangible benefits are real, they should not be dismissed simply because they are difficult to quantify.

Sensitivity analysis is not limited to assessing the impact of intangible benefits on a candidate investment's economic viability, as the following examples demonstrate.

EXAMPLE 13.6 Sensitivity Analysis for the SMP Investment

To illustrate how a sensitivity analysis might be performed, we consider once more the SMP investment: a $500,000 initial investment, annual savings of $92,500 for a 10-year period, and a salvage value of $50,000. As before, a 10 percent *MARR* applies.

Let's consider how sensitive the annual worth for the investment is to errors in estimating the initial investment, the annual savings, the salvage value, the investment's duration, and the *MARR*. Specifically, let's consider the impact on AW of each parameter for an error range of ±50 percent.

If it is assumed that all estimates are correct except that for annual receipts, the alternative's annual worth can be given as

$$AW(10\%) = -\$500,000(A|P\ 10\%, 10) + \$50,000(A|F\ 10\%, 10) + \$92,500(1 + X)$$

where X denotes the percent error (decimal equivalent) in estimating the value for annual savings. Plotting annual worth as a function of the percent error in estimating the value of annual savings yields the straight line having positive slope in Figure 13.4. Performing similar analyses for the initial investment required, the salvage value, the investment's duration (planning horizon), and the *MARR* yields the remaining results given in Figure 13.4.

(Note: For the example, we assumed the salvage value was $50,000, regardless of the investment's duration. In reality, salvage value depends on investment life. Also, we used annual instead of present worth in the sensitivity analysis because of the variability of the planning horizon.)

As shown in Figure 13.4, the investment's net annual worth is affected differently by errors in estimating the values of the various parameters. The net annual worth is relatively insensitive to changes in the parameters. Based on the slopes of the sensitivity curves, annual worth is most sensitive to errors in estimating the values of the initial investment, the annual savings, and the planning horizon. It is insensitive to changes in salvage value and is moderately sensitive to changes in the *MARR*.

The break-even values for the individual parameters are $587,649.62 for the initial investment, $78,235.43 for the annual savings, −$177,340.55 for the salvage value, 7.5767 years for the investment's duration, and 13.8 percent for the *MARR*. (As noted previously, the discounted payback period (DPBP) is the break-even value for the investment duration, and the internal rate of return (IRR) is the break-even value for the *MARR*.)

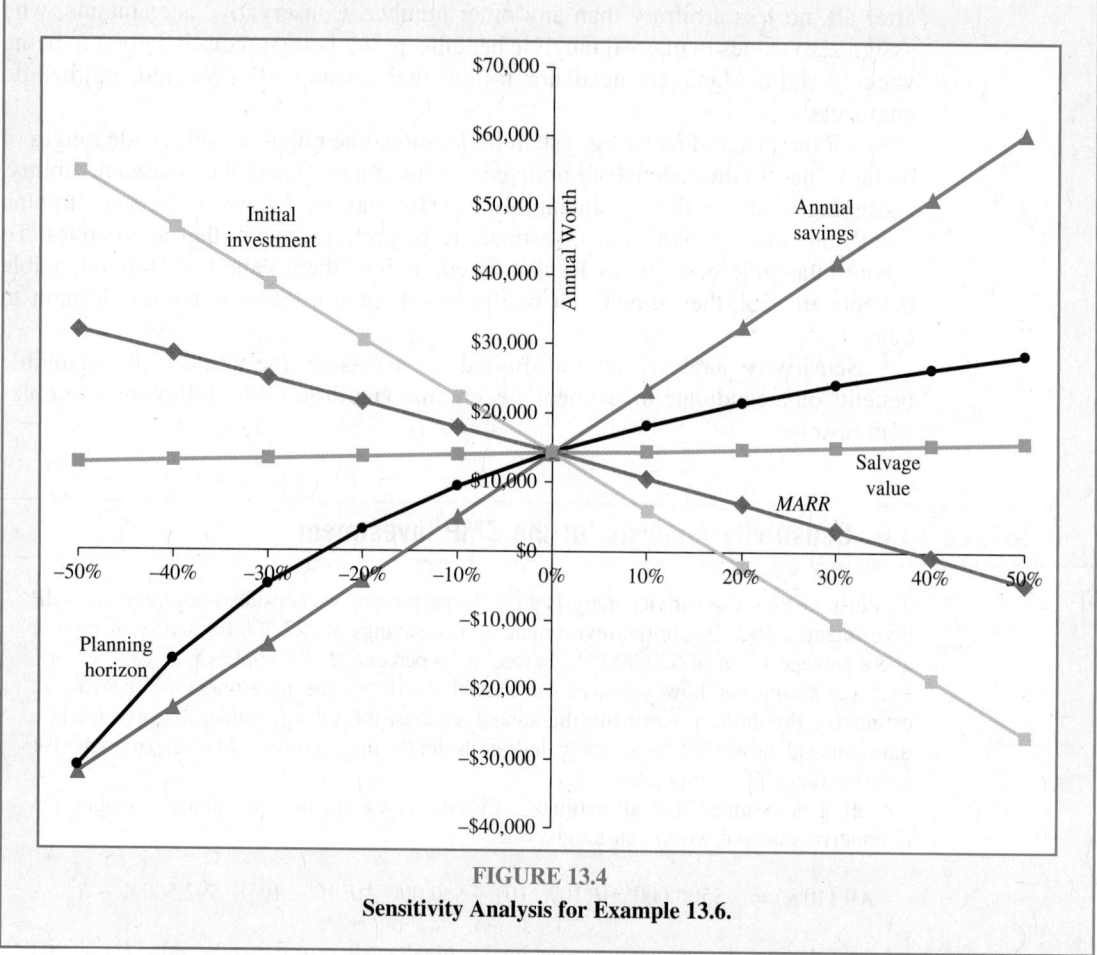

FIGURE 13.4
Sensitivity Analysis for Example 13.6.

The analysis depicted in Figure 13.4 examines the sensitivity of individual parameters, one at a time. In practice, estimation errors occur for more than one parameter, as shown in the following example.

EXAMPLE 13.7 Two-Parameter Sensitivity Analysis

An investment to modernize a distribution center is being considered. Specifically, automated storage and retrieval equipment has been proposed for the storage of pallet loads of product. The building has a projected life of 30 years, and the storage/retrieval equipment has a projected life of 15 years. A 15 percent *MARR* is being used. It is anticipated the new warehouse will require 70 fewer employees than the present system. Each employee costs approximately $27,500/year, including fringe benefits. The building is estimated to cost $3,750,000, and the material handling and storage equipment is estimated to cost $4,250,000. Annual operating and maintenance costs for the building and equipment are estimated to be $225,000/year more than the current operation. If the current warehouse is replaced with the automated warehouse, existing equipment can be sold at an estimated value of $750,000.

Using a 30-year planning horizon and assuming 15-year equipment will be replaced with equipment having a cash flow profile that is identical to the newly installed automated equipment, the annual worth for the investment is given by

$$AW = 70(\$27,500) - (\$3,750,000 - \$750,000)(A|P\,15\%,30) - \$4,250,000$$
$$\times (A|P\,15\%,15) - \$225,000$$

or, using the Excel® **PMT** function,

$$AW = 70*27500+PMT(15\%,30,3000000)+PMT(15\%,15,4250000)-225000$$
$$=\$516,276.93$$

The architectural and engineering estimate of \$3,750,000 for the building is believed to be accurate, as are the estimates of \$225,000 for annual operating and maintenance costs and \$750,000 for existing equipment. However, it is felt that the estimate of \$4,250,000 for the new automated warehouse equipment and the labor savings estimate of 70 employees are subject to error. A sensitivity analysis for these two parameters is to be performed on a before-tax basis.

Letting x denote the percent error in the estimate of equipment cost and letting y denote the percent error in estimating the annual labor savings, the automated warehouse will be justified economically if

$$AW = \$1,925,000(1 + y) - \$456,900.59 - \$726,822.47(1 + x) - \$225,000 \geq \$0$$

$$= \$516,276.90 - \$726,822.47x + \$1,925,000y \geq \$0$$

Solving for y,

$$y \geq -0.268196 + 0.37757x$$

Plotting the equation, as shown in Figure 13.5, indicates the favorable region $(AW > 0)$ lies above the break-even line; the unfavorable region $(AW < 0)$ lies below the break-even line.

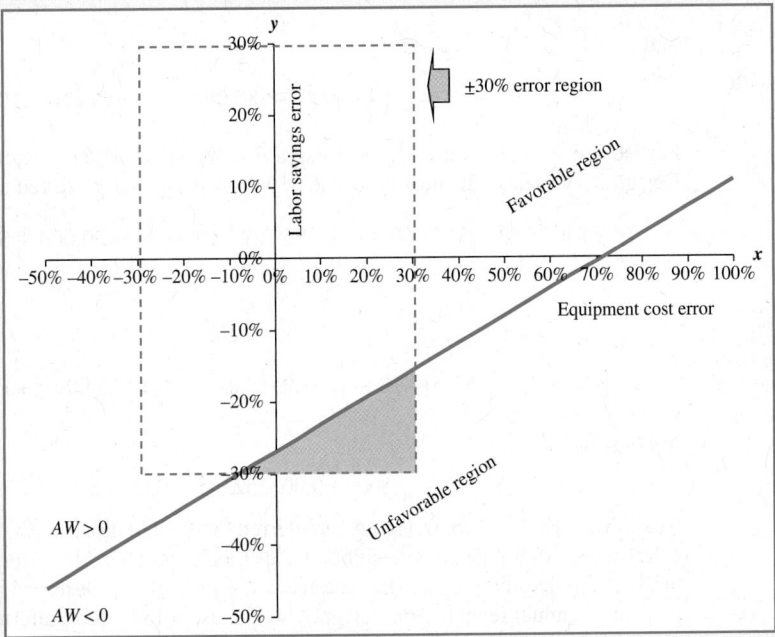

FIGURE 13.5
Sensitivity Analysis for Example 13.7.

If no errors are made in estimating the equipment cost—that is, $x = 0$—then up to a 26.82 percent reduction in labor savings can be tolerated. Likewise, if no errors are made in estimating the annual labor savings—that is, $y = 0$—then up to a 71 percent increase in equipment cost $(0.268196/0.37757)$ can occur, and the automated warehouse will continue to be justified economically.

Notice, very little of the ± 30 percent estimation error zone (shaded area) results in a negative annual worth. Consequently, it appears that the warehouse modernization is quite insensitive to errors in estimating the equipment cost, the labor savings, or both. However, the decision is more sensitive to errors in estimating labor savings than in estimating equipment costs.

EXAMPLE 13.8 Sensitivity Analysis for the Scream Machine Investment Problem

Recall, in previous chapters we considered two alternative designs for a new ride called the Scream Machine at a theme park in Florida. Design A had an initial cost of $300,000 and net annual after-tax revenues of $55,000; Design B had an initial investment of $450,000 and net annual after-tax revenues of $80,000. A 10 percent *MARR* was used over the 10-year planning horizon.

Letting x denote the error in estimating the annual revenue for Design A, and letting y denote the error in estimating the annual revenue for Design B, the present worth for each is as follows:

$$PW_A = -\$300,000 + \$55,000(1 + x)(P|A\ 10\%, 10)$$

and

$$PW_B = -\$450,000 + \$80,000(1 + y)(P|A\ 10\%, 10)$$

For Design A to be preferred over Design B, $PW(A) > PW(B)$. Therefore, assuming either Design A or Design B must be chosen, Design A will be preferred so long as

$$-\$300,000 + \$55,000(1 + x)(P|A\ 10\%, 10) > -\$450,000 + \$80,000(1 + y)$$
$$\times (P|A\ 10\%, 10)$$

or

$$\$3,614.18 - \$337,951.20x + \$491,565.00y < \$0$$

Solving for y,

$$y < -0.007352385 + 0.6875x$$

As shown in Figure 13.6, Design A is preferred for combinations of estimation errors that fall below the indifference diagonal plotted. Design B is preferred for error combinations above the indifference diagonal. If the estimates are correct for Design B, an increase of 1.07 percent in annual revenue for Design A will cause it to be the preferred choice. Likewise, assuming the estimates for Design A are correct, a decrease of 0.735 percent in annual revenue for Design B will make it no longer be the preferred choice. Therefore, the preferred design is sensitive to errors in estimating annual revenue.

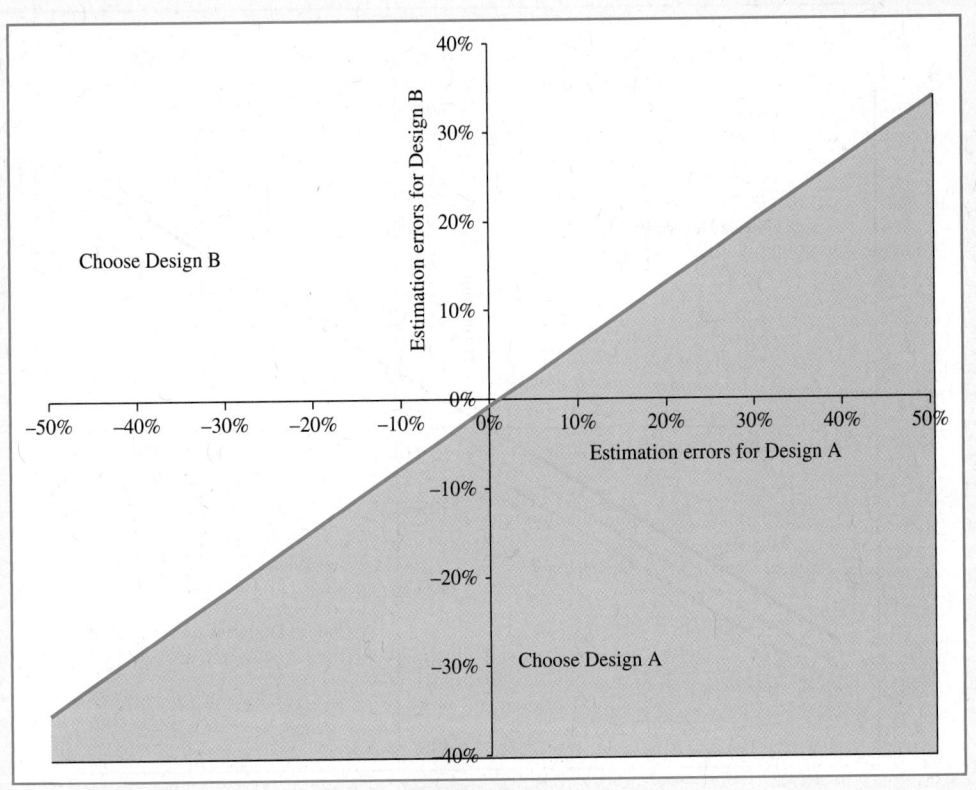

FIGURE 13.6
Sensitivity Analysis for Example 13.8.

EXAMPLE 13.9   Sensitivity Analysis for Three Parameters

In the previous example, suppose an additional parameter, the planning horizon, is to be considered, along with the estimation errors for annual revenue. Specifically, suppose the planning horizon can be either 7, 8, 9, or 10 years. How sensitive will the decision be between the two designs?

The indifference diagonal has already been plotted for $n = 10$. Equations for the diagonal when $n = 7$, 8, and 9 must be developed.

For $n = 7$, solving for y yields

$$y < 0.072635312 - 0.6875x$$

For $n = 8$, solving for y yields

$$y < 0.038957533 - 0.6875x$$

For $n = 9$, solving for y yields

$$y < 0.013076011 - 0.6875x$$

The resulting diagonals are shown in Figure 13.7. As before, combinations of errors in estimating annual revenue lying above the diagonal favor Design B; those lying below the diagonal favor Design A. (We excluded the do-nothing alternative in this analysis.)

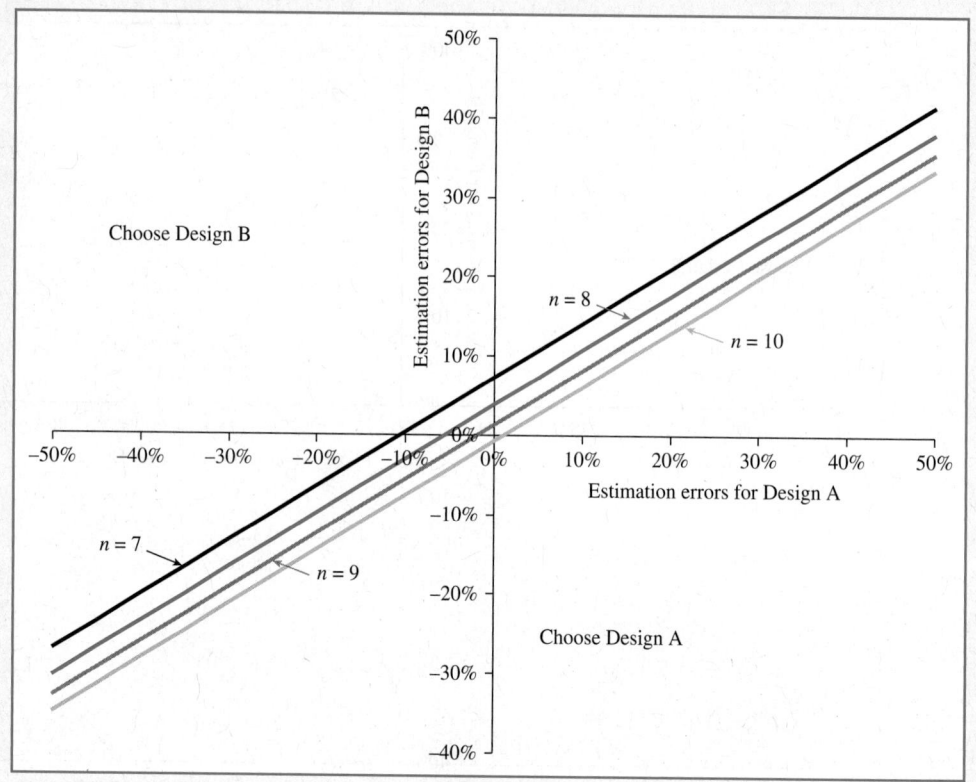

FIGURE 13.7
Sensitivity Analysis for Example 13.9.

Recall from Chapter 5, the DPBP for the investments in Designs A and B are 8.273 years and 8.674 years, respectively. Therefore, neither alternative will yield a positive-valued present worth for $n = 7$ unless the annual revenues are greater than originally estimated. In fact, for $n = 7$, a calculation establishes that the break-even values for x and y are 12.04 percent and 15.54 percent, respectively. Hence, unless annual revenue for Design A is at least 12.04 percent greater than originally estimated, then $PW(A) < 0$ when $n = 7$; similarly, unless annual revenue for Design B is at least 15.54 percent greater than originally estimated, then $PW(B) < 0$ when $n = 7$.

For $n = 8$, the break-even values for x and y are 2.24 percent and 5.44 percent, respectively. Hence, unless annual revenue for Design A is at least 2.24 percent greater than originally estimated, then $PW(A) < 0$ when $n = 8$; similarly, unless annual revenue for Design B is at least 5.44 percent greater than originally estimated, then $PW(B) < 0$ when $n = 8$.

For $n = 9$, the break-even values for x and y are −5.29 percent and −2.33 percent, respectively. Hence, annual revenue for Design A can be up to 5.29 percent less than originally estimated and still have $PW(A) > 0$ when $n = 9$; similarly, annual revenue for Design B can be up to 2.33 percent less than originally estimated and still have $PW(B) > 0$ when $n = 9$.

For $n = 10$, the break-even values for x and y are −11.23 percent and −8.46 percent, respectively. Hence, annual revenue for Design A can be up to 11.23 percent less than originally estimated and still have $PW(A) > 0$ when $n = 10$; similarly, annual revenues for Design B can be up to 8.46 percent less than originally estimated and still have $PW(B) > 0$ when $n = 10$.

A popular method of performing multiparameter sensitivity analysis is to provide three estimates for each parameter subject to estimation error. The estimates, typically, represent optimistic, pessimistic, and most likely values for each parameter. The following example illustrates this approach.

EXAMPLE 13.10 Multiparameter Sensitivity Analysis

For the previous example, suppose (for both designs) there is uncertainty concerning the values for the initial investments required and the annual revenue that will result. Specifically, suppose the estimates shown in Table 13.1 are available for the four parameters.

As shown, assuming the pessimistic scenario occurs for each, Design A is preferred. If, however, the optimistic or the most likely scenario occurs, then Design B is preferred.

TABLE 13.1
Optimistic, Pessimistic, and Most Likely Estimates, Plus Estimated Expected Values, for Four Parameters in Example 13.10.

Parameter	Optimistic	Pessimistic	Most Likely	Expected
Initial Investment (A)	$285,000	$310,000	$300,000	$299,166.67
Initial Investment (B)	$400,000	$510,000	$450,000	$451,666.67
Annual Revenue (A)	$65,000	$40,000	$55,000	$54,166.67
Annual Revenue (B)	$85,000	$70,000	$80,000	$79,166.67
PW_A	$114,396.86	−$64,217.32	$37,951.19	$33,664.05
PW_B	$122,288.20	−$79,880.30	$41,565.37	$34,778.23

In 1958, the use of three estimates was proposed by the developers of a project scheduling technique for the U.S. Navy's Polaris missile project. Called PERT (Project Evaluation and Review Technique),[2] three estimates were provided for activity times. A beta probability density function was assumed to approximate the distribution of activity times. The average or expected activity time was approximated as follows:

$$\text{Expected value} = [\text{pessimistic} + 4(\text{most likely}) + \text{optimistic}]/6 \qquad (13.1)$$

EXAMPLE 13.11 Using Approximations of Expected Values for the Multiple Parameters

Using Equation 13.1 to approximate the expected value for each of the four parameters for each design and computing the expected present worth yields the results shown in Table 13.1. Based on the expected values, Design B is preferred.

---

[2]See http://en.wikipedia.org/wiki/PERT for a description of the PERT algorithm.

EXAMPLE 13.12 Considering All Possible Combinations

In the previous example, it seems unlikely that pessimistic estimates will occur for all four parameters and for both designs. Likewise, it is unlikely that the optimistic estimates will occur for all four parameters for both designs. And, unfortunately, neither is it likely that the most likely estimates will be realized for each of the eight parameters (four for each design). Instead, combinations of pessimistic, optimistic, and most likely values will generally occur.

There are 81 possible combinations of the four parameters and three estimates ($3^4 = 81$) for each design. After computing the present worth for each design and for each possible combination, we show in Figure 13.8 the preferred design. In 41 cases of the 81 combinations considered, Design A has the greatest present worth. (Some might conclude that Design A is best because more than 50 percent of the combinations favor it. However, there is no reason to believe each combination is equally likely to occur. More will be said about this in the next section.)

E10 ▾ fx =IF(PV(10%,10,-$B10)-$A10>PV(10%,10,-E$3)-E$2,"A","B")

	A	B	C	D	E	F	G	H	I	J	K
1							Design B				
2			$400,000	$400,000	$400,000	$510,000	$510,000	$510,000	$450,000	$450,000	$450,000
3	Design A		$85,000	$70,000	$80,000	$85,000	$70,000	$80,000	$85,000	$70,000	$80,000
4	$285,000	$65,000	B	A	A	A	A	A	A	A	A
5	$285,000	$40,000	B	B	B	B	A	B	B	B	B
6	$285,000	$55,000	B	A	B	A	A	A	B	A	A
7	$310,000	$65,000	B	A	B	A	A	A	A	A	A
8	$310,000	$40,000	B	B	B	B	A	B	B	B	B
9	$310,000	$55,000	B	B	B	A	A	A	B	A	B
10	$300,000	$65,000	B	A	A	A	A	A	A	A	A
11	$300,000	$40,000	B	B	B	B	A	B	B	B	B
12	$300,000	$55,000	B	A	B	A	A	A	B	A	B
13											
14											
15											
16			=IF(PV(10%,10,-$B12)-$A12>PV(10%,10,-E$3)-E$2,"A","B")								
17											

FIGURE 13.8
Considering 81 Possible Combinations of 3 Estimates and 4 Parameters.

13-4 RISK ANALYSIS[3]

In performing break-even analyses, we seek to determine the value of a parameter that is, in essence, an indifference value. In other words, if the parameter takes on a value equal to the break-even value, then the present worth equals 0 and the internal rate of return equals the *MARR*. With sensitivity analysis, our desire is to gain an understanding of how the measure of economic worth behaves when parameter values are within a specified range; no knowledge is assumed as to the likelihood of the parameter taking on any particular value within the range.

Risk analysis is performed when probabilities can be assigned to various values of one or more parameters. We define *risk analysis* as the process of incorporating explicitly random variation in one or more parameters. For example, estimates of probabilities for possible values of annual savings, and estimates of probabilities for

---

[3]A basic understanding of probability theory is assumed for this section.

possible salvage values, might be used to analyze the economic worth of investing in a new machine tool.

> Risk analysis is performed when probabilities can be assigned to various values of one or more parameters. Risk analysis is defined as the process of incorporating explicitly random variation in one or more parameters.

Using either analytic or simulation approaches, risk analysis develops exact values or estimates for the expected value and standard deviation of the measure of economic worth. In addition, the probability of present worth, future worth, or annual worth being greater than 0 and the probability of internal rate of return or external rate of return being greater than the *MARR* are typically determined in risk analyses, either analytically or with simulation.

The magnitudes of cash flows, the planning horizon's duration, and the value of the *MARR* are candidates for probabilistic estimates. The cash flows occurring in a given year are often functions of several other factors, such as selling prices, market size and share, market growth rate, investment required, inflation rate, tax rates, operating costs, fixed costs, and salvage values of all assets. The values of a number of these random variables can be correlated with each other and can be autocorrelated.[4] Consequently, an analytical development of the probability distribution for the measure of economic worth is not easily achieved in most real-world situations. Thus, simulation is widely used in performing risk analyses.

13.4.1 Distributions

In comparison with sensitivity analyses, risk analyses attempt to reflect the imprecision inherent in assigning values to parameters in an engineering economic analysis. The imprecision is represented in the form of a probability distribution.

Probability distributions for the values of the parameters in question are often based on subjective probabilities. Occasionally, there might be historical data on which the probabilities are based. Typically, the more distant in the future an event is, the less precise is our estimate of the value of the event's outcome. Hence, letting the variance reflect our degree of precision, we expect the variance of the probability distributions to increase with time.

Among the probability distributions commonly used in risk analysis are the normal distribution and the beta distribution. Examples of these are depicted in Figures 13.9 and 13.10. For discussions of several probability distributions and their process generators in the context of simulation, see any number of simulation texts.

In some situations, the subjective probability distribution cannot be represented accurately using a well-known distribution. Instead, one must estimate directly the probability distribution for the random variable.

One approach to estimating the subjective probability distribution was introduced in the previous section—namely, providing optimistic, pessimistic, and most likely estimates for the random variable in question. The optimistic value should be one that is not expected to be exceeded more than, say, one percent of the time. A similar

---

[4]*Autocorrelation* means correlated with itself over time.

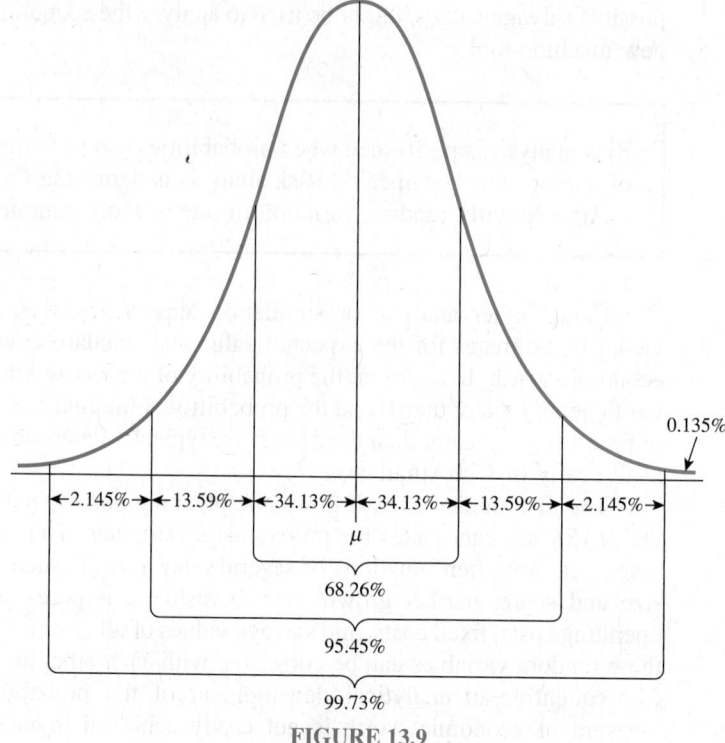

FIGURE 13.9
Normal Distribution.

standard applies to the pessimistic value. Using the optimistic and pessimistic values to establish practical limits on the range of values anticipated for the random variable, the probability of the most likely estimate being exceeded is projected. Next, a smooth curve is constructed, passing through the three estimates. This represents the cumulative distribution function for the random variable. Finally, the range is divided

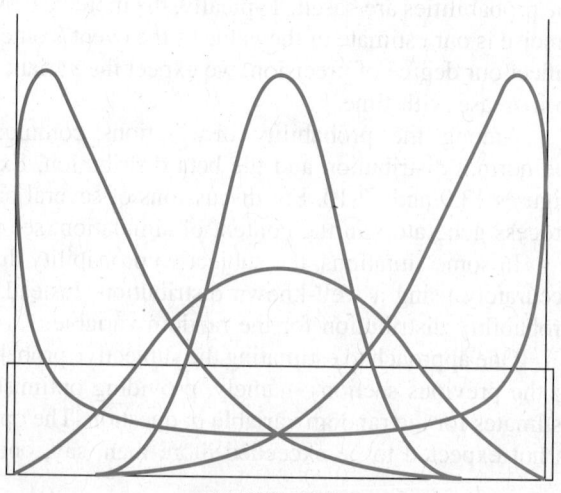

FIGURE 13.10
Sample Beta Distributions.

into an appropriate number of intervals, and individual probability estimates are obtained.

EXAMPLE 13.13 Developing Subjective Probabilities

To illustrate the process of developing subjective probabilities, suppose a probability distribution is to be created for the salvage value of a machine that will be used for 10 years. The machine has an initial cost of $15,000. Depending on the machine's condition, it is anticipated to have a salvage value from $0 to $3,000. The most likely estimate is $1,250. Based on a belief that the probability is 0.40 for the salvage value to be less than or equal to $1,250, the smooth curve depicted in Figure 13.11a is constructed.

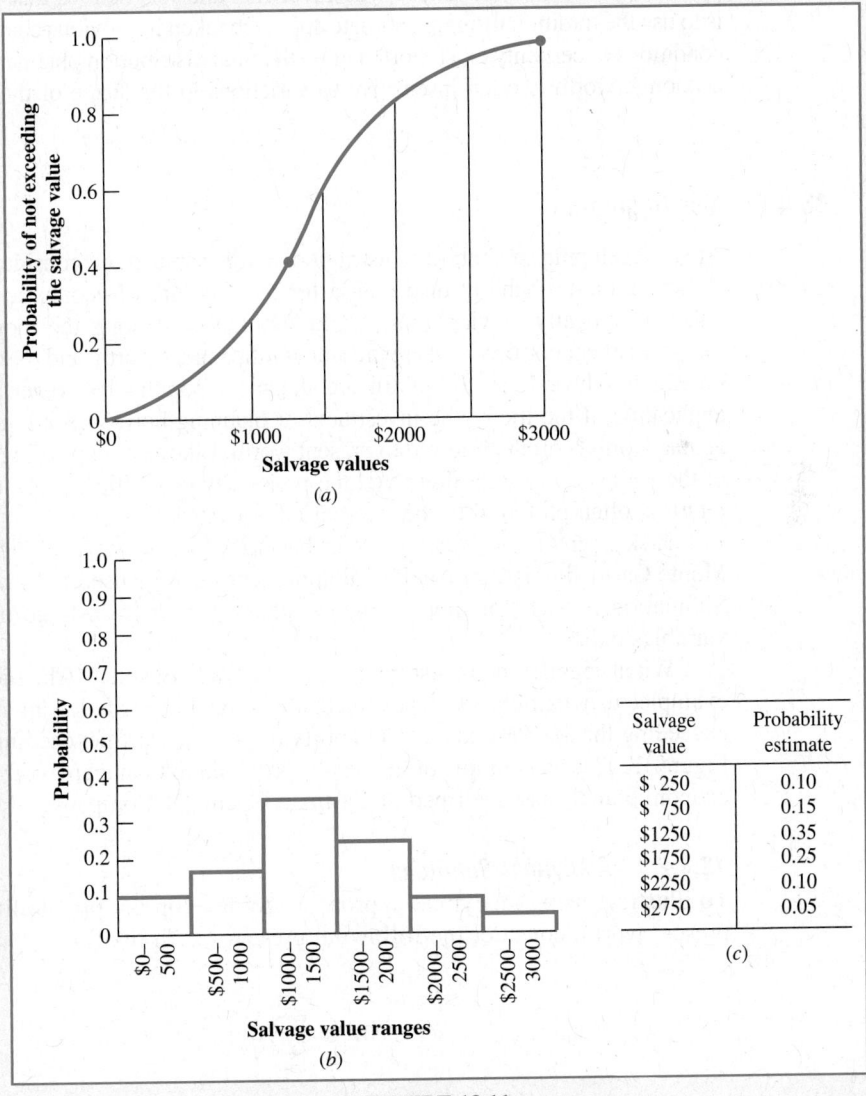

Salvage value	Probability estimate
$ 250	0.10
$ 750	0.15
$1250	0.35
$1750	0.25
$2250	0.10
$2750	0.05

(c)

FIGURE 13.11

Developing a Subjective Probability Distribution.

Using $500 intervals, the cumulative distribution function is transformed into the probability distribution shown in Figure 13.11b. Letting the midpoints of the intervals represent the probabilities associated with the intervals yields the probability mass function given in Figure 13.11c.

Clearly, the process described above is quite subjective. A large number of different curves can pass through the three estimates. However, if you are uncomfortable with the curve selected, then consider a variety of curves and determine how sensitive the outcome of the risk analysis is to the shape of the curve used.

Critics of risk analysis cite the degree of subjectivity involved in developing probability distributions. Those who favor risk analysis believe that the only alternative is to use the traditional single-estimate approach taken in previous chapters, which implies conditions of certainty exist. Fortunately, the final distribution obtained for the measure of economic worth is often insensitive to variations in the shape of the curve used.

13.4.2 Risk Aggregation

After developing probability distributions for parameters considered to be random variables, the probability distribution for the measure of economic worth is obtained, either analytically or via Monte Carlo simulation. Among the more commonly used measures of economic worth are present worth, annual worth, and rate of return. Of these, present worth and rate of return are the most popular. However, depending on the application, if the life of the investment or planning horizon is a random variable, then annual worth is often preferred to present worth. Likewise, depending on the magnitudes of the variances for cash flows and the possibility of multiple roots, the external rate of return is often preferred to the internal rate of return.

Risk aggregation is achieved in basically two ways: analytically and by using Monte Carlo simulation. Analytical approaches can be used for several simple cases. Simulation is used for more complex situations, where a large number of random variables exist.

When significant investments are involved, Eastman Chemical Company, for example, uses simulation to estimate the probability of the internal rate of return exceeding the *MARR* and the probability of present worth exceeding specified values. Figure 13.12 is an example of the results provided to management from an engineering economic analysis performed at Eastman Chemical Company.

13.4.2.1 Analytical Solutions

To illustrate using analytical approaches to develop the probability distribution for present worth, consider the following present worth relation:

$$PW = \sum_{t=0}^{n} A_t (1 + i)^{-t} \tag{13.2}$$

Random Cash Flows: Suppose the cash flows, A_t, are *random variables* with expected values $E(A)_t$ and variances $V(A)_t$.

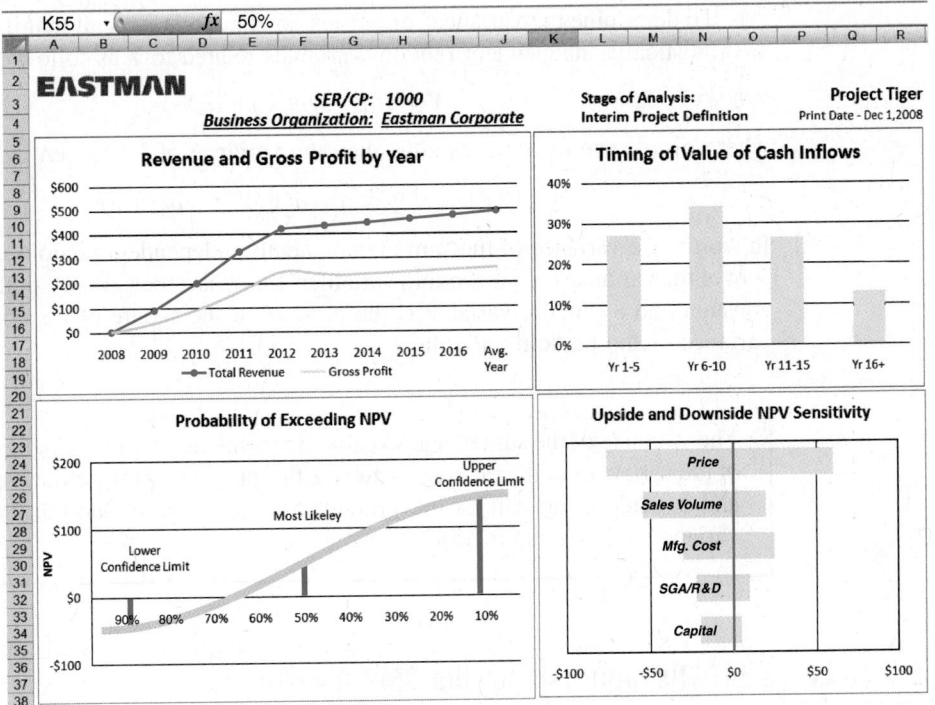

FIGURE 13.12

Example of Analyses Performed by EASTMAN.

Since the *expected value*[5] of a sum of random variables is given by the sum of the expected values of the random variables, the expected present worth is given by

$$E(PW) = \sum_{t=0}^{n} E[A_t(1+i)^{-t}] \tag{13.3}$$

Further, since the expected value of the product of a constant and a random variable is given by the product of the constant and the expected value of the random variable,

$$E(PW) = \sum_{t=0}^{n} E(A_t)(1+i)^{-t} \tag{13.4}$$

Hence, the expected present worth of a series of cash flows is found by summing the present worths of the expected values of the individual cash flows.

The expected value of a sum of random variables is the sum of the expected values of the random variables; the expected value of the product of a constant and a random variable is the product of the constant and the expected value of the random variable.

---

[5]Recall, the expected value of a random variable is obtained by summing over all values of the random variable the product of the value and the probability of its occurrence.

To determine the variance[6] of present worth, we first recall that if X_1, X_2, and X_3 are statistically independent random variables related to Y as follows,

$$Y = a_1X_1 + a_2X_2 + a_3X_3 \tag{13.5}$$

where a_1, a_2, and a_3 are constants, then the variance of Y is given by

$$V(Y) = a_1^2V(X_1) + a_2^2V(X_2) + a_3^2V(X_3) \tag{13.6}$$

In words, the variance of the sum of statistically independent random variables is the sum of the variances of the random variables. Likewise, the variance of the product of a constant and a random variable is the product of the square of the constant and the variance of the random variable.

The variance of the sum of statistically independent random variables is the sum of the variances of the random variables; the variance of the product of a constant and a random variable is the product of the square of the constant and the variance of the random variable.

EXAMPLE 13.14   Risk Analysis for the SMP Investment

To illustrate the calculation of the expected value and the variance of present worth, recall the SMP investment: $500,000 initial investment; $92,500 annual savings; $50,000 salvage value; 10-year planning horizon; and 10 percent *MARR*. Suppose the annual savings and the salvage value are random variables, distributed as shown in Table 13.2.

TABLE 13.2
Means, Variances, Standard Deviations, and Probability Distributions for Annual Savings and Salvage Value for Example 13.14.

A	p(A)	Ap(A)	A^2p(A)	SV	p(SV)	SVp(SV)	SV^2p(SV)
$75,000	0.070	$5,250	393,750,000	$40,000	0.10	$4,000	160,000,000
$80,000	0.095	$7,600	608,000,000	$45,000	0.20	$9,000	405,000,000
$85,000	0.131	$11,135	946,475,000	$50,000	0.40	$20,000	1,000,000,000
$90,000	0.178	$16,020	1,441,800,000	$55,000	0.20	$11,000	605,000,000
$95,000	0.183	$17,385	1,651,575,000	$60,000	0.10	$6,000	360,000,000
$100,000	0.181	$18,100	1,809,999,998	Sum	1.00	$50,000	2,530,000,000
$105,000	0.162	$17,010	1,786,050,000				
Sum	1.000	$92,500	8,637,649,998				
E(A) =	$92,500			E(SV) =	$50,000		
V(A) =	81,400,001.7			V(SV) =	30,000,000		
SD(A) =	$9,022.19			SD(SV) =	$5,477.23		

[6]Recall, the variance of a random variable equals the expected value of the square of the random variable less the square of the expected value of the random variable and the standard deviation of a random variable equals the square root of the variance of the random variable.

Computing the expected value for the annual cash flow gives \$92,500. Similarly, the expected value for the salvage value is \$50,000.

Applying Equation 13.6, the variance for annual savings is

$$V(A) = E(A^2) - [E(A)^2]$$
$$= (92,500)^2 - 8,637,649,998$$
$$= 81,400,001.7$$

and the variance for salvage value is

$$V(SV) = E(SV^2) - [E(SV)]^2$$
$$= (50,000)^2 - 2,530,000,000$$
$$= 30,000,000$$

Table 13.3 provides the results of applying the expected values and variances for the annual savings and salvage value to obtain the statistical parameters for the SMP investment's present worth. As noted, the expected present worth is \$87,649.62, and the variance of present worth is 334,461,261.82. Notice, the expected cash flow in the tenth year equals the sum of the expected annual savings and the expected salvage value; likewise, the variance of the cash flow in the tenth year equals the sum of the annual savings variance and the salvage value variance.

TABLE 13.3

Computing the Expected Value and Variance for the Present Worth of the SMP Investment, Plus the Probability of the Present Worth Being Greater than Zero.

				E(SV) =	\$50,000	
E(A) =	\$92,500			V(SV) =	30,000,000	
V(A) =	81,400,001.7			SD(SV) =	\$5,477.23	
SD(A) =	\$9,022.19					
EOY(t)	E(CF)	$(1.10)^{-t}$	$E(CF)(1.10)^{-t}$	V(CF)	$(1.10)^{-2t}$	$V(CF)(1.10)^{-2t}$
0	−\$500,000	1.0000	−\$500,000.00	0.0	1.0000	0.00
1	\$92,500	0.9091	\$84,090.91	81,400,001.7	0.8264	67,272,728.68
2	\$92,500	0.8264	\$76,446.28	81,400,001.7	0.6830	55,597,296.43
3	\$92,500	0.7513	\$69,496.62	81,400,001.7	0.5645	45,948,178.87
4	\$92,500	0.6830	\$63,178.74	81,400,001.7	0.4665	37,973,701.54
5	\$92,500	0.6209	\$57,435.22	81,400,001.7	0.3855	31,383,224.41
6	\$92,500	0.5645	\$52,213.84	81,400,001.7	0.3186	25,936,549.10
7	\$92,500	0.5132	\$47,467.13	81,400,001.7	0.2633	21,435,164.55
8	\$92,500	0.4665	\$43,151.93	81,400,001.7	0.2176	17,715,012.02
9	\$92,500	0.4241	\$39,229.03	81,400,001.7	0.1799	14,640,505.80
10	\$142,500	0.3855	\$54,939.92	111,400,001.7	0.1486	16,558,900.41
		E(PW) =	\$87,649.62		**V(PW) =**	334,461,261.82
					SD(PW) =	\$18,288.28
					Pr(PW>0)* =	0.999999176

*Central Limit Theorem approximation

Based on the Central Limit Theorem, we can expect the distribution of present worth to approximate a normal distribution. The Excel® **NORMSDIST** function can be used to approximate the probability of present worth being greater than 0. The syntax for the **NORMSDIST** function provides the probability of a normally distributed random variable with mean μ and standard deviation σ being less than or equal to z by entering =NORMSDIST$((z\text{-}\mu)/\sigma)$ in any cell. Due to the symmetry of the normal distribution, the probability of a normally distributed random variable with mean μ and standard deviation σ being greater than or equal to z can be obtained by entering =NORMSDIST$((\mu\text{-}z)/\sigma)$ in any cell. Hence, for $z = 0$,

$$\Pr(PW > 0) = \text{NORMSDIST}(E(PW)/SD(PW)) \tag{13.7}$$

where E(PW) and SD(PW) denote the expected value and standard deviation of present worth, respectively.

The Central Limit Theorem states that the distribution of the sum of independently distributed random variables approaches a normal distribution as the number of terms in the summation approaches infinity.

EXAMPLE 13.15 The Probability of the SMP Investment Being Profitable

Since the variance for the SMP investment is 334,461,261.82, the standard deviation is

$$SD(PW) = \sqrt{334,461,261.82}$$
$$= \$18,288.28$$

Therefore, for the SMP investment, based on the central limit theorem,

$$\Pr(PW > 0) = \text{NORMSDIST}(87649.62/18288.28)$$
$$= 0.999999177$$

Thus, the SMP machine is practically guaranteed to be a profitable investment.

Statistically Dependent Cash Flows: For the SMP investment, we assumed annual savings are statistically independent. In other words, we assumed the annual savings in any particular year are independent of the savings in every other year. While such an assumption is often valid, there are situations in which there is uncertainty about the annual savings the first year, with an expectation that subsequent years will produce savings identical to what occurs the first year. In such cases, the annual savings are *statistically dependent*. Since they are dependent over time, they are called *autocorrelated*. Not only are they autocorrelated, but they are also *perfectly correlated,* since knowing the value of annual savings the first year removes all uncertainty regarding the annual savings the remaining 9 years.

When random variables are perfectly correlated, recalling Equation 13.5, the standard deviation of Y is given by

$$SD(Y) = a_1 SD(X_1) + a_2 SD(X_2) + a_3 SD(X_3) \tag{13.8}$$

In words, the standard deviation of a sum of perfectly correlated random variables equals the sum of the standard deviations of the random variables. Likewise, the standard deviation of the product of a constant and a random variable is the product of the constant and the standard deviation of the random variable.

In Equation 13.2, suppose the cash flows, A_t, are *statistically dependent random variables* with expected values $E(A_t)$ and standard deviations $SD(A_t)$. In such a case, the standard deviation of the annual savings' present worth is given by

$$SD[PW(A)] = \sum_{t=0}^{n} SD(A_t)(1+i)^{-t} \qquad (13.9)$$

> The standard deviation of the sum of perfectly correlated random variables is the sum of the standard deviations of the random variables; the standard deviation of the product of a constant and a perfectly correlated random variable is the product of the constant and the standard deviation of the random variable.

EXAMPLE 13.16 The SMP Investment with Statistically Dependent Cash Flows

Suppose, in Example 13.14, the annual savings resulting from acquiring the SMP machine are perfectly autocorrelated. Applying Equation 13.9, as shown in Table 13.4, the standard deviation of the present worth of annual savings equals $55,437.48. Squaring the standard deviation gives a variance of 3,073,314,444.39. (Table 13.5 shows the results from an alternative approach to determine the variance of the present worth of annual savings. As expected, an identical result is obtained.)

Even though annual savings from year to year are statistically dependent, annual savings and the salvage value are statistically independent. Since the SMP investment's present worth equals the annual savings' present worth plus the salvage value's present

TABLE 13.4

Calculating the Standard Deviation and Variance for the Present Worth of the SMP Investment When the Cash Flows are Statistically Dependent and Perfectly Correlated.

$EOY(t)$	$SD(A_t)$	$(1.10)^{-t}$	$SD(A_t)(1.10)^{-t}$
0	0.00000	1.0000	0.00
1	9,022.19495	0.9091	8,202.00
2	9,022.19495	0.8264	7,456.36
3	9,022.19495	0.7513	6,778.51
4	9,022.19495	0.6830	6,162.28
5	9,022.19495	0.6209	5,602.07
6	9,022.19495	0.5645	5,092.79
7	9,022.19495	0.5132	4,629.81
8	9,022.19495	0.4665	4,208.92
9	9,022.19495	0.4241	3,826.29
10	9,022.19495	0.3855	3,478.45
		SD[PW(A)] =	$55,437.48
		V[PW(A)] =	3,073,314,444.39

TABLE 13.5

An Alternative Approach to Determine the Variance of Present Worth When the Cash Flows are Statistically Dependent and Perfectly Correlated.

Annual Savings	PW(Annual Savings)	p(A)	p(A)PW(A)	p(A)PW(A)²
$75,000	$460,842.53	0.070	$32,258.98	$14,866,308,810.88
$80,000	$491,565.37	0.095	$46,698.71	$22,955,468,589.24
$85,000	$522,288.20	0.131	$68,419.75	$35,734,830,810.85
$90,000	$553,011.04	0.178	$98,435.97	$54,436,175,348.62
$95,000	$583,733.88	0.183	$106,823.30	$62,356,378,347.48
$100,000	$614,456.71	0.181	$111,216.66	$68,337,825,823.37
$105,000	$645,179.55	0.162	$104,519.09	$67,433,576,766.13
		SUM =	$568,372.46	$326,120,564,496.57
		V[PW(A)] =		3,073,314,444.39

worth, the variance of present worth equals the variance of annual savings' present worth plus the variance of the salvage value's present worth.

The variance of the salvage value's present worth equals

$$V[PW(SV)] = V(SV)(1+i)^{-2n}$$
$$= 30,000,000(1.10)^{-20}$$
$$= 30,000,000(P|F\ i\%,2n)$$
$$= 4,459,308.84$$

Therefore, the variance and standard deviation of the SMP investment's present worth are

$$V(PW) = 3,073,314,444.39 + 4,459,308.84$$
$$= 3,077,773,753.23$$

and

$$SD(PW) = \sqrt{3,077,773,753.23}$$
$$= \$55,477.69$$

Using the Excel® NORMSDIST function, the probability of a positive-valued present worth can be approximated using the Central Limit Theorem as follows:

$$Pr(PW > 0) = \text{NORMSDIST}(87649.62/55477.69)$$
$$= 0.942936$$

Notice that the probability of the SMP investment being profitable is less when the annual savings are perfectly correlated. Even so, the chance of the SMP investment *not being profitable* is only slightly greater than 5 percent.

Random Sum of i.i.d. Random Variables: Another relationship among random variables that can be treated analytically is *the random sum of independent and identically distributed (i.i.d.) random variables.* By *random sum,* we mean the number of terms in the summation is a random variable; the elements being summed are also random variables. Specifically, if

$$Y = \sum_{j=1}^{N} X_j \tag{13.10}$$

where N is a discretely distributed random variable and X_j are *i.i.d.* random variables, then

$$E(Y) = E(N)E(X) \tag{13.11}$$

and

$$V(Y) = E(N)V(X) + V(N)[E(X)]^2 \tag{13.12}$$

> The expected value of the random sum of independent and identically distributed (i.i.d.) random variables is the product of the expected value of the random variable and the expected value of the number of terms in the summation; the variance of the random sum of i.i.d. random variables is the product of the expected value of the number of terms in the summation and the variance of the random variable plus the product of the variance of the number of terms in the summation and the square of the expected value of the random variable being summed.

Although one might be tempted to apply Equation 13.12 when the annual cash flows and the planning horizon are random variables, it is important to note that the set of X_j random variables must be identically distributed for Equation 13.12 to hold. Even if the discount rate is identically distributed, when either the future or present worth is computed, the random variable is raised to different powers over the summation. Hence, the X_j will not be identically distributed.

While Equation 13.12 cannot be used, for example, to determine the variance for present worth when the planning horizon is a random variable, it can be used in other ways, as the following example demonstrates.

EXAMPLE 13.17   Revisiting Gizmo Manufacturing

Recall Example 13.1, where the Gizmo Manufacturing Company was considering making and selling a new product. Recall, the following data were provided to management:

Sales price	$17.50/unit
Equipment cost	$250,000
Incremental overhead cost	$50,000/year
Sales and marketing cost	$150,000/year
Operating and maintenance cost	$25/operating hour
Production time/1,000 units	100 hours
Packaging and shipping cost	$0.50/unit
Planning horizon	5 years
Minimum attractive rate of return	15 percent

Also, recall the break-even sales value was 18,936.475 units.

Now, suppose that Gizmo will sell its new product through distributors and that the $17.50 sales price is what they charge its distributors. Distributors will sell the product for $25 each.

Gizmo is not sure how many distributors it can secure; therefore, the number of distributors is a random variable. The number of units each distributor sells is also a random variable.

Suppose the number of units a distributor sells is binomially distributed with a mean of 1,000 and a variance of 500. Also, suppose the number of distributors is discretely and uniformly distributed over the interval [16,25]; hence, the expected number of distributors is $(16 + 25)/2$, or 20.5, and the variance[7] is

$$[(25 - 16)^2 + 2(25 - 16)]/12$$

or 8.25.

From Equation 13.11, the expected number of units sold through distributors is 1,000(20.5), or 20,500. From Equation 13.12, the variance for the number of units sold through distributors is

$$500(20.5) + 8.25(1,000)^2$$

or 8,260,250.

Applying the Central Limit Theorem, the probability of Gizmo selling at least 18,936.475 units can be approximated using the Excel® **NORMSDIST** function:

$$\Pr(Y > 18,936.475) = \textbf{NORMSDIST(20500-18936.475)/SQRT(8260250)}$$
$$= \textbf{0.70678}$$

Therefore, there is a better than 70 percent chance of Gizmo breaking even in the sale of its product.

Notice, if Gizmo reduces the uncertainty in the number of distributors, the probability of breaking even increases. For example, if the number of distributors is uniformly distributed over the interval [19,22], the probability of breaking even increases to 0.91815.

Risk Analysis of Multiple Alternatives: Risk analysis can also be used when two or more alternatives are being compared. As shown in Figure 13.13, probability distributions for present worth can have different shapes and parameters (e.g., means and standard deviations). Depending on the situation, one might choose an investment with

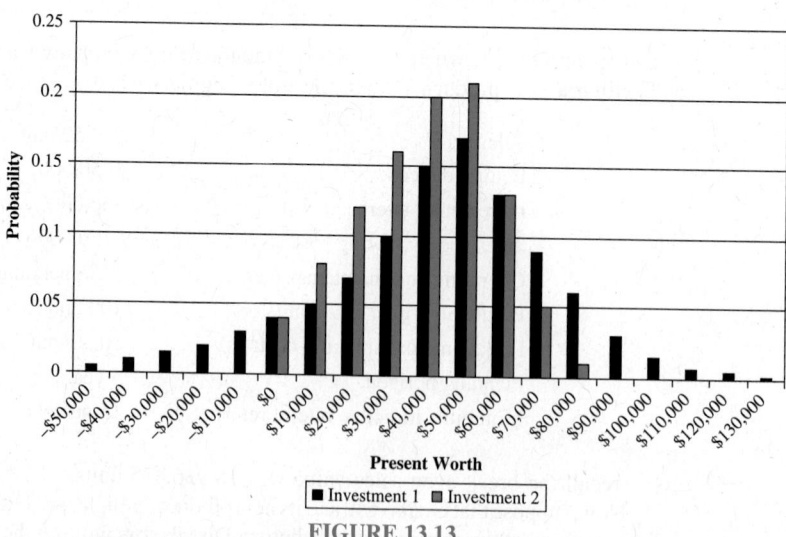

FIGURE 13.13

Probability Distribution for Present Worth for Two Investment Alternatives.

---

[7]For a discrete, uniform distribution (also called a *rectangular distribution*), [a,b], the mean is $(a + b)/2$ and the variance is $[(b - a)^2 + 2(b - a)]/12$.

a smaller expected value, if its standard deviation is significantly less than that for an investment with a larger expected value. Here, Investment 1 has a mean of $42,450 and a standard deviation of $30,495.86, with a 0.08 probability of a negative present worth; Investment 2 has a mean of $38,600 and a standard deviation of $18,221.96, with a zero probability of a negative present worth.

EXAMPLE 13.18   Risk Analysis for the Scream Machine Investment Problem

Recall the example involving two design alternatives (A and B) for a new ride (the Scream Machine) in a Florida theme park. Design A has an initial cost of $300,000 and net annual after-tax revenue of $55,000; Design B has an initial investment of $450,000 and net annual after-tax revenue of $80,000. A 10 percent *MARR* was used over the 10-year planning horizon. Now, suppose annual revenue for each machine is a statistically independent random variable. Further, suppose annual revenue for Design A is normally distributed with a mean of $55,000 and a standard deviation of $5,000; annual revenue for Design B is normally distributed with a mean of $80,000 and a standard deviation of $7,500. What is the probability of each design having a positive present worth? What is the probability of Design B having a greater present worth than Design A?

Since the annual revenues are statistically independent, normally distributed random variables, present worth will be normally distributed. The expected present worth for each design will be the same as in Chapter 5: $37,951.19 for Design A and $41,565.37 for Design B. Calculations for the variance and standard deviation for present worth for each design are summarized in Table 13.6. Also shown is the variance for the difference in cash flows,

TABLE 13.6
Risk Analysis for the Selection of the Scream Machine Design.

$EOY(t)$	$(1.10)^{-2t}$	$V(A_t)$	$V(A_t)(1.10)^{-2t}$	$V(B_t)$	$V(B_t)(1.10)^{-2t}$	$V(B_t - A_t)$	$V(B_t - A_t)(1.10)^{-2t}$
0	1.0000	0	0.0000	0	0.0000		
1	0.8264	25,000,000	20661157.0248	56,250,000	46487603.3058	81,250,000	67148760.3306
2	0.6830	25,000,000	17075336.3841	56,250,000	38419506.8643	81,250,000	55494843.2484
3	0.5645	25,000,000	14111848.2513	56,250,000	31751658.5655	81,250,000	45863506.8169
4	0.4665	25,000,000	11662684.5052	56,250,000	26241040.1368	81,250,000	37903724.6420
5	0.3855	25,000,000	9638582.2357	56,250,000	21686810.0304	81,250,000	31325392.2661
6	0.3186	25,000,000	7965770.4428	56,250,000	17922983.4962	81,250,000	25888753.9390
7	0.2633	25,000,000	6583281.3577	56,250,000	14812383.0547	81,250,000	21395664.4124
8	0.2176	25,000,000	5440728.3948	56,250,000	12241638.8882	81,250,000	17682367.2829
9	0.1799	25,000,000	4496469.7477	56,250,000	10117056.9324	81,250,000	14613526.6801
10	0.1486	25,000,000	3716090.7006	56,250,000	8361204.0764	81,250,000	12077294.7770

$V[PW(A)]$ = 101351949.0447		$V[PW(B\text{-}A)]$ = 329393834.3954
$SD[PW(A)]$ = $10,067.37		$SD[PW(B\text{-}A)]$ = $18,149.21
$\Pr[PW(A) > 0]^*$ = 0.999918		$\Pr[PW(B\text{-}A) > 0]^*$ = 0.578922
	$V[PW(B)]$ = 228041885.3507	
	$SD[PW(B)]$ = $15,101.06	
	$\Pr[PW(B{-}A) > 0]^*$ = 0.997043	

*Central Limit Theorem approximations

$(B - A)$. Notice, to determine which of the two designs is more profitable, we take advantage of $\Pr[PW(B) > PW(A)]$ being the same as $\Pr[PW(B - A) > 0]$.

Recall, the variance of the difference in two statistically independent random variables is the sum of the variances of the two random variables. Therefore, the variance of the difference in annual revenues equals the sum of $(5,000)^2$ for Design A and $(7,500)^2$ for Design B, or 81,250,000.

Notice, the probability of Design A having a positive present worth is 0.999918, the probability of Design B having a positive present worth is 0.997043, and the probability of Design B having a present worth greater than the present worth for Design A is 0.578922. Hence, the probability of Design A being the best choice economically is 0.421078, or there is a 58 percent chance that Design B is best and a 42 percent chance that Design A is best.

 The probabilities were calculated using the Excel® **NORMSDIST** function as follows:

$$\Pr[PW(A) > 0] = \text{NORMSDIST}(37951.19/10067.37)$$
$$= 0.999918$$

$$\Pr[PW(B) > 0] = \text{NORMSDIST}(41565.37/15101.06)$$
$$= 0.997043$$

$$\Pr[PW(B - A) > 0] = \text{NORMSDIST}(3614.18/18149.21)$$
$$= 0.578922$$

In the previous example, we assumed annual revenue was normally distributed. Recall, in Examples 13.10 through 13.12, we used the three-estimate approach to perform sensitivity analyses for the magnitude of the initial investment and the resulting annual revenue for the two designs. In Example 13.12, we considered all possible combinations of three estimates for four parameters (two parameters for each design). However, probabilities were not assigned to the 81 possible combinations. In the following example, we assign probabilities to each estimate and determine the probability that Design B is the preferred design, from a present worth perspective.

EXAMPLE 13.19 **Risk Analysis for the Scream Machine Investment Problem, Using the Three-Estimate Approach for Each Parameter**

We continue with the theme park investment problem. However, now we assume annual revenue resulting for each design is perfectly autocorrelated but is independent between designs. Hence, if the annual revenue for, say, Design A equals $65,000 in the first year, it will equal $65,000 each year for the rest of the planning horizon.

Here, we use the same optimistic, pessimistic, and most likely estimates of the parameters that were used in Examples 13.10 through 13.12. Now, though, we assign probabilities to each estimate, as given in Table 13.7. Computations establish that the expected investments for Designs A and B are $300,000 and $450,000, respectively. The expected annual revenues for Designs A and B are $55,000 and $80,000, respectively.

For each of the 81 possible combinations, Table 13.8 provides the probability of the combination occurring and the most economic choice between the two designs. To illustrate the calculations performed, consider the combination of an optimistic estimate for the initial investment required for Design A ($285,000), a most likely estimate for the annual revenue for Design A ($55,000), a pessimistic estimate for the initial investment required for Design

TABLE 13.7

Probability Distributions for Initial Investments and Annual Revenues for the Two Designs of the Scream Machine.

Design A			
Initial Investment	Probability	Annual Savings	Probability
$285,000	0.200	$40,000	0.150
$300,000	0.500	$55,000	0.625
$310,000	0.300	$65,000	0.225
Design B			
Initial Investment	Probability	Annual Savings	Probability
$400,000	0.25005	$70,000	0.125
$450,000	0.54200	$80,000	0.625
$510,000	0.20800	$85,000	0.250

B ($510,000), and an optimistic estimate for the annual revenue for Design B ($85,000). The probability of this combination occurring is (0.200)(0.625)(0.208)(0.250), or 0.00650.

Summing over the 81 possible combinations the probabilities when the economic choice is Design B results in a probability of 0.5673909. Notice how similar the result is to that obtained in the previous example, where annual revenue is assumed to be normally distributed *and* statistically independent *and* the initial investments were known with certainty.

TABLE 13.8

Preferred Design and Probability for Each Combination of Initial Investment and Annual Revenues for the Two Theme Park Design Alternatives.

Design A	Design B								
	$400,000 $85,000	$400,000 $70,000	$400,000 $80,000	$510,000 $85,000	$510,000 $70,000	$510,000 $80,000	$450,000 $85,000	$450,000 $70,000	$450,000 $80,000
$285,000 $65,000	B 0.002813	A 0.001407	A 0.007033	A 0.002340	A 0.001170	A 0.005850	A 0.006098	A 0.003049	A 0.015244
$285,000 $40,000	B 0.001875	B 0.000938	B 0.004688	B 0.001560	A 0.000780	B 0.003900	B 0.004065	B 0.002033	B 0.010163
$285,000 $55,000	B 0.007814	A 0.003907	B 0.019535	A 0.006500	A 0.003250	A 0.016250	B 0.016938	A 0.008469	A 0.042344
$310,000 $65,000	B 0.004220	A 0.002110	B 0.010549	A 0.003510	A 0.001755	A 0.008775	A 0.009146	A 0.004573	A 0.022866
$310,000 $40,000	B 0.002813	B 0.001407	B 0.007033	B 0.002340	A 0.001170	B 0.005850	B 0.006098	B 0.003049	B 0.015244
$310,000 $55,000	B 0.011721	B 0.005861	B 0.029303	A 0.009750	A 0.004875	A 0.024375	B 0.025406	A 0.012703	B 0.063516
$300,000 $65,000	B 0.007033	A 0.003516	A 0.017582	A 0.005850	A 0.002925	A 0.014625	A 0.015244	A 0.007622	A 0.038109
$300,000 $40,000	B 0.004688	B 0.002344	B 0.011721	B 0.003900	A 0.001950	B 0.009750	B 0.010163	B 0.005081	B 0.025406
$300,000 $55,000	B 0.019535	A 0.009768	B 0.048838	A 0.016250	A 0.008125	A 0.040625	B 0.042344	A 0.021172	B 0.105859

13.4.2.2 Simulation Solutions

Simulation, in the general sense, may be thought of as performing experiments on a model. Basically, simulation is an "if . . . , then . . ." device (i.e., *if* a certain input is specified, *then* the output can be determined). Some of the major reasons for using simulation in risk analysis include the following:

1. Except for the simplest problems, analytical solutions are difficult to obtain.
2. Simulation is useful in selling a system modification to management.
3. Simulation can be used as a verification of analytical solutions.
4. Simulation is very versatile.
5. Less background in mathematical analysis and probability theory is generally required.

Some of the major disadvantages of simulation are the following:

1. Simulation can be quite time-consuming.
2. Simulations introduce a source of randomness not present in analytical solutions (sampling error).
3. Monte Carlo simulations do not reproduce the input distribution exactly (especially the tails of the distribution).[8]
4. Validation of the simulation model is easily overlooked.
5. Simulation is so easily applied that it is often used when analytical solutions can be easily obtained at considerably less cost.

EXAMPLE 13.20 Monte Carlo Simulation

To illustrate the simulation approach in performing a risk analysis, consider an investment of $10,000 that returns A_t at the end of year t, with A_t being a statistically independent random variable. Using a *MARR* of 20 percent and a 4-year planning horizon, it is desired to use simulation to estimate the probability of the investment being unprofitable (or risky!). It is anticipated that the annual return each year will be either $2,000, $3,000, $4,000, or $5,000, with probabilities of occurrence equal to 0.1, 0.2, 0.3, and 0.4, respectively.

Based on the probability distribution for A_t, single-digit random numbers could be assigned to each value of the random variable in proportion to their probability of occurrence. However, because we will need two-digit random numbers in the next example, we will use them in this example.

Ten random numbers (00 through 09) designate an annual return of $2,000; twenty random numbers (10 through 29) designate an annual return of $3,000; thirty random numbers (30 through 59) designate an annual return of $4,000; and forty random numbers (60 thru 99) designate an annual return of $5,000.

Consulting a table of random numbers, such as Table 13.9, two-digit random numbers are selected, and the investment is simulated for a large number of trials. Beginning with Column 1, Row 1, and proceeding down the first column, the following sequence of four

---

[8]Latin hypercube simulation, included in Pallisade Corporation's @RISK software, uses stratified sampling of the input distributions to force sampling across the entire range of values of the random variables. It incorporates "sampling without replacement," because only one sample is drawn randomly from a stratification or stratum.

TABLE 13.9
Two-Digit Random Numbers.

72	71	87	95	73	76	60	87	33	84
48	05	12	09	42	86	10	66	68	74
61	86	49	48	39	90	13	07	80	82
26	48	46	47	60	75	80	73	97	13
05	42	50	49	18	92	78	02	72	82
11	77	40	78	07	21	36	53	86	73
73	26	97	62	71	70	41	69	18	92
39	32	86	85	19	85	78	30	27	18
40	56	22	12	66	67	28	56	29	38
09	71	64	20	07	69	40	15	99	29
23	40	63	18	53	99	76	97	86	13
18	99	49	83	84	90	28	57	73	05
67	02	03	40	34	58	82	90	50	54
66	10	50	06	71	40	35	91	72	73
93	44	25	83	60	76	25	8	34	99
19	84	84	01	41	53	92	51	39	08
25	76	84	73	12	76	36	83	61	53
62	31	29	24	81	95	69	11	10	12
47	25	46	28	88	97	78	04	27	59
85	09	07	53	92	23	78	62	83	31
93	90	23	66	65	86	06	48	99	94
89	85	58	67	30	70	11	28	60	52
15	80	86	91	79	92	40	16	16	3
57	94	93	01	05	45	72	82	6	56
44	71	33	53	46	93	88	48	33	31

random numbers is obtained: 72, 48, 61, and 26. This generates the following sequence of annual returns for the first simulated investment trial: $5,000, $4,000, $5,000, and $3,000. A computation establishes that the present worth for the first simulated investment trial is

$$PW(20\%) = NPV(20\%, 5000, 4000, 5000, 3000) - 10000$$
$$= \$1284.72$$

Obviously, one simulated investment is not sufficient to estimate the probability of the investment being profitable. Depending upon the desired level of accuracy, thousands of samples might be required. The results of 25 simulated investments are provided in Table 13.10. Based on this sample, an estimate of the probability of the investment being unprofitable is 0.32, since 8 of the 25 simulated investments had a negative present worth.

TABLE 13.10
Twenty-Five Monte Carlo Simulated Investments for Example 13.20.

Investment Trial	Year 1		Year 2		Year 3		Year 4		Present Worth MARR = 20%
	RN	Value	RN	Value	RN	Value	RN	Value	
1	72	$5,000	48	$4,000	61	$5,000	26	$3,000	$1,284.72
2	5	$2,000	11	$3,000	73	$5,000	39	$4,000	−$1,427.47
3	40	$4,000	9	$2,000	23	$3,000	18	$3,000	−$2,094.91
4	67	$5,000	66	$5,000	93	$5,000	19	$3,000	$1,979.17
5	25	$3,000	62	$5,000	47	$4,000	85	$5,000	$698.30
6	93	$5,000	89	$5,000	15	$3,000	57	$4,000	$1,304.01
7	44	$4,000	71	$5,000	5	$2,000	86	$5,000	$374.23
8	48	$4,000	42	$4,000	77	$5,000	26	$3,000	$451.39
9	32	$4,000	56	$4,000	71	$5,000	40	$4,000	$933.64
10	99	$5,000	2	$2,000	10	$3,000	44	$4,000	−$779.32
11	84	$5,000	76	$5,000	31	$4,000	25	$3,000	$1,400.46
12	9	$2,000	90	$5,000	85	$5,000	80	$5,000	$443.67
13	94	$5,000	71	$5,000	87	$5,000	12	$3,000	$1,979.17
14	49	$4,000	46	$4,000	50	$4,000	40	$4,000	$354.94
15	97	$5,000	86	$5,000	22	$3,000	64	$5,000	$1,786.27
16	63	$5,000	49	$4,000	3	$2,000	50	$4,000	$30.86
17	25	$3,000	84	$5,000	84	$5,000	29	$3,000	$312.50
18	46	$4,000	7	$2,000	23	$3,000	58	$4,000	−$1,612.65
19	86	$5,000	93	$5,000	33	$4,000	95	$5,000	$2,364.97
20	9	$2,000	48	$4,000	47	$4,000	49	$4,000	−$1,311.73
21	78	$5,000	62	$5,000	85	$5,000	12	$3,000	$1,979.17
22	20	$3,000	18	$3,000	83	$5,000	40	$4,000	−$594.14
23	6	$2,000	83	$5,000	1	$2,000	73	$5,000	−$1,292.44
24	24	$3,000	28	$3,000	53	$4,000	66	$5,000	−$690.59
25	67	$5,000	91	$5,000	1	$2,000	53	$4,000	$725.31
							% Negative =		32.0%

One should be cautious against drawing conclusions based on 25 simulated investments. In practice, it would be desirable to use a computer to simulate thousands of investments before estimating the probability of a negative present worth. In fact, we performed a Monte Carlo simulation of the investment, with 100,000 trials, and obtained an average present worth of $354.38 and an estimate of 0.37767 for the probability of the investment not being profitable.

The exact value of 0.3763 for $\Pr(PW < 0)$ can be obtained by enumerating the 4^4, or 256, possible combinations of four values of the random variable and a 4-year planning horizon. The E(PW), obtained from enumeration, is $354.94; as expected, it is identical to that obtained by using the expected annual return of $4,000.

$$\text{E}(PW) = \text{PV}(20\%, 4, -4000) - 10000$$
$$= \$354.94$$

EXAMPLE 13.21 Latin Hypercube Simulation

As noted previously, when using Monte Carlo simulation, many thousands of trials might be required to fully capture the tails of the distributions of the input parameters. Latin hypercube simulation overcomes this limitation of Monte Carlo simulation by using stratified sampling.

Figure 13.14 depicts the cumulative distribution function for the annual returns from a $10,000 investment. With Monte Carlo simulation, each point on the abscissa is equally likely to be chosen. With Latin hypercube simulation, the abscissa is divided into several equal-sized strata, with the number equal to the number of simulation trials to be performed. For the previous example, with 25 investment trials, there would be 25 strata formed, as shown in Figure 13.15.

Since Latin hypercube simulation uses "sampling without replacement," once an observation occurs within a particular strata, no additional observations can occur in the same strata. For the $10,000 investment, each year is treated separately.

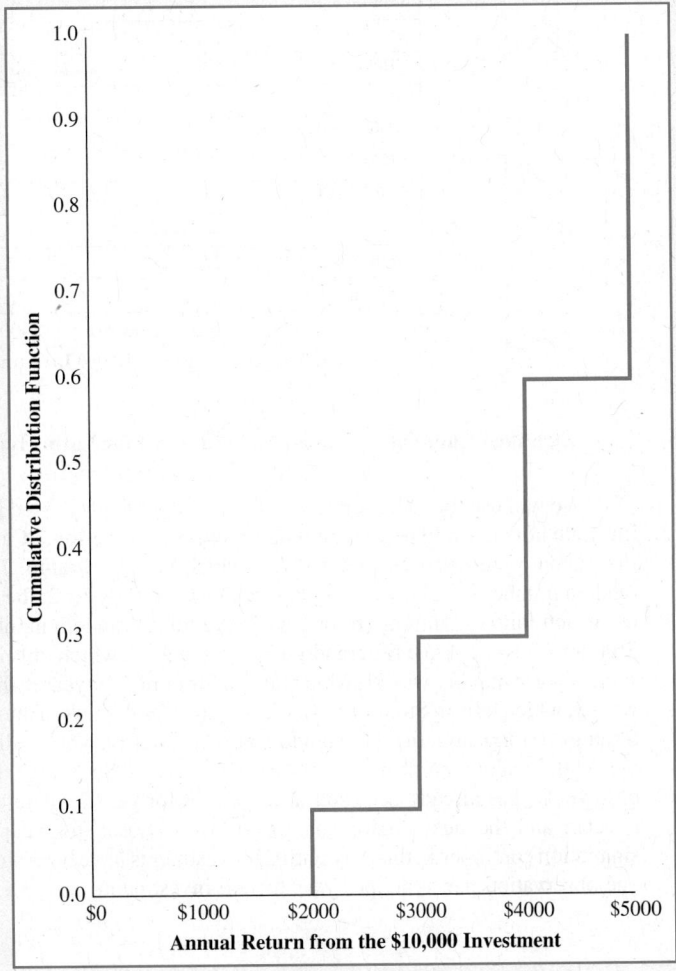

FIGURE 13.14

Cumulative Distribution Function for Example 13.21.

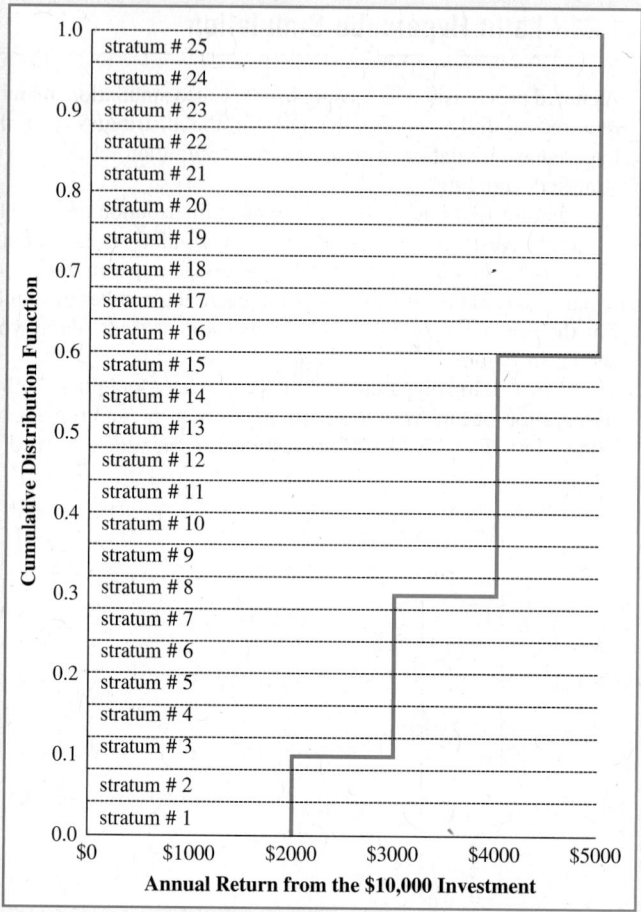

FIGURE 13.15

Stratified Cumulative Distribution Function for Latin Hypercube Simulation.

We will use the same sequence of random numbers as used in the previous example to illustrate how Latin hypercube simulation differs from Monte Carlo simulation. Recall, the first random number was 72 (or 0.72), which falls in Stratum 19 for year 1;[9] the second random number was 48, which falls in Stratum 13 for year 2; the third random number was 61, which falls in Stratum 16 for year 3; the fourth random number was 26, which falls in Stratum 7 for year 4; the fifth random number was 05, which falls in Stratum 2 for year 1; the sixth random number was 11, which falls in Stratum 3 for year 2; the seventh random number was 73, which falls in Stratum 19 for year 3; the eighth random number was 39, which falls in Stratum 10 for year 4; the ninth random number was 40, which falls in Stratum 11 for year 1; the tenth random number was 09, which falls in Stratum 3 for year 2. However, an observation has already occurred in Stratum 3 for year 2; therefore, random number 09 is rejected and the next random number (23) is chosen for year 2. The Latin hypercube simulation continues in this way until 25 investments have been simulated with no more than one observation per strata per year for the investment.

[9]The strata are defined as follows: [a,b). Therefore, since stratum 19 is defined by [72,76) and the random number is 72, then the random number is in stratum 19.

TABLE 13.11

Twenty-Five Randomly Selected Strata for the Latin Hypercube Simulation in Example 13.21.

Investment Trial	Year 1		Year 2		Year 3		Year 4	
	RN	Stratum	RN	Stratum	RN	Stratum	RN	Stratum
1	72	19	48	13	61	16	26	7
2	5	2	11	3	73	19	39	10
3	40	11	23	6	18	5	67	17
4	66	17	93	24	25	7	62	16
5	47	12	85	22	93	24	89	23
6	15	4	57	15	44	12	71	18
7	86	22	42	11	77	20	32	9
8	56	15	71	18	40	11	99	25
9	2	1	44	12	84	22	76	20
10	31	8	25	7	9	3	85	22
11	80	21	12	4	49	13	46	12
12	50	13	97	25	22	6	49	13
13	25	7	29	8	7	2	23	6
14	93	24	33	9	12	4	18	5
15	53	14	66	17	67	17	1	1
16	39	10	60	16	53	14	41	11
17	88	23	79	20	90	23	92	24
18	21	6	67	17	69	18	58	15
19	76	20	53	14	97	25	10	3
20	35	9	36	10	2	1	53	14
21	69	18	90	23	83	21	4	2
22	62	16	82	21	33	9	80	21
23	97	25	72	19	29	8	73	19
24	10	3	6	2	38	10	13	4
25	18	5	3	1	56	15	31	8

The results are provided in Tables 13.11 and 13.12. The conversion of random numbers to strata are provided in Table 13.11; monitoring the strata used for each investment year is required, since no more than one observation per strata can occur for each year. Notice, the percentage of the simulated investments resulting in a negative present worth is identical to that obtained using Monte Carlo simulation: 0.32. However, the average present worth obtained was quite different: $343.98 for Monte Carlo and $439.97 for Latin hypercube. (Recall from our discussion of analytical solutions that the expected present worth can be obtained by using the expected annual return of $4,000; the result is $354.94.)

To speed up the Latin hypercube simulation process, after an observation has occurred within a stratum, the stratum can be eliminated from further consideration ("sampling without replacement") and random numbers reallocated over the remaining strata. For example, for the $10,000 investment, after selecting the random number 72, we can eliminate Stratum 19 for year 1 and reassign the random numbers to the remaining 24 strata. (Obviously, the reassignment process is cumbersome when performing the simulation

TABLE 13.12

Twenty-Five Latin Hypercube Simulated Investments for Example 13.21.

Investment Trial	Year 1 RN	Year 1 Value	Year 2 RN	Year 2 Value	Year 3 RN	Year 3 Value	Year 4 RN	Year 4 Value	Present Worth MARR = 20%
1	72	$5,000	48	$4,000	61	$5,000	26	$3,000	$1,284.72
2	5	$2,000	11	$3,000	73	$5,000	39	$4,000	−$1,427.47
3	40	$4,000	23	$3,000	18	$3,000	67	$5,000	−$435.96
4	66	$5,000	93	$5,000	25	$3,000	62	$5,000	$1,786.27
5	47	$4,000	85	$5,000	93	$5,000	89	$5,000	$2,110.34
6	15	$3,000	57	$4,000	44	$4,000	71	$5,000	$3.86
7	86	$5,000	42	$4,000	77	$5,000	32	$4,000	$1,766.98
8	56	$4,000	71	$5,000	40	$4,000	99	$5,000	$1,531.64
9	2	$2,000	44	$4,000	84	$5,000	76	$5,000	−$250.77
10	31	$4,000	25	$3,000	9	$2,000	85	$5,000	−$1,014.66
11	80	$5,000	12	$3,000	49	$4,000	46	$4,000	$493.83
12	50	$4,000	97	$5,000	22	$3,000	49	$4,000	$470.68
13	25	$3,000	29	$3,000	7	$2,000	23	$3,000	−$2,812.50
14	93	$5,000	33	$4,000	12	$3,000	18	$3,000	$127.31
15	53	$4,000	66	$5,000	67	$5,000	1	$2,000	$663.58
16	39	$4,000	60	$5,000	53	$4,000	41	$4,000	$1,049.38
17	88	$5,000	79	$5,000	90	$5,000	92	$5,000	$2,943.67
18	21	$3,000	67	$5,000	69	$5,000	58	$4,000	$794.75
19	76	$5,000	53	$4,000	97	$5,000	10	$3,000	$1,284.72
20	35	$4,000	36	$4,000	2	$2,000	53	$4,000	−$802.47
21	69	$5,000	90	$5,000	83	$5,000	4	$2,000	$1,496.91
22	62	$5,000	82	$5,000	33	$4,000	80	$5,000	$2,364.97
23	97	$5,000	72	$5,000	29	$3,000	73	$5,000	$1,786.27
24	10	$3,000	6	$2,000	38	$4,000	13	$3,000	−$2,349.54
25	18	$3,000	3	$2,000	56	$4,000	31	$4,000	−$1,867.28
							% Negative =		32.0%

manually; however, as we shall subsequently see, it is relatively simple to do when using a computer.)

The "greedy" approach is another way to match random numbers to annual returns with Latin hypercube simulation: Instead of moving through the random number table until finding a feasible number, for a given random number, move through the annual returns until finding one that "can use" the random number. Table 13.13 provides the results using the greedy approach. Notice, the percentage of investments that had a negative present worth is 44 percent, and the average present worth is $340.90.

To allow a significantly greater sample size, we used a computer to perform a Latin hypercube simulation of the 4-year investment problem. Specifically, we used Pallisade Corporation's Excel®-based software @RISK 4.5 to simulate 100,000 investments. The result was an expected return of $354.94 and a 0.37761 probability of a negative present worth. To eliminate one source of sampling error, we used the same random number seed for

TABLE 13.13
Twenty-Five Latin Hypercube Simulated Investments Using a "Greedy" Approach for Example 13.21.

Investment Trial	Year 1 RN	Year 1 Value	Year 2 RN	Year 2 Value	Year 3 RN	Year 3 Value	Year 4 RN	Year 4 Value	Present Worth MARR = 20%
1	72	$5,000	48	$4,000	61	$5,000	26	$3,000	$1,284.72
2	5	$2,000	11	$3,000	73	$5,000	39	$4,000	−$1,427.47
3	40	$4,000	23	$3,000	9	$2,000	18	$3,000	−$1,979.17
4	67	$5,000	66	$5,000	93	$5,000	62	$5,000	$2,943.67
5	19	$3,000	25	$3,000	47	$4,000	85	$5,000	−$690.59
6	93	$5,000	89	$5,000	15	$3,000	57	$4,000	$1,304.01
7	44	$4,000	71	$5,000	5	$2,000	48	$4,000	−$108.02
8	86	$5,000	42	$4,000	77	$5,000	32	$4,000	$1,766.98
9	26	$3,000	56	$4,000	40	$4,000	71	$5,000	$3.86
10	99	$5,000	2	$2,000	44	$4,000	10	$3,000	−$682.87
11	76	$5,000	84	$5,000	31	$4,000	90	$5,000	$2,364.97
12	9	$2,000	80	$5,000	25	$3,000	94	$5,000	−$713.73
13	49	$4,000	71	$5,000	85	$5,000	46	$4,000	$1,628.09
14	22	$3,000	97	$5,000	64	$5,000	40	$4,000	$794.75
15	63	$5,000	29	$3,000	3	$2,000	7	$2,000	−$1,628.09
16	58	$4,000	93	$5,000	23	$3,000	78	$5,000	$952.93
17	33	$4,000	47	$4,000	83	$5,000	12	$3,000	$451.39
18	18	$3,000	62	$5,000	53	$4,000	20	$3,000	−$266.20
19	83	$5,000	6	$2,000	39	$4,000	1	$2,000	−$1,165.12
20	28	$3,000	53	$4,000	18	$3,000	73	$5,000	−$574.85
21	91	$5,000	19	$3,000	34	$4,000	66	$5,000	$976.08
22	1	$2,000	12	$3,000	71	$5,000	53	$4,000	−$1,427.47
23	70	$5,000	79	$5,000	88	$5,000	81	$5,000	$2,943.67
24	53	$4,000	36	$4,000	99	$5,000	30	$4,000	$933.64
25	36	$4,000	35	$4,000	56	$4,000	97	$5,000	$837.19
								% Negative =	44.0%

the Latin hypercube simulation as for the Monte Carlo simulation. The results obtained are shown below:

	Average	Pr(PW < 0)
Exact analytical solution	$354.94	0.3763
Monte Carlo simulation (25 trials)	$343.98	0.32
Monte Carlo simulation (100,000 trials)	$354.38	0.37767
Latin hypercube simulation (25 trials)	$439.97	0.32
Latin hypercube simulation (100,000 trials)	$354.94	0.37761

(The @RISK setup used for this and the previous example is shown in Table 13.14.)

TABLE 13.14

SetUp for the @RISK Simulation in Examples 13.20 and 13.21. (The Table was Generated with the Help of @RISK, a Product of Palisade Corporation, Ithaca, NY; www.palisade.com.).

	A EOY	B CF	C
1			
2	0	−$10,000.00	
3	1	$4,000.00	= RiskDiscrete({2000,3000,4000,5000}, {0.1,0.2,0.3,0.4})
4	2	$4,000.00	= RiskDiscrete({2000,3000,4000,5000}, {0.1,0.2,0.3,0.4})
5	3	$4,000.00	= RiskDiscrete({2000,3000,4000,5000}, {0.1,0.2,0.3,0.4})
6	4	$4,000.00	= RiskDiscrete({2000,3000,4000,5000}, {0.1,0.2,0.3,0.4})
7	**PW(20%) =**	$4,000.00	= RiskOutput("PW(20%)") + NPV(20%,B3:B6)+B2

Computer software is available to support simulation analyses. Among the vast array of options, we have found Pallisade Corporation's Excel®-based software, @RISK, to be easy to use. In addition, Microsoft's VBA (Visual Basic for Applications) software language can be used with Excel® to perform simulations of engineering economic investments.

@RISK software includes the option of using either Monte Carlo simulation or Latin Hypercube simulation. Practically every known probability distribution is included in @RISK's menu of input distributions. Among the discrete probability mass functions available are the binomial, discrete, discrete uniform (rectangular), hypergeometric, negative binomial, and Poisson distributions; the continuous probability density functions include, among others, the beta, chi square, Erlang, gamma, geometric, lognormal, normal, Pareto, PERT, triangular, uniform, and Weibull distributions.

The following examples illustrate the use of @RISK 4.5 simulation software in performing engineering economic analyses.

EXAMPLE 13.22   Monte Carlo Simulation of the SMP Investment

Recall, in Examples 13.14 and 13.15, we performed an analytical analysis of the SMP investment, with annual savings and salvage value assumed to be statistically independent random variables. The probability distributions used in previous examples are given in Table 13.15. The analytical solution yielded an expected present worth of $87,649.62, a variance for present worth of 334,461,261.82, and a 0.999999177 probability of a positive-valued present worth.

We also performed a Monte Carlo simulation using @RISK; 100,000 simulated investments yielded an average present worth of $87,677.55, a variance of 336,070,498, and an estimate of 0.999999135 (based on the central limit theorem) for the probability of a positive-valued present worth. The number of present worths that were greater than 0 totaled 100,000; not once was the present worth less than 0. This should not be surprising, since the expected number of instances of present worth being less than 0 is (0.000000823)(100,000),

TABLE 13.15
Probability Distributions for Example 13.22.

Annual Savings	Probability	Salvage Value	Probability
$75,000	0.070	$40,000	0.1
$80,000	0.095	$45,000	0.2
$85,000	0.131	$50,000	0.4
$90,000	0.178	$55,000	0.2
$95,000	0.183	$60,000	0.1
$100,000	0.181		
$105,000	0.162		

or 0.0823. The histogram obtained from the Monte Carlo simulation is provided in Figure 13.16.[10]

Since we can only determine the internal rate of return numerically, we did not consider the distribution of internal rate of return in Examples 13.14 and 13.15. However, with @Risk software and the Excel® **IRR** function, we can obtain an approximation of the distribution of IRR, as well as an estimate of the probability of IRR being less than the *MARR*. (Since $\Pr(IRR < MARR) = \Pr(PW < 0)$, we already know how many times IRR is less than 10 percent during the 100,000 simulation trials—zero!)

The Monte Carlo simulation yielded an estimate of 13.80126 percent for the expected internal rate of return for the SMP investment when annual savings and salvage value were statistically independent random variables. The sample standard deviation obtained for IRR was 0.7926308 percent. As noted, all simulated investments yielded an IRR value greater than or equal to the *MARR*. The histogram obtained from the Monte Carlo simulation is provided in Figure 13.17.

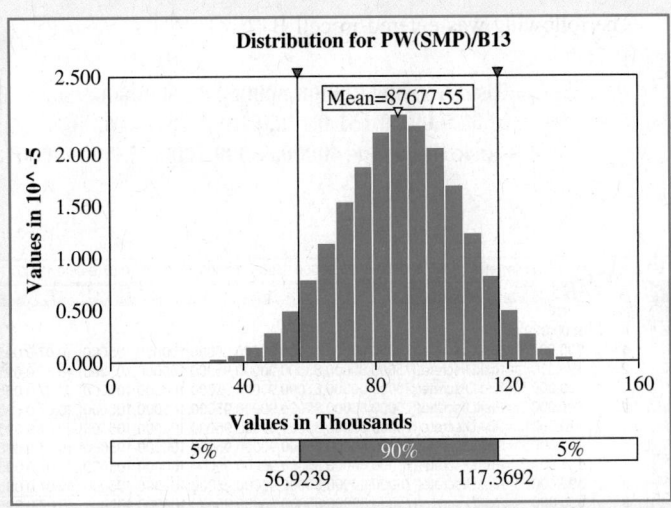

FIGURE 13.16

PW Histogram from 100,000 Simulation Trials in Example 13.22. (The Figure was Generated with the Help of @RISK, a Product of Palisade Corporation, Ithaca, NY; www.palisade.com.).

---

[10]Many of the figures and tables in this section were generated with the help of @RISK 4.5, a software product of Palisade Corporation, Ithaca, NY: www.palisade.com, or call 800-432-RISK (7475).

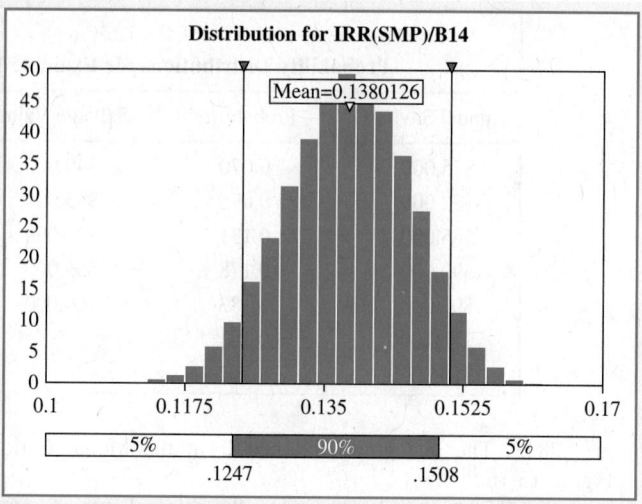

FIGURE 13.17

IRR Histogram from 100,000 Simulation Trials in Example 13.22. (The Figure was Generated with the Help of @RISK, a Product of Palisade Corporation, Ithaca, NY; www.palisade.com.).

The setup for the SMP investment, using @RISK, is shown in Figure 13.18. The following entries were made in cells B3:B11:

=RiskDiscrete({75000,80000,85000,90000,95000,100000,105000}, {0.07,0.095,0.131,0.178,0.183,0.181,0.162})

The following was entered in cell B12:

=RiskDiscrete({75000,80000,85000,90000,95000,100000,105000}, {0.07,0.095,0.131,0.178,0.183,0.181,0.162}) +RiskDiscrete ({40000,45000,50000,55000,60000}, {0.1,0.2,0.4,0.2,0.1})

	A	B	C	D	E	F	G	H	I	J	K	L	M
		B12	fx =RiskDiscrete({75000,80000,85000,90000,95000,100000,105000}, {0.07,0.95,0.131,0.178,0.183,0.181,0.162})+RiskDiscrete(										
1	EOY	CF											
2	0	-$500,000											
3	1	$90,000	=RiskDiscrete({75000,80000,85000,90000,95000,100000,105000}, {0.07,0.095,0.131,0.178,0.183,0.181,0.162})										
4	2	$90,000	=RiskDiscrete({75000,80000,85000,90000,95000,100000,105000}, {0.07,0.095,0.131,0.178,0.183,0.181,0.162})										
5	3	$90,000	=RiskDiscrete({75000,80000,85000,90000,95000,100000,105000}, {0.07,0.095,0.131,0.178,0.183,0.181,0.162})										
6	4	$90,000	=RiskDiscrete({75000,80000,85000,90000,95000,100000,105000}, {0.07,0.095,0.131,0.178,0.183,0.181,0.162})										
7	5	$90,000	=RiskDiscrete({75000,80000,85000,90000,95000,100000,105000}, {0.07,0.095,0.131,0.178,0.183,0.181,0.162})										
8	6	$90,000	=RiskDiscrete({75000,80000,85000,90000,95000,100000,105000}, {0.07,0.095,0.131,0.178,0.183,0.181,0.162})										
9	7	$90,000	=RiskDiscrete({75000,80000,85000,90000,95000,100000,105000}, {0.07,0.095,0.131,0.178,0.183,0.181,0.162})										
10	8	$90,000	=RiskDiscrete({75000,80000,85000,90000,95000,100000,105000}, {0.07,0.095,0.131,0.178,0.183,0.181,0.162})										
11	9	$90,000	=RiskDiscrete({75000,80000,85000,90000,95000,100000,105000}, {0.07,0.095,0.131,0.178,0.183,0.181,0.162})										
12	10	$140,000											
13	PW =	$72,288.20	=RiskOutput("PW(SMP)") + NPV(10%,B3:B12)+B2										
14	IRR =	13.149%	=RiskOutput("IRR(SMP)") + IRR(B2:B12)										
15			=RiskDiscrete({75000,80000,85000,90000,95000,100000,105000}, {0.07,0.095,0.131,0.178,0.183,0.181,0.162})										
16			+RiskDiscrete({40000,45000,50000,55000,60000}, {0.1,0.2,0.4,0.2,0.1})										
17													

FIGURE 13.18

Setup for @RISK Monte Carlo Simulation of Example 13.22. (The Figure was Generated with the Help of @RISK, a Product of Palisade Corporation, Ithaca, NY; www.palisade.com.).

In cells B13 and B14, the following entries were made:

$$=\text{RiskOutput(``PW(SMP)'')}+\text{NPV}(10\%,\text{B3:B12})+\text{B2}$$

and

$$=\text{RiskOutput(``IRR(SMP)'')}+\text{IRR(B2:B12)}$$

For the 10 input cells (B3:B12), the discrete probability distributions were entered. Notice, for EOY = 10, the sum of annual savings and salvage value occurs; therefore, the input is the sum of the two distributions.

EXAMPLE 13.23 Using Simulation with Dependent Random Variables

Recall, Example 13.16 considered the SMP investment when the annual savings were autocorrelated and salvage value was randomly distributed in the same manner as in the previous example. When the annual cash flows were statistically independent, we used the Excel® **NPV** function to determine present worth. When the annual cash flows are perfectly autocorrelated, the Excel® **PV** function is used, as shown in Figure 13.19. Likewise, notice that we use the Excel® **RATE** function to determine the IRR when the annual cash flows are perfectly autocorrelated; when they are statistically independent, we use the Excel® **IRR** function.

Based on 100,000 simulated investments, the average present worth is $87,556.22 and the average internal rate of return is 13.758 percent. The investment had a positive-valued present worth and an internal rate of return greater than the *MARR* 92.93 percent of the time. Recall, the analytical solution included an expected present worth of $87,649.62 and a probability of 0.942936 of the investment being profitable. Hence, the Monte Carlo simulation slightly underestimated the investment's profitability.

The histograms for present worth and internal rate of return produced by @**RISK** for the 100,000 simulated investments are shown in Figure 13.20. (@**RISK** provides a wealth of results; we have only scratched the surface in terms of the output statistics and reports provided by the program.)

	C2	▾	*fx* =RiskDiscrete({75000,80000,85000,90000,95000,100000,105000}, {0.07,0.95,0.131,0.178,0.183,0.181,0.162})							
	A	B	C	D	E	F	G	H	I	J
1	Initial Investment =		$500,000							
2	Annual Savings =		$90,000							
3	Salvage Value =		$50,000	=RiskDiscrete({40000,45000,50000,55000,60000}, {0.1,0.2,0.4,0.2,0.1})						
4		PW =	72288.204	=RiskOutput("PW(SMP) =") + PV(10%,10,-C2,-C3)-500000						
5		IRR =	0.131492	=RiskOutput() + RATE(10,C2,-C1,C3)						
6										
7										
8	=RiskDiscrete({75000,80000,85000,90000,95000,100000,105000}, {0.07,0.095,0.131,0.178,0.183,0.181,0.162})									
9										

FIGURE 13.19

Setup for @RISK Monte Carlo Simulation of Example 13.23. (The Figure was Generated with the Help of @RISK, a Product of Palisade Corporation, Ithaca, NY; www.palisade.com.).

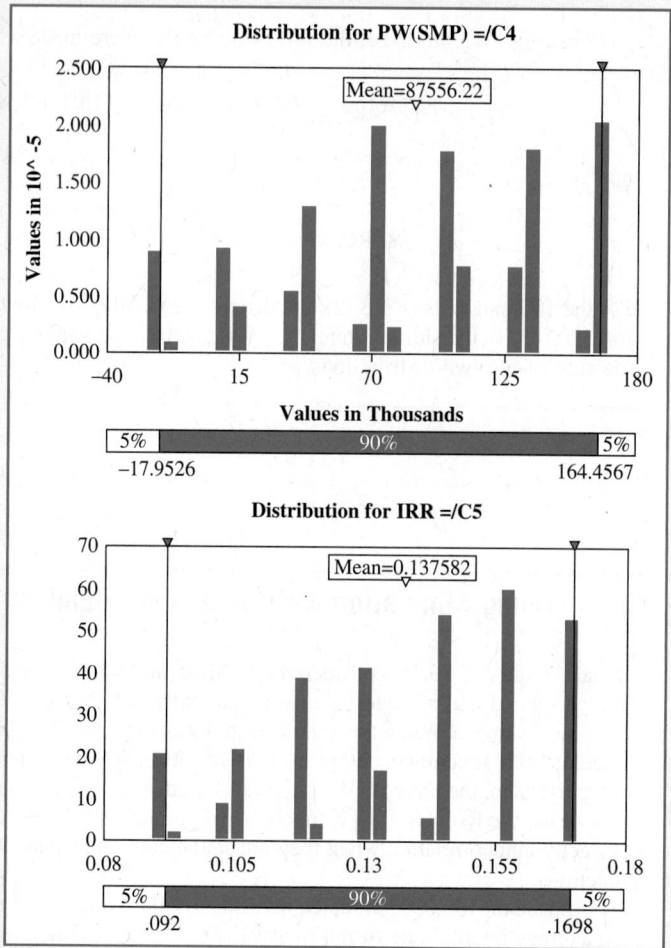

FIGURE 13.20

PW and IRR Histograms from 100,000 Simulation Trials in Example 13.23. (The Figure was Generated with the Help of @RISK, a Product of Palisade Corporation, Ithaca, NY; www.palisade.com.).

As noted previously, depending on the particular investment, when the planning horizon is a random variable, it is advisable to use annual, instead of present, worth as the measure of economic merit. The following example illustrates the use of annual worth.

EXAMPLE 13.24 **Using Simulation to Determine the Distribution of After-Tax Annual Worth When the Planning Horizon and Annual Growth Rates Are Random Variables**

Due to rapid changes in electronics manufacturing technology, there is considerable uncertainty regarding how long the SMP machine will be used. Based on recent experience, it is anticipated the machine will be replaced in 6, 7, 8, 9, or 10 years. The useful life of the

SMP machine is assumed to equal 6 plus X, where X is binomially distributed[11] with $n = 4$ and $p = 0.7$. Hence, the expected life is $6 + 4(0.7)$, or 8.8 years, and the variance is $4(0.7)(0.3)$, or 0.84.

Salvage value depends on the useful life and is assumed to be uniformly distributed with a range of \$40,000 and a mean equal to \$130,000 minus \$20,000 times the number of years the SMP machine is used beyond 6 years. Hence, if the useful life is 10 years, the mean salvage value equals $130,000 - 4(\$20,000)$, or \$50,000; also, for a 10-year life, salvage value is uniformly distributed between \$30,000 and \$70,000.

Annual savings the first year is normally distributed with a mean of \$92,500 and a standard deviation of \$2,500. Each year thereafter, annual savings increase by a growth rate that is uniformly distributed between 0 percent and 8 percent. Hence, the annual savings in year t equals the annual savings in year $t - 1$ times 1 plus the randomly distributed growth rate.

As before, a 10 percent after-tax *MARR* is used. The income tax rate is 40 percent, and the SMP machine qualifies as 5-year property with MACRS-GDS depreciation.

Notice, from Figure 13.21, how the taxable income and annual worth are calculated. Specifically, salvage value is ignored until the calculation of after-tax cash flow. Then, based on a 40 percent tax rate, after-tax cash flow is set equal to before-tax cash flow minus income taxes owed plus 60 percent of the applicable salvage value. The salvage value calculation occurs only if the randomly generated planning horizon coincides with the after-tax cash flow year in question. A number of Excel® **IF** functions are used in calculating ATCF and PW.

In computing after-tax present worth, the range of values over which the Excel® **NPV** function is used depends on the planning horizon's length. The embedded sequence of Excel® **IF**

H16			fx	=RiskOutput("AW(ATCF)")+PMT(10%,D2,-H15)						
	A	B	C	D	E	F	G	H	I	J	K
1			**1st Yr Savings:**	\$92,500	=RiskNormal(92500, 2500)						
2			**SMP Life:**	9		**10-Yr Life Salvage Value:**		\$50,000	=RiskUniform(30000, 70000)		
3	**EOY**	**Growth Rate**	**BTCF**	**True Salvage Value**	**DWO**	**TI***	**T***	**ATCF**			
4	0		-\$500,000					-\$500,000			
5	1		\$92,500		\$100,000.00	-\$7,500	-\$3,000	\$95,500			
6	2	4%	\$96,200		\$160,000.00	-\$63,800	-\$25,520	\$121,720			
7	3	4%	\$100,048		\$96,000.00	\$4,048	\$1,619	\$98,429			
8	4	4%	\$104,050		\$57,600.00	\$46,450	\$18,580	\$85,470			
9	5	4%	\$108,212		\$57,600.00	\$50,612	\$20,245	\$87,967			
10	6	4%	\$112,540	\$70,000	\$28,800.00	\$83,740	\$33,496	\$79,044	=C10-G10+0.6*IF(D2=A10,D10,0)		
11	7	4%	\$117,042	\$70,000	\$0	\$117,042	\$46,817	\$70,225	=C11-G11+0.6*IF(D2=A11,D11,0)		
12	8	4%	\$121,724	\$70,000	\$0	\$121,724	\$48,689	\$73,034	=C12-G12+0.6*IF(D2=A12,D12,0)		
13	9	4%	\$126,593	\$70,000	\$0	\$126,593	\$50,637	\$117,956	=C13-G13+0.6*IF(D2=A13,D13,0)		
14	10	4%	\$131,656	\$70,000	\$0	\$131,656	\$52,663	\$78,994	=C14-G14+0.6*IF(D2=A14,D14,0)		
15					=H2+20000*(10-D2)		**PW =**	\$39,112.77			
16					=C13*(1+B14)		**AW=**	\$6,791.56			
17			=RiskUniform(0, 0.08)				=C11-E11				
18	=6+RiskBinomial(4, 0.7)							=RiskOutput("AW(ATCF)") + PMT(10%,D2,-H15)			
19			=NPV(10%,I5:IF(D2=A10,H10,IF(D2=A11,H11,IF(D2=A12,H12,IF(D2=A13,H13,H14)))))+H4								
20											
21						*excluding salvage value					
22											

FIGURE 13.21

@RISK SetUp for Example 13.24. (The Figure was Generated with the Help of @RISK, a Product of Palisade Corporation, Ithaca, NY; www.palisade.com.).

[11]A binomially distributed random variable with parameters n and p has a mean of np and a variance of $np(1-p)$.

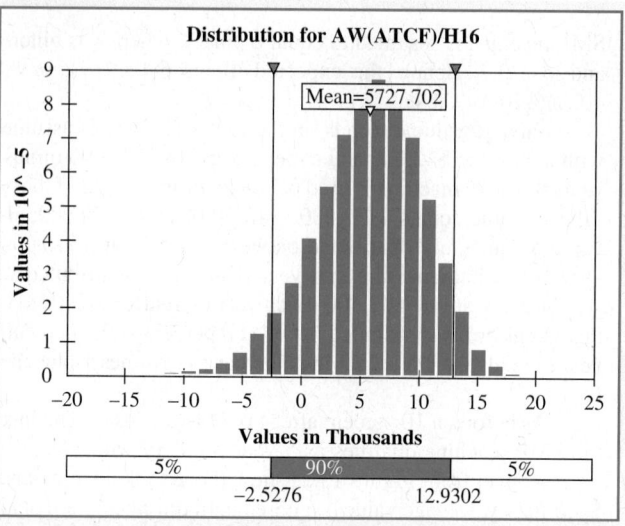

FIGURE 13.22

After-tax AW Histogram from 100,000 Simulation Trials in Example 13.24. (The Figure was Generated with the Help of @RISK, a Product of Palisade Corporation, Ithaca, NY; www.palisade.com.).

functions is used to specify the end point for the range of cash flows considered in the Excel® NPV calculation.

Once the after-tax present worth is known, the after-tax annual worth is easily calculated. Specifically, the Excel® **PMT** function is used, with the randomly generated planning horizon entered for the number of periods included in the Excel® **NPV** calculation, based on the after-tax *MARR*.

For the example, as shown in Figure 13.22, the average after-tax annual worth obtained from 100,000 simulated SMP investments is $5,727.70. A total of 11,292 investments had a negative after-tax annual worth. Therefore, 88.708 percent of the investments had a non-negative after-tax annual worth.

With a sample standard deviation of $4,692.40, the central limit theorem provides the following approximation for the percentage of investments that will have a positive-valued after-tax annual worth:

$$\text{Pr}(ATAW > 0) = \text{NORMSDIST}(5727.70/4692.40)$$
$$= 0.88888755$$

The simulation result (88.708 percent) is very close to the central limit theorem approximation (88.889 percent).

EXAMPLE 13.25 Simulating an Investment Portfolio's Value

When what is earned on investments and the amount invested each year are both statistically independent random variables, simulation is a far easier analysis tool than attempting to use exact probabilistic models.

Here, we are concerned with determining the expected future worth of an investment portfolio and the probability of the future worth being greater than $14,000 at the end of 3 years. Specifically, suppose the annual investment in a mutual fund is equally likely to be

	A	B	C	D	E	F	G	H	I
			fx	=RiskDiscrete({4000,4250,4500,4750,5000}. {0.2,0.2,2,0.2,0.2})					
1	t	MARR	Annual Investment						
2	1	7%	$4,500	=RiskDiscrete({4000,4250,4500,4750,5000}, {0.2,0.2,0.2,0.2,0.2})					
3	2	7%	$4,500	=RiskDiscrete({4000,4250,4500,4750,5000}, {0.2,0.2,0.2,0.2,0.2})					
4	3		$4,500	=RiskDiscrete({4000,4250,4500,4750,5000}, {0.2,0.2,0.2,0.2,0.2})					
5		FW =	$14,467.05	=RiskOutput("Portfolio Value =") + (C2*(1+B2)+C3)*(1+B3)+C4					
6									
7			=RiskDiscrete({0.06,0.065,0.07,0.075,0.08}, {0.2,0.2,0.2,0.2,0.2})						
8									

FIGURE 13.23

Setup for @RISK Monte Carlo Simulation of Example 13.25. (The Figure was Generated with the Help of @RISK, a Product of Palisade Corporation, Ithaca, NY; www.palisade.com.).

$4,000, $4,250, $4,500, $4,750, or $5,000. Similarly, it is equally likely that the annual return will be either 6 percent, 6.5 percent, 7 percent, 7.5 percent, or 8 percent.

Figure 13.23 provides the setup to simulate the investment over a 3-year period. Notice the entry in cell C5:

=RiskOutput("Portfolio Value=")+(C2*(1+B2)+C3)*(1+B3))+C4

The investment portfolio's future worth is obtained by determining the cumulative future worth (i.e., by moving each cash flow forward in time 1 year, using the simulated value for the mutual fund return).

By enumerating all possible combinations of investments and annual returns, the expected future worth can be obtained—$14,467.05, which is the same value obtained by assuming the annual deposits are equal to $4,500 and the annual return is equal to 7 percent. The probability of the portfolio having a value in excess of $14,000 was also obtained by enumerating all possible combinations; its value was 0.723125.

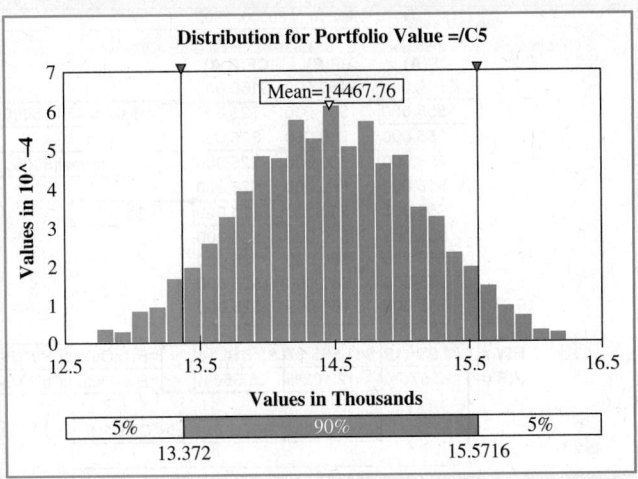

FIGURE 13.24

PW Histogram from 100,000 Simulation Trials in Example 13.25. (The Figure was Generated with the Help of @RISK, a Product of Palisade Corporation, Ithaca, NY; www.palisade.com.).

The results obtained from 100,000 simulated investments (using Monte Carlo simulation) included an average future worth of 14,467.76, and 74,673 of the 100,000 simulated investments had a future worth in excess of $14,000. Hence, the simulated future worth was almost identical to that obtained analytically, and the simulated probability of the investment portfolio having a value of at least $14,000 was slightly greater than the exact value obtained analytically. A histogram of the portfolio value after investing for 3 years is provided in Figure 13.24.

This example indicates the power of simulation. From cell C5 in Figure 13.23, it is obvious how one would expand the investment period to, say, 10 or more years. To do this analytically would be very tedious.

EXAMPLE 13.26   Simulating the Theme Park Investment Problem

Recall the theme park investment problem considered in many of the previous chapters and in this one. In Example 13.21, we presented analytical results for the two design alternatives being considered for the Scream Machine. Specifically, we estimated the probabilities of Design A being profitable, of Design B being profitable, and of Design B having a greater present worth than Design A. Here, we duplicate the analysis but with Monte Carlo simulation, and we assume net annual revenue produced by the new ride is a statistically independent random variable. Since the revenue in any given year is independent of the revenue in any other year, as shown in Figure 13.25, the Excel® NPV function is used to calculate present worth. The histograms for PW(A), PW(B), and PW(B − A) resulting from the 100,000 simulated investments are given in Figure 13.26. Of the 100,000 simulation trials, all but 12 resulted in a positive-valued present worth for Design A, all but 280 resulted in a positive-valued present worth for Design B, and 57,877 trials resulted in Design B having a greater present worth than Design A. Hence, the probability of Design B being the most economic was estimated to be equal to 0.57877.

Recall, solving analytically for the mean and variance for PW(A), PW(B), and PW(B − A) yielded probability estimates of 0.999918, 0.997043, and 0.578922,

C5		fx	=RiskNormal(80000, 7500)							
	A	B	C	D	E	F	G	H	I	J
1	EOY	CF(A)	CF(B)	CF(B-A)						
2	0	-$300,000	-$450,000	-$150,000						
3	1	$55,000	$80,000	$25,000		=RiskNormal(55000, 5000)				
4	2	$55,000	$80,000	$25,000						
5	3	$55,000	$80,000	$25,000		=RiskNormal(80000, 7500)				
6	4	$55,000	$80,000	$25,000						
7	5	$55,000	$80,000	$25,000		=C5-B5				
8	6	$55,000	$80,000	$25,000						
9	7	$55,000	$80,000	$25,000						
10	8	$55,000	$80,000	$25,000						
11	9	$55,000	$80,000	$25,000						
12	10	$55,000	$80,000	$25,000						
13	PW =	$37,951.19	$41,565.37	$3,614.18		=RiskOutput("PW(B-A)") + NPV(10%,D3:D12)+D2				
14	IRR =	12.870%	12.109%	10.558%		=RiskOutput("IRR(B-A)") + IRR(D2:D12)				
15										
16			=RiskOutput("IRR(B)") + IRR(C2:C12)							
17										
18		=RiskOutput("PW(A)") + NPV(10%,B3:B12)+B2								
19										

FIGURE 13.25

SetUp for @RISK Monte Carlo Simulation of Example 13.26. (The Figure Was Generated with the Help of @RISK, a Product of Palisade Corporation, Ithaca, NY; www.palisade.com.).

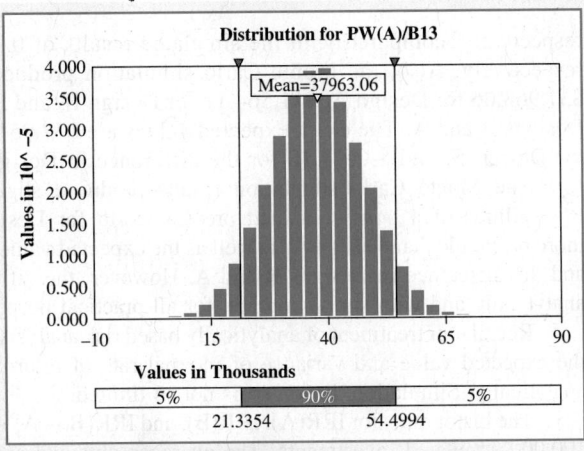

FIGURE 13.26a

PW Histogram from 100,000 Simulated Investments in Design A.

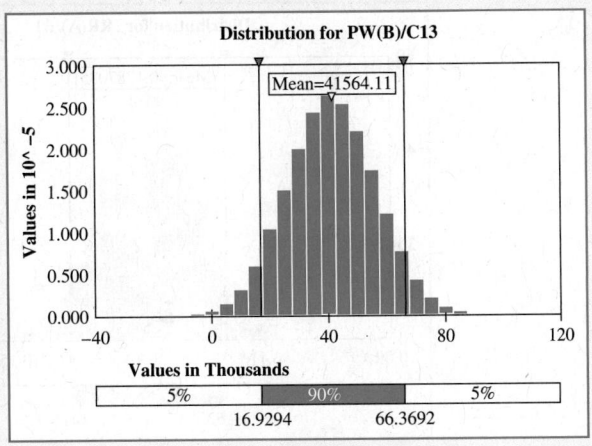

FIGURE 13.26b

PW Histogram from 100,000 Simulated Investments in Design B.

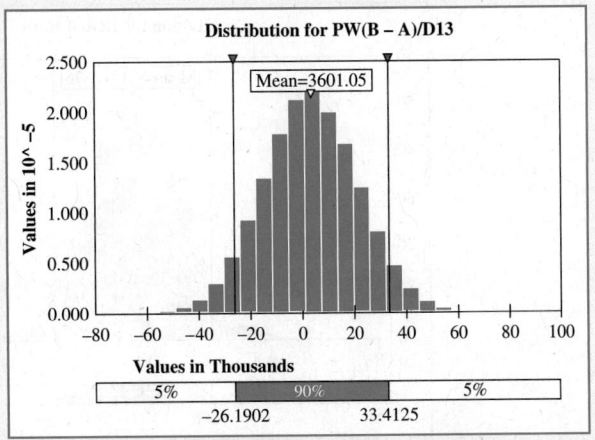

FIGURE 13.26c

PW Histogram from 100,000 Simulated Incremental Investments Between Designs B and A. (The Figures were Generated with the Help of @RISK, a Product of Palisade Corporation, Ithaca, NY; www.palisade.com.).

respectively, compared with the simulated results of 0.99988, 0.99720, and 0.57877, respectively. Also, the Monte Carlo simulation produced average present worths of $37,963.06 for Design A, $41,564.11 for Design B, and $3,601.05 for the difference in Designs B and A. The exact expected values are $37,951.19 for Design A, $41,565.37 for Design B, and $3,614.18 for the difference in Designs B and A.

The Monte Carlo simulation results produced slightly smaller estimates for the probabilities of a positive-valued present worth for Design A and of Design B being more profitable than Design A, as well as the expected values for present worth of Design B and the difference in Designs B and A. However, the differences in the results obtained analytically and with simulation are, for all practical purposes, negligible.

Recall, our treatment of analytically based risk analysis did not include calculations for the expected value and variance of internal rate of return, since we cannot obtain them analytically. Simulation, however, is not so limited.

The histograms for IRR(A), IRR(B), and IRR(B − A) are given in Figure 13.27 for the 100,000 simulated investments. The averages obtained are IRR(A) = 12.87035 percent, IRR(B) = 12.10875 percent, and IRR(B − A) = 10.53514 percent.

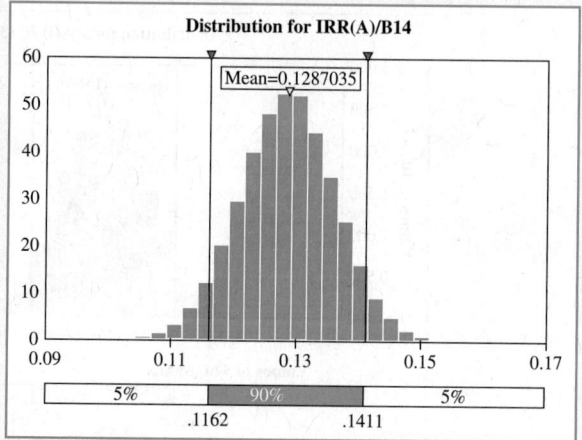

FIGURE 13.27a

IRR Histogram from 100,000 Simulated Investments in Design A.

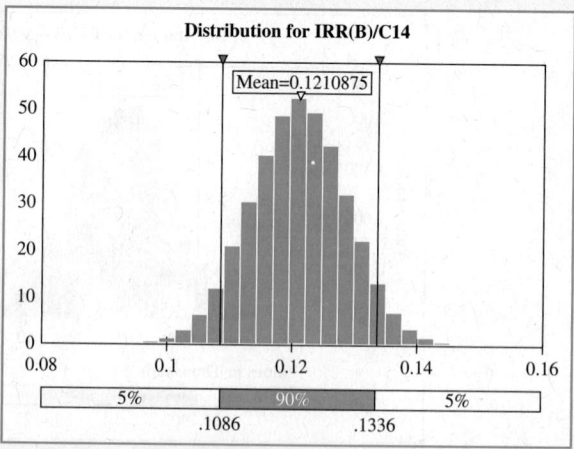

FIGURE 13.27b

IRR Histogram from 100,000 Simulated Investments in Design B. (The Figures were Generated with the Help of @RISK, a Product of Palisade Corporation, Ithaca, NY; www.palisade.com.).

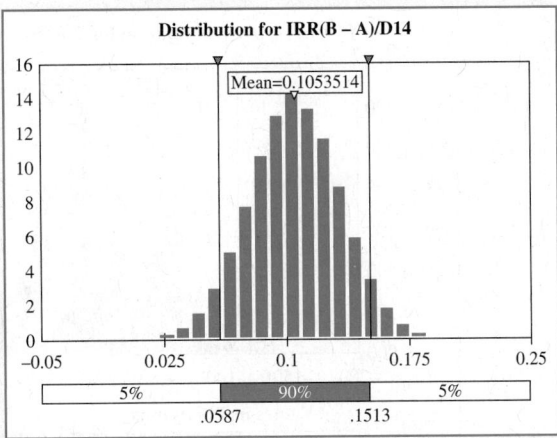

FIGURE 13.27

IRR Histogram from 100,000 Simulated Incremental Investments Between Designs B and A. (The Figure was Generated with the Help of @RISK, a Product of Palisade Corporation, Ithaca, NY; www.palisade.com.).

As noted on the histograms, in 90 percent of the simulation trials, IRR(A) was between 11.62 percent and 14.11 percent; similarly, 90 percent of the time, IRR(B) was between 10.86 percent and 13.36 percent; and, finally, 90 percent of the time, the incremental investment made in Design B had an internal rate of return between 5.87 percent and 15.13 percent.

EXAMPLE 13.27   Using the Three-Estimate Approach to Simulate the Theme Park Investment Problem

Recall, three estimates were provided for the initial investments required for the two Scream Machine designs, as well as the annual revenues resulting. In Example 13.19, we considered all 81 possible combinations of investments and annual revenues to determine the probability of Design B being the economic choice.

Figure 13.28 provides the @RISK setup for the simulation. Here, we assume the net annual revenues over the 10-year planning horizon are autocorrelated. Hence, the Excel®

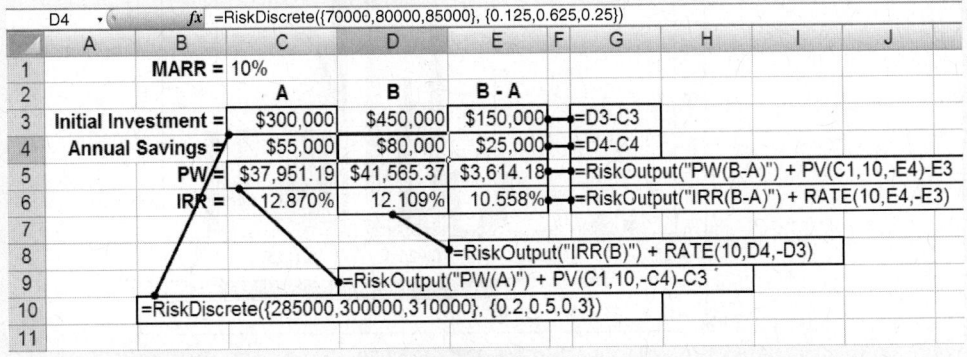

FIGURE 13.28

Setup for @RISK Monte Carlo Simulation of Example 13.27. (The Figure was Generated with the Help of @RISK, a Product of Palisade Corporation, Ithaca, NY; www.palisade.com.).

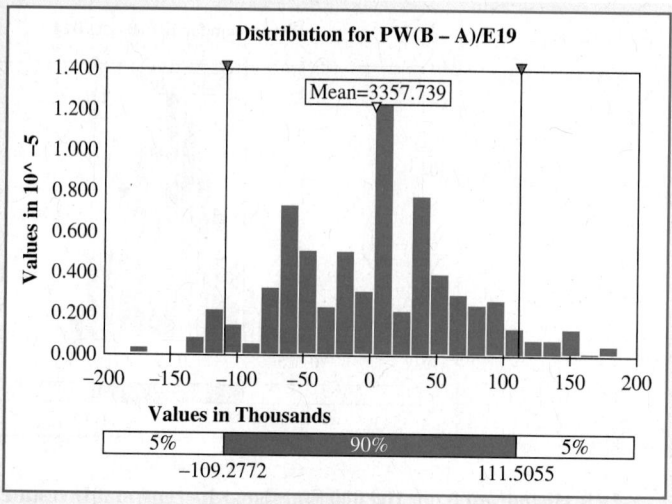

FIGURE 13.29

PW Histogram from 100,000 Simulated Incremental Investments Between Designs B and A.

PV and **RATE** functions are used to obtain values of PW and IRR. After performing 100,000 Monte Carlo simulation trials, the following results were obtained: The average simulated present worth was $37,936.07 for Design A; it was $41,293.81 for Design B; and it was $3,357.74 for the difference in cash flows for B and A, as shown in Figure 13.29. The simulated average internal rate of return was 12.7822 percent for Design A; it was 12.21019 percent for Design B; and it was 9.083892 percent for the incremental investment (B − A), as shown in Figure 13.30. *This is a very interesting result!*

Since $E[IRR(B − A)] < MARR = 10$ percent, it appears that Design B is not justified. However, $PW(B − A) = \$3,357.74 > 0$, so Design B is justified economically. *What happened?*

The answer lies in the **@RISK** output report. Specifically, the number of simulation trials that resulted in $PW > 0$ and, consequently, $IRR > MARR$, does not "match up" with

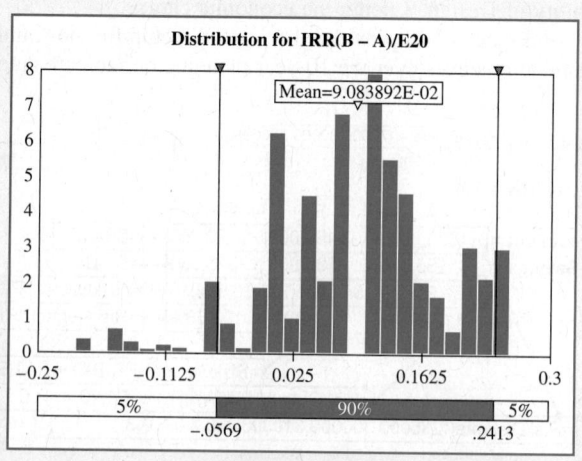

FIGURE 13.30

IRR Histogram from 100,000 Simulated Incremental Investments Between Designs B and A.

the number of simulation trials that resulted in IRR > MARR. In all previous examples, the simulated Pr($PW > 0$) and Pr(IRR > MARR) have been the same. However, that is not the case for this example.

Specifically, 84.973 percent of the simulated investments resulted in $PW(A) > 0$ and IRR(A) > MARR; 77.633 percent of the 100,000 trials resulted in $PW(B) > 0$ and IRR(B) > MARR. However, 56.745 percent of the simulation trials resulted in $PW(B − A) > 0$, while 48.408 percent resulted in IRR(B − A) > MARR. *What caused the 8.337 percent difference in the two probabilities for the incremental cash flow?*

As shown in Table 13.16, the @RISK output report indicates that three errors occurred in the first 25 simulated investments. For the 100,000 simulated investments, 8,337 errors

		TABLE 13.16				
		First 25 Simulation Trials for Example 13.24, Including 3 Error Reports. (The Table was Generated with the Help of @RISK, a Product of Palisade Corporation, Ithaca, NY; www.palisade.com.).				

@RISK Output Data Report Output Data						
Output Simulation Iteration / Cell	PW(A) 1 $C$5	PW(B) 1 $D$5	PW(B − A) 1 $E$5	IRR(A) 1 $C$6	IRR(B) 1 $D$6	IRR(B − A) 1 $E$6
1	$37,951.19	$41,565.37	$3,614.18	12.870%	12.109%	10.558%
2	$99,396.86	$91,565.37	−$7,831.49	17.257%	15.098%	8.144%
3	$27,951.19	$72,288.20	$44,337.01	12.060%	13.621%	16.952%
4	$37,951.19	−$18,434.63	−$56,385.82	12.870%	9.152%	3.303%
5	$114,396.86	$91,565.37	−$22,831.49	18.699%	15.098%	5.148%
6	$114,396.86	−$18,434.63	−$132,831.50	18.699%	9.152%	−6.766%
7	$27,951.19	$72,288.20	$44,337.01	12.060%	13.621%	16.952%
8	$37,951.19	$41,565.37	$3,614.18	12.870%	12.109%	10.558%
9	$99,396.86	$12,288.20	−$87,108.66	17.257%	10.558%	−0.877%
10	$37,951.19	$122,288.20	$84,337.02	12.870%	16.723%	Error
11	−$54,217.32	$41,565.37	$95,782.69	5.604%	12.109%	23.413%
12	$52,951.19	$72,288.20	$19,337.01	14.169%	13.621%	12.664%
13	$37,951.19	−$18,434.63	−$56,385.82	12.870%	9.152%	3.303%
14	$27,951.19	$41,565.37	$13,614.18	12.060%	12.109%	12.219%
15	$52,951.19	$41,565.37	−$11,385.82	14.169%	12.109%	8.368%
16	$37,951.19	$12,288.20	−$25,662.99	12.870%	10.558%	7.073%
17	$27,951.19	$91,565.37	$63,614.18	12.060%	15.098%	24.730%
18	$27,951.19	−$18,434.63	−$46,385.82	12.060%	9.152%	4.277%
19	$37,951.19	$122,288.20	$84,337.02	12.870%	16.723%	Error
20	−$39,217.32	$72,288.20	$111,505.52	6.691%	13.621%	24.133%
21	$37,951.19	$122,288.20	$84,337.02	12.870%	16.723%	Error
22	$89,396.86	$41,565.37	−$47,831.49	16.360%	12.109%	1.274%
23	$27,951.19	−$18,434.63	−$46,385.82	12.060%	9.152%	4.277%
24	$52,951.19	−$18,434.63	−$71,385.82	14.169%	9.152%	1.963%
25	$52,951.19	$91,565.37	$38,614.18	14.169%	15.098%	17.349%

TABLE 13.17

First 25 Simulated Investments for Example 13.24. (The Table was Generated with the Help of @RISK, a Product of Palisade Corporation, Ithaca, NY; www.palisade.com.).

@RISK Input Data Report
Input Data

Input Simulation Iteration / Cell	Initial Investment = / 1 $C$3	Initial Investment = / 1 $D$3	Annual Savings = / A 1 $C$4	Annual Savings = / B 1 $D$4
1	300000	450000	55000	80000
2	300000	400000	65000	80000
3	310000	450000	55000	85000
4	300000	510000	55000	80000
5	285000	400000	65000	80000
6	285000	510000	65000	80000
7	310000	450000	55000	85000
8	300000	450000	55000	80000
9	300000	510000	65000	85000
10	300000	400000	55000	85000
11	300000	450000	40000	80000
12	285000	450000	55000	85000
13	300000	510000	55000	80000
14	310000	450000	55000	80000
15	285000	450000	55000	80000
16	300000	510000	55000	85000
17	310000	400000	55000	80000
18	310000	510000	55000	80000
19	300000	400000	55000	85000
20	285000	450000	40000	85000
21	300000	400000	55000	85000
22	310000	450000	65000	80000
23	310000	510000	55000	80000
24	285000	510000	55000	80000
25	285000	400000	55000	80000

occurred. The investment/revenue combination that produced the three errors in the first 25 simulated investments are given in Table 13.17.

The following 12 combinations of investments and annual revenues for Designs A and B resulted in an error occurring using the Excel® **RATE** function:

{$285,000; $40,000; $400,000; $80,000}
{$285,000; $40,000; $400,000; $85,000}
{$300,000; $40,000; $400,000; $70,000}
{$310,000; $40,000; $400,000; $70,000}
{$300,000; $40,000; $400,000; $80,000}
{$300,000; $40,000; $400,000; $85,000}

{$300,000; $55,000; $400,000; $85,000}
{$300,000; $40,000; $450,000; $85,000}
{$310,000; $40,000; $400,000; $80,000}
{$310,000; $40,000; $400,000; $85,000}
{$310,000; $40,000; $450,000; $85,000}
{$310,000; $55,000; $400,000; $85,000}

Selecting the first combination when the Excel® RATE function is used, the following occurs:

$$IRR(B - A) = \text{RATE}(10,80000-40000,-400000+285000)$$
$$= \text{NUM!}$$

Yet, from Figure 13.31, if the Excel® IRR function is used, IRR(B − A) = 32.734 percent. As shown, a plot of PW versus *MARR* does not suggest any problems should arise in applying the Excel® RATE function. Excel® offers the following statement regarding the RATE function: "If the successive results of RATE do not converge to within 0.0000001 after 20 iterations, RATE returns the #NUM! error value." Repeated attempts to increase the number of iterations and adjust the RATE function parameters to obtain solutions for

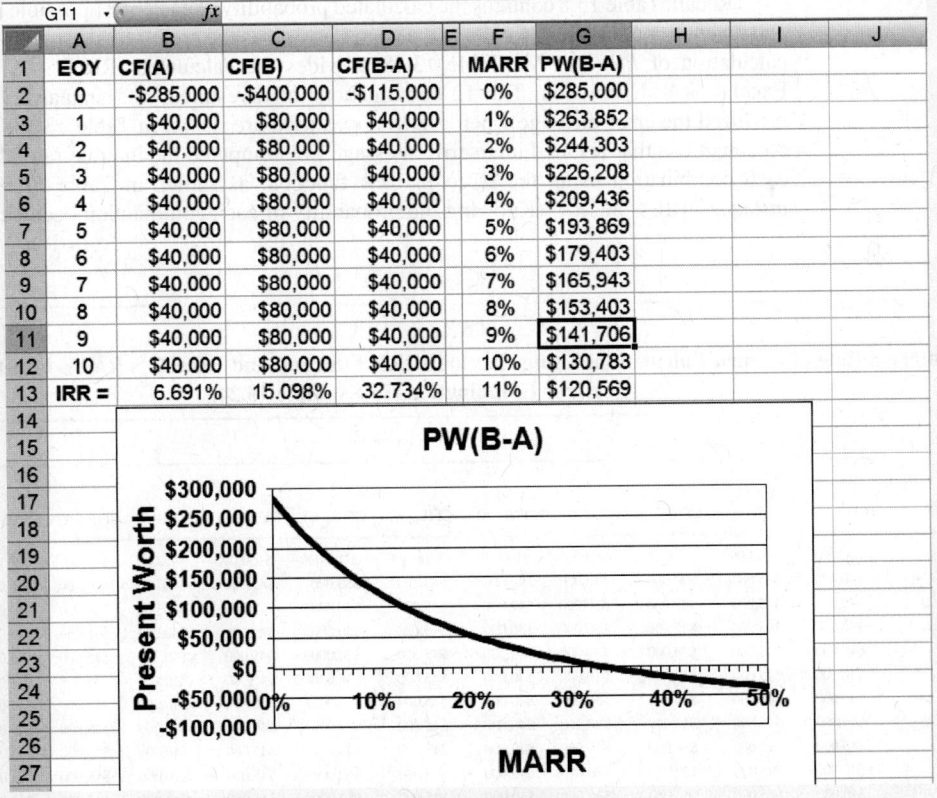

FIGURE 13.31

Excel® IRR Worksheet Function Solution for a Cash Flow Combination that Generated an Error Message with the Excel® RATE Worksheet Function.

TABLE 13.18

IRR Values Produced by Excel®'s RATE Function for All Combinations of Investments and Annual Returns for Example 13.24.

					Design B				
Design A		$400,000 $85,000	$400,000 $70,000	$400,000 $80,000	$510,000 $85,000	$510,000 $70,000	$510,000 $80,000	$450,000 $85,000	$450,000 $70,000	$450,000 $80,000
$285,000	$65,000	11.575%	−12.845%	5.148%	−2.086%	−20.872%	−6.766%	3.660%	−17.355%	−1.696%
$285,000	$40,000	#NUM!	22.720%	#NUM!	15.098%	5.604%	12.109%	24.133%	12.664%	20.481%
$285,000	$55,000	22.720%	5.148%	17.349%	5.604%	−6.766%	1.963%	12.664%	−1.696%	8.368%
$310,000	$65,000	17.963%	−9.471%	10.558%	0.000%	−19.571%	−4.916%	7.073%	−15.363%	1.274%
$310,000	$40,000	#NUM!	#NUM!	#NUM!	18.314%	8.144%	15.098%	#NUM!	16.952%	25.661%
$310,000	$55,000	#NUM!	10.558%	24.730%	8.144%	−4.916%	4.277%	16.952%	1.274%	12.219%
$300,000	$65,000	15.098%	−10.956%	8.144%	−0.877%	−20.115%	−5.692%	5.604%	−16.211%	0.000%
$300,000	$40,000	#NUM!	#NUM!	#NUM!	16.952%	7.073%	13.834%	#NUM!	15.098%	23.413%
$300,000	$55,000	#NUM!	8.144%	21.406%	7.073%	−5.692%	3.303%	15.098%	0.000%	10.558%

these combinations were unsuccessful. Hence, we were unable to use the Excel® RATE function to attain solutions for the 12 combinations given above.

Recall, Table 13.8 contains the calculated probability of each of 81 possible investment and revenue combinations for the two designs, as well as the preferred alternative based on a calculation of $PW(B − A)$. Table 13.18 provides the calculated IRR(B − A) using the Excel® RATE function. The 12 combinations of investment and annual revenues that produced the error message when @RISK was used are shown in Table 13.18. For the 12 combinations that resulted in an error message, we computed the internal rate of return for each combination using the Excel® IRR function, as shown in Table 13.19. In each instance, IRR > MARR. (Knowing the probability of each combination occurring, we can

TABLE 13.19

Internal Rate of Return Calculations Using Excel®'s IRR Function and Excel®'s RATE Function for the 12 Error Combinations in Example 13.24.

						Combination						
	1	2	3	4	5	6	7	8	9	10	11	12
EOY	CF(B−A)	CF(B−A)	CF(B−A)	CF(B−A)	CF(B−A)	CF(B−A)	CF(B−A)	CF(B−A)	CF(B−A)	CF(B−A)	CF(B−A)	CF(B−A)
0	−$115,000	−$115,000	−$100,000	−$90,000	−$100,000	−$100,000	−$100,000	−$150,000	−$90,000	−$90,000	−$140,000	−$90,000
1	$40,000	$45,000	$30,000	$30,000	$40,000	$45,000	$30,000	$45,000	$40,000	$45,000	$45,000	$30,000
2	$40,000	$45,000	$30,000	$30,000	$40,000	$45,000	$30,000	$45,000	$40,000	$45,000	$45,000	$30,000
3	$40,000	$45,000	$30,000	$30,000	$40,000	$45,000	$30,000	$45,000	$40,000	$45,000	$45,000	$30,000
4	$40,000	$45,000	$30,000	$30,000	$40,000	$45,000	$30,000	$45,000	$40,000	$45,000	$45,000	$30,000
5	$40,000	$45,000	$30,000	$30,000	$40,000	$45,000	$30,000	$45,000	$40,000	$45,000	$45,000	$30,000
6	$40,000	$45,000	$30,000	$30,000	$40,000	$45,000	$30,000	$45,000	$40,000	$45,000	$45,000	$30,000
7	$40,000	$45,000	$30,000	$30,000	$40,000	$45,000	$30,000	$45,000	$40,000	$45,000	$45,000	$30,000
8	$40,000	$45,000	$30,000	$30,000	$40,000	$45,000	$30,000	$45,000	$40,000	$45,000	$45,000	$30,000
9	$40,000	$45,000	$30,000	$30,000	$40,000	$45,000	$30,000	$45,000	$40,000	$45,000	$45,000	$30,000
10	$40,000	$45,000	$30,000	$30,000	$40,000	$45,000	$30,000	$45,000	$40,000	$45,000	$45,000	$30,000
IRR =	32.734%	37.512%	27.320%	31.113%	38.455%	43.811%	27.320%	27.320%	43.220%	49.078%	29.770%	31.113%
RATE =	#NUM!	#NUM!	#NUM!	#NUM!	#NUM!	#NUM!	#NUM!	#NUM!	#NUM!	#NUM!	#NUM!	#NUM!

compute the probability of a simulated trial having a combination that would produce an error message. From data in Tables 13.8 and 13.15, the probability of one of the 12 combinations being chosen is 0.084086. Of the 100,000 simulated investments, 8.337 percent produced an error message.)

This example highlighted the possible difficulties that can arise when using the IRR method to choose from among investment alternatives in a risky environment. Recall, in Chapter 8, we emphasized the need to use an incremental approach when comparing alternatives with the IRR method. For the example, in several instances, the simulated estimate of IRR(A) is less than the *MARR*; therefore, Design A would not be acceptable. Consequently, in those cases, Design B should not be compared to Design A.

The previous example illustrates why we recommend using the three "worth methods" (PW, AW, and FW) instead of the IRR method, especially when comparing mutually exclusive investment alternatives. It also reinforces the fact that the external rate of return can play an important role when performing risk analyses.

How might we compute the ERR in an @RISK simulation? We offer an approach in the following example.

EXAMPLE 13.28 Using the External Rate of Return in Risk Analyses

Recall from Chapter 8, when multiple negative values can occur, the Excel® **MIRR** function cannot be used to determine the ERR. Instead, an *alternative cash flow profile* is created, having negative values or zeroes in all but the last period; the cash flow for the last period in the planning horizon is the sum of (1) the future worth of all positive-valued cash flows and of (2) any negative-valued cash flow that occurs in the planning horizon's last period. Once the alternative cash flow profile has been created, the ERR is obtained by applying the Excel® **IRR** function to the alternative cash flow profile.

Continuing with the theme park investment and the autocorrelated net annual revenues, Figure 13.32 shows the inputs and outputs for the @RISK simulation, including the computations of PW, IRR, and ERR values for the investment in Design A; a similar setup is performed for the investment in Design B and for the incremental investment between Designs B and A. Table 13.20 shows the setup used to simulate 100,000 investments in Designs A and B.

	B3	▾	*fx* '=RiskPert(40000, 55000, 65000)		
	A	B	C	D	E
1	EOY	CF(A)	CF(A)⁻	CF(A)⁺	CF(A)
2	0	=RiskPert(-310000, -300000, -285000)	=IF(B2<0,B2,0)	=IF(B2>0,B2,0)	=C2
3	1	=RiskPert(40000, 55000, 65000)	=IF(B3<0,B3,0)	=IF(B3>0,B3,0)	=C3
4	2	=B3	=IF(B4<0,B4,0)	=IF(B4>0,B4,0)	=C4
5	3	=B3	=IF(B5<0,B5,0)	=IF(B5>0,B5,0)	=C5
6	4	=B3	=IF(B6<0,B6,0)	=IF(B6>0,B6,0)	=C6
7	5	=B3	=IF(B7<0,B7,0)	=IF(B7>0,B7,0)	=C7
8	6	=B3	=IF(B8<0,B8,0)	=IF(B8>0,B8,0)	=C8
9	7	=B3	=IF(B9<0,B9,0)	=IF(B9>0,B9,0)	=C9
10	8	=B3	=IF(B10<0,B10,0)	=IF(B10>0,B10,0)	=C10
11	9	=B3	=IF(B11<0,B11,0)	=IF(B11>0,B11,0)	=C11
12	10	=B3	=IF(B12<0,B12,0)	=IF(B12>0,B12,0)	=FV(10%,10,,-NPV(10%,D3:D12))+C12
13	PW =	=RiskOutput("PW(A)") + NPV(10%,B3:B12)+B2			
14	IRR =	=RiskOutput("IRR(A)") + IRR(B2:B12)			
15				ERR =	=RiskOutput("ERR(A)") + IRR(E2:E12)
16					

FIGURE 13.32

@RISK Setup for the Investment in Design A in Example 13.28.

TABLE 13.20

SetUp for @RISK Simulation of the Theme Park Investment Problem when the ERR is to be Determined. (The Table was Generated with the Help of @RISK, a Product of Palisade Corporation, Ithaca, NY; www.palisade.com.).

EOY	CF(A)	CF(A)⁻	CF(A)⁺	𝒞ℱ(𝒜)	CF(B)	CF(B)⁻	CF(B)⁺	𝒞ℱ(ℬ)	CF(B−A)	CF(B−A)⁻	CF(B−A)⁺	𝒞ℱ(ℬ−𝒜)
0	−$300,000	−$300,000	$0	−$300,000	−$451,667	−$451,667	$0	−$451,667	−$151,667	−$151,667	$0	−$151,667
1	$55,000	$0	$55,000	$0	$79,167	$0	$79,167	$0	$24,167	$0	$24,167	$0
2	$55,000	$0	$55,000	$0	$79,167	$0	$79,167	$0	$24,167	$0	$24,167	$0
3	$55,000	$0	$55,000	$0	$79,167	$0	$79,167	$0	$24,167	$0	$24,167	$0
4	$55,000	$0	$55,000	$0	$79,167	$0	$79,167	$0	$24,167	$0	$24,167	$0
5	$55,000	$0	$55,000	$0	$79,167	$0	$79,167	$0	$24,167	$0	$24,167	$0
6	$55,000	$0	$55,000	$0	$79,167	$0	$79,167	$0	$24,167	$0	$24,167	$0
7	$55,000	$0	$55,000	$0	$79,167	$0	$79,167	$0	$24,167	$0	$24,167	$0
8	$55,000	$0	$55,000	$0	$79,167	$0	$79,167	$0	$24,167	$0	$24,167	$0
9	$55,000	$0	$55,000	$0	$79,167	$0	$79,167	$0	$24,167	$0	$24,167	$0
10	$55,000	$0	$55,000	$876,558	$79,167	$0	$79,167	$1,261,713	$24,167	$0	$24,167	$385,154
PW =	$37,951				$34,778				−$3,173			
IRR =	12.870%				11.764%				9.511%			
ERR =				11.318%				10.819%				9.768%

Histograms obtained for the ERR are provided in Figure 13.33. Notice in Figure 13.33a that the average ERR(A) is 11.22107 percent; in Figure 13.33b, the average ERR(B) is 10.99528 percent; and, in Figure 13.33c, the average ERR(B − A) is 9.94132 percent. No errors were generated in producing the results for ERR. The percentage of simulated investments resulting in ERR(A) > *MARR* was 84.973 percent; in 77.633 percent of the 100,000 trials, ERR(B) > *MARR*; and 56.745 percent of the investment trials resulted in ERR(B − A) > *MARR*. The statistics are identical to those obtained for PW(A), PW(B), and *PW*(B − A).

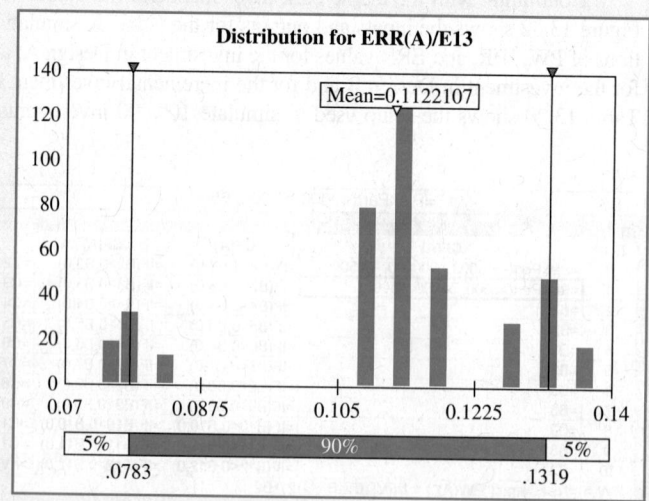

FIGURE 13.33a

Histogram for ERR(A) in Example 13.28. (The Figure was Generated with the Help of @RISK, a Product of Palisade Corporation, Ithaca, NY; www.palisade.com.).

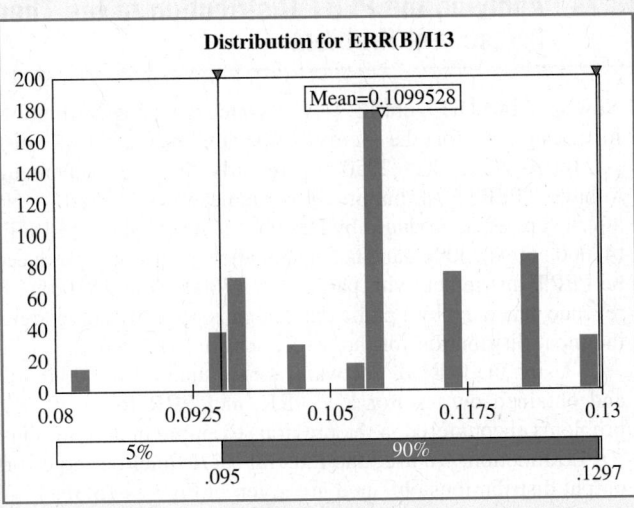

FIGURE 13.33b

Histogram for ERR(B) in Example 13.28.

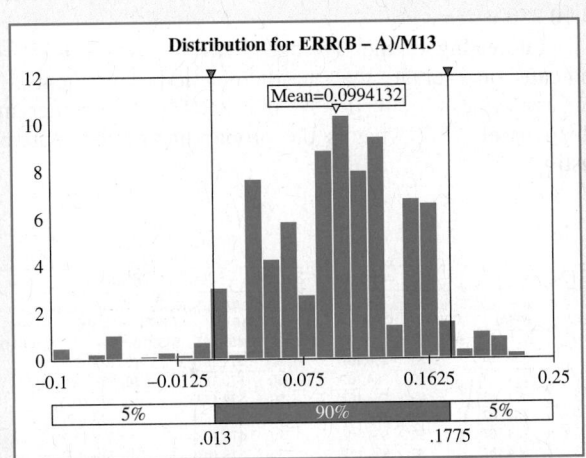

FIGURE 13.33c

Histogram for ERR(B − A) in Example 13.28. (The Figures were Generated with the Help of @RISK, a Product of Palisade Corporation, Ithaca, NY; www.palisade.com.).

In the previous examples, the three estimates (pessimistic, most likely, and optimistic) were used to simulate the investment in the Scream Machine design alternatives, A and B. Recall from our discussion of sensitivity analysis, the three-estimate approach originated with the PERT program in 1958. The @RISK menu of input distributions includes what is called the PERT distribution. Based on the beta distribution, the input parameters for the PERT distribution in @RISK are the three estimates previously cited. The following example applies the PERT distribution to the theme park investment problem.

EXAMPLE 13.29 Applying the PERT Distribution to the Theme Park Investment Problem

Now, as shown in Figure 13.34, we assume the input distribution for the investment required for Design A for the Scream Machine has a PERT distribution, with parameters $(-310000, -300000, -285000)$; similarly, the investment required for Design B is assumed to have a PERT distribution with parameters $(-510000, -450000, -400000)$, net annual after-tax revenue produced by Design A is assumed to be PERT distributed with parameters $(40000, 55000, 65000)$, and net annual after-tax revenue produced by Design B is assumed to be PERT distributed with parameters $(70000, 80000, 85000)$. We continue to assume that revenue generated by a particular design is perfectly autocorrelated. Figure 13.35 illustrates the input distribution for the investment in Design A.

Using the @**RISK** software, we simulated 100,000 investments in Designs A and B and obtained outputs for PW, IRR, and ERR for A, B, and B − A. (Because of the problems encountered in the previous example in determining the IRR using the Excel® **RATE** function, we used the Excel® **IRR** function; no errors were generated.) Sample output distributions obtained are given in Figures 13.36, 13.37, and 13.38, respectively, for $PW(B - A)$, $ERR(B - A)$, and $IRR(B - A)$. From output not shown, the average present worth for Design A is \$33,657.09; for Design B it is \$34,805.19; and the average difference in present worths is \$1,148.10. The average external rate of return for Design A is 11.142 percent; for Design B, it is 10.826 percent; and for the incremental investment $(B - A)$, it is 9.955 percent. The average internal rate of return for Design A is 12.526 percent; for design B, it is 11.799 percent; and for the incremental investment $(B - A)$, it is 10.289 percent.

Interestingly, the average $ERR(B - A) < MARR = 10$ percent, which would indicate, on average, that the incremental investment is not justified. Yet, based on average values for $PW(B - A)$ and $IRR(B - A)$, the incremental investment is justified, albeit barely. So, what is the probability of the incremental investment not being justified?

	C17	▾	fx	=RiskPert(-310000, -300000, -285000)								
	A	B	C	D	E	F	G	H	I	J	K	L	M
1	EOY	CF(A)	CF(A)⁻	CF(A)⁺	CF(A)	CF(B)	CF(B)⁻	CF(B)⁺	CF(B)	CF(B-A)	CF(B-A)⁻	CF(B-A)⁺	CF(B-A)
2	0	-$299,167	-$299,167	$0	-$299,167	-$451,667	-$451,667	$0	-$451,667	-$152,500	-$152,500	$0	-$152,500
3	1	$54,167	$0	$54,167	$0	$79,167	$0	$79,167	$0	$25,000	$0	$25,000	$0
4	2	$54,167	$0	$54,167	$0	$79,167	$0	$79,167	$0	$25,000	$0	$25,000	$0
5	3	$54,167	$0	$54,167	$0	$79,167	$0	$79,167	$0	$25,000	$0	$25,000	$0
6	4	$54,167	$0	$54,167	$0	$79,167	$0	$79,167	$0	$25,000	$0	$25,000	$0
7	5	$54,167	$0	$54,167	$0	$79,167	$0	$79,167	$0	$25,000	$0	$25,000	$0
8	6	$54,167	$0	$54,167	$0	$79,167	$0	$79,167	$0	$25,000	$0	$25,000	$0
9	7	$54,167	$0	$54,167	$0	$79,167	$0	$79,167	$0	$25,000	$0	$25,000	$0
10	8	$54,167	$0	$54,167	$0	$79,167	$0	$79,167	$0	$25,000	$0	$25,000	$0
11	9	$54,167	$0	$54,167	$0	$79,167	$0	$79,167	$0	$25,000	$0	$25,000	$0
12	10	$54,167	$0	$54,167	$863,277	$79,167	$0	$79,167	$1,261,713	$25,000	$0	$25,000	$398,436
13	ERR =	=C17			11.179%	=D18			10.819%				10.080%
14		=B3											
15	MARR =	10%		=RiskPert(-510000, -450000, -400000)					=RiskOutput("ERR(B)") + IRR(I2:I12)			
16		A	B	B-A									
17	Initial Investment =	-$299,167	-$451,667	-$152,500									
18	Annual Revenue =	$54,167	$79,167	$25,000									
19	PW =	$33,664	$34,778	$1,114									
20	IRR =	12.560%	11.764%	10.170%									
21				=RiskOutput("PW(B)") + NPV($C$15,F3:F12)+F2									
22			=RiskOutput("IRR(A)") + IRR(B2,B12)										
23	=RiskPert(40000, 55000, 65000)												
24													

FIGURE 13.34

@RISK setup for Example 13.29. (The Figure was Generated with the Help of @RISK, a Product of Palisade Corporation, Ithaca, NY; www.palisade.com.).

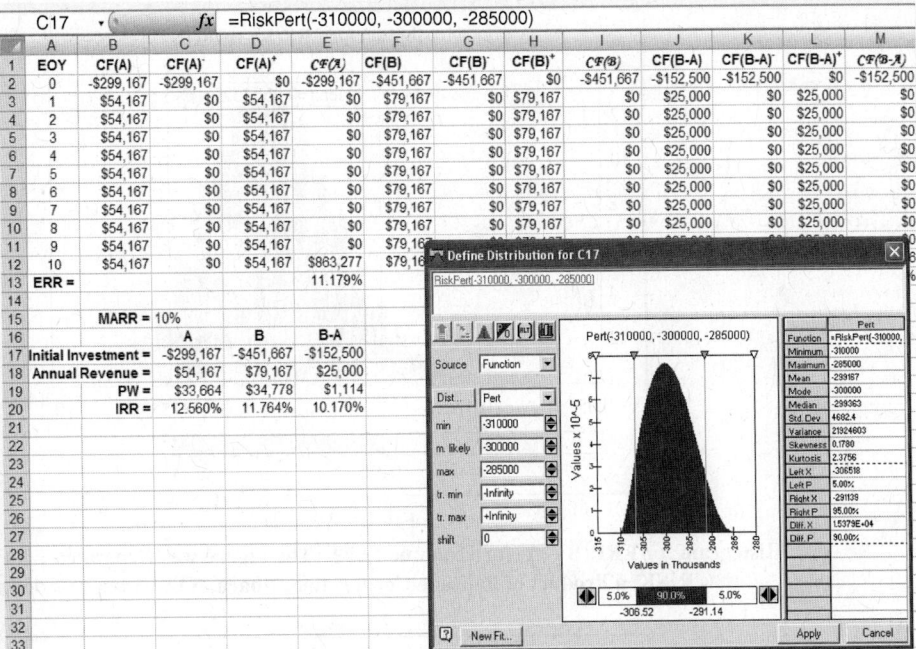

FIGURE 13.35

PERT Distribution for Investment in Design A. (The Figure was Generated with the Help of @RISK, a Product of Palisade Corporation, Ithaca, NY; www.palisade.com.).

From the output report, for the incremental investment, $\Pr[PW(\text{B} - \text{A}) < 0] = \Pr[\text{ERR}(\text{B} - \text{A}) < MARR] = \Pr[\text{IRR}(\text{B} - \text{A}) < MARR] = 0.49192$. Therefore, Design B has a greater probability of being the economic choice, as confirmed by the following results: $\Pr[PW(\text{A}) < 0] = \Pr[\text{ERR}(\text{A}) < MARR] = \Pr[\text{IRR}(\text{A}) < MARR] = 0.14129$ and $\Pr[PW(\text{B}) < 0] = \Pr[\text{ERR}(\text{B}) < MARR] = \Pr[\text{IRR}(\text{B}) < MARR] = 0.10399$.

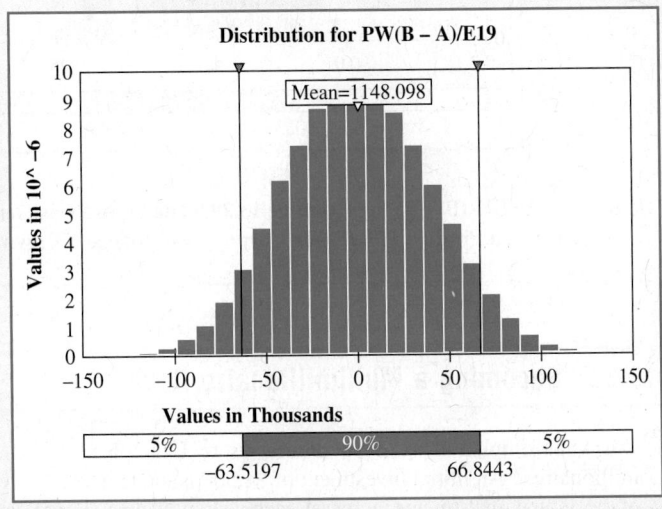

FIGURE 13.36

Histogram for PW(B − A) for Example 13.29. (The Figure was Generated with the Help of @RISK, a Product of Palisade Corporation, Ithaca, NY; www.palisade.com.).

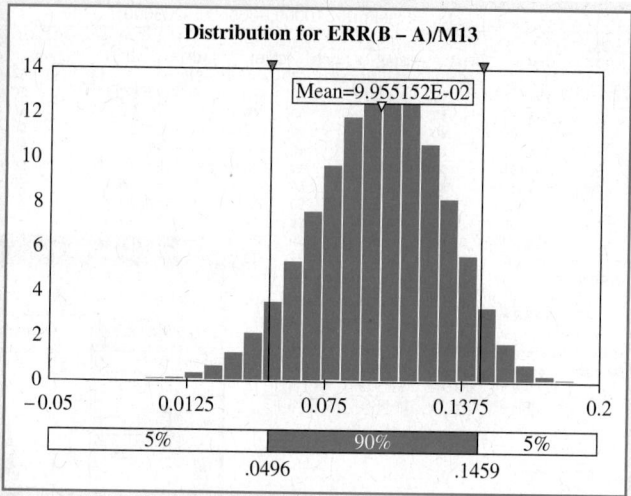

FIGURE 13.37

Histogram for ERR(B − A) for Example 13.29. (The Figure was Generated with the Help of @RISK, a Product of Palisade Corporation, Ithaca, NY; www.palisade.com.).

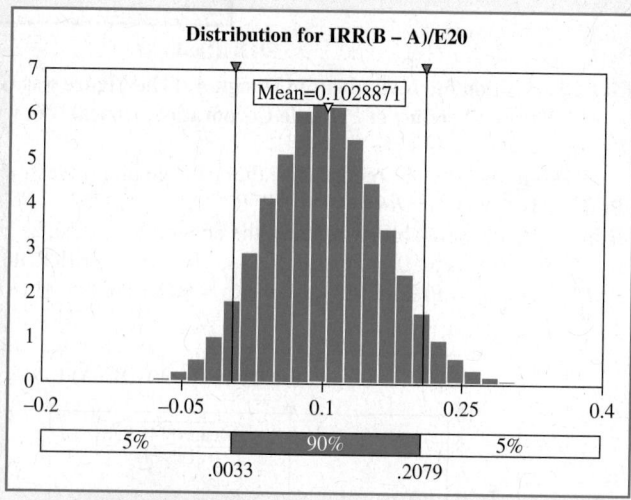

FIGURE 13.38

Histogram for IRR(B − A) for Example 13.29. (The Figure was Generated with the Help of @RISK, a Product of Palisade Corporation, Ithaca, NY; www.palisade.com.).

EXAMPLE 13.30   Becoming a Multimillionaire Revisited

Our final simulation example returns us to Example 3.21, titled "Becoming a Multimillionaire." An initial investment of $4,500 is made into an investment account. The size of the annual investments increases each year, with an average growth rate of 8 percent. The amount earned annually on the investment portfolio averages 6.86 percent. We wish to determine the probability of the investment portfolio having a value of $2,000,000 after 35 years of investing.

First, we specify a distribution for the growth rate for the annual investment's size. Specifically, we assume a PERT distribution, with a minimum increase of -5 percent, a most likely increase of 10.25 percent, and a maximum increase of 12 percent, giving an average growth rate of

$$[-0.05 + 4(0.1025) + 0.12]/6$$

or 8 percent.

Next, we specify a distribution for the annual earnings or growth rate for the investment portfolio. As with the annual investment's size, we assume a PERT distribution, with a minimum growth rate of -4 percent, a most likely growth rate of 7.79 percent, and a maximum growth rate of 14 percent, for an average of

$$[-0.04 + 4(0.0779) + 0.14]/6$$

or 6.86 percent.

We chose 8 percent and 6.86 percent as the averages, because they are the deterministic rates that produced an investment portfolio of $2,000,000 in 35 years in Example 3.20.

The @RISK setup is shown in Figure 13.39. The results of 100,000 Monte Carlo simulation trials are as follows: a mean portfolio value of $2,000,941.68; a minimum portfolio value of $1,022,881.81; a maximum portfolio value of $3,671,799.25; a sample standard deviation of $269,955.87; and 48.136 percent of the simulated investments have a portfolio value of at least $2,000,000. The histogram of the portfolio value is given in Figure 13.40; 90 percent of the simulated portfolios have values between $1,582,444.25 and $2,468,729.75.

To compare the results obtained using Monte Carlo with those obtained using Latin hypercube, the problem was resimulated. To minimize the variance in outputs, the random number seed used for the Latin hypercube was also used for Monte Carlo. The following Latin hypercube results were obtained: a mean portfolio value of $2,001,244.16; a minimum portfolio value of $1,023,027.75; a maximum portfolio value of $3,671,367.75; a sample standard deviation of $269,989.16; and 48.202 percent of the simulated investments have a portfolio

H14 =RiskPert(-0.05, 0.1025, 0.12)

	A	B	C	D	E	F	G	H	I	J	K
1	EOY	Annual Investment Growth Rate	Size of Annual Investment	Investment Portfolio Growth Rate	Value of Investment Portfolio		EOY	Annual Investment Growth Rate	Size of Annual Investment	Investment Portfolio Growth Rate	Value of Investment Portfolio
2	0		$4,500		$4,500		18	8.00%	$17,982	6.86%	$311,064
3	1	8.00%	$4,860	6.86%	$9,669		19	8.00%	$19,421	6.86%	$351,824
4	2	8.00%	$5,249	6.86%	$15,581		20	8.00%	$20,974	6.86%	$396,933
5	3	8.00%	$5,669	6.86%	$22,318		21	8.00%	$22,652	6.86%	$446,815
6	4	8.00%	$6,122	6.86%	$29,972		22	8.00%	$24,464	6.86%	$501,931
7	5	8.00%	$6,612	6.86%	$38,640		23	8.00%	$26,422	6.86%	$562,785
8	6	8.00%	$7,141	6.86%	$48,431		24	8.00%	$28,535	6.86%	$629,927
9	7	8.00%	$7,712	6.86%	$59,466		25	8.00%	$30,818	6.86%	$703,958
10	8	8.00%	$8,329	6.86%	$71,874		26	8.00%	$33,284	6.86%	$785,534
11	9	8.00%	$8,996	6.86%	$85,800		27	8.00%	$35,946	6.86%	$875,367
12	10	8.00%	$9,715	6.86%	$101,401		28	8.00%	$38,822	6.86%	$974,240
13	11	8.00%	$10,492	6.86%	$118,850		29	8.00%	$41,928	6.86%	$1,083,000
14	12	8.00%	$11,332	6.86%	$138,335		30	8.00%	$45,282	6.86%	$1,202,576
15	13	8.00%	$12,238	6.86%	$160,063		31	8.00%	$48,905	6.86%	$1,333,977
16	14	8.00%	$13,217	6.86%	$184,261		32	8.00%	$52,817	6.86%	$1,478,305
17	15	8.00%	$14,275	6.86%	$211,176		33	8.00%	$57,042	6.86%	$1,636,759
18	16	8.00%	$15,417	6.86%	$241,079		34	8.00%	$61,606	6.86%	$1,810,646
19	17	8.00%	$16,650	6.86%	$274,267		35	8.00%	$66,534	6.86%	$2,001,390
20											
21		=RiskPert(-0.05, 0.1025, 0.12)			=E18*(1+D19)+C19						
22									=RiskOutput("FW(Inv)") + K18*(1+J19)+I19		
23					=RiskPert(-0.04, 0.0779, 0.14)						
24											

FIGURE 13.39

@RISK Setup for Example 13.30.

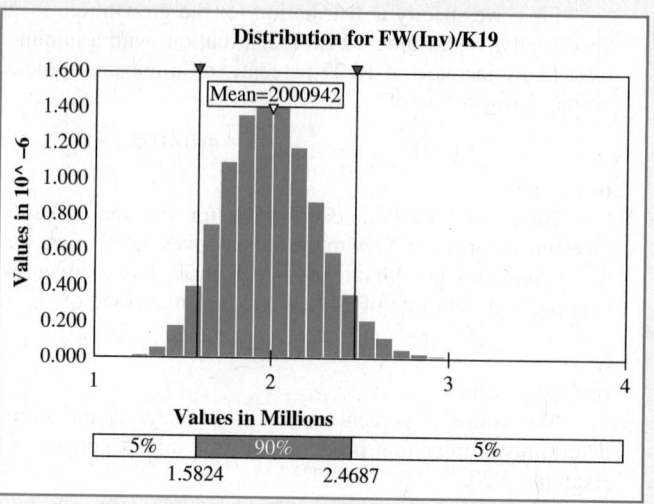

Histogram of the Future Worth of An Investment Portfolio, Based on 100,000 Monte Carlo Simulation Trials. (The Figure was Generated with the Help of @RISK, a Product of Palisade Corporation, Ithaca, NY; www.palisade.com.).

value of at least $2,000,000. The histogram of the portfolio value is given in Figure 13.41; 90 percent of the simulated portfolios have values between $1,583,106.50 and $2,469,397.25.

Using a laptop computer, the time required by @RISK to perform the Monte Carlo simulation was 4 minutes and 29 seconds; the Latin hypercube simulation took 4 minutes and 2 seconds. The @RISK output includes a sensitivity analysis of all inputs; seven of the ten most sensitive inputs were the investment portfolio growth rate, with the most sensitive being the growth rate for the last year, the next most sensitive being the growth rate for the

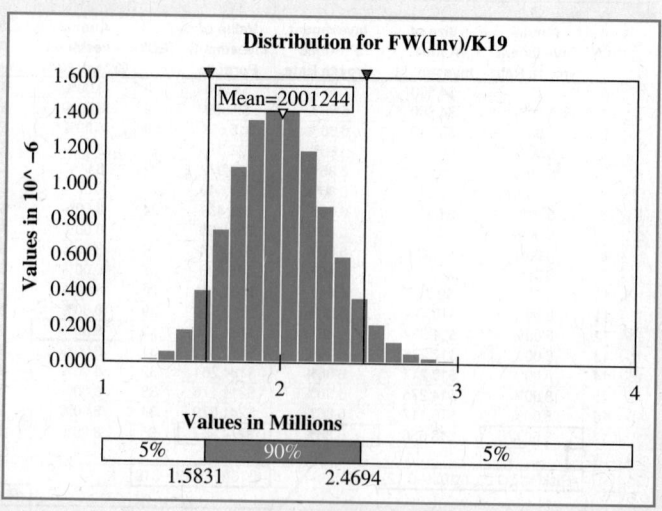

Histogram of the future worth of an investment portfolio, Based on 100,000 Latin Hypercube simulation trials. (The Figure was Generated with the Help of @RISK, a Product of Palisade Corporation, Ithaca, NY; www.palisade.com.)

Sensitivity			
Rank	Name	Regr	Corr
#1	Investment Portfolio Growth Rate / $J$19	0.224	0.214
#2	Investment Portfolio Growth Rate / $J$18	0.213	0.203
#3	Investment Portfolio Growth Rate / $J$17	0.210	0.196
#4	Investment Portfolio Growth Rate / $J$16	0.203	0.195
#5	Investment Portfolio Growth Rate / $J$15	0.192	0.188
#6	Investment Portfolio Growth Rate / $J$14	0.186	0.177
#7	Annual Investment Growth Rate / $B$3	0.184	0.174
#8	Investment Portfolio Growth Rate / $J$13	0.181	0.167
#9	Annual Investment Growth Rate / $B$4	0.176	0.166
#10	Annual Investment Growth Rate / $B$5	0.173	0.157
#11	Investment Portfolio Growth Rate / $J$12	0.170	0.158
#12	Annual Investment Growth Rate / $B$7	0.166	0.157
#13	Annual Investment Growth Rate / $B$6	0.166	0.150
#14	Investment Portfolio Growth Rate / $J$11	0.163	0.158
#15	Annual Investment Growth Rate / $B$8	0.160	0.152
#16	Investment Portfolio Growth Rate / $J$10	0.158	0.151

FIGURE 13.42

@RISK Sensitivity Analysis for Example 13.30. (The Figure was Generated with the Help of @RISK, a Product of Palisade Corporation, Ithaca, NY; www.palisade.com.).

next to last year, and so forth. The @RISK sensitivity analysis indicates that the "final legs of the marathon" play a critical role in the investment portfolio's final value. The sensitivity analysis performed by @RISK for this example is shown in Figure 13.42.

13-5 SUMMARY

In summary, an essential step in engineering economic analyses is performing supplementary analysis. Since perfect knowledge concerning the future seldom exists, it is important to understand the impact on an investment's economic worth when things do not go as planned.

In this chapter, we considered three approaches: break-even analysis, sensitivity analysis, and risk analysis. Break-even analysis is performed when it is desired to know the values of one or more parameters that will cause the investment to "break even" or have a negligible economic worth. Sensitivity analysis is performed when it is desired to gauge the impact on the economic worth if one or more parameters take on values over some specified range; typically, one is interested in knowing what percent change in a parameter's value will result in a different recommendation regarding the investment(s). Risk analysis incorporates probabilistic estimates with the values of the parameters; typically, one is interested in knowing the probability of an investment being profitable or the probability of the measure of economic worth having at least a particular value.

In performing risk analyses, we noted that, in some cases, analytical approaches can be used, and the probabilities of certain outcomes could be obtained mathematically. However, because such opportunities are limited, we discussed the use of simulation approaches for more complex situations.

Although many options are available in performing computer-based simulations, we focused on the @RISK software. Numerous investments were analyzed under probabilistic conditions using @RISK 4.5 software.[12] Both Monte Carlo and Latin hypercube simulation were used.

From the treatment of computer-based simulation, we noted the following:

1. The central limit theorem often provides a very good approximation, even when small sample sizes are used and when input distributions are not symmetrically distributed.

2. The Excel® PV and RATE functions are appropriate when cash flows are perfectly autocorrelated, but the Excel® NPV and IRR functions should be used when cash flows are statistically independent.

3. The Excel® RATE function will not always yield a result, even when a reasonable rate of return exists for an investment; internal rate of return calculations can prove problematic when considering incremental cash flows.

4. If a rate of return is desired when considering incremental cash flows, the external rate of return is more dependable than the internal rate of return.

Pit Stop #13—Superstitious? Chapter 13 Isn't Bad Luck, It's Just Risky!

1. True or False: In the absence of perfect information accurate investment decisions cannot be made.

2. True or False: Break-even analysis is a brand new concept, nothing like it has been presented previously in the book.

3. True or False: Sensitivity analysis is a technique used by psychologists to gauge a person's reaction to criticism.

4. True or False: Risk analyses are performed when complete uncertainty exists and no reasonable estimates can be made regarding the probability of occurrence of parameter values.

[12]Pinacle Corporation released @RISK 5.0 after we performed the simulations in the examples. We now use version 5.0 and recommend it to future users of the software.

5. True or False: Monte Carlo simulation is used in casinos, but has no application other than in roulette and other gambling establishments.

6. True or False: If the cost of producing one unit of product is uniformly distributed with a mean of 25¢ and a standard deviation of 10¢, then the cost of producing 1000 units of product will be distributed uniformly with a mean of $250 and a standard deviation of $100.

7. True or False: If producing one unit of product has a mean cost of 25¢ and a standard deviation of 10¢, then there will be a 0.999 probability of it costing less than $260 to produce 1000 units of product when the units are produced independently.

8. True or False: if producing one unit of produce has a mean cost of 25¢ and a standard deviation of 10¢, then there will be a 0.841 probability of it costing less than $260 to produce 1000 units of the costs of producing units of product are perfectly correlated.

9. True or False: If X and Y are independent random variables with expected values and variances of E(X), E(Y), V(X), and V(Y), respectively, then the expected value of the product of X and Y is equal to E(X)E(Y) and the variance of the product of X and Y is equal to V(X)V(Y).

10. True or False: @**RISK** simulation is limited to Latin Hypercube sampling.

DECISION TREE ANALYSIS

A companion technique to risk analysis is decision tree analysis. Although frequently used to analyze decision situations under random conditions, decision trees are also used when conditions are deterministic.

Tree structures can also be used to evaluate complex situations and to enumerate all possible combinations of outcomes. Consider, for example, the formation of investment alternatives from a set of investment proposals described in Example 1.5. Figure 13.A.1 depicts a tree-structured representation of all possible investment alternatives from three investment proposals. When $x_j = 1$, proposal j is included in the investment portfolio; when $x_j = 0$, proposal j is not included. As shown, with three investment proposals, eight mutually exclusive investment alternatives or portfolios can be formed, including the do-nothing alternative, or empty portfolio, $\{\emptyset\}$. Squares in the tree structure are called *decision nodes*; lines are called *branches*. Dj denotes the decision to include or exclude investment proposal j from the investment portfolio.

Decision trees are used when multiple decisions are to be made sequentially. As an example, medical decisions are typically sequential. Based on the results of a routine blood analysis, a physician may require additional medical tests and then may perform exploratory surgery, and, based on these findings, recommend additional treatment or surgery for the patient. Following surgery, the recuperative procedure may also be conditional and involve further sequential decisions made by the physician.

Sequential decisions are also common in the business and industrial world. For example, the number and type of material handling units to purchase may depend on the forecast of product demand in each of the next 5 years. In the field of quality control, sampling is concerned with sequential decisions. For example, if a sample of five units is taken from a production machine, subsequent actions taken with that machine may well depend on whether 0, 1, 2, 3, 4, or 5 defective units were found in the sample of five units.

Although decision trees can be used in deterministic conditions, our focus will be on using them when conditions are probabilistic. For that reason, we will add another symbol to the tree structure: a probability node, denoted by a circle. Working from left to right on the decision tree, the following sequence typically occurs: a decision is made, a probabilistic outcome occurs, a subsequent decision is made based on the probabilistic outcome, another probabilistic outcome occurs, and so forth.

Because we are interested in using decision trees in performing engineering economic analyses, we use one or more measures of economic worth in making our decisions. And because we are dealing with random variables, we rely on either expected values, such as expected present worth, or a probabilistic criterion, such as maximizing the probability of a positive-valued present worth.

In decision tree analysis, the solution is obtained by "working backward" through the tree. As such, calculations begin with the final nodes in the decision tree. We provide an example to illustrate this approach. (Since our purpose is to demonstrate how to perform decision tree analysis, the number of alternatives and possible outcomes is reduced significantly from what the firm in question faced.)

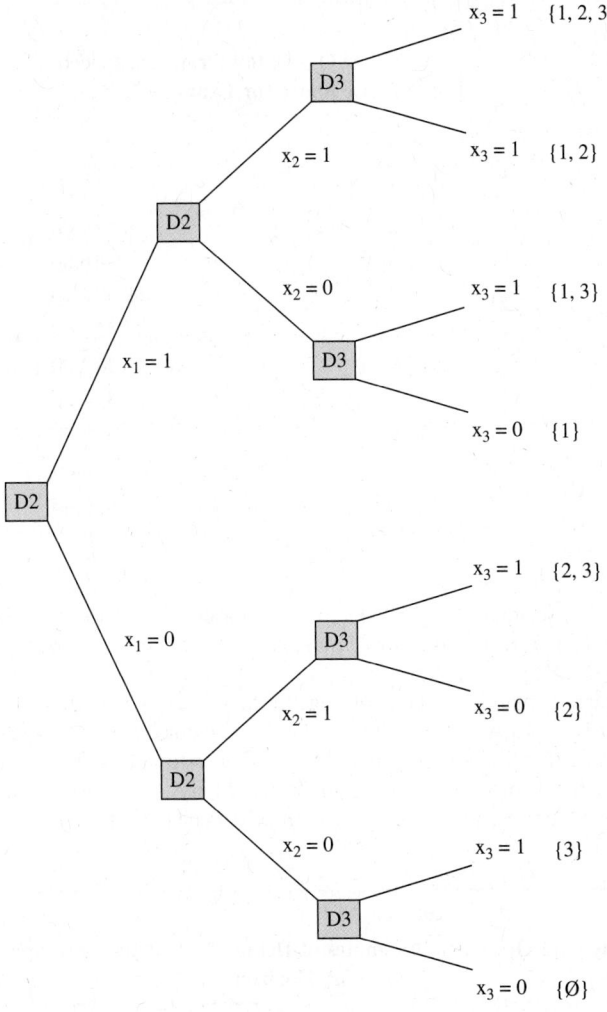

FIGURE 13.A.1
Using a Tree Structure to Form Investment Alternatives from Investment Proposals.

EXAMPLE 13.A.1   How Large a Warehouse to Lease?

A home goods manufacturing firm is undecided about the size of a distribution center (DC) it should lease. A developer has approached the firm with an offer to build to the firm's specifications either a 75,000 sq. ft. DC or a 150,000 sq. ft. DC. The developer has available existing warehouse space that can be leased to meet short-term needs. Hence, if demand exceeds the capacity of the leased DC, additional leased space can be secured, but at a premium price and at additional costs, due to extra handling.

If the smaller DC is leased, the developer is willing to expand it to 150,000 sq. ft. after 5 years—if the firm will enter into a 10-year contract. Specifically, the developer offers the following options to the firm:

1. Lease a 75,000 sq. ft. DC now, with the possibility of expanding it to 150,000 sq. ft. after 5 years.

2. Lease a 150,000 sq. ft. DC now, with no expansion needed in the foreseeable future.

TABLE 13.A.1

Cost of Over-Flow Premium Priced Lease Space for Example 13.A.1.

Year	$/sq.ft.
1	$12.00
2	$14.00
3	$16.00
4	$18.00
5	$20.00
6	$22.00
7	$24.00
8	$26.00
9	$28.00
10	$30.00

Leased space costs $7.50 per sq. ft. if leased now; if leased after 5 years, it will cost $12.50 per sq. ft. If premium space must be leased, the cost per square foot will be as shown in Table 13.A.1.

Yearly demand for space during the first 5 years is anticipated to be distributed as shown in Table 13.A.2. Depending on the demand during the first 5 years, different forecasts are provided for the next 5 years. Notice, three estimates are provided: pessimistic, most likely, and optimistic—or minimum, most likely, and maximum, depending on your terminology preference. Notice also, the estimates during the last 5 years depend on

TABLE 13.A.2

Pessimistic, Most Likely, and Optimistic Estimates of Demand for Warehouse Space Over the 10-Year Planning Horizon.

	Annual Demand for Leased Space								
Year	Pessimistic (0.1)			Most Likely (0.5)			Optimistic (0.4)		
1	25,000			50,000			60,000		
2	33,000			60,000			72,000		
3	41,000			70,000			84,000		
4	49,000			80,000			96,000		
5	57,000			90,000			108,000		
Year	Pessimistic 0.1	Most Likely 0.7	Optimistic 0.2	Pessimistic 0.3	Most Likely 0.4	Optimistic 0.3	Pessimistic 0.2	Most Likely 0.5	Optimistic 0.3
6	60,000	65,000	70,000	95,000	100,000	105,000	115,000	120,000	125,000
7	67,000	73,000	79,000	104,000	110,000	114,000	126,000	132,000	138,000
8	74,000	81,000	88,000	113,000	120,000	123,000	137,000	144,000	151,000
9	81,000	89,000	97,000	122,000	130,000	132,000	148,000	156,000	164,000
10	88,000	97,000	106,000	131,000	140,000	141,000	159,000	168,000	177,000

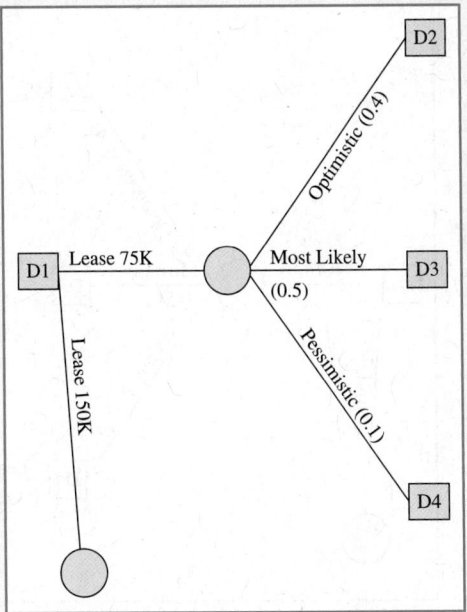

FIGURE 13.A.2
Creating a decision tree for Example 13.A.1.

whether the pessimistic, most likely, or optimistic outcomes occur during the first 5 years. If, for example, the most likely estimates are realized during the first 5 years, then the pessimistic, most likely, and optimistic estimates of 95,000, 100,000, and 105,000, respectively, will be provided for the sixth year. Finally, notice that different probability distributions are used for the final 5 years, depending on the demand during the first 5 years.

Lease payments are made at the beginning of the year. The firm uses a before-tax MARR of 15 percent. It is desired to make decisions that will minimize the expected present worth cost over the 10-year planning horizon.

In constructing the decision tree, we recognize that the first decision is how much space to lease initially from the developer: 75,000 sq. ft. or 150,000 sq. ft. Figure 13.A.2 illustrates the initial steps taken in constructing a decision tree for the example. Notice, if a decision is made to lease 75,000 sq. ft., then another decision must be made after 5 years. Recognizing that the decision might differ depending on the demand during the first 5 years, three decision nodes (D2, D3, and D4) are added to the decision tree.

As shown in Figure 13.A.3, if only 75,000 sq. ft. is leased initially, then a further decision is required after 5 years to either lease 75,000 sq. ft. from the developer or contract with the developer to increase the lease capacity to 150,000 sq. ft. Figure 13.A.4 shows the various demand possibilities and probabilities for the two-stage demand scenario.

Based on a 10-year planning horizon, a 15 percent MARR, and beginning-of-year (BOY) lease payments, the present worth is computed for each of the end branches on the tree. Table 13.A.3 provides the present worth calculations for leasing 75,000 sq. ft. for the 10-year period. Table 13.A.4 provides the present worth calculations for leasing 75,000 sq. ft. initially and leasing an additional 75,000 sq. ft. for the last 5 years. Table 13.A.5 provides the present worth calculations for the case of 150,000 sq. ft. being leased for the 10-year period. Figure 13.A.5 shows the complete decision tree.

Figure 13.A.6 shows the first reduction to the decision tree. The end branches and probability nodes are replaced with elliptically shaped expected value nodes, in which the expected values are recorded. To illustrate the calculations performed, consider decision

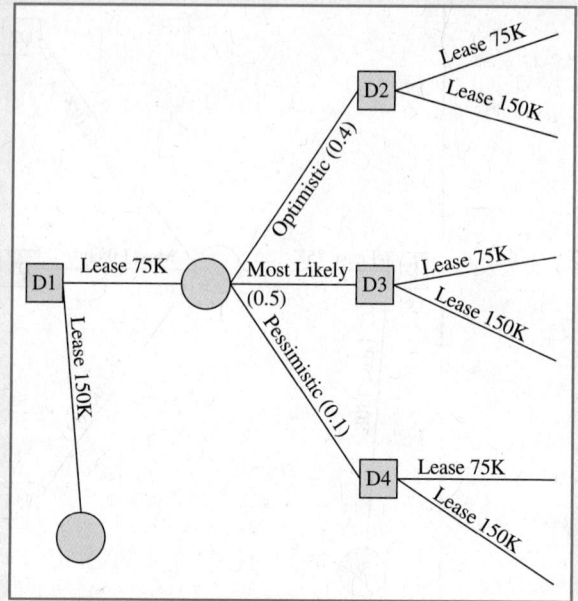

FIGURE 13.A.3
Expanding the Decision Tree.

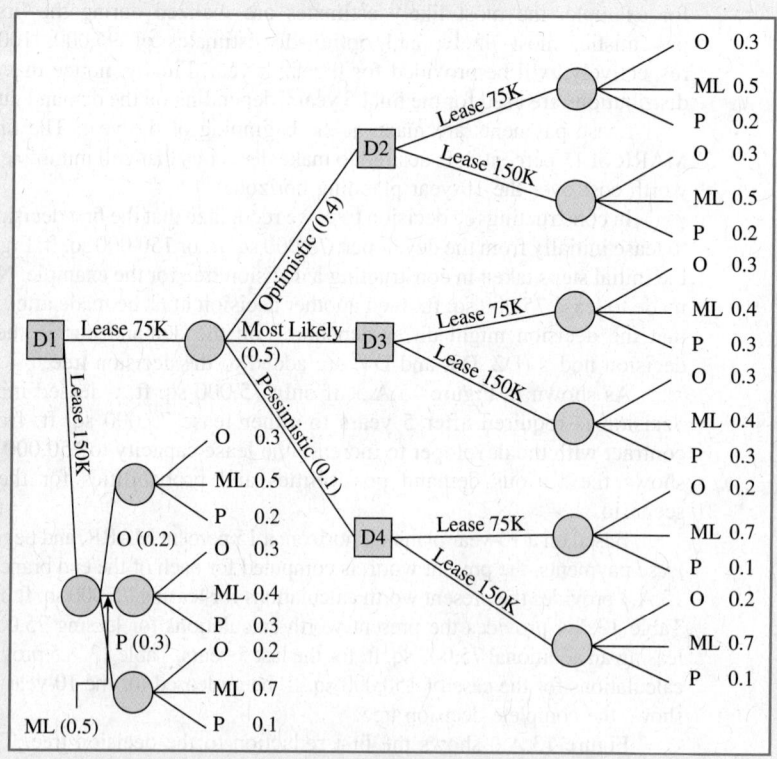

FIGURE 13.A.4
Adding Probabilities to the Decision Tree.

TABLE 13.A.3

Present Worth Calculations for the Alternative of Leasing 75,000 Sq. Ft. of Space Over the Entire 10-Year Planning Horizon.

	Yearly Lease Payments with 75,000 Sq. Ft. DC (no expansion)								
BOY	{P,P}	{P,ML}	{P,O}	{ML,P}	{ML,ML}	{ML,O}	{O,P}	{O,ML}	{O,O}
1	$562,500	$562,500	$562,500	$562,500	$562,500	$562,500	$562,500	$562,500	$562,500
2	$562,500	$562,500	$562,500	$562,500	$562,500	$562,500	$730,500	$730,500	$730,500
3	$562,500	$562,500	$562,500	$674,500	$674,500	$674,500	$946,500	$946,500	$946,500
4	$562,500	$562,500	$562,500	$886,500	$886,500	$886,500	$1,210,500	$1,210,500	$1,210,500
5	$702,500	$702,500	$702,500	$1,142,500	$1,142,500	$1,142,500	$1,522,500	$1,522,500	$1,522,500
6	$672,500	$892,500	$1,112,500	$1,222,500	$1,442,500	$1,662,500	$1,772,500	$1,882,500	$2,102,500
7	$850,500	$1,114,500	$1,378,500	$1,474,500	$1,738,500	$2,002,500	$2,098,500	$2,242,500	$2,506,500
8	$1,056,500	$1,368,500	$1,680,500	$1,758,500	$2,070,500	$2,382,500	$2,460,500	$2,642,500	$2,954,500
9	$1,290,500	$1,654,500	$2,018,500	$2,074,500	$2,438,500	$2,802,500	$2,858,500	$3,082,500	$3,446,500
10	$1,552,500	$1,972,500	$2,392,500	$2,422,500	$2,842,500	$3,262,500	$3,292,500	$3,562,500	$3,982,500
PW =	$4,210,878	$4,790,067	$5,369,255	$6,070,900	$6,650,088	$7,229,276	$8,163,686	$8,499,028	$9,078,216

node D2. If 75,000 sq. ft. are leased the last 5 years, the expected present worth cost (from Table 13.A.3) is

$$E(PW_{75K,75K}) = 0.3(\$9,078,216) + 0.5(\$8,499,028) + 0.2(\$8,163,686)$$
$$= \$8,605,716$$

Likewise, if 150,000 sq. ft. are leased after 5 years, the expected present worth cost (from Table 13.A.4) is

$$E(PW_{75K,150K}) = 0.3(\$7,272,031) + 0.5(\$6,854,101) + 0.2(\$6,655,252) = \$6,939,710$$

As shown, if 75,000 sq. ft. of space are leased for the duration of the planning horizon and the optimistic estimates of demand hold for the first 5 years, then the expected present worth lease cost is $8,605,718. Similarly, if the optimistic estimates of demand hold for the

TABLE 13.A.4

Present Worth Calculations for the Alternative of Leasing 75,000 Sq. Ft. of Space for 5 Years and Increasing the DC Capacity to 150,000 Sq. Ft. of Space after the 5th Year.

	Yearly Lease Payments with 75,000 Sq. Ft. DC, Plus Sq. Ft. Expansion								
BOY	{P,P}	{P,ML}	{P,O}	{ML,P}	{ML,ML}	{ML,O}	{O,P}	{O,ML}	{O,O}
1	$562,500	$562,500	$562,500	$562,500	$562,500	$562,500	$562,500	$562,500	$562,500
2	$562,500	$562,500	$562,500	$562,500	$562,500	$562,500	$730,500	$730,500	$730,500
3	$562,500	$562,500	$562,500	$674,500	$674,500	$674,500	$946,500	$946,500	$946,500
4	$562,500	$562,500	$562,500	$886,500	$886,500	$886,500	$1,210,500	$1,210,500	$1,210,500
5	$702,500	$702,500	$702,500	$1,142,500	$1,142,500	$1,142,500	$1,522,500	$1,522,500	$1,522,500
6	$1,500,000	$1,500,000	$1,500,000	$1,500,000	$1,500,000	$1,500,000	$1,500,000	$1,500,000	$1,500,000
7	$1,500,000	$1,500,000	$1,500,000	$1,500,000	$1,500,000	$1,500,000	$1,500,000	$1,500,000	$1,644,000
8	$1,500,000	$1,500,000	$1,500,000	$1,500,000	$1,500,000	$1,500,000	$1,500,000	$1,630,000	$1,942,000
9	$1,500,000	$1,500,000	$1,500,000	$1,500,000	$1,500,000	$1,640,000	$1,696,000	$1,920,000	$2,284,000
10	$1,500,000	$1,500,000	$1,500,000	$1,500,000	$1,530,000	$1,950,000	$1,980,000	$2,250,000	$2,670,000
PW =	$5,123,379	$5,123,379	$5,123,379	$5,672,674	$5,681,202	$5,846,358	$6,655,252	$6,854,101	$7,272,031

TABLE 13.A.5
Present Worth Calculations for the Alternative of Leasing 150,000 Sq. Ft. of Space for 10 Years.

Yearly Lease Payments with 150,000 Sq. Ft. DC

BOY	{P,P}	{P,ML}	{P,O}	{ML,P}	{ML,ML}	{ML,O}	{O,P}	{O,ML}	{O,O}
1	$1,125,000	$1,125,000	$1,125,000	$1,125,000	$1,125,000	$1,125,000	$1,125,000	$1,125,000	$1,125,000
2	$1,125,000	$1,125,000	$1,125,000	$1,125,000	$1,125,000	$1,125,000	$1,125,000	$1,125,000	$1,125,000
3	$1,125,000	$1,125,000	$1,125,000	$1,125,000	$1,125,000	$1,125,000	$1,125,000	$1,125,000	$1,125,000
4	$1,125,000	$1,125,000	$1,125,000	$1,125,000	$1,125,000	$1,125,000	$1,125,000	$1,125,000	$1,125,000
5	$1,125,000	$1,125,000	$1,125,000	$1,125,000	$1,125,000	$1,125,000	$1,125,000	$1,125,000	$1,125,000
6	$1,125,000	$1,125,000	$1,125,000	$1,125,000	$1,125,000	$1,125,000	$1,125,000	$1,125,000	$1,125,000
7	$1,125,000	$1,125,000	$1,125,000	$1,125,000	$1,125,000	$1,125,000	$1,125,000	$1,125,000	$1,269,000
8	$1,125,000	$1,125,000	$1,125,000	$1,125,000	$1,125,000	$1,125,000	$1,125,000	$1,255,000	$1,567,000
9	$1,125,000	$1,125,000	$1,125,000	$1,125,000	$1,125,000	$1,265,000	$1,321,000	$1,545,000	$1,909,000
10	$1,125,000	$1,125,000	$1,125,000	$1,125,000	$1,155,000	$1,575,000	$1,605,000	$1,875,000	$2,295,000
PW =	$6,493,032	$6,493,032	$6,493,032	$6,493,032	$6,501,560	$6,666,716	$6,693,551	$6,892,399	$7,310,329

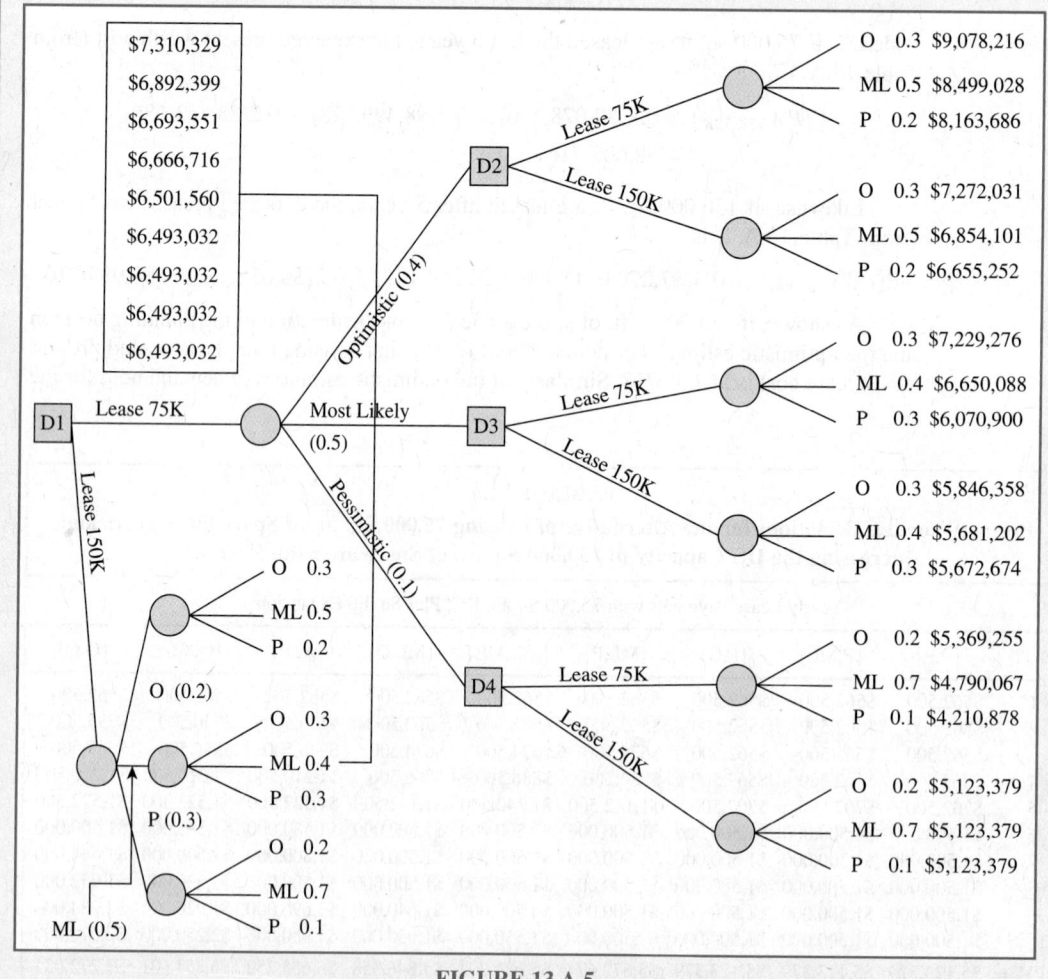

FIGURE 13.A.5
Adding Present Worths to Each Branch of the Decision Tree.

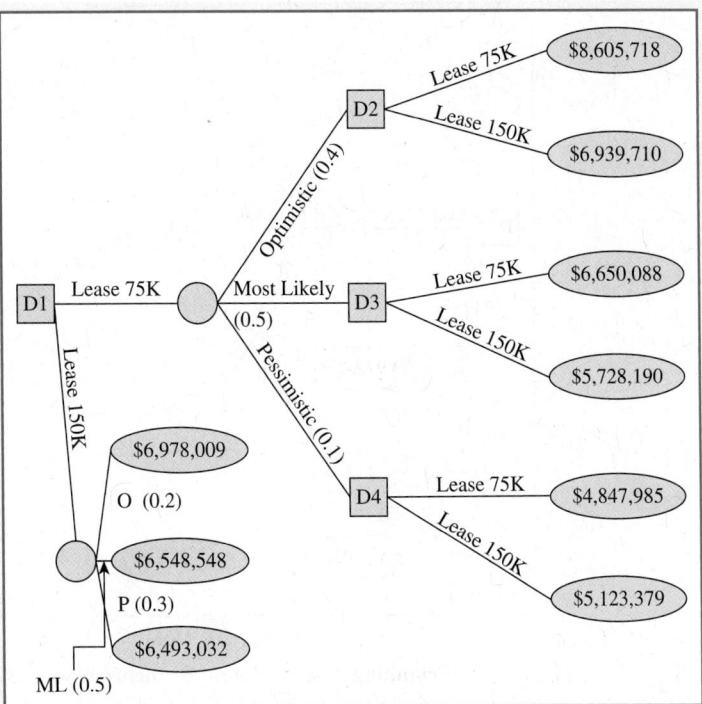

FIGURE 13.A.6

Replacing Branches with Expected Present Worth Values.

first 5 years and the DC is expanded to a total of 150,000 after the fifth year, then the expected present worth cost is $6,939,710.

Therefore, if the objective is to minimize expected present worth cost and one arrives at decision node D2, then the best course of action is to lease 150,000 sq. ft. for the remaining 5 years, since $E(PW_{75K,150K}) < E(PW_{75K,75K})$. Similar calculations are performed for decision nodes D3 and D4, resulting in the preferences shown in Figure 13.A.7.

As shown, if 75,000 sq. ft. of space is leased and the optimistic estimates of demand hold for the first 5 years, the firm will prefer to expand the DC after the fifth year. Hence, the "Lease 75K" branch is trimmed from the tree. Similarly, if the most likely estimates of demand hold for the first 5 years, the firm will prefer to expand the DC after the fifth year, and the "Lease 75K" branch is trimmed from the tree. However, if the pessimistic estimates of demand hold for the first 5 years, the firm will prefer to continue leasing 75,000 sq. ft. of space and the "Lease 150K" branch is trimmed from the tree.

As shown in Figure 13.A.8, since an initial decision to lease 150,000 sq. ft. of space does not require further decisions, we can compute its expected present worth cost: $6,714,781. Likewise, knowing the conditional optimum strategies if we initially lease 75,000 sq. ft. of space, we can compute the expected present worth cost: $6,124,778. Since the expected present worth cost of initially leasing 75,000 sq. ft. is less than the expected present worth cost of initially leasing 150,000 sq. ft., that is the recommended decision. After the firm experiences demand the first 5 years, a decision can be made to continue leasing 75,000 sq. ft. (if the pessimistic estimates are realized) or to have the DC expanded by 75,000 sq. ft. for the final 5 years of the planning horizon (if the most likely or optimistic estimates are realized). Of course, if the actual demand during the first 5 years varies significantly from the estimates, a new set of estimates for the final 5 years should be made and the appropriate decision made concerning the amount of space to lease.

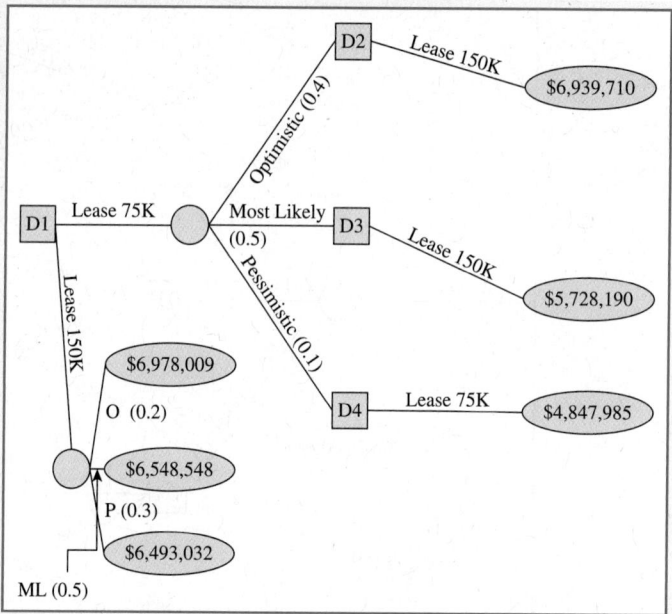

FIGURE 13.A.7
Trimming Non-Optimum Branches from the Tree.

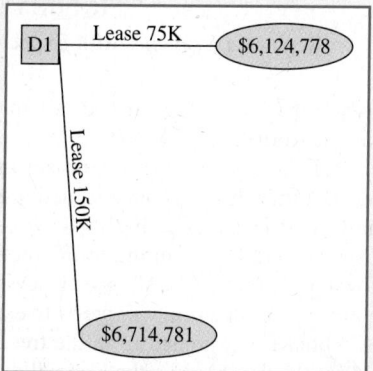

FIGURE 13.A.8
**Reducing the Tree to the Final Two Expected Values and Determining the Optimum
First Decision.**

EXAMPLE 13.A.2 **Accommodating Needed Manufacturing Space**

The Jax Tool and Engineering Company is a medium-sized, job-order machine shop and has
been in business for 10 years. During the past 2 years, sales have increased sharply and the
company is operating near capacity. A market test for a new product, electroplating tanks,
was very favorable. However, production floor space for a new product line is not readily
available in the existing facility. Management is considering three alternatives: do nothing,
rearrange an area of the existing floor space, and build an addition to the current facility.
Another factor to be considered is the possibility of competition from one other job-order

machine shop in the local area. If the electroplating tank venture is successful and the Jax Tool and Engineering Company cannot fully meet the market demand, it is likely that competition will occur. In performing a present worth analysis, a 5-year planning horizon and a 30 percent *MARR* is to be used.

Rearrangement does not require new construction, but machinery must be moved, some new machinery must be purchased, and new storage areas must be created. Weekly production is to be limited to 10 tanks on a two-shift operation. If there is competition the first year, Jax will probably take no further action; a present worth of $500,000 is estimated for this outcome.

On the other hand, if there is no competition the first year, Jax will not be able to meet the expected demand. Management estimates that there is a 40 percent chance that no competition will occur during the first year. If no competition occurs the first year, Jax must decide whether or not to expand the production line by building an addition to the facility.

Expanding the existing facility will be expensive. However, if expansion occurs now, it will preclude competition emerging. A present worth of $300,000 is estimated for this outcome. If there is no expansion, two outcomes are possible: the other local machine shop either will or will not enter the competition after 1 year. The probability of the other local machine shop entering the competition after 1 year is estimated to be 0.7. The present worth of this outcome is estimated to be $100,000; if no competition occurs in the second year, the firm's present worth is estimated to be $500,000. It is so unlikely that competition will occur after a 2-year period that a probability of 0 is assigned to this possibility.

The "Build Addition" alternative has greater initial and recurring costs than the "New Layout" alternative. However, with the addition, a capacity of 25 tanks per week will exist; it is anticipated this capacity will satisfy the market for a 5-year period.

With adequate production capacity initially, the chance of competition is small, approximately 20 percent. If no competition occurs, Jax's present worth will be $900,000. If competition emerges, then the reduced sales, coupled with the high annual fixed costs, will result in a present worth of −$1,000,000. A decision tree representation of the problem is given in Figure 13.A.9.

Based on an objective of maximizing expected present worth, a best decision is sought at D2, the most distant decision point. The expected values at D2 are

$$E(\text{Expansion}) = \$300,000$$

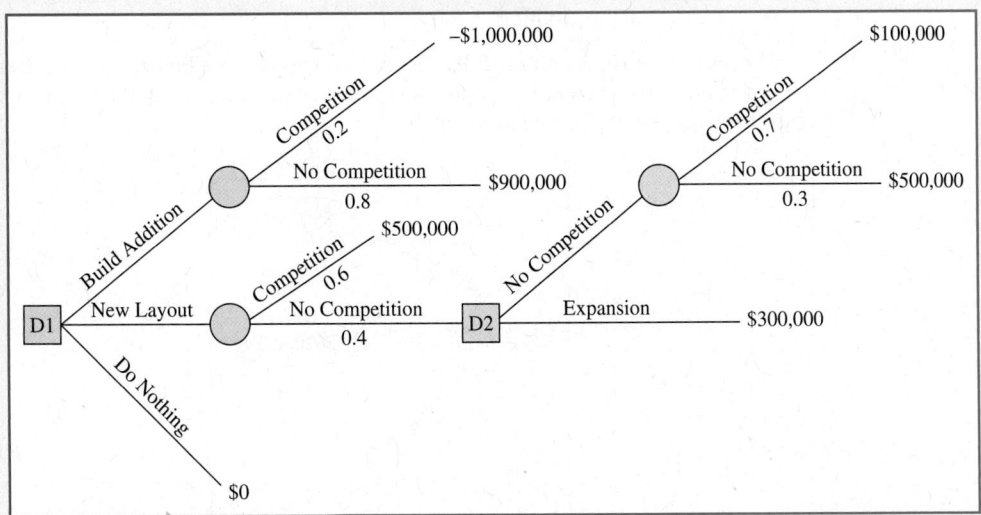

FIGURE 13.A.9

Jax Tool and Engineering Company Decision Tree.

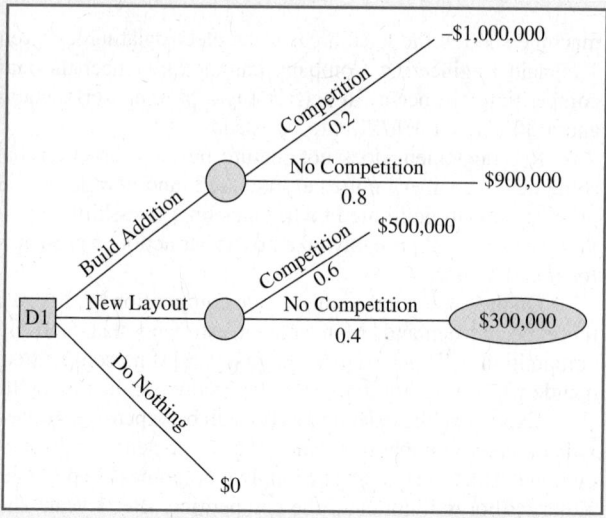

FIGURE 13.A.10

Jax Tool and Engineering Company–Reduced Decision Tree.

and

$$E(\text{No Expansion}) = \$100,000(0.7) + \$500,000(0.3)$$
$$= \$220,000$$

Thus, the alternative of expansion is chosen to maximize expected present worth, and this *best* value of $300,000 replaces D2 in the tree, as shown in Figure 13.A.10. From Figure 13.A.10, the expected values at D1 are calculated as

$$E(\text{Build Addition}) = -\$1,000,000(0.2) + \$900,000(0.8)$$
$$= \$520,000$$

$$E(\text{Rearrange}) = \$500,000(0.6) + \$300,000(0.4)$$
$$= \$420,000$$

$$E(\text{Do Nothing}) = \$0$$

The results are shown on the fully reduced decision tree in Figure 13.A.11. Based on maximizing expected present worth, the alternative of building an addition to the existing facility is recommended to management.

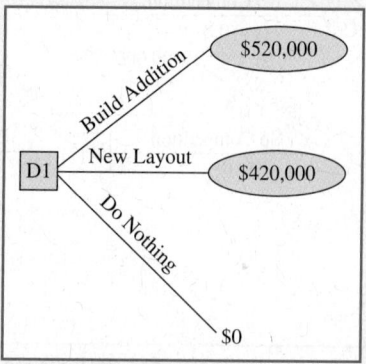

FIGURE 13.A.11

Jax Tool and Engineering Company–fully Reduced Decision Tree.

It is worth noting that choosing to build the addition exposes management to the possibility of a million-dollar negative present worth. (If management is interested in pursuing the alternative with the greatest probability of a positive-valued present worth, then the rearrangement alternative would be pursued, since it is guaranteed to have positive-valued present worth.)

 Tutoring problem available (at instructor's discretion) in *WileyPLUS*.

 Problem available (at instructor's discretion) in *WileyPLUS*.

Worked Problem Video available in *WileyPLUS*.

FE-LIKE PROBLEMS

1. If the total cost for producing widgets can be represented by $TC = 8,000 + 0.75X$, where X is the number of widgets produced and total revenue can be represented by $TR = 4.00X$, what is the break-even value for number of widgets produced?
   a. 1,684
   b. 2,000
   c. 2,462
   d. 3,763

   The next five questions refer to the following sensitivity graph:

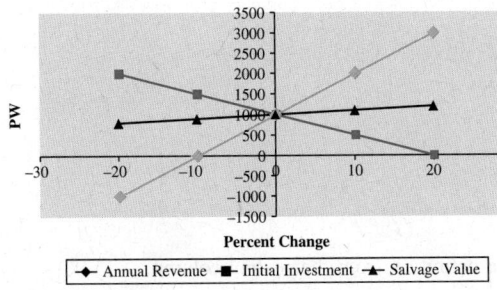

2. The analysis is most sensitive to changes in which component?
   a. Annual revenue
   b. Initial investment
   c. Salvage value
   d. Cannot be determined from the information given

3. The analysis is least sensitive to changes in which component?
   a. Annual revenue
   b. Initial investment
   c. Salvage value
   d. Cannot be determined from the information given

4. What is the numeric value of the present worth of the original project (i.e., no changes)?
   a. −10
   b. 20
   c. 1,000
   d. Cannot be determined from the information given

5. What percentage change in initial investment would cause the project to become unattractive?
   a. −10
   b. +20
   c. +1,000
   d. Cannot be determined from the information given

6. If a line for "annual expenses" was to be added to the graph, what slope would you expect the line to have?
   a. Positive slope (line rises as it goes left to right)
   b. Negative slope (line falls as it goes left to right)
   c. Zero slope (horizontal line)
   d. Infinite slope (vertical line)

7. Which of the following is not a method typically used for supplementary analysis of engineering economy problems?
   a. Break-even analysis
   b. Depreciation analysis
   c. Risk analysis
   d. Sensitivity analysis

8. The probability of weather-related crop damage during the growing season in a typical year is given by the following table. If the interest rate is 8 percent, what is the expected present worth of crop damage over the next 5 years?

Value of Crop Damage	Probability
$0	60%
$100,000	25%
$200,000	13%
$300,000	2%

    a. $57,000

    b. $167,000

    c. $240,000

    d. $285,000

9. Gooey Bites sells snack packs for $3 per pack. Variable expenses involved in producing snack packs are estimated to be $1 per pack, and fixed costs for operating the production line are estimated to be $14,000. How many snack packs must Gooey Bites sell to break even?

    a. 14,000

    b. 3,500

    c. 4,667

    d. 7,000

10. Reconsider the previous problem. After making changes to the production line, Gooey Bites made a profit of $36,000 by selling 20,000 snack packs. Variable costs were modified by the line changes, but fixed costs were unaffected. What is the new variable cost per pack?

    a. 0.33

    b. 0.50

    c. 1.00

    d. 1.50

PROBLEMS

Section 13.1

1. Uncertainty can impact many elements of an engineering economic analysis. Given the list of factors below, rank them from most to least uncertain, and briefly justify why you ranked them in that order.

Factor List (alphabetical)
First cost
MARR
Operating and maintenance costs
Planning horizon
Salvage value

2. Match the terms in the first column with an appropriate definition from the second column.

Terms

(a) Breakeven analysis

(b) Sensitivity analysis

(c) Risk analysis

Definitions

(1) Determining how the worth of an investment changes with changes in one or more parameters

(2) Determining probabilistic statements about the worth of an investment based on probabilistic values assigned to one or more parameters

(3) Determining the indifference value of a particular parameter

Section 13.2

3. Cecil's Manufacturing is considering producing a new product. The sales price would be $10.25 per unit. The cost of the equipment is $100,000. Operating and maintenance (O&M) costs are expected to be $3,500 annually. Based on a 7-year planning horizon and a *MARR* of 12 percent, determine the number of units that must be sold annually to achieve breakeven.

4. Reconsider Problem 3. Indicate whether each of the following statements is true or false by determining the new breakeven for each case. Each case is independent of the other cases.

   a. If the cost of the equipment doubles, the break-even volume will double.

   b. If the revenue per unit doubles, the break-even volume will halve.

   c. If the O&M costs double, the break-even volume will double.

5. The Fence Company is setting up a new production line to create top rails. The relevant data for two alternatives are shown below.

	Flow Line	Manufacturing Cell
Installed Cost	$15,000	$10,000
Expected Life	5 years	5 years
Salvage Value	$0	$0
Variable Cost per Top Rail	$6.00	$7.00

   a. Based on *MARR* of 8 percent, determine the annual rate of production for which the alternatives are equally economical.

   b. If it is estimated that production will be 300 top rails per year, which alternative is preferred, and what will be the total annual cost?

6. A manufacturer offers an inventor the choice of two contracts for the exclusive right to manufacture and market the inventor's patented design. Plan 1 calls for an immediate single payment of $50,000. Plan 2 calls for an annual payment of $2,000 plus a royalty of $1.00 for each unit sold. The remaining life of the patent is 10 years. *MARR* is 10 percent per year.

   a. What must be the uniform annual sales to make Plan 1 and Plan 2 equally attractive?

   b. If fewer than the number in Part a are schedule for production and sales, which plan is more attractive?

7. A pipeline contractor can purchase a needed truck for $40,000. Its estimated life is 6 years, and it has no salvage value. Maintenance is estimated to be $2,400 per year. Operating expense is $60 per day. The contractor can hire a similar unit for $150 per day. *MARR* is 7 percent.

   a. How many days per year must the truck's services be needed such that the two alternatives are equally costly?

   b. If the truck is needed for 180 days/year, should the contractor buy the truck or hire the similar unit? Determine the dollar amount of savings generated by using the preferred alternative rather than the nonpreferred.

8. A firm has the capacity to produce 650,000 units of product per year. At present, it is operating at 64 percent of capacity. The firm's income per unit is $1.00, annual fixed costs are $192,000, and variable costs are $0.376 per unit of product.

   a. What is the firm's current annual profit or loss?

   b. At what volume of product does the firm break even?

   c. What would be the profit or loss at 80 percent of capacity?

9. Spending $1,500 more today for a hybrid engine rather than a gasoline engine will result in annual fuel savings of $300. How many years must this savings continue in order to justify the extra investment if money is worth 10 percent per year, compounded annually?

10. A certain assembly requires rods varying in length from 0.25 to 4 inches long. The rods may be made from either brass or steel. The machining cost of brass rods is $0.0054 + $0.006L$ per piece, where L is the length of the rod in inches. For steel, the machining cost is $0.0072 + $0.010L$ per piece. Brass rods cost $0.022 per inch, and steel rods cost $0.007 per inch.

   a. What length will equalize the cost of brass versus steel?

   b. What type of rod should be used?

11. A portable generator is needed at a remote construction site. Two alternatives are being considered. Their annual fixed costs and operating and maintenance costs per hour are shown in the table below. The contractor runs three 8-hour shifts per day for 250 working days per year.

Generator	Fixed Costs ($/yr)	O&M Costs ($/hour)
1	$4,000	$7.00
2	$8,000	$5.50

   a. How many hours per shift is a generator needed if the contractor is indifferent between the two generators?

   b. If the site requires a generator for 2.5 hours per shift, which generator is preferred, and what is its estimated annual cost?

   c. If the site requires a generator for 5.5 hours per shift, which generator is preferred, and what is its estimated annual cost?

12. The Cooper Company is considering investing in a recuperator. The recuperator will have an initial cost of $20,000 and a service life of 10 years. Operating and maintenance costs for the first year are estimated to be $1,500, increasing by $100 every year thereafter. It is estimated that the salvage value of the recuperator will be 20 percent of its initial cost. The recuperator will result in equal annual fuel savings throughout its service life. Assuming *MARR* is 12 percent, what is the minimum value of fuel savings for which the recuperator is attractive?

13. Snow Valley Ski Resort has been contracting snow removal from its parking lots at a cost of $400/day. A snow-removal machine can be purchased for $25,000. The machine is estimated to have a useful life of 6 years with a zero salvage value at that time. Annual costs for operating and maintaining the equipment are estimated to be $5,000. Determine the break-even value for the number of days per year that snow removal is required in order to justify purchasing the snow-removal machine. *MARR* is 12 percent/year.

14. A small utility company is considering the purchase of a power-driven post-hole digger. The equipment costs $8,000, has an estimated life of 8 years, and has a salvage value of $1,000 at that time. Annual maintenance costs for the digger are estimated to be 15 percent of the first cost regardless of its level of usage. Operation costs are $40 per day with an output rate of 25 holes per day. At present, holes are manually dug at a rate of 1.5 per day by a laborer whose marginal cost is $11.20 per day. Determine the break-even value in holes per year. *MARR* is 8 percent.

15. To make a batch of 1,000 units, it is estimated that 120 direct labor hours are required at a cost of $10 per hour. Direct material costs are estimated at $1,500 per batch. The overhead costs are calculated based on an overhead rate of $7.50 per direct labor hour. The item can be readily purchased from a local vendor for $4 per unit.

   a. Should the item be manufactured or purchased?

   b. What is the break-even value for the overhead rate (dollars per direct labor hour)? Assume that the material costs, labor hours, and labor costs do not change.

16. A manufacturer of precision castings has the capacity to produce 1,000,000 castings per year. Each sells for $15. The variable cost per unit to produce the casting is $9 per casting. Annual fixed costs for the plant are $3,500,000.

   a. If the plant is currently operating at 50 percent of capacity, how much profit (loss) is being earned?

   b. What percent of production capacity is required for breakeven?

17. A new manufacturing plant costs $5 million to build. Operating and maintenance costs are estimated to be $45,000 per year, and a salvage value of 25 percent of the initial cost is expected. The units the plant produces are sold for $35 each. Sales and production are designed to run 365 days per year. The planning horizon is 10 years. Find the break-even value for the number of units sold per day for each of the following values of *MARR*:

   a. 5 percent

   b. 10 percent

   c. 15 percent

18. A subsidiary of a major furniture company manufactures wooden pallets. The plant has the capacity to produce 300,000 pallets per year. Presently the plant is operating at 70 percent of capacity. The selling price of the pallets is $18.25 per pallet, and the variable cost per pallet is $15.75. At zero output, the subsidiary plant's annual fixed costs are $550,000. This amount remains constant for any production rate between zero and plant capacity.

    a. With the present 70 percent of capacity production, what is the expected annual profit or loss for the subsidiary plant?

    b. What annual volume of sales (units) is required in order for the plant to break even?

    c. What would be the annual profit or loss if the plant was operating at 90 percent of capacity?

    d. If fixed costs could be reduced by 40 percent, what would be the new break-even sales volume?

19. Cowboy Metal Cutting produces a laser-cut part based on customer orders. The number of units requested on a customer's order for the laser-cut part can vary from 1 to 150. Cowboy has determined that three different cutting machines can be used to produce this part. An economic analysis of production costs has produced the data in the table below.

Cutting Tool ID	Fixed Cost Per Order	Variable Cost Per Unit
CT 1	$300	$9.00
CT 2	$750	$3.00
CT 3	$500	$5.00

    a. For all order sizes between 1 and 150, determine the preferred (most economical) cutting machine for an order of that size.

    b. For an order of size 75, what is the minimum cost production?

Section 13.3

20. You have been asked to perform a sensitivity analysis on a company's plan to modernize its facilities to determine the impact of possible errors in estimating the net annual savings. The initial investment in the modernization is $30,000. The expected net annual savings are $13,000. The salvage value is $7,000 after a 7-year planning horizon. MARR is 12 percent per year.

    a. Determine if the modernization is economically attractive based on the initial estimates and an annual worth (AW) analysis.

    b. Determine the AW if the net annual savings change by the following percentages from the initial estimate: −80 percent, −60 percent, −40 percent, −20 percent, +20 percent, +40 percent.

    c. Determine the percentage change in net annual savings that causes a reversal in the decision regarding the attractiveness of the project.

21. A pork-processing facility is considering installing either a storage facility or a holding pond. A biosystems engineer has been hired to evaluate the economic trade-offs for the two alternatives. The engineer estimates the cost of the storage facility to be $213,000, with annual costs for maintenance to be $3,200 per year. She estimates the cost of the pond to be $90,000, plus $45,000 for pumps and piping; annual operating and maintenance costs for the holding pond are estimated to be $8,500. The engineer estimates the life of the storage facility and the pond to be around 20 years but is concerned about the accuracy of this estimate. She decides to do a sensitivity analysis.

    a. Develop the equation she should use to determine how sensitive the economic decision is to changes in life. Use a MARR of 15 percent.

    b. Determine which alternative is preferred for lives ranging from 15 to 25 years in 1 year increments.

22. A new project will cost $80,000 initially and will last for 7 years, at which time its salvage value will be $2,500. Annual revenues are anticipated to be $15,000 per year. For a MARR of 12 percent/year, plot a sensitivity graph for annual worth versus initial cost, annual revenue, and salvage value, varying only one parameter at a time, each within the range of +/− 50 percent.

23. Plot a sensitivity graph for annual worth versus initial cost, annual revenue, and salvage value for the data in the table below. Vary only one parameter at a time, each within the range of −20 percent to +20 percent. *MARR* is 3 percent/year. Project life is 4 years. Based on your graph, which parameter shows the most sensitivity? The least?

Initial Cost	$120,000
Annual Revenue	$25,000
Salvage Value	$35,000

24. Plot a sensitivity graph for annual worth versus initial cost, annual revenue, and salvage value for the data in the table below. Vary only one parameter at a time, each within the range of −20 percent to +20 percent. *MARR* is 20 percent/year. Project life is 10 years. Based on your graph, which parameter shows the most sensitivity? The least?

Initial Cost	$800,000
Annual Revenue	$330,000
Salvage Value	$130,000

25. The cash flow estimates for a project are shown below. The initial cost is believed to be accurate, but the estimates of annual revenue and salvage value are subject to error. For a *MARR* of 3 percent/year, plot a two-factor sensitivity graph similar to Figure 13.5. Include a line that separates the favorable and unfavorable regions as well as a box showing the 20 percent error region. Project life is 4 years.

Initial Cost	$120,000
Annual Revenue	$25,000
Salvage Value	$35,000

26. A new project will cost $80,000 initially and will last for 7 years, at which time its salvage value will be $2,500. Annual revenues are anticipated to be $15,000 per year. The initial cost is believed to be accurate, but the estimates of annual revenue and salvage value are subject to error. For a *MARR* of 12 percent/year, plot a two-factor sensitivity graph similar to Figure 13.5. Include a line that separates the favorable and unfavorable regions as well as a box showing the 15 percent error region.

27. Initial estimates of the parameters for an investment are given below.

Parameter	Initial Estimate	Sensitivity
Initial Investment	$15,000	None
Net Annual Receipts	$2,500	−30%, 0%, +30%
Project Life	10 years	−20%, 0%, +20%
Salvage Value	$500	−50%, 0%, +50%
MARR	15% per year	None

You wish to do a multiparameter sensitivity analysis based on the sensitivities shown. AW is the preferred measure of worth.

a. How many values of AW need to be calculated?

b. Determine the AW values.

28. The owners of a discount motel chain are considering building a new motel. Optimistic, pessimistic, and most likely estimates of several key parameters have been obtained from the local builders and the chamber of commerce. These estimates are shown in the table below. The life of the motel is estimated to be 15 years, and MARR is 20 percent.

Parameter	Pessimistic	Most Likely	Optimistic
Initial Cost	$10,500,000	$8,875,000	$6,000,000
Annual Operating	$350,000	$175,000	$150,000
Annual Revenue	$1,500,000	$2,500,000	$3,500,000

   a. Based only on the pessimistic estimates, is the new motel economically attractive?
   b. Based only on the most likely estimates, is the new motel economically attractive?
   c. Based only on the optimistic estimates, is the new motel economically attractive?
   d. Based on a beta approximation of expected value estimates, is the new motel economically attractive?

29. Reconsider the data in Problem 28. Based on a present worth measure of worth, complete a multiparameter sensitivity analysis that examines all possible combinations of the estimates.

Section 13.4

30. A venture capitalist is considering investing $400,000 in a business start-up. It is expected that the start-up will generate annual receipts of $80,000 over a 10-year period. However, there is uncertainty with respect to the annual receipts. The standard deviation for annual receipts is estimated to be $5,000 each year. MARR is 10 percent/year. For the following questions, determine an analytical solution:
   a. Determine the expected value and standard deviation of present worth assuming annual receipts are statistically independent.
   b. Determine the expected value and standard deviation of present worth assuming annual receipts are perfectly correlated.

31. The parking superintendent is responsible for snow removal at his parking garage. The probabilities for the number of days per year requiring snow removal are shown in the chart below. These probabilities are independent from year to year. The superintendent can contract for snow removal at a cost of $500 per day. Alternatively, he can purchase a snow-removal machine for $40,000. It is expected to have a useful life of 10 years and no salvage value at that time. Annual costs for operating and maintaining the machine are estimated to be $14,000. MARR is 10 percent per year.

Number of Days Per Year	Probability
20	0.15
40	0.15
60	0.35
80	0.30
100	0.05

For the following questions, determine an analytical solution:
   a. Determine the mean and standard deviation of the present worth of the savings resulting from purchasing the snow-removal machine.
   b. Assuming the present worth is normally distributed, what is the probability of a positive present worth of the savings resulting from purchasing the machine?

For the following questions, determine a simulation solution using @RISK:

c. Using a Latin hypercube simulation with 10,000 iterations, estimate the mean and standard deviation of present worth and the probability of positive present worth.

d. Using a Monte Carlo simulation with 10,000 iterations, estimate the mean and standard deviation of present worth and the probability of positive present worth.

32. Main Electric is deciding whether to invest $19,700,000 in a new plant. An analyst forecasts that the plant will generate the independent random cash flows shown in the table below at the end of each year. *MARR* is 15 percent/year.

End of Year	Expected Net Cash Flow	Standard Deviation of Net Cash Flow
0	−$19,700,000	$0
1	$1,200,000	$120,000
2	$3,600,000	$240,000
3	$6,000,000	$650,000
4	$9,600,000	$750,000
5	$11,000,000	$1,080,000

For the following questions, determine an analytical solution:

a. Determine the mean and standard deviation of the present worth.

b. If the present worth is normally distributed, what is the probability that present worth is greater than 0?
For the following questions, determine a simulation solution using @RISK:
Assume each end-of-year cash flow is normally distributed with the mean and standard deviation shown in the table above.

c. Using a Latin hypercube simulation with 10,000 iterations, estimate the mean and standard deviation of present worth and the probability of positive present worth.

d. Using a Monte Carlo simulation with 10,000 iterations, estimate the mean and standard deviation of present worth and the probability of positive present worth.

33. An initial investment of $22,500 results in independent annual receipts of $6,250 until the end of the project life. The probability distribution for the project's life is shown in the table below. *MARR* is 15 percent/year.

Life (Years)	Probability
4	0.10
5	0.25
6	0.45
7	0.15
8	0.05

For the following questions, determine an analytical solution:

a. Determine the probability that the present worth of the project is greater than 0.

b. Determine the probability that the present worth of the project is greater than $1,000.
For the following questions, determine a simulation solution using @RISK:

c. Using a Latin hypercube simulation with 10,000 iterations, estimate the mean and standard deviation of present worth and the probability of positive present worth.

34. One of two mutually exclusive alternatives must be selected for implementation. Alternative A is an equipment purchase; Alternative B is a lease arrangement with annual payments. The characteristics of the two investments are shown in the table below. Use an 8-year planning horizon and a *MARR* of 15 percent/year.

Alt.	Parameter	Mean	Std. Dev.	Distribution
A	Initial Cost	$13,000	None	None
A	Annual Maintenance	$5,000	$500	Normal
A	Salvage Value	$2,000	$800	Normal
B	End-of-Year Lease Payment	$7,500	$750	Normal

For the following question, determine an analytical solution:

a. determine the probability that Alternative A is the preferred alternative.

For the following questions, determine a simulation solution using @RISK:

b. Using a Latin hypercube simulation with 10,000 iterations, estimate the probability that A is the preferred alternative.

c. Using a Monte Carlo simulation with 10,000 iterations, estimate the mean and standard deviation of present worth and the probability of positive present worth.

35. A new CNC mill is expected to cost $263,000 and have a useful life of 6 years. The net annual savings generated by the mill are independent from year to year and are estimated to follow a uniform distribution with a lower bound of $60,000 and an upper bound of $70,000. *MARR* is 12 percent/year.

For the following question, determine an analytical solution:

a. Determine the probability that the present worth of the CNC mill is positive.

For the following questions, determine a simulation solution using @RISK:

b. Using a Latin hypercube simulation with 10,000 iterations, estimate the probability that the present worth of the CNC mill is positive.

c. Using a Monte Carlo simulation with 10,000 iterations, estimate the mean and standard deviation of present worth; the present worth of the CNC mill is positive.

36. A project under consideration has a 10-year projected life. The initial investment for the project is estimated to have a mean of $10,000 and a standard deviation of $1,000. The annual receipts are independent, with each year's expected return having a mean of $1,800 and a standard deviation of $200. *MARR* is 12 percent.

For the following question, determine an analytical solution:

a. Determine the probability that the present worth is negative.

For the following questions, determine a simulation solution using @RISK:

Assume the initial investment and annual receipts are independent and normally distributed.

b. Using a Latin hypercube simulation with 10,000 iterations, estimate the probability that the present worth is negative.

c. Using a Monte Carlo simulation with 10,000 iterations, estimate the probability that the present worth is negative.

37. An investment of $5,000 is expected to generate the probabilistic returns shown in the table below over its 3-year life. Assume the annual cash flows are independent and that the distribution of present worth is normal.

EOY	Annual Return
1	$2,500 with probability 0.4 or $1,800 with probability 0.6
2	$3,000 with probability 0.5 or $2,000 with probability 0.5
3	$3,500 with probability 0.7 or $2,500 with probability 0.3

For the following question, determine an analytical solution using a MARR of 15%:

a. Determine the probability that the present worth is negative.

For the following questions, determine a simulation solution using @RISK:

b. Using a Latin hypercube simulation with 10,000 iterations, estimate the probability that the present worth is negative.

   c. Using a Monte Carlo simulation with 10,000 iterations, estimate the probability that the present worth is negative.

38. A proposed project has the following cash flow estimates:

End of Year	Mean Net Cash Flow	Standard Deviation of Cash Flow
0	−$800,000	$250,000
1	$1,000,000	$450,000
2	$1,000,000	$600,000

Assuming independent cash flows, a normally distributed net present value, and a minimum attractive rate of return of 15 percent, determine the following.

For the following questions, determine an analytical solution:

   a. The mean and standard deviation of net present value

   b. The probability that the net present value is negative

   c. The probability that the net present value is greater than $1,000,000

For the following questions, determine a simulation solution using @RISK:

Assume the initial investment and annual receipts are normally distributed.

   d. Using a Latin hypercube simulation with 10,000 iterations, estimate the probability that the present worth is negative.

   e. Using a Monte Carlo simulation with 10,000 iterations, estimate the probability that the present worth is negative.

39. A proposed project has the following cash flow estimates:

End of Year	Mean Net Cash Flow	Standard Deviation of Cash Flow
0	−$32,000	$1,000
1	$4,000	$2,000
2	$8,000	$3,000
3	$12,000	$5,000
4	$12,000	$6,000
5	$12,000	$7,000

Assuming independent cash flows, a normally distributed net present value, and a minimum attractive rate of return of 18 percent, determine the following:

For the following questions, determine an analytical solution:

   a. The mean and standard deviation of net present value

   b. The probability that the net present value is positive

   c. The probability that the net present value is greater than $5,000

For the following questions, determine a simulation solution using @RISK:

Assume the initial investment and annual receipts are normally distributed.

   d. Using a Latin hypercube simulation with 10,000 iterations, estimate the probability that the present worth is positive and is greater than $5,000.

   e. Using a Monte Carlo simulation with 10,000 iterations, estimate the probability that the present worth is positive and is greater than $5,000.

40. A $5,000 process improvement project is expected to increase annual expenses for the next 3 years by an average of $20,000, with a standard deviation of $3,000. The annual savings generated over the 3 years will average $24,000 with a standard deviation of $4,000. *MARR* is 20 percent. Assume independent cash flows.

For the following questions, determine an analytical solution:

a. Assuming that present worth is normally distributed, determine the probability that the process improvement will result in a loss.

b. Assuming that present worth is normally distributed, determine the probability that the process improvement will result in a present worth of $10,000 or greater.

For the following questions, determine a simulation solution using @RISK:

c. Using a Latin hypercube simulation with 10,000 iterations, estimate the probability that the process improvement will result in a loss and the probability that the present worth is $10,000 or greater.

d. Using a Monte Carlo simulation with 10,000 iterations, estimate the probability that that the process improvement will result in a loss and the probability that the present worth is $10,000 or greater.

41. Two mutually exclusive alternatives are being compared. The planning horizon is 10 years, and *MARR* is 12 percent. The cash flows for the alternatives are shown in the table below. All cash flows are normally distributed.

Alternative 1		Alternative 2	
Initial Investment	**Standard Deviation**	**Initial Investment**	**Standard Deviation**
$750,000	15,000	$750,000	150,000
Salvage Value	**Standard Deviation**	**Salvage Value**	**Standard Deviation**
$125,000	2,500	$125,000	25,000
Annual Revenue	**Standard Deviation**	**Annual Revenue**	**Standard Deviation**
$75,000	1,500	$75,000	15,000

For the following questions, determine a simulation solution using @RISK:

a. Using a Latin hypercube simulation with 10,000 iterations, determine the mean and standard deviation of the present worth of each alternative.

b. Using a Latin hypercube simulation with 10,000 iterations, determine the probability that Alternative 1 is preferred over Alternative 2.

42. An investment alternative requires an initial investment of $19,000 and has a life of 6 years. The annual returns for the investment are independent and defined by the discrete probability distribution shown in the table below.

Annual Return	Probability
$500	0.05
$2,000	0.15
$4,500	0.25
$6,000	0.35
$9,000	0.20

For the following question, determine an analytical solution using a MARR of 20%:

a. Determine the analytical expected value of present worth.

For the following questions, determine a simulation solution using @RISK:

b. Use Latin hypercube simulation with 25 trials to generate an estimate of the expected present value and the probability that the present worth will be less than 0.

c. Use Latin hypercube simulation with 100,000 trials to generate an estimate of the expected present value and the probability that the present worth will be less than 0.

d. Use Monte Carlo simulation with 25 trials to generate an estimate of the expected present value and the probability that the present worth will be less than 0.

e. Use Monte Carlo simulation with 100,000 trials to generate an estimate of the expected present value and the probability that the present worth will be less than 0.

Section 13.A

43. Your company is trying to decide whether to buy or lease snow-removal equipment. You have gathered all the relevant cost data and converted them to equivalent uniform annual costs (EUACs), as shown in the table below. The complicating factor in your evaluation is that the need for the snow-removal equipment might be heavy or light. You estimate that there is a 60 percent probability of heavy use and a 40 percent probability of light use.

Need	Lease	Buy
Light	$2,375	$3,000
Heavy	$4,250	$4,000

a. Draw a decision tree to represent this situation.

b. Using decision tree analysis, determine whether the new snow-removal equipment should be leased or bought.

44. A factory modernization team is considering a new compressor that costs $9,000 and has a 6-year useful life. The compressor's salvage value at the end of its 6-year life is zero. *MARR* is 20 percent/year. The expected annual savings from the compressor are not known with certainty and are estimated as shown in the table below.

Outcome	Probability	Annual Cost Savings
1	0.25	$3,500
2	0.40	$3,000
3	0.25	$2,300
4	0.10	$1,500

a. Draw a decision tree to represent this situation.

b. Using decision tree analysis, determine whether the new compressor should be purchased.

45. A company is evaluating the potential of a new product. Pursuing the new product can be implemented fully, partially, or not at all. The success of the new product depends upon consumer acceptance, which can be strong, average, or weak. The table below characterizes the situation.

Consumer Acceptance	Probability of Occurrence	PW of Full Implementation	PW of Partial Implementation	PW of Do Not Pursue
Strong	0.25	$78,000	$51,000	$0
Average	0.60	$28,000	$32,000	$0
Weak	0.15	−$55,000	−$10,000	$0

a. Draw a decision tree to represent this situation.

b. Using decision tree analysis, determine the preferred implementation plan.

46. We must decide between purchasing an automatic machine that costs $100,000 and will last 10 years and have a zero salvage value, or purchasing a manual machine that costs $40,000 and will last 5 years and have a zero salvage value. If we purchase the manual machine initially, after 5 years we must decide between a manual machine having the same characteristics as the first machine and a semiautomatic machine costing $80,000 that would have a $40,000 salvage value after 5 years of life. The annual operating costs for each of the machines are automatic, $20,000/year; manual $28,000/year; semiautomatic, $22,000/year.

a. Draw a decision tree to represent this situation.

b. Using a PW method with a *MARR* of 10 percent, determine what decisions should be made.

47. The manager of a university bookstore is trying to determine whether or not to advance purchase copies of a popular textbook. Her uncertainty is caused by the changing popularity of the course that requires the book. The table below characterizes the uncertainties as well as the present worths of her options.

Future Popularity of the Course	Probability	PW of Savings with Advanced Purchase
High	0.5	$200,000
Medium	0.3	−$40,000
Low	0.2	−$150,000

The bookstore manager can pay $6,000 for a student survey that will predict whether the course's popularity will go up or down. The table below indicates the results of past predictions using student surveys.

If the future popularity is going to be:	Then the probabilities that the survey will predict that the popularity will go up or down are:	
	Up	Down
High	0.9	0.1
Medium	0.4	0.6
Low	0.2	0.8

a. Draw a decision tree to represent this situation.

b. Determine whether or not the manager should advance-purchase the textbook or pay for the survey.

48. Consider an investment decision problem with two decision points. At the first decision point, the investor can select between Options A, B, or C, each of which has an uncertain outcome with the probabilities and present worths shown in the table below. If Option B is selected, there is a 60 percent chance that, before the termination of the investment, a futures contract will be triggered that will require the selection of Buyout Option 1 or Buyout Option 2. The probabilities and present worths associated with these buyout options are also shown in the table.

Option	Outcome Probability	Outcome PW
A	0.1	$10
A	0.6	$15
A	0.3	$1
C	0.2	−$5
C	0.5	$10
C	0.3	$20
B	0.4	$12 (no futures decision)
B	0.6	Futures decision required
B with Buyout Option 1	0.5	$7
B with Buyout Option 1	0.5	$10
B with Buyout Option 2	1.0	$8

a. Draw a decision tree to represent this situation.

b. Determine what decisions should be made.

Chapter 14

ECONOMIC ANALYSIS IN THE PUBLIC AND REGULATED SECTORS

(a) The futuristic monorail from 1962 served as one motivation for Seattle's interest in the "Green Line" monorail project. The sky needle is shown in the background. Courtesy Seattle Municipal Archives, Item No. 127805. (b) A Clyde Light and Power crew works on the City of Clyde, Ohio distribution system.

Seattle's "Green Line" Project

In 1962, Seattle, Washington, hosted what became commonly known as the Seattle World Fair. The Space Needle and a futuristic-looking monorail were built for the fair, and both are still prominent on the Seattle landscape. Fast-forward to November 2002, when the citizens of Seattle voted to approve a new "Green Line" monorail project, extending 14 miles and serving Seattle Center, downtown, and the stadium district. The new monorail would benefit the public by providing reliable, faster, and more frequent transit service in a busy and congested area. There would also be savings from not operating as many automobiles, and there would be a decrease in the number of accidents due to reduced exposure. Then, in November 2005, the citizens voted to kill the project. Let's look at a small piece of what happened as it relates to this chapter.

The three groups to benefit from the new Green Line would include current transit riders, new riders who choose to park their cars, and those who will continue to drive their cars but enjoy a slight decrease in delays due the reduced traffic. There would also be some negative benefits realized by the public. For example, traffic would be displaced with even more congestion during periods of construction in areas of current work. Some persons or businesses would be displaced, temporarily or permanently, to accommodate the new monorail extension. And some businesses that benefited from the vehicular traffic may lose customers due to rerouting of autos and buses away from their area.

So, should the city of Seattle undertake development, construction, and operation of the Green Line? Is this different from any other investment in terms of its economic evaluation? Could Seattle establish a planning horizon, identify capital expenditures and operational outlays, quantify in monetary terms the positive and negative benefits, and do a present worth analysis? Of course! In that sense, economic evaluation in the public sector is no different from industrial alternative evaluation. However, in the 1930s, the U.S. federal government adopted the cost-benefit (aka benefit-cost) approach for water resource projects, and it has been common ever since for projects in the public sector to be evaluated using benefit-cost analysis.

In Seattle's case, an analysis was performed to determine whether or not the benefits realized by the new monorail would justify the capital expenditure plus operating and maintenance costs. A 26-year planning horizon was used, including time for design and construction as well as 20 years of operation. All cost and benefit numbers were discounted to the beginning of the planning horizon's first year. They decided to do a benefit-cost analysis (they also did present worth and rate of return analyses resulting in the same recommendation). The only proposed alternative project was to improve the bus service. The monorail plan was then submitted to the voters and approved.

Some of the things quantified included travel time savings ($10.10 per hour), automobile cost savings at the IRS-approved rate for tax purposes, average trip length (5.77 miles), benefit of freed-up road capacity ($0.15 per vehicle-mile), accident reduction, and other positive and negative benefits. There is a benefit-cost ratio, B/C = 1.23 (over 1.00 is good), a net present worth of $390 million, and a 7.95 percent rate of return. Due to the uncertainty of estimates, sensitivity analyses were conducted to examine the effects of incorrect estimates on economic performance. Finally, the analysis was critiqued for strengths and weaknesses.

While the benefit-cost analysis appeared favorable, new projections on financing and the income stream showed a cost of $9 billion over 50 years. At this point, the mayor dropped his support, opponents launched a campaign to defeat the monorail, and the citizens voted it down.

*   *   *

Clyde Light and Power

The city of Clyde, Ohio, built its own electrical distribution system—Clyde Light and Power—in 1989. The system provides a dual-feed 69 KV transmission line and a 12,470 V distribution system. Clyde purchases its wholesale power, and its supplier has been American Electric Power Company (AEP). A year before the contract expired with AEP, the city manager addressed a letter to the customers in Clyde explaining why an increase in their electric energy rates will be necessary in the future. He noted that Clyde had sent out numerous requests for proposal (RFPs) to other power providers and that "extending the existing contract with modifications for a shorter period of time may be the most logical, if AEP agrees"; that is, he is suggesting that the short-term "fix" may be to extend the contract with AEP for 2 years beyond the current expiration. Of course, the necessary modifications primarily include a rate increase to cover higher charges from AEP during the extension. We all know that many factors around the world are increasing the cost of power.

AEP provided Clyde the details on their needs for a 2-year contract extension to provide wholesale power. Clyde took these numbers, plus their own operating costs, and prepared a schedule showing both the present rate and the proposed rate required in the future. In essence, Clyde presented its customers with a revenue requirements analysis (revenue requirements are those revenues needed to cover all costs of capital investment, operating, and maintenance). Clyde's city manager openly and factually communicated with its electric-power customers after having discussed these figures with the Clyde city council.

The revenue requirements analysis, which Clyde shared with its citizens, called for a 24-month term, simple pass-through of AEP's charges that include an increase of approximately $0.04/kWh. In addition, Clyde assumes a 2 percent per year growth in sales and a 3 percent inflation rate, and includes the costs for operating expenses, debt service, and tax transfer. The analysis projects the revenue requirements and customer rates needed for Clyde Light and Power to remain in business. In essence, it shows percentage increases of about 20 percent from present rates. Apparently the extension with AEP was accepted and proved successful, concluding at the end of 2007. Beginning January 1, 2008, Clyde began purchasing its power through AMP-Ohio.

So, what do Seattle and Clyde Light and Power have in common? Two things for sure: (1) Their proper economic analyses are different from, and yet equivalent to, industrial analyses, and (2) they use their own special brand of analysis, known in the public sector as *benefit-cost analysis* and in the public utility sector as *revenue requirements analysis.* Evaluation of projects in the public sector is discussed extensively in Section 14.1 through Section 14.8. Regulated public utilities are treated in Section 14.9 through Section 14.12.

> *Benefit-cost analyses* (public sector) and the *revenue requirements method* (regulated organizations) both (1) differ from traditional ATCF industrial analyses, and (2) are consistent with and equivalent to traditional analyses.

14-1   INTRODUCTION: THE NATURE OF PUBLIC PROJECTS

Government units fund projects using money taken, usually in the form of taxes, from the public. They then provide goods or services to the public that would be infeasible for individuals to provide on their own. While they are not in business to make a profit, it is important that they make wise investment decisions.

Projects should provide benefits for the public's greater good that exceed the costs of providing those benefits. The most frequently used method in evaluating government (local, state, or federal) projects is benefit-cost analysis. Cost-effectiveness analysis is also used but to a lesser extent.

Four classes cover the spectrum of projects that government enters: cultural development, protection, economic services, and natural resources. *Cultural development* is enhanced through education, recreation, and historic and similar institutions or preservations. *Protection* is achieved through military services, police and fire protection, and the judicial system. *Economic services* include transportation, power generation, and housing loan programs. *Natural resource* projects entail wildland management, pollution control, and flood control. Some projects belong in more than one area. For example, flood control is a form of assistance for some, provides transportation and power generation for others, and also relates to natural resource benefits.

Many government projects are huge, having first costs of tens or hundreds of millions of dollars. They may have long lives, such as 50 years for a bridge or a dam. The multiple-use concept is common, as in wildland management projects, where economic (timber), wildlife preservation (deer, squirrel), and recreation projects (camping, hiking) are each considered uses of importance. The benefits or enjoyment of some government projects are often completely out of proportion to the financial support of specific individuals or groups. Also, there are often multiple government agencies that have an interest in a project. For example, there is often federal support of state road projects. Finally, some public-sector projects are not easily evaluated due to difficulty in estimating benefits. Also, it may be many years before their benefits are realized.

14-2   BUILD-OPERATE-TRANSFER

Look at the following three public-sector examples. See if you can figure out what each has in common:

1. The Hudson-Bergen Light Rail (HBLR) is a 20.5-mile light-rail transit system that encompasses 32 stations and 5 regional park-and-ride lots running north–south on the New Jersey Hudson River waterfront in Hudson and Bergen counties.

2. The Las Vegas Monorail serves the heart of the resort corridor, east of Las Vegas Boulevard, linking the MGM Grand hotel-casino and the Sahara hotel-casino with 6.4 km (4 miles) of elevated dual-monorail guideway connecting seven stations.

3. Major enhancements to Route 3 North, an existing 21-mile limited-access highway running north and south between the I-95/128 circumferential highway around Boston and the New Hampshire border, designed to alleviate several significant transportation problems on this heavily utilized highway.

So, what do all three of these examples have in common? Each uses an interesting alternative approach to providing public projects that has surfaced in recent years. It involves using an integrated public-private partnership, with one form known as build-operate-transfer (BOT). In BOT, a private-sector partner such as a firm or consortium receives an exclusive authorization from the public sector to finance, design, construct, and operate a facility for a specified period, after which ownership is transferred back to the public sector. During that time, the private partner operates the facility and is allowed to assess appropriate tolls, fees, rentals, and charges stated in their contract to recover its investment and operating and maintenance costs in the project. One excellent source for learning about BOT is the Federal Highway Administration's Web site on public-private partnerships.[1] Figure 14.1 illustrates the continuum of responsibilities between the public and private sectors, including where BOTs and similar partnerships fall along the spectrum.

Traditionally, private-sector participation in public projects has been limited to separate planning, design, or construction contracts on a fee-for-service based on the public agency's specifications. Expanding the private-sector role allows the public

---

[1] **www.fhwa.dot.gov/ppp/bot.htm**, or search FHWA PPP

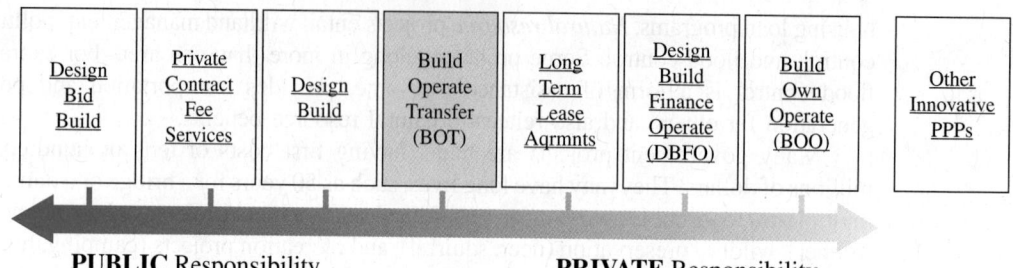

PUBLIC Responsibility   PRIVATE Responsibility

FIGURE 14.1

A Continuum of Responsibility from Public to Private (U.S. DOT).

agencies to tap private-sector technical, management, and financial resources in new ways to achieve greater cost and schedule certainty, supplementing in-house staff, innovative technology applications, specialized expertise, and access to private capital. Some BOT characteristics include the following items:

Responsibility. The advantage of the BOT approach is that it combines responsibility for usually disparate functions—design, construction, and maintenance—under a single entity. This allows the private partners to take advantage of many efficiencies. For example, the project design can be tailored to the construction equipment and materials to be used.

Life-Cycle Costing. The benefits of life-cycle costing—considering the economics throughout the entire birth-to-death life cycle—are particularly important, as more money is spent maintaining systems than on expansion.

Procurement Process. The public sector awards BOT contracts by competitive bid. Proposers respond to the specifications provided and are usually required to submit a single price for the facility's design, construction, and maintenance for whatever time period is specified. Proposers are also required to document their qualifications to accomplish the job.

Standard Specifications. While the potential exists to reap substantial rewards by utilizing the integrated BOT approach, the public sector must take great care to specify all standards to which they want their facilities designed, constructed, and maintained. Unless needs are identified up front as overall project specifications, they will not generally be met. This is important, because from design through operation, BOT contracts can extend for 20 years or more.

Since both the private and public sectors are involved, the economic analyses of projects utilize both private- and public-sector methods. Present worth, annual worth, and rate of return methods will prevail in the private sector, while benefit-cost ratio, benefits minus costs, and cost-effectiveness analyses are prevalent in the public sector.

14-3 OBJECTIVES IN PUBLIC PROJECT EVALUATION

When large, complex, lengthy, multiple-use projects are to be evaluated for their desirability, the criteria for the evaluation must first be agreed upon. We often point to guidance given in the Flood Control Act on June 22, 1936, which states that "the

Federal Government should improve or participate . . . if the benefits to whomsoever they may accrue are in excess of the estimated costs. . . . ''

The setting for modern evaluation of government projects dates to the River and Harbor Act of 1902, which ''required a board of engineers to report on the desirability of Army Corps of Engineers' river and harbor projects, taking into account the amount of commerce benefited and the cost.''

And the intellectual father of benefit-cost analysis is said to be the French economist and engineer Jules Dupuit, who in 1844 wrote the frequently cited study ''On the Measure of Utility of Public Works.'' The idea of benefit-cost analysis has been around for a long time!

Prest and Turvey[2] give a short, reasonable definition of benefit-cost analysis:

> A practical way of assessing the desirability of projects where it is important to take a long view (in the sense of looking at repercussions in the further, as well as the nearer, future) and a wide view (in the sense of allowing for side effects of many kinds on many persons, industries, regions etc.); that is, it implies the enumeration and evaluation of all the relevant costs and benefits.

The ''long view'' is merely considering the entire planning horizon, which is generally far longer for projects in the public sector than for those in the private sector. The ''wide view'' and the notion of evaluating all ''relevant costs and benefits'' probably spell out the greatest single difference between government and private economic evaluation—that is, government projects often affect many individuals, groups, and things, either directly or indirectly, for better or for worse. In evaluating these projects, the analyst tries to capture these effects on the public, quantify them, and make the measures in monetary terms. Positive effects are referred to as *benefits,* while negative effects are termed *disbenefits.* In contrast, the private-sector effects of primary importance are those that relate to *income* being returned to the organization. Costs of construction, financing, operation, and maintenance are estimated in much the same way in both the public and private sectors.

> Benefit-cost analyses take a ''long view'' and a ''wide view'' and evaluate monetized benefits, disbenefits, and costs.

14-4 GUIDELINES IN PUBLIC-SECTOR EVALUATION

Believe it or not, evaluating benefits does not always take place when regulations, policies, or projects are undertaken by government entities using tax dollars. Arrow et al.,[3] reporting on a blue-ribbon panel's findings in 1996, set out several guidelines

---

[2]Prest, A. R. and Turvey, Ralph, ''Cost-Benefit Analysis: A Survey,'' *Economic Journal,* 75, December 1965, 683–735.

[3]Arrow, Kenneth J., et.al., *Benefit-Cost Analysis in Environmental, Health, and Safety Regulation: A Statement of Principles,* American Enterprise Institute, The Annapolis Center, and Resources for the Future, AEI Press, La Vergne, TN, 1996.

for decision makers on using economic analyses to evaluate proposed policies. While that group focused on policies and regulations in environment, health, and safety, the guidelines transcend these areas and should be kept in mind on any government investment. The guidelines are summarized as follows:

1. *A benefit-cost analysis is a useful way of organizing a comparison of the favorable and unfavorable effects of proposed policies.* Benefit-cost analysis can help the decision maker better understand the implications of a decision, and it should play an important role in informing the decision-making process.

2. *Economic analysis can be useful in designing regulatory strategies that achieve a desired goal at the lowest possible cost.* Economic analysis can highlight the extent to which cost savings can be achieved by using alternative, more flexible approaches that reward performance.

3. *Congress should not preclude decision makers from considering the economic costs and benefits of different policies in the development of regulations. At the very least, agencies should be encouraged to use economic analysis to help set regulatory priorities.* Current planning in most regulatory agencies places insufficient emphasis on the likely benefits and costs of regulations and places excessive emphasis on politics and deadlines.

4. *Benefit-cost analysis should be required for all major regulatory decisions.* An important benefit of mandatory benefit-cost analysis is that it facilitates external monitoring of an agency's performance.

5. *Agencies should not be bound by a strict benefit-cost test but should be required to consider available benefit-cost analyses. For regulations whose expected costs far exceed expected benefits, agency heads should be required to present a clear explanation justifying the reasons for their decision.* There may be factors other than economic benefits and costs that agencies will want to weigh when making decisions, such as equity within and across generations. In addition, a decision maker may want to place greater weight on particular characteristics of a decision, such as potential irreversible consequences.

6. *For legislative proposals involving major health, safety, and environmental regulations, the Congressional Budget Office should do a preliminary benefit-cost analysis that can inform legislative decision making.* Because laws give rise to regulations, some kind of benefit-cost analysis is likely to be useful in informing the policy process.

> Arrow, et al, established six guiding principles for use by those in public service.

14-5   U.S. FEDERAL GOVERNMENT GUIDELINES

The *definitive document* for performing benefit-cost analysis or cost-effectiveness analysis of federal programs is the Office of Management and Budget's Circular No. A-94, Revised.[4] It is really worth a quick read and being a future reference. The

---

[4]www.whitehouse.gov/omb/circulars/a094/a094.html, or do a search on ''A-94''

document has 17 sections listed in the table of contents. In addition, at least once each year, the appropriate interest rates to be used for analyses are presented and available on the Web. While this document is focused on federal programs, it is highly applicable to state and local government programs as well.

OMB's Circular No. A-94, Revised is summarized in Appendix 14.A, which gives the title of all 17 sections in the document's table of contents, with comments on only those that are highly relevant to this text.

The Office of Management and Budget's (OMB) Circular No. A-94, Revised, is the *definitive document* today for those performing benefit-cost analyses.

EXAMPLE 14.1 Benefit-Cost Analysis Adapted from Circular No. A-94, Revised

Even though you may not yet have read Circular No. A-94, Revised in Appendix 14.A, you have learned enough up to this point to understand this example. Consider a 10-year public investment program that will commit the government to a stream of real or constant-dollar expenditures appearing in the Cost column of Figure 14.2. Real benefits appear in the Benefit column. Discounting takes place at a rate of 7 percent in accordance with guidance provided in OMB Circular A-94, Revised, Section 8b (see Appendix 14.A).

The present value of benefits is $1,424,102, and the present value of costs is $1,063,987, so the net present value of benefits minus costs is $360,115. The program is desirable when considered alone.

It is also common to calculate the ratio of benefits to costs, resulting in B/C = $1,424,102/1,063,987 = 1.33. When the B/C ratio is greater than 1.00, the program is desirable when considered alone.

			E10 ▾	*fx* =PV(0.07,A10,,-C10)		
	A	B	C	D	E	F
1	**EOY**	**Cost**	**Benefit**	**PW Costs**	**PW Benefits**	
2	0	$0	$0	$0	$0	
3	1	$100,000	$0	$93,458	$0	
4	2	$200,000	$0	$174,688	$0	
5	3	$300,000	$50,000	$244,889	$40,815	
6	4	$300,000	$100,000	$228,869	$76,290	
7	5	$200,000	$300,000	$142,597	$213,896	
8	6	$100,000	$400,000	$66,634	$266,537	
9	7	$50,000	$400,000	$31,137	$249,100	
10	8	$50,000	$400,000	$29,100	$232,804	
11	9	$50,000	$400,000	$27,197	$217,573	=PV(0.07,A11,,-C11)
12	10	$50,000	$250,000	$25,417	$127,087	=PV(0.07,A12,,-B12)
13		**PRESENT WORTH**		$1,063,987	$1,424,102	
14						

FIGURE 14.2

Costs and Benefits for Public Investment Program, $i = 7\%$**, Real (Constant)$.**

14-6 USING SEAT IN PUBLIC SECTOR EVALUATIONS

By now, it should be apparent that the analysis of programs, projects, and alternatives in the public sector uses the same principles and techniques (Chapter 1, Sections 2 and 3) used for economic analyses in general. The systematic economic analysis technique (SEAT) of Chapter 1, Section 4, can also be adapted to public-sector evaluations. The language used and the measures of merit are different, but the principles and techniques remain the same:

1. *Identify the feasible public-sector alternatives.* Each viable mutually exclusive and collectively exhaustive alternative, made up of one or more projects or programs, should be described thoroughly, specifying all of the good and bad effects that the alternative will have on the public. This includes effects directly on people, safety, environment, land values, recreation, and so on. All aspects of project development, operation, maintenance, and eventual salvage should be stated. In addition, all project contingencies and overall resource limitations should be identified.

2. *Define the planning horizon for the benefit-cost study.* The planning horizon for public-sector activities may be substantially longer than for industrial alternatives—perhaps 10, 20, and even 50 years. Of course, a common planning horizon should be used to compare all alternatives.

3. *Specify the discount rate.* There are many opinions on the appropriate discount rate to use in the public sector. Often, the rate is far too low, even 0.0 percent at times. A good guideline for most alternatives focused on the general public is to use the average rate of return on private-sector investments.

4. *Estimate the benefit and cost profiles in monetary terms for each alternative.* Each *benefit* or *disbenefit* during the planning horizon should be quantified insofar as possible. (Remember, *benefits* refer to desirable consequences on the public; *disbenefits* are negative effects.) Quantifying all *costs* and *incomes* refers to governmental expenditures and incomes received relating to the alternative over the planning horizon. Costs include all first and continuing costs of a project; incomes may result from tolls, fees, or other charges to the user public.

5. *Compare the alternatives using a measure of worth related to benefits and costs.* Benefit-cost analyses frequently use the *benefit-cost ratio* (B/C) or a measure of *benefits minus costs* ($B - C$). There are also *cost-effectiveness analyses* that are useful when either (1) the benefits attributed to all alternatives equal and the one with the lowest cost is selected, or (2) the costs of all alternatives are equal and the one with the highest benefits is selected. The mathematics underlying benefit-cost and cost-effectiveness analyses are presented in detail in the next section.

6. *Perform supplementary analyses.* Supplementary analyses in the form of risk analysis, sensitivity analysis, and break-even analysis may be performed. These are useful in benefit-cost analyses due to the relative uncertainties in quantifying many benefits or disbenefits. If a project decision or selection is very sensitive to, say, public benefits that are also somewhat unknown or intangible, it may be wise to do further research to ensure a good decision. All of these supplementary analysis methods are covered in Chapter 13.

7. *Select the preferred alternative.* Not only is the preferred alternative selected, but also all quantitative and qualitative supporting considerations should be recorded in detail. This is particularly true in the case of public-sector projects, due to the wide base of interested parties and the difficulty of quantifying monetarily the benefits and disbenefits.

The systematic economic analysis technique (SEAT), particularly steps 3 to 5, is illustrated through examples in sections 14-7 and 14-8.

Systematic Economic Analysis Technique

1. Identify the investment alternatives
2. Define the planning horizon
3. Specify the discount rate
4. Estimate the cash flows
5. Compare the alternatives
6. Perform supplementary analyses
7. Select the preferred investment

14-7   BENEFIT-COST AND COST-EFFECTIVENESS CALCULATIONS

Benefit-cost analysis is recommended for a formal economic analysis of government alternatives such as programs or projects. Its two most common forms are the benefit-cost ratio (B/C) or, equivalently, a measure of benefits minus costs ($B - C$). With either of these two forms, both the benefits (B) and costs (C) are typically expressed as present worth or annual worth monetary figures, using an appropriate discount rate for the time value of money. The mathematics of benefit-cost analysis is quite simple, although its application and quantification of benefits can be challenging.

If

B_{jt} = net public benefits associated with alternative j during year t, $t = 1, 2, \ldots, n$

C_{jt} = net government costs associated with alternative j during year t, $t = 0, 1, 2, \ldots, n$, and

i = appropriate interest or discount rate,

then the B/C criterion may be expressed mathematically, using the present worth of all net benefits over the present worth of all net costs, as

$$B/C_j(i) = \frac{\sum_{t=1}^{n} B_{jt}(1+i)^{-t}}{\sum_{t=0}^{n} C_{jt}(1+i)^{-t}} \tag{14.1}$$

Although Equation 14.1 is a ratio of present worths of benefits to costs, it could just as well be a ratio of annual worths of benefits to costs.

The benefits minus costs criterion ($B - C$) is expressed as

$$(B - C)_j(i) \sum_{t=0}^{n} (B_{jt} - C_{jt})(1+i)^{-t} \tag{14.2}$$

which is similar to the present worth method described in Chapter 5. It can be used directly to compare alternatives and will always be consistent with a proper B/C ratio analysis.

When two or more project alternatives are being compared using a B/C ratio, the analysis should be done on an incremental basis—that is, let the alternative with the lower present worth of costs be Alternative 1 and let the other be Alternative 2. Then, the incremental benefits of the second alternative over the first, $\Delta B_{2-1}(i)$, are divided by the incremental costs of the second over the first, $\Delta C_{2-1}(i)$—that is,

$$\Delta B/C_{2-1}(i) = \frac{\Delta B_{2-1}(i)}{\Delta C_{2-1}(i)} = \frac{\sum_{t=1}^{n}(B_{2t} - B_{1t})(1+i)^{-t}}{\sum_{t=0}^{n}(C_{2t} - C_{1t})(1+i)^{-t}} \qquad (14.3)$$

Note that if the first alternative is to do nothing, the incremental B/C ratio is also the straight B/C ratio for the second alternative. As long as $\Delta B/C_{2-1}(i)$ exceeds 1.0, Alternative 2 is preferable to Alternative 1; otherwise, Alternative 1 is preferred to Alternative 2. The winner of these is then compared on an incremental basis with another alternative. These pair-wise comparisons continue until all alternatives have been exhausted and only the best project remains. The procedure used is very similar to that specified for the rate of return method presented in Chapter 8.

> B/C analysis is useful for evaluating one project. Incremental $\Delta B/\Delta C$ analysis is required when comparing more than one alternative. $B - C$ analysis is useful for one or many alternatives.

With the $B - C$ criterion, an incremental basis may be used following the same rules as for the B/C ratio, preferring Alternative 2 to Alternative 1 as long as the following condition holds:

$$\Delta(B - C)_{2-1}(i) = \Delta B_{2-1}(i) - \Delta C_{2-1}(i) =$$

$$\sum_{t=1}^{n}[B_{2t}(i) - B_{1t}(i)](1+i)^{-t} - \sum_{t=0}^{n}[C_{2t}(i) - C_{1t}(i)](1+i)^{-t} \geq 0 \qquad (14.4)$$

The incremental basis of Equation 14.4 is not required when using the $B - C$ criterion, as long as benefits and costs are known for each alternative. In this case, Equation 14.2 could be used directly for each alternative and the maximum value selected.

Cost-effectiveness analysis is appropriate whenever it is unnecessary or impractical to consider the monetary value of the benefits provided by the alternatives being considered. This is the case whenever (1) each alternative has the same annual benefits expressed monetarily, or (2) each alternative has the same annual effects, but monetary values are not easily assigned to their benefits, such as in the analysis of defense systems. Cost-effectiveness analysis can also be used to compare alternatives with identical costs but differing benefits, in which case the alternative with the largest benefits would normally be favored.

When benefits or effects of all alternatives are considered equal,

$$C_{j\,\text{preferred}}(i) = \min \forall j \left(\sum_{t=0}^{n} C_{jt}(i)\right) \qquad (14.5)$$

And when the costs are identical for all alternatives,

$$B_{j\,\text{preferred}}(i) = \max \forall j \left(\sum_{t=0}^{n} B_{jt}(i)\right) \qquad (14.6)$$

EXAMPLE 14.2   *Cost-Effectiveness Analysis of Three Routes*

The state of Washington must decide between three highway alternatives to replace an old winding road. The length of the current route is 26 miles. Planners agree that the old road must be replaced or overhauled; they cannot keep it as is. Also, for simplicity, they decide to estimate all costs and benefits in real or constant-worth dollars. Alternative A is to overhaul and resurface the old road at a cost of $2 million/mile. Resurfacing will also cost $2 million/mile at the end of each 10-year period. Annual maintenance will cost $10,000/mile. Alternative B is to cut a new road following the terrain. It will be only 22 miles long. Its first cost will be $3 million/mile with resurfacing at 10-year intervals costing $2 million/mile with annual maintenance at $12,000/mile. Alternative C also involves a new highway to be built along a 20.5-mile straight line. Its first cost will be $4 million/mile with resurfacing at 10-year intervals costing $2 million/mile and with annual maintenance costing $20,000/mile. This increase over Routes A and B is due to additional roadside bank retention efforts.

The Washington planners initially believe the benefits will be equal to the public, regardless of which alternative is selected, so they decide to select the best alternative based on costs alone, known as a *cost-effectiveness study*. The planning horizon is 30 years, with negligible salvage value for each of the highways at that time. They begin by calculating the annual equivalent first cost and resurfacing cost of each alternative using a discount rate of 8 percent, followed by the annual maintenance cost.

Annualized first cost and resurfacing cost:

$$\text{Route A:} \quad AW(8\%) = 26[2,000,000 + 2,000,000(P|F\,8\%,10)$$
$$+ 2,000,000(P|F\,8\%,20)](A|P\,8\%,30)$$
$$= \$7,749,533/\text{year}$$

$$\text{Route B:} \quad AW(8\%) = 22[3,000,000 + 2,000,000(P|F\,8\%,10)$$
$$+ 2,000,000(P|F\,8\%,20)](A|P\,8\%,30)$$
$$= \$8,511,501/\text{year}$$

$$\text{Route C:} \quad AW(8\%) = 20.5[4,000,000 + 2,000,000(P|F\,8\%,10)$$
$$+ 2,000,000(P|F\,8\%,20)](A|P\,8\%,30)$$
$$= \$9,752,134/\text{year}$$

Annual maintenance cost:

Route A: ($10,000/mile-year)(26 miles)   = $260,000/year
Route B: ($12,000/mile-year)(22 miles)   = $264,000/year
Route C: ($20,000/mile-year)(20.5 miles) = $410,000/year

The total annual cost for each route is then

Route A: $8,009,533/year
Route B: $8,775,501/year
Route C: $10,162,134/year

Based on a cost-effectiveness study with the benefits of all alternatives assumed equal, Route A is the clear winner. All of this data and a summary of calculations are shown in Figure 14.3.

B17 ▾ (*fx* =PMT(B6,B7,PV(B6,10,,B9*B3)+PV(B6,20,,B10*B3))

	A	B	C	D	E
		Route A	**Route B**	**Route C**	
1					
2	**General info**				
3	**Miles**	26	22	20.5	
4					
5	**Government-related info**				
6	**Discount rate**	8.00%	8.00%	8.00%	
7	**Planning horizon in years**	30	30	30	
8	**First Cost $/mi**	$2,000,000	$3,000,000	$4,000,000	
9	**Resurfacing cost $/mi @10 yrs**	$2,000,000	$2,000,000	$2,000,000	
10	**Resurfacing cost $/mi @20 yrs**	$2,000,000	$2,000,000	$2,000,000	
11	**Maintenance $/mi-yr**	$10,000	$12,000	$20,000	
12					
13		**Summary of Annual Equivalent Government Costs**			
14		**Route A**	**Route B**	**Route C**	
15	**Government**				
16	**First cost of highway $/year**	$4,619,027	$5,862,611	$7,283,850	=-PMT(D6,D7,D8*D3)
17	**Resurfacing costs $/year**	$3,130,507	$2,648,890	$2,468,284	
18	**Maintenance costs $/year**	$260,000	$264,000	$410,000	=D11*D3
19	**Total $/year**	$8,009,533	$8,775,501	$10,162,134	=SUM(D16:D18)
20					
21		=PMT(D6,D7,PV(D6,10,,D9*D3)+PV(D6,20,,D10*D3))			
22					

FIGURE 14.3

Data and Calculations for Cost-Effectiveness Analysis of Three Routes.

EXAMPLE 14.3   Benefit-Cost Analysis of Three Routes

In Example 14.2, Route A is identified as the preferred alternative based on a cost-effectiveness study where all alternatives are assumed to have equal benefits. The Washington State agency reviewing the study questions the assumption of equal benefits and believes they may be significantly different for each of the three routes. While the government cost estimation is still good, the planners must now explicitly consider the benefits of each alternative to the public.

Traffic density along each of the three routes will fluctuate widely from day to day but will average 4,000 vehicles/day throughout the 365-day year. This volume is composed of 350 light trucks, 250 heavy trucks, and 80 motorcycles, and the remaining 3,320 are automobiles. The average operation cost for each of these vehicles is $0.70, $1.10, $0.30, and $0.60 per mile, respectively.

There will be a time savings because of the different distances along each of the routes, as well as different speeds that each of the routes will sustain. Route A will allow heavy trucks to average 35 miles/hour, while the other vehicles can maintain 45 miles/hour. For each of Routes B and C, these numbers are 40 miles/hour for heavy trucks and 50 miles/hour for other vehicles. The cost of time for all commercial traffic is valued at $25/hour and for noncommercial vehicles, $10/hour. Twenty-five percent of the automobiles and all of the trucks are considered commercial.

Finally, there is a significant safety factor to be included. An excessive number of accidents per year have occurred along the old winding road. Route A will reduce the number of vehicles involved in accidents to 105, and Routes B and C are expected to involve only 75 and 50 vehicles in accidents, respectively. The average cost per vehicle in an accident is estimated to be $18,000, considering actual property damages, lost time and wages, medical expenses, and other relevant costs.

The planners are now set to analyze the various benefits in monetary terms. Before doing so, they must quantify the costs of vehicle operation, time, and accidents.

The benefit-cost analysis includes the government first costs, resurfacing costs, and maintenance costs from Example 14.2, plus the public operational, time, and accident costs that follow.

Annual public operational costs are:

Route A: $[(350)(0.70) + (250)(1.10) + (80)(0.30) + (3,320)(0.60)](26)(365)$
$= \$24,066,640/\text{year}$

Route B: $[(350)(0.70) + (250)(1.10) + (80)(0.30) + (3,320)(0.60)](22)(365)$
$= \$24,066,640/\text{year}$

Route C: $[(350)(0.70) + (250)(1.10) + (80)(0.30) + (3,320)(0.60)](20.5)(365)$
$= \$24,066,640/\text{year}$

Annual public time costs:

Route A: $[(350)(1/45)(25) + (250)(1/35)(25) + (80)(1/45)(10)$
$\qquad + (3,320)(0.25)(1/45)(25) + (3,320)(0.75)(1/45)(10)](26)(365)$
$= \$13,335,710/\text{year}$

Route B: $[(350)(1/50)(25) + (250)(1/40)(25) + (80)(1/50)(10)$
$\qquad + (3,320)(0.25)(1/50)(25) + (3,320)(0.75)(1/50)(10)]](22)(365)$
$= \$10,119,808/\text{year}$

Route C: $[(350)(1/50)(25) + (250)(1/40)(25) + (80)(1/50)(10)$
$\qquad + (3,320)(0.25)(1/50)(25) + (3,320)(0.75)(1/50)(10)](20.5)(365)$
$= \$9,429,821/\text{year}$

Annual accident costs per vehicle:

Route A: $(105)(18,000) = \$1,890,000/\text{year}$
Route B: $(75)(18,000) = \$1,350,000/\text{year}$
Route C: $(50)(18,000) = \$900,000/\text{year}$

 All relevant government and public costs are summarized in Figure 14.4. The analysis follows.

The Washington planners want to compare the three alternative routes using benefit-cost criteria. Their first criterion is the popular benefit-cost ratio. Since they have not yet defined the "benefits" per se, public benefits are taken as the incremental reduction in user costs between each pair of alternatives evaluated. Then, the incremental benefits are compared against the respective incremental costs needed to achieve the incremental benefits.

The incremental benefits and costs for Route B as compared to Route A using a real discount rate of 8 percent are given as follows:

$$\Delta B_{B-A}(8\%) = \text{Public costs}_A(8\%) - \text{Public costs}_B(8\%)$$
$$\$39,292,350 - \$31,833,888 = \$7,458,462$$
$$\Delta C_{B-A}(8\%) = \text{Government costs}_B(8\%) - \text{Government costs}_A(8\%)$$
$$\$8,775,501 - \$8,009,533 = \$765,968$$

	Route A	Route B	Route C	
	Route A	**Route B**	**Route C**	
General info				
Miles	26	22	20.5	
Hvy truck speed miles/hour	35	40	40	
Other veh speed miles/hour	45	50	50	
Accidents/year	105	75	50	
Cost/accident	$18,000	$18,000	$18,000	
Government-related info				
Discount rate	8.00%	8.00%	8.00%	
Planning horizon in years	30	30	30	
First Cost $/mi	$2,000,000	$3,000,000	$4,000,000	
Resurfacing cost $/mi @10 yrs	$2,000,000	$2,000,000	$2,000,000	
Resurfacing cost $/mi @20 yrs	$2,000,000	$2,000,000	$2,000,000	
Maintenance $/mi-yr	$10,000	$12,000	$20,000	
Public-related info	**Vehicles/day**	**Op cost/mile**	**Time cost/veh hr**	
Light commercial trucks	350	$0.70	$25	
Heavy commercial trucks	250	$1.10	$25	
Motorcycles	80	$0.30	$10	
Commercial autos	830	$0.60	$25	
Noncommercial autos	2490	$0.60	$10	
Total vehicles	4000			
Automobiles	3320			
% commercial autos	25.00%			
% noncommercial autos	75.00%			

FIGURE 14.4

Summary of Data for Three Routes of Example 14.3.

That is, for an incremental expenditure of $765,968/year, the government can provide added benefits of $7,458,462/year for the public. The appropriate benefit-cost ratio is then

$$\Delta B/C_{B-A}(8\%) = \frac{\Delta B_{B-A}(8\%)}{\Delta C_{B-A}(8\%)} = \frac{\$7,458,462}{\$765,968} = 9.74$$

This clearly indicates that the additional funds for Route B are worthwhile, and Route B is desired over Route A.

Using a similar analysis, the benefits, costs, and $\Delta B/C$ ratio may now be calculated to determine whether or not Route C is preferable to Route B:

$$\Delta B_{C-B}(8\%) = \text{Public costs}_B(8\%) - \text{Public costs}_C(8\%)$$
$$\$31,833,888 - \$29,305,441 = \$2,528,447$$

$$\Delta C_{C-B}(8\%) = \text{Government costs}_C(8\%) - \text{Government costs}_B(8\%)$$
$$\$10,162,134 - \$8,775,501 = \$1,386,633$$

$$\Delta B_{C-B}(8\%) = \frac{\Delta B_{C-B}(8\%)}{\Delta C_{B-A}(8\%)} = \frac{\$2,528,447}{\$1,386,633} = 1.82$$

This benefit-cost ratio, being greater than 1.00, shows that the additional expenditure of $1,386,633/year to build and maintain Route C would provide commensurate benefits in public savings of $2,528,447/year. Of the three alternatives, Route C is preferred.

Figure 14.5 illustrates the benefit-cost calculations using Excel®.

| B38 | fx | =($B18*$C18+$B19*$C19+$B20*$C20+$B21*$C21+$B22*$C22)*B3*365 |

	A	B	C	D	E
29	Summary of Annual Equivalent Government and Public Costs				
30		Route A	Route B	Route C	
31	Government				
32	First cost of highway $/year	$4,619,027	$5,862,611	$7,283,850	=-PMT(D10,D11,D12*D3)
33	Resurfacing costs $/year	$3,130,507	$2,648,890	$2,468,284	
34	Maintenance costs $/year	$260,000	$264,000	$410,000	=D15*D3
35	Total $/year	$8,009,533	$8,775,501	$10,162,134	=SUM(D32:D34)
37	Public				
38	Operating costs	$24,066,640	$20,364,080	$18,975,620	
39	Time costs	$13,335,710	$10,119,808	$9,429,821	
40	Accident costs	$1,890,000	$1,350,000	$900,000	=D7*D6
41	Total $/year	$39,292,350	$31,833,888	$29,305,441	=SUM(D38:D40)
43	Benefit B to A		$7,458,462		
44	Cost B to A		$765,968		
45	B/C Ratio B to A	Prefer B to A	9.74		
47	Benefit C to B			$2,528,447	=C41-D41
48	Cost C to B			$1,386,633	=D35-C35
49	B/C Ratio C to B		Prefer C to B	1.82	=D47/D48
51	=PMT(D10,D11,PV(D10,10,,D13*D3)+PV(D10,20,,D14*D3))				
53	=($B18*$C18+$B19*$C19+$B20*$C20+$B21*$C21+$B22*$C22)*D3*365				
55	=($B18*$D18/D5+$B19*$D19/D4+$B20*$D20/D5+$B21*$D21/D5+$B22*$D22/D5)*D3*365				

FIGURE 14.5

Benefit-Cost Calculations for Example 14.3.

The next benefit-cost criterion takes advantage of the fact that if $\Delta B/C > 1$, $\Delta(B - C) > 0$—that is, the difference in incremental benefits and costs may be used in place of the incremental benefit-cost ratio.

EXAMPLE 14.4   Using Differences in Incremental Benefits and Costs

The following calculations use the difference in incremental benefits and costs for the previous example.

$$\Delta(B - C)_{B-A}(8\%) = \Delta B_{B-A}(8\%) - \Delta C_{B-A}(8\%)$$
$$= \$7,458,462 - \$765,968 = \$6,692,494/\text{year}$$

We again conclude that Route B is preferred to Route A, since $\Delta(B - C)_{B-A}(8\%) > 0$. Similarly,

$$\Delta(B - C)_{C-B}(8\%) = \Delta B_{C-B}(8\%) - \Delta C_{C-B}(8\%)$$
$$= \$2,528,447 - 1,386,633 = \$1,141,814/\text{year}$$

Again, Route C is worthy of the additional expenditure required over Route B, and Route C should be constructed.

Example 14.1 used the present worth of benefits and of costs to perform a benefit-cost analysis, using both the $B - C$ and the B/C measures. This was a very traditional analysis, and both the $B - C$ and B/C measures result in a consistent decision. In addition to present worth, the annual worth or future worth of benefits and costs would have worked just as well. Usually, either the present worth or annual worth is used.

Example 14.2 through Example 14.4 described a much richer problem. Example 14.2 took advantage of a cost-effectiveness analysis, simply comparing the costs of each alternative, since the Washington planners initially believed the benefits would be equal to the public, regardless of the alternative selected. In Example 14.3 and Examples 14.4, the planners decided there were actually differences in benefits between Routes A, B, and C. Since benefits were not identified directly, they were determined as the reduction in public costs in comparing one alternative to another. Both the B/C and $B - C$ measures were used, this time looking at incremental benefits and incremental costs, both of which were evaluated using annual worth. Of course, it would have been perfectly fine to use the present worth of all costs.

Usually the benefit-cost ratio B/C is used. This is unfortunate, because, just as in rate of return analyses in the private sector, the benefit-cost ratio B/C is easy to misuse and misinterpret, and it is very sensitive to classifying problem elements such as benefits or costs. These problems are discussed in the next section.

14-8 IMPORTANT CONSIDERATIONS IN EVALUATING PUBLIC PROJECTS

In Section 14.7, we noted that there are several pitfalls to using benefit-cost analyses, especially the B/C ratio, when analyzing government projects. Actually, opportunities for error pervade benefit-cost analyses from the initial philosophy right through to the interpretation of a B/C ratio. It is important to talk about the more significant of these, both to help prevent errors in analysis and to help those who may be reviewing a biased benefit-cost analysis.

The major topics to be considered include the following:

1. Point of view (national, state, local, individual)
2. Selection of the interest rate
3. Assessing benefit-cost factors
4. Overcounting
5. Unequal lives
6. Tolls, Fees, and User Charges
7. Multiple-use projects
8. Problems with the B/C ratio

> Benefit-cost analyses have their own challenges due to *interpretation* in the ''soft'' public sector, even though the principles are solid and ''hard.''

14.8.1 Point of View

The stance taken in analyzing a public-sector project can significantly affect the economic ''facts.'' The analyst may take any of several viewpoints, including those of

1. an individual or select group who will benefit or lose;
2. a particular governmental organization;

3. a local area such as a city or county;

4. a regional area such as a state;

5. the entire nation.

The first of these viewpoints is not particularly interesting from an economic analysis standpoint. Nonetheless, all too frequently, an isolated road is paved, a remote stretch of water or sewer line is extended under exceptional circumstances, or a seemingly ideal location for a public works facility is suddenly eliminated from consideration. In these cases, the benefit-cost analysis, its review, and the implementation decision are usually made by a group without external review.

The other four viewpoints are, however, of considerable interest to those involved in public works evaluation. Analyzing projects or project components from viewpoint 2—that of a particular government agency—is analogous to economic comparisons in private enterprise; that is, only the gains and losses to the organization involved are considered. This viewpoint, which seems contrary to benefit-cost optimization to the public as a whole, may be appropriate under certain circumstances.

EXAMPLE 14.5   Viewing a Project from an Organization Point of View

Consider a Corps of Engineers construction project in which the water table must be lowered in the immediate area so work can proceed. Any of several water cutoff or dewatering systems may be employed. Water cutoff techniques include driving a sheet pile diaphragm or using a bentonite slurry trench to cut off the water flow to the construction area. Dewatering methods include deep-well turbines, an eductor system, or wellpoints for lowering the water level. It is sometimes appropriate for the Corps to evaluate these different techniques from an "organization" point of view, since each of the feasible methods provides the same service or outcome—a dry construction site. Therefore, the most economical decision from the Corps' point of view is also correct from the public's view, since the benefits or contributions to the project are the same regardless of the method chosen.

The third point of view—that of a locality such as a city or county—is popular among local government employees and elected officials. However, seemingly localized projects often impact a much wider range of the citizenry than is apparent.

EXAMPLE 14.6   Viewing a Project from a "Local" County Point of View

County officials are to decide whether or not future refuse service should be county owned and operated or whether a private contractor should be employed. The job requires front-end-loader compaction trucks and roll on/roll off container capability. Primarily, rural roads are traveled, and from 1 container (a roadside picnic area) to 50 containers (a large rurally located industrial plant) must be collected at each stop. Front-end-loader containers range from 2 to 8 cubic yards, while roll on/off containers are sized from 15 to 45 cubic yards. Several trucks and drivers are required, including a base for operations and maintenance. The cost in dollars per ton of refuse collected, removed, and disposed of are given in Table 14.1.

County cost to provide service will be $85.70/ton. The county is not, however, required to pay the additional $21.69/ton for federal and state taxes, property taxes, or a return on appropriated money, as would a private firm.

TABLE 14.1
Cost Per Ton of Refuse Service.

Cost of refuse collection, removal, and disposal paid by county	$/ton
Labor	20.32
Materials, supplies, utilities	17.14
Maintenance and repair	18.78
Overhead	11.39
Depreciation	12.06
5% interest on half financed by bonds	6.01
Total cost to county	**$85.70/ton**
Costs avoided by county, but paid by private contractor	**$/ton**
Federal taxes foregone	6.25
State taxes foregone	0.67
Property taxes foregone	5.15
8% return on half financed by tax money	9.62
Total not paid by county	**$21.69/ton**

It is obvious from this example that a "local" county decision can affect a much wider public. Suppose, based on $85.70/ton, the county decides to own and operate the needed refuse service. The ramifications are several:

- The county will not pay federal taxes of $6.25/ton. Since the federal government's revenue requirements will be the same, this small burden will be passed along to and shared by taxpayers throughout the country. While this is inconsequential for one county's decision, consider the result if every town, city, and county took this attitude.

- Likewise, state taxes will be forgone, and the burden must be spread over the state. Providing refuse service at less cost to the populace, at the expense of the state, is tempting from a parochial point of view.

- Since the county does not have to pay property tax on facilities and equipment, the slack will be taken up by increasing the property tax rates in the county. The burden of increased property tax will be on county residents. However, it may be entirely disproportionate to their refuse service needs.

It could be argued that a regional or national perspective should be used in evaluating public works projects at every level, from local on up. Experience indicates that this will not happen, and the primary concern of most public officials is their own constituency.

Perhaps the best advice for evaluators and decision makers in the public realm is to examine multiple viewpoints—that is, project evaluators are often not in a position to decide on a single specific point of view. They should instead present a thorough analysis clearly indicating any benefits or costs that depend on the perspective taken. Similarly, decision makers should require multiple points of view so they can be aware of the kind and degree of repercussions resulting from their actions.

14.8.2 Selection of the Interest Rate

The interest rate or discount rate is another factor to be decided upon when evaluating public works projects. In Examples 14.2 to 14.4, regarding the route selection, the interest rate was taken at 8 percent with no question of the appropriateness of this figure. Actually, that 8 percent is very close to the real discount rate of 7 percent suggested for public investment in Section 8b of Circular A-94, Revised, in Appendix 14.A. Many analysts question the rate selected, with rates ranging from 0 percent to 15 percent (and even higher), comparable to interest rates used in the private sector. Of course, the interest rate significantly affects the net present worth or annual worth of benefits minus costs or the benefit-cost ratio in public-sector analyses.

EXAMPLE 14.7 The Effect of Interest Rates on Benefit-Cost Analyses

Three projects each have investments requiring $50,000. The annual benefits are $15,000, $9,000, and $5,000 for 5, 10, and 20 years, respectively. No project renewal will be performed, and benefits will cease after the time noted. The planning horizon is 20 years. The projects have the economic profile, as a function of the interest rate used, given in Table 14.2. Note that the present value of benefits minus costs of the best alternative for a given interest rate is in bold type.

TABLE 14.2
Analysis of Projects Using Different Discount Rates.

	Project A	Project B	Project C
Initial investment	$50,000	$50,000	$50,000
Annual benefits	$15,000/yr	$9000/yr	$5000/yr
Life in years	5 yr	10 yr	20 yr
	Present value of benefits - costs:		
0.0%	$25,000	$40,000	**$50,000**
1.0%	$22,801	$35,242	**$40,228**
2.0%	$20,702	$30,843	**$31,757**
3.0%	$18,696	**$26,772**	$24,387
4.0%	$16,777	**$22,998**	$17,952
5.0%	$14,942	**$19,496**	$12,311
6.0%	$13,185	**$16,241**	$7,350
7.0%	$11,503	**$13,212**	$2,970
8.0%	$9,891	**$10,391**	−$909
9.0%	**$8,345**	$7,759	−$4,357
10.0%	**$6,862**	$5,301	−$7,432

Example 14.7 shows that different decisions can be made, depending upon the interest rate used in the analysis to discount benefits and costs. Project C is best for low discount rates of 0 percent, 1 percent, and 2 percent. Project B is best for 3 percent through 8 percent, and A is best at 9 percent and 10 percent due to its benefits being much higher in the early years of the planning horizon.

Project C appears to be the best alternative when evaluated at 0 percent, because its long-lived but rather small benefits make it appear more attractive than it really is. Prior to 1940, the Soviet Union did not use discount rates and consequently invested huge sums in long-lived, capital-intensive projects. In the United States, the Water Resources Council evaluated 245 authorized Corps of Engineers projects. In about one-third of them, costs actually exceeded benefits when the discount rate was raised from 5.375 percent to 7 percent. The U.S. Office of Management and Budget (OMB) in Circular A-94, Revised (see Appendix 14.A) continues to specify a 7 percent discount rate for use in federal government public investments.

Before considering different schools of thought on the appropriate interest rate, it is helpful to know how public activities are financed.

Financing of Government Projects. There are several different ways in which units of government finance public-sector projects. These ways include:

1. taxation such as income tax, property tax, sales tax, and road user tax;

2. issuance of bonds or notes;

3. income-generating activities such as a municipally owned power plant, a toll road, or other activity where a charge is made to cover (or partially offset) the cost of the service performed.

These are the primary *sources* of government funds, and this money may be passed from one government authority to another by way of direct payments, loans, subsidies, and grants. Since federal funds are raised through tax money and federal borrowing, federal projects may be financed through direct payment where the government does not expect monetary return; however, the "return" is expressed through the benefits incurred by the public. Direct payment financing may be total, as in the case of many Corps of Engineers projects, or it may be partial—for example, 90 percent, as in cost sharing with states for interstates.

State and local public projects are financed from taxes or bonds. There are, however, constraints on bond financing. First, bond issues must be approved by the voters, sometimes with a supermajority of 60 percent or 67 percent. Second, in order to prevent excessive borrowing, states have limited the amount of bond debt that may be undertaken. Finally, there are also restrictions that govern the payback requirements and lives of the bonds.

Selecting the Interest or Discount Rate. Many philosophies for selecting the interest rate have surfaced over time. Most of these are aligned with one of the following positions:

1. *A 0% interest rate is appropriate when tax monies are used for financing.* Advocates argue that current taxes (e.g., highway user taxes) require no principal or interest payment at all and therefore should be considered "free" money and a 0 percent interest or discount rate applied. Counterarguments point out that a 0 percent (or >0 percent but very low) interest rate will allow very marginal projects to achieve a *B/C* ratio greater than 1, taking money away from other projects that are truly deserving.

2. *The interest value need only reflect society's rate of time preference (SRTP).* The SRTP reflects society's preference for consumption this year rather than next year. For example, the rate is 6 percent to 13 percent for a house, 8 percent to 20 percent for a new or used car, and so on. The "societal time preference rate" need bear no relation to the rates of return in the private sector, interest rates, or any other measurable market phenomena.

3. *The interest rate should match that paid by government for borrowed money.* Many people back the use of an interest rate matching that paid by government for

borrowed money. This seems reasonable in that government bonds are in direct competition with other investment opportunities available in the private sector. This is also a rate supported in Section 8c of the OMB's Circular A-94, Revised (see Appendix 14.A) for internal government investment (e.g., a new government building), among other things. Those opposed to these rates say they are too low because (1) of the tax-exempt status of government bonds, (2) they do not include a provision for risk, and (c) opportunities forgone in the private sector would have provided a far higher return.

4. *The appropriate interest rate is dictated by the opportunity cost of those investments forgone by private investors who pay taxes or purchase bonds.* This philosophy calls for an opportunity cost approach, taking into account many of the factors not considered in the pure cost of government borrowed money. It can be summarized well by a statement from Howe:[5] "No public project should be undertaken that would generate a rate of return less than the rate of return that would have been experienced on the private uses of funds that would be precluded by the financing of the public project (say, through taxes or bonds)." Empirical studies place the weighted average "private use of funds rate" at least two times that of government bonds.

5. *The appropriate interest rate is dictated by the opportunity cost of those investments forgone by government agencies due to budget constraints.* This last philosophy also requires an opportunity cost approach in which an artificial interest rate reflects the rates of return forgone on government projects by virtue of having insufficient funds. That interest rate is found by continuing to increase the value of i until only the projects remain having $B/C > 1$ or $B - C > 0$, which can be afforded with money available.

What conclusions can we reach from these philosophical arguments? What guidelines are available for public-works projects? Although no one answer is universally applicable, we recommend that the discount rate for public investments and regulatory programs that provide benefits and costs to the general public should approximate the average rate of return on private-sector investments, similar to Position 4 above. This was the consensus philosophy that led to the OMB's Circular A-94, Revised (see Appendix 14.A), which specifies the rate of 7 percent, applicable since 1992 and current as of this writing.

> Selection of the interest rate used in a benefit-cost evaluation is all over the board. Most experts recommend position #4. We agree.

14.8.3 Assessing Benefit-Cost Factors

Before starting a public-sector benefit-cost study, we know that placing a monetary figure on certain "social benefits" may be difficult. Actually, an even more fundamental problem is what factors to assess. Some insight is available by the following four types of factors discussed by Cohn:[6]

1. *Internal* effects are those operating directly or indirectly upon the individual(s) or organization(s) with which the analyst is concerned. Rides on Atlanta's MARTA or the

[5]Howe, Charles W., "The Opportunity Cost of Displaced Private Spending and the Social Discount Rate," Water Resources Research, 5 (5), 1969, pp. 947–957.

[6]Cohn, Elchanan, Public Expenditure Analysis, D.C. Heath, 1972.

METRO in Washington, D.C., are direct benefits, while materials used in their construction are direct costs. These effects are always included in a benefit-cost analysis.

2. *External technological (or real)* effects are those causing changes in the physical opportunities for consumption or production. For example, effects on navigation and water sport recreation due to a new hydroelectric plant fall into this category. These effects should be included in an analysis.

3. *External pecuniary* effects are changes in the distribution of incomes through changes in the prices of goods, services, and production factors. For example, increases in rents near a subway station are pecuniary in nature, since the benefits to landlords in the form of higher rentals are exactly equal to the costs incurred by the tenants. Therefore, there is no net change, and these effects can usually be ignored.

4. *Secondary effects* involve changes in the demand for and supply of goods, services, resources, and production factors arising from a particular project. As an example, phosphate mining in Idaho on government lands will bring instant population increases to nearby small towns. Secondary effects include increasing the incomes of various store owners; however, their increased sales are almost certainly offset by reduced sales of stores elsewhere. Only incremental incomes or losses, if any, arising from such effects should be included.

EXAMPLE 14.8 Internal and Secondary Effects

A small dam and reservoir are contemplated in an effort to reduce flood damage to homes and crops in a low area of northeastern Oklahoma. Annual damage to property averages approximately $1,900,000/year. The dam and reservoir will virtually eliminate damage to this region. No other benefits (e.g., irrigation, power generation, recreation) will be provided.

The *primary* benefit to the public will be prevention of the *internal effects* of $1,900,000/year in damage. However, the engineer argues that this will also cut back on money paid to contractors and servicemen for home and car repair, to health care units, for insurance premiums, and so forth. In other words, building a dam will provide disbenefits to those who would normally receive part of their livelihood from helping flood-damaged families. Should the engineer's evaluation include only the direct benefits to the flood-damage victims, or should the other disbenefits be included as well?

The disbenefits to those who would lose income if the dam and reservoir were built are considered *secondary effects*—that is, there would be a decrease in the demand for post-flood restoration goods and services. There would, however, be an increase in the demand for goods and services in constructing and maintaining the dam. Most analysts argue that only the *incremental* incomes or profits (losses or lost profits in this case) should be considered when secondary effects are involved.

The secondary effects of the flood-control dam and reservoir would be small, if not negligible. This is intuitively reasonable, because the dam's primary benefit to reduce home and crop damage represents the measure of its direct usefulness. The diseconomies described are, in fact, secondary and diffuse.

EXAMPLE 14.9 External Real Effects

What if, in Example 14.8, the dam and reservoir would cause a loss of agricultural land for grazing and crops? Should this loss be considered in the benefit-cost analysis? Yes, because it is an external real effect causing changes in the physical opportunities for consumption or production.

External technological effects are often well defined and included in benefit-cost analyses. External pecuniary effects, however, are not as apparent.

EXAMPLE 14.10   External Pecuniary Effects

A large irrigation project is being considered in the heart of cotton country. The irrigation will provide a significant effect on the quantity and quality of the cotton grown. This additional supply of cotton will, however, depress its price, lowering the profitability of other cotton growers. Also, the same effect will be felt throughout, say, the clothing industry, and manufacturers of cotton-substitutable products (products that may be used in place of cotton items) will likely have to reduce prices. At the same time, producers of cotton complementary goods (items that go well with cotton) will note increased demand, possibly with increased prices due to insufficient supply.

Which of these effects would we include in an evaluation of the irrigation project? None! Each of the effects described relates to changes in the distribution of incomes through changes in the prices of goods, services, and production factors. As such, they are considered external pecuniary effects, which are not "real" benefits or disbenefits, and therefore are not included.

As a guide, all identifiable effects of a project should be delineated. Some will clearly provide direct benefits or disbenefits to the public that should be counted. There may also be some factors that obviously should not be included. The third group—the controversial factors—should be studied and quantified if possible, and if they are not included in the benefit-cost evaluation, they should be documented as part of the record.

14.8.4 Overcounting

When trying to consider a large variety of effects in a benefit-cost analysis, it is common to overcount, or unknowingly count some factors twice.

EXAMPLE 14.11   Overcounting of Welfare Payments

Reconsider Example 14.10 involving a cotton irrigation system. The increased quantity of cotton will require that additional gin and seed mill hands be employed, removing a significant number of persons from the welfare rolls. The amount of their new wage, equal to the sum of their old welfare payments, plus some incremental amount, represents an *increase* in real output and constitutes a legitimate national benefit of the project. If we then add the *reduction* in welfare payments as another benefit to the country's taxpayers, we would be double-counting welfare payments—once from the standpoint of the recipient and again from the taxpayer's viewpoint.

14.8.5 Unequal Lives

When evaluating public-works projects having unequal lives, the principles are identical to those seen earlier. It is common for some projects to have a long life, while others have a short one. In such cases, the planning horizon will often coincide with the longest lived alternative.

We have already seen in Example 14.7 how one-shot public projects having different lives can yield different decisions, depending upon the discount rate used. Let's look at a similar example, this time modifying it to make several points.

EXAMPLE 14.12 Projects with Unequal Lives and Longer Planning Horizon

Two projects each have first costs of $200,000, with annual operating costs of $30,000. Project A is a large park with many well-made and safe pieces of equipment such as swings, slides, horizontal bars, and the like, ideal for families with young children to visit. Project A's life is only 15 years due to expected development in that area. Project B is a new fairgrounds arena for livestock shows, tractor pulls, horse shows, and so on, ideal for people of all ages to enjoy. It should last 30 years. Benefits realized by the public are estimated at $60,000/year for the park and $54,000/year for the fairgrounds arena. Let's look at these unequal-lived projects in three different ways.

First, assume each is a one-shot project. Project A, the large park, will have no benefits or costs after year 15. Project B, the new arena, will continue to provide benefits for 30 years. Suppose the analyst sets the planning horizon at 30 years. Which project is more attractive?

 Figure 14.6 shows that for interest rates up to 15.8 percent, Project B is the preferred choice. The Excel® tool GOAL SEEK is used to determine the interest rate at which Projects A and B are equally desirable.

	B14 ▾	fx =PV($A14,B$4,-B$3)-B$2	
	A	B	C	D
1		**A: Park**	**B: Arena**	
2	**Initial investment**	$200,000	$200,000	
3	**Annual benefits**	$60,000	$54,000	
4	**Life in years**	15	30	
5	**Salvage value**	$0	$0	
6	**Planning horizon**	30	30	
7	**Project renewed**	No	NA	
8	**Present value of benefits - costs:**			
9	0.0%	$700,000	$1,420,000	
10	5.0%	$422,779	$630,112	
11	10.0%	$256,365	$309,053	
12	15.0%	$150,842	$154,563	
13	20.0%	$80,528	$68,863	
14	15.8%	$138,080	$138,080	
15	**PV Difference at IRR**	$0	=B14-C14	
16				

Goal Seek
Set cell: $C$15
To value: 0
By changing cell: $A$14
OK   Cancel

FIGURE 14.6
Benefit-Cost Analysis with 30 Year Horizon.

EXAMPLE 14.13 Projects with Unequal Lives and Shorter Planning Horizon

Reconsidering Example 14.12, suppose both A and B remain one-shot projects; however, the analyst makes only one change and sets the planning horizon to 15 years. The salvage value of $30,000 for Project B, the arena, is established to account for the residual value of that asset after 15 years. Table 14.3 shows that there is no reasonable interest rate at which the two alternatives are equally desirable. Project A, the park, wins under every condition.

TABLE 14.3
Benefit-Cost Analysis with 15 Year Horizon.

	A: Park	B: Arena
Initial investment	$200,000	$200,000
Annual benefits	$60,000	$54,000
Annual costs	$30,000	$30,000
Life in years	15	30
Salvage value	$0	$30,000
Planning horizon	15	15
Project renewed	NA	NA
Present value of benefits - costs:		
0.0%	**$250,000**	$190,000
5.0%	**$111,390**	$63,542
10.0%	**$28,182**	−10,272
15.0%	−24,579	−55,976
20.0%	−59,736	−85,841
649354704.0%	−200,000	−200,000
PV Difference at IRR		$0

EXAMPLE 14.14 Projects with Unequal Lives, Renewal, and Longer Planning Horizon

Again consider Example 14.12 and suppose Project A, the park, can be renewed after 15 years using the same real-dollar (not inflated) estimates during the second 15 years. Also, the analyst goes back to using a 30-year planning horizon. Table 14.4 shows that Project B is preferred if the discount rate is under 6.3 percent.

TABLE 14.4
Benefit-Cost Analysis with 30 Year Horizon and Renewal of Park.

	A: Park	B: Arena
Initial investment	$200,000	$200,000
Annual benefits	$60,000	$54,000
Annual costs	$30,000	$30,000
Life in years	15	30
Salvage value	$0	$0
Planning horizon	30	30
Project renewed	Yes	NA
Present value of benefits - costs:		
0.0%	$500,000	**$520,000**
5.0%	$164,970	**$168,939**
10.0%	**$34,929**	$26,246
15.0%	−$27,600	−$42,416
20.0%	−$63,613	−$80,506
6.3%	$120,191	$120,191
PV Difference at IRR		$0

In summary, alternatives with unequal lives and renewal possibilities set up some interesting results that are heavily influenced by the interest rate and planning horizon used. It is helpful if the government agency has explicit guidelines for both the interest rate and the planning horizon. This will simplify the analysis requiring only that the benefits and costs for each year of the entire planning horizon be quantified, providing a benefit-cost analysis that is much less subject to arbitrary decisions.

14.8.6   Tolls, Fees, and User Charges

If a toll, fee, or user charge is regarded as a payment or partial payment for benefits derived, it can be argued that net benefits the user receives are reduced by the payment amount. Similarly, the payment amount decreases the operating cost of the project to the government. Thus, the B/C ratio will change, but the $B - C$ measure of merit will remain constant as long as total user benefits remain constant.

EXAMPLE 14.15   User Fees Applied

Suppose 35,000 people/year participate in fishing, skiing, camping, and other outdoor activities at a reservoir area. The equivalent uniform annual cost of the area is $150,000/year. The people, on average, receive recreational benefits in the amount of $6 each. The B/C ratio and the $B - C$ metric are

$$B/C = \$6(35,000)/\$150,000 = 1.4$$
$$B - C = \$6(35,000) - \$150,000 = \$60,000/\text{year.}$$

Based on either criterion, the public facility appears worthwhile.

Now suppose that a fee of $3.50/person is charged. The net benefits are now $6.00 − $3.50, or $2.50/person, and the government cost is reduced by $122,500/year. Thus, the B/C and $B - C$ measures are as follows:

$$B/C = (\$210,000 - \$122,500)/(\$150,000 - \$122,500) = 3.18$$
$$B - C = (\$210,000 - \$122,500) - (\$150,000 - \$122,500) = \$60,000/\text{year}$$

Note that B/C changed while $B - C$ did not. This phenomenon is discussed in the subsequent section, titled ''Problems with the B/C Ratio.''

It might be concluded that tolls, fees, and user charges are irrelevant, at least with respect to the $B - C$ measure of merit. This, however, is not true if the number of users or degree of use is linked to the fee charged, as it almost always will be.

EXAMPLE 14.16   User Fees Affect Number of Users

As an extreme, suppose that the 35,000 users of the public facility in the previous example receive different levels of benefits, but they average out to $6/person. The actual breakdown is that 28,000 persons perceive $3 worth of enjoyment, 3,500 persons perceive $6 worth, and 3,500 persons expect to derive $30 in recreational benefits. With a user fee of \$3.50/person, it is assumed only 7,000 will patronize the facility. Thus, the B/C and $B - C$ measures are

$$B/C = [\$30(3,500) + \$6(3,500) - \$3.50(7,000)]/[\$150,000 - \$3.50(7,000)]$$
$$= \$101,500/\$125,500 = 0.81$$
$$B - C = [\$30(3,500) + \$6(3,500) - (\$3.50)(7,000)] - [\$150,000 - (\$3.50)(7,000)]$$
$$= -\$24,000/\text{year}.$$

In this case, the reduction in demand due to a fee makes the costs exceed realized benefits. Thus, when tolls, fees, and user charges are expected, their effect on user demand, and therefore total user benefits, must be determined and taken into account.

14.8.7   Multiple-Use Projects

Multiple uses, and hence multiple benefits, for the public are often available at slight incremental costs over single-use projects. Of course, the incremental costs required for additional uses must provide at least a like worth of benefits.

EXAMPLE 14.17   Incremental Analysis of an Additional Use

An irrigation dam and reservoir will provide present worth benefits of \$80 million over the next 50 years. The present worth cost of the irrigation facility's construction, operation, and maintenance will be \$46.5 million. A single-purpose flood-control dam providing present worth benefits of \$19 million would cost a present worth of \$28.8 million. Suitable design modifications can be made to the irrigation dam and reservoir to provide the flood-control benefits, too, at a total package present worth cost of \$59 million. If sufficient funds are available, what should be done?

The irrigation project considered alone is worthwhile, providing a benefit-cost ratio of

$$B/C_{\text{irrigation}} = \$80,000,000/\$46,500,000 = 1.72.$$

As a single-purpose project, a flood-control dam would not provide benefits commensurate with its costs, yielding a B/C ratio of only

$$B/C_{\text{flood control}} = \$19,000,000/\$28,800,000 = 0.66.$$

As a multiple-use facility, however, the flood-control benefits may be provided at a sufficiently low incremental cost to be justifiable. The incremental B/C ratio is

$$\Delta B/\Delta C_{\text{irrigation(incremental over flood control)}} = \$19,000,000/(\$59,000,000 - \$46,500,000)$$
$$= 1.62.$$

The irrigation dam and reservoir, modified to include flood control, is worthwhile.

This example illustrates how multiple uses can draw on one another, providing economic benefits that could never have been provided using a single-purpose facility (e.g., the B/C flood-control ratio of 0.66). Multiple-purpose projects also have their problems. For example, it is frequently desirable to ''allocate'' a project's costs to its various uses.

EXAMPLE 14.18 Interesting Considerations in Multiple-Use Facilities

The Covanta Alexandria/Arlington Waste-to-Energy facility burns trash to generate electricity. In operation since 1988, it has processed over 3.8 million tons of trash. It even includes a recycling program to separate out such things as paper, aluminum, and glass to avoid incineration and instead be remade into useful new products. By 2010, the total trash generated in the jurisdictions Covanta covers is estimated at 338,000 tons!

When a city's refuse is used to fire a power-generation facility, this is a clear multiple-use project in the public sector. Obviously, electrical power is supplied to a segment of the city. In addition, the burning of refuse after processing substantially reduces the need for an expensive landfill operation. If such a facility is to be self-supporting, the construction, operation, and maintenance costs must be covered. It is here that things get interesting, especially in allocating between (1) the power generation and (2) the refuse disposal benefits provided in order to determine the user charges for electrical energy and refuse disposal. Arguments for cost allocation range from (1) no costs should be allocated to refuse disposal, because the refuse is being used in place of fuel oil or coal; in fact, a credit should be issued, to (2) refuse disposal should receive sufficient cost allocation to raise rates above those for conventional disposal to include the aesthetic benefits of having no unsightly public landfill.[7]

14.8.8 Problems with the *B/C* Ratio

There are two frequent problems with the *B/C* ratio that require an explanation and warning. Either can give misleading results that may cause an otherwise perfect analysis to point toward the wrong project.

First, it is sometimes difficult to decide whether an item is a benefit to the public or a cost savings to the government. Similarly, there is often uncertainty between disbenefits (negative benefits to the public) and costs.

EXAMPLE 14.19 Classification as a Disbenefit or a Cost?

A project provides equivalent annual benefits of $200,000 to some of the public, equivalent annual disbenefits of $100,000 to others, and annual costs of $25,000 incurred by the project and paid by the government agency. What is the benefit-cost ratio? Let us first calculate one form of the *B/C* ratio for the problem as stated:

$$B/C = (\$200,000 - \$100,000)/\$25,000 = 4.0$$

Such a high ratio leads one to believe that the project is outstanding.

Now, another analyst *incorrectly* decides that the $100,000 in disbenefits should be treated as a cost and calculates a *B/C* ratio of

$$B/C = \$200,000/(\$25,000 + \$100,000) = 1.60$$

which is considerably lower and apparently much less desirable.

Example 14.19 shows that a wide range of *B/C* ratios may be obtained on a single project simply by interpreting certain elements of the problem differently. The resolution of this problem is easy—the analyst can simply calculate the net benefits less the net costs, $B - C$.

---

[7]These extremes in arguments have actually been used by public officials of one major city.

EXAMPLE 14.20   Using $B - C$ Instead of B/C

Let us reconsider Example 14.19 and calculate the annual net benefits less net costs. The first analyst would have calculated (parentheses denote B and then C)

$$B - C = (\$200,000 - \$100,000) - (\$25,000) = \$75,000/\text{year}$$

and the second analyst would have calculated

$$B - C = (\$200,000) - (\$25,000 + \$100,000) = \$75,000/\text{year}$$

Calculating $B - C$ eliminates the inherent bias in the B/C ratio and does not require an incremental approach between alternatives where benefits and costs are known directly for each alternative—that is, if mutually exclusive alternatives are involved, over the same time horizon, the one having the highest $B - C$ value should be selected. Unfortunately, the B/C ratio is by far the more popular criterion of the two.

The potential for the other B/C problem was illustrated in the irrigation dam and reservoir problem in Example 14.17 —that is, when the B/C ratio is used, it should be based on *incremental benefits* and *incremental costs*, much like a rate-of-return analysis. To simply calculate the B/C ratio of each alternative and take the one with the largest ratio is incorrect and may lead to errors in project selection.

EXAMPLE 14.21   Need for Incremental Analysis with B/C Ratio

In the irrigation dam and reservoir problem of Example 14.17, we calculated the B/C for irrigation only to be

$$B/C_{\text{irrigation}} = \$80,000,000/\$46,500,000 = 1.72.$$

To compare this value against a total project B/C ratio of

$$B/C_{\text{irrigation(plus flood control)}} = (\$80,000,000 + \$19,000,000)/\$59,000,000 = 1.68$$

would cause us to select irrigation only, in error.

Finally, a related error is to require the incremental B/C ratio to be above that for the previous incremental B/C ratio. In the irrigation dam and reservoir problem of Example 14.17, if the incremental B/C ratio—$\Delta B/\Delta C_{\text{irrigation(incremental over flood control)}} = 1.62$—been compared against the value of $B/C_{\text{irrigation}} = 1.72$, again an incorrect conclusion would have resulted. As long as the incremental B/C ratio exceeds 1.0, the incremental benefits exceed the incremental costs. Again, the B/C ratio is closely akin to the rate-of-return criterion.

14-9   INTRODUCTION: THE REVENUE REQUIREMENTS METHOD

Utility firms that deliver services to the public are in business to make a return for their shareholders and yet are often not subjected to competition in the usual sense. As such, their performance and related charges are regulated by a public service commission or a corporation commission. The economic evaluation of project investments, known as the *revenue requirements method*, takes on a different and somewhat "inverted" approach, where the focus is not on maximization of present worth of after-tax cash flows. Rather, it is based on minimization of revenues required from the public to provide the goods or services that meet customer performance requirements. So, this section's purpose is twofold: (1) to acquaint the many engineers going into regulated organizations with a different type of economic analysis that they will see and use and (2) to convince them that the revenue requirements analysis is equivalent to the traditional ATCF analysis.

> The "Revenue Requirements" method used by regulated utilities, uses a different and "inverted" approach, and yet is still fully equivalent to traditional after-tax cash flow analyses.

Of course, we cannot forget the owners of the public utility! They are the ones who provide much of the capital for investment and assume much of the financial risk. In using the revenue requirements method, a fair return to the owners is explicitly included—that is, the utility should be allowed to recover, through rates charged to the public for products and services, all reasonable costs plus a fair return on their investment. Many organizations openly publish on the Web either specific revenue requirement analyses or the guidelines and considerations for doing so. For example, the "Issue Paper on System Revenue Requirements," published by the city of Austin, discusses appropriate bases for determining Austin's revenue requirements for rate-making purposes.[8]

14-10 DEFINITION OF TERMS

To develop the equation for determining revenue requirements, several terms must be defined:

P Initial investment

F Salvage value

n Project book life

C_t Annual expenses in year t associated with the project

$\hat{d}_t$ Depreciation in year t based on financial accounting

$\hat{B}_t$ Book value at end of year t based on financial accounting

d_t Depreciation in year t based on tax accounting

B_t Book value at end of year t based on tax accounting (note that this is not used!)

c Debt ratio (fraction of capital borrowed—assumed fixed over all assets)

i_e Cost of equity capital (interest rate earned on equity capital)

i_d Cost of debt capital (interest rate to borrow money)

$WACC$ Weighted average (after-tax) cost of capital

I_t Interest paid on debt

$TCBIT_t$ Total cost before income taxes

TI_t Taxable income in year t

itr Income tax rate paid on taxable income

T_t Income taxes paid in year t

R_t Return to owners in year t

FC_t Fixed charges (see explanation to follow) in year t

RR_t Revenue requirement in year t

Given this notation, we can develop a mathematical representation of revenue requirements. Note that there are two different depreciations involved, one for financial reporting and the other for determining income tax paid. Sometimes these are the same.

---

[8] www.ci.austin.tx.us/water/issue_paper1a.htm, or search on "revenue requirements method"

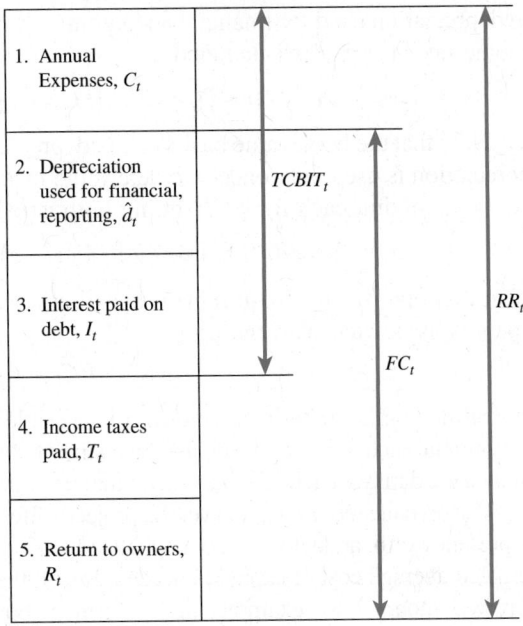

FIGURE 14.7

Components of Total Revenue Requirement in Year t.

The financial reporting depreciation method is often used to more closely reflect the actual lessening in value of the asset. The tax depreciation, which the IRS requires be used for tax-calculation purposes, may provide a significantly more aggressive write-off. The latter is shown in Chapters 9 and 10 to be more favorable economically.

Figure 14.7 illustrates the components of revenue that make up the total revenue requirement in a given year t. These are all expressed in dollars and include

1. annual expenses associated with project, C_t;
2. depreciation used for financial accounting, $\hat{d}_t$;
3. interest paid on debt, I_t;
4. income taxes paid, T_t;
5. return to owners, R_t;

The first three components of revenue are straightforward. They represent the total cost before income taxes, $TCBIT_t$. Determining the income tax paid, however, requires a roundabout way of writing the relevant equations.

14-11 DETERMINING THE MINIMUM REVENUE REQUIREMENT

Use of a fixed-charge concept is common in the utility industry. The fixed charges include items 2 through 5 above. So, we can write

$$FC_t = \hat{d}_t + I_t + T_t + R_t$$
$$= \hat{d}_t + i_d * c * \hat{B}_{t-1} + T_t + i_e * (1 - c) * \hat{B}_{t-1} \qquad (14.7)$$
$$= \hat{d}_t + [i_d * c + i_e * (1 - c)] * \hat{B}_{t-1} + T_t$$

To figure the income tax, we multiply the income-tax rate times the taxable income. Taxable income is determined as the total fixed charge minus the tax depreciation (*not* the depreciation used for financial accounting) minus the interest on borrowed money. Income tax in year t is calculated as

$$T_t = itr * TI_t = itr * [FC_t - d_t - i_d * c * \hat{B}_{t-1}] \tag{14.8}$$

Note that the book value based on tax depreciation is never needed or used; the tax depreciation is used only once—to determine income tax. Now, using Equations 14.7 and 14.8, solving each for FC_t, setting both equal, and rearranging terms results in

$$T_t = [itr/(1 - itr)] * [i_e * (1 - c) * \hat{B}_{t-1} + \hat{d}_t - d_t] \tag{14.9}$$

Then, the total revenue requirement is expressed as the fixed charge plus the annual expenses associated with the project.

$$RR_t = FC_t + C_t \tag{14.10}$$

Now, armed with the basic equations, it is possible to determine the minimum revenue requirement each year for a specific investment. Furthermore, different alternatives to satisfy a need may each be evaluated and their minimum revenue requirements compared.

The revenue requirements over the project's life are then usually expressed as an after-tax present worth, annual worth, or capitalized amount. For these calculations, the after-tax weighted average cost of capital is needed. Recall that the cost of debt capital (interest on borrowed money—for example, in the form of bonds) is deductible when calculating taxable income. Of course, the return on equity capital is not deductible, because it is paid from after-tax funds. The overall after-tax cost of capital also reflects the mix of borrowed and equity money in the project, assumed fixed over all assets in the firm. It is expressed as

$$WACC = (1 - itr) * c * i_d + (1 - c) * i_e \tag{14.11}$$

EXAMPLE 14.22 Determining Minimum Revenue Requirements

An electric utility needs to place an additional transmission and distribution plant to serve the growing needs of a set of commercial customers. The utility has prepared a plan and now wants to determine the minimum revenue requirements necessary to support the plan if implemented. The installation will cost $1.5 million and have a life of 25 years. Depreciation for financial reporting will follow the traditional straight-line method. Tax depreciation will follow MACRS-GDS over a 20-year recovery period. Annual expenses are projected to be $200,000 for year 1, increasing at $10,000 per year each year thereafter. The utility debt finances 40 percent of their investment at a rate of 8.5 percent. The remainder is equity funded, and it is desired to have a 14 percent return on the owners' capital. There is no salvage value at the end of the project's life, and the effective tax rate is 35 percent. We need to know the revenue-requirement profile for each year, including the present worth, annual worth, and capitalized cost.

A summary of the input factors is given in Figure 14.8, and the revenue requirement profile for the investment is given in Figure 14.9. To help understand the calculations in the spreadsheet, the following calculation hints are offered for year i, $i \geq 1$, unless otherwise noted:

$\hat{d}_t = (P - F)/n$ for traditional straight-line depreciation

$\hat{B}_0 = P$ and $\hat{B}_t = \hat{B}_{t-1} - \hat{d}_t$

$d_t = P * \text{MACRS Rate}_t$

Equity Return$_t$ $R_t = \hat{B}_{t-1} * (1 - c) * i_e$

Interest on Debt$_t$ $I_t = \hat{B}_{t-1} * c * i_d$

Income Taxes Paid$_t$ $T_t = ((itr/(1 - itr)) * ((1 - c) * i_e * \hat{B}_{t-1} + \hat{d}_t - d_t)$

Annual Expense$_t$ $C_t = $ As given

Revenue Requirement$_t$ $RR_t = C_t + \hat{d}_t + I_t + T_t + R_t$

$PWRR_t$ @ WACC $= RR_t/((1 + WACC)^t)$

MACRS Rate$_t$ = From MACRS-GDS Depreciation Tables

J22	fx	=$I22/(1+$J$10)^$A22

	A	B	C	D	E	F	G	H	I	J
1		ALL ACTUAL VALUES				NEEDED TO SHOW EQUIVALENCY BETWEEN				
2	P	INITIAL INVESTMENT	$1,500,000			REVENUE REQUIREMENTS AND ATCF METHODS				
3	F	SALVAGE VALUE	$0			GI_1	YR 1 GROSS INCOME			$400,000.00
4	C_1	YR 1 ANN EXPENSE	$200,000			ΔGI_1	INCREMENT ANN INC			$30,000.00
5	ΔC_t	INCREMENT ANN EXP	$10,000							
6	c	DEBT RATIO	40.00%			AFTER TAX RATE SUMMARY (CALCULATED VALUES)				
7	id	COST OF DEBT	8.50%							
8	ie	RETURN ON EQUITY	14.0000%			AFTER-TAX COST OF DEBT				5.53%
9	itr	TAX RATE	35.00%			RETURN ON EQUITY (ALREADY AFTER TAX)				14.00%
10	n	PROJECT BOOK LIFE	25			OVERALL AFTER-TAX COST OF CAPITAL				10.61%
11										
12	End of	SL Book	Unrecovered	Tax	Equity	Debt	Income	Annual	Revenue	PW RR
13	Year	Depreciation	Investment	Depreciation	Return	Payment	Tax	Expense	Requirement	@ WACC
14	t	d_t	$\hat{B}_t$	d_t			T_t	C_t	B+E+F+G+H	
15	A	B	C	D	E	F	G	H	I	J
16	0		$1,500,000.00							
17	1	$60,000.00	$1,440,000.00	$56,250.00	$126,000.00	$51,000.00	$69,865.38	$200,000.00	$506,865.38	$458,245.53
18	2	$60,000.00	$1,380,000.00	$108,285.00	$120,960.00	$48,960.00	$39,132.69	$210,000.00	$479,052.69	$391,556.56
19	3	$60,000.00	$1,320,000.00	$100,155.00	$115,920.00	$46,920.00	$40,796.54	$220,000.00	$483,636.54	$357,384.68
20	4	$60,000.00	$1,260,000.00	$92,655.00	$110,880.00	$44,880.00	$42,121.15	$230,000.00	$487,881.15	$325,939.11
21	5	$60,000.00	$1,200,000.00	$85,695.00	$105,840.00	$42,840.00	$43,155.00	$240,000.00	$491,835.00	$297,062.25
22	6	$60,000.00	$1,140,000.00	$79,275.00	$100,800.00	$40,800.00	$43,898.08	$250,000.00	$495,498.08	$270,567.49
23	7	$60,000.00	$1,080,000.00	$73,320.00	$95,760.00	$38,760.00	$44,390.77	$260,000.00	$498,910.77	$246,298.71
24	8	$60,000.00	$1,020,000.00	$67,830.00	$90,720.00	$36,720.00	$44,633.08	$270,000.00	$502,073.08	$224,084.49
25	9	$60,000.00	$960,000.00	$66,930.00	$85,680.00	$34,680.00	$42,403.85	$280,000.00	$502,763.85	$202,868.45
26	10	$60,000.00	$900,000.00	$66,915.00	$80,640.00	$32,640.00	$39,698.08	$290,000.00	$502,978.08	$183,486.93
27	11	$60,000.00	$840,000.00	$66,930.00	$75,600.00	$30,600.00	$36,976.15	$300,000.00	$503,176.15	$165,951.71
28	12	$60,000.00	$780,000.00	$66,915.00	$70,560.00	$28,560.00	$34,270.38	$310,000.00	$503,390.38	$150,097.07

FIGURE 14.8

Summary of Input Factors for Example 14.22.

J43	fx	=PMT(J10,D10,-J42)

	A	B	C	D	E	F	G	H	I	J	K
12	End of	SL Book	Unrecovered	Tax	Equity	Debt	Income	Annual	Revenue	PW RR	
13	Year	Depreciation	Investment	Depreciation	Return	Payment	Tax	Expense	Requirement	@ WACC	
14	t	d_t	$\hat{B}_t$	d_t			T_t	C_t	B+E+F+G+H		
15	A	B	C	D	E	F	G	H	I	J	
16	0		$1,500,000.00								
17	1	$60,000.00	$1,440,000.00	$56,250.00	$126,000.00	$51,000.00	$69,865.38	$200,000.00	$506,865.38	$458,245.53	
18	2	$60,000.00	$1,380,000.00	$108,285.00	$120,960.00	$48,960.00	$39,132.69	$210,000.00	$479,052.69	$391,556.56	
19	3	$60,000.00	$1,320,000.00	$100,155.00	$115,920.00	$46,920.00	$40,796.54	$220,000.00	$483,636.54	$357,384.68	
20	4	$60,000.00	$1,260,000.00	$92,655.00	$110,880.00	$44,880.00	$42,121.15	$230,000.00	$487,881.15	$325,939.11	
21	5	$60,000.00	$1,200,000.00	$85,695.00	$105,840.00	$42,840.00	$43,155.00	$240,000.00	$491,835.00	$297,062.25	
22	6	$60,000.00	$1,140,000.00	$79,275.00	$100,800.00	$40,800.00	$43,898.08	$250,000.00	$495,498.08	$270,567.49	
23	7	$60,000.00	$1,080,000.00	$73,320.00	$95,760.00	$38,760.00	$44,390.77	$260,000.00	$498,910.77	$246,298.71	
24	8	$60,000.00	$1,020,000.00	$67,830.00	$90,720.00	$36,720.00	$44,633.08	$270,000.00	$502,073.08	$224,084.49	
25	9	$60,000.00	$960,000.00	$66,930.00	$85,680.00	$34,680.00	$42,403.85	$280,000.00	$502,763.85	$202,868.45	
26	10	$60,000.00	$900,000.00	$66,915.00	$80,640.00	$32,640.00	$39,698.08	$290,000.00	$502,978.08	$183,486.93	
27	11	$60,000.00	$840,000.00	$66,930.00	$75,600.00	$30,600.00	$36,976.15	$300,000.00	$503,176.15	$165,951.71	
28	12	$60,000.00	$780,000.00	$66,915.00	$70,560.00	$28,560.00	$34,270.38	$310,000.00	$503,390.38	$150,097.07	
29	13	$60,000.00	$720,000.00	$66,930.00	$65,520.00	$26,520.00	$31,548.46	$320,000.00	$503,588.46	$135,752.76	
30	14	$60,000.00	$660,000.00	$66,915.00	$60,480.00	$24,480.00	$28,842.69	$330,000.00	$503,802.69	$122,783.21	
31	15	$60,000.00	$600,000.00	$66,930.00	$55,440.00	$22,440.00	$26,120.77	$340,000.00	$504,000.77	$111,049.17	
32	16	$60,000.00	$540,000.00	$66,915.00	$50,400.00	$20,400.00	$23,415.00	$350,000.00	$504,215.00	$100,439.72	
33	17	$60,000.00	$480,000.00	$66,930.00	$45,360.00	$18,360.00	$20,693.08	$360,000.00	$504,413.08	$90,840.95	
34	18	$60,000.00	$420,000.00	$66,915.00	$40,320.00	$16,320.00	$17,987.31	$370,000.00	$504,627.31	$82,162.13	
35	19	$60,000.00	$360,000.00	$66,930.00	$35,280.00	$14,280.00	$15,265.38	$380,000.00	$504,825.38	$74,310.08	
36	20	$60,000.00	$300,000.00	$66,915.00	$30,240.00	$12,240.00	$12,559.62	$390,000.00	$505,039.62	$67,210.57	
37	21	$60,000.00	$240,000.00	$33,465.00	$25,200.00	$10,200.00	$27,857.31	$400,000.00	$523,257.31	$62,955.41	
38	22	$60,000.00	$180,000.00	$0.00	$20,160.00	$8,160.00	$43,163.08	$410,000.00	$541,483.08	$58,899.05	
39	23	$60,000.00	$120,000.00	$0.00	$15,120.00	$6,120.00	$40,449.23	$420,000.00	$541,689.23	$53,269.57	
40	24	$60,000.00	$60,000.00	$0.00	$10,080.00	$4,080.00	$37,735.38	$430,000.00	$541,895.38	$48,178.14	
41	25	$60,000.00	$0.00	$0.00	$5,040.00	$2,040.00	$35,021.54	$440,000.00	$542,101.54	$43,573.34	
42					$1,638,000.00	$663,000.00			PWRR	$4,324,967.07	$4,324,967.07
43									ARR	$498,986.85	$498,986.85
44									CAPRR	$40,763,120.37	$40,763,120.37

FIGURE 14.9

Revenue Requirements Profile for Example 14.22.

If other alternatives are to be considered, they can be evaluated in like manner, and the alternative having the lowest PW, AW, or capitalized revenue requirements can be determined. Note that the after-tax overall cost of capital is $(1 - 0.35)*0.4*0.085 + (1 - 0.4)*0.14 = 0.1061$, or 10.61 percent. The resulting PWRR(10.61 percent) is $4,324,967.07. The AWRR (10.61 percent) is $498,986.85, and the capitalized revenue requirements CAPRR are $40,763,120.37.

14-12 SHOWING EQUIVALENCE BETWEEN REVENUE REQUIREMENT AND ATCF METHODS

It isn't terribly obvious how the revenue requirement method is related to the after-tax cash flow approach. Before presenting an example, consider that the ATCF approach requires a gross-income amount from which expenses, depreciation, loan principal and interest, and taxes are subtracted to determine the ATCF. The revenue requirement method did not specify a gross income! In fact, that is what it was trying to determine— the minimum amount of income necessary each year to meet the equity return rate i_e, also known as the *minimum revenue requirement*. So, to show equivalence between the revenue requirement method and the ATCF method, we will identify in an example a gross income GI_t for each year and apply it to both the revenue requirement and the ATCF approaches. Both should give the same result!

EXAMPLE 14.23 Equivalence between RR and ATCF Methods

Let's reconsider Example 14.22 in its entirety and add only a gross income per year of $400,000 in year 1, increasing by $30,000 per year thereafter through the 25-year life. First, let's apply the gross income to the revenue requirements determined in Example 14.22. Every additional dollar that the gross income exceeds the revenue requirement $(GI_t - RR_t)$ is taxable, just as was the taxable income TI_t in the original revenue requirement analysis. Of course, a negative value results in a negative tax. Whatever is left over after taxes is for the good of the owners, who can choose to keep it, reinvest it, or some mix of both.

Figure 14.10 shows the gross-income analysis appended to the right-hand side of the revenue requirements analysis spreadsheet. The after-tax $GI_t - RR_t$ values are then

	I42		fx =NPV(J10,I17:I41)						
	H	I	J	K	L	M	N	O	P	Q
12	Annual	Revenue	PW RR	MACRS						
13	Expense	Requirement	@ WACC	Rate %	Year	Gross	Gross Inc-	After-Tax	PW	
14	C_t	B+E+F+G+H			t	Income	Rev Reqs	GI_t-RR_t	PW(GI_t-RR_t)	
15	H	I	J	K	A	GI_t	GI_t-RR_t	(1-t)*(GI_t-RR_t)	Eval at i_e	
16					0					
17	$200,000.00	$506,865.38	$458,245.53	3.750%	1	$400,000.00	-$106,865.38	-$69,462.50	-$60,932.02	
18	$210,000.00	$479,052.69	$391,556.56	7.219%	2	$430,000.00	-$49,052.69	-$31,884.25	-$24,533.90	
19	$220,000.00	$483,636.54	$357,384.68	6.677%	3	$460,000.00	-$23,636.54	-$15,363.75	-$10,370.09	
20	$230,000.00	$487,881.15	$325,939.11	6.177%	4	$490,000.00	$2,118.85	$1,377.25	$815.44	
21	$240,000.00	$491,835.00	$297,062.25	5.713%	5	$520,000.00	$28,165.00	$18,307.25	$9,508.21	
22	$250,000.00	$495,498.08	$270,567.49	5.285%	6	$550,000.00	$54,501.92	$35,426.25	$16,139.72	
23	$260,000.00	$498,910.77	$246,298.71	4.888%	7	$580,000.00	$81,089.23	$52,708.00	$21,064.08	
24	$270,000.00	$502,073.08	$224,084.49	4.522%	8	$610,000.00	$107,926.92	$70,152.50	$24,592.59	
25	$280,000.00	$502,763.85	$202,868.45	4.462%	9	$640,000.00	$137,236.15	$89,203.50	$27,430.78	
26	$290,000.00	$502,978.08	$183,486.93	4.461%	10	$670,000.00	$167,021.92	$108,564.25	$29,284.53	
27	$300,000.00	$503,176.15	$165,951.71	4.462%	11	$700,000.00	$196,823.85	$127,935.50	$30,271.76	
28	$310,000.00	$503,390.38	$150,097.07	4.461%	12	$730,000.00	$226,609.62	$147,296.25	$30,572.68	
29	$320,000.00	$503,588.46	$135,752.76	4.462%	13	$760,000.00	$256,411.54	$166,667.50	$30,345.05	
30	$330,000.00	$503,802.69	$122,783.21	4.461%	14	$790,000.00	$286,197.31	$186,028.25	$29,710.57	
31	$340,000.00	$504,000.77	$111,049.17	4.462%	15	$820,000.00	$315,999.23	$205,399.50	$28,775.75	
32	$350,000.00	$504,215.00	$100,439.72	4.461%	16	$850,000.00	$345,785.00	$224,760.25	$27,621.16	
33	$360,000.00	$504,413.08	$90,840.95	4.462%	17	$880,000.00	$375,586.92	$244,131.50	$26,317.30	
34	$370,000.00	$504,627.31	$82,162.13	4.461%	18	$910,000.00	$405,372.69	$263,492.25	$24,916.13	
35	$380,000.00	$504,825.38	$74,310.08	4.462%	19	$940,000.00	$435,174.62	$282,863.50	$23,463.06	
36	$390,000.00	$505,039.62	$67,210.57	4.461%	20	$970,000.00	$464,960.38	$302,224.25	$21,990.36	
37	$400,000.00	$523,257.31	$62,955.41	2.231%	21	$1,000,000.00	$476,742.69	$309,882.75	$19,778.60	
38	$410,000.00	$541,483.08	$58,899.05	0.000%	22	$1,030,000.00	$488,516.92	$317,536.00	$17,738.14	
39	$420,000.00	$541,689.23	$53,269.57	0.000%	23	$1,060,000.00	$518,310.77	$336,902.00	$16,545.96	
40	$430,000.00	$541,895.38	$48,178.14	0.000%	24	$1,090,000.00	$548,104.62	$356,268.00	$15,348.30	
41	$440,000.00	$542,101.54	$43,573.34	0.000%	25	$1,120,000.00	$577,898.46	$375,634.00	$14,195.27	
42	PWRR	$4,324,967.07	$4,324,967.07					PWGI-RR(i_e)=	$390,629.45	
43	ARR	$498,986.85	$498,986.85							
44	CAPRR	$40,763,120.37	$40,763,120.37							

FIGURE 14.10

Gross Income Applied in Revenue Requirements Analysis for Example 14.23.

J76	▾	fx =NPV(D8,J51:J75)+J50							

	A	B	C	D	E	F	G	H	I	J
45										
46	End of	Capital	Gross	Annual	Tax	Loan	Debt	Taxable	Income	
47	Year	Expenditure	Income	Expenses	Depreciation	Principle	Payment	Income	Tax	ATCF
48	t	P	GI_t	C_t	d_t	Payment	LI_t	TI_t	T_t	$ATCF_t$
49								$GI_t-C_t-d_t-LI_t$	itr^*TI_t	
50	0	-$1,500,000.00				-$600,000.00				-$900,000.00
51	1		$400,000.00	$200,000.00	$56,250.00	$24,000.00	$51,000.00	$92,750.00	$32,462.50	$92,537.50
52	2		$430,000.00	$210,000.00	$108,285.00	$24,000.00	$48,960.00	$62,755.00	$21,964.25	$125,075.75
53	3		$460,000.00	$220,000.00	$100,155.00	$24,000.00	$46,920.00	$92,925.00	$32,523.75	$136,556.25
54	4		$490,000.00	$230,000.00	$92,655.00	$24,000.00	$44,880.00	$122,465.00	$42,862.75	$148,257.25
55	5		$520,000.00	$240,000.00	$85,695.00	$24,000.00	$42,840.00	$151,465.00	$53,012.75	$160,147.25
56	6		$550,000.00	$250,000.00	$79,275.00	$24,000.00	$40,800.00	$179,925.00	$62,973.75	$172,226.25
57	7		$580,000.00	$260,000.00	$73,320.00	$24,000.00	$38,760.00	$207,920.00	$72,772.00	$184,468.00
58	8		$610,000.00	$270,000.00	$67,830.00	$24,000.00	$36,720.00	$235,450.00	$82,407.50	$196,872.50
59	9		$640,000.00	$280,000.00	$66,930.00	$24,000.00	$34,680.00	$258,390.00	$90,436.50	$210,883.50
60	10		$670,000.00	$290,000.00	$66,915.00	$24,000.00	$32,640.00	$280,445.00	$98,155.75	$225,204.25
61	11		$700,000.00	$300,000.00	$66,930.00	$24,000.00	$30,600.00	$302,470.00	$105,864.50	$239,535.50
62	12		$730,000.00	$310,000.00	$66,915.00	$24,000.00	$28,560.00	$324,525.00	$113,583.75	$253,856.25
63	13		$760,000.00	$320,000.00	$66,930.00	$24,000.00	$26,520.00	$346,550.00	$121,292.50	$268,187.50
64	14		$790,000.00	$330,000.00	$66,915.00	$24,000.00	$24,480.00	$368,605.00	$129,011.75	$282,508.25
65	15		$820,000.00	$340,000.00	$66,930.00	$24,000.00	$22,440.00	$390,630.00	$136,720.50	$296,839.50
66	16		$850,000.00	$350,000.00	$66,915.00	$24,000.00	$20,400.00	$412,685.00	$144,439.75	$311,160.25
67	17		$880,000.00	$360,000.00	$66,930.00	$24,000.00	$18,360.00	$434,710.00	$152,148.50	$325,491.50
68	18		$910,000.00	$370,000.00	$66,915.00	$24,000.00	$16,320.00	$456,765.00	$159,867.75	$339,812.25
69	19		$940,000.00	$380,000.00	$66,930.00	$24,000.00	$14,280.00	$478,790.00	$167,576.50	$354,143.50
70	20		$970,000.00	$390,000.00	$66,915.00	$24,000.00	$12,240.00	$500,845.00	$175,295.75	$368,464.25
71	21		$1,000,000.00	$400,000.00	$33,465.00	$24,000.00	$10,200.00	$556,335.00	$194,717.25	$371,082.75
72	22		$1,030,000.00	$410,000.00	$0.00	$24,000.00	$8,160.00	$611,840.00	$214,144.00	$373,696.00
73	23		$1,060,000.00	$420,000.00	$0.00	$24,000.00	$6,120.00	$633,880.00	$221,858.00	$388,022.00
74	24		$1,090,000.00	$430,000.00	$0.00	$24,000.00	$4,080.00	$655,920.00	$229,572.00	$402,348.00
75	25	$0.00	$1,120,000.00	$440,000.00	$0.00	$24,000.00	$2,040.00	$677,960.00	$237,286.00	$416,674.00
76									PW(ATCF(i_e))=	$390,629.45
77										

FIGURE 14.11

After-Tax Cash Flow Analysis for Example 14.23.

discounted at the rate i_e, the return on equity, and found to be $390,629.45. Figure 14.11 shows a traditional ATCF analysis, similar to those in Chapter 10, that requires no additional explanation. Note that the PW of the ATCF values evaluated at the rate i_e is also $390,629.45, as it should be.

14-13 SUMMARY

The major takeaways from this chapter can be summarized as follows:

1. The public sector (cities, counties, states, federal government) most commonly use some form of benefit-cost analysis to evaluate, justify, and sell projects. Public utilities, whether regulated or not and whether public or private, often use a revenue requirements approach to explain their need for certain rate increases or decreases. Both are different from, and yet equivalent to, industrial economic analyses.

2. Government projects for which benefit-cost analyses are used include cultural development, protection, economic services, and natural resources. Many of these are huge, cost millions of dollars, and have long lives.

3. New methods of ''providing'' public projects have surfaced in recent years. Public-private partnerships, deciding who will design, build, finance, operate, and/ or transfer the project, make the most efficient use of those involved. One popular form of partnership today is build-operate-transfer (BOT).

4. Benefit-cost analysis is a practical way of assessing the desirability of projects where it is important to take long and wide views. Unfortunately, these analyses do not always occur when government units are using tax dollars.

5. The *definitive document* for performing benefit-cost analysis or cost-effectiveness analysis of federal programs is the Office of Management and Budget's Circular No. A-94, Revised. It is summarized in Appendix 14.A and is easily found online by searching for "A-94."

6. The systematic economic analysis technique (SEAT) of Chapter 1, Section 4, can be adapted to public-sector evaluations.

7. Benefit-cost analysis takes either of two forms: (1) a *B/C* ratio or (2) $B - C$ using the PW (or AW) of benefits and costs. When the *B/C* ratio is used to evaluate multiple alternatives, an incremental approach is necessary, just as in rate of return analyses.

8. Cost-effectiveness analyses are used to compare alternatives with identical costs but differing benefits, or identical benefits but different costs.

9. As with industrial economic analyses, care must be taken when selecting point of view, interest rate, assessment of benefits and costs, and other factors.

10. Public utility firms often evaluate project investments using the revenue requirements method, an "inverted" approach whereby the focus is upon minimization of revenues required rather than maximization of present worth. Even so, the revenue requirements method is equivalent to traditional maximization of present worth.

Pit Stop #14—Same Thing; Different Look!

1. True or False: Benefit-cost analysis is primarily used by regulated utilities.

2. True or False: Build-Operate-Transfer (BOT) makes use of a public-private partnership.

3. True or False: Benefits and disbenefits must be converted to monetary values to use benefit-cost analysis.

4. True or False: OMB's Circular No. A-94, Revised is the definitive document for benefit-cost analysis.

5. True or False: The seven step SEAT is only applicable to public sector evaluation after *extensive* modification.

6. True or False: The B/C ratio is directly applicable to evaluation of one or many alternatives.

7. True or False: The B−C evaluation is directly applicable to evaluation of one or many alternatives.

8. True or False: Some in the public sector recommend using an interest rate of 0% on any money from outside sources.

9. True or False: The Revenue Requirements method is not economically equivalent to the industrial ATCF approach.

10. True or False: The Revenue Requirements method determines the income that exactly "pays" for costs, depreciation, interest on borrowed money, taxes, and a desirable return to owners.

OMB CIRCULAR NO. A-94, REVISED, TABLE OF CONTENTS (*WITH COMMENTS THAT ARE VASTLY REDUCED AND PARAPHRASED*; SEE OMB CIRCULAR NO. A-94, REVISED FOR COMPLETE TEXT)

1. **Purpose.** This circular provides general guidance for conducting benefit-cost and cost-effectiveness analyses. It also provides specific guidance on the discount rates to be used in evaluating federal programs whose benefits and costs are distributed over time. The general guidance will serve as a checklist of whether an agency has considered and properly dealt with all of the elements for sound benefit-cost and cost-effectiveness analysis.

2. **Recission.**

3. **Authority.**

4. **Scope.** These guidelines apply to any analysis used to support government decisions to initiate, renew, or expand programs or projects that would result in a series of measurable benefits or costs extending for 3 or more years into the future. These guidelines apply specifically to (1) benefit-cost or cost-effectiveness analysis of federal programs or policies, (2) regulatory impact analysis, (3) analysis of decisions whether to lease or purchase, and (4) asset valuation and sale analysis.

   Specifically exempted from the scope of A-94 are (1) water-resource projects, (2) acquisition of commercial-type services, and (3) federal energy management programs, each of which has its own guideline—see A-94 for specifics. Note that these areas are *not* exempted from benefit-cost analysis or cost-effectiveness analysis; they simply have different guidelines.

5. **General Principles.** Benefit-cost analysis is the recommended technique to use in a formal economic analysis of government programs or projects. Cost-effectiveness analysis is a less comprehensive technique but can be appropriate when the benefits from competing alternatives are the same.

   a. Net Present Value and Related Outcome Measures. The standard criterion for deciding whether a government program can be justified on economic principles is *net present value*—the discounted monetized value of expected net benefits (i.e., benefits minus costs). Net present value is computed by assigning monetary values to benefits and costs, discounting future benefits and costs using an appropriate discount rate, and subtracting the sum total of discounted costs from the sum total of discounted benefits. When net present worth is not computable, (1) a comprehensive enumeration of the different types of benefits and costs, monetized or not, can be helpful in identifying the full range of program effects, and (2) quantifying benefits and costs is worthwhile, even when they may be physical measurements instead of monetary values.

b. **Cost-Effectiveness Analysis.** This technique is appropriate whenever it is unnecessary or impractical to consider the monetary value of benefits. This is the case whenever each alternative has the same annual benefits.

c. **Elements of Benefit-Cost or Cost-Effectiveness Analysis.** Analyses should be explicit about the underlying assumptions used to arrive at estimates of future benefits and costs. Multiple alternatives from (1) doing nothing; (2) direct purchase; (3) upgrading, renovating, sharing, or converting existing government property; and (4) leasing or contracting for services should be considered.

6. **Identifying and Measuring Benefits and Costs.** Social net benefits, and not the benefits and costs to the federal government, should be the basis for evaluating government programs or policies that affect private citizens or other levels of government.

a. **Identifying Benefits and Costs.** Both intangible and tangible benefits and costs should be recognized. The relevant cost concept is broader than private-sector production and compliance costs or government cash expenditures. Calculation of net present value should be based on incremental benefits and costs. Sunk costs and already-realized benefits should be ignored.

b. **Measuring Benefits and Costs.** The principle of *willingness-to-pay* provides an aggregate measure of what individuals are willing to forgo to obtain a given benefit. Market prices provide an invaluable starting point for measuring willingness-to-pay, but prices sometimes do not adequately reflect a good's true value to society. In some cases, market prices do not exist for a relevant benefit or cost, and other methods of valuing benefits may have to be employed. Measures derived from actual market behavior are preferred when they are available.

7. **Treatment of Inflation.** Note: Circular A-94 and this text have some slight terminology differences in Sections 7 and 8; these are summarized in Table 14.A.1

a. **Real or Nominal Values.** Economic analyses are often most readily accomplished using *real* or *constant-dollar* values (i.e., by measuring benefits and costs in units of stable purchasing power). Where future benefits and costs are given in *nominal* terms (i.e., in terms of the dollar's future purchasing power),

---

TABLE 14.A.1
Terminology Differences between OMB Circular A-94, Revised, and this Text

Terminology in OMB Circular No. A-94, Revised	Terminology in this Text
Real discount rate	Real interest rate
Rate of inflation	Inflation rate
Nominal discount rate	Combined interest rate
Alternative inflation estimate	Commodity escalation rate
Real or constant-dollar value	Constant-worth cash flow
Nominal value	Then-current cash flow

the analysis should use these values rather than convert them to constant dollars. Nominal and real values must not be combined in the same analysis. Logical consistency requires that analysis be conducted either in constant dollars or in terms of nominal values. This may require converting some nominal values to real values, or vice versa.

   b. Recommended Inflation Assumption. When a general inflation assumption is needed, the rate of increase in the gross domestic product deflator from the administration's economic assumptions for the analysis period is recommended. For projects or programs that extend beyond the 6-year budget horizon, the inflation assumption can be extended by using the inflation rate for the sixth year of the budget forecast.

8. **Discount Rate Policy.** In order to compute net present value, it is necessary to discount future benefits and costs. Benefits and costs are worth more if they are experienced sooner. All future benefits and costs, including those that are non-monetized, should be discounted.

   a. Real versus Nominal Discount Rates. The proper discount rate to use depends on whether the benefits and costs are measured in real or nominal terms. A real discount rate that has been adjusted to eliminate the effect of expected inflation should be used to discount constant-dollar or real benefits and costs. A nominal discount rate that reflects expected inflation should be used to discount nominal benefits and costs.

   b. Public Investment and Regulatory Analyses. In general, public investments and regulations displace both private investment and consumption. Constant-dollar benefit-cost analyses of proposed investments and regulations should report net present value and other outcomes determined using a real discount rate of 7 percent, a rate that approximates the marginal pretax rate of return on an average investment in the private sector in recent years (as written in 1992 and not modified since then). Analyses should show the sensitivity of the discounted net present value and other outcomes to discount rate variations. Analyses may include the *internal rate of return* implied by the stream of benefits and costs. While the internal rate of return does not generally provide an acceptable decision criterion, it does provide useful information.

   c. Cost-Effectiveness, Lease-Purchase, Internal Government Investment, and Asset Sales Analyses. The Treasury's borrowing rates should be used as discount rates in the following cases: (1) cost-effectiveness analyses that involve constant-dollar costs should use the real Treasury borrowing rate on marketable securities of comparable maturity to the period of analysis; (2) lease-purchase analyses of nominal lease payments should use the nominal Treasury borrowing rate on marketable securities of comparable maturity to the period of analysis; and (3) internal government investments that provide ''internal'' benefits that take the form of increased federal revenues or decreased federal costs should calculate the net present value using a comparable-maturity Treasury rate, either nominal or real, depending on how benefits and costs are measured. An example of an internal benefit would be an investment in an energy-efficient building system that reduces federal operating costs. This is unlike the case of a federally funded highway, which provides external benefits to society as a whole.

   Note: The real and nominal rates based on assumptions from the 2009 budget are presented in Table 14.A.2.

TABLE 14.A.2
Discount Rates for Cost-Effectiveness, Lease-Purchase, and Related Analyses

Real Discount Rates. A forecast of real interest rates from which the inflation premium has been removed and based on the economic assumptions from the 2009 Budget is presented below. These real rates are to be used for discounting real (constant-dollar) flows, as is often required in cost-effectiveness analysis.

Real Interest Rates on Treasury Notes and Bonds of Specified Maturities					
3-Year	**5-Year**	**7-Year**	**10-Year**	**20-Year**	**30-Year**
2.1%	2.3%	2.4%	2.6%	2.8%	2.8%

Nominal Discount Rates. A forecast of nominal or market interest rates for 2008 based on the economic assumptions from the 2009 Budget is presented below. These nominal rates are to be used for discounting nominal flows, which are often encountered in lease-purchase analysis.

Nominal Interest Rates on Treasury Notes and Bonds of Specified Maturities					
3-Year	**5-Year**	**7-Year**	**10-Year**	**20-Year**	**30-Year**
4.1%	4.3%	4.4%	4.6%	4.9%	4.9%

Linear interpolation for terms other than given in the table are recommended.

   To obtain the most current table use: http://www.whitehouse.gov/OMB/circulars/a094/a94appx-c.html or search on A-94 Appendix C

9. **Treatment of Uncertainty.** Estimates of benefits and costs are typically uncertain, and the effects of this uncertainty should be analyzed and reported. Useful information would include the key sources of uncertainty; expected value estimates of outcomes; the sensitivity of results to important sources of uncertainty; and, where possible, the probability distributions of benefits, costs, and net benefits.

10. **Incidence and Distributional Effects.** The principle of maximizing net present value of benefits is based on the premise that gainers could fully compensate the losers and still be better off. Sometimes, however, the losers are not compensated. When this is the case, such effects should be analyzed and discussed, along with the analysis of net present value. Distributional effects may be analyzed by grouping individuals or households according to income class, geographical region, demographic group (e.g., age), industry, or occupation. Where a policy is intended to benefit a specified subgroup of the population, such as the poor, the analysis should consider how effective the policy is in reaching its targeted group.

11. **Special Guidance for Public Investment.**

12. **Special Guidance for Regulatory Impact Analysis.**

13. **Special Guidance for Lease-Purchase Analysis.** One principal thrust of this section is that whenever a federal agency needs to acquire the use of a capital asset, it should do so in the way that is least expensive for the government as a whole. This means (1) lease-purchase analyses should compare the net discounted present value of the *life-cycle cost* of leasing with the full costs of buying or constructing an identical asset; (2) for purposes of lease-purchase analysis, an asset's *economic life* is its remaining or productive lifetime; and (3) the asset's *purchase price,* for purposes of lease-purchase analysis, is its fair market value, defined as the price a

willing buyer could reasonably expect to pay a willing seller in a competitive market to acquire the asset; and other considerations.

14. **Related Guidance.**

15. **Implementation.**

16. **Effective Date.**

17. **Interpretation.**

> **APPENDIX A. Definition of Terms**
> **APPENDIX B. Additional Guidance for Discounting**
> **APPENDIX C. Discount Rates for Cost-Effectiveness, Lease-Purchase, and**
> **Related Analyses** (reformatted and presented in Table 14.A.2)

Tutoring problem available (at instructor's discretion) in *WileyPLUS*.

Problem available (at instructor's discretion) in *WileyPLUS*.

Worked Problem Video available in *WileyPLUS*.

FE-LIKE PROBLEMS

1. When using the benefit/cost ratio measure of worth, what benchmark is the calculated ratio compared to in determining if an individual investment is attractive?

   a. 0.0
   b. *MARR*
   c. 1.0
   d. IRR

2. Consider a situation in which you do not know the timing or amounts of individual cash flows. However, you do know the discounted and summed values of the revenues, $\sum Rt*(P|F, MARR, t)$, and the discounted and summed values of the expenses, $\sum Ct*(P|F, MARR, t)$. Which of the following measures of worth can you calculate?

   i. PW
   ii. *B/C* ratio

      a. I only
      b. II only
      c. Both I and II
      d. Neither I nor II

3. Elm City is considering a replacement for its police radio. The benefits and costs of the replacement are shown below. What is the replacement's benefit/cost ratio if the effective annual interest rate is 8 percent?

   Purchase Cost: $7,000
   Annual Savings: $1,500

   Life: 15 years

   a. 3.21
   b. 1.83
   c. 1.76
   d. 1.34

4. A library shelving system has a first cost of $20,000 and a useful life of 10 years. The annual maintenance is expected to be $2,500. The annual benefits to the library staff are expected to be $9,000. If the effective annual interest rate is 10 percent, what is the benefit/cost ratio of the shelving system?

   a. 1.51
   b. 2.24
   c. 1.73
   d. 1.56

5. The two most common forms of benefit-cost analysis are

   a. *B/C* and *B − C*.
   b. *B/C* and *B*C*.
   c. *B+C* and *B − C*.
   d. *B − C* and *B*C*.

6. Which of the following would be least likely to use public sector economic analysis?

   a. A library board
   b. A public housing authority
   c. A travel agency
   d. A veteran's hospital

7. Which of the following are typical characteristics of public sector projects?

   i. Large first costs

   ii. Benefits that may be hard to quantify

   iii. Benefits that are realized quickly

     a. I and III only

     b. I and II only

     c. II and III only

     d. I, II, and III

8. An integrated public-private partnership to deliver public projects is known by which of the following acronyms?

   a. EOQ

   b. *DCF*

   c. IRR

   d. BOT

9. An approach to justifying public sector projects that minimizes revenues while still allowing a business to earn a fair return for its shareholders is

   a. Revenue requirements.

   b. Revenue effectivity.

   c. Cost-plus pricing.

   d. Activity-based costing.

10. When using a benefit-cost analysis to evaluate multiple alternatives, which of the following approaches is acceptable?

   a. Ranking approach only

   b. Incremental approach only

   c. Either incremental or ranking

   d. Neither incremental nor ranking

PROBLEMS

Section 14.1 to 14.6

1. Identify a public project that has been performed by a government unit at any level in your city, state, or country. Identify

   a. The main thrust or nature of the project.

   b. Who benefits from the project. If multiple groups benefit, list them from ''most benefited'' to ''least benefited'' in your opinion.

   c. What entity (or entities) pays for the project, both initially and ongoing.

   d. If there is a fee or a charge to enjoy the benefits.

   e. What you think is the planning horizon of the project.

2. Do an Internet search on ''build operate transfer.'' Identify a BOT project, preferably from your home continent (e.g., AF, AS, EU, Pacific, NA, SA), and copy a small portion of what you find (a page or less). Also, identify the project, those involved, the location, the agreement, and/or other highlights in 100 words or less.

3. Using an Internet-based search on ''build operate transfer,'' find an additional definition from a source other than used in Section 14.2. Copy and paste it, as well as any graphics, examples, pictures, data, statistics, and so on, limiting yourself to one page.

4. Identify one benefit and one disbenefit that would be realized by the public for the following projects:

   a. A monument memorializing a particularly unfortunate event

   b. A public library

   c. A Web site giving information on a region's (a state, a region in a state, a city, etc.) public recreation and education activities

   d. A public park with a playground

   e. Renovation of water access areas at a public recreational lake

5. Identify one each (1) benefit, (2) disbenefit, and (3) monetary cost that would impact each of the following projects:

   a. A new electrical distribution station in a developing part of the city, with feeds from the city power plant and from a regional electrical grid

   b. Annexation of an adjoining semirural area into the city limits

   c. Replacement of old school buses

    d. Renovation of rest stops having only picnic tables to now including clean restrooms, protected open-air shelters for picnics, designated pet-walking areas, and ample parking

    e. A new stadium/coliseum for sporting events

6. A new airport addition is under consideration. Five different proposals have all been "qualified" as satisfactory from functional, environmental, and aesthetic standpoints and now the airport board is in the benefit-cost analysis phase. Benefits and costs are summarized as follows:

Proposal	Benefits in $K/year	Costs in $K/year
#1	$1,800	$1,470
#2	$1,260	$1,300
#3	$1,590	$1,050
#4	$2,000	$1,800
#5	$1,550	$1,160

    a. Which addition should be adopted based on a proper B/C analysis?

    b. Which addition should be adopted based on a proper $B - C$ analysis?

Section 14.7

7. Flood damage in the Brush Creek area averages $7,000 annually. Civil engineers with floodplain expertise have designed a series of small dams to restrain the flow. They will cost $25,000 and will involve annual maintenance charges of $500. What is the anticipated benefit/cost ratio if the interest rate is 6 percent, the service life is 10 years, and the salvage value is $5,000?

8. The Oklahoma City Zoo has proposed adding to their Web site a major segment providing a virtual tour of the grounds and animals, suitable for both routine enjoyment and educational purposes in classrooms. Survey data indicate that this will have either a neutral or positive effect upon actual zoo attendance. The Web site will be professionally done and have an initial cost of $325,000. Upkeep, refreshing the videos, and developing videos for scientific research and entertainment will cost another $80,000 per year. The zoo is expected to be in operation for an indefinite period; however, a study period of only 10 years for the Web site is to be assumed, with only a residual (salvage) value of $60,000 for the archival value being anticipated. Interest is 7 percent. An estimated 100,000 persons will visit the e-zoo in the first year, increasing by 30,000 each year, and they will receive, on the average, an additional $0.80 of benefit per visit when the new area is complete. On the basis of B/C analysis, should the Web site be supported for funding?

9. Ten cavemen with a remaining average life expectancy of 10 years use a path from their cave to a spring some distance away. The path is not easily traveled due to 100 large stones that could be removed. The annual benefit to each individual if the stones were removed is $6. Each stone can be removed at a cost of $1. The interest rate is 2 percent.

    a. Compute the benefit/cost ratio for the individual if he alone removed the 100 stones.

    b. Compute the benefit/cost ratio for the individual if the task was undertaken collectively, with each individual removing 10 stones.

    c. What maximum amount may be charged by a manager who organizes the group effort if the minimum acceptable benefit/cost ratio is 2?

10. The Logan Public Library in IA serves long-term residents, "bedroom community" residents who work in Omaha, and all of Harrison County. A renovation is planned, especially to include access to more electronic volumes, modernized computer facilities, and quicker check-in and checkout. In addition, two small meeting rooms with modernized e-access are needed. The cost of the renovation, including cabling, will be $33,000, the new equipment will cost $21,000, and e-volume access initiation will be $17,500. Maintenance is expected to run an additional $3,500 per year, plus $4,000 for renewed e-volume access. The interest rate is 8 percent, the planning horizon is 10 years, and the building renovation is expected to have a salvage value of 30 percent, with no salvage value for equipment or e-volume access. It is estimated that an additional 2,500 visits to the library will occur in the first year, increasing by 500 per year thereafter. It is estimated that the average benefits due to the new facilities, equipment, and access will be $2.00 per person per visit.

    a. Should the city government vote to approve the plans? Use PW and calculate $B - C$.

    b. What is the smallest benefit per person that will make this project desirable?

11. Lincoln Park Zoo in Chicago is considering a renovation that will improve some physical facilities at a cost of $1,800,000. Addition of new species will cost another $310,000. Additional maintenance, food, and animal care and replacement will cost $145,000 in the first year, increasing by 3 percent each year thereafter. The zoo has been in operation since 1868 and is expected to continue indefinitely; however, it is common to use a 20-year planning horizon on all new investments. Salvage value on facilities after 20 years will be 40 percent of initial cost. Interest is 7 percent. An estimated 1.5 million visits per year are made to the zoo, and the cost remains free year-round. How much additional benefit per visit, on average, must the visitors perceive to justify the renovation?

12. The Boundary Waters Canoe Area Wilderness (BWCA) located in northeastern Minnesota has 1 million acres of wilderness, 1,000 waterways, and 1,500 miles of canoe routes. While some youth, for example those in the Boy Scouts, are on high-adventure treks for 10 days at a time, it is common to have the rest of their family take advantage of the opportunity to also enjoy the BWCA area. A new area for this purpose is to be developed and will have an equivalent annual cost of $30,000, including initial cost (design, clearing, potable water, restrooms, showers, road, etc.), operating, upkeep, and security. Approximately 250 families will camp for 8 days each during the summer season. Another 2,200 persons will be admitted for single-day use of the facilities during the summer season. Although there are currently no fees charged, the average family camping in the area is willing to pay $12.00/night for the privilege, with some willing to pay more and some less. The average day user would be willing to pay $4.00/day, again some more and some less.

   a. What is the anticipated *B/C* ratio of this recreation area?

   b. What is the value of *B − C*?

13. Recent development near Eugene, Oregon, has identified a need for improved access to Interstate 5 at one location. Civil engineers and public planners are considering three alternative access plans. Benefits are estimated for the public in general; disbenefits primarily affect some local proprietors who will see traffic pattern changes as undesirable. Costs are monetary for construction and upkeep, and savings are a reduction in cost of those operations today that will not be necessary in the future. All figures are relative to the present situation, retention of which is still an alternative, and are annualized over the 20-year planning horizon.

Alternative	A	B	C
Benefits	$200,000	$300,000	$400,000
Disbenefits	$37,000	$69,000	$102,000
Costs	$150,000	$234,000	$312,000
Savings	$15,000	$31,000	$42,000

   a. What is the *B/C* ratio for each of these alternatives?

   b. Using incremental *B/C* ratio analysis, which alternative should be selected?

   c. Determine the value of *B − C* for each alternative.

14. A highway is to be built connecting Maud and Bowlegs. Route A follows the old road and costs $4 million initially and $210,000/year thereafter. A new route, B, will cost $6 million initially and $180,000/year thereafter. Route C is an enhanced version of Route B with wider lanes, shoulders, and so on. Route C will cost $9 million at first, plus $260,000 per year to maintain. Benefits to the users, considering time, operation, and safety, are $500,000 per year for A, $850,000 per year for B, and $1,000,000 per year for C. Using a 7 percent interest rate, a 15-year study period, and a salvage value of 50 percent of first cost, determine which road should be constructed.

15. The city of Columbus has identified three options for a public recreation area suitable for informal family activities and major organized events. As with most alternatives today, there are benefits, disbenefits, costs, and some savings. These have been estimated with the help of an external planning consultant and are identified in the table below. In each case, these are annualized over a 10-year planning horizon.

	Option 1	Option 2	Option 3
Benefits	$400,000	$550,000	$575,000
Disbenefits	$78,000	$125,000	$180,000
Costs	$235,000	$390,000	$480,000
Savings	$25,000	$65,000	$90,000

a. Determine the B/C ratio for each project. Can you tell from these ratios which option should be selected?

b. Determine which option should be selected using the incremental B/C ratio.

c. Determine which option should be selected using $B - C$ for each option.

d. At what value of Option 2 costs are you indifferent between Option 1 and Option 2?

16. An improvement to the roadway is desired from Philmont Scout Ranch to Springer in northeastern New Mexico. Alternative N (for north) costs $2,400,000 initially and $155,000/year thereafter. Route SA (for south, Alternative A) will cost $4,200,000 initially, and $88,000/year thereafter. Route SB is the same as SA with wider lanes and shoulders. It costs $5,200,000 initially with maintenance at $125,000/year. User costs considering time, operation, and safety are $625,000 for N, $410,000 for SA, and $310,000 for SB. The salvage values for N, SA, and SB after 20 years are 20 percent of initial cost, respectively. Using a *MARR* of 7 percent and a 20-year study period, which should be constructed?

a. Use an incremental B/C analysis.

b. Use a $B - C$ analysis.

c. Which route is preferred if 0 percent interest is used?

17. A relocation of a short stretch of rural highway feeding into Route 390 northwest of Dallas is to be made to accommodate new growth. The existing road is now unsafe, and improving it is not an alternative. Alternate new route locations are designated as East and West. The initial investment by government highway agencies will be $3,500,000 for East and $5,000,000 for West. Annual highway maintenance costs will be $120,000 for East and $90,000 for the shorter location West. Relevant annual road user costs, considering vehicle operation, time en route, fuel, safety, mileage, and so on, are estimated as $880,000 for East and only $660,000 for West. Assume a 20-year service life and $i = 7$ percent.

a. Clearly identify the annual equivalent benefits and costs of route West over route East.

b. Compute the appropriate B/C ratio(s) and decide whether East or West should be constructed.

18. Lynchburg has two old four-lane roads that intersect, and traffic is controlled by a standard green, yellow, red stoplight. From each of the four directions, a left turn is permitted from the inner lane; however, this impedes the flow of traffic while a car is waiting to safely turn left. The light operates on a two-minute cycle with 60 seconds of green-yellow and 60 seconds of red for each direction. Approximately 10 percent of the 12,000 vehicles using the intersection each day are held up for an extra 2 full minutes and average 3 extra start-stop operations, solely due to the left-turn bottleneck. These delays are realized during 300 days per year. A start-stop costs 3 cents per vehicle, and the cost of the excess waiting is $18/hour for private traffic and $45/hour for commercial traffic. Approximately 3,000 of the vehicles are commercial, with the remainder being private. The potential benefit to the public is that the cost of extra waiting and start-stops can be reduced by 90 percent through a project to widen the intersection to include specific left-turn lanes and use of dedicated left-turn arrows. If the planning horizon is 10 years and the city uses a 7 percent interest rate, what is the most that can be invested in the project and maintain a B/C ratio of 1.0 or greater? There will be no additional maintenance cost.

19. The Great Plains Authority is trying to decide between coal, fuel oil 3, low-sulphur fuel oil, and natural gas for powering their electrical generators. Fuel forecasts indicate the following needs for the upcoming year, as well as the gradient each year thereafter.

Fuel	Year #1	Gradient Each Year Thereafter
Coal	770,000 tons	38,500 tons
Fuel oil 3	3,005,000 barrels	150,250 barrels
Low-sulphur fuel oil	2,800,000 barrels	140,000 barrels
Natural gas	$16,800 \times 10^6$ cubic feet	840×10^6 cubic feet

The cost of the fuel, transportation, and various pollution effects have been estimated as follows:

Fuel	Cost	Transportation and Storage	Health	Crops	Uncleanliness
Coal	$41/ton	$22.40/ton	$27.86/ton	$70.05/ton	$41.92/ton
Fuel oil 3	$71/barrel	$4.20/barrel	$2.25/barrel	$5.70/barrel	$3.45/barrel
Low-sulphur fuel oil	$102/barrel	$4.20/barrel	$0.69/barrel	$1.68/barrel	$1.02/barrel
Natural gas	$0.0080/ cubic foot	$0.0005/ cubic foot	$0.0000002/ cubic foot	$0.0000004/ cubic foot	$0.0000004/ cubic foot

Cost, transportation, and storage are in the "Cost" category, while health, crops, and uncleanliness are in the "Disbenefits" category.

a. Calculate the annual equivalent benefits and costs of these fuels considering a life of 20 years and $i = 7$ percent.

b. Use an incremental B/C analysis to determine the best fuel to use.

c. Use a $B - C$ analysis to determine the best fuel to use.

20. Highway 51 west of Stillwater is to undergo a major renovation due to growth patterns of the city and increased traffic due to university sporting events. The road used to be two lanes and has a 40-year-old two-lane steel bridge on the south side. When the highway was expanded to four lanes 30 years ago, a two-lane concrete bridge was used on the newer two lanes. It is still very functional and will be kept. Now the city must decide whether or not to replace the steel bridge with a modern concrete bridge. A new concrete bridge will cost $300,000, installed. It will require $2,500 maintenance per year, with $30,000 resurfacing every 15 years. The concrete bridge will last 60 years with salvage value decreasing linearly to $0 at that time. The existing steel bridge cost $150,000 when it was new, installed. If kept, it is good for another 20 years provided that some beams are replaced immediately due to rust at a cost of $115,000. Maintenance will cost $12,000 per year. It will require resurfacing now, and again in 10 years, at a cost of $30,000 each time. It has no salvage value now, nor will it in 20 years. The city has successfully set aside sufficient money, and even though the money came from the state, $i = 7$ percent. The benefits perceived by the public will be the same, regardless of which bridge is selected. Planning horizons used by the city are usually 20 years for roads. A concerned citizen presented the following analysis at a recent city council meeting:

Retain steel bridge:

> Yearly cost of bridge $150,000/40 = \$2,500$
> Maintenance $\$12,000 + \$30,000/10 + 2(\$30,000)/20 = \$18,000$
> Total cost $= \$20,500$/year

Replace with concrete bridge:

> Yearly cost of bridge $\$300,000/60 = \$5,000$
> Maintenance $\$2,500 + 3(\$30,000)/45 = \$4,500$
> Total cost $= \$9,500$/year

a. Critique the citizen's analysis listing any deficiencies you notice.

b. Prepare your own analysis using an annual cost comparison.

Section 14.8

21. A water distribution system using a new source of water is under consideration and found to have an unfortunately high net annual cost of $5,750,000 and net benefits of $4,250,000. Officials decide that by purchasing the small rural water system providing annual benefits of $450,000, by paying an annual equivalent of $260,000, and then annexing certain areas, the city will be of a size to qualify for federal assistance, where the federal government will pay 70 percent of the new distribution system. Officials argue that the benefit/cost ratio is now a whopping $(\$4,250,000 + \$450,000)/(1 - 0.7)(\$5,750,000) = 2.47$. A sharp-eyed commissioner contends the real ratio should be calculated as $(\$4,250,000 + \$450,000)/(\$260,000 + (1 - 0.7)(\$5,750,000)) = 2.37$.

a. Is either of these ratios right? Discuss your reasoning from different points of view.

b. Determine the *B/C* ratio from the standpoint of an impartial citizen outside the community.

22. The county commissioner is considering three alternatives to spread gravel over a rough dirt road leading to a public astronomical observatory associated with the local university. The first cost of each alternative occurs at end-of-year 0, and benefits are estimated for the following 3 years, after which additional maintenance will be required. If the commissioner does not select any of the alternatives, the road will remain a muddy and rutted mess at times. Use a benefit-cost analysis to determine the preferred alternative for each of the *MARR* values shown below.

End of Year	A	B	C
0	−$10,000	−$15,000	−$18,000
1	5,000	7,000	8,000
2	5,000	7,000	8,000
3	5,000	7,000	8,000

a. *MARR* is 0 percent.

b. *MARR* is 7 percent.

c. *MARR* is 14 percent.

23. Three government projects are being considered today, one each in education, health, and welfare. Only one of the three projects may be selected, and multiple investments in the same alternative (e.g., investing in two for health) is not permitted. Since our local U.S. representative has procured a lot of "free" federal money, the *MARR* being used is 0 percent. The PW of benefits, PW of costs, and *B/C* ratios for each of the three mutually exclusive alternatives, plus some other incremental analyses, are summarized:

Project	PW Benefits	PW Costs	*B/C* Ratio
Education	$1,200,000	$1,000,000	1.20
Health	$280,000	$200,000	1.40
Welfare	$300,000	$150,000	2.00
Δ(Education-Health)	$920,000	$800,000	1.15
Δ(Welfare-Health)	$20,000	−$50,000	−2.50
Δ(Education-Welfare)	$900,000	$850,000	1.06

a. Which project should be undertaken?

b. Numerically, show your reasoning in terms of the *B/C* ratio.

c. Numerically, show your reasoning in terms of $B - C$.

24. A city has proposed a new waste treatment plant that would eliminate contractor charges of $300,000 each year starting at the beginning of the first year. It will, however, require an end-of-year annual operating cost of 5 percent of the initial investment. The plant would also result in pollution-reduction benefits judged to be $450,000 per year at the end of each year for the next 25 years. The plant will have no salvage value. Interest is usually considered to be 7 percent, since that is what the city's taxpayers can receive on their money, on average. However, since the money for the waste treatment plant is coming from the federal government with a 0 percent interest rate, some members of the city's leadership argue that the applicable interest rate is 0 percent rather than 7 percent. You have been called in to recommend which of the two is the more appropriate interest rate and to do the benefit-cost analysis.

a. What interest rate do you propose be used?

b. Determine the maximum amount the city can afford to pay for the new waste treatment plant such that the benefit/cost ratio is over 1.0. Show all work, and use a benefit/cost ratio approach.

25. A county commissioner has eight projects available as summarized below. The remaining budget for the year is $243,000 for new projects. Operating and maintenance costs are separately funded and are not of concern. All eight

have a favorable *B/C* ratio at the cost of capital, $i = 6$ percent. To determine how to select the projects, it has been suggested that the commissioner raise the interest rate (*MARR*) until only those projects remain that continue to have a $B/C > 1$ and are within the commissioner's budget limits. Use a 10-year planning horizon.

Project #	First Cost	O&M Cost/Year	Residual Value at 10 Years	Benefits/Year
1	$100,800	$9,180	$49,000	$44,100
2	$82,800	$4,600	$24,500	$23,350
3	$126,000	$7,650	$36,700	$33,050
4	$117,000	$4,900	$44,400	$25,900
5	$91,800	$12,850	$49,000	$26,300
6	$104,400	$1,840	$24,500	$16,500
7	$77,400	$15,600	$9,200	$27,500
8	$57,200	$6,550	$0	$17,800

   a. Which projects are selected using the suggested approach?

   b. Does this approach guarantee an optimum selection of projects? Why or why not?

26. Three public works projects, each having a first cost of $770,000 and annual operating costs of $80,000, are proposed. The lives of Projects 1, 2, and 3 are 10, 15, and 20 years, respectively, after which the project will be over, providing no benefits and requiring no operating costs. None of the projects can be renewed—each is a one-shot project. The annual benefits over the lives of Projects 1, 2, and 3 will be $208,000, $195,000, and $190,000, respectively.

   a. Select only one project to be implemented. Use a present worth basis and a $B - C$ measure of worth. Public works projects are evaluated at 7 percent, and a 20-year planning horizon is to be used in this case.

   b. Determine the value of the annual benefit that will make the least desirable project equally attractive to the most desirable project.

27. A municipal government has two alternatives under consideration. Both include short-term use of land that otherwise will just sit unused for 5 years, after which it will be developed as a recycling center. The two short-term alternatives being considered include (1) facilities for baseball and soccer for children's leagues that can be used for the full 5 years, and (2) a temporary home for "citizen garden plots" while a new area is cleared and converted; this temporary home will be needed for only 3 years. *MARR* is 7 percent, and the planning horizon is 5 years. The baseball and soccer facilities will cost $120,000 and have a salvage value of $15,000 after 5 years, bringing an estimated benefit to citizens of $50,000 per year. The city garden plots will have an initial cost of $70,000 and a salvage value of $20,000 after 3 years, and will provide benefits of $45,000 per year. No other use for the land is planned in years 4 and 5 if the citizen garden plots are selected. At a budget meeting, the city planner, an avid gardener, recommends Alternative 2, "citizen garden plots," based upon an annual equivalent $B - C$ analysis as follows:

   $$AE_{B-C}\,(1)\,(7\%) = \$50,000 - (\$120,000 * (A|P\,7\%,5) - \$15,000 * (A|F\,7\%,5)) = \$23,341.48/\text{year}$$
   $$AE_{B-C}\,(2)\,(7\%) = \$45,000 - (\$70,000 * (A|P\,7\%,3) - \$20,000 * (A|F\,7\%,3)) = \$24,547.42/\text{year}$$

   Either accept or correct the analysis.

28. A public recreation area is under planning. The initial cost of the area is $1,800,000, and it will have maintenance costs of $200,000/year. It is estimated that 90,000 persons will visit the area each year. An estimated 40 percent of them will realize benefits of $3.00, 45 percent will get benefits of $4.50, and 15 percent will perceive benefits of $7.00 with a visit.

   a. Perform a benefit/cost ratio analysis to decide whether the area should be developed. Use a 30-year planning horizon, and $i = 6$ percent compounded annually.

   b. Suppose each person is charged $4 to enter the area. Perform a $B - C$ analysis to decide whether the area now should be developed, assuming those who receive a net negative benefit will not visit the recreation area.

29. Suppose Lincoln Park Zoo decided to charge admission just for the newly renovated area described in Problem 11. Suppose the price is set at the average perceived benefit per visit, reasoning that the renovation could then pay for itself over the planning horizon. What, if anything, is the flaw to this logic? Be specific.

30. Lincoln Park Zoo in Chicago is considering a renovation that will improve some physical facilities at a cost of $1,800,000. Addition of new species will cost another $310,000. Additional maintenance, food, and animal care and replacement will cost $145,000 in the first year, increasing by 3 percent each year thereafter. The zoo has been in operation since 1868 and is expected to continue indefinitely; however, it is common to use a 20-year planning horizon on all new investments. Salvage value on facilities after 20 years will be 40 percent of initial cost. An estimated 1.5 million visits per year are made to the zoo, and 2 percent of the visitors per year will perceive an additional benefit of $3 per visit due to the renovation, while 8 percent will perceive an additional benefit of $2, 20 percent perceive $1, and 70 percent perceive no additional benefit. Suppose an incremental fee is charged for entrance to the renovated area. Determine the annual financial gain or loss if the fee charged per visit is

   a. $0.50.
   b. $1.50.
   c. $2.50.
   d. $5.00.

31. The Boundary Waters Canoe Area Wilderness (BWCA) located in northeastern Minnesota has 1 million acres of wilderness, 1,000 waterways, and 1,500 miles of canoe routes. While some youth, for example those in the Boy Scouts, are on high-adventure treks for 10 days at a time, it is common to have the rest of their family take advantage of the opportunity to also enjoy the BWCA area. A new area for this purpose is to be developed and will have an equivalent annual cost of $30,000, including initial cost (design, clearing, potable water, restrooms, showers, road, etc.), operating, upkeep, and security. Approximately 250 families will camp for 8 days each during the summer season. Another 2,200 persons will be admitted for single-day use of the facilities during the summer season. Estimates are that 30 percent of the camping families perceive $7 in benefits, 60 percent receive $15, and 10 percent enjoy $25 of recreation. For the day users, 40 percent receive $3 in benefits, and 60 percent receive $5 in benefits. If a charge of $15 is charged to campers only and day users are charged $4, Campers and day users will use the facilities unless the charge exceeds their perceived benefits.

   a. calculate B/C.
   b. calculate $B - C$.

32. Near the state capitol, a heritage center houses historical artifacts of significance to the state dating from pre-statehood to the present. The center is particularly well done and serves as both a historical research facility and as simply an enjoyable place for families and guests to visit. A survey has determined that annual benefits of $3 each are now received by 12,000 visitors, $5 each by 14,000 visitors, $7 each by 6,000 visitors, and $10 each by 9,000 more visitors. The annualized cost of the heritage center is $250,000, considering investment, operations, and maintenance. It is proposed to charge $5.75, just under the average benefit received per visitor. Their analysis does explicitly recognize that there will be a disbenefit of $2.75 to 12,000 visitors and $0.75 to 14,000 more. The resulting B/C ratio is calculated as follows:

$$B/C = \frac{\$10(9,000) + \$7(6,000) + \$5(14,000) + \$3(12,000) - \$0.75(14,000) - \$2.75(12,000)}{\$250,000 - \$5.75(41,000)} = 13.65$$

The proponents of charging admission point to the huge B/C ratio, as well as the fact that nearly all of the annualized cost would be covered each year.

   a. Identify any problems or concerns with this analysis.
   b. Prepare your own B/C analysis if you believe this to be incorrect.

33. Opponents to charging an entrance fee as described in Problem 32 note that only 15,000 visitors will utilize the heritage center, and the benefits of $5(14,000) + $3(12,000) = $106,000 derived by the other 26,000 who do not visit will be lost. They argue that the true benefits are the $7(6,000) + $10(9,000) = $132,000, less a disbenefit of $3(12,000) + $5(14,000) = $106,000 for the visitors who will not pay the $5.75 to enter, thereby losing the previous recreational enjoyment from the heritage center. Their B/C ratio is as follows:

$$B/C = \frac{\$7(6,000) + \$10(9,000) - \$3(12,000) - \$5.00(14,000)}{\$250,000 - \$5.75(15,000)} = 0.16$$

   a. Identify any problems or concerns with this analysis.
   b. Prepare your own $B - C$ analysis if you believe this to be incorrect.

34. For the heritage center described in Problem 32, note that a survey that has determined that annual benefits of $3 each are now received by 12,000 visitors, $5 each by 14,000 visitors, $7 each by 6,000 visitors, and $10 each by 9,000 more visitors. Also, the annualized cost of the heritage center is $250,000, considering investment, operations, and maintenance. Build a spreadsheet that will properly reflect the B/C ratio (the formulas given in Problems 32 or 33 may or may not be right). Then, use SOLVER to determine

    a. the non-negative visitor charge that maximizes annual income to the heritage center.

    b. the non-negative visitor charge that maximizes the B/C ratio.

    c. the non-negative visitor charge that maximizes annual income to the heritage center and assures a B/C > 1.0.

35. The federal government is planning a hydroelectric project for a river basin. The project will provide electrical energy to the local area and to the grid. With some enhancements to the basic plan, this project can also provide flood control, irrigation, and recreation benefits. Three enhancement alternatives, in addition to doing nothing, are considered. Each will have more or less cost and impact as follows:

Alternative	DN	A	B	C
Initial Cost	$0	$2,000,000	$4,500,000	$9,000,000
Annual Operating and Maintenance Cost	$0	$200,000	$280,000	$450,000
Flood Control Savings to Community	$0	$250,000	$350,000	$500,000
Irrigation Benefits to Community	$0	$350,000	$450,000	$600,000
Recreation Benefits to Community	$0	$100,000	$200,000	$350,000

    The interest rate is 5 percent, and the life of each of the enhancement alternatives is estimated to be 50 years.

    a. Calculate both the benefit/cost ratio and the value of $B - C$ for each alternative. Is the best alternative the one with the maximum benefit/cost ratio?

    b. If the interest rate is 8 percent, which alternative will be preferred?

    c. Perform an incremental B/C analysis to confirm your answer to Part b.

36. The following costs and benefits have been listed for a government-built, owned, and operated dam and reservoir that will be used for both flood control and electrical power generation.

Investment:

    Dam, including access roads, survey, clearing, and construction: $47,000,000

    Hydroelectric generator and transmission equipment: $24,275,000

    Land and right-of-way purchase: $3,300,000

    Highway relocation: $4,200,000

    Miscellaneous: $800,000

Operating and maintenance costs: 5 percent of total investment each year

Annual income to project from paying customers: $9,500,000

Annual benefits to public:

    Reduction in flood losses: $1,252,000

    Enhancement in property value: $525,000

    Value (before paying) to customers of having power available: $11,875,000

    (Note that the benefits or value perceived due to having power available are higher than the rates paid for the use of energy, so there is still a net benefit received.)

The planning horizon is 50 years and $i = 8$ percent.

    a. Determine whether or not the project pays for itself if none of the benefits or disbenefits are considered.

    b. Determine the B/C ratio of PW net benefits to PW net costs.

    c. Determine the PW value of $B - C$, and determine if the project is now favorable.

37. A new public school in Knoxville is proposed and will replace one older facility and affect school changes for several middle school students. The following estimates apply:

Category	Amount in $/Year
Benefits	2,350,000
Disbenefits	1,640,000
Costs	1,800,000
Savings	1,450,000

a. Calculate the B/C ratio.
b. Calculate $B - C$.
c. Mistakenly treating disbenefits as costs and savings as benefits, recalculate B/C.
d. Mistakenly treating disbenefits as costs and savings as benefits, recalculate $B - C$.
e. Set benefits to the value that makes (benefits-disbenefits) equal to (costs-savings) and repeat Parts a–d. What can you say about your new values of a–d?
f. When the B/C ratio in Part a is 1.0, what is the B/C ratio in Part c?
g. Which is easier to explain, B/C or $B - C$?

Section 14.11

38. Consider 1 year of a utility company's financial results. The company pays income tax of $9,000,000, where the tax rate is 40 percent. Debt is $80,000,000 and the interest rate on debt is 7 percent. Depreciation on a total unrecovered investment of $190,000,000 is 6.677 percent. Book and tax depreciation methods are the same. Total cost before income taxes is $56,000,000.
a. How much money is paid to interest on debt?
b. What is the depreciation charge?
c. What is the annual expense?
d. What is the amount of the return to owners?
e. What are the total revenue requirements for this year?

39. Consider 1 year of a utility company's financial results. The company pays income tax of $6,000,000, where the tax rate is 40 percent. Debt is $75,000,000 and the interest rate on debt is 10 percent. Depreciation on a total unrecovered investment of $150,000,000 is 7.219 percent. Book and tax depreciation methods are the same. Total cost before income taxes is $39,000,000.
a. How much money is paid to interest on debt?
b. What is the depreciation charge?
c. What is the annual expense?
d. What is the amount of the return to owners?
e. What are the total revenue requirements for this year?

40. Consider 1 year of a utility company's financial results. The company pays income tax of $5,500,000, where the tax rate is 40 percent. Debt is $70,000,000 and the interest rate on debt is 10 percent. Depreciation for financial accounting is $8,000,000. The initial investment was $200,000,000, and the MACRS(20) tax rate is 5.285%. Total annual cost before income taxes is $37,000,000.
a. How much money is paid to interest on debt?
b. What is the financial depreciation charge?
c. What is the tax depreciation charge?
d. What is the annual expense?
e. What is the amount of the return to owners?
f. What are the total revenue requirements for this year?

41. Consider year 7 of a utility company's financial results. The company pays income tax of $7,112,000, where the tax rate is 40 percent. Debt is $100,000,000 and the interest rate on debt is 9 percent. Depreciation for financial accounting purposes using straight-line depreciation is $10,000,000 per year. Depreciation for tax purposes on an initial investment of $250,000,000 is MACRS(20), or 4.888 percent. Total cost before income taxes is $52,000,000.

   a. How much money is paid to interest on debt?

   b. What is the financial depreciation charge?

   c. What is the tax depreciation charge?

   d. What is the annual expense?

   e. What is the amount of the return to owners?

   f. What are the total revenue requirements for this year?

42. A utility is preparing documentation for the Corporation Commission regarding revenue requirements during the next year. The company is 30 percent debt financed at an average interest rate of 6 percent, and the unrecovered investment is $40,000,000. The yearly expenses are $2,500,000 and the depreciation is $3,800,000. Fixed charges are $8,800,000. Both book and tax depreciation follow the same MACRS schedule, and the tax rate is 40 percent.

   a. What is the taxable income?

   b. What is the income tax paid?

   c. What are the equity earnings (return to owners)?

   d. How much money is equity financed?

   e. What is the percentage return on equity to owners?

   f. What is the revenue requirement for the year?

   g. If revenue received exactly matches the revenue requirements, determine the after-tax cash flow for the year if none of the debt principle is paid off during the year.

43. A utility is submitting their petition to their regulatory agency to justify rates for the upcoming year. Their proposal is based upon revenue requirements. The company has 45 percent of their investment financed by debt at an average interest rate of 8 percent. The book value of the assets is $85,000,000. Annual expenses are $6,000,000 and the depreciation write-off is $7,800,000. Fixed charges are $18,500,000. Both book and tax depreciation follow the same MACRS schedule, and the tax rate is 40 percent.

   a. What is the taxable income?

   b. What is the income tax paid?

   c. What are the equity earnings (return to owners)?

   d. How much money is equity financed?

   e. What is the percentage return on equity to owners?

   f. What is the revenue requirement for the year?

   g. If revenue received exactly matches the revenue requirements, determine the after-tax cash flow for the year if none of the debt principle is paid off during the year.

44. The first 5 years of a revenue requirements analysis for a public utility is presented below. The fraction of total capitalization that is debt is 35 percent. Answer the following questions.

EOY	UNRECOV BOOK INVEST	BOOK DEPR	UNRECOV TAX INVEST	TAX DEPR	DEBT RETURN	EQUITY RETURN	INCOME TAX	ANNUAL EXPENSES
0	$90,000.00		$90,000.00					
1	$86,625.00	$3,375.00	$86,625.00	$3,375.00	$1,890.00	$7,020.00	$4,680.00	$15,000.00
2	$80,127.90	$6,497.10	$80,127.90	$6,497.10	$1,819.13	$6,756.75	$4,504.50	$15,000.00
3	$74,118.60	$6,009.30	$74,118.60	$6,009.30	$1,682.69	$6,249.98	$4,166.65	$15,000.00
4	$68,559.30	$5,559.30	$68,559.30	$5,559.30	$1,556.49	$5,781.25	$3,854.17	$15,000.00
5	$63,417.60	$5,141.70	$63,417.60	$5,141.70	$1,439.75	$5,347.63	$3,565.08	$15,000.00

a. What is the amount of the investment?

b. What is the MACRS recovery period?

c. What is the cost of borrowed capital (as a percent)?

d. What is the revenue requirement in year 1?

45. Virginia Natural Gas Company (VNGC) must provide a regulation and metering unit to a new subdivision near Norfolk. They already own right-of-way and must now install the equipment at a cost of $170,000 with operating and maintenance costs of $9,000 per year. The useful life of the equipment is 25 years with no salvage value after that time. VNGC borrows 48 percent of their capital, and the rate is 8.5 percent over 25 years with uniform principal payments plus interest on the remaining principal. Tax depreciation follows MACRS-GDS (20), and financial depreciation is straight line in equal amounts over the full 25 years. The effective tax rate is 40 percent, and the WACC is 11 percent.

a. What is the revenue requirement for the third year?

b. What is the return on equity capital?

c. What is the present worth of the revenue requirements over the entire 25 years?

46. Determine the annual revenue requirements for the experimental trial of an environmentally friendly waste separator used to segregate burnable, glass, ferrous, nonferrous metals, and plastic items. Details follow:

Initial cost: $780,000

Useful life and planning horizon: 4 years

Salvage value: $0

Financial depreciation: straight line, no half-year convention

Tax depreciation MACRS (3): special approval obtained for this experimental trial

Income tax rate: 40 percent

Maintenance: 5 percent of initial cost, per year

Percentage of borrowed funds: 45 percent

Interest on borrowed money: 11 percent

Required return on equity: 14 percent

Use a spreadsheet approach similar to that presented in Section 14.11.

Section 14.12

47. Consolidated Rural Electric Coop (CREC) provides reliable electrical service to a large rural community. "Reading" the meters is very troublesome and costly due to the distance between service points, poorly kept narrow roads, locks on gates, distance to service inside property, dogs, and so on. They propose to place a meter conversion and maintenance facility whereby meters can be converted to permit remote access for information on usage, tampering, and need for maintenance. This area will also serve as their maintenance and calibration facility. The infrastructure is available, and only the equipment for the new area must be purchased at a cost of $95,000. The additional cost is expected to be $20,000 in the first year, increasing by a $2,000 gradient each subsequent year. The anticipated useful life and planning horizon is 7 years. Due to obsolescence, no salvage value is expected. The equipment is considered to be for the manufacture of electronic components and has a MACRS-GDS property class of 5 years. Financial accounting follows the straight-line method, with equal depreciation write-off over each of the 7 years. CREC borrows 45 percent of all capital, and the average rate is 9 percent, with this loan paid back in equal annual principal amounts plus interest over 7 years. The remainder is equity capital, and the Corporation Commission permits an earnings rate of 13 percent on it. The effective tax rate is 40 percent.

a. Determine the revenue requirement during each of the 7 years.

b. Determine the annual worth of the revenue requirements using the after-tax WACC as the appropriate discount factor (interest rate).

c. Using a gross income of $50,000 during each of the 7 years, develop the ATCF analysis and show that the revenue requirements method and the ATCF method are equivalent using the methods of Section 14.12 and Example 14.23.

Chapter 15

CAPITAL BUDGETING

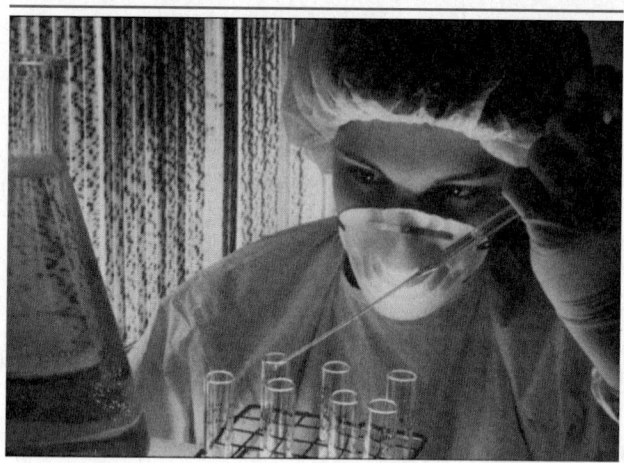

(a) Abbott's commitment to scientific investigation has led to breakthrough innovations that have changed the practice of medicine. Here, a scientist is shown performing DNA research. (Courtesy of Abbott) (b) At Abbott's state-of-the-art biologics plant in Barceloneta, Puerto Rico, an environmental technician is shown checking a water sample at a state one station. The plant processes its waste water in three stages before sending it to the municipal waste water treatment plant. (Courtesy of Abbott)

Abbott Laboratories

Founded by Dr. Wallace C. Abbott more than a century ago, incorporated in 1900, and headquartered in Abbott Park, Illinois, Abbott Laboratories is a global, broad-based health care products company with four reportable revenue segments: pharmaceutical, nutritional, diagnostic, and vascular products. Its chairman and CEO, Miles D. White, a mechanical engineering graduate from Stanford, noted, ''There's one fundamental fact that everyone at Abbott Laboratories understands: the purpose of our company is to improve lives.''

In 2010, Abbott was named to the Dow Jones Sustainability Index for the sixth consecutive year and, for the first time, it was recognized by *Fortune* magazine as the most admired company in the health care industry.

As of December 31, 2010, Abbott employed approximately 91,400 people around the world. About half of its employees are located in the United States and half are located elsewhere. Although the majority of its facilities are located in the U.S., Abbott has manufacturing facilities in 15 other countries. In addition to 25 owned and leased plants in the United States and Puerto Rico, Abbott has plants in Argentina, Brazil, Canada, England, France, Germany, Ireland, Italy, Japan, Mexico, Pakistan, Singapore, Spain, Sweden, and the Netherlands.

Abbott's sales in 2010 totaled $35.2 billion. Capital expenditures of $1.02 billion occurred in upgrading and expanding manufacturing, research and development, and investments in information technology and administrative support facilities in all four of Abbott's business segments.

As is true of health care innovators, Abbott invests heavily in R&D: $3.7 billion in 2010, the majority of which was concentrated in pharmaceutical products. Developing and bringing a new drug to market consumes, on average, $800 million and 10 years.

Health care technology is an R&D-intensive industry, it is highly competitive, and it is very dynamic. Changes occur rapidly. Consequently, firms in the industry must be highly adaptable. Their very survival might depend on the speed with which an acquisition or divestiture is made, or how quickly a new product is brought to market.

Leveraging R&D investments, every effort is made at Abbott to launch new products faster than the competition. Therefore, Abbott must manage its R&D portfolio carefully. Many opportunities exist for investment, but wise choices must be made.

15-1   INTRODUCTION

What do you do when you have far more economically attractive investments than can be funded with the available investment capital? Nice problem to have, isn't it? It is certainly better than the reverse—having more investment capital available than fiscally attractive investments. But, still, the question must be answered: How do you choose from among a set of really, really good investments?

The "abundance of riches" scenario occurs far more frequently than you might imagine. Pharmaceutical, chemical, and semiconductor companies, among others, typically must make choices among investments. They must forgo making some investments that will generate returns significantly greater than their cost of capital.

Indeed, companies that employ large numbers of engineers are frequently faced with deciding how to ration scarce investment capital. Otherwise, the engineers are not as effective as they should be.

Thus far in the text, we have addressed how to determine if an investment is fiscally attractive and, when multiple investment alternatives that are mutually exclusive are available, which one is the most attractive economically. Here, though, we address a different task: determining the investment portfolio when there are many economically viable investments available that are independent, rather than mutually exclusive.

Frequently, choices must be made from among such diverse investments as R&D to produce new products, expand existing production lines, acquire companies that are attractive strategically and financially, upgrade and maintain existing buildings, replace existing equipment, and so forth. And, of course, companies must spend capital in some areas in which the returns are difficult to measure or are nonexistent, such as those involving health, safety, and environmental and governmental regulations.

The amount of money a company budgets for capital expenditures (often called CAP EX or Cap-X) generally varies from year to year. It ranges from being significantly higher than annual depreciation to a level substantially below annual depreciation, depending on market conditions; and it depends on a combination of recent history and near-term future expansion plans, the condition of the overall economy, and other similar factors. However, it is not a positive sign regarding a company's fiscal health if its capital expenditures are substantially less than its annual depreciation over a prolonged period of time.

Why not borrow the money necessary to make investments when the after-tax present worth will be positive after including the cost of debt service? For publicly traded companies, the stock market usually reacts negatively when a firm's ratio of debt-to-equity capital increases significantly. Likewise, issuing additional stock to obtain equity capital is viewed negatively by shareholders, because it dilutes the fraction of the firm's assets represented by a share of stock. In addition, rating agencies will downgrade a company when its debt-to-equity ratio increases dramatically, causing the company's cost of capital to increase and making the investment community nervous. So, the reality is, a firm will not always be able to invest in projects that have positive after-tax present worths; choices will have to be made.

Typically, companies create a hierarchy of approval levels for capital expenditures. Such practices generate what are called *size gates*. For example, in a corporation with multibillion-dollar sales, one might allow capital expenditures requiring less than a million dollars to be approved by the head of a division, those requiring more than a million dollars but less than 10 million dollars to be approved by the head of a business unit within the corporation, those requiring more than 10 million dollars but less than 30 million dollars to be approved by the corporation's chief financial officer, and those requiring more than 30 million dollars to be approved by the board of directors.

Although the numbers vary from company to company, size gates are frequently used in large firms. As examples, Eastman Chemical Company and Motorola Corporation use them.

Where size gates occur, choices must be made, and the selection process does not occur only at the organization's highest levels. Division heads, business heads, chief financial officers, and boards of directors frequently must choose from among attractive investment alternatives. How do they do it? That is the subject of this chapter.

This chapter deals with *comparing alternatives, performing supplementary analysis* (where we perform sensitivity analysis), and *selecting the preferred investments* (where the investment portfolio is developed). In this chapter, we show

1. how to formulate a capital budgeting problem with independent, *indivisible* investments as a binary linear programming problem and how to solve (using

---

Systematic Economic Analysis Technique

1. Identify the investment alternatives
2. Define the planning horizon
3. Specify the discount rate
4. Estimate the cash flows
5. **Compare the alternatives**
6. **Perform supplementary analyses**
7. **Select the preferred investment**

Excel®'s **SOLVER** tool) reasonably sized problems by maximizing the investment portfolio's present worth;

2. how to add mutually exclusive, contingent, "either/or," and other constraints to a formulation of a capital budgeting problem involving *indivisible* investments; and how to determine (using **SOLVER**) the investment portfolio that maximizes its present worth;

3. how to formulate a capital budgeting problem involving independent, *divisible* investments as a linear programming problem and how to solve (using **SOLVER**) reasonably sized problems by maximizing the investment portfolio's present worth or by "filling the investment portfolio bucket" with investments ranked in order of their internal rates of return;

4. how to add mutually exclusive, contingent, "either/or" and other constraints to a formulation of a capital budgeting problem involving *divisible* investments and how to determine (using **SOLVER**) the investment portfolio that maximizes its present worth; and

5. how to analyze the sensitivity of the optimum investment portfolio to changes in the *MARR* and the limitation on capital.

15-2   THE CLASSICAL CAPITAL BUDGETING PROBLEM

Choosing from among a set of investments those that will be pursued, subject to a limitation on capital available for investment, is generally referred to as the *capital rationing problem* or the *capital budgeting problem*. We chose the latter because it is more commonly used in the engineering economics literature. Our focus in this chapter is on quantitative approaches to optimize financial returns when capital is limited; we refer to the capital allocation problem as the *capital budgeting problem*.

15.2.1   Mathematical Formulation of the Classical Capital Budgeting Problem

A mathematical formulation of the capital budgeting problem involves several parameters and a set of binary decision variables, $\{x_j, \ j = 1, \ldots, n\}$, where n is the number of investment opportunities. When x_j equals 1, investment opportunity j is to be included in the investment portfolio; when x_j equals 0, the jth opportunity is not included in the portfolio. We let the magnitude of the investment in opportunity j be denoted c_j and let the total amount of investment capital available be C. The final parameter required is the present worth of investment j, PW_j.

Based on an investor's objective of maximizing the investment portfolio's present worth, the capital budgeting problem can be formulated as follows:

$$\text{Maximize} \quad PW_1 x_1 + PW_2 x_2 + \cdots + PW_{n-1} x_{n-1} + PW_n x_n \qquad (15.1)$$

$$\text{subject to} \quad c_1 x_1 + c_2 x_2 + \cdots + c_{n-1} x_{n-1} + c_n x_n \leq C \qquad (15.2)$$

$$x_j = (0,1) \ j = 1, \ldots, n \qquad (15.3)$$

Since x_j equals 1 when the investment is included in the portfolio and equals 0 otherwise, Equation 15.1 is the present worth for the investment portfolio. The first constraint (Equation 15.2) assures that the total investment required for the portfolio is no greater than the amount of capital available. The second constraint (Equation 15.3) affirms that the decision variables are binary.

The mathematical optimization problem is a binary linear programming (BLP) problem. Several approaches can be used to solve it. Enumeration is one way; however, we do not recommend forming all possible combinations of the n investments and, for those not exceeding the capital limit, choosing the one having the greatest present worth. For problems with few investments, that might be feasible, but for a relatively small example with n equal to 10, there are 2^{10}, or 1,024, possible solutions.

Alternately, one could solve the BLP formulation of the capital budgeting problem using an approach developed by Lori and Savage.[1] However, it is neither simply explained nor easily understood.

When faced with solving a binary linear programming problem, we will use the Excel® **SOLVER** tool instead of enumeration or the Lori-Savage solution method. It is well suited for small-sized problems of this type.

$$\text{Maximize} \quad \sum_{\forall j} PW_j x_j$$

$$\text{Subject to} \quad \sum_{\forall j} c_j x_j \leq C$$

$$x_j \in (0,1)_{\forall j}$$

EXAMPLE 15.1   Solving a Capital Budgeting Problem with the Excel® SOLVER Tool

To illustrate using **SOLVER** in solving a BLP formulation of the capital budgeting problem, suppose you are presented with five different investment opportunities with the parameters given in Table 15.1.

Notice, the data in Table 15.1 are the same as for Example 8.4, which illustrated the need for incremental analysis when using the internal rate of return (IRR) to compare

TABLE 15.1
Characteristics of Five Investment Opportunities.

Investment Opportunity	1	2	3	4	5
Initial Investment	$15,000.00	$25,000.00	$40,000.00	$50,000.00	$70,000.00
Annual Return	$3,750.00	$5,000.00	$9,250.00	$11,250.00	$14,250.00
Salvage Value	$15,000.00	$25,000.00	$40,000.00	$50,000.00	$70,000.00
Present Worth	$4,718.79	$2,247.04	$9,212.88	$10,111.69	$7,415.24
Internal Rate of Return	25.00%	20.00%	23.13%	22.50%	20.36%

---

[1]Lorie, J. and L. Savage, ''Three Problems in Rationing Capital,'' *Journal of Business*, October 1955, pp. 229–239.

mutually exclusive investment alternatives. Since the investor fully recoups the initial investment at the end of the investment period, the IRR is the same regardless of how long the investment is held. However, since we are now interested in maximizing the investment portfolio's present worth, we need to know the durations for the investments. Here, we use a 10-year investment period to compute the investments' present worths. As before, we use an 18 percent before-tax *MARR* in the analysis.

An important difference in Example 15.1 and Example 8.4 is that now *we consider the investments to be independent, not mutually exclusive.* Hence, depending on the amount of money the investor has, the investment portfolio can consist of multiple investments. Also, notice that one of the investments considered in Example 8.4 has been omitted; its IRR equaled 15 percent, which is less than the required return of 18 percent.

We need to know one additional thing: the amount of investment capital available. For the example, suppose the investor has $100,000 available to invest.

The following BLP problem is to be solved:

Maximize $\$4,718.79x_1 + \$2,247.00x_2 + \$9,212.88x_3 + \$10,111.69x_4 + \$7,415.24x_5$

subject to $\$15,000x_1 + \$25,000x_2 + \$40,000x_3 + \$50,000x_4 + \$70,000x_5 \leq \$100,000$

$x_j = (0,1) \quad j = 1, \ldots, 5$

A spreadsheet is created from the data provided in Table 15.1, as shown in Figure 15.1. Row 7 initializes the values of the decision variables x_j, $j = 1, \ldots, 5$; although any initial values can be assigned to the decision variables, it is advisable to either set all values equal to 0 or set all values equal to 1. In this case, we assigned values of 1 to all the decision variables. Row 8 contains the products of the corresponding entries in rows 2 and 7. The Excel® sum worksheet function is used in cell G8, where =SUM(B8:F8) represents Equation 15.1, the objective function for the BLP. Row 9 contains the products of the corresponding entries from rows 5 and 7; G9 contains =SUM(B9:F9), the portfolio present worth. Finally, G10 is the amount of investment capital available.

	A	B	C	D	E	F	G
		B7		*fx* 1			
	A	B	C	D	E	F	G
1	**Investment Opportunity**	**1**	**2**	**3**	**4**	**5**	
2	**Initial Investment**	$15,000.00	$25,000.00	$40,000.00	$50,000.00	$70,000.00	
3	**Annual Return**	$3,750.00	$5,000.00	$9,250.00	$11,250.00	$14,250.00	
4	**Salvage Value**	$15,000.00	$25,000.00	$40,000.00	$50,000.00	$70,000.00	
5	**Present Worth**	$4,718.79	$2,247.04	$9,212.88	$10,111.69	$7,415.24	
6	**Internal Rate of Return**	25.00%	20.00%	23.13%	22.50%	20.36%	
7	**Value of x**	**1**	**1**	**1**	**1**	**1**	
8	**Portfolio Investment**	$15,000.00	$25,000.00	$40,000.00	$50,000.00	$70,000.00	$200,000.00
9	**Portfolio Present Worth**	$4,718.79	$2,247.04	$9,212.88	$10,111.69	$7,415.24	$33,705.65
10	**MARR = 18%**					**Cap Constraint**	$100,000.00

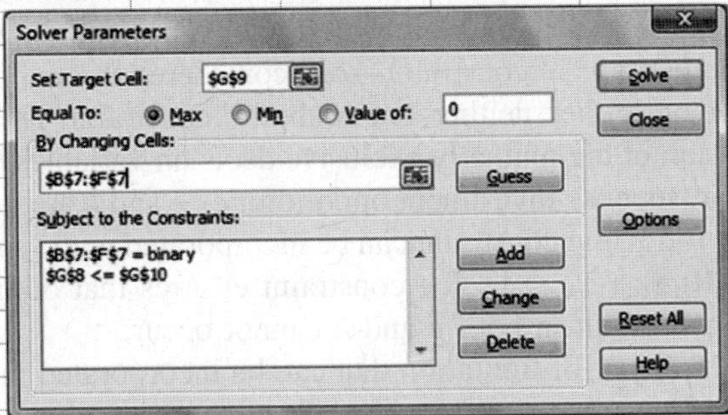

Solver Parameters

Set Target Cell: $G$9

Equal To: ● Max ○ Min ○ Value of: 0

By Changing Cells:

$B$7:$F$7

Subject to the Constraints:

$B$7:$F$7 = binary
$G$8 <= $G$10

[Solve] [Close] [Guess] [Options] [Add] [Change] [Reset All] [Delete] [Help]

FIGURE 15.1

Spreadsheet Setup to Solve Example 15.1 Using the Excel® SOLVER Tool.

	G9		fx	=SUM(B9:F9)		

	A	B	C	D	E	F	G
1	Investment Opportunity	1	2	3	4	5	
2	Initial Investment	$15,000.00	$25,000.00	$40,000.00	$50,000.00	$70,000.00	
3	Annual Return	$3,750.00	$5,000.00	$9,250.00	$11,250.00	$14,250.00	
4	Salvage Value	$15,000.00	$25,000.00	$40,000.00	$50,000.00	$70,000.00	
5	Present Worth	$4,718.79	$2,247.04	$9,212.88	$10,111.69	$7,415.24	
6	Internal Rate of Return	25.00%	20.00%	23.13%	22.50%	20.36%	
7	Value of x	0	0	1	1	0	
8	Portfolio Investment	$0.00	$0.00	$40,000.00	$50,000.00	$0.00	$90,000.00
9	Portfolio Present Worth	$0.00	$0.00	$9,212.88	$10,111.69	$0.00	$19,324.57
10	MARR = 18%					Cap Constraint	$100,000.00
11							

FIGURE 15.2

Optimum Solution to Example 15.1, Using the Excel® SOLVER Tool.

Using the Excel® SOLVER tool, we obtain the optimum solution to the BLP problem, as depicted in Figure 15.2. Notice, based on Equation 15.1, the target cell for SOLVER is G9, the present worth of the investment portfolio. Recall, G9 is to be maximized. The BLP problem is to be solved by changing cells B7 through F7, as indicated. Two constraints are added: $B$7:$F$7=binary and $G$8<=$G$10. The first constraint implements Equation 15.3; the latter implements Equation 15.2.

The optimum investment portfolio consists of two investments: 3 and 4. The total amount of capital required is $90,000, and the resulting present worth for the portfolio is $19,324.57. Recall, since the salvage value equals the initial investment, the IRR for the optimum portfolio can be easily computed: IRR$\{3, 4\} = (\$9,250 + \$11,250)/\$90,000 = 22.78\%$.

15.2.2 Adding Constraints to the Mathematical Formulation

A nice feature of the Excel® SOLVER tool is its ability to handle additional constraints incorporated in the BLP formulation of the capital budgeting problem. For example, suppose not all investment opportunities are independent. In particular, suppose investment opportunity k cannot be pursued unless investment opportunity j is pursued; in other words, suppose k is contingent on j. In such a case, the following constraint can be added to the SOLVER parameters: $x_k \leq x_j$. The constraint ensures that x_k cannot equal 1 if x_j equals 0. In fact, the only way x_k can equal 1 is for x_j to equal 1.

Another type of constraint—one considered throughout the text—is the mutually exclusive or "either, neither, but not both" constraint. This takes the form of requiring that the sum of the mutually exclusive decision variables be less than or equal to 1. In particular, suppose investment opportunities g and h are mutually exclusive. In such a case, the following constraint can be incorporated in the spreadsheet for solution using SOLVER: $x_g + x_h \leq 1$. The constraint ensures that both x_g and x_h cannot equal 1; hence, investment in both g and h cannot occur.

A third type of limitation that can be incorporated in the BLP formulation is the "either/or" contingent constraint. To illustrate the concept, suppose opportunity r cannot be pursued unless either opportunity s or opportunity t is pursued. (If both opportunities s and t are pursued, then opportunity r can also be pursued.) In such a case, the following constraint can be incorporated in the spreadsheet for solution using the Excel® SOLVER tool: $x_r \leq x_s + x_t$. The constraint ensures that x_r cannot equal 1 unless at least one of the two opportunities (s and t) equals 1.

Finally, a fourth type of limitation that the Excel® SOLVER tool can accommodate is the "at least, but not more than" constraint. For instance, suppose at least u but not more than v investments can be funded. In this case, the sum of the decision variables must be greater than or equal to u and less than or equal to v. Thus, two constraints must be added to the set of SOLVER parameters, both keying on a cell that contains the sum of the decision variables.

EXAMPLE 15.2 Adding Contingent Constraints

For the data given in Example 15.1, suppose Investment Opportunity 3 is contingent on Investment Opportunity 2. What will be the optimum investment portfolio?

Adding the constraint, $x_3 \leq x_2$ to the Excel's® SOLVER parameters takes the form $\$D\$7<=\$C\$7$. As shown in Figure 15.3, the optimum portfolio is $\{1,2,4\}$. The contingent constraint reduces the present worth from \$19,324.57 to \$17,077.53.

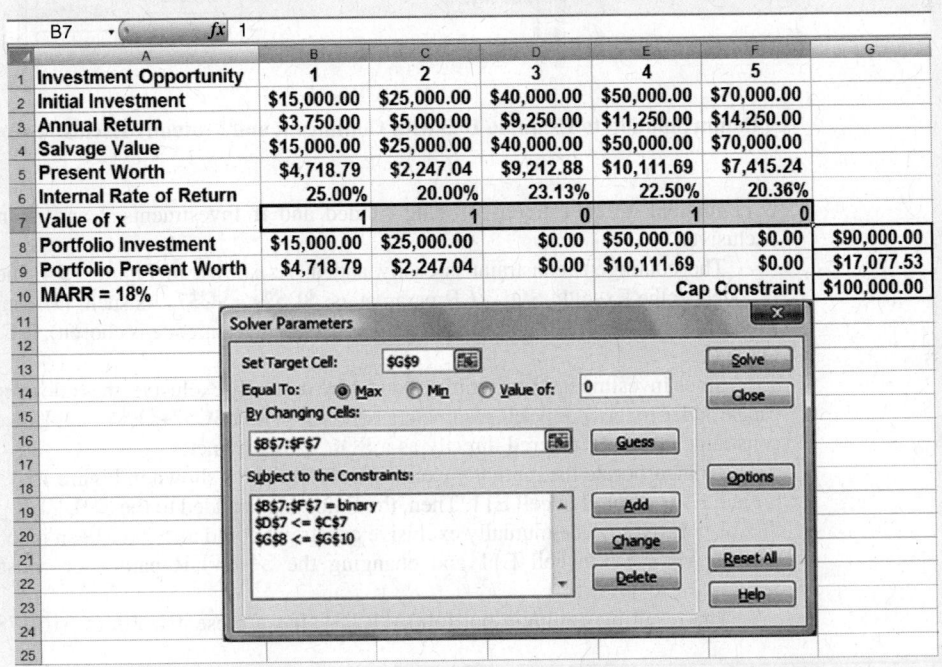

FIGURE 15.3
Optimum Solution to Example 15.2 with a Contingent Constraint.

EXAMPLE 15.3 Adding Mutually Exclusive and Contingent Constraints

To illustrate the combination of mutually exclusive and contingent constraints, consider the cash flow profiles given in Table 15.1 for five investment opportunities. Using a *MARR* of 10 percent and a capital limit of \$100,000, determine the optimum portfolio if Investment 3

	B7	▾	*fx*	1		
	A	B	C	D	E	F	G
1	Investment Opportunity	1	2	3	4	5	
2	Initial Investment	$15,000.00	$25,000.00	$40,000.00	$50,000.00	$70,000.00	
3	Annual Return	$3,750.00	$5,000.00	$9,250.00	$11,250.00	$14,250.00	
4	Salvage Value	$15,000.00	$25,000.00	$40,000.00	$50,000.00	$70,000.00	
5	Present Worth	$4,718.79	$2,247.04	$9,212.88	$10,111.69	$7,415.24	
6	Internal Rate of Return	25.00%	20.00%	23.13%	22.50%	20.36%	
7	Value of x	1	1	1	0	0	
8	Portfolio Investment	$15,000.00	$25,000.00	$40,000.00	$0.00	$0.00	$80,000.00
9	Portfolio Present Worth	$4,718.79	$2,247.04	$9,212.88	$0.00	$0.00	$16,178.71
10	MARR = 18%					Cap Constraint	$100,000.00
11				Mutually Exclusive Constraint	1	=C7+E7	

Solver Parameters

Set Target Cell: $G$9

Equal To: ● Max ○ Min ○ Value of: 0

By Changing Cells:

$B$7:$F$7

Subject to the Constraints:

$B$7:$F$7 = binary
$D$7 <= $C$7
$E$11 <= 1
$G$8 <= $G$10

Solve Close Guess Options Add Change Delete Reset All Help

FIGURE 15.4

Optimum Solution to Example 15.3 with Contingent and Mutually Exclusive Constraints.

is contingent on Investment 2 being funded and if Investments 2 and 4 are mutually exclusive.

The contingent constraint is easily added. As shown in Figure 15.4, the following is added to the Excel® SOLVER parameters: $D$7<=$C$7. As such, D7 cannot equal 1 (Investment 3 cannot be chosen) unless C7 equals 1 (Investment 2 is chosen); if C7 = 0, then D7 = 0.

Since Investment Opportunities 2 and 4 are mutually exclusive, the following constraint can be added to the SOLVER parameters: $x_2 + x_4 \leq 1$, or $C$7+$E$7<=1. However, such a constraint cannot be entered directly as a SOLVER parameter.

To incorporate the mutually exclusive constraint, as shown in Figure 15.4, the sum of C7 and E7 is entered in cell E11. Then, the following is added to the SOLVER parameters: $E$11<=1. (Note: The mutually exclusive constraint could also have been incorporated by entering =C7*E7 in cell E11 and changing the SOLVER parameter constraint from $E$11<=1 to $E$11=0.)

The resulting optimum portfolio, {1,2,3}, has a present worth of $16,178.71.

EXAMPLE 15.4 Incorporating Either/Or Constraints

To illustrate the incorporation of both mutually exclusive and either/or constraints in the BLP formulation of a capital budgeting problem, consider the data provided in Table 15.2 for six investment opportunities. Using a *MARR* of 10 percent and a capital limit of $100,000, determine the optimum investment portfolio when Investment Opportunities

TABLE 15.2
Data for Example 15.4.

EOY	CF(1)	CF(2)	CF(3)	CF(4)	CF(5)	CF(6)
0	−$15,000.00	−$18,000.00	−$20,000.00	−$25,000.00	−$30,000.00	−$40,000.00
1	$4,500.00	$3,000.00	$4,000.00	$4,500.00	$6,000.00	$15,000.00
2	$4,500.00	$4,500.00	$5,000.00	$4,500.00	$9,000.00	$15,000.00
3	$4,500.00	$6,000.00	$6,000.00	$4,500.00	$12,000.00	$25,000.00
4	$4,500.00	$7,500.00	$7,000.00	$4,500.00	$15,000.00	$0.00
5	$4,500.00	$9,000.00	$8,000.00	$4,500.00	$0.00	$0.00

1 and 2 are mutually exclusive and Investment Opportunity 6 is contingent on either or both of Investment Opportunities 3 and 4 being funded.

As shown in Figure 15.5, the optimum investment portfolio is {1,3,4,6}, and the portfolio's present worth is $12,265.06. Notice that the mutually exclusive and either/or contingent constraints were handled by establishing a cell for each. In this case, the mutually exclusive constraint was handled by setting D13 equal to the sum of B9 and C9 and including within the Excel® **SOLVER** parameters the constraint $D$13<=1. This implemented the constraint $x_1 + x_2 \leq 1$.

The either/or contingent constraint was handled by setting D14 equal to the sum of D9 and E9 and including within the **SOLVER** parameters the constraint $G$9<=$D$14. This implemented the constraint $x_6 \leq x_3 + x_4$.

(As an exercise, show that {1,2,3,6} will be the optimum investment portfolio with a present worth of $12,564.48 if the mutually exclusive and the either/or contingent constraints are eliminated.)

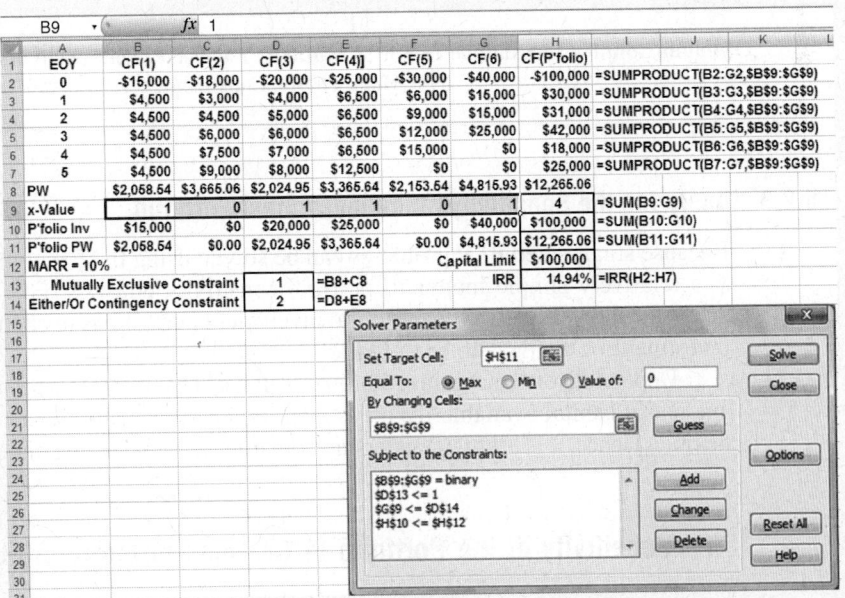

FIGURE 15.5
Optimum Solution to Example 15.4 with Mutually Exclusive and "Either/Or" Contingent Constraints.

EXAMPLE 15.5 Incorporating "At Most" and "At Least" Constraints

In the previous example, suppose at most three and at least two investments must be made. As shown in Figure 15.6, when the "at most" [$H$9<=3] and "at least" [$H$9>=2] constraints are added to those already included in Example 15.4, the optimum investment portfolio is {2,4,6}. The resulting present worth for the investment portfolio is $11,846.63; its IRR is 15.70 percent.

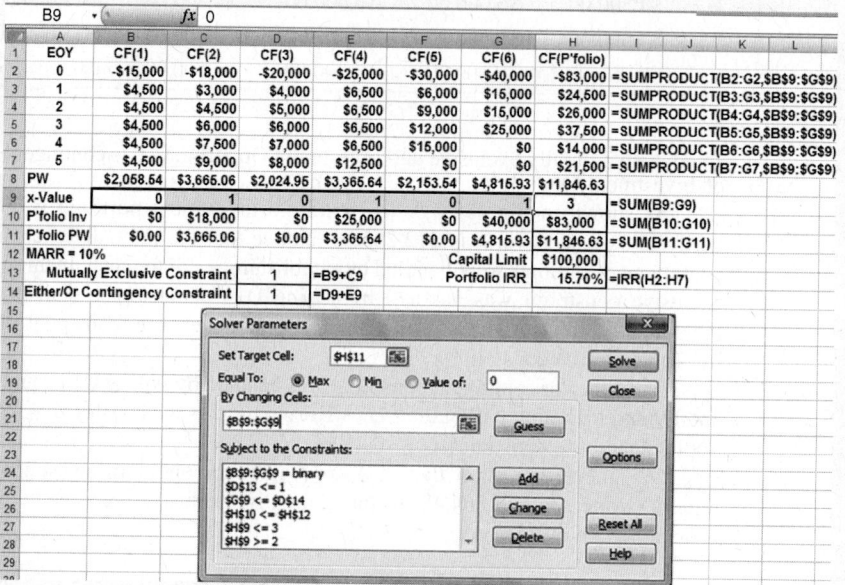

FIGURE 15.6

Optimum Solution to Example 15.5 with Mutually Exclusive, Contingent and "At Least, but Not More Than" Constraints.

15.2.3 Analyzing the Sensitivity of the Investment Portfolio

Because small-sized BLP problems can be solved using the Excel® SOLVER tool, it is a relatively simple matter to perform sensitivity analysis. For example, one can determine how sensitive the optimum investment portfolio is to changes in the limit on investment or changes to the *MARR*.

Depending on the organization's overall fiscal conditions, limitations placed on the amount of capital available for investment in a particular fiscal year can be somewhat flexible. Hence, it is useful to understand the impact of increasing or decreasing the limit.

EXAMPLE 15.6 Sensitivity of the Portfolio to Changes in the Capital Limit

Returning to the data from Example 15.1, what effect does the capital limit have on the optimum investment portfolio?

After using the Excel® SOLVER tool to determine the optimum investment portfolio for capital limits ranging from the minimum required to pursue any investment opportunity

TABLE 15.3
Optimum Investment Portfolios for Various Values of Investment Capital for Example 15.1.

Capital Available for Investment	Optimum Portfolio	Portfolio PW	Portfolio IRR	Capital Available for Investment	Optimum Portfolio	Portfolio PW	Portfolio IRR
$15,000	{1}	$4,718.79	25.00%	$110,000	{1,3,4}	$24,044.36	23.10%
$20,000	{1}	$4,718.79	25.00%	$115,000	{1,3,4}	$24,045.36	23.10%
$25,000	{1}	$4,718.79	25.00%	$120,000	{1,3,4}	$24,046.36	23.10%
$30,000	{1}	$4,718.79	25.00%	$125,000	{1,3,4}	$24,047.36	23.10%
$35,000	{1}	$4,718.79	25.00%	$130,000	{1,2,3,4}	$26,290.40	22.50%
$40,000	{3}	$9,212.88	23.13%	$135,000	{1,2,3,4}	$26,291.40	22.50%
$45,000	{3}	$9,212.88	23.13%	$140,000	{1,2,3,4}	$26,292.40	22.50%
$50,000	{4}	$10,111.69	22.50%	$145,000	{1,2,3,4}	$26,293.40	22.50%
$55,000	{1,3}	$13,931.67	23.64%	$150,000	{1,2,3,4}	$26,294.40	22.50%
$60,000	{1,3}	$13,932.67	23.64%	$155,000	{1,2,3,4}	$26,295.40	22.50%
$65,000	{1,4}	$14,830.48	23.08%	$160,000	{3,4,5}	$26,739.81	21.72%
$70,000	{1,4}	$14,831.48	23.08%	$165,000	{3,4,5}	$26,740.81	21.72%
$75,000	{1,4}	$14,832.48	23.08%	$170,000	{3,4,5}	$26,741.81	21.72%
$80,000	{1,2,3}	$16,178.71	22.50%	$175,000	{1,3,4,5}	$31,458.60	22.00%
$85,000	{1,2,3}	$16,179.71	22.50%	$180,000	{1,3,4,5}	$31,459.60	22.00%
$90,000	{3,4}	$19,324.57	22.78%	$185,000	{1,3,4,5}	$31,460.60	22.00%
$95,000	{3,4}	$19,325.57	22.78%	$190,000	{1,3,4,5}	$31,461.60	22.00%
$100,000	{3,4}	$19,326.57	22.78%	$195,000	{1,3,4,5}	$31,462.60	22.00%
$105,000	{1,3,4}	$24,043.36	23.10%	$200,000	{1,2,3,4,5}	$33,705.65	21.75%

($15,000) to the capital required to pursue all opportunities ($200,000), the results shown in Table 15.3 are obtained. As shown, if the investment limit is reduced to $90,000, the optimum portfolio does not change. However, if the investment limit is increased to $105,000, then the optimum portfolio changes from {3,4} to {1,3,4}, and the present worth increases from $19,324.57 to $24,043.36. Hence, by increasing the investment capital limit by $5,000, the present worth of the optimum investment portfolio increases by $4,716.79. This is an incredible return. In fact, the incremental IRR for the $5,000 investment is 75 percent. Clearly, the investor should endeavor to secure an additional $5,000 in order to add Investment Opportunity 1 to the investment portfolio.

As discussed in Chapter 4, many factors are considered when determining the value of the *MARR* to be used in performing engineering economic analyses and justifications. Consequently, it is useful to determine the impact of changes in the *MARR* on the optimum investment portfolio when capital budgeting is required.

EXAMPLE 15.7 Sensitivity of the Portfolio to Changes in the *MARR*

Consider the cash flow profiles given in Table 15.4 for six independent investment opportunities. Given a *MARR* of 10 percent, the optimum investment portfolio

TABLE 15.4
Cash Flow Data for Example 15.7.

EOY	CF(1)	CF(2)	CF(3)	CF(4)]	CF(5)	CF(6)
0	−$15,000.00	−$18,000.00	−$20,000.00	−$22,000.00	−$35,000.00	−$40,000.00
1	$4,500.00	$10,000.00	$4,000.00	$6,500.00	$6,000.00	$10,000.00
2	$4,500.00	$7,500.00	$5,000.00	$6,000.00	$6,900.00	$10,000.00
3	$4,500.00	$5,000.00	$6,000.00	$5,500.00	$7,935.00	$10,000.00
4	$4,500.00	$2,500.00	$7,000.00	$5,000.00	$9,125.25	$10,000.00
5	$4,500.00	$5,000.00	$8,000.00	$8,500.00	$15,494.04	$15,000.00

is $\{1,2,3,4\}$, as shown in Figure 15.7. However, it is desirable to know how sensitive the optimum portfolio is to different *MARR* values in the interval [0%,26%].

To analyze the sensitivity of the portfolio to different *MARR* values, we used the Excel® **SOLVER** tool to determine the optimum investment portfolio for *MARR* values over the desired interval. Specifically, we were interested in determining the ranges of *MARR* values over which the optimum investment portfolio did not change. The results of the analysis are given in Table 15.5, which provides the makeup of the optimum portfolio and its IRR for various ranges of *MARR* values.

From the example, it is evident that the optimum portfolio will be different for different ranges of *MARR* values. Specifically, for the example, for *MARR* values less than 8.11 percent, the optimum portfolio is $\{2,3,4,6\}$, with an IRR of 14.01 percent;

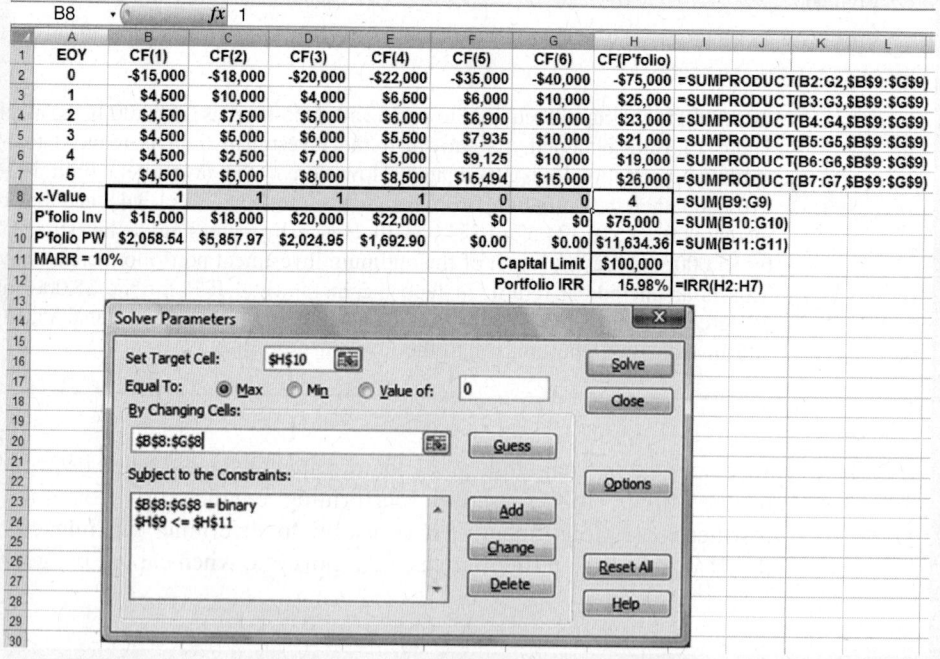

FIGURE 15.7
Optimum Investment Portfolio for Example 15.7.

TABLE 15.5
Sensitivity Analysis Results for Example 15.7.

MARR Range	Optimum Portfolio	IRR
[0.00%,8.10%]	{2,3,4,6}	14.01%
[8.11%,8.64%]	{1,2,3,6}	14.48%
[8.65%,12.89%]	{1,2,3,4}	15.98%
[12.90%,13.45%]	{1,2,3}	17.30%
[13.46%,15.23%]	{1,2}	20.17%
[15.24%,25.07%]	{2}	25.07%

for *MARR* values between 8.11 percent and 8.65 percent, the optimum portfolio is {1,2,3,6}, with an IRR of 14.48 percent; for *MARR* values between 8.65 percent and 12.90 percent, the optimum portfolio is {1,2,3,4}, with an IRR of 15.98 percent; for *MARR* values from 12.90 percent to 13.46 percent, the optimum portfolio is {1,2,3}, with an IRR of 17.30 percent; for *MARR* values from 13.46 percent to 15.24 percent, the optimum portfolio is {1,2}, with an IRR of 20.17 percent; and for *MARR* values greater than 15.24 percent but less than or equal to 25.07 percent, the optimum portfolio is {2}, with an IRR of 25.07 percent. For *MARR* values greater than 25.07 percent, no investment should be made.

The choice of *MARR* values to test was guided by plotting the present worth of each investment for *MARR* values ranging from 0 percent to 26 percent. A plot of the present worths is provided in Figure 15.8.

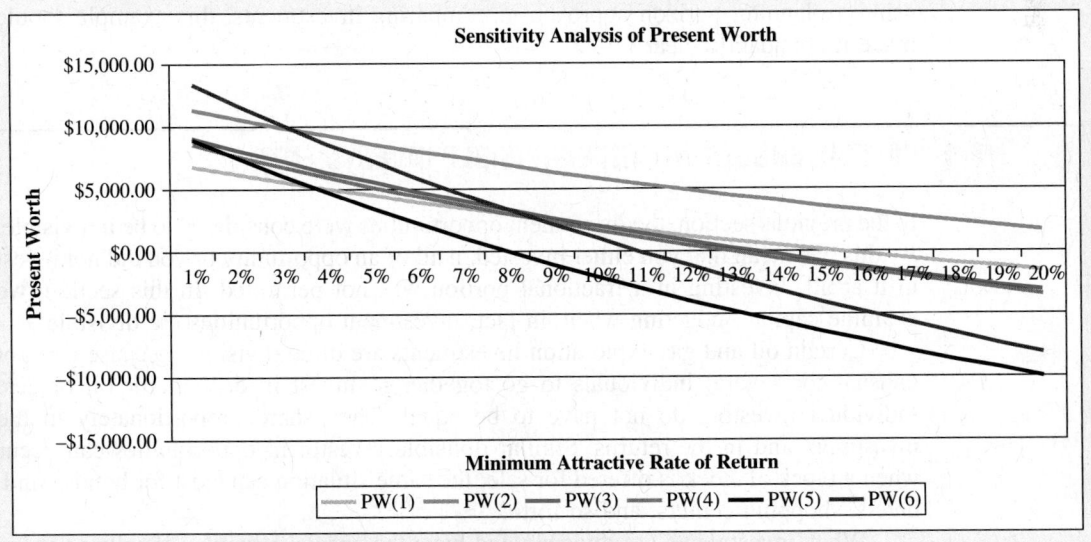

FIGURE 15.8
Sensitivity Analysis of Present Worth for Each Investment Considered in Example 15.7.

15-3   UNEQUAL INVESTMENT DURATIONS

Example 15.4 included investments that appeared to be of different durations. In particular, Table 15.2 included an alternative (5) with a 4-year duration and another (6) with a 3-year duration—all other investments have durations of 5 years. Yet, a present worth analysis was performed. Was this a correct thing to do?

Recall, in our discussion of unequal-lived investments, we recommended using a planning horizon and making explicit the cash flows that will occur each year during the planning horizon for each investment. In Example 15.4, the durations of Investments 5 and 6 could have been 5 years, but the net cash flows in particular years equaled 0. On the other hand, they could have represented investments that would last only 4 and 3 years, respectively.

Had we used annual worth instead of present worth to form the investment portfolio in Example 15.4, and had we used durations of 4 and 3 years for Investments 5 and 6, respectively, then an implicit assumption would have been made that the planning horizon was 60 years—the least common multiple of 3, 4, and 5 years. Furthermore, it would have been assumed that each investment would have been succeeded by investments having identical cash flow profiles. In the case of Investments 1, 2, 3, and 4, it would have been assumed that five successive replacements would occur with the very same cash flow profiles as shown for the original investments. Likewise, 14 successors would have been assumed for Investment 5, and 19 successors would have been assumed for Investment 6.

But what if Investments 5 and 6 were extraordinary investments of short duration that would not be expected to reoccur? To assume repetitive and identical life cycles over a 60-year period would make no sense at all. That is one of the reasons why, in Chapter 1, we recommended selecting a planning horizon and enumerating for each and every year of the planning horizon the cash flows that would result for each investment being considered. (If you did not fully appreciate why we have emphasized using a planning horizon approach in comparing investments, this example should make it abundantly clear.)

15-4   CAPITAL BUDGETING WITH DIVISIBLE INVESTMENTS

In the previous section, the investment opportunities were considered to be indivisible. By this, we mean that you either invested in all of an opportunity or you did not invest in it at all. Investing in a fractional portion was not permitted. In this section, we examine capital budgeting when, in fact, investment opportunities are divisible.

Certain oil and gas exploration investments are often divisible, because it is not unusual for several individuals to go together to invest in drilling for oil or gas. Individual investors do not have to be equal. They share proportionately in the investment and in the returns. Similar divisible investment opportunities can occur when a block of stock is offered for sale; the same situation can exist for bonds, land, hotels, shopping centers, and so forth.

When investments are divisible and have the special structure of salvage value equaling the investment and annual returns being a uniform series, the capital budgeting problem is solved using "pick the lowest hanging fruit first" approach. Specifically, the investments are ranked in decreasing order of their individual internal rates of return, and investments are chosen sequentially until the money runs out.

EXAMPLE 15.8 Optimizing the Investment Portfolio When Investments Are Divisible and Have a Special Structure

TABLE 15.6
Data for Example 15.8.

	Economically Viable Investments				
	1	2	3	4	5
IRR	25.00%	20.00%	23.13%	22.50%	20.36%
Annual Return	$3,750.00	$5,000.00	$9,250.00	$11,250.00	$14,250.00
Investment	$15,000.00	$25,000.00	$40,000.00	$50,000.00	$70,000.00
	Economically Viable Investments Sorted by IRR				
	1	3	4	5	2
IRR	25.00%	23.13%	22.50%	20.36%	20.00%
Annual Return	$3,750.00	$9,250.00	$11,250.00	$14,250.00	$5,000.00
Investment	$15,000.00	$40,000.00	$50,000.00	$70,000.00	$25,000.00
Cumulative Investment	$15,000.00	$55,000.00	$105,000.00	$175,000.00	$200,000.00

Continuing to use the data from Example 15.1, suppose each of the five investment opportunities is divisible. Ranking the investment opportunities in decreasing order of their internal rates of return results in the following order of investment opportunities: 1, 3, 4, 5, 2, as shown in Table 15.6.

Next, the cumulative investment is determined, summing investments across the columns, as shown in the bottom row of Table 15.6. Since $100,000 is available for investment, the optimum portfolio includes a full investment in Opportunities 1 and 3 and a partial investment in Opportunity 4. Specifically, $45,000 is to be invested in Opportunity 4, yielding an annual return of (0.9)$11,250.00, or $10,125.00. The present worth of the portfolio equals $23,032.19. The IRR for the portfolio equals 23.13 percent.

The solution procedure for capital budgeting with divisible investment opportunities having the special structure of this example is illustrated in Figure 15.9.

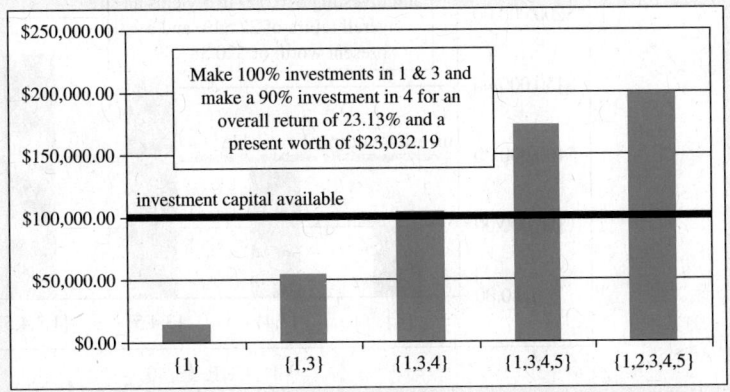

FIGURE 15.9
Solving a Capital Budgeting Problem When Investments Are Divisible: Example 15.8.

You might have noticed that we ranked investment opportunities on the basis of their internal rates of return. Yet, in Chapter 8, we were emphatic about not ranking investments on the basis of internal rates of return. In fact, we argued that, when using IRR, each increment of investment had to be justified by having its incremental IRR be greater than the *MARR*.

What's the difference? Why is it okay to rank investment opportunities by IRR here, but it wasn't acceptable to do so in Chapter 8 ? We are dealing with different kinds of investments. First, they have a special structure. Second, in Chapter 8, we considered mutually exclusive investments that could not be pursued partially; at most one investment is made, and it is made fully, not partially. Here, more than one investment can be pursued, fully or partially.

Not only do the rules change for IRR, but they also change for present worth. Recall, in Chapter 5, we recommended ranking investments on the basis of their present worths and choosing the one that had the greatest present worth. However, when multiple and partial investments can be made, ranking on the basis of present worth can suboptimize an investment portfolio.

EXAMPLE 15.9 Performing Capital Budgeting Incorrectly with Divisible Investments

Continuing to use the data from Example 15.1 but assuming the investments are divisible, what investment portfolio would be recommended if investments are ranked on the basis of present worth and opportunities are added to the investment portfolio (fully or partially) until the capital limit is met?

Using present worth ranking, an investment limit of $100,000 produces the sub-optimum portfolio shown in Figure 15.10.

Notice, using a present worth ranking to determine the investment portfolio reduces the portfolio's overall present worth from $23,032.19 to $20,383.89. If present worth ranking is the basis for forming the investment portfolio, the IRR on the $100,000 investment will be reduced from 23.13 percent to 22.54 percent.

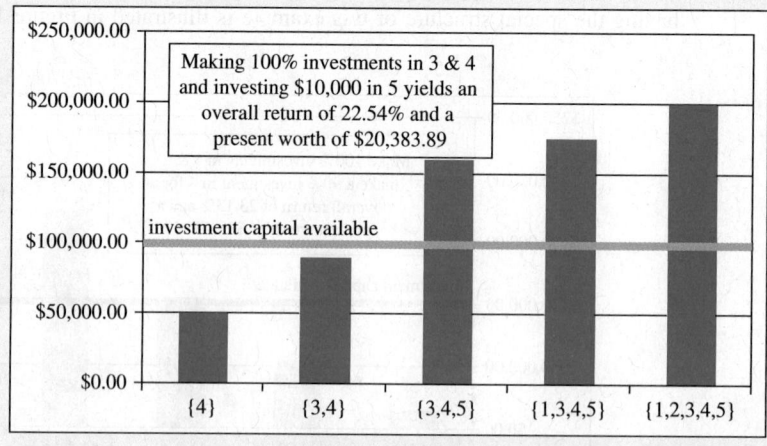

FIGURE 15.10

A Suboptimum Investment Portfolio, Based on Ranking Present Worths with Divisible Investments.

15-5 USING EXCEL® TO SOLVE THE CAPITAL BUDGETING PROBLEM WITH DIVISIBLE INVESTMENTS

In dealing with independent, divisible investments, the solution to the capital budgeting problem is relatively simple when investments have a special structure. However, when not all of the investments are independent or have that structure, an alternative to ranking on the basis of IRR is required. The Excel® SOLVER tool, again, provides a ready mechanism for solving such problems.

With divisible investments, the decision variable is changed from investing fully $(x_j = 1)$ versus not investing at all $(x_j = 0)$ in investment j to investing wholly, partially, or not at all $(0 \leq p_j \leq 1)$ in investment j, where p_j is the decision variable representing the percentage of investment j to be pursued. The capital budgeting problem with divisible investments can be formulated mathematically as follows:

$$\text{Maximize} \quad PW_1 p_1 + PW_2 p_2 + \cdots + PW_{n-1} p_{n-1} + PW_n p_n \tag{15.4}$$

$$\text{subject to} \quad c_1 p_1 + c_2 p_2 + \cdots + c_{n-1} p_{n-1} + c_n p_n \leq C \tag{15.5}$$

$$0 \leq p_j \leq 1 \, j = 1, \ldots, n \tag{15.6}$$

The objective function to be maximized (Equation 15.4) is the present worth of the investment portfolio. The first constraint (Equation 15.5) assures that the total investment required for the portfolio is no greater than the amount of capital available. The second constraint (Equation 15.6) allows the decision variables to have values ranging from 0 percent to 100 percent.

$$\text{Maximize} \quad \sum_{\forall j} PW_j p_j$$

$$\text{Subject to} \quad \sum_{\forall j} c_j p_j \leq C$$

$$0 \leq p_j \leq 1 \, \forall j$$

EXAMPLE 15.10 Optimizing the Investment Portfolio with the Excel® SOLVER Tool When Investments Are Divisible

To illustrate using the Excel® SOLVER tool to determine the optimum investment portfolio when investments are divisible, Example 15.8 is solved, as shown in Figure 15.11. As expected, SOLVER produces the same solution as obtained in Example 15.8.

Notice, the objective function (Equation 15.4) and constraints (Equations 15.5 and 15.6) are incorporated in the solver parameters. Also, notice that the constraint $0 \leq p_j \leq 1$ is implemented by using two constraints: $B$7:$F$7<=1$ and $B$7:$F$7>=0$.

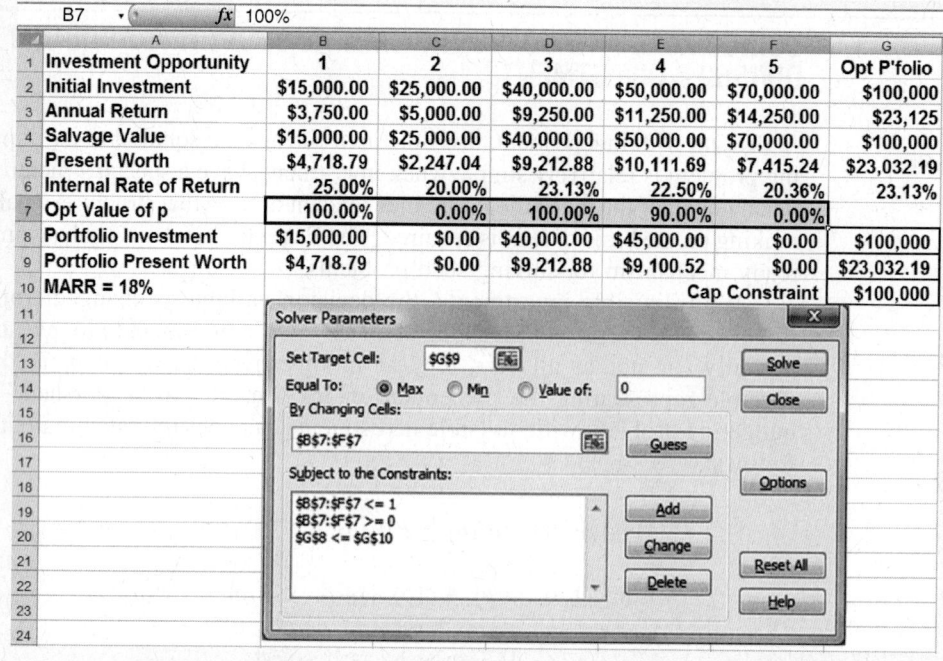

	A	B	C	D	E	F	G
1	Investment Opportunity	1	2	3	4	5	Opt P'folio
2	Initial Investment	$15,000.00	$25,000.00	$40,000.00	$50,000.00	$70,000.00	$100,000
3	Annual Return	$3,750.00	$5,000.00	$9,250.00	$11,250.00	$14,250.00	$23,125
4	Salvage Value	$15,000.00	$25,000.00	$40,000.00	$50,000.00	$70,000.00	$100,000
5	Present Worth	$4,718.79	$2,247.04	$9,212.88	$10,111.69	$7,415.24	$23,032.19
6	Internal Rate of Return	25.00%	20.00%	23.13%	22.50%	20.36%	23.13%
7	Opt Value of p	100.00%	0.00%	100.00%	90.00%	0.00%	
8	Portfolio Investment	$15,000.00	$0.00	$40,000.00	$45,000.00	$0.00	$100,000
9	Portfolio Present Worth	$4,718.79	$0.00	$9,212.88	$9,100.52	$0.00	$23,032.19
10	MARR = 18%					Cap Constraint	$100,000

FIGURE 15.11
Excel® SOLVER Solution for Independent Divisible Investments.

The advantage of using the Excel® SOLVER tool versus ranking investments based on their internal rates of return is the ability to incorporate additional constraints and handle investments without the special structure. For instance, if contingent and mutually exclusive constraints exist, the ranking approach does not work. However, SOLVER can accommodate such constraints, as the following example demonstrates.

EXAMPLE 15.11 Incorporating Mutually Exclusive and Contingent Constraints

In the previous example, suppose Investments 1 and 2 are mutually exclusive and Investments 3 and 4 are mutually exclusive. Further, suppose Investment 5 is contingent on Investment 3 being funded.

The Excel® SOLVER setup and solution are shown in Figure 15.12. The mutually exclusive constraints were implemented by entering the product of B7 and C7 in D11 and entering 1 minus the product of D7 and E7 in D12 and adding the constraints: $D$11=0 and $D$12=1. If an investment is made in Investment 1 or Investment 2, then there must be a zero investment in the other; the same logic holds for Investments 3 and 4.

The contingent constraint is incorporated by requiring that nothing be invested in Investment 5 unless something is invested in 3. This was accomplished by using the Excel® IF function; in D13,=IF(D7=0,0,1) was entered. Therefore, a value of 0 or 1 occurs in D13; zero if no investment is made in Investment 3 and 1 if some investment is made in Investment 3. The following SOLVER constraint was added: $F$7<=$D$13. If D13 = 0, then F7 must equal 0 and nothing will be invested in Investment 5;

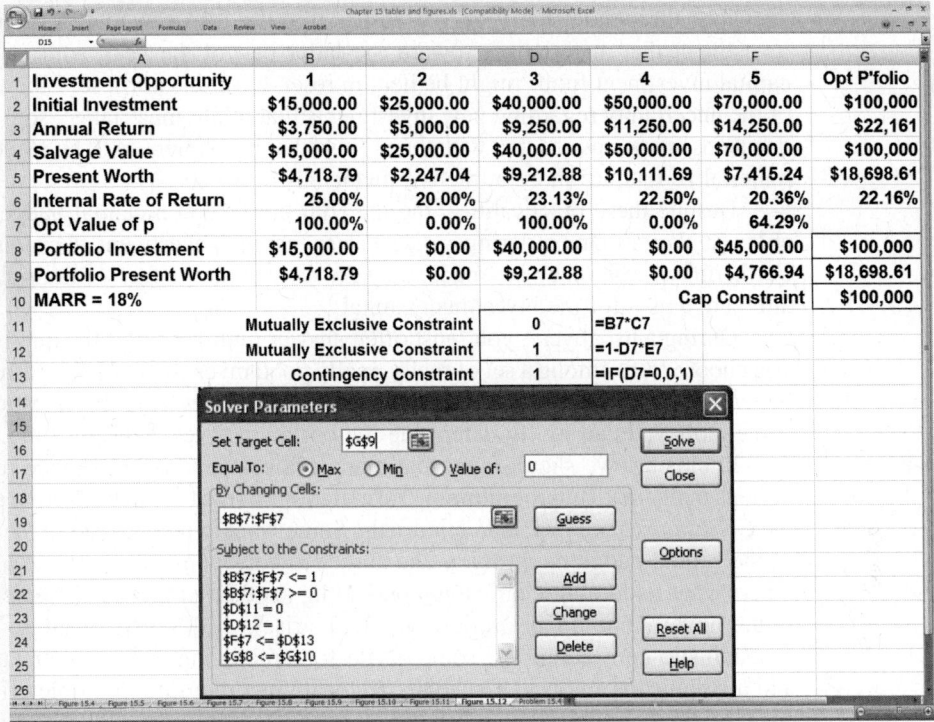

FIGURE 15.12

Excel® SOLVER Solution for Dependent Divisible Investments.

if $D13 = 1$, then something is invested in Investment 3 and no additional constraint is required for the amount invested in Investment 5. The optimum portfolio, {100% of 1, 100% of 3, 64.29% of 5}, has a present worth of $18,698.61 and an IRR of 22.16 percent.[2]

15-6 PRACTICAL CONSIDERATIONS IN CAPITAL BUDGETING

There are several practical considerations we should mention relative to capital budgeting. For example, even though a capital investment limit is established for a fiscal year, it is seldom the case that all prospective investments will be known or available for analysis at a particular point in time during the year.

Instead of determining at the beginning of a fiscal year which of a known set of investment opportunities will be funded, it is more common to make capital investment

---

[2]The Excel® SOLVER tool had difficulty recognizing both mutually exclusive constraints when they were formulated identically. For that reason, the second mutually exclusive constraint was formulated as $1 - p_3p_4 = 1$, which requires that $p_3p_4 = 0$. Also, SOLVER does not always produce an optimum solution; often, the solution depends on the starting point for the search performed. Hence, we recommend that a solution be obtained by starting with all decision variables equal to 0, followed by a starting solution having all decision variables equal to 1; if inconsistencies occur, randomly generate a starting solution. The Excel® SOLVER tool does not perform well in solving a mixed-integer programming problem with many *side constraints*, such as sets of *mutually exclusive*, *contingent*, *at least*, and at most constraints. For other than simple problems, more powerful mathematical programming software should be used.

decisions throughout the year. To ensure that the firm can fund a highly attractive investment that materializes toward the latter part of the year, some portion of the capital investment funds might be held in reserve for this purpose. Likewise, because of the uncertainty regarding new investments that might materialize, some investment decisions are postponed, but with the proviso that investments will be made if no others materialize that are more attractive financially.

Despite these practicalities, the material presented on capital budgeting is valuable. At various times during a fiscal year, capital investment decisions are made. Furthermore, when they are made, they are done so in the face of multiple competing alternative uses for the investment capital.

During a fiscal year, you must often answer multiple times the question, How do you choose from among a set of really, really good investments? Hopefully, you have a better idea of the considerations that should go into answering this question as well as some tools you can use to determine the optimum investment portfolio.

In closing, we should note that many criticisms have been made regarding the various mathematical programming formulations of the capital budgeting problem that have been presented in research journals. Some want to incorporate in the formulation of the capital budgeting problem the ability to borrow money at stated interest rates, others want to do multiyear capital budgeting (as though they are prescient regarding future investment opportunities that will arise), still others want to incorporate probabilistic considerations, some argue for optimizing a firm's annual cash flow, and a significant number of scholars advocate incorporating multiple criteria. While each of these preferences might be appropriate for specific applications, we are confident that including such formulations in this introductory text would be a mistake. For those who wish to pursue capital budgeting beyond the brief introduction offered in this chapter, we direct you to the vast capital budgeting and capital rationing literature.

15-7 SUMMARY

In the chapter, we introduced the challenges a manager faces when capital requirements for economically attractive investments exceed the capital available for investment. The takeaway messages from the chapter are

1. the process of forming an investment portfolio from among economically attractive investment opportunities is called *capital rationing* or *capital budgeting*;

2. optimum investment portfolios can be determined by formulating a binary linear programming problem, which can be solved using the Excel® **SOLVER** tool;

3. Excel® can be used to perform sensitivity analysis, including analyzing the sensitivity of the amount of investment capital available and the *MARR* used on the optimum investment portfolio;

4. constraints can be added to the capital budgeting problem when not all investment opportunities are independent;

5. not all investments are alike—not only in terms of differences in the cash flows, but also in terms of the ability to pursue a portion of an investment;

6. when the choice about an investment opportunity is to fund it wholly versus not funding it at all, the optimum portfolio is determined using binary linear programming to maximize the portfolio's present worth; and

7. to obtain the optimum investment portfolio when partial funding of investments is allowed and they have a special structure, you can optimize the portfolio using the Excel® SOLVER tool or by (a) ranking the investment opportunities on their internal rates of return, not their present worths, and (b) forming the portfolio by "filling the investment bucket," starting with the opportunity having the greatest IRR and proceeding sequentially until the "investment bucket" is full.

Pit Stop #15—The Finish Line Is In Sight!

1. True or False: When several independent, indivisible investments are available, form the investment portfolio so that the present worth of the portfolio is maximized.

2. True or False: If independent, indivisible investments 3 and 4 are mutually exclusive, then $X_3 + X_4 \le 1$ is added as a constraint to the BLP formulation.

3. True or False: If indivisible investment 2 is contingent on indivisible investment 1 being funded, then $X_2 - X_1 \le 0$ is added as a constraint to the BLP formulation.

4. True or False: When multiple independent, divisible investments are available, form the investment portfolio so that the internal rate of return is maximized.

5. True or False: When multiple independent divisible investments with a special structure are available, add investments to the portfolio on the basis of their IRR, moving from the largest to the smallest IRR until the capacity limit is reached.

Tutoring problem available (at instructor's discretion) in *WileyPLUS*.

Problem available (at instructor's discretion) in *WileyPLUS*.

Worked Problem Video available in *WileyPLUS*.

FE-LIKE PROBLEMS

1. Sarah is considering two investment proposals. Proposal A is to purchase a new computer. Proposal B is to purchase a new printer. She will not buy the printer unless she buys the computer. The relationship between Proposals A and B is best described by which of the following?

   a. B and A are mutually exclusive

   b. B is contingent on A

   c. A is contingent on B

   d. Not enough information is given to determine a relationship

2. Consider a capital budgeting formulation where the binary variables x_1 and x_2 are used to represent the acceptance $(x_i = 1)$ or rejection $(x_i = 0)$ of each alternative. A mutual exclusivity constraint between the two alternatives can be represented by which of the following?

   a. $x_1 + x_2 < = 1$

   b. $x_2 < = x_1$

   c. $x_1 + x_2 > = 1$

   d. $x_1 < = x_2$

3. Consider a capital budgeting formulation where the binary variables x_1 and x_2 are used to represent the acceptance $(x_i = 1)$ or rejection $(x_i = 0)$ of each alternative. The requirement that x_2 is contingent upon x_1 can be represented by which of the following?

   a. $x_1 + x_2 < = 1$

   b. $x_2 < = x_1$

   c. $x_1 + x_2 > = 1$

   d. $x_1 < = x_2$

4. Consider a capital budgeting formulation where the binary variables x_1 and x_2 are used to represent the acceptance $(x_i = 1)$ or rejection $(x_i = 0)$ of each alternative. The requirement that the null alternative is not feasible can be represented by which of the following?

   a. $x_1 + x_2 < \; = 1$

   b. $x_2 < \; = x_1$

   c. $x_1 + x_2 > \; = 1$

   d. $x_1 < \; = x_2$

5. Sebastian is about to compare a set of mutually exclusive and indivisible alternatives using a ranking approach. Which of the following is not an appropriate measure of worth?

   a. Present worth

   b. Future worth

   c. Annual worth

   d. Internal rate of return

6. If six investment proposals are under consideration, how many investment combinations must be evaluated if a complete enumeration approach is being used?

   a. 6

   b. $2*6 = 12$

   c. $6^2 = 36$

   d. $2^6 = 64$

7. Which of the following is not an approach that can be used to perform a capital budgeting economic analysis?

   a. Box-Jenkins algorithm

   b. Excel® SOLVER

   c. Exhaustive enumeration

   d. Lori-Savage formulation

8. To determine an optimal portfolio of investments when the available choices are divisible, the investment choices should first be ranked in increasing order based on which of the following?

   a. FW

   b. Initial investment

   c. IRR

   d. PW

9. Consider the following binary linear programming formulation of a capital budgeting problem.

$$\text{Max} \quad 1{,}200\,x_1 + 600\,x_2 + 950\,x_3 + 1{,}650\,x_4$$
$$\text{s.t.} \quad 15{,}000\,x_1 + 20{,}000\,x_2 + 25{,}000\,x_3$$
$$+30{,}000\,x_4 < \; = 70{,}000$$
$$x_1 + x_2 < \; = 1$$
$$x_4 < \; = x_3$$
$$x_1, x_2, x_3, x_4 = (0,1)$$

The first cost of project x_3 is

   a. $70,000.

   b. $25,000.

   c. $950.

   d. x_4.

10. Consider the following binary linear programming formulation of a capital budgeting problem.

$$\text{Max} \quad 1{,}200\,x_1 + 600\,x_2 + 950\,x_3 + 1{,}650\,x_4$$
$$\text{s.t.} \quad 15{,}000\,x_1 + 20{,}000\,x_2 + 25{,}000\,x_3$$
$$+30{,}000\,x_4 < \; = 70{,}000$$
$$x_1 + x_2 < \; = 1$$
$$x_4 < \; = x_3$$
$$x_1, x_2, x_3, x_4 = (0,1)$$

Projects x_3 and x_4 are

   a. mutually exclusive.

   b. related, where x_3 is contingent on x_4.

   c. related, where x_4 is contingent on x_3.

   d. not related.

11. Consider the following binary linear programming formulation of a capital budgeting problem.

$$\text{Max} \quad 1{,}200\,x_1 + 600\,x_2 + 950\,x_3 + 1{,}650\,x_4$$
$$\text{s.t.} \quad 15{,}000\,x_1 + 20{,}000\,x_2 + 25{,}000\,x_3$$
$$+30{,}000\,x_4 < \; = 70{,}000$$
$$x_1 + x_2 < \; = 1$$
$$x_4 < \; = x_3$$
$$x_1, x_2, x_3, x_4 = (0,1)$$

The capital budget limit is

   a. $90,000.

   b. $70,000.

   c. $30,000.

   d. $4,400.

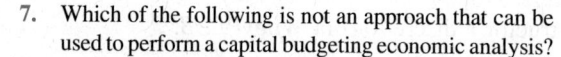

PROBLEMS

Sections 15.2.1, 15.2.2, and 15.2.3

1. True or false: In solving a classical capital budgeting problem using binary linear programming (BLP), the objective function can be either the sum of present worths or the sum of annual worths without affecting the optimum investment portfolio.

2. Aerotron Radio Inc. has $250,000 available, and its engineering staff has proposed the following *indivisible* investments. With each, Aerotron can exit at the end of its planning horizon of 5 years and have its initial investment returned. In addition, each year Aerotron will receive the annual return shown below. *MARR* is 12 percent.

Investment	1	2	3	4	5
Initial Investment	$75,000	$65,000	$50,000	$80,000	$100,000
Annual Return	$10,800	$12,000	$7,500	$13,750	$15,750

Section 15.2.1

For the original problem:

a. Which investments should Aerotron select for the optimum portfolio?

b. What is the present worth for the optimum investment portfolio?

c. What is the IRR for the optimum investment portfolio?

Section 15.2.2

In addition to the original problem statement, let Investments 1 and 4 be mutually exclusive and Investment 3 be contingent on Investment 2:

d. Now, which alternatives should Aerotron select?

e. What is the present worth for the optimum investment portfolio?

f. What is the IRR for the optimum investment portfolio?

Section 15.2.3

Consider the original problem using SOLVER for sensitivity analysis:

g. Determine the optimum portfolio (state the investments selected and the portfolio PW) using (1) the current limit on investment capital, (2) plus 20 percent, and (3) minus 20 percent.

h. Determine the optimum portfolio (state the investments selected and the portfolio PW) using (1) the current *MARR*, (2) plus 20 percent, and (3) minus 20 percent.

3. Polaris Industries has $1,250,000 available for additional innovations on the Victory Vision motorcycle. These include the five *indivisible*, equal-lived alternatives, each of which guarantees the investment can be exited after 6 years with the initial investment returned. In addition, each year Polaris will receive an annual return as noted below. *MARR* is 15 percent.

Investment	1	2	3	4	5
Initial Investment	$350,000	$300,000	$250,000	$500,000	$400,000
Annual Return	$90,000	$85,000	$75,000	$130,000	$115,000

Section 15.2.1

For the original problem:

a. Which alternatives should Polaris select for the optimum portfolio?

b. What is the present worth for the optimum investment portfolio?

c. What is the IRR for the portfolio?

Section 15.2.2

In addition to the original problem statement, Polaris has noted that Investments 1, 2, and 4 are mutually exclusive, and marketing believes at least 3 investments must be made.

d. Which alternatives should now be selected?

e. What is the present worth for the optimum investment portfolio?

f. What is the IRR for the optimum investment portfolio?

Section 15.2.3

Return to the original problem statement using SOLVER for sensitivity analysis:

g. Determine the optimum portfolio (state the investments selected and the portfolio PW) using (1) the current limit on investment capital, (2) plus 20 percent, and (3) minus 20 percent.

h. Determine the optimum portfolio (state the investments selected and the portfolio PW) using (1) the current *MARR*, (2) plus 20 percent, and (3) minus 20 percent.

4. CustomMetalworks is considering expanding their cable fabrication business for towers, rigging, winches, and many other uses. They have available $250,000 for investment and have identified the following *indivisible* alternatives, each of which will provide an exit with full return of the investment at the end of a 5-year planning horizon. Each year, CustomMetalworks will receive an annual return as noted below. *MARR* is 12 percent.

Investment	1	2	3	4	5
Initial Investment	$25,000	$40,000	$85,000	$100,000	$65,000
Annual Return	$7,500	$12,000	$20,000	$22,000	$17,000

Section 15.2.1

For the original problem:

a. Which alternatives should CustomMetalworks select?

b. What is the present worth for the optimum investment portfolio?

c. What is the IRR for the optimum investment portfolio?

Section 15.2.2

In addition to the original opportunity statement, CustomMetalworks has determined that Investments 3 and 4 are mutually exclusive and that Investment 5 is contingent on either Investment 1 or 2 being funded.

d. Now, which alternatives should be selected?

e. What is the present worth for the optimum investment portfolio?

f. What is the IRR for the optimum investment portfolio?

Section 15.2.3

Reconsider the original problem using SOLVER for sensitivity analysis:

g. Determine the optimum portfolio (state the investments selected and the portfolio PW) using (1) the current limit on investment capital, (2) plus 20 percent, and (3) minus 20 percent.

h. Determine the optimum portfolio (state the investments selected and the portfolio PW) using (1) the current *MARR*, (2) plus 20 percent, and (3) minus 20 percent.

5. Gymnastics4Life (G4L) is a high-end facility for beginning, intermediate, and elite gymnasts. The latter are drawn from the nearby region for exclusive and dedicated training. In order to maintain their edge, G4L trustees wish to invest up to $350,000 in new methods for critical evaluation and training and are considering the following independent, *indivisible*, investments that guarantee return of the initial investment at the end of a 7-year planning horizon. In addition, G4L will receive annual returns as noted below. *MARR* is 12 percent.

Investment	1	2	3	4	5
Initial Investment	$150,000	$130,000	$100,000	$160,000	$200,000
Annual Return	$24,000	$22,000	$15,000	$25,000	$30,000

Section 15.2.1

For the original problem:

a. Which alternatives should G4L select to form the optimum portfolio?

b. What is the present worth for the optimum portfolio?

c. What is the IRR for the optimum investment portfolio?

Section 15.2.2

During review, the G4L trustees judge Investments 2 and 5 to be mutually exclusive.

d. Which alternatives should now be selected?

e. What is the present worth for G4L's new optimum investment portfolio?

f. What is the IRR for the portfolio?

Section 15.2.3

Consider the original problem using SOLVER for sensitivity analysis:

g. Determine the optimum portfolio (state the investments selected and the portfolio PW) using (1) the current limit on investment capital, (2) plus 20 percent, and (3) minus 20 percent.

h. Determine the optimum portfolio (state the investments selected and the portfolio PW) using (1) the current *MARR*, (2) plus 20 percent, and (3) minus 20 percent.

6. Yaesu America wishes to enhance their already fine line of electronic equipment for commercial and individual use. Their engineering staff has proposed five independent, *indivisible*, equal-lived investments, cutting across different product lines, with each estimated to return the initial investment if it is exited after a 5-year planning horizon. In addition, each year, Yaesu is projected to receive an annual return as noted below. They have available $1,250,000 to invest, and their *MARR* is 10 percent.

Investment	1	2	3	4	5
Initial Investment	$400,000	$300,000	$200,000	$600,000	$500,000
Annual Return	$50,000	$36,000	$25,000	$69,000	$55,000

Section 15.2.1

For the original problem:

a. Which alternatives should Yaesu America select as optimal?

b. What is the present worth for the selected portfolio?

c. What is the IRR for the optimum set of investments?

Section 15.2.2

In addition to the original problem statement, Yaesu America has noted that Investment 4 is contingent on Investment 2.

d. Now, which alternatives should be selected?

e. What is the present worth for the portfolio?

f. What is the IRR for the portfolio?

Section 15.2.3

Consider the original opportunity statement using SOLVER for sensitivity analysis:

g. Determine the optimum portfolio (state the investments selected and the portfolio PW) using (1) the current limit on investment capital, (2) plus 20 percent, and (3) minus 20 percent.

h. Determine the optimum portfolio (state the investments selected and the portfolio PW) using (1) the current *MARR*, (2) plus 20 percent, and (3) minus 20 percent.

7. Your consulting firm has been doing well, and you believe it is time to add a new, related area of engineering services. To do so, you have identified the following five independent, *indivisible*, equal-lived investments, each of which guarantees you can exit it after 4 years and have your initial investment returned to you. Each year, you receive an annual return as noted below. Your *MARR* is 10 percent, and you have $250,000 to invest.

Investment	1	2	3	4	5
Initial Investment	$45,000	$60,000	$85,000	$100,000	$75,000
Annual Return	$4,000	$7,000	$9,000	$12,000	$11,000

Section 15.2.1

For the original problem:

a. Which alternatives should you select to form the optimum portfolio?

b. What is the present worth of your selected portfolio?

c. What is the IRR for the optimum portfolio?

Section 15.2.2

In addition to the original problem statement, you now believe that Investments 4 and 5 should be considered mutually exclusive.

d. Which alternatives should you now select?

e. What is the present worth for this portfolio?

f. What is the IRR now?

Section 15.2.3

Reconsider the original problem using SOLVER for sensitivity analysis:

g. Determine the optimum portfolio (state the investments selected and the portfolio PW) using (1) the current limit on investment capital, (2) plus 20 percent, and (3) minus 20 percent.

h. Determine the optimum portfolio (state the investments selected and the portfolio PW) using (1) the current *MARR*, (2) plus 20 percent, and (3) minus 20 percent.

8. A laboratory within Bayer is considering the five *indivisible* investment proposals below to further upgrade their diagnostic capabilities to ensure continued leadership and state-of-the-art performance. The laboratory uses a 10-year planning horizon, has a *MARR* of 10 percent, and has a capital limit of $1,000,000.

Investment	1	2	3	4	5
Initial Investment	$300,000	$400,000	$450,000	$500,000	$600,000
Annual Receipts	$205,000	$230,000	$245,000	$260,000	$290,000
Annual Disbursements	$125,000	$130,000	$140,000	$135,000	$150,000
Salvage Value	$50,000	$50,000	$60,000	$75,000	$75,000

Section 15.2.1

For the original opportunity statement:

a. Which alternatives should be selected to form the optimum portfolio for the lab?

b. What is the present worth for the optimum investment portfolio?

c. What is the IRR for the portfolio?

Section 15.2.2

In addition to the original opportunity statement, Bayer declares that Investments 2 and 4 are mutually exclusive, Investment 5 is contingent on 2 being funded, and at least two investments must be made.

d. Now, which alternatives should Bayer select?

e. What is the present worth for the resulting investment portfolio?

f. What is the resulting IRR?

Section 15.2.3

Again consider the original opportunity statement using SOLVER for sensitivity analysis:

g. Determine the optimum portfolio (state the investments selected and the portfolio PW) using (1) the current limit on investment capital, (2) plus 20 percent, and (3) minus 20 percent.

h. Determine the optimum portfolio (state the investments selected and the portfolio PW) using (1) the current *MARR*, (2) plus 20 percent, and (3) minus 20 percent.

9. A division of ConocoPhillips is involved in their periodic capital budgeting activity, and the engineering and operations staffs have identified 10 *indivisible* investments with cash flow parameters shown below. ConocoPhillips uses a 10-year planning horizon and a *MARR* of 10 percent in evaluating such investments. The division's capital limit for this budgeting cycle is $2,500,000.

Investment	1	2	3	4	5
Initial Investment	$150,000	$200,000	$225,000	$275,000	$350,000
Annual Return	$35,000	$38,000	$45,000	$60,000	$75,000
Salvage Value	$25,000	$50,000	$22,500	$27,500	$55,000
Investment	6	7	8	9	10
Initial Investment	$400,000	$475,000	$500,000	$550,000	$600,000
Annual Return	$95,000	$110,000	$85,000	$120,000	$125,000
Salvage Value	$75,000	$50,000	$100,000	$75,000	$75,000

Section 15.2.1

For the original problem statement:

a. Which alternatives should ConocoPhillips select?

b. What is the present worth of the optimum portfolio?

c. What is the IRR for the portfolio?

Section 15.2.2

In addition to the original problem statement, ConocoPhillips has noted that Investments 1 and 3 are mutually exclusive, Investment 4 is contingent on either Investment 2 or Investment 5 being funded, and at least five investments must be made.

d. Which alternatives should now be selected?

e. What is the present worth for the new portfolio?

f. What is the IRR for the investment portfolio?

Section 15.2.3

Consider the original problem using SOLVER for sensitivity analysis:

g. Determine the optimum portfolio (state the investments selected and the portfolio PW) using (1) the current limit on investment capital, (2) plus 20 percent, and (3) minus 20 percent.

h. Determine the optimum portfolio (state the investments selected and the portfolio PW) using (1) the current *MARR*, (2) plus 20 percent, and (3) minus 20 percent.

10. A lending firm is considering six independent and *indivisible* investment alternatives that can be exited with a full refund of the initial investment at any time the firm chooses. A total of $200,000 is available for investment, and the *MARR* is 10 percent. (Note: There is no planning horizon specified, so the firm can choose any number of years they wish—the optimum portfolio and the IRR will remain the same since the initial investment and the salvage value are the same, and the annual returns are constant each year.)

Alternative	1	2	3	4	5	6
Initial Investment	$25,000	$35,000	$30,000	$40,000	$60,000	$50,000
Annual Return	$2,600	$3,750	$3,050	$4,775	$6,750	$5,850

Section 15.2.1

For the original problem:

a. Which alternatives should the lending firm select as optimal?

b. What is the present worth for the optimum portfolio?

c. What is the IRR for the portfolio?

Section 15.2.2

Several possible constraints have been identified for additional analysis by the lending firm. Determine (1) the optimum investment portfolio, (2) the present worth, and (3) the IRR when

d. Investments 4 and 5 are mutually exclusive.

e. Investment 1 is contingent on Investment 2 being pursued.

f. exactly four investments must be pursued.

g. all of the constraints of Parts d, e, and f are considered simultaneously.

Section 15.2.3

Reconsider the original problem using SOLVER for sensitivity analysis:

h. Determine the optimum portfolio (state the investments selected and the portfolio PW) using (1) the current limit on investment capital, (2) plus 20 percent, and (3) minus 20 percent.

i. Determine the optimum portfolio (state the investments selected and the portfolio PW) using (1) the current *MARR*, (2) plus 20 percent, and (3) minus 20 percent.

11. Rex Electric has decided to move into low-rise (2 to 8 floors) commercial building electrical wiring. After great success in upscale residential and small commercial wiring, they have identified four independent and *indivisible* investments, any or all of which will help make the move to the next level. Rex Electric's *MARR* is 10 percent, and $500,000 is available for investment immediately, with $175,000 available for follow-up investment the next year.

Section 15.2.1

a. Which alternatives should be selected by Rex Electric?

b. What is the present worth for the selected investment portfolio?

c. What is the IRR for the optimum portfolio?

EOY	CF(1)	CF(2)	CF(3)	CF(4)
0	−$50,000	−$125,000	−$200,000	−$250,000
1	−$100,000	−$75,000	$50,000	$75,000
2	$50,000	$70,000	$50,000	$75,000
3	$50,000	$70,000	$50,000	$75,000
4	$50,000	$70,000	$50,000	$75,000
5	$50,000	$70,000	$75,000	$75,000
6	$50,000	$70,000	$75,000	$85,000
7	$50,000	$70,000	$75,000	$85,000
8	$50,000	$70,000	$75,000	$85,000
9	$50,000	$70,000	$75,000	$85,000
10	$75,000	$100,000	$75,000	$100,000

Section 15.2.3

Using SOLVER for sensitivity analaysis,

d. determine the optimum portfolio (state the investments selected and the portfolio PW) using (1) the current limit on investment capital, (2) plus 20 percent, and (3) minus 20 percent.

e. determine the optimum portfolio (state the investments selected and the portfolio PW) using (1) the current *MARR*, (2) plus 20 percent, and (3) minus 20 percent.

12. Consider six *mutually exclusive* and *indivisible* investment alternatives that will fully refund the initial investment to BASF in their catalyst unit at the end of 3 years. The annual returns are as shown below, and a *MARR* of 12 percent is used.

Alternative	1	2	3	4	5	6
Initial Investment	$40,000	$80,000	$60,000	$100,000	$150,000	$120,000
Annual Return	$5,200	$10,050	$7,500	$13,550	$18,700	$15,700

Sections 15.2.1 and 15.2.2

a. Which alternative should be selected by BASF? *Use the IRR method* to determine the preferred alternative. You might wish to refer to Section 8.3 for this. Specify the IRR for the preferred investment. You may use Excel® if desired.

b. Use Excel® and SOLVER to select the preferred investment based on PW. State both the PW and IRR.

13. Consider six *mutually exclusive* and *indivisible* investment alternatives being evaluated by Pioneer Cookware in their stainless-steel kitchenware group. At the end of 5 years, each investment will end and the initial investment will be fully returned to the investor. Based on the annual returns shown below and a *MARR* of 10 percent, determine the preferred alternative.

Alternative	1	2	3	4	5	6
Initial Investment	$20,000	$40,000	$30,000	$50,000	$75,000	$60,000
Annual Return	$2,100	$4,400	$3,050	$5,700	$8,200	$6,650

Sections 15.2.1 and 15.2.2

a. Which alternative should Pioneer Cookware select? *Use the IRR method* to determine the preferred alternative. You might wish to refer to Section 8.3 for this. Specify the IRR for the preferred investment. You may use Excel® if desired.

b. Use Excel® and SOLVER to select the preferred investment based on PW. State both the PW and IRR.

14. Consider six *mutually exclusive* and *indivisible* investment alternatives under evaluation by TranSystems in their bridge and structure design group. At any time TranSystems chooses to exit the investment, their initial financial outlay will be refunded, in addition to the annual returns earned. Based on the data shown below and a *MARR* of 10 percent, determine the preferred alternative. (Note: There is no planning horizon specified, so pick any number of years you like—the optimum portfolio and the IRR will remain the same, since the "initial investment" and the "salvage value" are the same, and the annual returns are constant each year. The PW will differ depending upon number of year selected, and yet will be a consistent measure.)

Alternative	1	2	3	4	5	6
Initial Investment	$25,000	$35,000	$30,000	$40,000	$60,000	$50,000
Annual Return	$2,600	$3,750	$3,050	$4,775	$6,750	$5,850

Sections 15.2.1 and 15.2.2

a. Which alternative should TranSystems select? *Use the IRR method* to determine the preferred alternative. You might wish to refer to Section 8.3 for this. Specify the IRR for the preferred investment. You may use Excel® if desired.

b. Use Excel® and SOLVER to select the preferred investment based on PW. State both the PW and IRR.

15. The city of Clyde, Ohio, is using the binary linear programming (BLP) formulation of a capital budgeting problem shown below. Assume $175,000 is available for investment and all investments are *indivisible*; *MARR* is 12 percent and $n = 10$ years. Given the incomplete SOLVER parameter box shown, respond to Parts a–f below if it is desired to obtain an optimum investment portfolio.

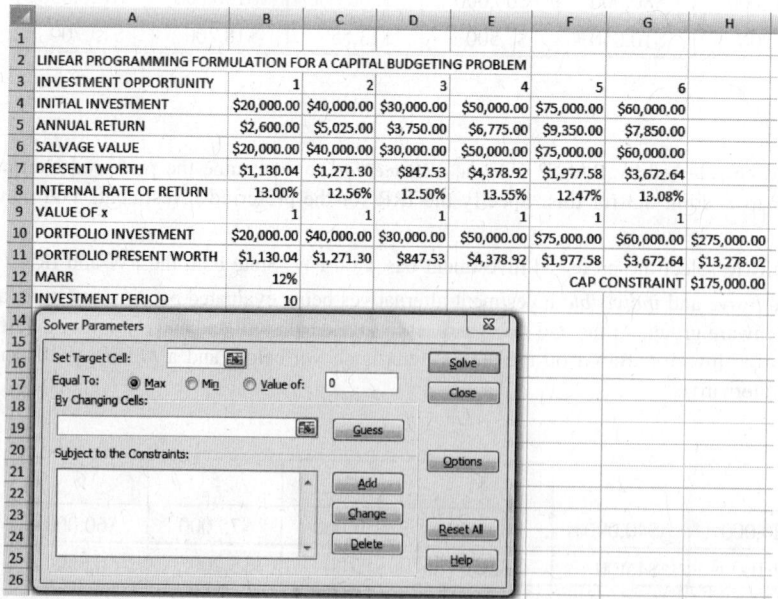

Section 15.2.1

a. Specify the contents of the target cell.

b. Specify the contents for "By Changing Cells:"

c. Specify all constraints to be added.

Section 15.2.2

d. Now, suppose the original problem is modified so that Investments 1 and 2 are mutually exclusive. Show how you would incorporate that constraint in SOLVER.

e. Now, suppose the original problem is modified so Investment 2 is contingent on Investment 3 being pursued. Show how you would incorporate that constraint in SOLVER.

f. Now, suppose the original problem is modified to specify that at least three and no more than four investments can be pursued. Show how you would incorporate that constraint in SOLVER.

16. The American Radio Relay League is using a binary linear programming (BLP) formulation to select from among several possible investments. Each investment continues for 5 years. Given the incomplete SOLVER parameter box shown, respond to Parts a–f below in order to obtain the optimum investment portfolio. Assume $180,000 is available for investment and all investments are *indivisible*.

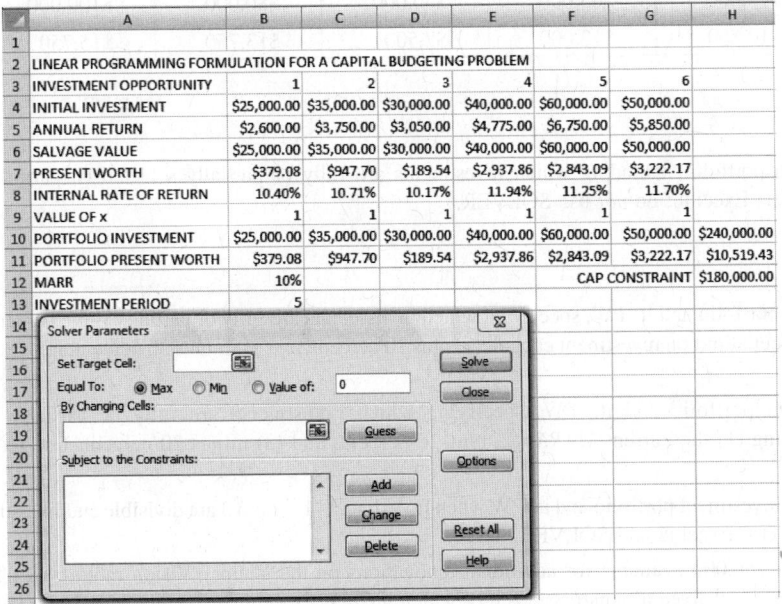

	A	B	C	D	E	F	G	H
1								
2	LINEAR PROGRAMMING FORMULATION FOR A CAPITAL BUDGETING PROBLEM							
3	INVESTMENT OPPORTUNITY	1	2	3	4	5	6	
4	INITIAL INVESTMENT	$25,000.00	$35,000.00	$30,000.00	$40,000.00	$60,000.00	$50,000.00	
5	ANNUAL RETURN	$2,600.00	$3,750.00	$3,050.00	$4,775.00	$6,750.00	$5,850.00	
6	SALVAGE VALUE	$25,000.00	$35,000.00	$30,000.00	$40,000.00	$60,000.00	$50,000.00	
7	PRESENT WORTH	$379.08	$947.70	$189.54	$2,937.86	$2,843.09	$3,222.17	
8	INTERNAL RATE OF RETURN	10.40%	10.71%	10.17%	11.94%	11.25%	11.70%	
9	VALUE OF x	1	1	1	1	1	1	
10	PORTFOLIO INVESTMENT	$25,000.00	$35,000.00	$30,000.00	$40,000.00	$60,000.00	$50,000.00	$240,000.00
11	PORTFOLIO PRESENT WORTH	$379.08	$947.70	$189.54	$2,937.86	$2,843.09	$3,222.17	$10,519.43
12	MARR	10%					CAP CONSTRAINT	$180,000.00
13	INVESTMENT PERIOD	5						
14								
15								
16								
17								
18								
19								
20								
21								
22								
23								
24								
25								
26								

Solver Parameters

Set Target Cell:

Equal To: ● Max ○ Min ○ Value of: 0

By Changing Cells:

Guess

Subject to the Constraints:

Add

Change

Delete

Solve

Close

Options

Reset All

Help

Section 15.2.1

a. Specify the contents of the target cell.

b. Specify the contents for "By Changing Cells:"

c. Specify all constraints to be added.

Section 15.2.2

d. Now, suppose the original problem is modified so that Investments 4 and 5 are mutually exclusive. Show how you would incorporate that constraint in SOLVER.

e. Now, suppose the original problem is modified so that Investment 6 is contingent on Investment 5 being pursued. Show how you would incorporate that constraint in SOLVER.

f. Now, suppose the original problem is modified so that exactly three investments must be pursued. Show how you would incorporate that constraint in SOLVER.

Sections 15.4 and 15.5

17. True or false: In solving a capital budgeting problem involving investment opportunities that are divisible (i.e., you can invest in portions of the opportunities instead of "all or nothing"), you rank the opportunities on the basis of present worth and add to the portfolio opportunities and fractions of opportunities, beginning with the largest present worth, until "the investment bucket is filled."

18. True or false: In solving a capital budgeting problem involving investment opportunities that are divisible (i.e., you can invest in portions of the opportunities instead of "all or nothing"), you rank the opportunities on the basis of internal rate of return and add to the portfolio opportunities and fractions of opportunities, beginning with the largest internal rate of return, until "the investment bucket is filled."

19. Aerotron Radio Inc. has $250,000 available, and its engineering staff has proposed the following *divisible* investments. With each, Aerotron can exit at the end of its planning horizon of 5 years and have its initial investment returned. In addition, each year Aerotron will receive the annual return shown below. *MARR* is 12 percent

Investment	1	2	3	4	5
Initial Investment	$75,000	$65,000	$50,000	$80,000	$100,000
Annual Return	$10,800	$12,000	$7,500	$13,750	$15,750

Section 15.4

a. Determine the optimum portfolio, including which investments are fully or partially selected (if partial, give percentage). You may use Excel®; do *not* use SOLVER.

Section 15.5

b. Determine the optimum portfolio and its PW, specifying which investments are fully or partially (give percentage) selected using (1) the current limit on investment capital, (2) plus 20 percent, and (3) minus 20 percent. Use Excel® and SOLVER. (15.5)

c. Determine the optimum portfolio and its PW, specifying which investments are fully or partially (give percentage) selected using (1) the current *MARR*, (2) plus 20 percent, and (3) minus 20 percent. Use Excel® and SOLVER.

d. Determine the optimum investment portfolio and its PW when Investments 1, 2, and 3 are divisible and Investments 4 and 5 are indivisible. Use Excel® and SOLVER.

20. Polaris Industries has $1,250,000 available for additional innovations on the Victory Vision motorcycle. These include the five *divisible*, equal-lived alternatives, each of which guarantees the investment can be exited after 6 years with the initial investment returned. In addition, each year Polaris will receive an annual return as noted below. *MARR* is 15 percent.

Investment	1	2	3	4	5
Initial Investment	$350,000	$300,000	$250,000	$500,000	$400,000
Annual Return	$90,000	$85,000	$75,000	$130,000	$115,000

Section 15.4

a. Determine the optimum portfolio, including which investments are fully or partially selected (if partial, give percentage). You may use Excel®; do *not* use SOLVER.

Section 15.5

b. Determine the optimum portfolio and its PW, specifying which investments are fully or partially (give percentage) selected using (1) the current limit on investment capital, (2) plus 20 percent, and (3) minus 20 percent. Use Excel® and SOLVER.

c. Determine the optimum portfolio and its PW, specifying which investments are fully or partially (give percentage) selected using (1) the current *MARR*, (2) plus 20 percent, and (3) minus 20 percent. Use Excel® and SOLVER.

d. Determine the optimum investment portfolio and its PW when Investments 1, 2, and 3 are indivisible and Investments 4 and 5 are divisible. Use Excel® and SOLVER.

21. CustomMetalworks is considering expanding their cable fabrication business for towers, rigging, winches, and many other uses. They have $250,000 available for investment and have identified the following *divisible* alternatives, each of which will provide an exit with full return of the investment at the end of a 5-year planning horizon. Each year, CustomMetalworks will receive an annual return as noted below. *MARR* is 12 percent.

Investment	1	2	3	4	5
Initial Investment	$25,000	$40,000	$85,000	$100,000	$65,000
Annual Return	$7,500	$12,000	$20,000	$22,000	$17,000

Section 15.4

a. Determine the optimum portfolio, including which investments are fully or partially selected (if partial, give percentage). You may use Excel®; do not use SOLVER.

Section 15.5

b. Determine the optimum portfolio and its PW, specifying which investments are fully or partially (give percentage) selected using (1) the current limit on investment capital, (2) plus 20 percent, and (3) minus 20 percent. Use Excel® and SOLVER.

c. Determine the optimum portfolio and its PW, specifying which investments are fully or partially (give percentage) selected using (1) the current *MARR*, (2) plus 20 percent, and (3) minus 20 percent. Use Excel® and SOLVER.

d. Determine the optimum investment portfolio and its PW when Investments 1, 2, and 5 are divisible and Investments 3 and 4 are indivisible. Use Excel® and SOLVER.

22. Gymnastics4Life (G4L) is a high-end facility for beginning, intermediate, and elite gymnasts. The latter are drawn from the nearby region for exclusive and dedicated training. In order to maintain their edge, G4L trustees wish to invest up to $350,000 in new methods for critical evaluation and training and are considering the following independent, *divisible*, investments, each of which guarantees return of the initial investment at the end of a 7-year planning horizon. In addition, G4L will receive annual returns as noted below. *MARR* is 12 percent

Investment	1	2	3	4	5
Initial Investment	$150,000	$130,000	$100,000	$160,000	$200,000
Annual Return	$24,000	$22,000	$15,000	$25,000	$30,000

Section 15.4

a. Determine the optimum portfolio, including which investments are fully or partially selected (if partial, give percentage). You may use Excel®; do *not* use SOLVER.

Section 15.5

b. Determine the optimum portfolio and its PW, specifying which investments are fully or partially (give percentage) selected using (1) the current limit on investment capital, (2) plus 20 percent, and (3) minus 20 percent. Use Excel® and SOLVER.

c. Determine the optimum portfolio and its PW, specifying which investments are fully or partially (give percentage) selected using (1) the current *MARR*, (2) plus 20 percent, and (3) minus 20 percent. Use Excel® and SOLVER.

d. Determine the optimum investment portfolio and its PW when Investments 1 and 2 are divisible and Investments 3, 4, and 5 are indivisible. Use Excel® and SOLVER.

23. Yaesu America wishes to enhance their already fine line of electronic equipment for commercial and individual use. Their engineering staff has proposed five independent, *divisible*, equal-lived investments, cutting across different product lines, with each estimated to return the initial investment if it is exited after a 5-year planning horizon. In addition, each year, Yaesu is projected to receive an annual return as noted below. They have available $1,250,000 to invest, and their *MARR* is 10 percent.

Investment	1	2	3	4	5
Initial Investment	$400,000	$300,000	$200,000	$600,000	$500,000
Annual Return	$50,000	$36,000	$25,000	$69,000	$55,000

Section 15.4

a. Determine the optimum portfolio, including which investments are fully or partially selected (if partial, give percentage). You may use Excel®; do *not* use SOLVER.

Section 15.5

b. Determine the optimum portfolio and its PW, specifying which investments are fully or partially (give percentage) selected using (1) the current limit on investment capital, (2) plus 20 percent, and (3) minus 20 percent. Use Excel® and SOLVER.

c. Determine the optimum portfolio and its PW, specifying which investments are fully or partially (give percentage) selected using (1) the current *MARR*, (2) plus 20 percent, and (3) minus 20 percent. Use Excel® and SOLVER.

d. Determine the optimum investment portfolio and its PW when Investments 2 and 4 are divisible and Investments 1, 3, and 5 are indivisible. Use Excel® and SOLVER.

24. Your consulting firm has been doing well, and you believe it is time to add a new, related area of engineering services. To do so, you have identified the following five independent, *divisible*, equal-lived investments, each of which guarantees you can exit it after 4 years and have your initial investment returned to you. Each year, you receive an annual return as noted below. Your *MARR* is 10 percent, and you have $250,000 to invest.

Investment	1	2	3	4	5
Initial Investment	$45,000	$60,000	$85,000	$100,000	$75,000
Annual Return	$4,000	$7,000	$9,000	$12,000	$11,000

Section 15.4

a. Determine the optimum portfolio, including which investments are fully or partially selected (if partial, give percentage). You may use Excel®; do *not* use SOLVER.

Section 15.5

b. Determine the optimum portfolio and its PW, specifying which investments are fully or partially (give percentage) selected using (1) the current limit on investment capital, (2) plus 20 percent, and (3) minus 20 percent. Use Excel® and SOLVER.

c. Determine the optimum portfolio and its PW, specifying which investments are fully or partially (give percentage) selected using (1) the current *MARR*, (2) plus 20 percent, and (3) minus 20 percent. Use Excel® and SOLVER.

d. Determine the optimum investment portfolio and its PW when Investments 2 and 4 are indivisible and Investments 1, 3, and 5 are divisible. Use Excel® and SOLVER.

25. A laboratory within Bayer is considering the five *divisible* investment proposals below to further upgrade their diagnostic capabilities to ensure continued leadership and state-of-the-art performance. The laboratory uses a 10-year planning horizon, has a *MARR* of 10 percent, and has a capital limit of $1,000,000.

Investment	1	2	3	4	5
Initial Investment	$300,000	$400,000	$450,000	$500,000	$600,000
Annual Receipts	$205,000	$230,000	$245,000	$260,000	$290,000
Annual Disbursements	$125,000	$130,000	$140,000	$135,000	$150,000
Salvage Value	$50,000	$50,000	$60,000	$75,000	$75,000

Section 15.4

a. Determine the optimum portfolio, including which investments are fully or partially selected (if partial, give percentage). You may use Excel®; do *not* use SOLVER.

Section 15.5

b. Determine the optimum portfolio and its PW, specifying which investments are fully or partially (give percentage) selected using (1) the current limit on investment capital, (2) plus 20 percent, and (3) minus 20 percent. Use Excel® and SOLVER.

c. Determine the optimum portfolio and its PW, specifying which investments are fully or partially (give percentage) selected using (1) the current *MARR*, (2) plus 20 percent, and (3) minus 20 percent. Use Excel® and SOLVER.

d. Determine the optimum investment portfolio and its PW when all investments except Investment 3 are divisible, at least two investments must be pursued fully or partially, and no more than three can be pursued fully or partially.

26. A division of ConocoPhillips is involved in their periodic capital budgeting activity, and the engineering and operations staffs have identified 10 *divisible* investments with cash flow parameters shown below. ConocoPhillips uses a 10-year planning horizon and a *MARR* of 10 percent in evaluating such investments. The division's capital limit for this budgeting cycle is $2,500,000.

Investment	1	2	3	4	5
Initial Investment	$150,000	$200,000	$225,000	$275,000	$350,000
Annual Return	$35,000	$38,000	$45,000	$60,000	$75,000
Salvage Value	$25,000	$50,000	$22,500	$27,500	$55,000
Investment	6	7	8	9	10
Initial Investment	$400,000	$475,000	$500,000	$550,000	$600,000
Annual Return	$95,000	$110,000	$85,000	$120,000	$125,000
Salvage Value	$75,000	$50,000	$100,000	$75,000	$75,000

Section 15.4

a. Determine the optimum portfolio, including which investments are fully or partially selected (if partial, give percentage). You may use Excel®; do *not* use SOLVER.

Section 15.5

b. Determine the optimum portfolio and its PW, specifying which investments are fully or partially (give percentage) selected using (1) the current limit on investment capital, (2) plus 20 percent, and (3) minus 20 percent. Use Excel® and SOLVER.

c. Determine the optimum portfolio and its PW, specifying which investments are fully or partially (give percentage) selected using (1) the current *MARR*, (2) plus 20 percent, and (3) minus 20 percent. Use Excel® and SOLVER.

d. Determine the optimum investment portfolio and its PW when Investments 1 through 5 are divisible and Investments 6 through 10 are indivisible. Use Excel® and SOLVER.

e. Determine the optimum investment portfolio and its PW when Investments 1 through 5 are indivisible and Investments 6 through 10 are divisible. Use Excel® and SOLVER.

f. Determine the optimum investment portfolio and its PW when all of the following conditions must be met simultaneously: Investments 1, 3, and 5 are mutually exclusive; investment 4 is contingent on either Investment 2 or Investment 5 being fully or partially funded; at least five investments must be made, albeit partially; Investments 1 through 5 are indivisible, and Investments 6 through 10 are divisible. Use Excel® and SOLVER.

27. A lending firm is considering six independent and *divisible* investment alternatives that can be exited with a full refund of the initial investment at any time the firm chooses. A total of $200,000 is available for investment, and the *MARR* is 10 percent. (Note: There is no planning horizon specified, so the firm can choose any number of years they wish—the optimum portfolio and the IRR will remain the same, since the initial investment and the salvage value are the same, and the annual returns are constant each year.)

Alternative	1	2	3	4	5	6
Initial Investment	$25,000	$35,000	$30,000	$40,000	$60,000	$50,000
Annual Return	$2,600	$3,750	$3,050	$4,775	$6,750	$5,850

Section 15.4

a. Determine the optimum portfolio, including which investments are fully or partially selected (if partial, give percentage). You may use Excel®; do *not* use SOLVER.

Section 15.5

b. Determine the optimum portfolio and its PW, specifying which investments are fully or partially (give percentage) selected using (1) the current limit on investment capital, (2) plus 20 percent, and (3) minus 20 percent. Use Excel® and SOLVER.

c. Determine the optimum portfolio and its PW, specifying which investments are fully or partially (give percentage) selected using (1) the current *MARR*, (2) plus 20 percent, and (3) minus 20 percent. Use Excel® and SOLVER.

d. Determine the optimum investment portfolio and its PW when Investments 1 through 3 are indivisible and Investments 4 through 6 are divisible. Use Excel® and SOLVER.

e. Determine the optimum investment portfolio when all of the investments are divisible, but fractional investments are limited to 0 percent, 25 percent, 50 percent, 75 percent, or 100 percent. Use Excel® and SOLVER.

28. Rex Electric has decided to move into low-rise (2 to 8 floors) commercial building electrical wiring. After great success in upscale residential and small commercial wiring, they have identified four independent and *divisible* investments, any or all of which will help make the move to the next level. Rex Electric's *MARR* is 10 percent, and $500,000 is available for investment immediately, with $175,000 available for follow-up investment the next year.

EOY	CF(1)	CF(2)	CF(3)	CF(4)
0	−$50,000	−$125,000	−$200,000	−$250,000
1	−$100,000	−$75,000	$50,000	$75,000
2	$50,000	$70,000	$50,000	$75,000
3	$50,000	$70,000	$50,000	$75,000
4	$50,000	$70,000	$50,000	$75,000
5	$50,000	$70,000	$75,000	$75,000
6	$50,000	$70,000	$75,000	$85,000
7	$50,000	$70,000	$75,000	$85,000
8	$50,000	$70,000	$75,000	$85,000
9	$50,000	$70,000	$75,000	$85,000
10	$75,000	$100,000	$75,000	$100,000

Section 15.4

a. Determine the optimum portfolio, including which investments are fully or partially selected (if partial, give percentage). You may use Excel®; do *not* use SOLVER.

Section 15.5

b. Determine the optimum portfolio and its PW, specifying which investments are fully or partially (give percentage) selected using (1) the current limit on investment capital at the end of year 0, (2) plus 20 percent, and (3) minus 20 percent. Use Excel® and SOLVER.

c. Determine the optimum portfolio and its PW, specifying which investments are fully or partially (give percentage) selected using (1) the current *MARR*, (2) plus 20 percent, and (3) minus 20 percent. Use Excel® and SOLVER.

d. Determine the optimum investment portfolio and its PW when Investments 2 and 4 are indivisible, Investments 1 and 3 are divisible, and only $125,000 in investment capital will be available for follow-up investment at the end of year 1. Use Excel® and SOLVER.

Chapter 16

OBTAINING AND ESTIMATING CASH FLOWS

Starbucks purchases and roasts high quality whole bean coffees and sells them along with a variety of pastries and confections primarily through its company operated retail stores.

Starbucks Coffee

In 1971 in Seattle's Pike Place Market, a small coffee shop opened its doors for the first time. Like most new businesses, it had its share of successes and false starts, but slowly and surely it began to grow. Over the next 20 years the little coffee shop expanded both its menu and its presence in the US Northwest, growing to 116 outlets. In 1991, success led to the stock market, the company "went public" by offering stock on the Nasdaq National Market under the trading symbol "SBUX." Today, we know this company as the leading retailer and roaster of specialty coffees in the world, Starbucks. As of October 2010, Starbucks employed approximately 137,000 employees and welcomed guests into more than 16,800 locations in 50 countries.

In 2010, Starbucks' total sales revenue was $10.7 billion, up from $697 million in 1996. This represents a remarkable 20 percent compound annual growth rate! Over the same period, Starbucks net profits grew at an even more astounding 25 percent compound annual growth rate. Without question, Starbucks has achieved remarkable success in its 40 year history. In addition to these accounting measures of success, Starbucks succeeds in other ways too. Accolades include being named one of the most recognizable brand names in the world, being named one of the top 100 best businesses to work for, and being named one of the 100 best corporate citizens.

How does Starbucks achieve these remarkable results? Undoubtedly, there are many explanations, including the way Starbucks supports key decision makers with appropriate and timely information. This support includes collecting, summarizing, and reporting relevant financial information in a timely manner to internal managers and external decision makers. This is the world of accounting.

O ne of this chapter's purposes is to briefly explore, from an engineering economy perspective, the world of accounting. Accounting is a broad and complex discipline. Our purpose here is not to cover these topics to the same depth and breadth that an accountant would; rather, our purpose is to enable the engineering economist to be conversant with accountants and to have an understanding of the sources, development, and uses of typical accounting data.

A second purpose of this chapter is to address the topic of estimating cash flows. Frequently, cash flow estimation is based upon discovering the patterns underlying past cash flows and extrapolating them into the future, thus implying a reliance on accounting data from prior periods. In still other cases, the cash flows associated with engineering economic analysis cannot be extrapolated from history. Other types of estimating techniques are required for these situations.

16-1   INTRODUCTION

Engineering economic analysis is primarily concerned with comparing alternative projects on the basis of an economic measure of effectiveness. The comparison process utilizes a variety of cost terminologies and cost concepts. To begin our discussion of cost terminology, we exemplify a typical production situation.

EXAMPLE 16.1   Cost Terminology Introductory Example

Let us assume that the primary business of a small manufacturing firm is job-shop machining—that is, the firm produces a variety of products and component parts according to customer orders. Any given order may be for only five parts or as many a several hundred. The firm has periodically received orders to manufacture a part, which we will identify as Part Number 163H, for the B&K Corporation. The part has been manufactured in a four-step production sequence consisting of (1) sawing bar stock to length, (2) machining on an engine lathe, (3) machining on an upright drill press, and (4) packaging. The unit cost to produce Part Number 163H by this sequence has been $25, where the unit cost is comprised of the major cost elements of direct labor, direct materials, and overhead (prorated costs for insurance, taxes, electric power, marketing expenses, etc.). The firm is now in the process of negotiations with the B&K Corporation to obtain a contract for producing 10,000 of these parts over a 4-year period, or an average of 2,500 units/year. A contract for this volume of parts is highly desirable, but in order to obtain the contract, the firm must lower the unit cost.

An engineer for the firm has been assigned to determine production methods to lower the unit cost. After study, the engineer recommends the purchase of a small turret lathe. With the turret lathe, the processing sequence of Part Number 163H would consist essentially of (1) machining bar stock on the turret lathe and (2) packaging. The estimated unit cost for Part Number 163H by this production method would be $15. Furthermore, the production rate with the new method would be increased over the old method, because the turret lathe would replace the sawing, engine lathe, and drill press operations.

If the turret lathe is purchased, the saw, engine lathe, and drill press would not be sold but would be kept for other jobs for which the firm may receive orders. The turret lathe would be reserved for the production of Part Number 163H, but about 25 percent excess production capacity could be devoted to other jobs.

The incremental investment required to purchase the turret lathe and the new tooling required, as well as installing the machine, is $50,000. The turret lathe's physical life is judged to be about 15 years, but assume that federal tax laws permit the investment capital to be recovered through annual depreciation charges in 5 years. At the end of 5 years, the firm estimates the turret lathe's salvage value would be $25,000. If the maximum unit price the B&K Corporation will pay for Part Number 163H is $22, should the firm accept the contract for 10,000 parts and then purchase the turret lathe in order to execute the contract?

Using the techniques and methods presented in previous chapters, we could answer this question. However, that is not our purpose here. The example situation has been cited to illustrate that considerable research and investigation is required to determine or estimate the cost figures used in economic decision making. This cost information is typically obtained from a variety of sources, such as company production records, accounting records, manufacturer's catalogs and technical specifications, publications from the U.S. Government Printing Office, and others. To make effective comparisons and intelligent recommendations, an engineering economist must therefore be familiar with cost terminology, cost factors, and estimating techniques used by different specialists.

16-2   COST TERMINOLOGY

In this section, cost definitions and concepts are considered from five different viewpoints: (1) life cycle, (2) past/future, (3) manufacturing cost structure, (4) fixed/ variable, and (5) average/marginal. Each viewpoint offers unique advantages with respect to economic decision making. The viewpoint to be used in analyzing a particular decision depends upon the analysis's purpose. Frequently, multiple viewpoints are employed in a single analysis. Examining a decision-making situation from multiple viewpoints can help ensure that all relevant costs (and revenues) have been considered prior to conducting the analysis. Further, it helps to ensure that the identified costs and revenues are correctly documented and incorporated within the analysis.

Five Cost Viewpoints

1. Life Cycle Viewpoint
2. Past/Future Viewpoint
3. Manufacturing Cost Structure Viewpoint
4. Fixed/Variable Viewpoint
5. Average/Marginal Viewpoint

16.2.1   Life Cycle Viewpoint

The life cycle viewpoint deals with costs and revenues based upon when they occur within an asset's service life. The term *asset* should be interpreted in the general sense as a machine, a unit of equipment, a product line, a project, a building, a system, and so forth. The life cycle viewpoint includes design and development costs, fabrication and testing costs, operating and maintenance costs, operating revenues, and salvage value.

This textbook is primarily concerned with economic justification of engineering projects, the replacement of existing projects or assets, and the economic comparison of alternative projects. For the purposes of these types of analysis, we will define the life cycle viewpoint to consist of (1) first cost, (2) operating and maintenance costs and revenues, and (3) salvage value.

First Cost

The first cost of an asset is the total initial investment required to get the asset ready for service; such costs are usually nonrecurring during the asset's life. For the purchase of a machine tool, its first cost may consist of the following major elements: (1) the basic machine cost, (2) costs for training personnel, (3) shipping and installation costs, (4) initial tooling costs, and (5) supporting equipment costs. The installation costs may include, for example, preparing a foundation; vibration and noise insulation; providing heat, light, and power supply; and cost of testing. Supporting equipment costs may include computer-control hardware and software and a spare-parts inventory.

For other projects, a different set of first cost elements may be appropriate. Some projects may include working capital for inventories; accounts receivable; and cash for wages, materials, and so forth. In any case, the emphasis here is that an item's first cost normally involves more cost elements than just the basic purchase price. Whether the first cost elements are aggregated or maintained separately depends on income-tax considerations and whether or not a before-tax or after-tax economic analysis is desired. Certain income-tax laws and depreciation methods were presented in Chapters 9 and 10, so we won't elaborate on this particular point here.

Operating and Maintenance Costs and Revenues

Operating and maintenance costs are recurring costs that are necessary to operate and maintain an item during its useful life. Operating costs usually consist of labor, material, and overhead items. Depending upon the accounting system a firm uses, a wide range of cost factors may be included in the major cost classification of overhead. Typical overhead items are fuel or electric power, insurance premiums, inventory charges, indirect labor (as opposed to direct labor), administrative and management expenses, and so forth. It is usually assumed that operating and maintenance costs are annual costs, but maintenance costs may not be on a recurring, annual basis—that is, a regular annual schedule of minor or preventive maintenance may be followed, or it could be policy that maintenance is performed only when necessary, such as when a major overhaul is required. In most cases, the maintenance policy would consist of both preventive maintenance and maintenance on an as-needed basis. In any case, repair and upkeep result in costs that must be recognized in the economic analysis of engineering projects.

Operating revenues are revenues that result from having and using the asset. In many cases, these revenues are estimated as recurring annual cash flows. They may have a consistent pattern (such as a uniform, gradient, or geometric series), or they may exhibit no consistent pattern and need to be estimated for each year individually. In the case of manufacturing assets and projects, the revenues are typically based on estimates of the volume and revenue generated by the parts that utilize the asset or result from the project.

Salvage Value

When an item's life cycle ends, disposal costs usually result. These may include labor and material costs to remove the item; shipping costs; or special costs, such as that for disposing of hazardous materials. Although disposal costs may be incurred at the end of the life cycle, most items have some monetary value at the time of their disposal. This value is the market or trade-in value (i.e., the actual dollar worth for which the item may be sold at the time of disposal). After deducting the cost of disposal from the market value at disposal, the resulting net dollar worth is termed the *salvage value*.

The market value, the disposal costs, and the salvage value are usually not known with certainty and therefore must be estimated. For an item that satisfies the IRS definition of a capital asset and that decreases in value over time through physical deterioration, the IRS has approved depreciation methods that can serve to estimate the rate of deterioration and consequent decrease in the asset's value. The capital asset's value at the end of a given accounting period during the asset's life is termed the *book value. Scrap value,* on the other hand, refers only to the value of the material of which the item is made. For example, a 4-year-old automobile may have a scrap value of $500 but a market value of $5,000. A distinction between these terms is generally not important for evaluating potential investment projects; therefore, we use *salvage value* to denote the end-of-life value. For example, a trade-in value of $3,000 minus disposal costs of $500 equals a net salvage value of $2,500.

The life cycle viewpoint obviously involves a time horizon, and the end of an item's life may be judged from either a functional or an economic point of view. An item's economic life is generally shorter than its functional life. For example, an engine lathe may remain functional for 15 years or more, but because of periodic advancements in machine design technology, newer engine lathes have higher production rates; therefore, an engine lathe's economically useful life may be only 10 years. An item's economic life is usually a matter of company policy, which is greatly influenced by income-tax considerations.

16.2.2 Past/Future Viewpoint

The past/future viewpoint deals with costs and revenues based upon when they occur relative to "time now." This viewpoint incorporates more than just a timeline; it also includes concepts related to past and future cash flows such as sunk costs, opportunity costs, and cost of capital. Each of these is explained in more detail in the examples and paragraphs that follow.

EXAMPLE 16.2 Past Costs and Sunk Costs

Past costs are historical costs that have occurred for the item under consideration. Sunk costs are past costs that are unrecoverable. The distinction is perhaps best made through examples. Assume that an investor purchases 100 shares of common stock in the JHP Corporation through a broker at $25/share. In addition, the investor pays $85 in brokerage fees and other charges. Just 2 months later, and before receiving any dividend payments, the purchaser resells the 100 shares of common stock through the same broker at $35/share minus $105 for selling expenses. The purchaser realizes a net profit of $810

($3500 − $2,500 − $85 − $105) on these transactions. At the time of sale, the $2,500 and $85 are past costs, but because these are recovered after the sales transaction, sunk costs are not incurred. If, on the other hand, the investor sold the 100 shares 2 months after purchase and the market price was $20/share, with a $70 charge for selling fees, the investor would incur a capital loss of $655 ($2,000 − $2,500 − $85 − $70). In this instance, some of the past costs would be recovered, but the $655 capital loss would be a sunk cost. If the investor reasons that the market price will decline further or if he simply needs the money, the $655 sunk cost should be ignored if the shares are to be sold for $20 each. However, sunk costs are not totally irrelevant to a present decision. They may qualify as capital losses and serve to offset capital gains or other taxable income and thus reduce income-taxes paid. Past costs and sunk costs provide information that can improve the accuracy of estimating future costs for similar items.

EXAMPLE 16.3 Another Example of Sunk Costs

Another example of sunk costs is the purchase and sale of a piece of equipment. Assume the equipment is purchased for $10,000, and the salvage value at the end of 5 years of service is estimated to be $5,000. For illustrative purposes, we will further assume that the annual decrease in the equipment's value through depreciation is $1,000 per year. The $1,000 annual cost of depreciation is a cost of production that, in theory, should be allocated to the equipment's output. After allocating this and other manufacturing costs, general and administrative costs, and marketing costs to each unit of production, the total unit cost is determined. A profit is then added to each unit of production in order to arrive at the unit selling price. Thus, when a unit is sold, a portion of each sales dollar returns a portion of the depreciation expense. In this illustration, it is assumed that sales will return, or recover, the total estimated depreciation expense of $5,000 (first cost minus estimated salvage value) for the 5-year period. However, if the equipment has a market value of over $2,000 at the end of 5 years, there is a $3,000 ($5,000 − $2,000) sunk cost. The $3,000 capital loss represents an error in estimating the rate of depreciation, and the owner cannot insist that the equipment is worth $5,000 when the market value for the 5-year-old equipment is, in fact, only $2,000. If the equipment is kept, it is argued that the true value being kept is thus only $2,000.

All costs that may occur in the future are termed *future costs*. These may include operating costs for labor and materials, maintenance costs, overhaul costs, and disposal costs. In any case, by virtue of occurring in the future, these costs are rarely known with certainty and must therefore be estimated. This is also true for future revenues or savings if these are involved in a given project. Estimates of future costs or revenues are uncertain and subject to error.

The cost of forgoing an opportunity to earn interest, or a return, on investment funds is termed an *opportunity cost*. This concept is best explained through examples. If a person has $1,000 and stores this cash in a home safe, she is forgoing the opportunity to earn interest on the money by establishing a savings account in a local bank that pays, for example, 5 percent annual compound interest. (Of course, investments other than savings accounts are possible). For a 1-year period, the person is forgoing the opportunity to earn $(0.05)($1,000) = 50. The $50 amount is thus termed the opportunity cost associated with storing the $1,000 in the home safe.

EXAMPLE 16.4   Opportunity Cost

Assume that a person has $5,000 cash on hand. This amount is considered equity capital if the $5,000 was not borrowed (i.e., there is no debt obligation involved). The person has available secure investment opportunities such as establishing a personal savings account in a commercial bank or purchasing other financial instruments. From the available investment opportunities, suppose the optimum combination of risk (security level) and interest yield on the investment results in a 10 percent annual interest. Thus, the investment of $5,000 would yield $(0.10)(\$5,000) = \$500$ each year. If, instead of investing the $5,000, the person purchases an automobile for the same amount, he will forgo the opportunity to earn $500 interest/year. The $500 amount is again termed an annual opportunity cost associated with purchasing the automobile.

The same logic applies in defining an annual opportunity cost for investments in business and engineering projects. For example, purchasing production machinery with $20,000 of equity funds prevents this money from being invested elsewhere with greater security and/or higher profit potential. This concept of opportunity cost is fundamental to the study of engineering economy and is a cost element that is included in virtually all methodologies for comparing alternative projects.

In manufacturing and retailing, one of the most common uses of the term *opportunity cost* is in conjunction with inventory. Holding inventory (raw material, work-in-process (WIP), or finished goods) is said to carry a high opportunity cost. For example, in the last fiscal year, Starbucks reported inventories of over $600 million in their financial reports. Most of these inventory items were likely planned and needed to provide the availability of products and high levels of customer service that patrons have come to expect from Starbucks. However, these inventories do not come without cost. If we assume that Starbucks could identify improvement projects that would return 15 percent if funded, then the $600 million tied up in inventories carries a $90 million opportunity cost. These types of realizations have companies like Starbucks constantly striving to find ways to maintain high levels of customer service while simultaneously lowering investments in inventories.

In Chapter 4, we discussed the concept of opportunity costs under the heading of *MARR*. Some individuals define *MARR* based on the cost of capital. As used in this text, the term *cost of capital* refers to the cost of obtaining funds for financing projects through debt obligations and/or equity sources. Debt funds are usually obtained from external sources by (1) borrowing money from banks or other financial organizations (e.g., insurance companies and pension funds) and (2) issuing bonds. These debt obligations are normally long-term and result in interest payments on, say, a monthly, quarterly, semiannual, or annual basis. The interest payments are thus a cost of borrowed capital. Financing projects through issuing bonds is a method of obtaining capital funds that may be less familiar to the reader than borrowing money from a bank. Some elaboration of bonds is therefore appropriate.

Bonds are issued by various organizational units, including partnerships, corporations (profit or nonprofit), governmental units (municipal, state, and federal), or other legal entities. The sale of bonds represents a legal debt of the issuing organization; as such, bonds are generally secured (or guaranteed) by the organization's assets (examples are mortgage bonds or collateral bonds). Debenture bonds, on the other hand, are promissory notes or just a promise to pay. In any case, the purchaser of a bond has legal claim to the assets of the issuing organization but has no ownership privileges in it. In the sense that bonds are debt obligations and not ownership shares, they are considered a more secure investment than either common or preferred stock. This statement should not be taken as a universal truth, however, since the security level for a bond or a stock depends on many factors, economic and otherwise; the principal factor is the financial soundness of the issuing unit. Additional details on interest payments for bank loans and interest payments for bonds were presented in Chapter 3.

Another method of financing engineering projects is through the use of equity funds, which are generally obtained from one or both of the following sources: (1) common or preferred stock authorized by the company and sold through brokers to investors, or (2) earnings accumulated from prior years and retained by the company. Both of these sources of funds incur an opportunity cost. Chapter 4 presented details on calculating these costs. Additional information related to a company's equity funding is presented later in the "General Accounting Principles" section.

16.2.3   Manufacturing Cost Structure Viewpoint

The manufacturing cost structure viewpoint looks at a product's selling price and breaks this price into its constituent pieces. A typical cost structure for a manufactured item, adapted from Ostwald,[1] is shown in Figure 16.1. Before examining the details of this figure, two general comments are appropriate. First, while this figure specifically targets a manufacturing cost structure, the major elements (the boxes in the figure) would remain essentially unchanged in other environments (retail, service, etc.). The changes you would see in these other environments are the labels shown for the various combinations. For example, at Starbucks, Cost of Goods Manufactured would likely be referred to as Cost of Sales, while Factory Overhead would be referred to as Store Operating Expenses.

The second general comment about Figure 16.1 deals with the size of the boxes in the figure. Just because the boxes appear to be approximately equal in height does not mean the costs are approximately equal. The relative sizes of these component pieces can and does vary dramatically between sectors (manufacturing, retail, etc.), between industries within sectors, and between companies within industries. The purpose of the figure is to show the structure of selling price, not the relative size of the constituent pieces.

The cost of goods sold, as shown in Figure 16.1, is the total cost of manufacturing and marketing a product. An amount of profit is added to this total cost to arrive at a selling price. Such a cost structure is helpful in arriving at a unit cost, which is a primary objective of cost accounting. The term *cost of goods sold,* as used here, has a different meaning than when used in general accounting practice, particularly for retail businesses. General accounting defines this term to be beginning-of-the period inventory plus purchases minus end-of-period inventory. Different meanings for the same terminology are unfortunate, but they do occur in the literature and in practice, and the reader is cautioned on this point. To simplify the treatment of the total cost of goods sold (as defined by Figure 16.1), the major cost elements can be defined as direct material, direct labor, and overhead costs.

Direct material costs and direct labor costs are the costs of material and labor that are easily measured and can be conveniently allocated to a specific operation, product, or project. Indirect costs for both labor and material, on the other hand, are either very difficult or impossible to assign directly to a specific operation, product, or project. The expense of directly assigning such costs is prohibitive, and costs are therefore considered to be indirect for accounting purposes.

---

[1]Ostwald, P. F. and T. S. McLaren, *Cost Analysis and Estimating for Engineering and Management,* 4th Revised Edition, Prentice Hall, 2003.

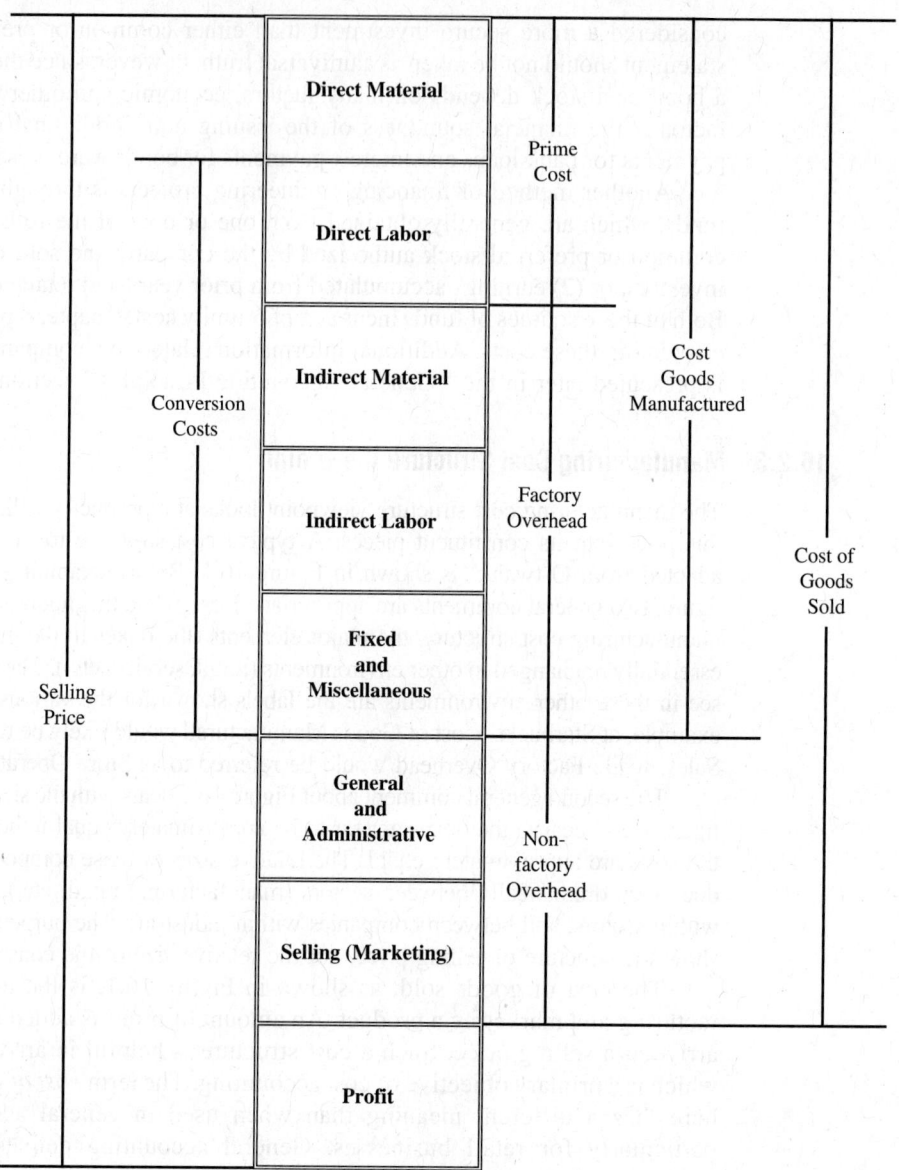

FIGURE 16.1
Manufacturing Cost Structure.

EXAMPLE 16.5 Direct and Indirect Costs

As an example of these different cost elements, suppose the raw material for a given part is a rectangular gray iron casting. The casting is milled on five sides, the unmachined surface is painted and air-dried, and then four through holes are drilled and tapped. The finished parts are stacked in wooden boxes, 30 per box, and are delivered to a customer.

In this example, the direct labor required per part to machine, paint, and package is probably readily determined. The labor required to receive the raw materials, handle parts between workstations, load boxes onto a truck, and deliver material to the customer is less easily identified and assigned to each part. This labor would be classified as *indirect*, especially if the labor in receiving, handling, shipping, and delivery is responsible for dealing with many different parts during the normal workday. The unit purchase price of the gray iron casting is an identifiable direct material cost. The cost of paint used per part may or may not be easily determined; if it is not, it is an example of indirect material cost. Also, any lubricating oils used during the machining processes would be an indirect material cost, not readily assigned on a cost-per-part basis.

Overhead costs consist of all costs of manufacturing other than direct material and direct labor, including indirect labor and indirect material. A given firm may identify different overhead categories, such as factory overhead, general and administrative overhead, and marketing expenses. Furthermore, overhead amounts may be allocated to a total plant, departments within a plant, or even to a given piece of equipment. Typical specific items of cost included in the general category of overhead are indirect materials, indirect labor, taxes, insurance premiums, rent, maintenance and repairs, supervisory and administrative personnel (technical, sales, and management), and utilities (water, electric power, etc.). Depreciation expenses are also usually included in the general overhead but may occasionally be considered a part of direct costs. It is the task of cost accounting to assign a proportionate amount of these costs to various products manufactured or to services provided by a business organization. This topic is addressed in more detail later in this chapter.

16.2.4 Fixed and Variable Viewpoint

Fixed costs do not vary in proportion to the quantity of output. General administrative expenses, taxes and insurance, rent, building and equipment depreciation, and utilities are examples of cost items that are usually invariant with production volume and hence are termed *fixed costs*. Such costs may be fixed only over a given range of production; they may then change and be fixed for another range of production. Hence the concept of a *relevant range* is frequently associated with fixed costs. For example, lighting costs in a manufacturing plant may be considered fixed for single-shift operation, regardless of how many units are produced. However, if demand warrants adding a second shift, lighting costs will increase to a new, higher valued, fixed cost. In this case, we would define lighting costs to be fixed with two relevant ranges. This suggests that fixed costs can, in some cases, be represented graphically as a step function. The reader is cautioned to recognize that if the width of the relevant ranges becomes small, the cost may be more appropriately treated as a variable cost rather than a fixed cost.

Variable costs vary in proportion to quantity of output. These costs are usually for direct material and direct labor. For instance, in Example 16.5, gray iron casting was used to produce a part. This cost was presented to illustrate direct material cost, since it can be directly traced to the product produced. The cost of the castings is also an example of a variable cost. This is the case since the cost of castings is directly proportional to the number of parts produced. In other words, if the factory produces and sells 1,000 parts, there will be an associated cost of 1,000 times the purchase price of the castings.

This example also illustrates another point—the notion of multiple viewpoints within a single analysis. If we are using the manufacturing cost structure viewpoint, the cost of castings is direct material. If we are using the fixed variable viewpoint, the cost of castings is a variable cost. The fact that this cost can be classified in two ways does not constitute a flaw in our representation scheme; it simply means the way we interpret a particular cost is dependent upon the viewpoint we have adopted. The intent of having and using multiple viewpoints is to facilitate communication with different audiences and to help the engineering economist ensure that all relevant costs have been incorporated in the analysis. Embracing the second of these two points is best assured by questioning each alternative's cash flows from each of the various viewpoints. For example, the engineering economist might ask, "Have we considered all costs within the manufacturing cost structure?" and "Have we considered all fixed or variable costs?" and "What (if any) of these costs we are considering are sunk costs?" and so on.

Many cost items have both fixed and variable components. For example, a plant maintenance department may have a constant number of maintenance personnel at fixed salaries over a wide range of production output. However, the amount of maintenance work done and replacement parts required on equipment may vary in proportion to production output. Thus, total annual maintenance costs for a plant over several years would consist of both fixed and variable components. Indirect labor, equipment depreciation, and electrical power are other cost items that may consist of fixed and variable components. Determining the fixed and variable portion of such a cost item may not be possible; if it is possible, the expense of establishing detailed measurement techniques and accounting records may be prohibitive. A comprehensive discussion on this issue is beyond the scope of this book, and the reader is referred to books on general cost accounting for further information.

Certain total costs (TC) can be expressed as the sum of fixed costs (FC) and variable costs (VC). As an example, the total annual cost for operating a personal automobile for a given year might be expressed as

$$TC(x) = FC + VC(x) \tag{16.1}$$

where x = miles per year. Costs for insurance, license tags, depreciation, certain maintenance, and interest on borrowed money if the automobile was financed are essentially fixed costs, independent of the miles traveled per year. Expenses for gasoline, oil, tire replacements, and certain maintenance are proportional to, or functional with, the mileage per year. One could argue that depreciation expenses are comprised of both fixed and variable components, since wear and tear on an automobile increases as the number of miles driven increases. We will not pursue that argument here. Arbitrarily assigning numerical values to the total cost function, assume that

$$TC(x) = \$950 + \$0.15x$$

is a valid relationship for a given year in question (the relevant range is restricted to a given year, since actual depreciation expenses, and hence the fixed expenses, may vary from year to year). This relationship is linear in terms of x, miles driven. In general, the variable cost component of total cost is not always linear function. However, in many real situations, the relationship is sufficiently linear as to make the assumption of a linear relationship reasonable. The reader is cautioned not to make this assumption without first examining the data. Figure 16.2 graphically illustrates the total cost function.

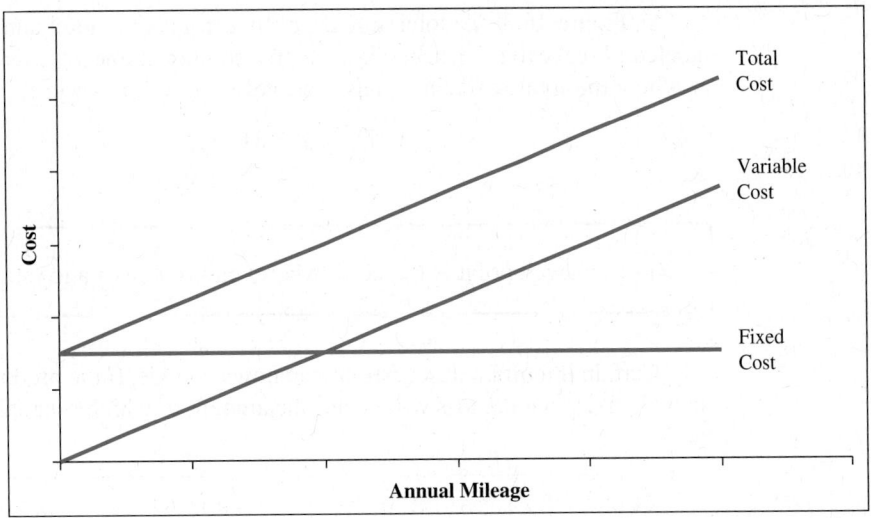

FIGURE 16.2

Total Annual Cost as a Function of Mileage.

Now let us consider Figure 16.2 as a total cost function for a production line in a manufacturing firm where the output from the line is a single product. Furthermore, let it be assumed that each unit of production can be sold for $R and that the total revenue (TR) is a linear function of the production quantity:

$$\text{TR}(x) = \$Rx \qquad (16.2)$$

Adding this functional relationship to Figure 16.2 and modifying the terminology for this example yields Figure 16.3.

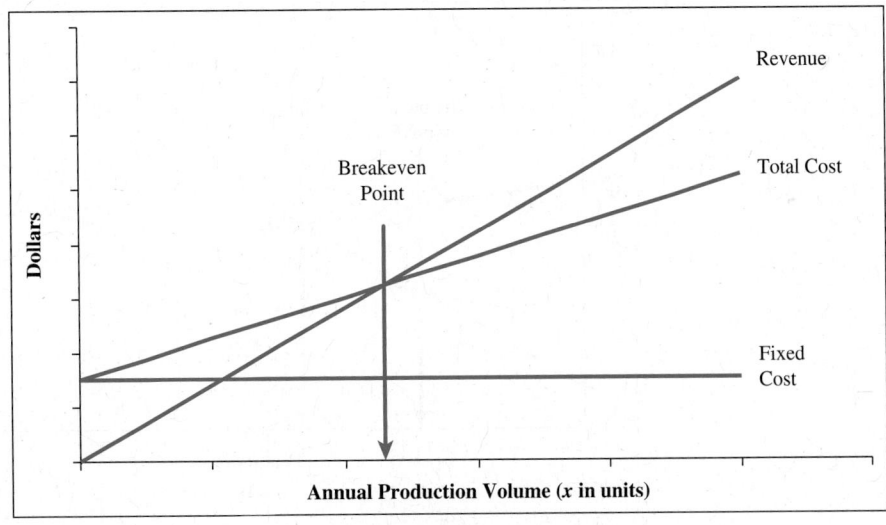

FIGURE 16.3

Revenue and Cost as a Function of Production Volume.

In Figure 16.3, the total annual revenue equals the total annual cost at the point labeled "breakeven." The break-even production volume, referred to as x^*, is the point at which the total revenue equals the total cost, as shown in Equation 16.3.

$$\text{TR}(x^*) = \text{TC}(x^*)$$
$$= \text{FC} + \text{VC}(x^*) \tag{16.3}$$

> The breakeven point is the point where total revenues and total costs are equal.

Certain important observations can now be made. If the production volume is less than x^*, an annual net loss will occur, the amount of which is equal to $\text{TC}(x) - \text{TR}(x)$,

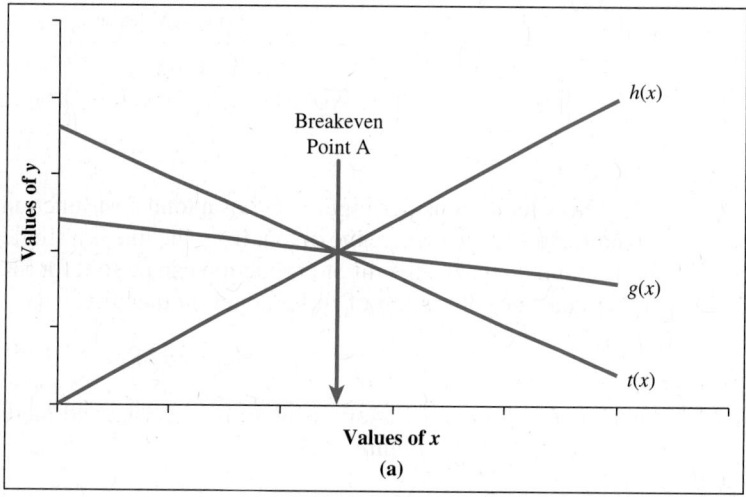

(a)

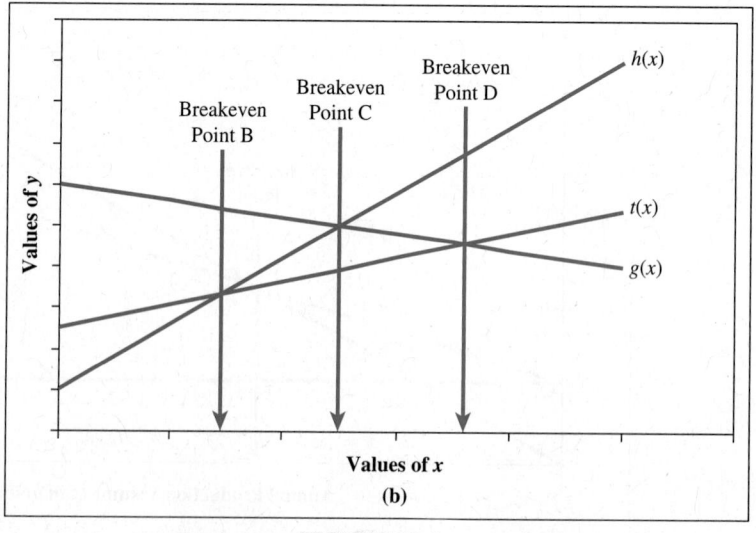

(b)

FIGURE 16.4
Breakeven Points (a) Single, (b) Multiple.

evaluated for a particular value of x. By the same token, if the production volume is greater than x^*, then an annual net revenue or profit will result. The amount of annual profit is equal to $\text{TR}(x) - \text{TC}(x)$, evaluated for a particular value of x.

It is generally desirable to have a low break-even value. For the general example of Figure 16.3, this can be accomplished in three ways: (1) increasing the slope of the total revenue line, (2) decreasing the slope of the variable cost line, and (3) decreasing the magnitude of the fixed cost line. Increasing the slope of the total revenue line means increasing the product's selling price, which may be a poor marketing strategy in a competitive market environment where sales would be lost. Fixed costs, although not literally fixed in all cases, can be difficult to reduce. Thus, reducing variable costs for direct material and labor usually offers the first point of attack for the engineer or analyst for profit improvement.

The concept of break-even analysis is general. Assuming that a break-even point exists for two relationships—$y = g(.)$ and $y = h(.)$—that are functions of a single variable x, the value of x for breakeven, say x^*, may be determined from equating $g(x) = h(x)$ and solving for x^*. The concept can be extended to more than two functions of a single variable, say $y = h(x)$, $y = g(x)$, and $y = t(x)$. If these are all linear functions, then Figure 16.4 depicts two of the possible results.

In Figure 16.4a, all three functions intersect at a single point; thus, a single value of x^* can be determined (Point A). In Figure 16.4b, there is no unique break-even value of x involving all three functional relationships. The linear equations $y = h(x)$ and $y = t(x)$ intersect at Point B, which is the break-even value for these two relationships. Point C is the break-even value for $y = h(x)$ and $y = g(x)$. Point D is the break-even value for $y = g(x)$ and $y = t(x)$.

The concept of break-even analysis also extends to nonlinear functions, with one or more break-even values and functions of more than a single variable, which may be of linear or nonlinear form. However, examples and problems dealing only with functions of a single variable will be presented in this chapter.

EXAMPLE 16.6   Break-Even Point for Production

The cost of tooling and direct labor required to set up for a machining job on a turret lathe is $300. Once set up, the variable cost to produce one finished unit consists of $2.50 for material and $1.00 for labor to operate the lathe. For simplicity, it is assumed these are the only relevant fixed and variable costs. If each finished unit can be sold for $5, determine (1) the production quantity required to break even and (2) the net profit (or loss) if the lot size is 1,000 units.

Letting $x = $ the production volume in units, then

$$R(x) = TC(x) = FC + VC(x)$$

and

$$\$5.00x = \$300 + (\$2.50 + \$1.00)x$$

Simplifying and solving for x yields x^* (the break-even value):

$$x^* = \$300/\$1.50 = 200 \text{ units}$$

For a production output of 1,000 units, the net profit, P, is calculated to be

$$P = \$5(1,000 \text{ units}) - (\$2.50 + \$1.00)(1,000 \text{ units}) - \$300 = \$1,200$$

EXAMPLE 16.7 *Alternative Analysis Using Breakeven*[2]

This example concerns selecting between two alternative methods of processing crude oil in a producing oil field, where the basis for the decision is the number of barrels of crude oil processed per year. The two methods of processing the crude oil are (1) a manually operated tank battery or (2) an automated tank battery. The tank batteries consist of heaters, treaters, storage tanks, and so forth, that remove salt water and sediment from crude oil prior to its entrance to pipelines for transport to an oil refinery.

For each alternative, fixed costs and variable costs are involved. Fixed costs include items such as pumper labor; maintenance (fixed over the production quantity of interest); taxes; certain energy costs (power to operate control panels and motors in continuous operation); and, for manual tank batteries, a cost for oil "shrinkage." Variable costs for chemical additives, heating, and noncontinuous operating motors are proportionate with the volume of oil being processed. This relationship is assumed to be linear over the production quantity of interest. The necessary data are given in Tables 16.1 and 16.2 and are considered valid for production quantities up to 1,000 barrels/day (365,000 barrels/yr).

In addition to the fixed and variable costs given in Table 16.1 for the automatic tank battery operation, other annual fixed costs are

$$D_1 = \text{annual cost of depreciation and interest} = \$3,082$$

$$M_1 = \text{annual cost of maintenance, taxes, and labor} = \$5,485$$

TABLE 16.1
Cost Data for Automatic Tank Battery Operations.

COST	$/day
Fixed cost	
Control panel power	0.15
Circulating pump power (3 hp)	0.82
Maintenance	1.00
Meter Calibration	0.40
Chemical pump power (1/4 hp)	0.32
Total Fixed Cost	**$2.69**
Fixed Cost per year = $2.69 × 365 = $982	
Variable Cost	
Pipeline pump (5 hp @ 50% utilization)	0.63
Chemical additives (7.5 qt/day)	3.75
Inhibitor (2 qt/day)	1.00
Gas (10.8 mcf/day × $0.0275/mcf)	0.30
Total Variable Cost	**$5.68**
Variable cost per barrel = 0.01136/bbl @ 500 bbl/day	

[2]This example, with slight modification, is taken from Ferguson, E.J. and J.E. Shamblin, "Break-Even Analysis," *The Journal of Industrial Engineering*, 18 (8), August 1967 with permission of the publisher.

TABLE 16.2
Cost Data for Manual Tank Battery Operation.

COST	$/day
Fixed cost	
Chemical pump power	0.16
Circulating pump power	0.82
Total Fixed Cost	**$0.98**
Fixed Cost per year = $0.98 × 365 = $358	
Variable Cost	
Chemical additives (7.5 qt/day)	3.75
(10.8 mcf/day × $0.0275/mcf)	0.30
Total Variable Cost	**$4.05**
Variable cost per barrel = 0.00810/bbl @ 500 bbl/day	

Letting x = the number of barrels of oil processed per year, the total annual cost, $TC_1(x)$, for the automatic tank battery operations is given by

$$TC_1(x) = FC_1 + VC_1(x)$$
$$= (\$982 + \$3,082 + \$5,485) + \$0.01136x$$
$$= \$9,549 + \$0.01136x$$

In addition to the fixed and variable costs given in Table 16.2 for the manual tank battery operations, other annual fixed costs are

$$D_2 = \text{annual cost of depreciation and interest} = \$2,017$$
$$M_2 = \text{annual cost of maintenance, taxes, and labor} = \$7,921$$

Then, the total annual cost, $TC_2(x)$, for the manual tank battery operation is given by

$$TC_2(x) = FC_2 + VC_2(x)$$
$$= (\$358 + \$2,017 + \$7,921) + \$0.00810x$$
$$= \$10,296 + \$0.00810x$$

By equating the two total cost functions, the break-even production volume can be determined as

$$TC_1(x) = TC_2(x)$$
$$\$9,549 + \$0.01136x = \$10,296 + \$0.00810x$$
$$x^* = 229,141 \text{ barrels/year}$$

The interpretation of the break-even point in this example is that $x^* = 229,141$ barrels/year is the point of indifference between the choice of the two alternatives. If production volume is less than x^*, then the first alternative, or the automatic tank battery operation, would be preferred. For instance, if $x = 200,000$ barrels/year, then $TC_1(x) = \$11,821$ and $TC_2(x) = \$11,916$. Similarly, if production volume is greater than x^*, the manual tank battery operation would be preferred. In our particular case, it would now be necessary to obtain a production estimate from the field engineers. Once determined, we could recommend which processing option is preferred.

16.2.5   Average and Marginal Viewpoint

The average/marginal viewpoint deals with costs expressed in terms of units of output. While this sounds similar to variable cost, the concept here is significantly different. The average cost is the ratio of total costs incurred divided by the number of units produced while incurring those costs. The marginal cost is the incremental cost associated with increasing the output by one unit. The definition of marginal cost changes slightly if the output is continuous (e.g., gallons of paint) rather than discrete (e.g., number of automobiles). This difference is explored more fully in the material that follows.

The average cost of one unit of output (unit cost) is the ratio of total cost to the quantity of output (miles traveled, production volume, etc.); that is,

$$AC(x) = \frac{TC(x)}{x} \tag{16.4}$$

where

$AC(x) = $ average cost per unit of x

$TC(x) = $ total cost for x units of output

$x = $ output quantity

The average cost is usually a variable function of the output quantity and normally decreases with an increasing output quantity. Using the automobile example from Section 16.2.4, which had a total cost function of $\$(950 + 0.15x)$, the average cost, in dollars per mile, is given by

$$AC(x) = \frac{950 + 0.15x}{x} = \frac{950}{x} + 0.15$$

If the automobile travels 10,000 miles/year, then the average operating cost is $\$(950/10,000 + 0.15) = \$0.245$/mile. For a total annual travel distance of 20,000 miles, the average operating cost decreases to $\$0.1975$/mile. This can be explained by noting that as the output quantity x increases, the proportion of the fixed cost allocated to each unit of output decreases. This relationship is a fundamental economic principle often referred to as the *economies of scale,* which underlies the economic benefits of mass production. Such a relationship assumes that the variable cost coefficient remains constant over the range of the output variable x. In a production environment, it is possible that the variable cost coefficient will increase as the production volume increases due to increased maintenance expenses, defective product, and so on.

For a total cost function that is continuous in the variable x, marginal cost is defined as the derivative of the total cost function (dependent variable) with respect to x, or $dTC(x)/dx$. This is true for continuous functions that are linear or nonlinear in the variable x. In the special case of a continuous total cost function that is linear in x, such as $TC(x) = \$950 + 0.15x$, then $dTC(x)/dx = \$0.15$. In this case, marginal cost is the constant value $\$0.15$ and is the cost required to increase the output quantity x by one unit.

If the total cost function is discontinuous and defined only for discrete values of x (for example, $x = 1,2,3,\ldots$), then difference equations must be used to determine marginal costs. For example, $TC(6) - TC(5)$ is the marginal cost of increasing the output quantity from $x = 5$ to $x = 6$. Thus, in the discrete case, marginal cost is always the cost required to increase the output quantity x by one unit at a specified level of output. This is true for discrete total cost functions regardless of whether they are linear or nonlinear.

Two additional observations are noteworthy with respect to average and marginal cost. First, examine the average cost equation above and consider what happens as x, the number produced, grows ever larger. As x increases, the proportion of the fixed cost assigned to each unit grows increasingly smaller, approaching 0 in the limit. This implies that, under the assumptions above, the average cost converges to the marginal cost. In the limit (when x is infinity) the average cost equals the marginal cost.

A second observation is related to the emerging concept of *economies of scope*. In contrast to economies of scale, which encourages large production runs to drive down average cost, economies of scope suggests that fixed costs be driven as low as possible, ideally to 0. Note that in terms of our average cost equation above, this implies that the point of attack is to reduce the $950 numerator of the fixed cost term. Similar to the economies of scale approach, the limiting case for average cost is the $0.15 marginal cost per unit. However, unlike economies of scale, economies of scope strives to disconnect the ideal average cost from the production volume. Thus, costs are reduced due to the elimination (or at least minimization) of the need to create large inventories to drive down average cost. This approach has the added advantage of enhancing both cost performance and production flexibility.

EXAMPLE 16.8 **Marginal Cost**

For a certain production process, fixed costs are $60,000. Variable costs are $30 per unit of production. Therefore, the total cost function is given by $TC(x) = 60,000 + 30x$. What is the marginal cost at $x = 10$? $x = 20$?

There are two ways to solve this problem: (1) difference equations, and (2) differentiation. For purposes of illustration, both approaches will be demonstrated.

Difference Equations

Marginal cost at 10 = total cost at 11 − total cost at 10

$$MC(10) = TC(11) - TC(10)$$
$$MC(10) = [\$60,000 + \$30(11)] - [\$60,000 + \$30(10)]$$
$$MC(10) = \$60,330 - \$60,300$$
$$MC(10) = \$30$$

Similarly,

$$MC(20) = TC(21) - TC(20)$$
$$MC(20) = [\$60,000 + \$30(21)] - [\$60,000 + \$30(20)]$$
$$MC(20) = \$60,630 - \$60,600$$
$$MC(20) = \$30$$

Differentiation

Marginal cost at 10 = first derivative of the total cost function evaluated at 10

$$MC(x) = d/dx\, TC(x)$$
$$MC(x) = d/dx\, [\$60,000 + \$30x]$$
$$MC(x) = \$30$$

therefore

$$MC(10) = \$30 \text{ and } MC(20) = \$30$$

TABLE 16.3
Relationship Between Marginal Cost and Total Cost.
If $MC(x) > 0$ then $TC(x + 1) > TC(x)$
If $MC(x) = 0$ then $TC(x + 1) = TC(x)$
If $MC(x) < 0$ then $TC(x + 1) < TC(x)$

TABLE 16.4
Relationship Between Marginal Cost and Average Cost.
If $MC(x) < AC(x)$ then $AC(x + 1) < AC(x)$
If $MC(x) = AC(x)$ then $AC(x + 1) = AC(x)$
If $MC(x) > AC(x)$ then $AC(x + 1) > AC(x)$

The concept of marginalism is general and applies to other mathematical functions as well. For example, marginal revenues can be determined from total revenue functions, marginal profit values can be determined from total profit functions, and so forth. Marginal revenue (profit) is the additional revenue (profit) received from selling one more unit of the output quantity x at a specified level of output.

Marginal and average values corresponding to a specified output quantity are generally different. If the marginal cost is smaller than the average cost, an increase in output will result in a reduction of average cost. This can be seen by recalling the now familiar automobile problem, when $TC(x) = \$950 + \$0.15x$. The average cost is $AC(x) = \$950/x + \$0.15$ and the marginal cost is $MC(x) = \$0.15$. Thus, for all nonnegative finite values of x, marginal cost is always smaller than the average cost, and the unit cost will continue to decrease as x is increased. Such a relationship is not true in general for nonlinear total cost functions. Tables 16.3 and 16.4 summarize the relationships between marginal cost and total cost (Table 16.3) and between marginal cost and average cost (Table 16.4). The following example illustrates some of these cost, revenue, and profit relationships.

EXAMPLE 16.9 Cost, Revenue, and Profit Relationships

A small firm blends and bags chemicals, primarily for home gardening purposes. The market area for the firm is local, and all sales are to wholesale distributors. For one pesticide dust product, sales and production cost records over the past 10 seasons have been reviewed and analyzed. The following equations approximate the relationships among selling price, sales volume, production costs, and profit before income taxes. (The functional form for selling price implicitly reflects a fundamental relationship between price and demand. Namely, as the selling price is decreased, demand for the item increases. Alternatively, in order to increase the demand, the selling price must be reduced).

Let t = number of tons per season

$SP(t)$ = selling price in order to sell t tons

$\quad = \$(800 - 0.8t)$

$TR(t)$ = total revenue when t tons are sold at a particular selling price

$\quad =$ selling price X demand

$\quad = \$(800 - 0.8t)t$

$\quad = \$(800t - 0.8t^2)$

$\text{MR}(t)$ = the marginal revenue at a sales volume of t tons

$\qquad = d\text{TR}(t)/dt = \$(800 - 1.6t)$

$\text{TC}(t)$ = the total production cost for t tons

$\qquad = \$(10{,}000 + 400t)$

$\text{TP}(t)$ = total profit when t tons are sold

$\qquad = \text{TR}(t) - \text{TC}(t)$

$\qquad = \$(800t - 0.8t^2) - \$(10{,}000 + 400t)$

$\qquad = \$(-0.8t^2 + 400t - 10{,}000)$

$\text{AP}(t)$ = average profit per ton when t tons are sold

$\qquad = \text{TP}(t)/t$

$\qquad = \$(-0.8t + 400 - 10{,}000/t)$

The equations apply for the range $0 <\, = t < 1{,}000$. Figure 16.5 illustrates the total revenue, total cost, and total profit curves for this example. Refer to this figure while reading the discussion below.

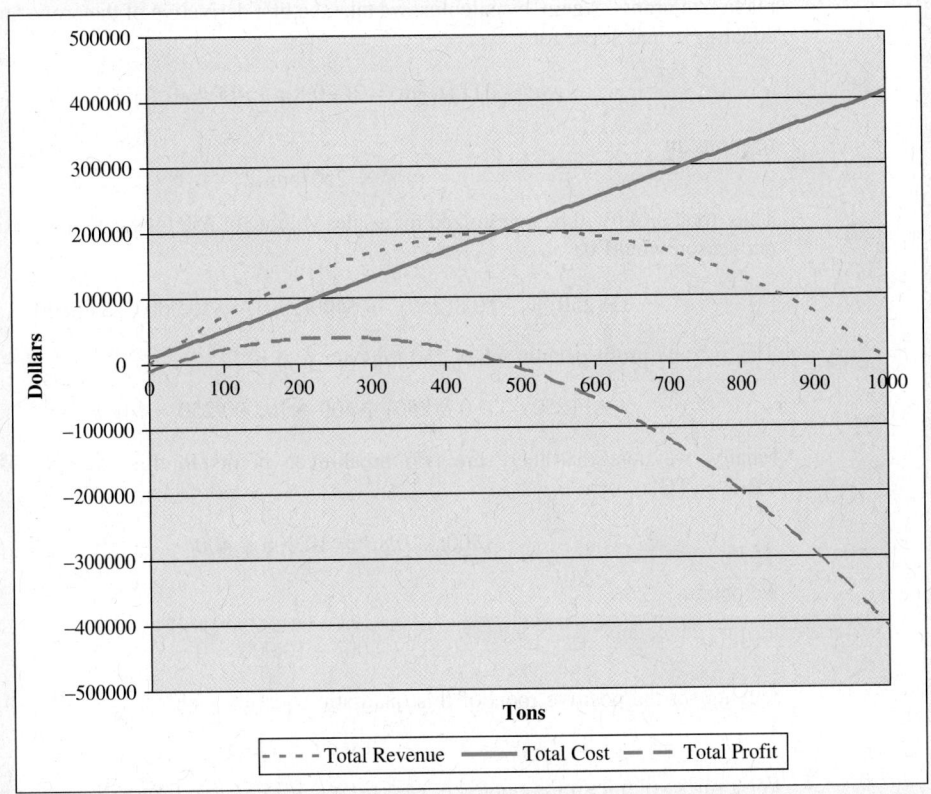

FIGURE 16.5

Total Revenue, Total Cost, and Total Profit as a Function of Tons.

We first determine that the total revenue will be maximized when 500 tons are produced and sold per season—that is, by calculus, we take the first derivative of the revenue function, set it equal to 0, and solve for t.

$$dTR(t)/dt = 800 - 2(0.8)t = 0$$

resulting in

$$t^* = 500 \text{ tons}$$

The total revenue with a sales volume of 500 tons is

$$TR(500) = \$800(500) - \$0.8(500)^2$$
$$= \$200,000$$

The marginal revenue at the output level of 500 tons is

$$MR(500) = \$800 - \$1.6(500) = 0$$

Thus, the rate of change in the $TR(t)$ function with respect to t is 0 when $TR(t)$ is evaluated at $t = 500$. The $TR(t)$ function is strictly concave with a unique maximum value at $TR(500)$. For sales from $t = 1$ to 500, the total revenue function is increasing at a decreasing rate. For sales volumes from $t = 500$ to 1,000, total revenues are decreasing at an increasing rate.

Maximizing total revenues is not the issue in this example, however. We wish to maximize profits. Again, by calculus, we take the first derivative of the profit function, set it equal to 0, and solve for t.

$$dTP(t)/dt = 2(-0.8)t + 400 = 0$$

resulting in

$$t^* = 250 \text{ tons}$$

Thus, total profit will be maximized for a sales volume of 250 tons, and the maximum profit per season would be

$$TP(250) = -\$0.8(250)^2 + \$400(250) - \$10,000 = \$40,000$$

The average profit per ton when 250 tons are sold is

$$AP(250) = -0.8(250) + 400 - 10,000/250 = \$160/\text{ton}$$

Finally, we note that there are two break-even points in this example. By equating $TR(t) = TC(t)$, or

$$800t - 0.8t^2 = 10,000 + 400t$$

we obtain

$$-0.8t^2 + 400t - 10,000 = 0$$

Solving for the positive roots of this quadratic equation yields

$$t = 26.39 \text{ and } t = 473.61$$

For a sales volume in the range $26.39 <= t <= 473.61$, the firm will make a profit. Sales volumes outside this range will result in total costs exceeding total revenues and a net loss to this firm.

16-3 COST ESTIMATION

The Association for the Advancement of Cost Engineering International (www. aacei.org) defines cost estimating as

> a predictive process used to quantify, cost, and price the resources required by the scope of an asset investment option, activity or project. As a predictive process, estimating must address risks and uncertainties. The outputs of estimating are used primarily as inputs for budgeting, cost or value analysis, decision making in business, asset and project planning, or for project cost and schedule control processes.

Webster's New Collegiate Dictionary states that *estimate,* "the comprehensive term, implies personal judgment the significance of which can only be made clear by the context." These definitions make it clear that estimating, in particular cost estimating, is not an exact science. Rather, it is an approximation that involves the availability and relevancy of appropriate historical data, personal judgments based on the estimator's experience, and the time frame available for completing the estimating activity.

Cost estimation is one of the most difficult challenges an engineering economist faces. It is difficult because it involves future events that are not (cannot be) known with certainty. Nonetheless, estimation of the amounts and timing of future cash flows is a necessary part of engineering economic analysis.

> Cost estimation is one of the most difficult challenges an engineering economist faces.

Many different terms pertain to the general subject of estimation. This text will not attempt to enumerate and explain all the terms exhaustively. Selected terminology will be given as needed to explain the topics. Furthermore, an in-depth study of estimation procedures and the accuracy of estimated values is the study of mathematical statistics and probability theory, about which a vast literature exists.

It is difficult to state precisely in quantitative terms the relationship between the accuracy of an estimate and the cost of making the estimate. Intuitively, as more detailed information is obtained to provide the basis for an estimate and as more mathematical preciseness is exercised in calculating the estimate, the more accurate the estimate should be. However, as the level of detail increases, the cost involved in making the estimate increases. Ostwald and McLaren[3] have conceptualized this notion by the function

$$C_T = C(M) + C(E) \tag{16.5}$$

where

C_T = the total cost of making the estimate in dollars

$C(M)$ = the functional cost of making the estimate in dollars

$C(E)$ = the functional cost of errors in the estimate in dollars.

[3]Ibid.

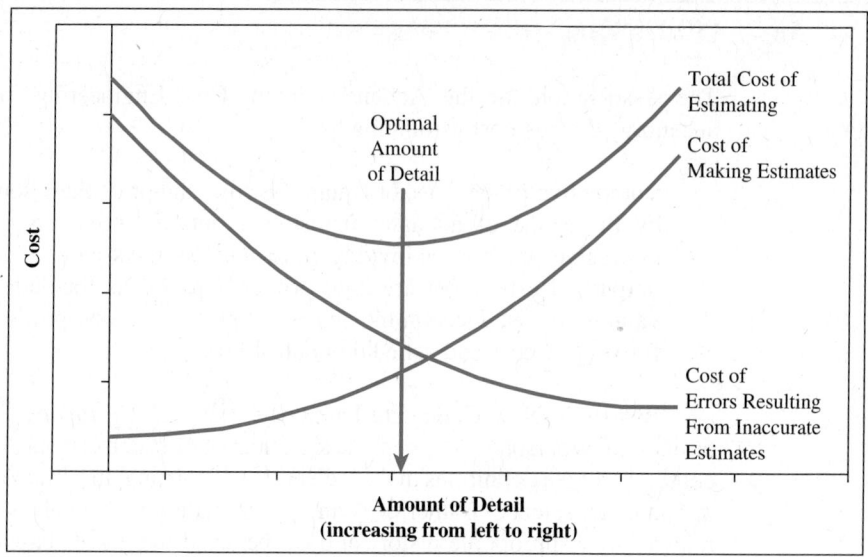

FIGURE 16.6
Cost of Detail in Estimating.

As depicted in Figure 16.6, the optimal amount of detail is that which minimizes the total cost of estimating. Since the curves for C(M) and C(E) are in general nonlinear, the minimum cost will not necessarily occur at the point of the two curves' intersection. Quantitatively determining the optimal amount of detail is at best difficult and may be a practical impossibility. However, this concept of the total cost of an estimate varying with the amount of detail involved in making the estimate is realistic and is important to the general subject of estimation. In the abbreviated discussion on cost estimation techniques that follows, we note that the individual techniques are based on varying amounts of detail with implied differences in the cost of making the estimate.

16.3.1   Project Estimation

In this textbook, we are concerned with estimation in the specific context of comparing alternative engineering investment projects and making a selection from these projects. The annual revenues or savings, the initial and annual recurring costs, the life of a project, and the future salvage value of capital assets such as buildings and equipment that may be associated with a given project are rarely, if ever, known with certainty.

For all categories of estimated items previously mentioned, four classes of estimates, based on accuracy and degree of detail, can be defined: (1) order-of-magnitude estimates, (2) preliminary estimates for feasibility studies, (3) semidetailed estimates for budget authorization, and (4) detailed estimates for execution and control.

Order-of-magnitude estimates are useful for concept screening and are usually gross estimates based on experience and judgment and made without formal examination of the details involved. Preliminary estimates are useful for feasibility studies and are also gross estimates, but more consideration is given to detail in making the estimate than for order-of-magnitude estimates. Key subelements of the overall task are individually estimated; engineering specifications are considered, and so forth. Semidetailed estimates are useful for budget authorization and are made by expanding the list of individually estimated items from key subelements to all major subelements. Finally, detailed estimates, which are used for execution and control, consider each subelement individually. Detailed estimates are expected to result in the most accurate estimate of actual cost. In preparing the estimate, each subelement of the overall task is considered, and an attempt is made to assign a realistic cost to it. Pricing a product or contract bidding usually involves detailed estimates of the costs involved.

Given the uncertainty inherent in cost estimating, a systematic approach is called for. The FAA's *Life Cycle Cost Estimating Handbook*[4] suggests the following six-step process:

1. Plan the estimate
2. Research, collect, and analyze data
3. Develop the estimate structure
4. Determine the estimating methodologies
5. Compute the cost estimate
6. Document and present the estimate

Planning the Estimate

Planning the estimate focuses on determining its intended use and the initial identification of an anticipated estimating methodology. The four-category classification scheme outlined earlier in this section (order-of-magnitude, etc.) or a more comprehensive five-level classification scheme available to members of the Association for the Advancement of Cost Engineering International (www.aacei.org) are useful in defining the estimate's intended use. Appropriate time and attention are warranted at this step of the estimating process, since this step provides the framework for the remainder of the estimating process.

Data Research, Collection, and Analysis

The second step—data research, collection, and analysis—includes (1) determining the availability of the data required by the initial methodology, (2) collecting the data, and (3) assessing the applicability of the collected data. Part 1 of this effort focuses on an initial determination of the availability of data sources to support the categories of data and the anticipated methodology of the estimating process. If data sources are available, then initial collection can proceed; if not, a different approach must be considered. As data collection begins, the types of data collected generally fall within two broad categories: cost estimating relationship and historical cost. Relationship data is used in conjunction with mathematical functions to estimate a factor of interest (dependent variable) based on one or more related factors (independent variables). Historical data is typically time-series data that represents or is directly related to the factor of interest. The final part of this step involves

[4]The FAA Life Cycle Cost Estimating Handbook is available at www.faa.gov.

assessing the applicability of the collected data. It is not uncommon at this stage that iterations to earlier parts of this step, and potentially back to the planning step, are required.

Developing the Estimate Structure

During the initial data collection, broad categories of cost were identified, assessed for data availability, and initial data collected. At the current stage (developing structure), the initial data requirements are refined with additional detail, and additional structure is added. This involves breaking down the broad categories into discrete cost elements. Frequently the discrete cost elements are derived and validated by considering the various cost viewpoints presented in Section 16.2. This process minimizes the chances that a cost element will be overlooked or omitted.

Determining the Estimating Methodology

The choice of a good estimating methodology is an important factor in developing a good estimate. Three primary methodologies are (1) parametric estimating, (2) estimating by analogy, and (3) engineering estimates. Each of these methods is discussed in more detail in Section 16.3.2.

Computing the Cost Estimate

At this step, the data, the estimate structure, and the methodology come together to facilitate the calculation of the estimate itself. Frequently, a spreadsheet model is used to support the calculations and documentation of the process. In addition to the quality of the estimate, the engineering economist frequently incorporates two additional issues at this step: time phasing of the estimate and consideration of the impact of inflation.

Documenting and Presenting the Estimate

The estimating task is not finished when numbers are determined. The estimate must be carefully documented and presented to the decision maker in a style and format that communicates effectively. Four key concerns are important. First, the documentation process should be completed concurrently with the estimate's development. Postponing documentation until after the estimating process is complete inherently leads to incomplete documentation.

Second, documentation should be complete and step by step. The estimator should not arbitrarily assume that the decision maker has in-depth knowledge of the items being estimated or the estimating process.

Third, the documentation should contain sufficient information to allow replication or enhancement of the estimate. Frequently, at this stage, the estimate will transfer into the decision maker's hands. As the decision-making process proceeds, refinements to the estimate are likely. The documentation should support this likelihood.

Fourth, in many cases, the estimate documentation will be the primary means through which the credibility of the estimate and the estimator will be judged. Poor documentation leads to poor credibility, which leads to the decision maker lacking confidence in the estimate.

16.3.2 Estimating Methodologies

Three primary methodologies for estimating are (1) parametric estimating, (2) estimating by analogy, and (3) engineering estimates. Each of these methods is discussed in more detail below.

Parametric Estimating

Parametric estimating develops estimates based on characteristics or features of the item being estimated. This process relies on a proven or assumed causal relationship between the characteristic and the cost. The relationships are usually expressed mathematically, frequently resulting from a regression analysis. (Detailed presentation of regression analysis is beyond the scope of this text, but note that Excel® includes a significant suite of regression tools. Additional regression capabilities for Excel® are available as add-ins.) The primary advantage of the parametric method is that it can quickly produce good-quality estimates with limited project detail. The primary disadvantage is that parametric estimates do not produce low-level detail, and they assume that the relationships represented in regressed data are truly cause and effect and that they will continue similarly into the future.

Estimating by Analogy

Forecasting by analogy is based on the premise that no new project is totally new. Many, if not most, new projects and systems evolve from their predecessors. As such, many of the cost elements and cost relationships can be approximated from the predecessor. The idea is that costs for similar elements are best estimated from the predecessor. For components that have evolved, adjustments are made for complexity and technical or physical differences. The primary advantage of the analogy method is that, if a good analogy can be found, it facilitates development of a low-level forecast relatively quickly. The primary disadvantage is identifying and verifying that the selected analogy is, in fact, appropriate.

Engineering Estimating

The engineering estimating method is also referred to as *bottom-up estimating*. The process starts at the lowest level of detail available for the project, considers each cost element, and builds up to the total cost estimate. Detailed engineering estimating takes relatively large amounts of time and requires detailed information about the project. The primary advantage of this method is that the level of detail gives high credibility to the estimate developed. The primary disadvantage is that the time and information requirements are high.

16.3.3 General Sources of Data

There are many sources for providing data to make the various estimates required in comparing alternative investment projects. Sources may be either internal or external to the firm. Examples of sources within a firm are sales records, production control records, inventory records, quality control records, purchasing department records, work measurement and other industrial engineering studies, maintenance records, and personnel records. The accounting system can and usually does serve as an important, if not primary, internal source of detailed estimates on operating costs, maintenance costs, and material costs, among others.

Sources of data external to the firm may be grouped into two general classes: (1) published information that is generally available and (2) information (published or otherwise) available on request. Available published information includes the vast literature of trade journals, professional society journals, U.S. government publications, reference handbooks, other books, and technical directories. Information not generally available except by request includes many sources listed in the previous category. For instance, many professional societies and trade associations publish handbooks, other books, special reports, and research bulletins that are available on request. Manufacturers of equipment and distributors of equipment are excellent sources of technical data, and most will readily supply this information without charge. Additionally, various government agencies, commercial banks (particularly holding companies involved in leasing buildings and equipment), and research organizations (commercial, governmental, industrial, and educational) may be sources of data to aid the estimating process.

Estimates of the functionally useful physical life of a piece of equipment may be obtained from manufacturers and suppliers. Alternatively, if a company repeatedly buys a particular piece of equipment and keeps accurate maintenance records, these records may be used to obtain an estimate of the item's functional life. For example, suppose records reveal that 100 percent of the items survive the first 3 years of service. Then, 10 percent of the items fail in the fourth year, 20 percent fail in the fifth year, 50 percent in the sixth year, 15 percent in the seventh year, and the remaining 5 percent fail in the eighth year. A weighted-average time to failure for this equipment is $[(0.10)(4) + (0.20)(5) + (0.50)(6) + (0.15)(7) + (0.05)(8)]$, or 5.85 years. This is an estimate of this particular item's functional life.

The texts by Ostwald and McLaren (footnote 1) and by Stewart, Johannes, and Wyskida[5] provide detailed presentations of well-founded general methodologies for cost estimating. The interested reader is referred to these texts for additional detail.

16-4 GENERAL ACCOUNTING PRINCIPLES

As already mentioned, the engineer should have some understanding of basic accounting practice and cost accounting techniques in order to obtain data from the firm's accounting system. The study of accounting is commonly divided into financial accounting and managerial accounting. Managerial accounting (particularly the subcategory of cost accounting) is more important to the engineer as a source of data for making cost estimates pertinent to engineering projects. Cost accounting will therefore receive the greater emphasis in this text. Our treatment of accounting is general and high level and is directed toward fundamental accounting concepts rather than a comprehensive treatment of accounting detail.

Accounting is the language of business. Without an understanding of this language, it is virtually impossible for an engineer to acquire and correctly interpret the data needed for economic analysis or to communicate the results of an analysis in meaningful and significant terms to managers. Learning this language is also crucial for engineers who aspire to progress through a technical career track to higher levels of authority and responsibility within a company.

The American Institute of Certified Public Accountants defines *accounting* as ''the art of recording, classifying and summarizing in a significant manner and in terms of money, transactions and events which are, in part at least, of a financial character, and interpreting the results thereof.'' This definition embodies the four key elements of an accounting system: recording, classifying, summarizing, and interpreting the financial data of an organization, whether profit or nonprofit. General accounting

---

[5]Stewart, R. D., J. D. Johannes, and R. M. Wyskida, *Cost Estimator's Reference Manual,* 2nd ed., John Wiley & Sons, 2001.

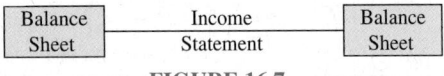

FIGURE 16.7

Relationship Between Balance Sheets and Income Statements.

information is summarized in two basic financial reports: the balance sheet and the income statement. These two financial statements will be the focus of our treatment of accounting.

The balance sheet provides a statement of a firm's financial condition at a point in time and lists the values of the assets, liabilities, and net worth of the firm. The income statement details the revenues and expenses incurred by a firm during a period of time, usually a month, quarter, or year. The two statements are closely related. The income statement summarizes the financial activities that occur between two balance sheets. The balance sheet reflects the financial condition as a result of the activities reported in the income statement. This relationship is illustrated in Figure 16.7.

16.4.1   Balance Sheet

The items listed on a balance sheet are usually classified into three main groups: assets, liabilities, and net worth items. Subgroups may also be identified, such as current and fixed assets or current and fixed liabilities. Assets are properties owned by the firm, and liabilities are debts owed by the firm against these assets. The dollar difference between assets and liabilities is the net worth of the business, which measures the investment made by the owners or stockholders of the business plus any accumulated profits left in the business by the owners or stockholders. Another term for net worth is *owners' equity*.

A balance sheet provides a statement of the financial condition of a firm at a point in time.

The fundamental accounting equation is defined as

$$\text{Assets} - \text{Liabilities} = \text{Net Worth}$$

Rewriting, we have the more common form of the fundamental equation of accounting:

$$\text{Assets} = \text{Liabilities} + \text{Net Worth} \tag{16.6}$$

The Fundamental Equation of Accounting

$$\text{Assets} = \text{Liabilities} + \text{Net Worth}$$

The usual format of a balance sheet follows the equation in this form. This can be observed in the condensed version of Starbucks's balance sheet for fiscal year 2006, shown in Figure 16.8. Note in the figure that total assets ($4,428,941 for the fiscal year

Fiscal Year Ended	in thousand, except earnings per share	
	Oct 1, 2006	Oct 1, 2005
ASSETS		
Current Assets		
Cash and Equivalents	$ 312,606	$ 173,809
Short Term Investments	141,038	133,227
Accounts Receivable	224,271	190,762
Inventories	636,222	546,299
Prepaid Expenses and other	126,874	94,429
Deferred Income Taxes	88,777	70,808
Total Current Assets	1,529,788	1,209,334
Long Term Investments	5,811	60,475
Equity and other Investments	219,093	201,089
Property, Plant, and Equipment	2,287,899	1,842,019
Other Assets	186,917	72,893
Other Intangible Assets	37,955	35,09
Goodwill	161,478	92,474
Total Assets	$ 4,428,941	$ 3,513,693
Liabilities and Shareholders' Equity		
Current Liabilities		
Accounts Payable	$ 340,937	$ 220,975
Accrued Compensation	288,963	232,354
Accrued Occupancy Costs	54,868	44,496
Accrued Taxes	94,010	78,293
Short-Term Borrowing	700,000	277,000
Other Accrued Expenses	224,154	198,082
Deferred Revenue	231,926	175,048
Current Portion of Long Term	762	748
Total Current Liabilities	1,935,620	1,226,996
Long Term Debt	1,958	2,870
Other Long Term Liabilities	262,857	193,565
Total Liabilities	2,200,435	1,423,431
Shareholders' Equity		
Common Stock	756	767
Additional Paid-In Capital	–	90,201
Other Additional Paid-In Capital	39,393	39,393
Retained Earnings	2,151,084	1,938,987
Accumulated Other Comprehensive Income	37,273	20,914
Total Shareholders' Equity	2,228,506	2,090,262
Total Liabilities and Shareholders' Equity	$ 4,428,941	$ 3,513,693

FIGURE 16.8

Starbucks' Condensed Consolidated Balance Sheet.

ended October 1, 2006) equals the sum of total liabilities ($2,200,435) plus total net worth (called ''shareholders equity'' on Starbucks's balance sheet) ($2,228,506). The double underline under the balancing totals is the accountant's verification that the balance sheet is indeed balanced according to the fundamental equation of accounting.

Usually each of the broad categories on the balance sheet (assets, liabilities, and net worth) are divided into subcategories. While reading the following material, the reader is encouraged to review Starbucks's balance sheet (Figure 16.8) to reinforce and confirm the points made. Current assets include cash and other assets that can be readily converted into cash; a period of 1 year or one business cycle is usually assumed as a criterion for conversion. Similarly, current liabilities are the debts that are due and payable within 1 year (or one business cycle) from the date of the balance sheet in question. Typical current-asset items are cash, accounts receivable, notes receivable, raw material inventory, work in process, finished goods inventory, and prepaid expenses.

By contrast, fixed assets are the properties the firm owns that are not readily converted into cash within 1 year, and fixed liabilities are long-term debts due and payable after 1 year from the balance sheet's date. Fixed-asset items are land, buildings, equipment, furniture, and fixtures. Items that are typically listed under current liabilities are accounts payable, notes payable, interest payable, taxes payable, prepaid income, and dividends payable. Fixed liabilities include notes payable, bonds payable, mortgages payable, and so forth. Net worth items appearing on a balance sheet are less standard and, to a degree, depend on whether the business is a sole proprietorship, a partnership, or a corporation. The corporation's size is also an influencing factor on item designation. However, items such as capital stock, retained earnings, capital surplus, or earned surplus appear under the net worth group.

To better understand balance sheets, we will examine several parts of a small tool manufacturing company's balance sheet, shown in Table 16.5. Of first importance, note that this sample balance sheet is ''balanced'' since assets = liabilities + net worth (i.e., the fundamental equation of accounting holds). Note the fixed-asset portion of the balance sheet. The building originally cost $200,000, and depreciation expenses have been charged annually, so the total depreciation charges (as of the balance sheet's date) have been $50,000, the amount entered as depreciation reserve for the building. In theory, the depreciation reserve is an accumulated amount of funds held to repurchase the asset when its functionally useful life terminates. The first cost of the depreciable asset (building, in this case) minus the amount in the depreciation reserve equals the book value. If the book value was a true estimate of the salvage, or market, value, then the sum of the amount in the depreciation reserve plus the book value provides the firm with an amount of funds equal to the original purchase price. This sum can be applied toward the purchase of a replacement asset. Typically, however, the market value of the asset when sold differs from the book value. The difference results in either a capital gain or loss and affects the firm's income taxes.

A similar explanation applies to the fixed asset account equipment. In this particular balance sheet, the equipment account is an aggregate for all the equipment owned by the company instead of an individual listing of each equipment item. There could be separate equipment accounts, grouped according to equipment class. In any case, a company normally keeps individual records on equipment items, which are then summarized on the balance sheet.

The net worth section of the balance sheet in Table 16.5 contains three entries, which summarize the company's ownership (or equity) accounts. The common stock account reflects the ownership position of stockholders, frequently referred to as

TABLE 16.5
Example Balance Sheet.

BuiltRite Tool and Engineering Company
Balance Sheet as of December 31, 2006

ASSETS

Current Assets

Cash		$25,000	
Accounts Receivable (net)		115,000	
Raw Materials		8,500	
Work In Process		7,000	
Finished Goods		3,000	
Small Tools		12,500	
Total Current Assets			$171,000

Fixed Assets

Land		$30,000	
Building	$200,000		
Less depreciation reserve	50,000	150,000	
Equipment	$750,000		
Less depreciation reserve	150,000	600,000	
Office Equipment		10,000	
Total Fixed Assets			$790,000
Total Assets			$961,000

LIABILITIES AND CAPITAL

Current Liabilities

Accounts Payable		32,000	
Taxes Payable		15,000	
Total Current Liabilities			47,000

Fixed Liabilities

Mortgage loan payable		$130,000	
Equipment loan payable		350,000	
Total Fixed Liabilities			$480,000
Total Liabilities			$527,000

Capital

Common Stock		$325,000	
Retained Earnings		80,000	
Earned Surplus (current year)		29,000	
Total Capital			$434,000
Total Liabilities and Capital			$961,000

contributed capital. The reporting of contributed capital accounts on a balance sheet is subject to several legal requirements, depending on the nature of the contributed capital (e.g., common stock, preferred stock, par value, no par value). Discussion of these issues is beyond the scope of this text.

The next two entries in the net worth section of Table 16.5 summarize the equity generated through the operation of the business rather than through investor contributions. These accounts are frequently referred to as *earned capital*. The retained earnings account summarizes the surplus (or deficit) of earnings over expenses that have been held by the company (i.e., retained) for accounting periods prior to the current period. The earned surplus account highlights this same information for the current period and should match the net profit (or loss) reflected on the current income statement.

16.4.2 Income Statement

The second basic financial report compiled by the accounting system is the income statement, or profit and loss statement. For the current accounting period, the income statement provides management with (1) a summary of the revenues received, (2) a summary of the expenses incurred to obtain the revenues, and (3) the profit or loss resulting from business operations. The income statement's format varies widely (more so than for balance sheets), and the revenue and expense items depend on the type of business involved. Figure 16.9 shows a condensed version of Starbucks's income statement (referred to as a *statement of earnings*).

> An income statement provides a statement of the revenues and expenses incurred by a firm during a period of time.

The income statement usually begins with a revenues section. Revenues are generated from the sale of products or services marketed by the firm. Next, the income statement reflects the direct costs associated with generating the sales revenue. This section is generally referred to as the *cost of goods*. For a manufacturing company (Table 16.6), the cost of goods section usually includes the costs incurred in producing the product. For a retail company (Table 16.7 and Figure 16.9), this section includes the costs incurred in acquiring the retail goods to be sold. In either case, the result of subtracting the cost of goods from the sales is gross profit. Gross profit is not always shown as a separate line on an income statement. For example, Tables 16.6 and 16.7 show a gross profit line, but Starbucks (Figure 16.9) does not.

After gross profit is determined, other operating expenses of the business are incorporated. This section includes all expenses that are not incorporated in the cost of goods. Generally this consists of general and administrative expenses as well as the marketing expenses. The subtraction of these costs from gross profit results in net profit before taxes. Subtracting taxes results in the net income (or loss) for the period. This final value is transferred to the earned surplus line on the balance sheet.

The format for the income statement in Table 16.6 is oversimplified, even for a small manufacturing firm. For example, the ''cost of goods sold'' entry may be considerably more detailed to reflect multiple product lines, the depreciation items may be detailed to a greater extent to reflect multiple classes of assets, and several common expense items—such as employee benefits contributions, insurance premiums, and advertising—are not included. Similarly, the income statement in Table 16.7 is highly simplified. This format is typical for a retail business, and the major difference in form concerns the method of determining the ''cost of goods sold'' item.

Actual balance sheets and income statements use the same general formats as the ones illustrated above but usually contain more detail, as was seen in the Starbucks examples. Starbucks's financial statements were extracted from their December 14,

Fiscal Year Ended	in thousand, except earnings per share	
	Oct 1, 2006	**Oct 1, 2005**
Net Revenues		
Company Operated Retail	$ 6,583,098	$ 5,391,927
Specialty		
Licensing	860,676	673,015
Foodservice and other	343,168	304,358
Total Specialty	1,203,844	977,373
Total Net Revenues	7,786,942	6,369,300
Cost of Sales including Occupancy	3,178,791	2,605,212
Store Operating Expenses	2,687,815	2,165,911
Other Operating Expenses	260,087	197,024
Depreciation and Amortization Expenses	387,211	340,169
General and Administrative Expenses	473,023	357,114
Subtotal Operating Expenses	6,986,927	5,665,430
Income from Equity Investments	93,937	76,648
Operating Income	893,952	780,518
Interest and Other Income	12,291	15,829
Earnings before Income Taxes	906,243	796,347
Income Taxes	324,770	301,977
Earnings before effect of accounting change	581,473	494370
Cumulative effect of accounting change	17,214	—
Net Earnings	$ 564,259	$ 494,370
Per Common Share		
Net Earnings—basic	$ 0.74	$ 0.63
Net Earnings—diluted	$ 0.71	$ 0.61
Weighted Average Shares Outstanding		
Basic	766,114	789,570
Diluted	792,556	815,417

FIGURE 16.9

Starbucks' Condensed Consolidated Statement of Earnings.

2006, Form 10-K, which is a required disclosure statement that publicly held companies file with the SEC (Securities and Exchange Commission). Starbucks's balance sheet (Figure 16.8) and income statement (Figure 16.9) are both referred to as *comparative statements,* since they show more than 1 fiscal year and therefore provide an opportunity for the reader to make year-to-year comparisons.

16.4.3 Ratio Analysis

An important topic related to the interpretation of balance sheets and income statements is ratio analysis, a common practice that examines relationships between the values found on these statements. Ratio analysis is not critical to an engineer focused solely on the accounting function as a source of data for economic analysis.

TABLE 16.6

Example Income Statement—Manufacturing.

BuiltRite Tool and Engineering Company
Income Statement
For Year Ended December 31, 2006

Net Sales		$1,200,000
Less Cost of Goods Manufactured		
Direct Labor	$420,000	
Direct Materials	302,000	
Indirect Labor	112,000	
Depreciation	98,000	
Repairs and Maintenance	41,500	
Utilities	11,500	985,000
Gross Profit		$215,000
Other Expenses		
Marketing	$49,000	
General and Administrative	76,000	
Interest payments	35,000	160,000
Net Income before Taxes		$55,000
Less Income Taxes		26,000
Net Income (posted to Earned Surplus)		$29,000

TABLE 16.7

Example Income Statement—Retail.

BuiltRite Tool and Engineering Company
Income Statement
For Year Ended December 31, 2006

Net Sales		$1,200,000
Less Cost of Goods Sold		
Inventory, December 31, 20x5	$26,000	
Plus purchases	432,000	
Total	$458,000	
Less Inventory, December 31, 2006	44,000	414,000
Gross Profit		$786,000
Less Expenses		
Direct Labor	$420,000	
Depreciation—Building	10,000	
Depreciation—Equipment	30,000	
Repairs and Maintenance	41,500	
Indirect Labor	218,000	
Utilities	9,800	
Supplies	1,700	731,000
Net Income before Taxes		$55,000
Less Income Taxes		26,000
Net Income (posted to Earned Surplus)		$29,000

However, to interpret a company's accounting statements to determine the attractiveness of a company's stock as a potential investment or to determine the economic health of a company as a potential employer, ratio analysis is of fundamental importance. If the reader's interest is focused solely on data sourcing, this section can be skipped with no loss of continuity for the remainder of the chapter.

Before proceeding to a presentation of several popular ratio calculations, it is important to bear in mind that the values of the ratios themselves are neither good nor bad. They can only be interpreted in comparison to the ratios of peer group companies or to an individual's personal expectations of a company's performance. Ratios are only rough guides to interpreting financial statements; they are not mathematical conclusions. Ratios are generally used in one of three ways to draw conclusions about a company's financial health: (1) comparison with a company's historic values of the same ratio to spot trends or changes in performance, (2) comparison with expected or desired performance benchmarks available from financial analysts, and (3) comparison with competitors within the same industry to measure competitive performance or position.

Uses of Ratio Analysis

1. Comparison to a company's historic values to spot trends and/or changes in performance
2. Comparison to expected or desired benchmarks
3. Comparison to competitor's performance

Generally, the analysis of financial statements focus on three primary areas: (1) the company's earning power, (2) the short-term liability obligations, and (3) the long-term liability obligations. We will use the financial statements of Carson's Cutlery Company to illustrate the calculation of several common ratios in each of these areas. Table 16.8 contains comparative balance sheets (two balance sheets displayed side by side) for the years 2005 and 2006. Table 16.9 contains comparative income statements for the years 2005 and 2006.

Areas of Focus of Ratio Analysis

1. Earning power
2. Short-term liability obligations
3. Long-term liability obligations

The viability of maintaining a company's financial health depends upon its earning power. Firms must earn and sustain profit over the long term to survive. The following ratios are commonly used to assess earning power:

$$\text{Return on Assets Employed} = \frac{\text{Net Income}}{\text{Average Total Assets}} \tag{16.7}$$

$$\text{Return on Owner's Equity} = \frac{\text{Net Income}}{\text{Average Owner's Equity}} \tag{16.8}$$

TABLE 16.8
Carson's Cutlery Company Comparative Balance Sheet.

Carson's Cutlery
Comparative Balance Sheet
as of December 31, 2005 and 2006

ASSETS	2006	2005
Current Assets		
Cash	$61,750	$83,520
Accounts Receivable (net)	195,000	130,500
Inventory	65,000	50,000
Prepaid Expenses	22,750	31,900
Total Current Assets	$344,500	$295,920
Fixed Assets		
Machinery	$208,000	$187,830
Furniture	74,750	72,500
Other	22,750	23,750
Total Assets	$650,000	$580,000
LIABILITIES AND CAPITAL		
Current Liabilities		
Notes Payable	$92,950	$87,000
Accounts Payable	147,212	109,653
Taxes Payable	69,438	64,920
Total Current Liabilities	$309,600	$261,573
Fixed Liabilities		
Loans	$100,000	$90,000
Total Liabilities	$409,600	$351,573
Capital		
Stock	$100,000	$100,000
Retained Earnings	88,427	77,397
Earned Surplus	51,973	51,030
Total Capital	$240,400	$228,427
Total Liabilities and Capital	$650,000	$580,000

The calculation of earning power ratios for Carson's Cutlery for 2006 are shown below:

$$\text{Return on Assets Employed} = \frac{\$51,973}{(\$580,000 + 650,000)/2} = 0.0845 \text{ or } 8.45\%$$

$$\text{Return on Owner's Equity} = \frac{\$51,973}{(\$228,427 + \$240,400)/2} = 0.2217 \text{ or } 22.17\%$$

The second major area of focus in ratio analysis is short-term liability obligations. This is referred to as *liquidity*. These ratios measure a company's ability to meet its current obligations. The following ratios are commonly used to measure liquidity:

$$\text{Current Ratio} = \frac{\text{Current Assets}}{\text{Current Liabilities}} \qquad (16.9)$$

TABLE 16.9		
Carson's Cutlery Company Comparative Income Statement.		

Carson's Cutlery
Comparative Income Statement
For Years Ended December 31, 2005 and 2006

	2006	2005
Net Sales	$1,625,450	$1,450,000
Cost of Goods Sold		
Beginning Inventory	$50,000	$40,000
Direct Materials	406,000	350,000
Direct Labor	801,500	700,000
Factory Overhead	94,603	90,000
Total	$1,352,103	$1,180,000
Less: Ending Inventory	65,000	50,000
Cost of Goods Sold	$1,287,103	$1,130,000
Gross Profit	$338,347	$320,000
Other Operating Expenses		
Selling Expenses	$43,980	$37,200
Depreciation & Amortization	58,122	53,791
General and Administrative	122,484	120,580
Total Other Operating Expenses	$224,586	$211,570
Net Operating Income	$113,761	$108,430
Less: Interest Expenses	$21,600	$18,000
Less: Income Taxes	40,188	39,400
Net Income	$51,973	$51,030

$$\text{Acid Test Ratio} = \frac{\text{Cash} + \text{Accounts Receivable} + \text{ShortTerm Investments}}{\text{Current Liabilities}} \quad (16.10)$$

$$\text{Accounts Receivable Turnover} = \frac{\text{Net Sales}}{\text{Average Accounts Receivable}} \quad (16.11)$$

$$\text{Inventory Turnover} = \frac{\text{Cost of Goods Sold}}{\text{Average Inventory}} \quad (16.12)$$

The calculation of liquidity ratios for Carson's Cutlery for 2006 is shown below.

$$\text{Current Ratio} = \frac{\$344,500}{\$309,600} = 1.112$$

$$\text{Acid Test Ratio} = \frac{\$61,750 + \$195,000 + \$0}{\$309,600} = 0.829$$

$$\text{Accounts Receivable Turnover} = \frac{\$1,625,450}{(\$130,500 + \$195,000)/2} = 9.98$$

$$\text{Inventory Turnover} = \frac{\$1,287,103}{(\$50,000 + \$65,000)/2} = 22.38$$

The final major area of focus in ratio analysis is long-term liability obligations. This is referred to as *solvency*. These ratios measure a company's ability to meet its long-term obligations based on its current debt structure. The following ratios are commonly used to measure solvency:

$$\text{Debt to Equity Ratio} = \frac{\text{Total Liabilities}}{\text{Total Capital Worth}} \qquad (16.13)$$

$$\text{Times Interest Earned Ratio} = \frac{\text{Net Income Before Taxes and Interest}}{\text{Interest Charges}} \qquad (16.14)$$

$$\text{Operating Income to Total Assets Ratio} = \frac{\text{Net Operating Income}}{\text{Total Assets}} \qquad (16.15)$$

The calculation of solvency ratios for Carson's Cutlery for 2006 is shown below:

$$\text{Debt to Equity Ratio} = \frac{\$409,600}{\$240,400} = 1.70$$

$$\text{Times Interest Earned Ratio} = \frac{\$113,761}{\$21,600} = 5.27$$

$$\text{Operating Income to Total Assets Ratio} = \frac{\$113,761}{\$650,000} = 0.1750, \text{ or } 17.50\%$$

Two other measures may be encountered when the financial analysis is focused on a company's ability to earn a profit through its operations. This focus is achieved by excluding certain nonoperating expenses (or revenues) from earnings. Earnings before interest and taxes (EBIT) considers a company's revenues less its operating expenses. Interest charges (or revenues) and taxes are excluded from EBIT. EBIT may also be referred to as *operating earnings, operating profit,* or *operating income.* Earnings before interest, taxes, depreciation and amortization (EBITDA) takes this one step further by excluding noncash expenses (depreciation and amortization) from the earnings consideration. The following calculations define these measures:

$$\text{EBIT} = \text{Net Income} + \text{Income Taxes} + \text{Interest Expense} \qquad (16.16)$$

$$\text{EBITDA} = \text{Net Income} + \text{Income Taxes} + \text{Interest Expense}$$
$$+ \text{Depreciation} + \text{Amortization} \qquad (16.17)$$

The calculation of these measures for Carson's Cutlery for 2006 is shown below:

$$\text{EBIT} = \$51,973 + \$40,188 + \$21,600 = \$113,761$$
$$\text{EBITDA} = \$51,973 + \$40,188 + \$21,600 + \$58,122 = \$171,883$$

It is worth noting that EBIT was already shown on the income statement under *net operating income.*

As stated earlier, ratios provide a useful and powerful means to express the relationships found in balance sheets and income statements. These ratios are generally only useful when compared to a meaningful set of standards or expectations, which typically take the form of previous year's results, peer group comparisons, or industry averages. Many variations to the names and calculation formulas presented above can be found in financial literature. The reader is cautioned to ensure that ratios are calculated in consistent ways before making comparisons.

16-5   COST ACCOUNTING PRINCIPLES

The balance sheet and the income statement in Section 16.4 are sometimes considerably removed, both in time and in detail, from data required for engineering project level decision making. In these cases, more important to the engineer as a source of cost information is the cost accounting system within a particular firm. The firm may be involved in manufacturing or providing services, and if it is involved in manufacturing, production may be on a job-shop or process basis. There are some fundamental differences in cost accounting procedures for determining manufacturing costs versus determining the cost of providing a service; also, there are differences in accounting procedures if manufacturing is on a job-shop or process basis. In order to concentrate on basic principles instead of details, the cost accounting system assumed will be that of a job-shop manufacturing firm. Thus, the emphasis will be on determining the per-order costs for a job order.

16.5.1   Traditional Cost Allocation Methods

The total cost of producing any job order consists of direct material, direct labor, and overhead costs. Our approach here will not split the overhead cost into factory overhead, general overhead, and marketing expenses in order to simplify the presentation. Direct materials for a given job order may include purchased parts and in-house fabricated parts. The cost for purchased materials is determined primarily from purchase invoices. The cost for fabricated parts is determined primarily from the job cost system. Direct labor expended on a job order is normally recorded by operators on labor time cards, and the direct labor cost is determined by applying the appropriate labor cost rates. The labor rates, as determined by the accounting system, will normally include the cost of employee fringe benefits in addition to the basic hourly rate. Determining direct material and direct labor costs can be problematic in some situations, but both are generally more readily determined than the overhead cost.

Overhead costs typically cannot be allocated as direct charges to any single job order and therefore must be prorated among all the job orders on some rational basis. Three popular methods of allocating overhead costs to manufacturing jobs are in wide use today: (1) allocation based on direct labor hours, (2) allocation based on direct labor dollars, and (3) allocation based on direct labor dollars plus direct material dollars (prime costs). These methods can be applied at any desired manufacturing unit level (i.e., an entire plant, specific departments, work centers, machines, or job orders). Step-by-step procedures for using each of these methods to (1) determine an appropriate overhead rate and (2) use this rate to estimate overhead on a specific job are outlined below. Example 16.10, which follows the step-by-step procedures, illustrates their application.

Traditional methods for allocating overhead

1. Allocation based on direct labor hours
2. Allocation based on direct labor dollars
3. Allocation based on prime dollars

Allocate Overhead Based on Direct Labor Hours

1. Determine (or estimate) values for previous period direct labor hours and overhead cost for the manufacturing unit

2. Calculate the rate per direct labor hour:

$$\text{Rate} = \frac{\text{overhead cost}}{\text{direct labor hours}} \qquad (16.18)$$

3. Determine (or estimate) the number of direct labor hours required by the particular job for which overhead cost is being estimated
4. Calculate the overhead cost for the job:

$$\text{Estimated overhead} = \text{rate} \times \text{estimated direct labor hours}$$

Allocate Overhead Based on Direct Labor Dollars

1. Determine (or estimate) values for previous period direct labor dollars and overhead cost for the manufacturing unit
2. Calculate the percentage ratio of overhead cost to direct labor dollars:

$$\text{Ratio} = \frac{\text{overhead cost}}{\text{direct labor dollars}} \times 100\% \qquad (16.19)$$

3. Determine (or estimate) the direct labor dollars required by the particular job for which overhead cost is being estimated
4. Calculate the overhead cost for the job:

$$\text{Estimated overhead} = \text{ratio} \times \text{estimated direct labor dollars}$$

Allocate Overhead Based on Direct Labor Dollars and Direct Material Dollars

1. Determine (or estimate) values for previous period direct labor dollars, direct material dollars, and overhead cost for the manufacturing unit
2. Calculate the percentage ratio of overhead cost to direct labor dollars plus direct material dollars:

$$\text{Ratio} = \frac{\text{overhead cost}}{\text{direct labor dollars} + \text{direct material dollars}} \times 100\% \qquad (16.20)$$

3. Determine (or estimate) the direct labor dollars and direct material dollars required by the particular job for which overhead cost is being estimated
4. Calculate the overhead cost for the job:

$$\text{Estimated overhead} = \text{ratio} \times (\text{estimated direct labor dollars}$$
$$+ \text{estimated direct material dollars})$$

EXAMPLE 16.10 Traditional Methods of Overhead Allocation

The overhead allocation for a job is to be estimated. Assume the direct labor hours for the job are estimated to be 40 hours at a rate of $12.50 per hour. Direct material costs are estimated at $850. The overhead calculations are to be based on the following cost totals collected during the previous accounting period.

Total direct labor hours	48,000
Total direct labor dollars	$480,000
Total direct material dollars	$600,000
Total overhead costs	$360,000

Using the step-by-step procedures above, we will calculate the overhead allocation based on (a) direct labor hours, (b) direct labor dollars, and (c) direct labor dollars plus direct material dollars.

a. Direct labor hours

Step 1: Previous period direct labor hours $= 48,000$
Previous period overhead cost $= \$360,000$

Step 2: Rate per direct labor hour $= \$360,000/48,000 = \$7.50/\text{hour}$

Step 3: Estimated direct labor hours for job $= 40$

Step 4: Estimate overhead $= \$7.50/\text{hour} \times 40\,\text{hours} = \$300$

b. Direct labor dollars

Step 1: Previous period direct labor dollars $= \$480,000$
Previous period overhead cost $= \$360,000$

Step 2: Percentage ratio per direct labor dollar $= (\$360,000/\$480,000) \times 100\% = 75\%$

Step 3: Estimated direct labor dollars for job $= 40\,\text{hours} \times \$12.50/\text{hour} = \$500$

Step 4: Estimate overhead $= 75\% \times \$500 = \$375$

c. Direct labor dollars + direct material dollars

Step 1: Previous period direct labor dollars $= \$480,000$
Previous period direct material dollars $= \$600,000$
Previous period overhead cost $= \$360,000$

Step 2: Percentage ratio per (direct labor dollar + direct material dollar) $= [\$360,000/(\$480,000 + \$600,000)] \times 100\% = 33.33\%$

Step 3: Estimated direct labor dollars + direct material dollars for job $= (40\,\text{hours} \times \$12.50/\text{hour}) + \$850 = \$1,350$

Step 4: Estimate overhead $= 33.33\% \times \$1,350 = \$450$

Determining the overhead cost for a job order by the rate per direct labor hour method will yield the same result as the percentage of direct labor cost method, provided that the rate per direct labor hour used on the job in question is equal to the average factory labor rate. The "percentage of prime cost" method will necessarily yield a different assignment of overhead to a job order than the other two methods. The choice among these three methods varies by company; indeed, cost accountants use other methods in distributing overhead costs in some cases. The rate per direct labor hour method is perhaps the most commonly used. Whatever method is chosen for distributing overhead costs to job orders in a current year, the rates or percentages are based on the previous year's cost figures. Thus, overhead rates may change from year to year within a particular firm.

Since an average overhead rate for the entire factory may very well be too gross an estimate when actual overhead costs differ among departments within the factory, cost accounting may determine individual overhead rates for departments or cost centers. In addition, the hourly rates for direct labor may vary among these cost centers. A further refinement is to determine overhead rates for individual machines within cost centers. Then, as particular job orders progress through cost centers (departments or machines), the direct labor time (or machine time) spent on the job order in the various cost centers is recorded, the appropriate labor or machine rates and overhead rates are applied, and the total cost for the job is calculated.

The following example illustrates the variety of methods used to distribute overhead to a given cost center; the total overhead for the cost center will then be distributed to particular products by yet another method.

EXAMPLE 16.11   Overhead Allocation to Departments

TABLE 16.10
Data for Example 16.6.

	Department A	Department B	Total
Direct Material Cost	$720,000	$240,000	$960,000
Direct Labor Cost	$260,000	$140,000	$400,000
Direct Labor Hours	25,200	16,200	41,400
Number of Employees	14	9	23
First Cost of Equipment	$250,000	$200,000	$450,000
Annual Depreciation	$25,000	$20,000	$45,000
Other Factory Overhead			$150,000
General Overhead			$350,000

The information in Table 16.10 has been accumulated for the Deetco Company's two departments during the past year. Deetco distributes depreciation overhead based on (1) the first cost of equipment in each department, (2) a zero salvage value of the equipment in 10 years, and (3) a straight-line rate of depreciation. All overhead other than depreciation is first distributed to each department according to the number of employees in each department, and then an overhead rate per direct labor hour is computed for each department.

What price should the company quote on Job Order D if raw material costs are estimated as $900; estimated direct labor hours required in Departments A and B are 30 hours and 100 hours, respectively; and profit is to be set at 25 percent of selling price?

For Department A, the total overhead allocation is determined as follows:

Annual depreciation	$25,000
Other factory overhead (14/23)($150,000)	$91,000
General overhead (14/23)($350,000)	$213,043
TOTAL	$329,347

Thus, the overhead rate for Department A per direct labor hour is

$$\text{Rate} = \frac{\$329,347}{25,200} = \$13.07 \text{ per direct labor hour}$$

For Department B, the total overhead allocation is calculated as follows:

Annual depreciation	$20,000
Other factory overhead (9/23)($150,000)	$58,696
General overhead (9/23)($350,000)	$136,957
TOTAL	$215,653

Thus, the overhead rate for Department B per direct labor hour is

$$\text{Rate} = \frac{\$215,653}{16,200} = \$13.31 \text{ per direct labor hour}$$

The estimated total cost for Job Order D is then computed as

Direct material cost	$900
Direct labor cost A ($260,000/25,200)(30 hours)	$309.52
Overhead cost A ($13.07)(30 hours)	$392.10
Direct labor B ($140,000/16,200)(100 hours)	$864.20
Overhead cost B ($13.31)(100 hours)	$1,331
TOTAL	$3,796.82

If x = the selling price of Job Order D, then

$$x = \text{total cost} + \text{profit}$$
$$x = \$3,796.82 + (0.25)x$$

solving for x yields

$$x = \frac{\$3,796.82}{0.75}$$

thus,

$$x = \$5,062.43$$

16.5.2 Activity Based Costing

A relatively new entrant in the field of cost accounting is activity-based costing (ABC). This has emerged due to the dramatic changes that have occurred, and continue to occur, in the nature and characteristics of manufacturing costs. Historically, direct labor and direct material constituted the most significant elements of the cost of goods. Overhead was the smallest element and hence was allocated based on direct labor or prime costs (see Section 16.5.1). In many cases today, it is no longer accurate to assume that direct labor is the largest element in the cost pool and overhead the smallest. With the introduction and implementation of computer-controlled and automated manufacturing systems, it is not unusual for overhead costs to dominate the cost of producing items. Frequently, in fact, direct labor is the least significant in the cost pool and overhead the largest.

ABC is designed to meet the challenge of a changing cost mix by associating manufacturing costs with activities that drive them. First, costs must be identified by categories. These need not (and probably should not) be associated with products or organizational units; rather, they are associated with clearly defined cost categories or cost pools. Typical examples of cost pools include material handling costs, energy costs, tooling costs, or maintenance costs.

> Activity based costing is designed to associate costs with the activities which drive them.

Next, the activities that drive the significant cost pools must be identified. These are to be monitored and controlled under ABC. This task is difficult and complex. Many companies have never considered their processes from the cost driver or value-added point of view. The newness of this approach and the implicit challenge of considering activities from a new perspective make this task a significant undertaking. Examples of cost-driving activities include machine hours for energy costs, material moves or truck hours for material handling costs, and machine hours or production volume for tooling and maintenance costs.

Next, the expected (or actual) rate of activity for each of the cost drivers is used to predict (or monitor) the costs associated with each cost pool. Such activity-based accounting of costs can be used as a basis to eliminate high-cost activities, particularly if they generate low value added. Similarly, ABC analysis can be used to focus the attention of process improvement activities toward those activities that drive high costs. Better still, product and process redesign can focus on changes that ultimately eliminate the activation of high-cost driver activities.

Many companies are employing ABC to make activity-based decisions that result from a more realistic allocation of costs than was previously possible. In many cases, ABC-generated process and product redesigns have been impressive when measured in terms of cost reduction and profit improvement. Activity-based costing does, however, require information sharing and a cross-functional perspective that is new to most companies. A vast literature exists for ABC and its derivative management philosophy, activity-based management. The interested reader is encouraged to explore this literature, particularly the text by Kaplan and Anderson[6] and the text by Cokins.[7]

16.5.3 Standard Costs

Although the first task of cost accounting is to determine per-item or per-order costs, another major purpose is to interpret financial data so that management can (1) measure changes in production efficiency and (2) judge the adequacy of production performance. Establishing cost standards can be of great assistance in achieving these objectives. A standard-cost system involves, in advance of manufacture, (1) the preparation of standard rates for material, labor, and overhead, and (2) the application of these rates to the standard quantities of material and labor required for a job order, or for each production operation required to complete the job order.

Since a process-type manufacturing firm, such as an oil refinery, outputs the same product (or a few products) over a long time period, cost standards are more readily determined for process firms than for job-shop firms, where the variety of output is large and varies with customer order. However, the number and type of production operations required to complete various job orders are finite for a given manufacturing firm. Each job order is, of course, made up of single units. Thus, a standard amount of material, standard labor times, and machine times can be determined for each unit. It is usually the responsibility of the firm's work measurement function to determine these standard quantities. Then, by applying standard unit material costs and standard labor rates, standard unit costs for material, labor, and overhead can be determined. The standard costs then serve as a basis for measuring production efficiency and performance over time. Deviations from standard costs may be caused by several factors, especially (1) raw material price variations and (2) actual quantities of material and labor used versus the standard amounts of these items. This latter factor is of primary concern in determining production efficiency and performance, measures of which provide information to management to aid in cost control.

16.5.4 Economic Value Added

Since the mid-1980s, a management tool called *economic value added (EVA)* has been used by an impressive set of firms to make investment decisions. It focuses

[6]Kaplan, R. S. and S. R. Anderson, *Time-Driven Activity Based Costing,* Harvard Business School Press, 2007.
[7]Cokins, G., *Activity-Based Cost Management, Making It Work,* McGraw-Hill, 1996.

management's attention on an important objective: adding value for the shareholders. In fact, it has been the principal tool used by upper management within the Coca-Cola Company. EVA is used to facilitate decisions regarding major capital investment, as well as acquisitions and divestitures. It has also been used to analyze products and operating units to determine the economic winners and losers within the firm's portfolio of products and businesses.

Basically, EVA is a management tool that examines the difference between the net operating profit after taxes and the cost of capital, which includes the cost of both debt and equity capital.[8] Hence, the interest charges and bond rates that contribute to the cost of debt capital are combined with the cost to the shareholders of providing the firm with equity capital (by purchasing its stock).

> EVA is a management tool that examines the difference between the net operating profit after taxes and the cost of capital.

Many firms that adopted EVA found that few of their managers knew how much capital was tied up in their business units. Moreover, the managers did not have an accurate understanding of the true cost of capital. EVA seeks to remedy this by focusing attention on adding value for the shareholder through more effective use of capital. The result of an increased emphasis on effective use of capital should be lower inventories, fewer warehouses, and so on.

Stern Stewart, a corporate financial advisory service, is generally credited with the development of EVA. Stern Stewart argues that there are four ways to create value for the shareholder:

1. Increase profitability without using additional capital (e.g., increase profit margins and increase sales without using additional capital).
2. Invest in projects that earn more than the cost of capital.
3. Free up capital that earns less than the cost of capital.
4. Use debt to reduce the cost of capital.

Real estate, equipment, facilities, working capital, and inventories are examples of capital being used within the firm. Other, not so obvious, examples of capital are investments in training and in research and development. The investments in training result in increased value of the firm's human capital. While it is not easy to quantify the value of capital in R&D and in training, they should not be overlooked in the quest for value.

The three examples below illustrate how EVA is calculated and how it can be used to improve economic decision making.

EXAMPLE 16.12 Economic Value Added—Example 1

Two firms (A and B) are being considered for acquisition. The assets of the firms are $100 million and $200 million, respectively. Both are debt free; hence, the equity equals the assets. The annual operating profits for the firms are $40 million and $70 million, respectively. Taxes equal 40 percent of operating profit. Consequently, the annual net

---

[8]Stern, J. M., J. S. Shiely, and I. Ross, *The EVA Challenge,* Wiley, 2001.

incomes for the firms are $24 million and $42 million, respectively. Dividing the net income by equity yields return on equity of 24 percent and 21 percent, respectively. The cost of capital is 12 percent. Which firm is best from a shareholder value point of view? Some would choose A, because it has the greatest ROE (return on equity) or ROA (return on assets). However, B maximizes value for shareholders.

To determine the EVA, subtract the cost of capital from net operating profit after taxes (NOPAT). For A, this yields $24 million − 0.12($100 million) = $12 million. For B, the EVA equals $42 million − 0.12($200 million) = $18 million. (As was the case with the IRR method, one cannot choose the alternative that has the greatest return on equity; instead, incremental net operating profits should be compared with the cost of capital.)

It has long been known that maximizing return on investment is not the right objective. In 1924, Donaldson Brown, chief financial officer of General Motors Corporation, noted, "The object of management is not necessarily the highest rate of return on capital, but . . . to assure profit with each increment of volume that will at least equal the economic cost of additional capital required."[9]

EXAMPLE 16.13 Economic Value Added—Example 2

Consider two firms, C and D, each with a 12 percent cost of capital. The financial data for the two firms (in $M's) are

	Firm C	Firm D
Equity	$100	$200
Annual Operating Profit	$25	$35
Taxes (40 percent)	$10	$14
Net Income	$15	$21

On the basis of net income generated, one might conclude that D is the better-performing company. However, for C there is a capital cost of $12 and an EVA of $3; whereas for D there is a capital cost of $24 and an EVA of −$3. Therefore, firm C is superior to firm D in adding value for the shareholder.

EXAMPLE 16.14 Economic Value Added—Example 3

There are several ways to compute EVA. The method used in the previous examples was

	Firm C	Firm D
Capital Invested	$100	$200
Operating Profit	$25	$35
Taxes (40 percent)	$10	$14
Net Operating Profit After Taxes (NOPAT)	$15	$21
Cost of Capital (12 percent)	$12	$24
EVA	+$3	−$3

---

[9]Viewgraphs used in EVA seminar conducted by Stern Stewart & Co.

Alternatively, EVA can be computed as follows:

	Firm C	Firm D
Return on Assets	15%	10.5%
Cost of Capital	12%	12%
Difference	+3%	−1.5%
EVA = difference × assets	+$3	−$3

16-6 SUMMARY

In this chapter, we provided an introduction to the language and techniques of accountants, financial analysts, and managers. The "takeaway" messages from this chapter can be summarized as follows:

1. To be successful in developing and selling engineering designs and projects, the engineer must learn to communicate effectively in the language of accounting.

2. Cost information is best understood and interpreted by considering it from one or more of five cost viewpoints: life cycle, past/future, manufacturing cost structure, fixed/variable, and average/marginal.

3. Cost estimation is a complex and challenging task that must incorporate the trade-off between the cost of making the estimate and the consequences of an inaccurate estimate.

4. Cost estimation can be thought of hierarchically. Order of magnitude estimates can be broken down into preliminary estimates that can be further broken down into detailed estimates.

5. The two most important accounting documents are the balance sheet and the income statement. The balance sheet shows what a company's assets, liabilities, and net worth are at a point in time. The income statement shows the revenues and expenses a company incurred over a period of time.

6. Ratio analysis can be used to meaningfully interpret the values found on balance sheets and income statements.

7. Cost accounting focuses on allocating overhead costs to specific products or orders. Traditional methods include allocation by direct labor hours, direct labor dollars, and prime dollars.

8. Activity-based costing is an emerging area of accounting that more accurately connects costs with the activities that drive them.

9. Economic value added is an emerging technique to focus management's attention to shareholder value by connecting profit with cost of capital.

Pit Stop #16—Does Accounting Count as a Foreign Language in Engineering?

 1. True or False: When conducting an economic analysis, an engineer should consider costs from one and only one cost viewpoint.

 2. True or False: The cost of foregoing an opportunity to earn interest, or a return, on investment funds is referred to as a sunk cost.

 3. True or False: Prime cost is the sum of direct material cost and direct labor cost.

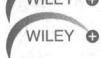 4. True or False: If the cost function for producing x units is $TC(x) = 700 + 0.6x$ and the revenue function is $TR(x) = 2.0x$; then the breakeven value is 500 units.

 5. True or False: The average cost function for Question 4 is given by $AC(x) = 500 + 1.4x$

 6. True or False: The tradeoff being considered when determining the level of detail of an estimate is the cost of making the estimate versus the cost of errors resulting from an inaccurate estimate.

 7. True or False: An income statement shows the assets, liabilities, and net worth of a firm at a point in time.

 8. True or False: The fundamental equation of accounting states that assets = liabilities + net worth

 9. True or False: EBIT can also be referred to as operating earnings.

10. True or False: In cost accounting, the acronym ABC refers to a Pareto analysis of costs where A items are most important, C items are least important, and B items are somewhere between.

 11. True or False: EVA is a management tool that focuses manager's attention on adding value for the shareholders.

 Tutoring problem available (at instructor's discretion) in *WileyPLUS*.

 Problem available (at instructor's discretion) in *WileyPLUS*.

 Worked Problem Video available in *WileyPLUS*.

FE-LIKE PROBLEMS

 1. On a balance sheet, a corporation's economic obligations to nonowners are called

    a. owners' equity.

    b. liabilities.

    c. assets.

    d. retained earnings.

2. The information below has been extracted from the books of the Shelley Company. Which of the following represents Shelley's current ratio?

    a. 0.76

    b. 1.48

Current Assets		Current Liabilities	
Cash	$86	Accounts payable	$78
Accounts receivable	$130	Wages payable	$68
Inventory	$140	Taxes payable	$28
Total	$356	Total	$174

    c. 2.05

    d. 2.51

3. The fundamental equation used within an accounting balance sheet is

    a. net profit = gross profit − expenses − taxes.

    b. assets + liabilities = net worth.

    c. assets + liabilities + net worth = 0.

    d. assets = liabilities + net worth.

4. Marginal cost is

    a. any cost occurring after "time now."

    b. the ratio of total cost to total quantity of output.

    c. the market value of an asset at the end of its life less its disposal costs.

    d. the incremental cost of producing one more unit of output.

5. The three major categories that comprise cost of goods manufactured are

    a. material, labor, and overhead.

    b. average, marginal, and instantaneous.

    c. past, present, and future.

    d. initial, operating, and salvage.

6. The total cost equation for producing X widgets is given by $TC = \$1,000 + \$6X$. The average cost per widget for producing 500 widgets is closest to which of the following?

    a. $1,000

    b. $6

    c. $8

    d. $4,000

7. The total cost equation for producing X widgets is given by $TC = \$1,000 + \$6X$. The variable cost per widget is closest to which of the following?

    a. $1,000

    b. $6

    c. $8

    d. $4,000

8. The total cost equation for producing X widgets is given by $TC = \$1,000 + \$6X$. The marginal cost per widget at a production level of 300 units is closest to which of the following?

    a. $2,800

    b. $6

    c. $8

    d. $4,000

9. Fixed cost is

    a. any cost that does not vary with the quantity of output.

    b. the ratio of total cost to total quantity of output.

    c. the market value of an asset at the end of its life less its disposal costs.

    d. the incremental cost of producing one more unit of output.

10. When an organization considers its work-in-process, how should it be classified on a balance sheet?

    a. Asset

    b. Liability

    c. Net worth

    d. Expense

PROBLEMS

Section 16.1

1. Reconsider the scenario presented in Example 16.1, which details a firm considering purchasing a small turret lathe to manufacture part number 163H for the B&K Corporation.

    a. What additional assumptions/data would be required to complete an economic analysis to determine if the turret lathe should be purchased?

    b. What source(s) would you pursue to obtain the data you identified in Part a?

    c. Given the facts and data presented, as well as any additional assumptions you made and data you acquired, should the turret lathe be purchased?

Section 16.2

2. Match the terms in the first column with the appropriate definition in the second column.

Terms	Definitions
(a) First cost	(1) Any cost occurring after "time now"
(b) Average cost	(2) The total initial investment required to get an asset ready for service

(c) Fixed cost

(d) Overhead cost

(e) Marginal cost

(f) Opportunity cost

(g) Salvage value

(h) Sunk cost

(i) Variable cost

(j) Past cost

(k) Maintenance costs

(l) Future cost

(m) Cost of debt capital

(3) The ratio of total cost to total quantity of output

(4) The market value of an asset at the end of its life less its disposal costs

(5) The cost of obtaining fund through debt obligations

(6) The incremental cost of producing one more unit of output

(7) Any past cost or portion of past cost that is not recovered

(8) The recurring costs that are necessary to operate and maintain an asset

(9) Any cost that varies with the quantity of output

(10) Any cost occurring prior to "time now"

(11) Any cost that does not vary with the quantity of output

(12) The cost of forgoing an opportunity to earn interest on funds

(13) All cost in manufacturing other than direct material and direct labor

3. A firm has the capacity to produce 1,000,000 units of a product each year. At present, it is operating at 70 percent of capacity. The firm's annual revenue is $700,000. Annual fixed costs are $300,000, and the variable costs are $0.50 per unit.

   a. What is the firm's annual profit or loss?

   b. At what volume of sales does the firm break even?

   c. What will be the profit or loss if the plant runs at 90 percent of capacity assuming a constant income per unit and constant variable cost per unit?

   d. At what percent of capacity would the firm have to run to earn a profit of $90,000?

4. Two production methods are being considered for making thermal dryers. Method 1 has a fixed cost of $1,000 and a variable cost of $20 per unit. Method 2 has a fixed cost of $400 and a variable cost of $100 per unit. For what range of production volumes would you prefer each method?

5. The maker of Winglow is purchasing a new stamping machine. Two options are being considered, Rooney and Blair. The sales forecast for Winglow is 8,000 units for next year. If purchased, the Rooney will increase plant fixed costs by $20,000 and reduce variable costs by $5.60 per unit. The Blair would increase fixed costs by $5,000 and reduce variable costs by $4.00 per unit. If variable costs are now $20 per unit, which machine should be purchased?

6. Product X is sold for $500 per unit. The total cost of production per year, including capital recovery and a return, is given by the expression

$$TC = 0.04n^3 - 700n + 50{,}000$$

where n is the number of units sold. If TC represents the total of all fixed and variable costs, determine the following:

   a. The value of n that maximizes profit

   b. The maximum profit for a year

   c. The fixed cost per year

7. The cost curve for producing widgets passes through the following points and is piecewise linear in between.

Units Produced	0	200	400	600
Costs	$600	$1,200	$1,600	$1,800

   a. What is the fixed cost of producing 600 widgets?

   b. What is the variable cost of producing 600 widgets?

   c. What is the cost per unit if only 400 widgets are produced?

   d. What is the incremental cost of producing the 100th widget?

   e. What is the incremental cost of producing the 500th widget?

   f. What is the fixed cost per unit for producing 1,000 widgets?

   g. What is the variable cost per unit for producing 1,000 widgets?

8. A manufacturer of precision cutting tools has the capacity to make 1,000,000 cutting tools per year. Each sells for $15. The variable cost per unit to produce the cutting tools is $9 each. Annual fixed costs for the manufacturer are $3,500,000.

    a. If the plant is operating at 50 percent of design capacity, how much profit (loss) is being earned?

    b. At what percent of capacity must the plant operate to break even?

    c. What is the cost per tool when operating at the level you determined in Part b?

9. A new engineering building at a state university is to contain 10,000,000 square feet. The total cost of the building (TC) is given by the following expression:

$$TC = (200 + 80X + 2X^2)A$$

where X = number of floors and A = floor area in ft^2/floor.

    a. Create a table that shows the total building cost, average cost per floor, and marginal cost per floor (using the difference equation approach) for configurations ranging from 1 floor to 12 floors, inclusive. (Hint: You may want to create the table using your favorite spreadsheet program.)

    b. Based on your table, what is the optimal number of floors for the building? Justify your answer based on the "total cost" column.

    c. Justify your answer in Part b based on the "marginal cost per floor" column.

    d. Demonstrate, using differential calculus, that your answer in Parts b and c is correct. (Note: For this part, assume that X is a continuous variable.)

 10. The KMP Metal Machining Company produces widgets according to customer order. The company has determined that widgets can be produced on three different machine tools: M1, M2, or M3. An analysis of widget production cost reveals the following data:

Machine Tool	Fixed Cost/Order	Variable Cost/Unit
M1	$300	$9
M2	$750	$3
M3	$500	$5

    a. Using a graphical approach, determine the most economical machine tool to use for all order sizes between 1 and 200 units. In other words, determine the subranges within the overall range of 1 to 200 for which each machine tool is preferred.

    b. Using an algebraic approach, determine the most economical machine tool to use for all order sizes between 1 and 200 units. (Hint: Determine the subranges within the overall range of 1 to 200 for which each machine tool is preferred.)

    c. For an order of size 75, which machine tool should be used to produce the order, and what is the total production cost?

    d. For an order of size 160, assume that the preferred (most economical) machine is unavailable. What penalty (expressed in dollars of additional production cost) must be paid if the second most economical machine is used? The third?

11. Two processes are put in place for production. Neither will be removed. Process R is designed to produce 10,000 units per year and has a fixed cost of $90,000 per year. Process T has the same design capacity and has a fixed cost of $80,000 per year. Process R produces the initial 4,000 units at a variable cost of $8 per unit and the next 6,000 units at a variable cost of $17 per unit. Process T produces the first 5,000 units at a variable cost of $9 each and produces the next 5,000 at $5 each. Assume that the fixed costs are incurred even if no production is assigned to the process.

    a. What should be the loads assigned to Processes R and T if demand for the product is 5,500 units?

    b. What is the total cost and average cost per unit for Part a?

    c. What should be the loads assigned to Processes R and T if demand for the product is 9,500 units?

    d. What is the total cost and average cost per unit for Part c?

12. The variable cost of producing specialty value-added stainless-steel tubing varies according to the quantity produced per year. The variable cost is $500 per ton from 0 to 700 tons. Above this level, the variable cost is different. At this time, we are producing 600 tons per year, and the average cost per ton is $800. Next year, we anticipate ramping up production to 1,000 tons, and the projected average cost for all 1,000 tons will be $710 per ton.

a. What is the current fixed cost?

b. If the fixed cost holds constant next year, what is the variable cost of production for tons above 700 tons?

Section 16.3

13. Find three Web sites where "cost estimating" is a topic.

    a. State the URL for each of the sites.

    b. Identify the one you would likely find most useful if you wanted to learn more about cost estimating.

    c. In 25 words or less, what does the site you identified in Part b have that is most useful?

14. A distributor has learned that an estimate for the packaging and processing costs can be predicted based on the weight of an order. To this end, a regression analysis is performed resulting in the mixed cost function: $cost = 63.63 + 0.279\ weight$.

    a. What is the fixed cost within this cost function?

    b. What is the marginal cost within this cost function?

    c. What was the independent variable within the regression analysis?

    d. What was the dependent variable within the regression analysis?

    e. What is the estimated cost for a package weighing 600 pounds?

    f. The regression analysis reports an r^2 of 0.9824. Interpret the meaning of this value.

15. For each of the situations below, identify a potential source of analogy data for the costs under each of the following cases: (1) this project/activity is a first of its kind for the company, and (2) this project/activity is similar to projects that the company has completed before.

    a. Construction of a high-rise in New York City

    b. Construction of a two-lane bridge in a rural Oklahoma county

    c. Acquisition of a punch press to be used by a manufacturing company in California

    d. Hiring an information technology manager to oversee new network services

16. A circuit board manufacturer is trying to determine the appropriate cost driver for estimating the cost of circuit board assembly support. The list of potential cost drivers has been narrowed to three: direct labor hours, number of circuit boards completed, and average cycle time. In preparation for a simple linear regression analysis, a data collection activity has been completed. The results of the data collection are shown in the table below. Use this data to complete the following:

    a. Determine a regression line for each of the three possible cost drivers. *For each* possible driver:

        (i) plot a graph of the cost driver versus the support cost;

        (ii) determine and clearly state the regression equation; and

        (iii) determine and clearly state the associated r^2.

    b. Which driver do you recommend?

    c. What percentage of the data does your driver and regression equation explain?

Week	Circuit Board Assembly Support Cost	Direct Labor Hours	Number of Boards Completed	Average Cycle Time
1	$66,402	7,619	2,983	186.44
2	$56,943	7,678	2,830	139.14
3	$60,337	7,816	2,413	151.13
4	$50,096	7,659	2,221	138.30
5	$64,241	7,646	2,701	158.63
6	$60,846	7,765	2,656	148.71
7	$43,119	7,685	2,495	105.85
8	$63,412	7,962	2,128	174.02
9	$59,283	7,793	2,127	155.30
10	$60,070	7,732	2,127	162.20

11	$53,345	7,771	2,338	142.97
12	$65,027	7,842	2,685	176.08
13	$58,220	7,940	2,602	150.19
14	$65,406	7,750	2,029	194.06
15	$35,268	7,954	2,136	100.51
16	$46,394	7,768	2,046	137.47
17	$71,877	7,764	2,786	197.44
18	$61,903	7,635	2,822	164.69
19	$50,009	7,849	2,178	141.95
20	$49,327	7,869	2,244	123.37
21	$44,703	7,576	2,195	128.25
22	$45,582	7,557	2,370	106.16
23	$43,818	7,569	2,016	131.41
24	$62,122	7,672	2,515	154.88
25	$52,403	7,653	2,942	140.07

Section 16.4

WILEY **17.** Determine the missing values below to produce a valid balance sheet.

BALANCE SHEET
Year Ending December 31, 2004

ASSETS

Cash		(a)
Accounts receivable		$8,000
Raw materials inventory		$10,000
Work-in-process inventory		$15,000
Finished goods inventory		$18,500
Land		$30,000
Building	$80,000	
Less: Depreciation reserve	$8,000	(b)
Equipment	(c)	
Less: Depreciation reserve	$4,000	$36,000
TOTAL ASSETS		$283,727

LIABILITIES

Notes payable	$25,000
Accounts payable	(d)
Declared dividends	$20,000
TOTAL LIABILITIES	$51,000

NET WORTH

Common stock	$200,000
Retained earnings	(e)
TOTAL NET WORTH	(f)
TOTAL LIABILITIES & NET WORTH	(g)

18. Following is a list of balance sheet accounts for Branman Co. as of December 31, 2005.

   a. Classify each of the following accounts as an asset, liability, or net worth.

Account	Balance	Account	Balance
Cash	$45,000	Declared dividends payable	$20,000
Accounts receivable	$8,000	Finished goods inventory	$18,500
Notes payable	$25,000	Land	$30,000
Raw materials inventory	$10,000	Net building (less depreciation)	$72,000
Common stock	$100,000	Net equipment (less depreciation)	$36,000
Work-in-process inventory	$15,000	Retained earnings	??????
Accounts payable	$6,000		

   b. What is the balance in the Retained Earnings account if this data forms a valid balance sheet?

19. The Scott Company shows the following alphabetical list of account balances as of December 31, 2006.

Account	Balance	Account	Balance
Accounts payable	$50,000	Finished goods	$30,000
Accounts receivable	$80,000	Land value	$115,000
Accrued taxes	$20,000	Long-term mortgages	$390,000
Buildings (net value)	$205,000	Notes payable	$60,000
Cash	$40,000	Raw material inventory	$40,000
Dividends payable	$20,000	Stockholder's equity	$150,000
Equipment (net value)	$180,000		

   a. Construct a balance sheet for Scott Company as of December 31, 2006.

   b. Demonstrate that the fundamental accounting equation holds by stating the dollar values of the terms in the equation.

20. In addition to the account balances in the previous problem, Scott Company recorded the following summary transactions for the year ending December 31, 2006.

Category	Amount
Administrative expenses	$30,000
Factory depreciation	$30,000
Direct labor charges	$70,000
Factory overhead	$35,000
General interest payments	$40,000
Raw material expenses	$90,000
Sales	$400,000
Taxes paid	$20,000

Construct an income statement for Scott Company for the period 1/1/2006 to 12/31/2006.

WILEY ⊕ **21.**   Betty Smith is the owner of Accurate Tax Service. For the year ending April 30, 2007, the following information is available for this service business. At the *beginning* of this accounting period, the balance in the Betty Smith, Capital account was $32,000. Following is a summary of activities *during* this accounting period:

Betty Smith, capital withdrawn: $18,600
Revenue from income tax preparation: $71,300
Revenue from monthly clients: $43,800
Salaries expense: $12,500
Advertising expense: $900
Rent expense: $6,000
Automobile expense: $1,300
Office supplies expense: $7,500.

  Note: You should assume that all profit (or loss) accrued during this accounting period is absorbed into the Betty Smith, Capital account at the end of the period.

  Following are the account balances at the *end* of this accounting period (except Betty Smith, Capital):

Cash: $62,500
Accounts receivable: $3,700
Office furniture and fixtures: $11,300
Office machines and computers: $15,000
Automobile: $9,500
Accounts payable: $1,700

   a.   Prepare an income statement for the year ending April 30, 2007.

   b.   Prepare a balance sheet as of April 30, 2007.

22.   As published in its annual report, the balance sheet and income statements of JanCo include the items shown below (listed alphabetically). All balances are as shown on the statements; no additional transaction processing or adjustments are required.

Accounts payable	$12,000
Accounts receivable	$21,000
Advertising expense	$600
Cash	$22,950
Common stock	$54,000
Cost of goods sold	$15,000
Depreciation expense	$300
Inventory	$14,400

Notes payable	$6,000
Prepaid rent	$1,050
Property, plant, and equipment	$15,300
Rent expense	$2,100
Retained earnings	$1,500
Sales revenue	$27,000
Wages expense	$7,500
Wages payable	$1,200

   a.   Prepare a balance sheet for JanCo.

   b.   Prepare an income statement for JanCo.

WILEY ⊕ **23.**   As published in its annual report, the consolidated balance sheet of Packers includes the items shown below (listed alphabetically).

Accounts payable	?	Other assets	$30,350
Accounts receivable	$8,739	Other liabilities	$57,786
Capital in excess of par value	$ 187,506	Property, plant, and equipment	$103,684
Cash	$92,827	Retained earnings	$35,097
Common stock at par value	$402	Total assets	$378,045
Inventory	?	Total liabilities	?
Long-term liabilities	$9,474	Total liabilities and net worth	?
Notes payable	$11,195	Total net worth	?

a. Determine the values for the missing items.

b. Prepare a balance sheet for Packers.

24. The annual report from a major energy company contains the following: Net income represented 9 percent return on average total assets of approximately $27 billion and a 19 percent return on average stockholders' equity. Net income per gallon on products sold worldwide averaged $0.035. Net income was $0.04 on each dollar of revenue. Based on this information, determine the following:

   a. Net income

   b. Total revenues

   c. Average stockholders' equity

   d. Gallons of products sold

WILEY 25. Consider the comparative balance sheet and income statement for Starbucks provided in Figures 16.8 and 16.9. Based on these financial statements, determine the following for the year ending October 1, 2006:

   a. Return on assets employed

   b. Return on owner's equity

   c. Current ratio

   d. Acid test ratio

   e. Accounts receivable turnover

   f. Inventory turnover

   g. Debt to equity ratio

   h. Operating income to total assets

   i. EBIT

   j. EBITDA

26. Find three Web sites where "financial ratios" is a topic.

   a. State the URL for each of the sites.

   b. Identify the one you would likely find most useful if you wanted to learn more about financial ratios.

   c. In 25 words or less, what does the site you identified in Part b have that is most useful?

   d. List the names and formulas for at least three additional financial ratios not stated in the chapter.

Section 16.5

WILEY 27. The Bryant Company manufactures a custom-designed part for the aerospace industry. Within the production facility, there are five operating departments. The sequence of departments through which the part passes during production is shown in the table below. The table also contains other production information. Two units of product can be obtained from one 4' × 4' sheet of aluminum that costs $3.50 per square foot. Overhead costs to produce a lot of size 10,000 are estimated to be $304,000.

Sequence	Dept	Avg. Labor ($/hr)	Avg. Prod. Time (min/part)	Floor Space (sq. ft.)
1	Cutting	$20.00	3.0	1,300
2	Stamping	$18.20	1.0	1,600
3	Trimming	$17.20	2.0	1,200
4	Assemble	$16.00	5.0	2,000
5	Package	$14.40	0.5	1,500

a. Assume that no other production costs exist. Determine the total cost of producing a 10,000-unit lot.

b. Determine the cost per piece of producing a 10,000-unit lot.

c. Assume that overhead is distributed on the basis of floor space. What is the overhead assigned to each department?

28. EmKay Company is divided into two departments for accounting purposes. The direct labor hours and overhead costs for the last year are as follows:

Department	Direct Labor Hours	Overhead Costs
A	900	$13,500
B	1,350	$27,000

What selling price should the company quote on Job Order A54 if the following conditions apply?
- Raw material costs are estimated as $750
- Estimated direct labor hours required in Departments A and B are 25 hours and 50 hours, respectively
- Workers in both departments earn $15 per hour
- Overhead costs *in each department* are allocated based on an overhead rate per direct labor hour
- Profit is to be 25 percent of total cost

29. For a small manufacturing firm, a current-period job that requires 35 hours of direct labor is to be allocated $437.50 of overhead cost based on a rate developed from previous period data. The following additional information is available:
- Overhead is allocated based on direct labor hours.
- One thousand direct labor hours were expended in the previous period.
- The previous period's average labor rate was $10/hour.
- The current period's average labor rate is $10/hour.

   a. What were the overhead costs for the previous period?

   b. If overhead for the job in question had been allocated based on direct labor dollars, how much overhead cost would have been allocated? (If you did not get an answer to Part a, you may assume a value of $15,000 for previous period overhead costs.)

30. To make a batch of 1,000 units of a certain item, it is estimated that 120 direct labor hours are required at a cost of $10/hour. Direct material costs are estimated at $1,500 per batch. The overhead costs are calculated based on an overhead rate of $7.50 per direct labor hour. The item can be readily purchased from a local vendor for $4 per unit.

   a. Should the item be made or purchased?

   b. Over what range of overhead rate is your answer in Part a valid?

31. Consider the following table (shown in two parts):

EOY	REVENUE	OPERATING EXPENSES	DEPRECIATION	NET OPERATING PROFIT	TAXES
8	$2,765,000	$2,379,200	$38,400	$347,400	$138,960
9	$2,765,000	$2,379,200	$23,040	$362,760	$145,104
10	$2,765,000	$2,379,200	$13,824	$371,976	$148,790

EOY	NOPAT	CAPITAL	COST OF CAPITAL	CAPITAL CHARGE	EVA (ECON PROFIT)
8	$208,440	$57,600	0.1	$9,600	XXX
9	$217,656	$34,560	0.1	XXX	
10	$223,186	$20,736	0.1		

   a. What is the EVA in year 8?

   b. What is the capital charge in year 9?

32. Consider the following table (shown in two parts):

   a. What is the EVA in year 5?

   b. What is the capital charge in year 6?

EOY	REVENUE	OPERATING EXPENSES	DEPRECIATION	NET OPERATING PROFIT	TAXES
5	$2,765,000	$2,379,200	$49,536	$336,264	$134,506
6	$2,765,000	$2,379,200	$49,536	$336,264	$134,506
7	$2,765,000	$2,379,200	$48,768	$337,032	$134,813

EOY	NOPAT	CAPITAL	COST OF CAPITAL	CAPITAL CHARGE	EVA (ECON PROFIT)
5	$201,758	$74,304	0.1	$12,384	XXX
6	$201,758	$144,768	0.1	XXX	
7	$202,219	$96,000	0.1		

33. A company is considering purchasing a new piece of machinery at a cost $60,000. It is expected to generate revenues of $20,000 per year for 4 years against $3,000 of annual operating expenses. The machinery is MACRS 3-year property. The tax rate is 30 percent. *MARR* is 10 percent. What is the EVA for year 3?

34. Given the following information for Live Wire Electronics, construct an income statement for the month ending June 30.

Sales	$500,000
Cost of goods sold	$170,000
Administration cost	$75,000
Advertising expense	$25,000
Taxes	$70,000

35. A company is considering purchasing a new piece of machinery at a cost $50,000. It is expected to generate revenues of $25,000 per year for 4 years against $1,500 of annual operating expenses. The machinery is MACRS 3-year property. The tax rate is 40 percent. *MARR* is 10 percent. What is the EVA for year 3?

36. Cost Center D within the Welding Department of the Mizer Corporation collected the following data during 2004.

Cost Center D Overhead Expenses: $4,800
Cost Center D Direct Labor Hours: 2,800
Cost Center D Direct Labor Cost: $11,200
Cost Center D Direct Material Cost: $3,000

Compute the 2005 cost center overhead rate by the following methods:

a. Percentage of direct labor cost
b. Percentage of prime cost
c. Rate per direct labor hour
d. Mizer Corp. has adopted the direct labor hours method of overhead allocation. The New Orders Department has just received an order that requires an estimated 125 hours of direct labor in Cost Center D. What is the estimated overhead charge for this job in Cost Center D?

37. Find three Web sites where "activity-based costing" (ABC) is a topic.
a. State the URL for each of the sites.
b. Identify the one you would likely find most useful if you wanted to learn more about ABC.
c. In 25 words or less, what does the site you identified in Part b have that is most useful?

38. Find three Web sites where "economic value added" (EVA) is a topic.
a. State the URL for each of the sites.
b. Identify the one you would likely find most useful if you wanted to learn more about EVA.
c. In 25 words or less, what does the site you identified in Part b have that is most useful?

39. Skrunchy Company produces two products, Lower and Upper. The following two tables give pertinent information about these two products.

Category	Lower	Upper
Direct labor	$700,000	$1,000,000
Direct material	$2,000,000	$1,500,000
Direct labor hours	28,000	25,000
Quantity produced	20,000	10,000
Total overhead	$2,500,000	

ABC Activity	Driver	Cost	Lower	Upper
Rework	Hours	$1,800,000	4,000 hours	42,500 hours
Material handling	Moves	$700,000	40,000 moves	20,000 moves

    a. What is the cost per unit of Upper if Skrunchy uses traditional overhead allocation based on direct labor hours?

    b. What is the cost per unit of Upper if Skrunchy uses activity-based costing to allocate overhead?

40. Reconsider Problem 39.

    a. What is the cost per unit of Lower if Skrunchy uses traditional overhead allocation based on direct labor hours?

    b. What is the cost per unit of Lower if Skrunchy uses activity-based costing to allocate overhead?

41. LockTite Company produces two products, Pretty Safe (PS) and Virtually Impenetrable (VI). The following two tables give pertinent information about these products.

Category	PS	VI
Number produced	3,000	2,000
Direct material cost	$350,000	$150,000
Direct labor hours	5,000 hours	10,000 hours
Direct labor cost	$100,000	$200,000
Total overhead	$750,000	

ABC Activity	Driver	Cost	PS	VI
Production	Machine hours	$500,000	1,000 hours	4,000 hours
Engineering	Engineering hours	$250,000	2,000 hours	3,000 hours

    a. What is the cost per unit of Pretty Safe if LockTite uses traditional overhead allocation based on number of units produced?

    b. What is the cost per unit of Pretty Safe if LockTite uses activity-based costing to allocate overhead?

42. Reconsider Problem 41.

    a. What is the cost per unit of Virtually Impenetrable if LockTite uses traditional overhead allocation based on number of units produced?

    b. What is the cost per unit of Virtually Impenetrable if LockTite uses activity-based costing to allocate overhead?

TABLE A-a-1

	Single Sums		Uniform Series				Gradient Series	
	To Find F	To Find P	To Find F	To Find A	To Find P	To Find A	To Find P	To Find A
	Given P	Given F	Given A	Given F	Given A	Given P	Given G	Given G
n	(F|P i%,n)	(P|F i%,n)	(F|A,i%,n)	(A|F i%,n)	(P|A,i%,n)	(A|P i%,n)	(P|G i%,n)	(A|G i%,n)
1	1.00250	0.99751	1.00000	1.00000	0.99751	1.00250	0.00000	0.00000
2	1.00501	0.99502	2.00250	0.49938	1.99252	0.50188	0.99502	0.49938
3	1.00752	0.99254	3.00751	0.33250	2.98506	0.33500	2.98009	0.99834
4	1.01004	0.99006	4.01503	0.24906	3.97512	0.25156	5.95028	1.49688
5	1.01256	0.98759	5.02506	0.19900	4.96272	0.20150	9.90065	1.99501
6	1.01509	0.98513	6.03763	0.16563	5.94785	0.16813	14.82630	2.49272
7	1.01763	0.98267	7.05272	0.14179	6.93052	0.14429	20.72235	2.99001
8	1.02018	0.98022	8.07035	0.12391	7.91074	0.12641	27.58391	3.48689
9	1.02273	0.97778	9.09053	0.11000	8.88852	0.11250	35.40614	3.98335
10	1.02528	0.97534	10.11325	0.09888	9.86386	0.10138	44.18420	4.47940
11	1.02785	0.97291	11.13854	0.08978	10.83677	0.09228	53.91328	4.97503
12	1.03042	0.97048	12.16638	0.08219	11.80725	0.08469	64.58858	5.47025
13	1.03299	0.96806	13.19680	0.07578	12.77532	0.07828	76.20532	5.96504
14	1.03557	0.96565	14.22979	0.07028	13.74096	0.07278	88.75874	6.45943
15	1.03816	0.96324	15.26537	0.06551	14.70420	0.06801	102.24409	6.95339
16	1.04076	0.96084	16.30353	0.06134	15.66504	0.06384	116.65666	7.44694
17	1.04336	0.95844	17.34429	0.05766	16.62348	0.06016	131.99172	7.94008
18	1.04597	0.95605	18.38765	0.05438	17.57953	0.05688	148.24459	8.43279
19	1.04858	0.95367	19.43362	0.05146	18.53320	0.05396	165.41059	8.92510
20	1.05121	0.95129	20.48220	0.04882	19.48449	0.05132	183.48508	9.41698
21	1.05383	0.94892	21.53341	0.04644	20.43340	0.04894	202.46341	9.90845
22	1.05647	0.94655	22.58724	0.04427	21.37995	0.04677	222.34096	10.39951
23	1.05911	0.94419	23.64371	0.04229	22.32414	0.04479	243.11313	10.89014
24	1.06176	0.94184	24.70282	0.04048	23.26598	0.04298	264.77534	11.38036
25	1.06441	0.93949	25.76457	0.03881	24.20547	0.04131	287.32301	11.87017
26	1.06707	0.93714	26.82899	0.03727	25.14261	0.03977	310.75160	12.35956
27	1.06974	0.93481	27.89606	0.03585	26.07742	0.03835	335.05657	12.84853
28	1.07241	0.93248	28.96580	0.03452	27.00989	0.03702	360.23340	13.33709
29	1.07510	0.93015	30.03821	0.03329	27.94004	0.03579	386.27760	13.82523
30	1.07778	0.92783	31.11331	0.03214	28.86787	0.03464	413.18468	14.31296
36	1.09405	0.91403	37.62056	0.02658	34.38647	0.02908	592.49878	17.23058
40	1.10503	0.90495	42.01320	0.02380	38.01986	0.02630	728.73988	19.16735
48	1.12733	0.88705	50.93121	0.01963	45.17869	0.02213	1040.05520	23.02092
50	1.13297	0.88263	53.18868	0.01880	46.94617	0.02130	1125.77667	23.98016
52	1.13864	0.87824	55.45746	0.01803	48.70484	0.02053	1214.58847	24.93774
55	1.14720	0.87168	58.88194	0.01698	51.32644	0.01948	1353.52863	26.37098
60	1.16162	0.86087	64.64671	0.01547	55.65236	0.01797	1600.08454	28.75142
72	1.19695	0.83546	78.77939	0.01269	65.81686	0.01519	2265.55685	34.42214
75	1.20595	0.82922	82.37922	0.01214	68.31075	0.01464	2447.60694	35.83048
80	1.22110	0.81894	88.43918	0.01131	72.42595	0.01381	2764.45681	38.16942
84	1.23335	0.81080	93.34192	0.01071	75.68132	0.01321	3029.75923	40.03312
90	1.25197	0.79874	100.78845	9.9218E−03	80.50382	0.01242	3446.86997	42.81623
96	1.27087	0.78686	108.34739	9.2296E−03	85.25460	0.01173	3886.28316	45.58444
100	1.28362	0.77904	113.44996	8.8145E−03	88.38248	0.01131	4191.24173	47.42163
108	1.30952	0.76364	123.80926	8.0769E−03	94.54530	0.01058	4829.01247	51.07618
120	1.34935	0.74110	139.74142	7.1561E−03	103.56175	9.6561E−03	5852.11160	56.50843
132	1.39040	0.71922	156.15817	6.4038E−03	112.31206	8.9038E−03	6950.01441	61.88128
144	1.43269	0.69799	173.07425	5.7779E−03	120.80407	8.2779E−03	8117.41331	67.19487
180	1.56743	0.63799	226.97269	4.4058E−03	144.80547	6.9058E−03	1.1987E+04	82.78122
240	1.82075	0.54922	328.30200	3.0460E−03	180.31091	5.5460E−03	1.9399E+04	107.58631
360	2.45684	0.40703	582.73688	1.7160E−03	237.18938	4.2160E−03	3.6264E+04	152.89019
480	3.31515	0.30165	926.05950	1.0798E−03	279.34176	3.5798E−03	5.3821E+04	192.66991
600	4.47331	0.22355	1389.32309	7.1977E−04	310.58071	3.2198E−03	7.0581E+04	227.25400

TABLE A-a-2

	Single Sums		Uniform Series				Gradient Series	
	To Find F Given P (F|P i%,n)	To Find P Given F (P|F i%,n)	To Find F Given A (F|A i%,n)	To Find A Given F (A|F i%,n)	To Find P Given A (P|A i%,n)	To Find A Given P (A|P i%,n)	To Find P Given G (P|G i%,n)	To Find A Given G (A|G i%,n)
n								
1	1.00500	0.99502	1.00000	1.00000	0.99502	1.00500	0.00000	0.00000
2	1.01003	0.99007	2.00500	0.49875	1.98510	0.50375	0.99007	0.49875
3	1.01508	0.98515	3.01502	0.33167	2.97025	0.33667	2.96037	0.99667
4	1.02015	0.98025	4.03010	0.24813	3.95050	0.25313	5.90111	1.49377
5	1.02525	0.97537	5.05025	0.19801	4.92587	0.20301	9.80260	1.99003
6	1.03038	0.97052	6.07550	0.16460	5.89638	0.16960	14.65519	2.48545
7	1.03553	0.96569	7.10588	0.14073	6.86207	0.14573	20.44933	2.98005
8	1.04071	0.96089	8.14141	0.12283	7.82296	0.12783	27.17552	3.47382
9	1.04591	0.95610	9.18212	0.10891	8.77906	0.11391	34.82436	3.96675
10	1.05114	0.95135	10.22803	0.09777	9.73041	0.10277	43.38649	4.45885
11	1.05640	0.94661	11.27917	0.08866	10.67703	0.09366	52.85264	4.95013
12	1.06168	0.94191	12.33556	0.08107	11.61893	0.08607	63.21360	5.44057
13	1.06699	0.93722	13.39724	0.07464	12.55615	0.07964	74.46023	5.93018
14	1.07232	0.93256	14.46423	0.06914	13.48871	0.07414	86.58346	6.41896
15	1.07768	0.92792	15.53655	0.06436	14.41662	0.06936	99.57430	6.90691
16	1.08307	0.92330	16.61423	0.06019	15.33993	0.06519	113.42380	7.39403
17	1.08849	0.91871	17.69730	0.05651	16.25863	0.06151	128.12311	7.88031
18	1.09393	0.91414	18.78579	0.05323	17.17277	0.05823	143.66343	8.36577
19	1.09940	0.90959	19.87972	0.05030	18.08236	0.05530	160.03602	8.85040
20	1.10490	0.90506	20.97912	0.04767	18.98742	0.05267	177.23221	9.33419
21	1.11042	0.90056	22.08401	0.04528	19.88798	0.05028	195.24341	9.81716
22	1.11597	0.89608	23.19443	0.04311	20.78406	0.04811	214.06109	10.29929
23	1.12155	0.89162	24.31040	0.04113	21.67568	0.04613	233.67676	10.78060
24	1.12716	0.88719	25.43196	0.03932	22.56287	0.04432	254.08203	11.26107
25	1.13280	0.88277	26.55912	0.03765	23.44564	0.04265	275.26856	11.74072
26	1.13846	0.87838	27.69191	0.03611	24.32402	0.04111	297.22805	12.21953
27	1.14415	0.87401	28.83037	0.03469	25.19803	0.03969	319.95231	12.69751
28	1.14987	0.86966	29.97452	0.03336	26.06769	0.03836	343.43317	13.17467
29	1.15562	0.86533	31.12439	0.03213	26.93302	0.03713	367.66255	13.65099
30	1.16140	0.86103	32.28002	0.03098	27.79405	0.03598	392.63241	14.12649
36	1.19668	0.83564	39.33610	0.02542	32.87102	0.03042	557.55983	16.96205
40	1.22079	0.81914	44.15885	0.02265	36.17223	0.02765	681.33469	18.83585
48	1.27049	0.78710	54.09783	0.01849	42.58032	0.02349	959.91881	22.54372
50	1.28323	0.77929	56.64516	0.01765	44.14279	0.02265	1035.69659	23.46242
52	1.29609	0.77155	59.21803	0.01689	45.68975	0.02189	1113.81615	24.37781
55	1.31563	0.76009	63.12577	0.01584	47.98145	0.02084	1235.26857	25.74471
60	1.34885	0.74137	69.77003	0.01433	51.72556	0.01933	1448.64580	28.00638
72	1.43204	0.69830	86.40886	0.01157	60.33951	0.01657	2012.34779	33.35041
75	1.45363	0.68793	90.72650	0.01102	62.41365	0.01602	2163.75249	34.66794
80	1.49034	0.67099	98.06771	0.01020	65.80231	0.01520	2424.64551	36.84742
84	1.52037	0.65773	104.07393	9.6086E−03	68.45304	0.01461	2640.66405	38.57628
90	1.56655	0.63834	113.31094	8.8253E−03	72.33130	0.01383	2976.07688	41.14508
96	1.61414	0.61952	122.82854	8.1414E−03	76.09522	0.01314	3324.18460	43.68454
100	1.64667	0.60729	129.33370	7.7319E−03	78.54264	0.01273	3562.79343	45.36126
108	1.71370	0.58353	142.73990	7.0057E−03	83.29342	0.01201	4054.37473	48.67581
120	1.81940	0.54963	163.87935	6.1021E−03	90.07345	0.01110	4823.50506	53.55080
132	1.93161	0.51770	186.32263	5.3670E−03	96.45960	0.01037	5624.58677	58.31029
144	2.05075	0.48763	210.15016	4.7585E−03	102.47474	9.7585E−03	6451.31165	62.95514
180	2.45409	0.40748	290.81871	3.4386E−03	118.50351	8.4386E−03	9031.33557	76.21154
240	3.31020	0.30210	462.04090	2.1643E−03	139.58077	7.1643E−03	1.3416E+04	96.11309
360	6.02258	0.16604	1004.51504	9.9551E−04	166.79161	5.9955E−03	2.1403E+04	128.32362
480	10.95745	0.09126	1991.49073	5.0214E−04	181.74758	5.5021E−03	2.7588E+04	151.79491
600	19.93596	0.05016	3787.19108	2.6405E−04	189.96787	5.2640E−03	3.1974E+04	168.31425

TABLE A-a-3

	Single Sums		Uniform Series				Gradient Series	
n	To Find F Given P (F|P i%,n)	To Find P Given F (P|F i%,n)	To Find F Given A (F|A i%,n)	To Find A Given F (A|F i%,n)	To Find P Given A (P|A i%,n)	To Find A Given P (A|P i%,n)	To Find P Given G (P|G i%,n)	To Find A Given G (A|G i%,n)
1	1.00750	0.99256	1.00000	1.00000	0.99256	1.00750	0.00000	0.00000
2	1.01506	0.98517	2.00750	0.49813	1.97772	0.50563	0.98517	0.49813
3	1.02267	0.97783	3.02256	0.33085	2.95556	0.33835	2.94083	0.99502
4	1.03034	0.97055	4.04523	0.24721	3.92611	0.25471	5.85250	1.49066
5	1.03807	0.96333	5.07556	0.19702	4.88944	0.20452	9.70581	1.98506
6	1.04585	0.95616	6.11363	0.16357	5.84560	0.17107	14.48660	2.47821
7	1.05370	0.94904	7.15948	0.13967	6.79464	0.14717	20.18084	2.97011
8	1.06160	0.94198	8.21318	0.12176	7.73661	0.12926	26.77467	3.46077
9	1.06956	0.93496	9.27478	0.10782	8.67158	0.11532	34.25438	3.95019
10	1.07758	0.92800	10.34434	0.09667	9.59958	0.10417	42.60641	4.43836
11	1.08566	0.92109	11.42192	0.08755	10.52067	0.09505	51.81736	4.92529
12	1.09381	0.91424	12.50759	0.07995	11.43491	0.08745	61.87398	5.41097
13	1.10201	0.90743	13.60139	0.07352	12.34235	0.08102	72.76316	5.89541
14	1.11028	0.90068	14.70340	0.06801	13.24302	0.07551	84.47197	6.37860
15	1.11860	0.89397	15.81368	0.06324	14.13699	0.07074	96.98758	6.86055
16	1.12699	0.88732	16.93228	0.05906	15.02431	0.06656	110.29735	7.34126
17	1.13544	0.88071	18.05927	0.05537	15.90502	0.06287	124.38875	7.82072
18	1.14396	0.87416	19.19472	0.05210	16.77918	0.05960	139.24940	8.29894
19	1.15254	0.86765	20.33868	0.04917	17.64683	0.05667	154.86708	8.77592
20	1.16118	0.86119	21.49122	0.04653	18.50802	0.05403	171.22969	9.25165
21	1.16989	0.85478	22.65240	0.04415	19.36280	0.05165	188.32527	9.72614
22	1.17867	0.84842	23.82230	0.04198	20.21121	0.04948	206.14200	10.19939
23	1.18751	0.84210	25.00096	0.04000	21.05331	0.04750	224.66820	10.67139
24	1.19641	0.83583	26.18847	0.03818	21.88915	0.04568	243.89233	11.14216
25	1.20539	0.82961	27.38488	0.03652	22.71876	0.04402	263.80295	11.61168
26	1.21443	0.82343	28.59027	0.03498	23.54219	0.04248	284.38879	12.07996
27	1.22354	0.81730	29.80470	0.03355	24.35949	0.04105	305.63869	12.54701
28	1.23271	0.81122	31.02823	0.03223	25.17071	0.03973	327.54162	13.01281
29	1.24196	0.80518	32.26094	0.03100	25.97589	0.03850	350.08668	13.47737
30	1.25127	0.79919	33.50290	0.02985	26.77508	0.03735	373.26310	13.94069
36	1.30865	0.76415	41.15272	0.02430	31.44681	0.03180	524.99236	16.69462
40	1.34835	0.74165	46.44648	0.02153	34.44694	0.02903	637.46933	18.50583
48	1.43141	0.69861	57.52071	0.01739	40.18478	0.02489	886.84045	22.06906
50	1.45296	0.68825	60.39426	0.01656	41.56645	0.02406	953.84863	22.94756
52	1.47483	0.67804	63.31107	0.01580	42.92762	0.02330	1022.58522	23.82115
55	1.50827	0.66301	67.76883	0.01476	44.93161	0.02226	1128.78691	25.12233
60	1.56568	0.63870	75.42414	0.01326	48.17337	0.02076	1313.51888	27.26649
72	1.71255	0.58392	95.00703	0.01053	55.47685	0.01803	1791.24629	32.28818
75	1.75137	0.57098	100.18331	9.9817E−03	57.20267	0.01748	1917.22249	33.51631
80	1.81804	0.55004	109.07253	9.1682E−03	59.99444	0.01667	2132.14723	35.53908
84	1.87320	0.53385	116.42693	8.5891E−03	62.15396	0.01609	2308.12830	37.13566
90	1.95909	0.51044	127.87899	7.8199E−03	65.27461	0.01532	2577.99605	39.49462
96	2.04892	0.48806	139.85616	7.1502E−03	68.25844	0.01465	2853.93524	41.81073
100	2.11108	0.47369	148.14451	6.7502E−03	70.17462	0.01425	3040.74530	43.33112
108	2.24112	0.44620	165.48322	6.0429E−03	73.83938	0.01354	3419.90409	46.31545
120	2.45136	0.40794	193.51428	5.1676E−03	78.94169	0.01267	3998.56214	50.65210
132	2.68131	0.37295	224.17484	4.4608E−03	83.60642	0.01196	4583.57014	54.82318
144	2.93284	0.34097	257.71157	3.8803E−03	87.87109	0.01138	5169.58283	58.83144
180	3.83804	0.26055	378.40577	2.6427E−03	98.59341	0.01014	6892.60143	69.90935
240	6.00915	0.16641	667.88687	1.4973E−03	111.14495	8.9973E−03	9494.11617	85.42103
360	14.73058	0.06789	1830.74348	5.4623E−04	124.28187	8.0462E−03	1.3312E+04	107.11448
480	36.10990	0.02769	4681.32027	2.1361E−04	129.64090	7.7136E−03	1.5513E+04	119.66198
600	88.51826	0.01130	1.1669E+04	8.5696E−05	131.82705	7.5857E−03	1.6673E+04	126.47762

TABLE A-a-4

	Single Sums		Uniform Series				Gradient Series	
n	To Find F Given P $(F\|P\,i\%,n)$	To Find P Given F $(P\|F\,i\%,n)$	To Find F Given A $(F\|A\,i\%,n)$	To Find A Given F $(A\|F\,i\%,n)$	To Find P Given A $(P\|A\,i\%,n)$	To Find A Given P $(A\|P\,i\%,n)$	To Find P Given G $(P\|G\,i\%,n)$	To Find A Given G $(A\|G\,i\%,n)$
1	1.01000	0.99010	1.00000	1.00000	0.99010	1.01000	0.00000	0.00000
2	1.02010	0.98030	2.01000	0.49751	1.97040	0.50751	0.98030	0.49751
3	1.03030	0.97059	3.03010	0.33002	2.94099	0.34002	2.92148	0.99337
4	1.04060	0.96098	4.06040	0.24628	3.90197	0.25628	5.80442	1.48756
5	1.05101	0.95147	5.10101	0.19604	4.85343	0.20604	9.61028	1.98010
6	1.06152	0.94205	6.15202	0.16255	5.79548	0.17255	14.32051	2.47098
7	1.07214	0.93272	7.21354	0.13863	6.72819	0.14863	19.91681	2.96020
8	1.08286	0.92348	8.28567	0.12069	7.65168	0.13069	26.38120	3.44777
9	1.09369	0.91434	9.36853	0.10674	8.56602	0.11674	33.69592	3.93367
10	1.10462	0.90529	10.46221	0.09558	9.47130	0.10558	41.84350	4.41792
11	1.11567	0.89632	11.56683	0.08645	10.36763	0.09645	50.80674	4.90052
12	1.12683	0.88745	12.68250	0.07885	11.25508	0.08885	60.56868	5.38145
13	1.13809	0.87866	13.80933	0.07241	12.13374	0.08241	71.11263	5.86073
14	1.14947	0.86996	14.94742	0.06690	13.00370	0.07690	82.42215	6.33836
15	1.16097	0.86135	16.09690	0.06212	13.86505	0.07212	94.48104	6.81433
16	1.17258	0.85282	17.25786	0.05794	14.71787	0.06794	107.27336	7.28865
17	1.18430	0.84438	18.43044	0.05426	15.56225	0.06426	120.78340	7.76131
18	1.19615	0.83602	19.61475	0.05098	16.39827	0.06098	134.99569	8.23231
19	1.20811	0.82774	20.81090	0.04805	17.22601	0.05805	149.89501	8.70167
20	1.22019	0.81954	22.01900	0.04542	18.04555	0.05542	165.46636	9.16937
21	1.23239	0.81143	23.23919	0.04303	18.85698	0.05303	181.69496	9.63542
22	1.24472	0.80340	24.47159	0.04086	19.66038	0.05086	198.56628	10.09982
23	1.25716	0.79544	25.71630	0.03889	20.45582	0.04889	216.06600	10.56257
24	1.26973	0.78757	26.97346	0.03707	21.24339	0.04707	234.18002	11.02367
25	1.28243	0.77977	28.24320	0.03541	22.02316	0.04541	252.89446	11.48312
26	1.29526	0.77205	29.52563	0.03387	22.79520	0.04387	272.19566	11.94092
27	1.30821	0.76440	30.82089	0.03245	23.55961	0.04245	292.07016	12.39707
28	1.32129	0.75684	32.12910	0.03112	24.31644	0.04112	312.50472	12.85158
29	1.33450	0.74934	33.45039	0.02990	25.06579	0.03990	333.48630	13.30444
30	1.34785	0.74192	34.78489	0.02875	25.80771	0.03875	355.00207	13.75566
36	1.43077	0.69892	43.07688	0.02321	30.10751	0.03321	494.62069	16.42848
40	1.48886	0.67165	48.88637	0.02046	32.83469	0.03046	596.85606	18.17761
48	1.61223	0.62026	61.22261	0.01633	37.97396	0.02633	820.14601	21.59759
50	1.64463	0.60804	64.46318	0.01551	39.19612	0.02551	879.41763	22.43635
52	1.67769	0.59606	67.76889	0.01476	40.39419	0.02476	939.91752	23.26863
55	1.72852	0.57853	72.85246	0.01373	42.14719	0.02373	1032.81478	24.50495
60	1.81670	0.55045	81.66967	0.01224	44.95504	0.02224	1192.80614	26.53331
72	2.04710	0.48850	104.70993	9.5502E−03	51.15039	0.01955	1597.86733	31.23861
75	2.10913	0.47413	110.91285	9.0161E−03	52.58705	0.01902	1702.73397	32.37934
80	2.21672	0.45112	121.67152	8.2189E−03	54.88821	0.01822	1879.87710	34.24920
84	2.30672	0.43352	130.67227	7.6527E−03	56.64845	0.01765	2023.31531	35.71704
90	2.44863	0.40839	144.86327	6.9031E−03	59.16088	0.01690	2240.56748	37.87245
96	2.59927	0.38472	159.92729	6.2528E−03	61.52770	0.01625	2459.42979	39.97272
100	2.70481	0.36971	170.48138	5.8657E−03	63.02888	0.01587	2605.77575	41.34257
108	2.92893	0.34142	192.89258	5.1842E−03	65.85779	0.01518	2898.42008	44.01029
120	3.30039	0.30299	230.03869	4.3471E−03	69.70052	0.01435	3334.11485	47.83486
132	3.71896	0.26889	271.89586	3.6779E−03	73.11075	0.01368	3761.69441	51.45200
144	4.19062	0.23863	319.06156	3.1342E−03	76.13716	0.01313	4177.46642	54.86764
180	5.99580	0.16678	499.58020	2.0017E−03	83.32166	0.01200	5330.06592	63.96975
240	10.89255	0.09181	989.25537	1.0109E−03	90.81942	0.01101	6878.60156	75.73933
360	35.94964	0.02782	3494.96413	2.8613E−04	97.21833	0.01029	8720.43230	89.69947
480	118.64773	8.4283E−03	1.1765E+04	8.5000E−05	99.15717	0.01008	9511.15793	95.92002
600	391.58340	2.5537E−03	3.9058E+04	2.5603E−05	99.74463	0.01003	9821.23859	98.46384

TABLE A-a-5

	Single Sums		Uniform Series				Gradient Series	
	To Find F Given P (F|P i%,n)	To Find P Given F (P|F i%,n)	To Find F Given A (F|A i%,n)	To Find A Given F (A|F i%,n)	To Find P Given A (P|A i%,n)	To Find A Given P (A|P i%,n)	To Find P Given G (P|G i%,n)	To Find A Given G (A|G i%,n)
n								
1	1.01250	0.98765	1.00000	1.00000	0.98765	1.01250	0.00000	0.00000
2	1.02516	0.97546	2.01250	0.49689	1.96312	0.50939	0.97546	0.49689
3	1.03797	0.96342	3.03766	0.32920	2.92653	0.34170	2.90230	0.99172
4	1.05095	0.95152	4.07563	0.24536	3.87806	0.25786	5.75687	1.48447
5	1.06408	0.93978	5.12657	0.19506	4.81784	0.20756	9.51598	1.97516
6	1.07738	0.92817	6.19065	0.16153	5.74601	0.17403	14.15685	2.46377
7	1.09085	0.91672	7.26804	0.13759	6.66273	0.15009	19.65715	2.95032
8	1.10449	0.90540	8.35889	0.11963	7.56812	0.13213	25.99494	3.43479
9	1.11829	0.89422	9.46337	0.10567	8.46234	0.11817	33.14870	3.91720
10	1.13227	0.88318	10.58167	0.09450	9.34553	0.10700	41.09733	4.39754
11	1.14642	0.87228	11.71394	0.08537	10.21780	0.09787	49.82011	4.87581
12	1.16075	0.86151	12.86036	0.07776	11.07931	0.09026	59.29670	5.35202
13	1.17526	0.85087	14.02112	0.07132	11.93018	0.08382	69.50717	5.82616
14	1.18995	0.84037	15.19638	0.06581	12.77055	0.07831	80.43196	6.29824
15	1.20483	0.82999	16.38633	0.06103	13.60055	0.07353	92.05186	6.76825
16	1.21989	0.81975	17.59116	0.05685	14.42029	0.06935	104.34806	7.23620
17	1.23514	0.80963	18.81105	0.05316	15.22992	0.06566	117.30207	7.70208
18	1.25058	0.79963	20.04619	0.04988	16.02955	0.06238	130.89580	8.16591
19	1.26621	0.78976	21.29677	0.04696	16.81931	0.05946	145.11145	8.62767
20	1.28204	0.78001	22.56298	0.04432	17.59932	0.05682	159.93161	9.08738
21	1.29806	0.77038	23.84502	0.04194	18.36969	0.05444	175.33919	9.54502
22	1.31429	0.76087	25.14308	0.03977	19.13056	0.05227	191.31742	10.00062
23	1.33072	0.75147	26.45737	0.03780	19.88204	0.05030	207.84986	10.45415
24	1.34735	0.74220	27.78808	0.03599	20.62423	0.04849	224.92039	10.90564
25	1.36419	0.73303	29.13544	0.03432	21.35727	0.04682	242.51321	11.35507
26	1.38125	0.72398	30.49963	0.03279	22.08125	0.04529	260.61282	11.80245
27	1.39851	0.71505	31.88087	0.03137	22.79630	0.04387	279.20402	12.24778
28	1.41599	0.70622	33.27938	0.03005	23.50252	0.04255	298.27192	12.69106
29	1.43369	0.69750	34.69538	0.02882	24.20002	0.04132	317.80191	13.13230
30	1.45161	0.68889	36.12907	0.02768	24.88891	0.04018	337.77969	13.57150
36	1.56394	0.63941	45.11551	0.02217	28.84727	0.03467	466.28302	16.16385
40	1.64362	0.60841	51.48956	0.01942	31.32693	0.03192	559.23198	17.85148
48	1.81535	0.55086	65.22839	0.01533	35.93148	0.02783	759.22956	21.12993
50	1.86102	0.53734	68.88179	0.01452	37.01288	0.02702	811.67385	21.92950
52	1.90784	0.52415	72.62710	0.01377	38.06773	0.02627	864.94093	22.72110
55	1.98028	0.50498	78.42246	0.01275	39.60169	0.02525	946.22770	23.89362
60	2.10718	0.47457	88.57451	0.01129	42.03459	0.02379	1084.84285	25.80834
72	2.44592	0.40884	115.67362	8.6450E−03	47.29247	0.02115	1428.45610	30.20472
75	2.53879	0.39389	123.10349	8.1232E−03	48.48897	0.02062	1515.79039	31.26052
80	2.70148	0.37017	136.11880	7.3465E−03	50.38666	0.01985	1661.86513	32.98225
84	2.83911	0.35222	147.12904	6.7968E−03	51.82219	0.01930	1778.83839	34.32581
90	3.05881	0.32692	164.70501	6.0715E−03	53.84606	0.01857	1953.83026	36.28548
96	3.29551	0.30344	183.64106	5.4454E−03	55.72457	0.01795	2127.52438	38.17929
100	3.46340	0.28873	197.07234	5.0743E−03	56.90134	0.01757	2242.24109	39.40577
108	3.82528	0.26142	226.02255	4.4243E−03	59.08651	0.01692	2468.26361	41.77373
120	4.44021	0.22521	275.21706	3.6335E−03	61.98285	0.01613	2796.56945	45.11844
132	5.15400	0.19402	332.31981	3.0091E−03	64.47807	0.01551	3109.35041	48.22338
144	5.98253	0.16715	398.60208	2.5088E−03	66.62772	0.01501	3404.60974	51.09900
180	9.35633	0.10688	668.50676	1.4959E−03	71.44964	0.01400	4176.90718	58.45945
240	19.71549	0.05072	1497.23948	6.6790E−04	75.94228	0.01317	5101.52883	67.17640
360	87.54100	0.01142	6923.27961	1.4444E−04	79.08614	0.01264	5997.90267	75.84012
480	388.70068	2.5727E−03	3.1016E+04	3.2241E−05	79.79419	0.01253	6284.74422	78.76193
600	1725.91392	5.7940E−04	1.3799E+05	7.2467E−06	79.95365	0.01251	6368.48047	79.65216

TABLE A-a-6

	Single Sums		Uniform Series				Gradient Series	
n	To Find F Given P (F|P i%,n)	To Find P Given F (P|F i%,n)	To Find F Given A (F|A i%,n)	To Find A Given F (A|F i%,n)	To Find P Given A (P|A i%,n)	To Find A Given P (A|P i%,n)	To Find P Given G (P|G i%,n)	To Find A Given G (A|G i%,n)
1	1.01500	0.98522	1.00000	1.00000	0.98522	1.01500	0.00000	0.00000
2	1.03023	0.97066	2.01500	0.49628	1.95588	0.51128	0.97066	0.49628
3	1.04568	0.95632	3.04522	0.32838	2.91220	0.34338	2.88330	0.99007
4	1.06136	0.94218	4.09090	0.24444	3.85438	0.25944	5.70985	1.48139
5	1.07728	0.92826	5.15227	0.19409	4.78264	0.20909	9.42289	1.97023
6	1.09344	0.91454	6.22955	0.16053	5.69719	0.17553	13.99560	2.45658
7	1.10984	0.90103	7.32299	0.13656	6.59821	0.15156	19.40176	2.94046
8	1.12649	0.88771	8.43284	0.11858	7.48593	0.13358	25.61574	3.42185
9	1.14339	0.87459	9.55933	0.10461	8.36052	0.11961	32.61248	3.90077
10	1.16054	0.86167	10.70272	0.09343	9.22218	0.10843	40.36748	4.37721
11	1.17795	0.84893	11.86326	0.08429	10.07112	0.09929	48.85681	4.85118
12	1.19562	0.83639	13.04121	0.07668	10.90751	0.09168	58.05708	5.32267
13	1.21355	0.82403	14.23683	0.07024	11.73153	0.08524	67.94540	5.79169
14	1.23176	0.81185	15.45038	0.06472	12.54338	0.07972	78.49944	6.25824
15	1.25023	0.79985	16.68214	0.05994	13.34323	0.07494	89.69736	6.72231
16	1.26899	0.78803	17.93237	0.05577	14.13126	0.07077	101.51783	7.18392
17	1.28802	0.77639	19.20136	0.05208	14.90765	0.06708	113.93999	7.64306
18	1.30734	0.76491	20.48938	0.04881	15.67256	0.06381	126.94349	8.09973
19	1.32695	0.75361	21.79672	0.04588	16.42617	0.06088	140.50842	8.55394
20	1.34686	0.74247	23.12367	0.04325	17.16864	0.05825	154.61536	9.00569
21	1.36706	0.73150	24.47052	0.04087	17.90014	0.05587	169.24532	9.45497
22	1.38756	0.72069	25.83758	0.03870	18.62082	0.05370	184.37976	9.90180
23	1.40838	0.71004	27.22514	0.03673	19.33086	0.05173	200.00058	10.34618
24	1.42950	0.69954	28.63352	0.03492	20.03041	0.04992	216.09009	10.78810
25	1.45095	0.68921	30.06302	0.03326	20.71961	0.04826	232.63103	11.22758
26	1.47271	0.67902	31.51397	0.03173	21.39863	0.04673	249.60654	11.66460
27	1.49480	0.66899	32.98668	0.03032	22.06762	0.04532	267.00017	12.09918
28	1.51722	0.65910	34.48148	0.02900	22.72672	0.04400	284.79585	12.53132
29	1.53998	0.64936	35.99870	0.02778	23.37608	0.04278	302.97790	12.96102
30	1.56308	0.63976	37.53868	0.02664	24.01584	0.04164	321.53101	13.38829
36	1.70914	0.58509	47.27597	0.02115	27.66068	0.03615	439.83026	15.90092
40	1.81402	0.55126	54.26789	0.01843	29.91585	0.03343	524.35682	17.52773
48	2.04348	0.48936	69.56522	0.01437	34.04255	0.02937	703.54615	20.66667
50	2.10524	0.47500	73.68283	0.01357	34.99969	0.02857	749.96361	21.42772
52	2.16887	0.46107	77.92489	0.01283	35.92874	0.02783	796.87737	22.17938
55	2.26794	0.44093	84.52960	0.01183	37.27147	0.02683	868.02846	23.28936
60	2.44322	0.40930	96.21465	0.01039	39.38027	0.02539	988.16739	25.09296
72	2.92116	0.34233	128.07720	7.8078E−03	43.84467	0.02281	1279.79379	29.18927
75	3.05459	0.32738	136.97278	7.3007E−03	44.84160	0.02230	1352.56005	30.16306
80	3.29066	0.30389	152.71085	6.5483E−03	46.40732	0.02155	1473.07411	31.74228
84	3.49259	0.28632	166.17264	6.0178E−03	47.57863	0.02102	1568.51404	32.96677
90	3.81895	0.26185	187.92990	5.3211E−03	49.20985	0.02032	1709.54387	34.73987
96	4.17580	0.23947	211.72023	4.7232E−03	50.70168	0.01972	1847.47253	36.43810
100	4.43205	0.22563	228.80304	4.3706E−03	51.62470	0.01937	1937.45061	37.52953
108	4.99267	0.20029	266.17777	3.7569E−03	53.31375	0.01876	2112.13479	39.61708
120	5.96932	0.16752	331.28819	3.0185E−03	55.49845	0.01802	2359.71143	42.51851
132	7.13703	0.14011	409.13539	2.4442E−03	57.32571	0.01744	2588.70855	45.15789
144	8.53316	0.11719	502.21092	1.9912E−03	58.85401	0.01699	2798.57842	47.55119
180	14.58437	0.06857	905.62451	1.1042E−03	62.09556	0.01610	3316.90537	53.41614
240	35.63282	0.02806	2308.85437	4.3312E−04	64.79573	0.01543	3870.69117	59.73682
360	212.70378	4.7014E−03	1.4114E+04	7.0854E−05	66.35324	0.01507	4310.71648	64.96618
480	1269.69754	7.8759E−04	8.4580E+04	1.1823E−05	66.61416	0.01501	4415.74120	66.28833
600	7579.23459	1.3194E−04	5.0522E+05	1.9794E−06	66.65787	0.01500	4438.58047	66.58749

TABLE A-a-7

	Single Sums		Uniform Series				Gradient Series	
	To Find F Given P (F|P i%,n)	To Find P Given F (P|F i%,n)	To Find F Given A (F|A i%,n)	To Find A Given F (A|F i%,n)	To Find P Given A (P|A i%,n)	To Find A Given P (A|P i%,n)	To Find P Given G (P|G i%,n)	To Find A Given G (A|G i%,n)
n								
1	1.01750	0.98280	1.00000	1.00000	0.98280	1.01750	0.00000	0.00000
2	1.03531	0.96590	2.01750	0.49566	1.94870	0.51316	0.96590	0.49566
3	1.05342	0.94929	3.05281	0.32757	2.89798	0.34507	2.86447	0.98843
4	1.07186	0.93296	4.10623	0.24353	3.83094	0.26103	5.66334	1.47832
5	1.09062	0.91691	5.17809	0.19312	4.74786	0.21062	9.33099	1.96531
6	1.10970	0.90114	6.26871	0.15952	5.64900	0.17702	13.83671	2.44941
7	1.12912	0.88564	7.37841	0.13553	6.53464	0.15303	19.15057	2.93062
8	1.14888	0.87041	8.50753	0.11754	7.40505	0.13504	25.24345	3.40895
9	1.16899	0.85544	9.65641	0.10356	8.26049	0.12106	32.08698	3.88439
10	1.18944	0.84073	10.82540	0.09238	9.10122	0.10988	39.65354	4.35695
11	1.21026	0.82627	12.01484	0.08323	9.92749	0.10073	47.91623	4.82662
12	1.23144	0.81206	13.22510	0.07561	10.73955	0.09311	56.84886	5.29341
13	1.25299	0.79809	14.45654	0.06917	11.53764	0.08667	66.42596	5.75733
14	1.27492	0.78436	15.70953	0.06366	12.32201	0.08116	76.62270	6.21836
15	1.29723	0.77087	16.98445	0.05888	13.09288	0.07638	87.41495	6.67653
16	1.31993	0.75762	18.28168	0.05470	13.85050	0.07220	98.77919	7.13182
17	1.34303	0.74459	19.60161	0.05102	14.59508	0.06852	110.69257	7.58424
18	1.36653	0.73178	20.94463	0.04774	15.32686	0.06524	123.13283	8.03379
19	1.39045	0.71919	22.31117	0.04482	16.04606	0.06232	136.07832	8.48048
20	1.41478	0.70682	23.70161	0.04219	16.75288	0.05969	149.50799	8.92431
21	1.43954	0.69467	25.11639	0.03981	17.44755	0.05731	163.40134	9.36529
22	1.46473	0.68272	26.55593	0.03766	18.13027	0.05516	177.73847	9.80341
23	1.49036	0.67098	28.02065	0.03569	18.80125	0.05319	192.49999	10.23868
24	1.51644	0.65944	29.51102	0.03389	19.46069	0.05139	207.66706	10.67111
25	1.54298	0.64810	31.02746	0.03223	20.10878	0.04973	223.22138	11.10069
26	1.56998	0.63695	32.57044	0.03070	20.74573	0.04820	239.14512	11.52744
27	1.59746	0.62599	34.14042	0.02929	21.37173	0.04679	255.42098	11.95135
28	1.62541	0.61523	35.73788	0.02798	21.98695	0.04548	272.03215	12.37243
29	1.65386	0.60465	37.36329	0.02676	22.59160	0.04426	288.96226	12.79069
30	1.68280	0.59425	39.01715	0.02563	23.18585	0.04313	306.19544	13.20613
36	1.86741	0.53550	49.56613	0.02018	26.54275	0.03768	415.12498	15.63986
40	2.00160	0.49960	57.23413	0.01747	28.59423	0.03497	492.01087	17.20665
48	2.29960	0.43486	74.26278	0.01347	32.29380	0.03097	652.60539	20.20838
50	2.38079	0.42003	78.90222	0.01267	33.14121	0.03017	693.70101	20.93167
52	2.46485	0.40570	83.70547	0.01195	33.95972	0.02945	735.03220	21.64424
55	2.59653	0.38513	91.23105	0.01096	35.13545	0.02846	797.33210	22.69310
60	2.83182	0.35313	104.67522	9.5534E−03	36.96399	0.02705	901.49545	24.38848
72	3.48721	0.28676	142.12628	7.0360E−03	40.75645	0.02454	1149.11809	28.19476
75	3.67351	0.27222	152.77206	6.5457E−03	41.58748	0.02405	1209.77384	29.08986
80	4.00639	0.24960	171.79382	5.8209E−03	42.87993	0.02332	1309.24819	30.53289
84	4.29429	0.23287	188.24499	5.3122E−03	43.83614	0.02281	1387.15838	31.64417
90	4.76538	0.20985	215.16462	4.6476E−03	45.15161	0.02215	1500.87981	33.24089
96	5.28815	0.18910	245.03739	4.0810E−03	46.33703	0.02158	1610.47158	34.75560
100	5.66816	0.17642	266.75177	3.7488E−03	47.06147	0.02125	1681.08862	35.72112
108	6.51204	0.15356	314.97378	3.1749E−03	48.36790	0.02067	1816.18525	37.54939
120	8.01918	0.12470	401.09620	2.4932E−03	50.01709	0.01999	2003.02686	40.04685
132	9.87514	0.10126	507.15073	1.9718E−03	51.35632	0.01947	2170.82384	42.26985
144	12.16063	0.08223	637.75045	1.5680E−03	52.44385	0.01907	2320.13512	44.24036
180	22.70885	0.04404	1240.50595	8.0612E−04	54.62653	0.01831	2668.57763	48.85131
240	64.30730	0.01555	3617.56017	2.7643E−04	56.25427	0.01778	3001.26781	53.35183
360	515.69206	1.9391E−03	2.9411E+04	3.4001E−05	57.03205	0.01753	3219.08332	56.44341
480	4135.42921	2.4181E−04	2.3625E+05	4.2327E−06	57.12904	0.01750	3257.88395	57.02676
600	3.3163E+04	3.0154E−05	1.8950E+06	5.2772E−07	57.14113	0.01750	3264.17380	57.12476

TABLE A-a-8

	Single Sums		Uniform Series				Gradient Series	
n	To Find F Given P (F|P i%,n)	To Find P Given F (P|F i%,n)	To Find F Given A (F|A i%,n)	To Find A Given F (A|F i%,n)	To Find P Given A (P|A i%,n)	To Find A Given P (A|P i%,n)	To Find P Given G (P|G i%,n)	To Find A Given G (A|G i%,n)
1	1.02000	0.98039	1.00000	1.00000	0.98039	1.02000	0.00000	0.00000
2	1.04040	0.96117	2.02000	0.49505	1.94156	0.51505	0.96117	0.49505
3	1.06121	0.94232	3.06040	0.32675	2.88388	0.34675	2.84581	0.98680
4	1.08243	0.92385	4.12161	0.24262	3.80773	0.26262	5.61735	1.47525
5	1.10408	0.90573	5.20404	0.19216	4.71346	0.21216	9.24027	1.96040
6	1.12616	0.88797	6.30812	0.15853	5.60143	0.17853	13.68013	2.44226
7	1.14869	0.87056	7.43428	0.13451	6.47199	0.15451	18.90349	2.92082
8	1.17166	0.85349	8.58297	0.11651	7.32548	0.13651	24.87792	3.39608
9	1.19509	0.83676	9.75463	0.10252	8.16224	0.12252	31.57197	3.86805
10	1.21899	0.82035	10.94972	0.09133	8.98259	0.11133	38.95510	4.33674
11	1.24337	0.80426	12.16872	0.08218	9.78685	0.10218	46.99773	4.80213
12	1.26824	0.78849	13.41209	0.07456	10.57534	0.09456	55.67116	5.26424
13	1.29361	0.77303	14.68033	0.06812	11.34837	0.08812	64.94755	5.72307
14	1.31948	0.75788	15.97394	0.06260	12.10625	0.08260	74.79992	6.17862
15	1.34587	0.74301	17.29342	0.05783	12.84926	0.07783	85.20213	6.63090
16	1.37279	0.72845	18.63929	0.05365	13.57771	0.07365	96.12881	7.07990
17	1.40024	0.71416	20.01207	0.04997	14.29187	0.06997	107.55542	7.52564
18	1.42825	0.70016	21.41231	0.04670	14.99203	0.06670	119.45813	7.96811
19	1.45681	0.68643	22.84056	0.04378	15.67846	0.06378	131.81388	8.40732
20	1.48595	0.67297	24.29737	0.04116	16.35143	0.06116	144.60033	8.84328
21	1.51567	0.65978	25.78332	0.03878	17.01121	0.05878	157.79585	9.27599
22	1.54598	0.64684	27.29898	0.03663	17.65805	0.05663	171.37947	9.70546
23	1.57690	0.63416	28.84496	0.03467	18.29220	0.05467	185.33090	10.13169
24	1.60844	0.62172	30.42186	0.03287	18.91393	0.05287	199.63049	10.55468
25	1.64061	0.60953	32.03030	0.03122	19.52346	0.05122	214.25924	10.97445
26	1.67342	0.59758	33.67091	0.02970	20.12104	0.04970	229.19872	11.39100
27	1.70689	0.58586	35.34432	0.02829	20.70690	0.04829	244.43113	11.80433
28	1.74102	0.57437	37.05121	0.02699	21.28127	0.04699	259.93924	12.21446
29	1.77584	0.56311	38.79223	0.02578	21.84438	0.04578	275.70639	12.62138
30	1.81136	0.55207	40.56808	0.02465	22.39646	0.04465	291.71644	13.02512
36	2.03989	0.49022	51.99437	0.01923	25.48884	0.03923	392.04045	15.38087
40	2.20804	0.45289	60.40198	0.01656	27.35548	0.03656	461.99313	16.88850
48	2.58707	0.38654	79.35352	0.01260	30.67312	0.03260	605.96572	19.75559
50	2.69159	0.37153	84.57940	0.01182	31.42361	0.03182	642.36059	20.44198
52	2.80033	0.35710	90.01641	0.01111	32.14495	0.03111	678.78489	21.11638
55	2.97173	0.33650	98.58653	0.01014	33.17479	0.03014	733.35269	22.10572
60	3.28103	0.30478	114.05154	8.7680E–03	34.76089	0.02877	823.69753	23.69610
72	4.16114	0.24032	158.05702	6.3268E–03	37.98406	0.02633	1034.05570	27.22341
75	4.41584	0.22646	170.79177	5.8551E–03	38.67711	0.02586	1084.63929	28.04344
80	4.87544	0.20511	193.77196	5.1607E–03	39.74451	0.02516	1166.78677	29.35718
84	5.27733	0.18949	213.86661	4.6758E–03	40.52552	0.02468	1230.41912	30.36159
90	5.94313	0.16826	247.15666	4.0460E–03	41.58693	0.02405	1322.17008	31.79292
96	6.69293	0.14941	284.64666	3.5131E–03	42.52943	0.02351	1409.29734	33.13699
100	7.24465	0.13803	312.23231	3.2027E–03	43.09835	0.02320	1464.75275	33.98628
108	8.48826	0.11781	374.41288	2.6708E–03	44.10951	0.02267	1569.30251	35.57742
120	10.76516	0.09289	488.25815	2.0481E–03	45.35539	0.02205	1710.41605	37.71142
132	13.65283	0.07324	632.64148	1.5807E–03	46.33776	0.02158	1833.47151	39.56755
144	17.31509	0.05775	815.75446	1.2259E–03	47.11235	0.02123	1939.79497	41.17381
180	35.32083	0.02831	1716.04157	5.8274E–04	48.58440	0.02058	2174.41310	44.75537
240	115.88874	8.6290E–03	5744.43676	1.7408E–04	49.56855	0.02017	2374.87999	47.91102
360	1247.56113	8.0156E–04	6.2328E+04	1.6044E–05	49.95992	0.02002	2483.56794	49.71121
480	1.3430E+04	7.4459E–05	6.7146E+05	1.4893E–06	49.99628	0.02000	2498.02683	49.96426
600	1.4458E+05	6.9167E–06	7.2289E+06	1.3833E–07	49.99965	0.02000	2499.77521	49.99585

TABLE A-a-9

	Single Sums		Uniform Series				Gradient Series	
	To Find F Given P (F|P i%,n)	To Find P Given F (P|F i%,n)	To Find F Given A (F|A i%,n)	To Find A Given F (A|F i%,n)	To Find P Given A (P|A i%,n)	To Find A Given P (A|P i%,n)	To Find P Given G (P|G i%,n)	To Find A Given G (A|G i%,n)
n								
1	1.03000	0.97087	1.00000	1.00000	0.97087	1.03000	0.00000	0.00000
2	1.06090	0.94260	2.03000	0.49261	1.91347	0.52261	0.94260	0.49261
3	1.09273	0.91514	3.09090	0.32353	2.82861	0.35353	2.77288	0.98030
4	1.12551	0.88849	4.18363	0.23903	3.71710	0.26903	5.43834	1.46306
5	1.15927	0.86261	5.30914	0.18835	4.57971	0.21835	8.88878	1.94090
6	1.19405	0.83748	6.46841	0.15460	5.41719	0.18460	13.07620	2.41383
7	1.22987	0.81309	7.66246	0.13051	6.23028	0.16051	17.95475	2.88185
8	1.26677	0.78941	8.89234	0.11246	7.01969	0.14246	23.48061	3.34496
9	1.30477	0.76642	10.15911	0.09843	7.78611	0.12843	29.61194	3.80318
10	1.34392	0.74409	11.46388	0.08723	8.53020	0.11723	36.30879	4.25650
11	1.38423	0.72242	12.80780	0.07808	9.25262	0.10808	43.53300	4.70494
12	1.42576	0.70138	14.19203	0.07046	9.95400	0.10046	51.24818	5.14850
13	1.46853	0.68095	15.61779	0.06403	10.63496	0.09403	59.41960	5.58720
14	1.51259	0.66112	17.08632	0.05853	11.29607	0.08853	68.01413	6.02104
15	1.55797	0.64186	18.59891	0.05377	11.93794	0.08377	77.00020	6.45004
16	1.60471	0.62317	20.15688	0.04961	12.56110	0.07961	86.34770	6.87421
17	1.65285	0.60502	21.76159	0.04595	13.16612	0.07595	96.02796	7.29357
18	1.70243	0.58739	23.41444	0.04271	13.75351	0.07271	106.01367	7.70812
19	1.75351	0.57029	25.11687	0.03981	14.32380	0.06981	116.27882	8.11788
20	1.80611	0.55368	26.87037	0.03722	14.87747	0.06722	126.79866	8.52286
21	1.86029	0.53755	28.67649	0.03487	15.41502	0.06487	137.54964	8.92309
22	1.91610	0.52189	30.53678	0.03275	15.93692	0.06275	148.50939	9.31858
23	1.97359	0.50669	32.45288	0.03081	16.44361	0.06081	159.65661	9.70934
24	2.03279	0.49193	34.42647	0.02905	16.93554	0.05905	170.97108	10.09540
25	2.09378	0.47761	36.45926	0.02743	17.41315	0.05743	182.43362	10.47677
26	2.15659	0.46369	38.55304	0.02594	17.87684	0.05594	194.02598	10.85348
27	2.22129	0.45019	40.70963	0.02456	18.32703	0.05456	205.73090	11.22554
28	2.28793	0.43708	42.93092	0.02329	18.76411	0.05329	217.53197	11.59298
29	2.35657	0.42435	45.21885	0.02211	19.18845	0.05211	229.41367	11.95582
30	2.42726	0.41199	47.57542	0.02102	19.60044	0.05102	241.36129	12.31407
36	2.89828	0.34503	63.27594	0.01580	21.83225	0.04580	313.70284	14.36878
40	3.26204	0.30656	75.40126	0.01326	23.11477	0.04326	361.74994	15.65016
48	4.13225	0.24200	104.40840	9.5778E–03	25.26671	0.03958	455.02547	18.00890
50	4.38391	0.22811	112.79687	8.8655E–03	25.72976	0.03887	477.48033	18.55751
52	4.65089	0.21501	121.69620	8.2172E–03	26.16624	0.03822	499.51915	19.09021
55	5.08215	0.19677	136.07162	7.3491E–03	26.77443	0.03735	531.74111	19.86004
60	5.89160	0.16973	163.05344	6.1330E–03	27.67556	0.03613	583.05261	21.06742
72	8.40002	0.11905	246.66724	4.0540E–03	29.36509	0.03405	693.12255	23.60363
75	9.17893	0.10895	272.63086	3.6680E–03	29.70183	0.03367	717.69785	24.16342
80	10.64089	0.09398	321.36302	3.1117E–03	30.20076	0.03311	756.08652	25.03534
84	11.97642	0.08350	365.88054	2.7331E–03	30.55009	0.03273	784.54337	25.68056
90	14.30047	0.06993	443.34890	2.2556E–03	31.00241	0.03226	823.63021	26.56665
96	17.07551	0.05856	535.85019	1.8662E–03	31.38122	0.03187	858.63770	27.36151
100	19.21863	0.05203	607.28773	1.6467E–03	31.59891	0.03165	879.85405	27.84445
108	24.34559	0.04108	778.18627	1.2850E–03	31.96416	0.03129	917.60126	28.70719
120	34.71099	0.02881	1123.69957	8.8992E–04	32.37302	0.03089	963.86347	29.77366
132	49.48957	0.02021	1616.31893	6.1869E–04	32.65979	0.03062	999.75206	30.61110
144	70.56029	0.01417	2318.67634	4.3128E–04	32.86092	0.03043	1027.33721	31.26319
180	204.50336	4.8899E–03	6783.44532	1.4742E–04	33.17034	0.03015	1076.33852	32.44883
240	1204.85263	8.2998E–04	4.0128E+04	2.4920E–05	33.30567	0.03002	1103.54910	33.13397
360	4.1822E+04	2.3911E–05	1.3940E+06	7.1735E–07	33.33254	0.03000	1110.79761	33.32473
480	1.4517E+06	6.8886E–07	4.8389E+07	2.0666E–08	33.33331	0.03000	1111.09932	33.33300
600	5.0389E+07	1.9846E–08	1.6796E+09	5.9537E–10	33.33333	0.03000	1111.11069	33.33332

4.00% Time Value of Money Factors Discrete Compounding 4.00%

TABLE A-a-10

	Single Sums		Uniform Series				Gradient Series	
	To Find F Given P	To Find P Given F	To Find F Given A	To Find A Given F	To Find P Given A	To Find A Given P	To Find P Given G	To Find A Given G
n	$(F|P\ i\%,n)$	$(P|F\ i\%,n)$	$(F|A\ i\%,n)$	$(A|F\ i\%,n)$	$(P|A\ i\%,n)$	$(A|P\ i\%,n)$	$(P|G\ i\%,n)$	$(A|G\ i\%,n)$
1	1.04000	0.96154	1.00000	1.00000	0.96154	1.04000	0.00000	0.00000
2	1.08160	0.92456	2.04000	0.49020	1.88609	0.53020	0.92456	0.49020
3	1.12486	0.88900	3.12160	0.32035	2.77509	0.36035	2.70255	0.97386
4	1.16986	0.85480	4.24646	0.23549	3.62990	0.27549	5.26696	1.45100
5	1.21665	0.82193	5.41632	0.18463	4.45182	0.22463	8.55467	1.92161
6	1.26532	0.79031	6.63298	0.15076	5.24214	0.19076	12.50624	2.38571
7	1.31593	0.75992	7.89829	0.12661	6.00205	0.16661	17.06575	2.84332
8	1.36857	0.73069	9.21423	0.10853	6.73274	0.14853	22.18058	3.29443
9	1.42331	0.70259	10.58280	0.09449	7.43533	0.13449	27.80127	3.73908
10	1.48024	0.67556	12.00611	0.08329	8.11090	0.12329	33.88135	4.17726
11	1.53945	0.64958	13.48635	0.07415	8.76048	0.11415	40.37716	4.60901
12	1.60103	0.62460	15.02581	0.06655	9.38507	0.10655	47.24773	5.03435
13	1.66507	0.60057	16.62684	0.06014	9.98565	0.10014	54.45462	5.45329
14	1.73168	0.57748	18.29191	0.05467	10.56312	0.09467	61.96179	5.86586
15	1.80094	0.55526	20.02359	0.04994	11.11839	0.08994	69.73550	6.27209
16	1.87298	0.53391	21.82453	0.04582	11.65230	0.08582	77.74412	6.67200
17	1.94790	0.51337	23.69751	0.04220	12.16567	0.08220	85.95809	7.06563
18	2.02582	0.49363	25.64541	0.03899	12.65930	0.07899	94.34977	7.45300
19	2.10685	0.47464	27.67123	0.03614	13.13394	0.07614	102.89333	7.83416
20	2.19112	0.45639	29.77808	0.03358	13.59033	0.07358	111.56469	8.20912
21	2.27877	0.43883	31.96920	0.03128	14.02916	0.07128	120.34136	8.57794
22	2.36992	0.42196	34.24797	0.02920	14.45112	0.06920	129.20242	8.94065
23	2.46472	0.40573	36.61789	0.02731	14.85684	0.06731	138.12840	9.29729
24	2.56330	0.39012	39.08260	0.02559	15.24696	0.06559	147.10119	9.64790
25	2.66584	0.37512	41.64591	0.02401	15.62208	0.06401	156.10400	9.99252
26	2.77247	0.36069	44.31174	0.02257	15.98277	0.06257	165.12123	10.33120
27	2.88337	0.34682	47.08421	0.02124	16.32959	0.06124	174.13846	10.66399
28	2.99870	0.33348	49.96758	0.02001	16.66306	0.06001	183.14235	10.99092
29	3.11865	0.32065	52.96629	0.01888	16.98371	0.05888	192.12059	11.31205
30	3.24340	0.30832	56.08494	0.01783	17.29203	0.05783	201.06183	11.62743
36	4.10393	0.24367	77.59831	0.01289	18.90828	0.05289	253.40520	13.40181
40	4.80102	0.20829	95.02552	0.01052	19.79277	0.05052	286.53030	14.47651
48	6.57053	0.15219	139.26321	7.1806E−03	21.19513	0.04718	347.24455	16.38322
50	7.10668	0.14071	152.66708	6.5502E−03	21.48218	0.04655	361.16385	16.81225
52	7.68659	0.13010	167.16472	5.9821E−03	21.74758	0.04598	374.56381	17.22324
55	8.64637	0.11566	191.15917	5.2312E−03	22.10861	0.04523	393.68897	17.80704
60	10.51963	0.09506	237.99069	4.2018E−03	22.62349	0.04420	422.99665	18.69723
72	16.84226	0.05937	396.05656	2.5249E−03	23.51564	0.04252	481.01697	20.45519
75	18.94525	0.05278	448.63137	2.2290E−03	23.68041	0.04223	493.04083	20.82062
80	23.04980	0.04338	551.24498	1.8141E−03	23.91539	0.04181	511.11614	21.37185
84	26.96500	0.03709	649.12512	1.5405E−03	24.07287	0.04154	523.94309	21.76488
90	34.11933	0.02931	827.98333	1.2078E−03	24.26728	0.04121	540.73692	22.28255
96	43.17184	0.02316	1054.29603	9.4850E−04	24.42092	0.04095	554.93118	22.72360
100	50.50495	0.01980	1237.62370	8.0800E−04	24.50500	0.04081	563.12487	22.98000
108	69.11951	0.01447	1702.98772	5.8720E−04	24.63831	0.04059	576.89491	23.41455
120	110.66256	9.0365E−03	2741.56402	3.6476E−04	24.77409	0.04036	592.24276	23.90573
132	177.17433	5.6442E−03	4404.35813	2.2705E−04	24.85890	0.04023	602.84668	24.25074
144	283.66180	3.5253E−03	7066.54508	1.4151E−04	24.91187	0.04014	610.10550	24.49056
180	1164.12891	8.5901E−04	2.9078E+04	3.4390E−05	24.97852	0.04003	620.59757	24.84525
240	1.2246E+04	8.1658E−05	3.0613E+05	3.2666E−06	24.99796	0.04000	624.45902	24.98040
360	1.3552E+06	7.3790E−07	3.3880E+07	2.9516E−08	24.99998	0.04000	624.99290	24.99973
480	1.4997E+08	6.6680E−09	3.7492E+09	2.6672E−10	25.00000	0.04000	624.99992	25.00000
600	1.6596E+10	6.0255E−11	4.1490E+11	2.4102E−12	25.00000	0.04000	625.00000	25.00000

TABLE A-a-11

	Single Sums		Uniform Series				Gradient Series	
	To Find F Given P	To Find P Given F	To Find F Given A	To Find A Given F	To Find P Given A	To Find A Given P	To Find P Given G	To Find A Given G
n	$(F\|P\ i\%,n)$	$(P\|F\ i\%,n)$	$(F\|A\ i\%,n)$	$(A\|F\ i\%,n)$	$(P\|A\ i\%,n)$	$(A\|P\ i\%,n)$	$(P\|G\ i\%,n)$	$(A\|G\ i\%,n)$
1	1.05000	0.95238	1.00000	1.00000	0.95238	1.05000	0.00000	0.00000
2	1.10250	0.90703	2.05000	0.48780	1.85941	0.53780	0.90703	0.48780
3	1.15763	0.86384	3.15250	0.31721	2.72325	0.36721	2.63470	0.96749
4	1.21551	0.82270	4.31013	0.23201	3.54595	0.28201	5.10281	1.43905
5	1.27628	0.78353	5.52563	0.18097	4.32948	0.23097	8.23692	1.90252
6	1.34010	0.74622	6.80191	0.14702	5.07569	0.19702	11.96799	2.35790
7	1.40710	0.71068	8.14201	0.12282	5.78637	0.17282	16.23208	2.80523
8	1.47746	0.67684	9.54911	0.10472	6.46321	0.15472	20.96996	3.24451
9	1.55133	0.64461	11.02656	0.09069	7.10782	0.14069	26.12683	3.67579
10	1.62889	0.61391	12.57789	0.07950	7.72173	0.12950	31.65205	4.09909
11	1.71034	0.58468	14.20679	0.07039	8.30641	0.12039	37.49884	4.51444
12	1.79586	0.55684	15.91713	0.06283	8.86325	0.11283	43.62405	4.92190
13	1.88565	0.53032	17.71298	0.05646	9.39357	0.10646	49.98791	5.32150
14	1.97993	0.50507	19.59863	0.05102	9.89864	0.10102	56.55379	5.71329
15	2.07893	0.48102	21.57856	0.04634	10.37966	0.09634	63.28803	6.09731
16	2.18287	0.45811	23.65749	0.04227	10.83777	0.09227	70.15970	6.47363
17	2.29202	0.43630	25.84037	0.03870	11.27407	0.08870	77.14045	6.84229
18	2.40662	0.41552	28.13238	0.03555	11.68959	0.08555	84.20430	7.20336
19	2.52695	0.39573	30.53900	0.03275	12.08532	0.08275	91.32751	7.55690
20	2.65330	0.37689	33.06595	0.03024	12.46221	0.08024	98.48841	7.90297
21	2.78596	0.35894	35.71925	0.02800	12.82115	0.07800	105.66726	8.24164
22	2.92526	0.34185	38.50521	0.02597	13.16300	0.07597	112.84611	8.57298
23	3.07152	0.32557	41.43048	0.02414	13.48857	0.07414	120.00868	8.89706
24	3.22510	0.31007	44.50200	0.02247	13.79864	0.07247	127.14024	9.21397
25	3.38635	0.29530	47.72710	0.02095	14.09394	0.07095	134.22751	9.52377
26	3.55567	0.28124	51.11345	0.01956	14.37519	0.06956	141.25852	9.82655
27	3.73346	0.26785	54.66913	0.01829	14.64303	0.06829	148.22258	10.12240
28	3.92013	0.25509	58.40258	0.01712	14.89813	0.06712	155.11011	10.41138
29	4.11614	0.24295	62.32271	0.01605	15.14107	0.06605	161.91261	10.69360
30	4.32194	0.23138	66.43885	0.01505	15.37245	0.06505	168.62255	10.96914
36	5.79182	0.17266	95.83632	0.01043	16.54685	0.06043	206.62370	12.48719
40	7.03999	0.14205	120.79977	8.2782E-03	17.15909	0.05828	229.54518	13.37747
48	10.40127	0.09614	188.02539	5.3184E-03	18.07716	0.05532	269.24673	14.89431
50	11.46740	0.08720	209.34800	4.7767E-03	18.25593	0.05478	277.91478	15.22326
52	12.64281	0.07910	232.85617	4.2945E-03	18.41807	0.05429	286.10125	15.53372
55	14.63563	0.06833	272.71262	3.6669E-03	18.63347	0.05367	297.51040	15.96645
60	18.67919	0.05354	353.58372	2.8282E-03	18.92929	0.05283	314.34316	16.60618
72	33.54513	0.02981	650.90268	1.5363E-03	19.40379	0.05154	345.14853	17.78769
75	38.83269	0.02575	756.65372	1.3216E-03	19.48497	0.05132	351.07215	18.01759
80	49.56144	0.02018	971.22882	1.0296E-03	19.59646	0.05103	359.64605	18.35260
84	60.24224	0.01660	1184.84483	8.4399E-04	19.66801	0.05084	365.47273	18.58209
90	80.73037	0.01239	1594.60730	6.2711E-04	19.75226	0.05063	372.74879	18.87120
96	108.18641	9.2433E-03	2143.72821	4.6648E-04	19.81513	0.05047	378.55553	19.10436
100	131.50126	7.6045E-03	2610.02516	3.8314E-04	19.84791	0.05038	381.74922	19.23372
108	194.28725	5.1470E-03	3865.74499	2.5868E-04	19.89706	0.05026	386.82363	19.44125
120	348.91199	2.8661E-03	6958.23971	1.4371E-04	19.94268	0.05014	391.97505	19.65509
132	626.59580	1.5959E-03	1.2512E+04	7.9924E-05	19.96808	0.05008	395.14839	19.78900
144	1125.27603	8.8867E-04	2.2486E+04	4.4473E-05	19.98223	0.05004	397.08516	19.87192
180	6517.39184	1.5344E-04	1.3033E+05	7.6730E-06	19.99693	0.05001	399.38626	19.97238
240	1.2174E+05	8.2143E-06	2.4348E+06	4.1072E-07	19.99984	0.05000	399.95729	19.99803
360	4.2476E+07	2.3542E-08	8.4953E+08	1.1771E-09	20.00000	0.05000	399.99982	19.99999
480	1.4821E+10	6.7474E-11	2.9641E+11	3.3737E-12	20.00000	0.05000	400.00000	20.00000
600	5.1711E+12	1.9338E-13	1.0342E+14	9.6692E-15	20.00000	0.05000	400.00000	20.00000

TABLE A-a-12

	Single Sums		Uniform Series				Gradient Series	
n	To Find F Given P (F|P i%,n)	To Find P Given F (P|F i%,n)	To Find F Given A (F|A i%,n)	To Find A Given F (A|F i%,n)	To Find P Given A (P|A i%,n)	To Find A Given P (A|P i%,n)	To Find P Given G (P|G i%,n)	To Find A Given G (A|G i%,n)
1	1.06000	0.94340	1.00000	1.00000	0.94340	1.06000	0.00000	0.00000
2	1.12360	0.89000	2.06000	0.48544	1.83339	0.54544	0.89000	0.48544
3	1.19102	0.83962	3.18360	0.31411	2.67301	0.37411	2.56924	0.96118
4	1.26248	0.79209	4.37462	0.22859	3.46511	0.28859	4.94552	1.42723
5	1.33823	0.74726	5.63709	0.17740	4.21236	0.23740	7.93455	1.88363
6	1.41852	0.70496	6.97532	0.14336	4.91732	0.20336	11.45935	2.33040
7	1.50363	0.66506	8.39384	0.11914	5.58238	0.17914	15.44969	2.76758
8	1.59385	0.62741	9.89747	0.10104	6.20979	0.16104	19.84158	3.19521
9	1.68948	0.59190	11.49132	0.08702	6.80169	0.14702	24.57677	3.61333
10	1.79085	0.55839	13.18079	0.07587	7.36009	0.13587	29.60232	4.02201
11	1.89830	0.52679	14.97164	0.06679	7.88687	0.12679	34.87020	4.42129
12	2.01220	0.49697	16.86994	0.05928	8.38384	0.11928	40.33686	4.81126
13	2.13293	0.46884	18.88214	0.05296	8.85268	0.11296	45.96293	5.19198
14	2.26090	0.44230	21.01507	0.04758	9.29498	0.10758	51.71284	5.56352
15	2.39656	0.41727	23.27597	0.04296	9.71225	0.10296	57.55455	5.92598
16	2.54035	0.39365	25.67253	0.03895	10.10590	0.09895	63.45925	6.27943
17	2.69277	0.37136	28.21288	0.03544	10.47726	0.09544	69.40108	6.62397
18	2.85434	0.35034	30.90565	0.03236	10.82760	0.09236	75.35692	6.95970
19	3.02560	0.33051	33.75999	0.02962	11.15812	0.08962	81.30615	7.28673
20	3.20714	0.31180	36.78559	0.02718	11.46992	0.08718	87.23044	7.60515
21	3.39956	0.29416	39.99273	0.02500	11.76408	0.08500	93.11355	7.91508
22	3.60354	0.27751	43.39229	0.02305	12.04158	0.08305	98.94116	8.21662
23	3.81975	0.26180	46.99583	0.02128	12.30338	0.08128	104.70070	8.50991
24	4.04893	0.24698	50.81558	0.01968	12.55036	0.07968	110.38121	8.79506
25	4.29187	0.23300	54.86451	0.01823	12.78336	0.07823	115.97317	9.07220
26	4.54938	0.21981	59.15638	0.01690	13.00317	0.07690	121.46842	9.34145
27	4.82235	0.20737	63.70577	0.01570	13.21053	0.07570	126.85999	9.60294
28	5.11169	0.19563	68.52811	0.01459	13.40616	0.07459	132.14200	9.85681
29	5.41839	0.18456	73.63980	0.01358	13.59072	0.07358	137.30959	10.10319
30	5.74349	0.17411	79.05819	0.01265	13.76483	0.07265	142.35879	10.34221
36	8.14725	0.12274	119.12087	8.3948E−03	14.62099	0.06839	170.03866	11.62977
40	10.28572	0.09722	154.76197	6.4615E−03	15.04630	0.06646	185.95682	12.35898
48	16.39387	0.06100	256.56453	3.8977E−03	15.65003	0.06390	212.03505	13.54854
50	18.42015	0.05429	290.33590	3.4443E−03	15.76186	0.06344	217.45738	13.79643
52	20.69689	0.04832	328.28142	3.0462E−03	15.86139	0.06305	222.48229	14.02666
55	24.65032	0.04057	394.17203	2.5370E−03	15.99054	0.06254	229.32225	14.34112
60	32.98769	0.03031	533.12818	1.8757E−03	16.16143	0.06188	239.04279	14.79095
72	66.37772	0.01507	1089.62859	9.1774E−04	16.41558	0.06092	255.51462	15.56537
75	79.05692	0.01265	1300.94868	7.6867E−04	16.45585	0.06077	258.45274	15.70583
80	105.79599	9.4522E−03	1746.59989	5.7254E−04	16.50913	0.06057	262.54931	15.90328
84	133.56500	7.4870E−03	2209.41674	4.5261E−04	16.54188	0.06045	265.21627	16.03302
90	189.46451	5.2780E−03	3141.07519	3.1836E−04	16.57870	0.06032	268.39461	16.18912
96	268.75903	3.7208E−03	4462.65050	2.2408E−04	16.60465	0.06022	270.79093	16.30814
100	339.30208	2.9472E−03	5638.36806	1.7736E−04	16.61755	0.06018	272.04706	16.37107
108	540.79597	1.8491E−03	8996.59954	1.1115E−04	16.63585	0.06011	273.93570	16.46659
120	1088.18775	9.1896E−04	1.8120E+04	5.5188E−05	16.65135	0.06006	275.68459	16.55629
132	2189.64755	4.5669E−04	3.6477E+04	2.7414E−05	16.65906	0.06003	276.64619	16.60636
144	4406.00107	2.2696E−04	7.3417E+04	1.3621E−05	16.66288	0.06001	277.17002	16.63398
180	3.5897E+04	2.7858E−05	5.9826E+05	1.6715E−06	16.66620	0.06000	277.68647	16.66165
240	1.1842E+06	8.4449E−07	1.9736E+07	5.0669E−08	16.66665	0.06000	277.77417	16.66646
360	1.2886E+09	7.7605E−10	2.1476E+10	4.6563E−11	16.66667	0.06000	277.77777	16.66667
480	1.4022E+12	7.1316E−13	2.3370E+13	4.2789E−14	16.66667	0.06000	277.77778	16.66667
600	1.5259E+15	6.5536E−16	2.5431E+16	3.9322E−17	16.66667	0.06000	277.77778	16.66667

TABLE A-a-13

	Single Sums		Uniform Series				Gradient Series	
	To Find F Given P $(F\|P\ i\%,n)$	To Find P Given F $(P\|F\ i\%,n)$	To Find F Given A $(F\|A\ i\%,n)$	To Find A Given F $(A\|F\ i\%,n)$	To Find P Given A $(P\|A\ i\%,n)$	To Find A Given P $(A\|P\ i\%,n)$	To Find P Given G $(P\|G\ i\%,n)$	To Find A Given G $(A\|G\ i\%,n)$
n								
1	1.07000	0.93458	1.00000	1.00000	0.93458	1.07000	0.00000	0.00000
2	1.14490	0.87344	2.07000	0.48309	1.80802	0.55309	0.87344	0.48309
3	1.22504	0.81630	3.21490	0.31105	2.62432	0.38105	2.50603	0.95493
4	1.31080	0.76290	4.43994	0.22523	3.38721	0.29523	4.79472	1.41554
5	1.40255	0.71299	5.75074	0.17389	4.10020	0.24389	7.64666	1.86495
6	1.50073	0.66634	7.15329	0.13980	4.76654	0.20980	10.97838	2.30322
7	1.60578	0.62275	8.65402	0.11555	5.38929	0.18555	14.71487	2.73039
8	1.71819	0.58201	10.25980	0.09747	5.97130	0.16747	18.78894	3.14654
9	1.83846	0.54393	11.97799	0.08349	6.51523	0.15349	23.14041	3.55174
10	1.96715	0.50835	13.81645	0.07238	7.02358	0.14238	27.71555	3.94607
11	2.10485	0.47509	15.78360	0.06336	7.49867	0.13336	32.46648	4.32963
12	2.25219	0.44401	17.88845	0.05590	7.94269	0.12590	37.35061	4.70252
13	2.40985	0.41496	20.14064	0.04965	8.35765	0.11965	42.33018	5.06484
14	2.57853	0.38782	22.55049	0.04434	8.74547	0.11434	47.37181	5.41673
15	2.75903	0.36245	25.12902	0.03979	9.10791	0.10979	52.44605	5.75829
16	2.95216	0.33873	27.88805	0.03586	9.44665	0.10586	57.52707	6.08968
17	3.15882	0.31657	30.84022	0.03243	9.76322	0.10243	62.59226	6.41102
18	3.37993	0.29586	33.99903	0.02941	10.05909	0.09941	67.62195	6.72247
19	3.61653	0.27651	37.37896	0.02675	10.33560	0.09675	72.59910	7.02418
20	3.86968	0.25842	40.99549	0.02439	10.59401	0.09439	77.50906	7.31631
21	4.14056	0.24151	44.86518	0.02229	10.83553	0.09229	82.33932	7.59901
22	4.43040	0.22571	49.00574	0.02041	11.06124	0.09041	87.07930	7.87247
23	4.74053	0.21095	53.43614	0.01871	11.27219	0.08871	91.72013	8.13685
24	5.07237	0.19715	58.17667	0.01719	11.46933	0.08719	96.25450	8.39234
25	5.42743	0.18425	63.24904	0.01581	11.65358	0.08581	100.67648	8.63910
26	5.80735	0.17220	68.67647	0.01456	11.82578	0.08456	104.98137	8.87733
27	6.21387	0.16093	74.48382	0.01343	11.98671	0.08343	109.16556	9.10722
28	6.64884	0.15040	80.69769	0.01239	12.13711	0.08239	113.22642	9.32894
29	7.11426	0.14056	87.34653	0.01145	12.27767	0.08145	117.16218	9.54270
30	7.61226	0.13137	94.46079	0.01059	12.40904	0.08059	120.97182	9.74868
36	11.42394	0.08754	148.91346	6.7153E−03	13.03521	0.07672	141.19902	10.83213
40	14.97446	0.06678	199.63511	5.0091E−03	13.33171	0.07501	152.29277	11.42335
48	25.72891	0.03887	353.27009	2.8307E−03	13.73047	0.07283	169.49812	12.34467
50	29.45703	0.03395	406.52893	2.4598E−03	13.80075	0.07246	172.90512	12.52868
52	33.72535	0.02965	467.50497	2.1390E−03	13.86212	0.07214	176.00368	12.69673
55	41.31500	0.02420	575.92859	1.7363E−03	13.93994	0.07174	180.12433	12.92146
60	57.94643	0.01726	813.52038	1.2292E−03	14.03918	0.07123	185.76774	13.23209
72	130.50646	7.6625E−03	1850.09222	5.4051E−04	14.17625	0.07054	194.63648	13.72976
75	159.87602	6.2548E−03	2269.65742	4.4060E−04	14.19636	0.07044	196.10351	13.81365
80	224.23439	4.4596E−03	3189.06268	3.1357E−04	14.22201	0.07031	198.07480	13.92735
84	293.92554	3.4022E−03	4184.65058	2.3897E−04	14.23711	0.07024	199.30463	13.99895
90	441.10298	2.2670E−03	6287.18543	1.5905E−04	14.25333	0.07016	200.70420	14.08122
96	661.97663	1.5106E−03	9442.52329	1.0590E−04	14.26413	0.07011	201.70162	14.14047
100	867.71633	1.1525E−03	1.2382E+04	8.0765E−05	14.26925	0.07008	202.20008	14.17034
108	1490.89820	6.7074E−04	2.1284E+04	4.6983E−05	14.27613	0.07005	202.90990	14.21323
120	3357.78838	2.9782E−04	4.7954E+04	2.0853E−05	14.28146	0.07002	203.51031	14.24997
132	7562.38275	1.3223E−04	1.0802E+05	9.2576E−06	14.28383	0.07001	203.80529	14.26826
144	1.7032E+04	5.8713E−05	2.4330E+05	4.1102E−06	14.28488	0.07000	203.94887	14.27726
180	1.9457E+05	5.1395E−06	2.7796E+06	3.5977E−07	14.28564	0.07000	204.06737	14.28479
240	1.1275E+07	8.8694E−08	1.6107E+08	6.2086E−09	14.28571	0.07000	204.08131	14.28569
360	3.7858E+10	2.6414E−11	5.4083E+11	1.8490E−12	14.28571	0.07000	204.08163	14.28571
480	1.2712E+14	7.8666E−15	1.8160E+15	5.5066E−16	14.28571	0.07000	204.08163	14.28571
600	4.2684E+17	2.3428E−18	6.0977E+18	1.6400E−19	14.28571	0.07000	204.08163	14.28571

TABLE A-a-14

	Single Sums		Uniform Series				Gradient Series	
n	To Find F Given P (F|P i%,n)	To Find P Given F (P|F i%,n)	To Find F Given A (F|A i%,n)	To Find A Given F (A|F i%,n)	To Find P Given A (P|A i%,n)	To Find A Given P (A|P i%,n)	To Find P Given G (P|G i%,n)	To Find A Given G (A|G i%,n)
1	1.08000	0.92593	1.00000	1.00000	0.92593	1.08000	0.00000	0.00000
2	1.16640	0.85734	2.08000	0.48077	1.78326	0.56077	0.85734	0.48077
3	1.25971	0.79383	3.24640	0.30803	2.57710	0.38803	2.44500	0.94874
4	1.36049	0.73503	4.50611	0.22192	3.31213	0.30192	4.65009	1.40396
5	1.46933	0.68058	5.86660	0.17046	3.99271	0.25046	7.37243	1.84647
6	1.58687	0.63017	7.33593	0.13632	4.62288	0.21632	10.52327	2.27635
7	1.71382	0.58349	8.92280	0.11207	5.20637	0.19207	14.02422	2.69366
8	1.85093	0.54027	10.63663	0.09401	5.74664	0.17401	17.80610	3.09852
9	1.99900	0.50025	12.48756	0.08008	6.24689	0.16008	21.80809	3.49103
10	2.15892	0.46319	14.48656	0.06903	6.71008	0.14903	25.97683	3.87131
11	2.33164	0.42888	16.64549	0.06008	7.13896	0.14008	30.26566	4.23950
12	2.51817	0.39711	18.97713	0.05270	7.53608	0.13270	34.63391	4.59575
13	2.71962	0.36770	21.49530	0.04652	7.90378	0.12652	39.04629	4.94021
14	2.93719	0.34046	24.21492	0.04130	8.24424	0.12130	43.47228	5.27305
15	3.17217	0.31524	27.15211	0.03683	8.55948	0.11683	47.88566	5.59446
16	3.42594	0.29189	30.32428	0.03298	8.85137	0.11298	52.26402	5.90463
17	3.70002	0.27027	33.75023	0.02963	9.12164	0.10963	56.58832	6.20375
18	3.99602	0.25025	37.45024	0.02670	9.37189	0.10670	60.84256	6.49203
19	4.31570	0.23171	41.44626	0.02413	9.60360	0.10413	65.01337	6.76969
20	4.66096	0.21455	45.76196	0.02185	9.81815	0.10185	69.08979	7.03695
21	5.03383	0.19866	50.42292	0.01983	10.01680	0.09983	73.06291	7.29403
22	5.43654	0.18394	55.45676	0.01803	10.20074	0.09803	76.92566	7.54118
23	5.87146	0.17032	60.89330	0.01642	10.37106	0.09642	80.67259	7.77863
24	6.34118	0.15770	66.76476	0.01498	10.52876	0.09498	84.29968	8.00661
25	6.84848	0.14602	73.10594	0.01368	10.67478	0.09368	87.80411	8.22538
26	7.39635	0.13520	79.95442	0.01251	10.80998	0.09251	91.18415	8.43518
27	7.98806	0.12519	87.35077	0.01145	10.93516	0.09145	94.43901	8.63627
28	8.62711	0.11591	95.33883	0.01049	11.05108	0.09049	97.56868	8.82888
29	9.31727	0.10733	103.96594	9.6185E−03	11.15841	0.08962	100.57385	9.01328
30	10.06266	0.09938	113.28321	8.8274E−03	11.25778	0.08883	103.45579	9.18971
36	15.96817	0.06262	187.10215	5.3447E−03	11.71719	0.08534	118.28355	10.09490
40	21.72452	0.04603	259.05652	3.8602E−03	11.92461	0.08386	126.04220	10.56992
48	40.21057	0.02487	490.13216	2.0403E−03	12.18914	0.08204	137.44276	11.27584
50	46.90161	0.02132	573.77016	1.7429E−03	12.23348	0.08174	139.59279	11.41071
52	54.70604	0.01828	671.32551	1.4896E−03	12.27151	0.08149	141.51214	11.53177
55	68.91386	0.01451	848.92320	1.1780E−03	12.31861	0.08118	144.00645	11.69015
60	101.25706	9.8759E−03	1253.21330	7.9795E−04	12.37655	0.08080	147.30001	11.90154
72	254.98251	3.9218E−03	3174.78140	3.1498E−04	12.45098	0.08031	152.10756	12.21652
75	321.20453	3.1133E−03	4002.55662	2.4984E−04	12.46108	0.08025	152.84485	12.26577
80	471.95483	2.1188E−03	5886.93543	1.6987E−04	12.47351	0.08017	153.80008	12.33013
84	642.08934	1.5574E−03	8013.61677	1.2479E−04	12.48053	0.08012	154.37137	12.36897
90	1018.91509	9.8144E−04	1.2724E+04	7.8592E−05	12.48773	0.08008	154.99254	12.41158
96	1616.89019	6.1847E−04	2.0199E+04	4.9508E−05	12.49227	0.08005	155.41120	12.44059
100	2199.76126	4.5459E−04	2.7485E+04	3.6384E−05	12.49432	0.08004	155.61073	12.45452
108	4071.60456	2.4560E−04	5.0883E+04	1.9653E−05	12.49693	0.08002	155.88006	12.47347
120	1.0253E+04	9.7532E−05	1.2815E+05	7.8034E−06	12.49878	0.08001	156.08846	12.48829
132	2.5819E+04	3.8731E−05	3.2272E+05	3.0986E−06	12.49952	0.08000	156.18004	12.49489
144	6.5016E+04	1.5381E−05	8.1269E+05	1.2305E−06	12.49981	0.08000	156.21991	12.49779
180	1.0382E+06	9.6322E−07	1.2977E+07	7.7057E−08	12.49999	0.08000	156.24768	12.49983
240	1.0512E+08	9.5126E−09	1.3140E+09	7.6101E−10	12.50000	0.08000	156.24997	12.50000
360	1.0778E+12	9.2779E−13	1.3473E+13	7.4223E−14	12.50000	0.08000	156.25000	12.50000
480	1.1051E+16	9.0489E−17	1.3814E+17	7.2391E−18	12.50000	0.08000	156.25000	12.50000
600	1.1331E+20	8.8257E−21	1.4163E+21	7.0605E−22	12.50000	0.08000	156.25000	12.50000

TABLE A-a-15

	Single Sums		Uniform Series				Gradient Series	
	To Find F Given P	To Find P Given F	To Find F Given A	To Find A Given F	To Find P Given A	To Find A Given P	To Find P Given G	To Find A Given G
n	$(F \vert P \; i\%,n)$	$(P \vert F \; i\%,n)$	$(F \vert A \; i\%,n)$	$(A \vert F \; i\%,n)$	$(P \vert A \; i\%,n)$	$(A \vert P \; i\%,n)$	$(P \vert G \; i\%,n)$	$(A \vert G \; i\%,n)$
1	1.09000	0.91743	1.00000	1.00000	0.91743	1.09000	0.00000	0.00000
2	1.18810	0.84168	2.09000	0.47847	1.75911	0.56847	0.84168	0.47847
3	1.29503	0.77218	3.27810	0.30505	2.53129	0.39505	2.38605	0.94262
4	1.41158	0.70843	4.57313	0.21867	3.23972	0.30867	4.51132	1.39250
5	1.53862	0.64993	5.98471	0.16709	3.88965	0.25709	7.11105	1.82820
6	1.67710	0.59627	7.52333	0.13292	4.48592	0.22292	10.09238	2.24979
7	1.82804	0.54703	9.20043	0.10869	5.03295	0.19869	13.37459	2.65740
8	1.99256	0.50187	11.02847	0.09067	5.53482	0.18067	16.88765	3.05117
9	2.17189	0.46043	13.02104	0.07680	5.99525	0.16680	20.57108	3.43123
10	2.36736	0.42241	15.19293	0.06582	6.41766	0.15582	24.37277	3.79777
11	2.58043	0.38753	17.56029	0.05695	6.80519	0.14695	28.24810	4.15096
12	2.81266	0.35553	20.14072	0.04965	7.16073	0.13965	32.15898	4.49102
13	3.06580	0.32618	22.95338	0.04357	7.48690	0.13357	36.07313	4.81816
14	3.34173	0.29925	26.01919	0.03843	7.78615	0.12843	39.96333	5.13262
15	3.64248	0.27454	29.36092	0.03406	8.06069	0.12406	43.80686	5.43463
16	3.97031	0.25187	33.00340	0.03030	8.31256	0.12030	47.58491	5.72446
17	4.32763	0.23107	36.97370	0.02705	8.54363	0.11705	51.28208	6.00238
18	4.71712	0.21199	41.30134	0.02421	8.75563	0.11421	54.88598	6.26865
19	5.14166	0.19449	46.01846	0.02173	8.95011	0.11173	58.38679	6.52358
20	5.60441	0.17843	51.16012	0.01955	9.12855	0.10955	61.77698	6.76745
21	6.10881	0.16370	56.76453	0.01762	9.29224	0.10762	65.05094	7.00056
22	6.65860	0.15018	62.87334	0.01590	9.44243	0.10590	68.20475	7.22322
23	7.25787	0.13778	69.53194	0.01438	9.58021	0.10438	71.23594	7.43574
24	7.91108	0.12640	76.78981	0.01302	9.70661	0.10302	74.14326	7.63843
25	8.62308	0.11597	84.70090	0.01181	9.82258	0.10181	76.92649	7.83160
26	9.39916	0.10639	93.32398	0.01072	9.92897	0.10072	79.58630	8.01556
27	10.24508	0.09761	102.72313	9.7349E−03	10.02658	0.09973	82.12410	8.19064
28	11.16714	0.08955	112.96822	8.8520E−03	10.11613	0.09885	84.54191	8.35714
29	12.17218	0.08215	124.13536	8.0557E−03	10.19828	0.09806	86.84224	8.51538
30	13.26768	0.07537	136.30754	7.3364E−03	10.27365	0.09734	89.02800	8.66566
36	22.25123	0.04494	236.12472	4.2350E−03	10.61176	0.09424	99.93194	9.41709
40	31.40942	0.03184	337.88245	2.9596E−03	10.75736	0.09296	105.37619	9.79573
48	62.58524	0.01598	684.28041	1.4614E−03	10.93358	0.09146	112.96246	10.33170
50	74.35752	0.01345	815.08356	1.2269E−03	10.96168	0.09123	114.32507	10.42952
52	88.34417	0.01132	970.49077	1.0304E−03	10.98534	0.09103	115.51926	10.51577
55	114.40826	8.7406E−03	1260.09180	7.9359E−04	11.01399	0.09079	117.03621	10.62614
60	176.03129	5.6808E−03	1944.79213	5.1419E−04	11.04799	0.09051	118.96825	10.76832
72	495.11702	2.0197E−03	5490.18906	1.8214E−04	11.08867	0.09018	121.59166	10.96560
75	641.19089	1.5596E−03	7113.23215	1.4058E−04	11.09378	0.09014	121.96458	10.99396
80	986.55167	1.0136E−03	1.0951E+04	9.1319E−05	11.09985	0.09009	122.43064	11.02994
84	1392.59819	7.1808E−04	1.5462E+04	6.4674E−05	11.10313	0.09006	122.69793	11.05075
90	2335.52658	4.2817E−04	2.5939E+04	3.8552E−05	11.10635	0.09004	122.97576	11.07256
96	3916.91189	2.5530E−04	4.3510E+04	2.2983E−05	11.10827	0.09002	123.15295	11.08660
100	5529.04079	1.8086E−04	6.1423E+04	1.6281E−05	11.10910	0.09002	123.23350	11.09302
108	1.1017E+04	9.0769E−05	1.2240E+05	8.1700E−06	11.11010	0.09001	123.33666	11.10131
120	3.0987E+04	3.2272E−05	3.4429E+05	2.9045E−06	11.11075	0.09000	123.40978	11.10724
132	8.7156E+04	1.1474E−05	9.6839E+05	1.0326E−06	11.11098	0.09000	123.43855	11.10960
144	2.4514E+05	4.0793E−06	2.7238E+06	3.6714E−07	11.11107	0.09000	123.44976	11.11052
180	5.4547E+06	1.8333E−07	6.0608E+07	1.6500E−08	11.11111	0.09000	123.45640	11.11108
240	9.6020E+08	1.0415E−09	1.0669E+10	9.3731E−11	11.11111	0.09000	123.45679	11.11111
360	2.9754E+13	3.3609E−14	3.3060E+14	3.0248E−15	11.11111	0.09000	123.45679	11.11111
480	9.2197E+17	1.0846E−18	1.0244E+19	9.7617E−20	11.11111	0.09000	123.45679	11.11111
600	2.8569E+22	3.5003E−23	3.1744E+23	3.1502E−24	11.11111	0.09000	123.45679	11.11111

TABLE A-a-16

	Single Sums		Uniform Series				Gradient Series	
n	To Find F Given P (F|P i%,n)	To Find P Given F (P|F i%,n)	To Find F Given A (F|A i%,n)	To Find A Given F (A|F i%,n)	To Find P Given A (P|A i%,n)	To Find A Given P (A|P i%,n)	To Find P Given G (P|G i%,n)	To Find A Given G (A|G i%,n)
1	1.10000	0.90909	1.00000	1.00000	0.90909	1.10000	0.00000	0.00000
2	1.21000	0.82645	2.10000	0.47619	1.73554	0.57619	0.82645	0.47619
3	1.33100	0.75131	3.31000	0.30211	2.48685	0.40211	2.32908	0.93656
4	1.46410	0.68301	4.64100	0.21547	3.16987	0.31547	4.37812	1.38117
5	1.61051	0.62092	6.10510	0.16380	3.79079	0.26380	6.86180	1.81013
6	1.77156	0.56447	7.71561	0.12961	4.35526	0.22961	9.68417	2.22356
7	1.94872	0.51316	9.48717	0.10541	4.86842	0.20541	12.76312	2.62162
8	2.14359	0.46651	11.43589	0.08744	5.33493	0.18744	16.02867	3.00448
9	2.35795	0.42410	13.57948	0.07364	5.75902	0.17364	19.42145	3.37235
10	2.59374	0.38554	15.93742	0.06275	6.14457	0.16275	22.89134	3.72546
11	2.85312	0.35049	18.53117	0.05396	6.49506	0.15396	26.39628	4.06405
12	3.13843	0.31863	21.38428	0.04676	6.81369	0.14676	29.90122	4.38840
13	3.45227	0.28966	24.52271	0.04078	7.10336	0.14078	33.37719	4.69879
14	3.79750	0.26333	27.97498	0.03575	7.36669	0.13575	36.80050	4.99553
15	4.17725	0.23939	31.77248	0.03147	7.60608	0.13147	40.15199	5.27893
16	4.59497	0.21763	35.94973	0.02782	7.82371	0.12782	43.41642	5.54934
17	5.05447	0.19784	40.54470	0.02466	8.02155	0.12466	46.58194	5.80710
18	5.55992	0.17986	45.59917	0.02193	8.20141	0.12193	49.63954	6.05256
19	6.11591	0.16351	51.15909	0.01955	8.36492	0.11955	52.58268	6.28610
20	6.72750	0.14864	57.27500	0.01746	8.51356	0.11746	55.40691	6.50808
21	7.40025	0.13513	64.00250	0.01562	8.64869	0.11562	58.10952	6.71888
22	8.14027	0.12285	71.40275	0.01401	8.77154	0.11401	60.68929	6.91889
23	8.95430	0.11168	79.54302	0.01257	8.88322	0.11257	63.14621	7.10848
24	9.84973	0.10153	88.49733	0.01130	8.98474	0.11130	65.48130	7.28805
25	10.83471	0.09230	98.34706	0.01017	9.07704	0.11017	67.69640	7.45798
26	11.91818	0.08391	109.18177	9.1590E−03	9.16095	0.10916	69.79404	7.61865
27	13.10999	0.07628	121.09994	8.2576E−03	9.23722	0.10826	71.77726	7.77044
28	14.42099	0.06934	134.20994	7.4510E−03	9.30657	0.10745	73.64953	7.91372
29	15.86309	0.06304	148.63093	6.7281E−03	9.36961	0.10673	75.41463	8.04886
30	17.44940	0.05731	164.49402	6.0792E−03	9.42691	0.10608	77.07658	8.17623
36	30.91268	0.03235	299.12681	3.3431E−03	9.67651	0.10334	85.11938	8.79650
40	45.25926	0.02209	442.59256	2.2594E−03	9.77905	0.10226	88.95254	9.09623
48	97.01723	0.01031	960.17234	1.0415E−03	9.89693	0.10104	94.02168	9.50009
50	117.39085	8.5186E−03	1163.90853	8.5917E−04	9.91481	0.10086	94.88887	9.57041
52	142.04293	7.0401E−03	1410.42932	7.0900E−04	9.92960	0.10071	95.63512	9.63132
55	189.05914	5.2894E−03	1880.59142	5.3175E−04	9.94711	0.10053	96.56192	9.70754
60	304.48164	3.2843E−03	3034.81640	3.2951E−04	9.96716	0.10033	97.70101	9.80229
72	955.59382	1.0465E−03	9545.93818	1.0476E−04	9.98954	0.10010	99.14189	9.92458
75	1271.89537	7.8623E−04	1.2709E+04	7.8685E−05	9.99214	0.10008	99.33171	9.94099
80	2048.40021	4.8819E−04	2.0474E+04	4.8842E−05	9.99512	0.10005	99.56063	9.96093
84	2999.06275	3.3344E−04	2.9981E+04	3.3355E−05	9.99667	0.10003	99.68657	9.97198
90	5313.02261	1.8822E−04	5.3120E+04	1.8825E−05	9.99812	0.10002	99.81178	9.98306
96	9412.34365	1.0624E−04	9.4113E+04	1.0625E−05	9.99894	0.10001	99.88738	9.98980
100	1.3781E+04	7.2566E−05	1.3780E+05	7.2571E−06	9.99927	0.10001	99.92018	9.99274
108	2.9540E+04	3.3852E−05	2.9539E+05	3.3854E−06	9.99966	0.10000	99.96005	9.99634
120	9.2709E+04	1.0786E−05	9.2708E+05	1.0787E−06	9.99989	0.10000	99.98598	9.99871
132	2.9096E+05	3.4369E−06	2.9096E+06	3.4369E−07	9.99997	0.10000	99.99512	9.99955
144	9.1316E+05	1.0951E−06	9.1316E+06	1.0951E−07	9.99999	0.10000	99.99831	9.99984
180	2.8228E+07	3.5426E−08	2.8228E+08	3.5426E−09	10.00000	0.10000	99.99993	9.99999
240	8.5950E+09	1.1635E−10	8.5950E+10	1.1635E−11	10.00000	0.10000	100.00000	10.00000
360	7.9683E+14	1.2550E−15	7.9683E+15	1.2550E−16	10.00000	0.10000	100.00000	10.00000
480	7.3874E+19	1.3537E−20	7.3874E+20	1.3537E−21	10.00000	0.10000	100.00000	10.00000
600	6.8487E+24	1.4601E−25	6.8487E+25	1.4601E−26	10.00000	0.10000	100.00000	10.00000

TABLE A-a-17

	Single Sums		Uniform Series				Gradient Series	
	To Find F Given P $(F\|P\ i\%,n)$	To Find P Given F $(P\|F\ i\%,n)$	To Find F Given A $(F\|A\ i\%,n)$	To Find A Given F $(A\|F\ i\%,n)$	To Find P Given A $(P\|A\ i\%,n)$	To Find A Given P $(A\|P\ i\%,n)$	To Find P Given G $(P\|G\ i\%,n)$	To Find A Given G $(A\|G\ i\%,n)$
n								
1	1.11000	0.90090	1.00000	1.00000	0.90090	1.11000	0.00000	0.00000
2	1.23210	0.81162	2.11000	0.47393	1.71252	0.58393	0.81162	0.47393
3	1.36763	0.73119	3.34210	0.29921	2.44371	0.40921	2.27401	0.93055
4	1.51807	0.65873	4.70973	0.21233	3.10245	0.32233	4.25020	1.36995
5	1.68506	0.59345	6.22780	0.16057	3.69590	0.27057	6.62400	1.79226
6	1.87041	0.53464	7.91286	0.12638	4.23054	0.23638	9.29721	2.19764
7	2.07616	0.48166	9.78327	0.10222	4.71220	0.21222	12.18716	2.58630
8	2.30454	0.43393	11.85943	0.08432	5.14612	0.19432	15.22464	2.95847
9	2.55804	0.39092	14.16397	0.07060	5.53705	0.18060	18.35204	3.31441
10	2.83942	0.35218	16.72201	0.05980	5.88923	0.16980	21.52170	3.65442
11	3.15176	0.31728	19.56143	0.05112	6.20652	0.16112	24.69454	3.97881
12	3.49845	0.28584	22.71319	0.04403	6.49236	0.15403	27.83878	4.28793
13	3.88328	0.25751	26.21164	0.03815	6.74987	0.14815	30.92896	4.58216
14	4.31044	0.23199	30.09492	0.03323	6.98187	0.14323	33.94489	4.86187
15	4.78459	0.20900	34.40536	0.02907	7.19087	0.13907	36.87095	5.12747
16	5.31089	0.18829	39.18995	0.02552	7.37916	0.13552	39.69533	5.37938
17	5.89509	0.16963	44.50084	0.02247	7.54879	0.13247	42.40945	5.61804
18	6.54355	0.15282	50.39594	0.01984	7.70162	0.12984	45.00743	5.84389
19	7.26334	0.13768	56.93949	0.01756	7.83929	0.12756	47.48563	6.05739
20	8.06231	0.12403	64.20283	0.01558	7.96333	0.12558	49.84227	6.25898
21	8.94917	0.11174	72.26514	0.01384	8.07507	0.12384	52.07712	6.44912
22	9.93357	0.10067	81.21431	0.01231	8.17574	0.12231	54.19116	6.62829
23	11.02627	0.09069	91.14788	0.01097	8.26643	0.12097	56.18640	6.79693
24	12.23916	0.08170	102.17415	9.7872E−03	8.34814	0.11979	58.06561	6.95552
25	13.58546	0.07361	114.41331	8.7402E−03	8.42174	0.11874	59.83220	7.10449
26	15.07986	0.06631	127.99877	7.8126E−03	8.48806	0.11781	61.49004	7.24430
27	16.73865	0.05974	143.07864	6.9892E−03	8.54780	0.11699	63.04334	7.37539
28	18.57990	0.05382	159.81729	6.2571E−03	8.60162	0.11626	64.49652	7.49818
29	20.62369	0.04849	178.39719	5.6055E−03	8.65011	0.11561	65.85418	7.61310
30	22.89230	0.04368	199.02088	5.0246E−03	8.69379	0.11502	67.12098	7.72056
36	42.81808	0.02335	380.16441	2.6304E−03	8.87859	0.11263	73.07116	8.23004
40	65.00087	0.01538	581.82607	1.7187E−03	8.95105	0.11172	75.77886	8.46592
48	149.79695	6.6757E−03	1352.69958	7.3926E−04	9.03022	0.11074	79.17988	8.76832
50	184.56483	5.4182E−03	1668.77115	5.9924E−04	9.04165	0.11060	79.73405	8.81853
52	227.40232	4.3975E−03	2058.20294	4.8586E−04	9.05093	0.11049	80.20238	8.86123
55	311.00247	3.2154E−03	2818.20424	3.5484E−04	9.06168	0.11035	80.77119	8.91349
60	524.05724	1.9082E−03	4755.06584	2.1030E−04	9.07356	0.11021	81.44610	8.97620
72	1833.38837	5.4544E−04	1.6658E+04	6.0031E−05	9.08595	0.11006	82.24254	9.05162
75	2507.39877	3.9882E−04	2.2785E+04	4.3888E−05	9.08728	0.11004	82.33975	9.06099
80	4225.11275	2.3668E−04	3.8401E+04	2.6041E−05	9.08876	0.11003	82.45294	9.07197
84	6414.01865	1.5591E−04	5.8300E+04	1.7153E−05	9.08949	0.11002	82.51269	9.07781
90	1.1997E+04	8.3355E−05	1.0905E+05	9.1698E−06	9.09015	0.11001	82.56954	9.08341
96	2.2439E+04	4.4565E−05	2.0398E+05	4.9024E−06	9.09050	0.11000	82.60205	9.08663
100	3.4064E+04	2.9356E−05	3.0967E+05	3.2293E−06	9.09064	0.11000	82.61551	9.08797
108	7.8502E+04	1.2738E−05	7.1365E+05	1.4013E−06	9.09079	0.11000	82.63107	9.08953
120	2.7464E+05	3.6412E−06	2.4967E+06	4.0053E−07	9.09088	0.11000	82.64035	9.09047
132	9.6080E+05	1.0408E−06	8.7345E+06	1.1449E−07	9.09090	0.11000	82.64329	9.09077
144	3.3613E+06	2.9750E−07	3.0557E+07	3.2725E−08	9.09091	0.11000	82.64421	9.09087
180	1.4392E+08	6.9481E−09	1.3084E+09	7.6429E−10	9.09091	0.11000	82.64462	9.09091
240	7.5425E+10	1.3258E−11	6.8568E+11	1.4584E−12	9.09091	0.11000	82.64463	9.09091
360	2.0714E+16	4.8276E−17	1.8831E+17	5.3103E−18	9.09091	0.11000	82.64463	9.09091
480	5.6889E+21	1.7578E−22	5.1717E+22	1.9336E−23	9.09091	0.11000	82.64463	9.09091
600	1.5624E+27	6.4005E−28	1.4203E+28	7.0405E−29	9.09091	0.11000	82.64463	9.09091

TABLE A-a-18

	Single Sums		Uniform Series				Gradient Series	
	To Find F Given P	To Find P Given F	To Find F Given A	To Find A Given F	To Find P Given A	To Find A Given P	To Find P Given G	To Find A Given G
n	$(F|P\ i\%,n)$	$(P|F\ i\%,n)$	$(F|A\ i\%,n)$	$(A|F\ i\%,n)$	$(P|A\ i\%,n)$	$(A|P\ i\%,n)$	$(P|G\ i\%,n)$	$(A|G\ i\%,n)$
1	1.12000	0.89286	1.00000	1.00000	0.89286	1.12000	0.00000	0.00000
2	1.25440	0.79719	2.12000	0.47170	1.69005	0.59170	0.79719	0.47170
3	1.40493	0.71178	3.37440	0.29635	2.40183	0.41635	2.22075	0.92461
4	1.57352	0.63552	4.77933	0.20923	3.03735	0.32923	4.12731	1.35885
5	1.76234	0.56743	6.35285	0.15741	3.60478	0.27741	6.39702	1.77459
6	1.97382	0.50663	8.11519	0.12323	4.11141	0.24323	8.93017	2.17205
7	2.21068	0.45235	10.08901	0.09912	4.56376	0.21912	11.64427	2.55147
8	2.47596	0.40388	12.29969	0.08130	4.96764	0.20130	14.47145	2.91314
9	2.77308	0.36061	14.77566	0.06768	5.32825	0.18768	17.35633	3.25742
10	3.10585	0.32197	17.54874	0.05698	5.65022	0.17698	20.25409	3.58465
11	3.47855	0.28748	20.65458	0.04842	5.93770	0.16842	23.12885	3.89525
12	3.89598	0.25668	24.13313	0.04144	6.19437	0.16144	25.95228	4.18965
13	4.36349	0.22917	28.02911	0.03568	6.42355	0.15568	28.70237	4.46830
14	4.88711	0.20462	32.39260	0.03087	6.62817	0.15087	31.36242	4.73169
15	5.47357	0.18270	37.27971	0.02682	6.81086	0.14682	33.92017	4.98030
16	6.13039	0.16312	42.75328	0.02339	6.97399	0.14339	36.36700	5.21466
17	6.86604	0.14564	48.88367	0.02046	7.11963	0.14046	38.69731	5.43530
18	7.68997	0.13004	55.74971	0.01794	7.24967	0.13794	40.90798	5.64274
19	8.61276	0.11611	63.43968	0.01576	7.36578	0.13576	42.99790	5.83752
20	9.64629	0.10367	72.05244	0.01388	7.46944	0.13388	44.96757	6.02020
21	10.80385	0.09256	81.69874	0.01224	7.56200	0.13224	46.81876	6.19132
22	12.10031	0.08264	92.50258	0.01081	7.64465	0.13081	48.55425	6.35141
23	13.55235	0.07379	104.60289	9.5600E−03	7.71843	0.12956	50.17759	6.50101
24	15.17863	0.06588	118.15524	8.4634E−03	7.78432	0.12846	51.69288	6.64064
25	17.00006	0.05882	133.33387	7.5000E−03	7.84314	0.12750	53.10464	6.77084
26	19.04007	0.05252	150.33393	6.6519E−03	7.89566	0.12665	54.41766	6.89210
27	21.32488	0.04689	169.37401	5.9041E−03	7.94255	0.12590	55.63689	7.00491
28	23.88387	0.04187	190.69889	5.2439E−03	7.98442	0.12524	56.76736	7.10976
29	26.74993	0.03738	214.58275	4.6602E−03	8.02181	0.12466	57.81409	7.20712
30	29.95992	0.03338	241.33268	4.1437E−03	8.05518	0.12414	58.78205	7.29742
36	59.13557	0.01691	484.46312	2.0641E−03	8.19241	0.12206	63.19703	7.71409
40	93.05097	0.01075	767.09142	1.3036E−03	8.24378	0.12130	65.11587	7.89879
48	230.39078	4.3405E−03	1911.58980	5.2312E−04	8.29716	0.12052	67.40684	8.12408
50	289.00219	3.4602E−03	2400.01825	4.1666E−04	8.30450	0.12042	67.76241	8.15972
52	362.52435	2.7584E−03	3012.70289	3.3193E−04	8.31035	0.12033	68.05756	8.18950
55	509.32061	1.9634E−03	4236.00505	2.3607E−04	8.31697	0.12024	68.40821	8.22513
60	897.59693	1.1141E−03	7471.64111	1.3384E−04	8.32405	0.12013	68.81003	8.26641
72	3497.01610	2.8596E−04	2.9133E+04	3.4325E−05	8.33095	0.12003	69.25301	8.31274
75	4913.05584	2.0354E−04	4.0934E+04	2.4430E−05	8.33164	0.12002	69.30310	8.31806
80	8658.48310	1.1549E−04	7.2146E+04	1.3861E−05	8.33237	0.12001	69.35943	8.32409
84	1.3624E+04	7.3398E−05	1.1353E+05	8.8084E−06	8.33272	0.12001	69.38797	8.32717
90	2.6892E+04	3.7186E−05	2.2409E+05	4.4625E−06	8.33302	0.12000	69.41397	8.32999
96	5.3080E+04	1.8840E−05	4.4232E+05	2.2608E−06	8.33318	0.12000	69.42806	8.33152
100	8.3522E+04	1.1973E−05	6.9601E+05	1.4368E−06	8.33323	0.12000	69.43364	8.33214
108	2.0680E+05	4.8356E−06	1.7233E+06	5.8028E−07	8.33329	0.12000	69.43976	8.33281
120	8.0568E+05	1.2412E−06	6.7140E+06	1.4894E−07	8.33332	0.12000	69.44312	8.33318
132	3.1389E+06	3.1858E−07	2.6158E+07	3.8230E−08	8.33333	0.12000	69.44407	8.33329
144	1.2229E+07	8.1772E−08	1.0191E+08	9.8126E−09	8.33333	0.12000	69.44434	8.33332
180	7.2318E+08	1.3828E−09	6.0265E+09	1.6593E−10	8.33333	0.12000	69.44444	8.33333
240	6.4912E+11	1.5405E−12	5.4093E+12	1.8487E−13	8.33333	0.12000	69.44444	8.33333
360	5.2298E+17	1.9121E−18	4.3582E+18	2.2945E−19	8.33333	0.12000	69.44444	8.33333
480	4.2136E+23	2.3733E−24	3.5113E+24	2.8479E−25	8.33333	0.12000	69.44444	8.33333
600	3.3948E+29	2.9457E−30	2.8290E+30	3.5348E−31	8.33333	0.12000	69.44444	8.33333

TABLE A-a-19

	Single Sums		Uniform Series				Gradient Series	
	To Find F Given P	To Find P Given F	To Find F Given A	To Find A Given F	To Find P Given A	To Find A Given P	To Find P Given G	To Find A Given G
n	(F|P i%,n)	(P|F i%,n)	(F|A i%,n)	(A|F i%,n)	(P|A i%,n)	(A|P i%,n)	(P|G i%,n)	(A|G i%,n)
1	1.15000	0.86957	1.00000	1.00000	0.86957	1.15000	0.00000	0.00000
2	1.32250	0.75614	2.15000	0.46512	1.62571	0.61512	0.75614	0.46512
3	1.52088	0.65752	3.47250	0.28798	2.28323	0.43798	2.07118	0.90713
4	1.74901	0.57175	4.99338	0.20027	2.85498	0.35027	3.78644	1.32626
5	2.01136	0.49718	6.74238	0.14832	3.35216	0.29832	5.77514	1.72281
6	2.31306	0.43233	8.75374	0.11424	3.78448	0.26424	7.93678	2.09719
7	2.66002	0.37594	11.06680	0.09036	4.16042	0.24036	10.19240	2.44985
8	3.05902	0.32690	13.72682	0.07285	4.48732	0.22285	12.48072	2.78133
9	3.51788	0.28426	16.78584	0.05957	4.77158	0.20957	14.75481	3.09223
10	4.04556	0.24718	20.30372	0.04925	5.01877	0.19925	16.97948	3.38320
11	4.65239	0.21494	24.34928	0.04107	5.23371	0.19107	19.12891	3.65494
12	5.35025	0.18691	29.00167	0.03448	5.42062	0.18448	21.18489	3.90820
13	6.15279	0.16253	34.35192	0.02911	5.58315	0.17911	23.13522	4.14376
14	7.07571	0.14133	40.50471	0.02469	5.72448	0.17469	24.97250	4.36241
15	8.13706	0.12289	47.58041	0.02102	5.84737	0.17102	26.69302	4.56496
16	9.35762	0.10686	55.71747	0.01795	5.95423	0.16795	28.29599	4.75225
17	10.76126	0.09293	65.07509	0.01537	6.04716	0.16537	29.78280	4.92509
18	12.37545	0.08081	75.83636	0.01319	6.12797	0.16319	31.15649	5.08431
19	14.23177	0.07027	88.21181	0.01134	6.19823	0.16134	32.42127	5.23073
20	16.36654	0.06110	102.44358	9.7615E−03	6.25933	0.15976	33.58217	5.36514
21	18.82152	0.05313	118.81012	8.4168E−03	6.31246	0.15842	34.64479	5.48832
22	21.64475	0.04620	137.63166	7.2658E−03	6.35866	0.15727	35.61500	5.60102
23	24.89146	0.04017	159.27638	6.2784E−03	6.39884	0.15628	36.49884	5.70398
24	28.62518	0.03493	184.16784	5.4298E−03	6.43377	0.15543	37.30232	5.79789
25	32.91895	0.03038	212.79302	4.6994E−03	6.46415	0.15470	38.03139	5.88343
26	37.85680	0.02642	245.71197	4.0698E−03	6.49056	0.15407	38.69177	5.96123
27	43.53531	0.02297	283.56877	3.5265E−03	6.51353	0.15353	39.28899	6.03190
28	50.06561	0.01997	327.10408	3.0571E−03	6.53351	0.15306	39.82828	6.09600
29	57.57545	0.01737	377.16969	2.6513E−03	6.55088	0.15265	40.31460	6.15408
30	66.21177	0.01510	434.74515	2.3002E−03	6.56598	0.15230	40.75259	6.20663
36	153.15185	6.5295E−03	1014.34568	9.8586E−04	6.62314	0.15099	42.58717	6.43006
40	267.86355	3.7332E−03	1779.09031	5.6209E−04	6.64178	0.15056	43.28299	6.51678
48	819.40071	1.2204E−03	5456.00475	1.8328E−04	6.65853	0.15018	43.99967	6.60802
50	1083.65744	9.2280E−04	7217.71628	1.3855E−04	6.66051	0.15014	44.09583	6.62048
52	1433.13697	6.9777E−04	9547.57978	1.0474E−04	6.66201	0.15010	44.17154	6.63036
55	2179.62218	4.5880E−04	1.4524E+04	6.8851E−05	6.66361	0.15007	44.25583	6.64142
60	4383.99875	2.2810E−04	2.9220E+04	3.4223E−05	6.66515	0.15003	44.34307	6.65298
72	2.3455E+04	4.2634E−05	1.5636E+05	6.3954E−06	6.66638	0.15001	44.42209	6.66360
75	3.5673E+04	2.8033E−05	2.3781E+05	4.2050E−06	6.66648	0.15000	44.42918	6.66456
80	7.1751E+04	1.3937E−05	4.7833E+05	2.0906E−06	6.66657	0.15000	44.43639	6.66555
84	1.2549E+05	7.9686E−06	8.3661E+05	1.1953E−06	6.66661	0.15000	44.43963	6.66600
90	2.9027E+05	3.4450E−06	1.9351E+06	5.1676E−07	6.66664	0.15000	44.44222	6.66636
96	6.7142E+05	1.4894E−06	4.4761E+06	2.2341E−07	6.66666	0.15000	44.44343	6.66652
100	1.1743E+06	8.5156E−07	7.8287E+06	1.2773E−07	6.66666	0.15000	44.44384	6.66658
108	3.5923E+06	2.7838E−07	2.3948E+07	4.1757E−08	6.66666	0.15000	44.44423	6.66664
120	1.9219E+07	5.2031E−08	1.2813E+08	7.8046E−09	6.66667	0.15000	44.44440	6.66666
132	1.0283E+08	9.7249E−09	6.8553E+08	1.4587E−09	6.66667	0.15000	44.44444	6.66667
144	5.5016E+08	1.8177E−09	3.6677E+09	2.7265E−10	6.66667	0.15000	44.44444	6.66667
180	8.4258E+10	1.1868E−11	5.6172E+11	1.7802E−12	6.66667	0.15000	44.44444	6.66667
240	3.6939E+14	2.7072E−15	2.4626E+15	4.0608E−16	6.66667	0.15000	44.44444	6.66667
360	7.0994E+21	1.4086E−22	4.7329E+22	2.1129E−23	6.66667	0.15000	44.44444	6.66667
480	1.3645E+29	7.3289E−30	9.0965E+29	1.0993E−30	6.66667	0.15000	44.44444	6.66667
600	2.6224E+36	3.8133E−37	1.7483E+37	5.7199E−38	6.66667	0.15000	44.44444	6.66667

TABLE A-a-20

	Single Sums		Uniform Series				Gradient Series	
	To Find F Given P	To Find P Given F	To Find F Given A	To Find A Given F	To Find P Given A	To Find A Given P	To Find P Given G	To Find A Given G
n	(F|P i%,n)	(P|F i%,n)	(F|A i%,n)	(A|F i%,n)	(P|A i%,n)	(A|P i%,n)	(P|G i%,n)	(A|G i%,n)
1	1.18000	0.84746	1.00000	1.00000	0.84746	1.18000	0.00000	0.00000
2	1.39240	0.71818	2.18000	0.45872	1.56564	0.63872	0.71818	0.45872
3	1.64303	0.60863	3.57240	0.27992	2.17427	0.45992	1.93545	0.89016
4	1.93878	0.51579	5.21543	0.19174	2.69006	0.37174	3.48281	1.29470
5	2.28776	0.43711	7.15421	0.13978	3.12717	0.31978	5.23125	1.67284
6	2.69955	0.37043	9.44197	0.10591	3.49760	0.28591	7.08341	2.02522
7	3.18547	0.31393	12.14152	0.08236	3.81153	0.26236	8.96696	2.35259
8	3.75886	0.26604	15.32700	0.06524	4.07757	0.24524	10.82922	2.65581
9	4.43545	0.22546	19.08585	0.05239	4.30302	0.23239	12.63287	2.93581
10	5.23384	0.19106	23.52131	0.04251	4.49409	0.22251	14.35245	3.19363
11	6.17593	0.16192	28.75514	0.03478	4.65601	0.21478	15.97164	3.43033
12	7.28759	0.13722	34.93107	0.02863	4.79322	0.20863	17.48106	3.64703
13	8.59936	0.11629	42.21866	0.02369	4.90951	0.20369	18.87651	3.84489
14	10.14724	0.09855	50.81802	0.01968	5.00806	0.19968	20.15765	4.02504
15	11.97375	0.08352	60.96527	0.01640	5.09158	0.19640	21.32687	4.18866
16	14.12902	0.07078	72.93901	0.01371	5.16235	0.19371	22.38852	4.33688
17	16.67225	0.05998	87.06804	0.01149	5.22233	0.19149	23.34820	4.47084
18	19.67325	0.05083	103.74028	9.6395E−03	5.27316	0.18964	24.21231	4.59161
19	23.21444	0.04308	123.41353	8.1028E−03	5.31624	0.18810	24.98769	4.70026
20	27.39303	0.03651	146.62797	6.8200E−03	5.35275	0.18682	25.68130	4.79778
21	32.32378	0.03094	174.02100	5.7464E−03	5.38368	0.18575	26.30004	4.88514
22	38.14206	0.02622	206.34479	4.8463E−03	5.40990	0.18485	26.85061	4.96324
23	45.00763	0.02222	244.48685	4.0902E−03	5.43212	0.18409	27.33942	5.03292
24	53.10901	0.01883	289.49448	3.4543E−03	5.45095	0.18345	27.77249	5.09498
25	62.66863	0.01596	342.60349	2.9188E−03	5.46691	0.18292	28.15546	5.15016
26	73.94898	0.01352	405.27211	2.4675E−03	5.48043	0.18247	28.49353	5.19914
27	87.25980	0.01146	479.22109	2.0867E−03	5.49189	0.18209	28.79149	5.24255
28	102.96656	9.7119E−03	566.48089	1.7653E−03	5.50160	0.18177	29.05371	5.28096
29	121.50054	8.2304E−03	669.44745	1.4938E−03	5.50983	0.18149	29.28416	5.31489
30	143.37064	6.9749E−03	790.94799	1.2643E−03	5.51681	0.18126	29.48643	5.34484
36	387.03680	2.5837E−03	2144.64890	4.6628E−04	5.54120	0.18047	30.26771	5.46230
40	750.37834	1.3327E−03	4163.21303	2.4020E−04	5.54815	0.18024	30.52692	5.50218
48	2820.56655	3.5454E−04	1.5664E+04	6.3840E−05	5.55359	0.18006	30.75871	5.53853
50	3927.35686	2.5462E−04	2.1813E+04	4.5844E−05	5.55414	0.18005	30.78561	5.54282
52	5468.45169	1.8287E−04	3.0375E+04	3.2922E−05	5.55454	0.18003	30.80573	5.54604
55	8984.84112	1.1130E−04	4.9910E+04	2.0036E−05	5.55494	0.18002	30.82675	5.54943
60	2.0555E+04	4.8650E−05	1.1419E+05	8.7574E−06	5.55529	0.18001	30.84648	5.55264
72	1.4980E+05	6.6757E−06	8.3220E+05	1.2016E−06	5.55552	0.18000	30.86132	5.55507
75	2.4612E+05	4.0630E−06	1.3673E+06	7.3135E−07	5.55553	0.18000	30.86238	5.55525
80	5.6307E+05	1.7760E−06	3.1281E+06	3.1968E−07	5.55555	0.18000	30.86335	5.55541
84	1.0917E+06	9.1603E−07	6.0648E+06	1.6489E−07	5.55555	0.18000	30.86374	5.55548
90	2.9470E+06	3.3933E−07	1.6372E+07	6.1079E−08	5.55555	0.18000	30.86402	5.55553
96	7.9556E+06	1.2570E−07	4.4198E+07	2.2626E−08	5.55555	0.18000	30.86413	5.55554
100	1.5424E+07	6.4833E−08	8.5690E+07	1.1670E−08	5.55556	0.18000	30.86416	5.55555
108	5.7977E+07	1.7248E−08	3.2210E+08	3.1047E−09	5.55556	0.18000	30.86419	5.55555
120	4.2251E+08	2.3668E−09	2.3473E+09	4.2602E−10	5.55556	0.18000	30.86420	5.55556
132	3.0791E+09	3.2477E−10	1.7106E+10	5.8458E−11	5.55556	0.18000	30.86420	5.55556
144	2.2439E+10	4.4565E−11	1.2466E+11	8.0216E−12	5.55556	0.18000	30.86420	5.55556
180	8.6848E+12	1.1514E−13	4.8249E+13	2.0726E−14	5.55556	0.18000	30.86420	5.55556
240	1.7852E+17	5.6017E−18	9.9177E+17	1.0083E−18	5.55556	0.18000	30.86420	5.55556
360	7.5426E+25	1.3258E−26	4.1903E+26	2.3864E−27	5.55556	0.18000	30.86420	5.55556
480	3.1869E+34	3.1379E−35	1.7705E+35	5.6482E−36	5.55556	0.18000	30.86420	5.55556
600	1.3465E+43	7.4267E−44	7.4805E+43	1.3368E−44	5.55556	0.18000	30.86420	5.55556

TABLE A-a-21

	Single Sums		Uniform Series				Gradient Series	
	To Find F Given P	To Find P Given F	To Find F Given A	To Find A Given F	To Find P Given A	To Find A Given P	To Find P Given G	To Find A Given G
n	$(F\|P\ i\%,n)$	$(P\|F\ i\%,n)$	$(F\|A\ i\%,n)$	$(A\|F\ i\%,n)$	$(P\|A\ i\%,n)$	$(A\|P\ i\%,n)$	$(P\|G\ i\%,n)$	$(A\|G\ i\%,n)$
1	1.20000	0.83333	1.00000	1.00000	0.83333	1.20000	0.00000	0.00000
2	1.44000	0.69444	2.20000	0.45455	1.52778	0.65455	0.69444	0.45455
3	1.72800	0.57870	3.64000	0.27473	2.10648	0.47473	1.85185	0.87912
4	2.07360	0.48225	5.36800	0.18629	2.58873	0.38629	3.29861	1.27422
5	2.48832	0.40188	7.44160	0.13438	2.99061	0.33438	4.90612	1.64051
6	2.98598	0.33490	9.92992	0.10071	3.32551	0.30071	6.58061	1.97883
7	3.58318	0.27908	12.91590	0.07742	3.60459	0.27742	8.25510	2.29016
8	4.29982	0.23257	16.49908	0.06061	3.83716	0.26061	9.88308	2.57562
9	5.15978	0.19381	20.79890	0.04808	4.03097	0.24808	11.43353	2.83642
10	6.19174	0.16151	25.95868	0.03852	4.19247	0.23852	12.88708	3.07386
11	7.43008	0.13459	32.15042	0.03110	4.32706	0.23110	14.23296	3.28929
12	8.91610	0.11216	39.58050	0.02526	4.43922	0.22526	15.46668	3.48410
13	10.69932	0.09346	48.49660	0.02062	4.53268	0.22062	16.58825	3.65970
14	12.83918	0.07789	59.19592	0.01689	4.61057	0.21689	17.60078	3.81749
15	15.40702	0.06491	72.03511	0.01388	4.67547	0.21388	18.50945	3.95884
16	18.48843	0.05409	87.44213	0.01144	4.72956	0.21144	19.32077	4.08511
17	22.18611	0.04507	105.93056	9.4401E−03	4.77463	0.20944	20.04194	4.19759
18	26.62333	0.03756	128.11667	7.8054E−03	4.81219	0.20781	20.68048	4.29752
19	31.94800	0.03130	154.74000	6.4625E−03	4.84350	0.20646	21.24390	4.38607
20	38.33760	0.02608	186.68800	5.3565E−03	4.86958	0.20536	21.73949	4.46435
21	46.00512	0.02174	225.02560	4.4439E−03	4.89132	0.20444	22.17423	4.53339
22	55.20614	0.01811	271.03072	3.6896E−03	4.90943	0.20369	22.55462	4.59414
23	66.24737	0.01509	326.23686	3.0653E−03	4.92453	0.20307	22.88671	4.64750
24	79.49685	0.01258	392.48424	2.5479E−03	4.93710	0.20255	23.17603	4.69426
25	95.39622	0.01048	471.98108	2.1187E−03	4.94759	0.20212	23.42761	4.73516
26	114.47546	8.7355E−03	567.37730	1.7625E−03	4.95632	0.20176	23.64600	4.77088
27	137.37055	7.2796E−03	681.85276	1.4666E−03	4.96360	0.20147	23.83527	4.80201
28	164.84466	6.0663E−03	819.22331	1.2207E−03	4.96967	0.20122	23.99906	4.82911
29	197.81359	5.0553E−03	984.06797	1.0162E−03	4.97472	0.20102	24.14061	4.85265
30	237.37631	4.2127E−03	1181.88157	8.4611E−04	4.97894	0.20085	24.26277	4.87308
36	708.80187	1.4108E−03	3539.00937	2.8256E−04	4.99295	0.20028	24.71078	4.94914
40	1469.77157	6.8038E−04	7343.85784	1.3617E−04	4.99660	0.20014	24.84691	4.97277
48	6319.74872	1.5823E−04	3.1594E+04	3.1652E−05	4.99921	0.20003	24.95807	4.99240
50	9100.43815	1.0988E−04	4.5497E+04	2.1979E−05	4.99945	0.20002	24.96978	4.99451
52	1.3105E+04	7.6309E−05	6.5518E+04	1.5263E−05	4.99962	0.20002	24.97825	4.99603
55	2.2645E+04	4.4160E−05	1.1322E+05	8.8324E−06	4.99978	0.20001	24.98675	4.99757
60	5.6348E+04	1.7747E−05	2.8173E+05	3.5495E−06	4.99991	0.20000	24.99423	4.99894
72	5.0240E+05	1.9904E−06	2.5120E+06	3.9809E−07	4.99999	0.20000	24.99923	4.99986
75	8.6815E+05	1.1519E−06	4.3407E+06	2.3038E−07	4.99999	0.20000	24.99954	4.99991
80	2.1602E+06	4.6291E−07	1.0801E+07	9.2583E−08	5.00000	0.20000	24.99980	4.99996
84	4.4794E+06	2.2324E−07	2.2397E+07	4.4648E−08	5.00000	0.20000	24.99990	4.99998
90	1.3376E+07	7.4763E−08	6.6878E+07	1.4953E−08	5.00000	0.20000	24.99996	4.99999
96	3.9939E+07	2.5038E−08	1.9970E+08	5.0076E−09	5.00000	0.20000	24.99999	5.00000
100	8.2818E+07	1.2075E−08	4.1409E+08	2.4149E−09	5.00000	0.20000	24.99999	5.00000
108	3.5610E+08	2.8082E−09	1.7805E+09	5.6164E−10	5.00000	0.20000	25.00000	5.00000
120	3.1750E+09	3.1496E−10	1.5875E+10	6.2991E−11	5.00000	0.20000	25.00000	5.00000
132	2.8309E+10	3.5324E−11	1.4154E+11	7.0649E−12	5.00000	0.20000	25.00000	5.00000
144	2.5241E+11	3.9619E−12	1.2620E+12	7.9237E−13	5.00000	0.20000	25.00000	5.00000
180	1.7891E+14	5.5895E−15	8.9453E+14	1.1179E−15	5.00000	0.20000	25.00000	5.00000
240	1.0081E+19	9.9198E−20	5.0404E+19	1.9840E−20	5.00000	0.20000	25.00000	5.00000
360	3.2007E+28	3.1243E−29	1.6004E+29	6.2486E−30	5.00000	0.20000	25.00000	5.00000
480	1.0162E+38	9.8402E−39	5.0812E+38	1.9680E−39	5.00000	0.20000	25.00000	5.00000
600	3.2266E+47	3.0992E−48	1.6133E+48	6.1984E−49	5.00000	0.20000	25.00000	5.00000

TABLE A-a-22

	Single Sums		Uniform Series				Gradient Series	
	To Find F Given P (F|P i%,n)	To Find P Given F (P|F i%,n)	To Find F Given A (F|A i%,n)	To Find A Given F (A|F i%,n)	To Find P Given A (P|A i%,n)	To Find A Given P (A|P i%,n)	To Find P Given G (P|G i%,n)	To Find A Given G (A|G i%,n)
n								
1	1.25000	0.80000	1.00000	1.00000	0.80000	1.25000	0.00000	0.00000
2	1.56250	0.64000	2.25000	0.44444	1.44000	0.69444	0.64000	0.44444
3	1.95313	0.51200	3.81250	0.26230	1.95200	0.51230	1.66400	0.85246
4	2.44141	0.40960	5.76563	0.17344	2.36160	0.42344	2.89280	1.22493
5	3.05176	0.32768	8.20703	0.12185	2.68928	0.37185	4.20352	1.56307
6	3.81470	0.26214	11.25879	0.08882	2.95142	0.33882	5.51424	1.86833
7	4.76837	0.20972	15.07349	0.06634	3.16114	0.31634	6.77253	2.14243
8	5.96046	0.16777	19.84186	0.05040	3.32891	0.30040	7.94694	2.38725
9	7.45058	0.13422	25.80232	0.03876	3.46313	0.28876	9.02068	2.60478
10	9.31323	0.10737	33.25290	0.03007	3.57050	0.28007	9.98705	2.79710
11	11.64153	0.08590	42.56613	0.02349	3.65640	0.27349	10.84604	2.96631
12	14.55192	0.06872	54.20766	0.01845	3.72512	0.26845	11.60195	3.11452
13	18.18989	0.05498	68.75958	0.01454	3.78010	0.26454	12.26166	3.24374
14	22.73737	0.04398	86.94947	0.01150	3.82408	0.26150	12.83341	3.35595
15	28.42171	0.03518	109.68684	9.1169E−03	3.85926	0.25912	13.32599	3.45299
16	35.52714	0.02815	138.10855	7.2407E−03	3.88741	0.25724	13.74820	3.53660
17	44.40892	0.02252	173.63568	5.7592E−03	3.90993	0.25576	14.10849	3.60838
18	55.51115	0.01801	218.04460	4.5862E−03	3.92794	0.25459	14.41473	3.66979
19	69.38894	0.01441	273.55576	3.6556E−03	3.94235	0.25366	14.67414	3.72218
20	86.73617	0.01153	342.94470	2.9159E−03	3.95388	0.25292	14.89320	3.76673
21	108.42022	9.2234E−03	429.68087	2.3273E−03	3.96311	0.25233	15.07766	3.80451
22	135.52527	7.3787E−03	538.10109	1.8584E−03	3.97049	0.25186	15.23262	3.83646
23	169.40659	5.9030E−03	673.62636	1.4845E−03	3.97639	0.25148	15.36248	3.86343
24	211.75824	4.7224E−03	843.03295	1.1862E−03	3.98111	0.25119	15.47109	3.88613
25	264.69780	3.7779E−03	1054.79118	9.4805E−04	3.98489	0.25095	15.56176	3.90519
26	330.87225	3.0223E−03	1319.48898	7.5787E−04	3.98791	0.25076	15.63732	3.92118
27	413.59031	2.4179E−03	1650.36123	6.0593E−04	3.99033	0.25061	15.70019	3.93456
28	516.98788	1.9343E−03	2063.95153	4.8451E−04	3.99226	0.25048	15.75241	3.94574
29	646.23485	1.5474E−03	2580.93941	3.8746E−04	3.99381	0.25039	15.79574	3.95506
30	807.79357	1.2379E−03	3227.17427	3.0987E−04	3.99505	0.25031	15.83164	3.96282
36	3081.48791	3.2452E−04	1.2322E+04	8.1156E−05	3.99870	0.25008	15.94808	3.98831
40	7523.16385	1.3292E−04	3.0089E+04	3.3235E−05	3.99947	0.25003	15.97661	3.99468
48	4.4842E+04	2.2301E−05	1.7936E+05	5.5753E−06	3.99991	0.25001	15.99536	3.99893
50	7.0065E+04	1.4272E−05	2.8026E+05	3.5682E−06	3.99994	0.25000	15.99692	3.99929
52	1.0948E+05	9.1344E−06	4.3790E+05	2.2836E−06	3.99996	0.25000	15.99795	3.99953
55	2.1382E+05	4.6768E−06	8.5528E+05	1.1692E−06	3.99998	0.25000	15.99890	3.99974
60	6.5253E+05	1.5325E−06	2.6101E+06	3.8312E−07	3.99999	0.25000	15.99961	3.99991
72	9.4956E+06	1.0531E−07	3.7982E+07	2.6328E−08	4.00000	0.25000	15.99997	3.99999
75	1.8546E+07	5.3920E−08	7.4184E+07	1.3480E−08	4.00000	0.25000	15.99998	4.00000
80	5.6598E+07	1.7668E−08	2.2639E+08	4.4171E−09	4.00000	0.25000	15.99999	4.00000
84	1.3818E+08	7.2370E−09	5.5271E+08	1.8093E−09	4.00000	0.25000	16.00000	4.00000
90	5.2711E+08	1.8971E−09	2.1084E+09	4.7428E−10	4.00000	0.25000	16.00000	4.00000
96	2.0108E+09	4.9732E−10	8.0431E+09	1.2433E−10	4.00000	0.25000	16.00000	4.00000
100	4.9091E+09	2.0370E−10	1.9636E+10	5.0926E−11	4.00000	0.25000	16.00000	4.00000
108	2.9260E+10	3.4176E−11	1.1704E+11	8.5439E−12	4.00000	0.25000	16.00000	4.00000
120	4.2580E+11	2.3485E−12	1.7032E+12	5.8714E−13	4.00000	0.25000	16.00000	4.00000
132	6.1961E+12	1.6139E−13	2.4785E+13	4.0348E−14	4.00000	0.25000	16.00000	4.00000
144	9.0166E+13	1.1091E−14	3.6066E+14	2.7727E−15	4.00000	0.25000	16.00000	4.00000
180	2.7784E+17	3.5991E−18	1.1114E+18	8.9978E−19	4.00000	0.25000	16.00000	4.00000
240	1.8130E+23	5.5157E−24	7.2521E+23	1.3789E−24	4.00000	0.25000	16.00000	4.00000
360	7.7198E+34	1.2954E−35	3.0879E+35	3.2384E−36	4.00000	0.25000	16.00000	4.00000
480	3.2870E+46	3.0422E−47	1.3148E+47	7.6056E−48	4.00000	0.25000	16.00000	4.00000
600	1.3996E+58	7.1448E−59	5.5984E+58	1.7862E−59	4.00000	0.25000	16.00000	4.00000

TABLE A-a-23

	Single Sums		Uniform Series				Gradient Series	
n	To Find F Given P (F|P i%,n)	To Find P Given F (P|F i%,n)	To Find F Given A (F|A i%,n)	To Find A Given F (A|F i%,n)	To Find P Given A (P|A i%,n)	To Find A Given P (A|P i%,n)	To Find P Given G (P|G i%,n)	To Find A Given G (A|G i%,n)
1	1.30000	0.76923	1.00000	1.00000	0.76923	1.30000	0.00000	0.00000
2	1.69000	0.59172	2.30000	0.43478	1.36095	0.73478	0.59172	0.43478
3	2.19700	0.45517	3.99000	0.25063	1.81611	0.55063	1.50205	0.82707
4	2.85610	0.35013	6.18700	0.16163	2.16624	0.46163	2.55243	1.17828
5	3.71293	0.26933	9.04310	0.11058	2.43557	0.41058	3.62975	1.49031
6	4.82681	0.20718	12.75603	0.07839	2.64275	0.37839	4.66563	1.76545
7	6.27485	0.15937	17.58284	0.05687	2.80211	0.35687	5.62183	2.00628
8	8.15731	0.12259	23.85769	0.04192	2.92470	0.34192	6.47995	2.21559
9	10.60450	0.09430	32.01500	0.03124	3.01900	0.33124	7.23435	2.39627
10	13.78585	0.07254	42.61950	0.02346	3.09154	0.32346	7.88719	2.55122
11	17.92160	0.05580	56.40535	0.01773	3.14734	0.31773	8.44518	2.68328
12	23.29809	0.04292	74.32695	0.01345	3.19026	0.31345	8.91732	2.79517
13	30.28751	0.03302	97.62504	0.01024	3.22328	0.31024	9.31352	2.88946
14	39.37376	0.02540	127.91255	7.8178E−03	3.24867	0.30782	9.64369	2.96850
15	51.18589	0.01954	167.28631	5.9778E−03	3.26821	0.30598	9.91721	3.03444
16	66.54166	0.01503	218.47220	4.5772E−03	3.28324	0.30458	10.14263	3.08921
17	86.50416	0.01156	285.01386	3.5086E−03	3.29480	0.30351	10.32759	3.13451
18	112.45541	8.8924E−03	371.51802	2.6917E−03	3.30369	0.30269	10.47876	3.17183
19	146.19203	6.8403E−03	483.97343	2.0662E−03	3.31053	0.30207	10.60189	3.20247
20	190.04964	5.2618E−03	630.16546	1.5869E−03	3.31579	0.30159	10.70186	3.22754
21	247.06453	4.0475E−03	820.21510	1.2192E−03	3.31984	0.30122	10.78281	3.24799
22	321.18389	3.1135E−03	1067.27963	9.3696E−04	3.32296	0.30094	10.84819	3.26462
23	417.53905	2.3950E−03	1388.46351	7.2022E−04	3.32535	0.30072	10.90088	3.27812
24	542.80077	1.8423E−03	1806.00257	5.5371E−04	3.32719	0.30055	10.94326	3.28904
25	705.64100	1.4172E−03	2348.80334	4.2575E−04	3.32861	0.30043	10.97727	3.29785
26	917.33330	1.0901E−03	3054.44434	3.2739E−04	3.32970	0.30033	11.00452	3.30496
27	1192.53329	8.3855E−04	3971.77764	2.5178E−04	3.33054	0.30025	11.02632	3.31067
28	1550.29328	6.4504E−04	5164.31093	1.9364E−04	3.33118	0.30019	11.04374	3.31526
29	2015.38126	4.9618E−04	6714.60421	1.4893E−04	3.33168	0.30015	11.05763	3.31894
30	2619.99564	3.8168E−04	8729.98548	1.1455E−04	3.33206	0.30011	11.06870	3.32188
36	1.2646E+04	7.9075E−05	4.2151E+04	2.3724E−05	3.33307	0.30002	11.10074	3.33049
40	3.6119E+04	2.7686E−05	1.2039E+05	8.3061E−06	3.33324	0.30001	11.10711	3.33223
48	2.9463E+05	3.3941E−06	9.8211E+05	1.0182E−06	3.33332	0.30000	11.11053	3.33317
50	4.9793E+05	2.0083E−06	1.6598E+06	6.0250E−07	3.33333	0.30000	11.11075	3.33323
52	8.4150E+05	1.1884E−06	2.8050E+06	3.5651E−07	3.33333	0.30000	11.11089	3.33327
55	1.8488E+06	5.4090E−07	6.1626E+06	1.6227E−07	3.33333	0.30000	11.11101	3.33330
60	6.8644E+06	1.4568E−07	2.2881E+07	4.3704E−08	3.33333	0.30000	11.11108	3.33332
72	1.5993E+08	6.2529E−09	5.3309E+08	1.8759E−09	3.33333	0.30000	11.11111	3.33333
75	3.5136E+08	2.8461E−09	1.1712E+09	8.5383E−10	3.33333	0.30000	11.11111	3.33333
80	1.3046E+09	7.6653E−10	4.3486E+09	2.2996E−10	3.33333	0.30000	11.11111	3.33333
84	3.7260E+09	2.6839E−10	1.2420E+10	8.0516E−11	3.33333	0.30000	11.11111	3.33333
90	1.7985E+10	5.5603E−11	5.9949E+10	1.6681E−11	3.33333	0.30000	11.11111	3.33333
96	8.6808E+10	1.1520E−11	2.8936E+11	3.4559E−12	3.33333	0.30000	11.11111	3.33333
100	2.4793E+11	4.0333E−12	8.2645E+11	1.2100E−12	3.33333	0.30000	11.11111	3.33333
108	2.0225E+13	4.9444E−13	6.7416E+12	1.4833E−13	3.33333	0.30000	11.11111	3.33333
120	4.7120E+13	2.1223E−14	1.5707E+14	6.3668E−15	3.33333	0.30000	11.11111	3.33333
132	1.0978E+15	9.1091E−16	3.6593E+15	2.7327E−16	3.33333	0.30000	11.11111	3.33333
144	2.5577E+16	3.9098E−17	8.5255E+16	1.1729E−17	3.33333	0.30000	11.11111	3.33333
180	3.2345E+20	3.0917E−21	1.0782E+21	9.2751E−22	3.33333	0.30000	11.11111	3.33333
240	2.2203E+27	4.5040E−28	7.4009E+27	1.3512E−28	3.33333	0.30000	11.11111	3.33333
360	1.0462E+41	9.5586E−42	3.4873E+41	2.8676E−42	3.33333	0.30000	11.11111	3.33333
480	4.9296E+54	2.0286E−55	1.6432E+55	6.0857E−56	3.33333	0.30000	11.11111	3.33333
600	2.3228E+68	4.3052E−69	7.7427E+68	1.2915E−69	3.33333	0.30000	11.11111	3.33333

TABLE A-a-24

	Single Sums		Uniform Series				Gradient Series	
	To Find F Given P	To Find P Given F	To Find F Given A	To Find A Given F	To Find P Given A	To Find A Given P	To Find P Given G	To Find A Given G
n	$(F|P\ i\%,n)$	$(P|F\ i\%,n)$	$(F|A\ i\%,n)$	$(A|F\ i\%,n)$	$(P|A\ i\%,n)$	$(A|P\ i\%,n)$	$(P|G\ i\%,n)$	$(A|G\ i\%,n)$
1	1.40000	0.71429	1.00000	1.00000	0.71429	1.40000	0.00000	0.00000
2	1.96000	0.51020	2.40000	0.41667	1.22449	0.81667	0.51020	0.41667
3	2.74400	0.36443	4.36000	0.22936	1.58892	0.62936	1.23907	0.77982
4	3.84160	0.26031	7.10400	0.14077	1.84923	0.54077	2.01999	1.09234
5	5.37824	0.18593	10.94560	0.09136	2.03516	0.49136	2.76373	1.35799
6	7.52954	0.13281	16.32384	0.06126	2.16797	0.46126	3.42778	1.58110
7	10.54135	0.09486	23.85338	0.04192	2.26284	0.44192	3.99697	1.76635
8	14.75789	0.06776	34.39473	0.02907	2.33060	0.42907	4.47129	1.91852
9	20.66105	0.04840	49.15262	0.02034	2.37900	0.42034	4.85849	2.04224
10	28.92547	0.03457	69.81366	0.01432	2.41357	0.41432	5.16964	2.14190
11	40.49565	0.02469	98.73913	0.01013	2.43826	0.41013	5.41658	2.22149
12	56.69391	0.01764	139.23478	7.1821E–03	2.45590	0.40718	5.61060	2.28454
13	79.37148	0.01260	195.92869	5.1039E–03	2.46850	0.40510	5.76179	2.33412
14	111.12007	8.9993E–03	275.30017	3.6324E–03	2.47750	0.40363	5.87878	2.37287
15	155.56810	6.4281E–03	386.42024	2.5879E–03	2.48393	0.40259	5.96877	2.40296
16	217.79533	4.5915E–03	541.98833	1.8451E–03	2.48852	0.40185	6.03764	2.42620
17	304.91347	3.2796E–03	759.78367	1.3162E–03	2.49180	0.40132	6.09012	2.44406
18	426.87885	2.3426E–03	1064.69714	9.3923E–04	2.49414	0.40094	6.12994	2.45773
19	597.63040	1.6733E–03	1491.57599	6.7043E–04	2.49582	0.40067	6.16006	2.46815
20	836.68255	1.1952E–03	2089.20639	4.7865E–04	2.49701	0.40048	6.18277	2.47607
21	1171.35558	8.5371E–04	2925.88894	3.4178E–04	2.49787	0.40034	6.19984	2.48206
22	1639.89781	6.0979E–04	4097.24452	2.4407E–04	2.49848	0.40024	6.21265	2.48658
23	2295.85693	4.3557E–04	5737.14232	1.7430E–04	2.49891	0.40017	6.22223	2.48998
24	3214.19970	3.1112E–04	8032.99925	1.2449E–04	2.49922	0.40012	6.22939	2.49253
25	4499.87958	2.2223E–04	1.1247E+04	8.8911E–05	2.49944	0.40009	6.23472	2.49444
26	6299.83141	1.5873E–04	1.5747E+04	6.3504E–05	2.49960	0.40006	6.23869	2.49587
27	8819.76398	1.1338E–04	2.2047E+04	4.5358E–05	2.49972	0.40005	6.24164	2.49694
28	1.2348E+04	8.0987E–05	3.0867E+04	3.2397E–05	2.49980	0.40003	6.24382	2.49773
29	1.7287E+04	5.7848E–05	4.3214E+04	2.3140E–05	2.49986	0.40002	6.24544	2.49832
30	2.4201E+04	4.1320E–05	6.0501E+04	1.6529E–05	2.49990	0.40002	6.24664	2.49876
36	1.8223E+05	5.4877E–06	4.5556E+05	2.1951E–06	2.49999	0.40000	6.24947	2.49980
40	7.0004E+05	1.4285E–06	1.7501E+06	5.7140E–07	2.50000	0.40000	6.24985	2.49994
48	1.0331E+07	9.6795E–08	2.5828E+07	3.8718E–08	2.50000	0.40000	6.24999	2.50000
50	2.0249E+07	4.9385E–08	5.0622E+07	1.9754E–08	2.50000	0.40000	6.24999	2.50000
52	3.9688E+07	2.5197E–08	9.9220E+07	1.0079E–08	2.50000	0.40000	6.25000	2.50000
55	1.0890E+08	9.1824E–09	2.7226E+08	3.6730E–09	2.50000	0.40000	6.25000	2.50000
60	5.8571E+08	1.7073E–09	1.4643E+09	6.8293E–10	2.50000	0.40000	6.25000	2.50000
72	3.3206E+10	3.0115E–11	8.3015E+10	1.2046E–11	2.50000	0.40000	6.25000	2.50000
75	9.1118E+10	1.0975E–11	2.2779E+11	4.3899E–12	2.50000	0.40000	6.25000	2.50000
80	4.9005E+11	2.0406E–12	1.2251E+12	8.1624E–13	2.50000	0.40000	6.25000	2.50000
84	1.8826E+12	5.3118E–13	4.7065E+12	2.1247E–13	2.50000	0.40000	6.25000	2.50000
90	1.4175E+13	7.0547E–14	3.5438E+13	2.8219E–14	2.50000	0.40000	6.25000	2.50000
96	1.0673E+14	9.3693E–15	2.6683E+14	3.7477E–15	2.50000	0.40000	6.25000	2.50000
100	4.1002E+14	2.4389E–15	1.0250E+15	9.7557E–16	2.50000	0.40000	6.25000	2.50000
108	6.0510E+15	1.6526E–16	1.5128E+16	6.6105E–17	2.50000	0.40000	6.25000	2.50000
120	3.4306E+17	2.9150E–18	8.5764E+17	1.1660E–18	2.50000	0.40000	6.25000	2.50000
132	1.9449E+19	5.1416E–20	4.8623E+19	2.0566E–20	2.50000	0.40000	6.25000	2.50000
144	1.1026E+21	9.0691E–22	2.7566E+21	3.6276E–22	2.50000	0.40000	6.25000	2.50000
180	2.0093E+26	4.9768E–27	5.0233E+26	1.9907E–27	2.50000	0.40000	6.25000	2.50000
240	1.1769E+35	8.4971E–36	2.9422E+35	3.3988E–36	2.50000	0.40000	6.25000	2.50000
360	4.0373E+52	2.4769E–53	1.0093E+53	9.9076E–54	2.50000	0.40000	6.25000	2.50000
480	1.3850E+70	7.2201E–71	3.4626E+70	2.8880E–71	2.50000	0.40000	6.25000	2.50000
600	4.7514E+87	2.1046E–88	1.1878E+88	8.4186E–89	2.50000	0.40000	6.25000	2.50000

TABLE A-a-25

| | Single Sums | | Uniform Series | | | | Gradient Series | |
	To Find F Given P (F|P i%,n)	To Find P Given F (P|F i%,n)	To Find F Given A (F|A i%,n)	To Find A Given F (A|F i%,n)	To Find P Given A (P|A i%,n)	To Find A Given P (A|P i%,n)	To Find P Given G (P|G i%,n)	To Find A Given G (A|G i%,n)
1	1.50000	0.66667	1.00000	1.00000	0.66667	1.50000	0.00000	0.00000
2	2.25000	0.44444	2.50000	0.40000	1.11111	0.90000	0.44444	0.40000
3	3.37500	0.29630	4.75000	0.21053	1.40741	0.71053	1.03704	0.73684
4	5.06250	0.19753	8.12500	0.12308	1.60494	0.62308	1.62963	1.01538
5	7.59375	0.13169	13.18750	0.07583	1.73663	0.57583	2.15638	1.24171
6	11.39063	0.08779	20.78125	0.04812	1.82442	0.54812	2.59534	1.42256
7	17.08594	0.05853	32.17188	0.03108	1.88294	0.53108	2.94650	1.56484
8	25.62891	0.03902	49.25781	0.02030	1.92196	0.52030	3.21963	1.67518
9	38.44336	0.02601	74.88672	0.01335	1.94798	0.51335	3.42773	1.75964
10	57.66504	0.01734	113.33008	8.8238E−03	1.96532	0.50882	3.58380	1.82352
11	86.49756	0.01156	170.99512	5.8481E−03	1.97688	0.50585	3.69941	1.87134
12	129.74634	7.7073E−03	257.49268	3.8836E−03	1.98459	0.50388	3.78419	1.90679
13	194.61951	5.1382E−03	387.23901	2.5824E−03	1.98972	0.50258	3.84585	1.93286
14	291.92926	3.4255E−03	581.85852	1.7186E−03	1.99315	0.50172	3.89038	1.95188
15	437.89389	2.2837E−03	873.78778	1.1444E−03	1.99543	0.50114	3.92236	1.96567
16	656.84084	1.5224E−03	1311.68167	7.6238E−04	1.99696	0.50076	3.94519	1.97560
17	985.26125	1.0150E−03	1968.52251	5.0800E−04	1.99797	0.50051	3.96143	1.98273
18	1477.89188	6.7664E−04	2953.78376	3.3855E−04	1.99865	0.50034	3.97293	1.98781
19	2216.83782	4.5109E−04	4431.67564	2.2565E−04	1.99910	0.50023	3.98105	1.99143
20	3325.25673	3.0073E−04	6648.51346	1.5041E−04	1.99940	0.50015	3.98677	1.99398
21	4987.88510	2.0049E−04	9973.77019	1.0026E−04	1.99960	0.50010	3.99078	1.99579
22	7481.82764	1.3366E−04	1.4962E+04	6.6838E−05	1.99973	0.50007	3.99358	1.99706
23	1.1223E+04	8.9105E−05	2.2443E+04	4.4556E−05	1.99982	0.50004	3.99554	1.99795
24	1.6834E+04	5.9403E−05	3.3666E+04	2.9703E−05	1.99988	0.50003	3.99691	1.99857
25	2.5251E+04	3.9602E−05	5.0500E+04	1.9802E−05	1.99992	0.50002	3.99786	1.99901
26	3.7877E+04	2.6401E−05	7.5752E+04	1.3201E−05	1.99995	0.50001	3.99852	1.99931
27	5.6815E+04	1.7601E−05	1.1363E+05	8.8006E−06	1.99996	0.50001	3.99898	1.99952
28	8.5223E+04	1.1734E−05	1.7044E+05	5.8671E−06	1.99998	0.50001	3.99930	1.99967
29	1.2783E+05	7.8226E−06	2.5567E+05	3.9114E−06	1.99998	0.50000	3.99951	1.99977
30	1.9175E+05	5.2151E−06	3.8350E+05	2.6076E−06	1.99999	0.50000	3.99967	1.99984
36	2.1842E+06	4.5784E−07	4.3683E+06	2.2892E−07	2.00000	0.50000	3.99997	1.99998
40	1.1057E+07	9.0438E−08	2.2115E+07	4.5219E−08	2.00000	0.50000	3.99999	2.00000
48	2.8339E+08	3.5287E−09	5.6677E+08	1.7644E−09	2.00000	0.50000	4.00000	2.00000
50	6.3762E+08	1.5683E−09	1.2752E+09	7.8416E−10	2.00000	0.50000	4.00000	2.00000
52	1.4346E+09	6.9703E−10	2.8693E+09	3.4852E−10	2.00000	0.50000	4.00000	2.00000
55	4.8419E+09	2.0653E−10	9.6839E+09	1.0326E−10	2.00000	0.50000	4.00000	2.00000
60	3.6768E+10	2.7197E−11	7.3537E+10	1.3599E−11	2.00000	0.50000	4.00000	2.00000
72	4.7706E+12	2.0962E−13	9.5411E+12	1.0481E−13	2.00000	0.50000	4.00000	2.00000
75	1.6101E+13	6.2109E−14	3.2201E+13	3.1055E−14	2.00000	0.50000	4.00000	2.00000
80	1.2226E+14	8.1790E−15	2.4453E+14	4.0895E−15	2.00000	0.50000	4.00000	2.00000
84	6.1896E+14	1.6156E−15	1.2379E+15	8.0780E−16	2.00000	0.50000	4.00000	2.00000
90	7.0504E+15	1.4184E−16	1.4101E+16	7.0918E−17	2.00000	0.50000	4.00000	2.00000
96	8.0308E+16	1.2452E−17	1.6062E+17	6.2260E−18	2.00000	0.50000	4.00000	2.00000
100	4.0656E+17	2.4597E−18	8.1312E+17	1.2298E−18	2.00000	0.50000	4.00000	2.00000
108	1.0420E+19	9.5972E−20	2.0839E+19	4.7986E−20	2.00000	0.50000	4.00000	2.00000
120	1.3519E+21	7.3969E−22	2.7038E+21	3.6984E−22	2.00000	0.50000	4.00000	2.00000
132	1.7541E+23	5.7010E−24	3.5081E+23	2.8505E−24	2.00000	0.50000	4.00000	2.00000
144	2.2758E+25	4.3940E−26	4.5517E+25	2.1970E−26	2.00000	0.50000	4.00000	2.00000
180	4.9708E+31	2.0117E−32	9.9416E+31	1.0059E−32	2.00000	0.50000	4.00000	2.00000
240	1.8277E+42	5.4714E−43	3.6554E+42	2.7357E−43	2.00000	0.50000	4.00000	2.00000
360	2.4709E+63	4.0471E−64	4.9418E+63	2.0236E−64	2.00000	0.50000	4.00000	2.00000
480	3.3404E+84	2.9936E−85	6.6809E+84	1.4968E−85	2.00000	0.50000	4.00000	2.00000
600	4.5160E+105	2.2143E−106	9.0320E+105	1.1072E−106	2.00000	0.50000	4.00000	2.00000

TABLE A-b-1

j	4%	5%	6%	10%	15%
n	To Find P Given A_1 $(P|A_1\ i\%, j\%, n)$	To Find P Given A_1 $(P|A_1\ i\%, j\%, n)$	To Find P Given A_1 $(P|A_1\ i\%, j\%, n)$	To Find P Given A_1 $(P|A_1\ i\%, j\%, n)$	To Find P Given A_1 $(P|A_1\ i\%, j\%, n)$
1	0.96154	0.96154	0.96154	0.96154	0.96154
2	1.92308	1.93232	1.94157	1.97855	2.02478
3	2.88462	2.91244	2.94044	3.05424	3.20048
4	3.84615	3.90198	3.95853	4.19198	4.50053
5	4.80769	4.90104	4.99619	5.39536	5.93808
6	5.76923	5.90971	6.05381	6.66817	7.52769
7	6.73077	6.92807	7.13177	8.01441	9.28542
8	7.69231	7.95622	8.23046	9.43832	11.22907
9	8.65385	8.99426	9.35028	10.94438	13.37830
10	9.61538	10.04228	10.49163	12.53732	15.75485
11	10.57692	11.10038	11.65493	14.22217	18.38277
12	11.53846	12.16866	12.84060	16.00422	21.28864
13	12.50000	13.24720	14.04907	17.88908	24.50186
14	13.46154	14.33612	15.28078	19.88268	28.05494
15	14.42308	15.43550	16.53618	21.99129	31.98383
16	15.38462	16.54546	17.81573	24.22156	36.32828
17	16.34615	17.66609	19.11988	26.58050	41.13223
18	17.30769	18.79749	20.44910	29.07553	46.44429
19	18.26923	19.93978	21.80389	31.71450	52.31821
20	19.23077	21.09304	23.18474	34.50572	58.81340
21	20.19231	22.25740	24.59214	37.45797	65.99559
22	21.15385	23.43295	26.02660	40.58055	73.93743
23	22.11538	24.61981	27.48865	43.88327	82.71927
24	23.07692	25.81807	28.97882	47.37654	92.42996
25	24.03846	27.02786	30.49764	51.07134	103.16775
26	25.00000	28.24929	32.04567	54.97930	115.04126
27	25.96154	29.48245	33.62347	59.11272	128.17062
28	26.92308	30.72748	35.23162	63.48461	142.68867
29	27.88462	31.98447	36.87069	68.10872	158.74228
30	28.84615	33.25355	38.54128	72.99961	176.49387
36	34.61538	41.12844	49.26152	108.87422	330.16651
40	38.46154	46.63525	57.12012	140.45012	498.11856
48	46.15385	58.30188	74.75307	229.42525	1124.62271
50	48.07692	61.36078	79.59740	258.63957	1377.12975
52	50.00000	64.47879	84.62985	291.32200	1685.87657
55	52.88462	69.26914	92.54728	347.76220	2282.59383
60	57.69231	77.56509	106.79116	465.73578	3779.49708
72	69.23077	99.17238	147.05700	928.96423	1.2651E+04
75	72.11538	104.97315	158.64571	1102.25501	1.7109E+04
80	76.92308	115.01897	179.49439	1464.47438	2.8290E+04
84	80.76923	123.40898	197.66360	1837.00923	4.2299E+04
90	86.53846	136.61179	227.64978	2578.64714	7.7332E+04
96	92.30769	150.59485	261.26658	3617.00726	1.4137E+05
100	96.15385	160.37302	285.90974	4530.94462	2.1137E+05
108	103.84615	181.08887	341.20357	7106.25392	4.7246E+05
120	115.38462	215.29361	441.66933	1.3946E+04	1.5789E+06
132	126.92308	253.66061	567.93591	2.7354E+04	5.2762E+06
144	138.46154	296.69635	726.62925	5.3636E+04	1.7632E+07
180	173.07692	459.85139	1491.78806	4.0412E+05	6.5799E+08
240	230.76923	894.10062	4784.77465	1.1697E+07	2.7421E+11
360	346.15385	3034.33576	4.7492E+04	9.7997E+09	4.7624E+16
480	461.53846	9782.36045	4.6745E+05	8.2098E+12	8.2712E+21
600	576.92308	3.1058E+04	4.5971E+06	6.8779E+15	1.4365E+27

TABLE A-b-2

j	4%	5%	6%	10%	15%
	To Find P Given A_1 $(P|A_1\ i\%,j\%,n)$	To Find P Given A_1 $(P|A_1\ i\%,j\%,n)$	To Find P Given A_1 $(P|A_1\ i\%,j\%,n)$	To Find P Given A_1 $(P|A_1\ i\%,j\%,n)$	To Find P Given A_1 $(P|A_1\ i\%,j\%,n)$
n					
1	0.95238	0.95238	0.95238	0.95238	0.95238
2	1.89569	1.90476	1.91383	1.95011	1.99546
3	2.83002	2.85714	2.88444	2.99536	3.13789
4	3.75545	3.80952	3.86429	4.09037	4.38912
5	4.67206	4.76190	4.85348	5.23753	5.75951
6	5.57995	5.71429	5.85208	6.43932	7.26042
7	6.47919	6.66667	6.86020	7.69834	8.90426
8	7.36986	7.61905	7.87791	9.01731	10.70467
9	8.25205	8.57143	8.90532	10.39908	12.67654
10	9.12584	9.52381	9.94251	11.84666	14.83622
11	9.99131	10.47619	10.98959	13.36316	17.20157
12	10.84854	11.42857	12.04663	14.95189	19.79219
13	11.69760	12.38095	13.11374	16.61626	22.62955
14	12.53857	13.33333	14.19101	18.35989	25.73712
15	13.37154	14.28571	15.27855	20.18656	29.14066
16	14.19657	15.23810	16.37644	22.10020	32.86834
17	15.01375	16.19048	17.48478	24.10497	36.95104
18	15.82314	17.14286	18.60369	26.20521	41.42257
19	16.62482	18.09524	19.73325	28.40546	46.31995
20	17.41887	19.04762	20.87356	30.71048	51.68376
21	18.20536	20.00000	22.02474	33.12526	57.55840
22	18.98436	20.95238	23.18688	35.65504	63.99254
23	19.75593	21.90476	24.36009	38.30528	71.03944
24	20.52016	22.85714	25.54447	41.08172	78.75749
25	21.27711	23.80952	26.74013	43.99037	87.21058
26	22.02686	24.76190	27.94718	47.03753	96.46873
27	22.76946	25.71429	29.16573	50.22980	106.60861
28	23.50499	26.66667	30.39588	53.57407	117.71419
29	24.23351	27.61905	31.63774	57.07760	129.87745
30	24.95510	28.57143	32.89143	60.74796	143.19911
36	29.14256	34.28571	40.66835	86.74607	254.42803
40	31.80357	38.09524	46.10418	108.57764	370.48860
48	36.82956	45.71429	57.61414	166.54883	777.78913
50	38.02707	47.61905	60.63061	184.73840	934.98968
52	39.20189	49.52381	63.70481	204.70155	1123.55905
55	40.92249	52.38095	68.42678	238.35462	1479.25741
60	43.68262	57.14286	76.60133	306.01168	2336.99669
72	49.79223	68.57143	97.87584	549.73617	6982.21820
75	51.21312	71.42857	103.58345	635.06433	9176.29941
80	53.49248	76.19048	113.46432	806.61043	1.4467E+04
84	55.23904	80.00000	121.71321	975.66772	2.0821E+04
90	57.73668	85.71429	134.68804	1296.23897	3.5946E+04
96	60.09495	91.42857	148.42217	1720.02329	6.2051E+04
100	61.59356	95.23810	158.02193	2075.89057	8.9291E+04
108	64.42406	102.85714	178.34867	3020.85487	1.8488E+05
120	68.28353	114.28571	211.88030	5294.18080	5.5083E+05
132	71.72430	125.71429	249.45136	9267.03237	1.6411E+06
144	74.79180	137.14286	291.54847	1.6210E+04	4.8891E+06
180	82.13812	171.42857	450.78476	8.6604E+04	1.2928E+08
240	89.94066	228.57143	872.69322	1.4120E+06	3.0342E+10
360	96.80953	342.85714	2933.63852	3.7519E+08	1.6714E+15
480	98.98810	457.14286	9361.32092	9.9691E+10	9.2066E+19
600	99.67906	571.42857	2.9408E+04	2.6489E+13	5.0714E+24

TABLE A-b-3

n	j 4% To Find P Given A_1 $(P\|A_1\ i\%,j\%,n)$	5% To Find P Given A_1 $(P\|A_1\ i\%,j\%,n)$	6% To Find P Given A_1 $(P\|A_1\ i\%,j\%,n)$	10% To Find P Given A_1 $(P\|A_1\ i\%,j\%,n)$	15% To Find P Given A_1 $(P\|A_1\ i\%,j\%,n)$
1	0.94340	0.94340	0.94340	0.94340	0.94340
2	1.86899	1.87789	1.88679	1.92239	1.96689
3	2.77712	2.80357	2.83019	2.93833	3.07729
4	3.66812	3.72052	3.77358	3.99261	4.28196
5	4.54231	4.62882	4.71698	5.08667	5.58892
6	5.40000	5.52855	5.66038	6.22201	7.00685
7	6.24151	6.41979	6.60377	7.40020	8.54517
8	7.06714	7.30262	7.54717	8.62285	10.21410
9	7.87720	8.17712	8.49057	9.89164	12.02473
10	8.67197	9.04337	9.43396	11.20831	13.98909
11	9.45174	9.90146	10.37736	12.57466	16.12024
12	10.21680	10.75144	11.32075	13.99257	18.43234
13	10.96743	11.59341	12.26415	15.46399	20.94074
14	11.70389	12.42743	13.20755	16.99093	23.66213
15	12.42646	13.25359	14.15094	18.57549	26.61457
16	13.13539	14.07195	15.09434	20.21985	29.81770
17	13.83095	14.88259	16.03774	21.92626	33.29278
18	14.51339	15.68559	16.98113	23.69706	37.06293
19	15.18295	16.48101	17.92453	25.53469	41.15317
20	15.83987	17.26892	18.86792	27.44166	45.59071
21	16.48440	18.04941	19.81132	29.42059	50.40501
22	17.11677	18.82252	20.75472	31.47419	55.62808
23	17.73721	19.58835	21.69811	33.60530	61.29462
24	18.34594	20.34695	22.64151	35.81682	67.44227
25	18.94319	21.09839	23.58491	38.11179	74.11190
26	19.52917	21.84275	24.52830	40.49337	81.34781
27	20.10409	22.58008	25.47170	42.96482	89.19810
28	20.66816	23.31046	26.41509	45.52953	97.71492
29	21.22159	24.03394	27.35849	48.19102	106.95487
30	21.76458	24.75060	28.30189	50.95294	116.97934
36	24.81401	28.91080	33.96226	69.85616	197.75529
40	26.66171	31.55569	37.73585	85.00510	278.24756
48	29.96041	36.55392	45.28302	122.94741	544.24595
50	30.70949	37.74537	47.16981	134.32393	642.55541
52	31.43057	38.91444	49.05660	146.57525	758.26765
55	32.46196	40.62702	51.88679	166.74105	971.35170
60	34.05522	43.37529	56.60377	205.75398	1465.53354
72	37.31332	49.46326	67.92453	334.90762	3915.15469
75	38.01797	50.88009	70.75472	377.20874	5002.55747
80	39.10649	53.15376	75.47170	459.04485	7524.44829
84	39.90566	54.89669	79.24528	536.34890	1.0428E+04
90	40.99585	57.39024	84.90566	676.05776	1.7012E+04
96	41.96830	59.74594	90.56604	850.53743	2.7747E+04
100	42.55752	61.24360	94.33962	990.36455	3.8444E+04
108	43.60947	64.07384	101.88679	1340.57814	7.3795E+04
120	44.91528	67.93642	113.20755	2104.89599	1.9623E+05
132	45.95427	71.38371	124.52830	3297.00464	5.2178E+05
144	46.78096	74.46038	135.84906	5156.33978	1.3874E+06
180	48.37851	81.84409	169.81132	1.9634E+04	2.6080E+07
240	49.48291	89.71927	226.41509	1.8143E+05	3.4660E+09
360	49.94742	96.70363	339.62264	1.5459E+07	6.1217E+13
480	49.99465	98.94307	452.83019	1.3171E+09	1.0812E+18
600	49.99946	99.66111	566.03774	1.1221E+11	1.9096E+22

TABLE A-b-4

j	4%	5%	6%	10%	15%
n	To Find P Given A_1 $(P\|A_1\ i\%,j\%,n)$	To Find P Given A_1 $(P\|A_1\ i\%,j\%,n)$	To Find P Given A_1 $(P\|A_1\ i\%,j\%,n)$	To Find P Given A_1 $(P\|A_1\ i\%,j\%,n)$	To Find P Given A_1 $(P\|A_1\ i\%,j\%,n)$
1	0.90909	0.90909	0.90909	0.90909	0.90909
2	1.76860	1.77686	1.78512	1.81818	1.85950
3	2.58122	2.60518	2.62930	2.72727	2.85312
4	3.34951	3.39586	3.44278	3.63636	3.89190
5	4.07590	4.15059	4.22668	4.54545	4.97789
6	4.76267	4.87102	4.98207	5.45455	6.11325
7	5.41198	5.55870	5.71000	6.36364	7.30022
8	6.02587	6.21512	6.41145	7.27273	8.54113
9	6.60628	6.84171	7.08740	8.18182	9.83846
10	7.15503	7.43981	7.73877	9.09091	11.19475
11	7.67385	8.01073	8.36645	10.00000	12.61270
12	8.16436	8.55570	8.97130	10.90909	14.09509
13	8.62813	9.07589	9.55417	11.81818	15.64487
14	9.06659	9.57244	10.11583	12.72727	17.26509
15	9.48114	10.04642	10.65708	13.63636	18.95896
16	9.87308	10.49886	11.17864	14.54545	20.72982
17	10.24364	10.93073	11.68123	15.45455	22.58117
18	10.59398	11.34297	12.16555	16.36364	24.51668
19	10.92522	11.73647	12.63226	17.27273	26.54017
20	11.23839	12.11208	13.08199	18.18182	28.65563
21	11.53448	12.47063	13.51538	19.09091	30.86725
22	11.81442	12.81287	13.93300	20.00000	33.17940
23	12.07909	13.13956	14.33543	20.90909	35.59664
24	12.32932	13.45140	14.72324	21.81818	38.12376
25	12.56590	13.74906	15.09694	22.72727	40.76575
26	12.78958	14.03319	15.45705	23.63636	43.52783
27	13.00106	14.30441	15.80407	24.54545	46.41546
28	13.20100	14.56330	16.13846	25.45455	49.43434
29	13.39003	14.81042	16.46070	26.36364	52.59045
30	13.56876	15.04631	16.77122	27.27273	55.89002
36	14.45402	16.25279	18.41108	32.72727	79.08675
40	14.89870	16.88904	19.31845	36.36364	98.36852
48	15.53791	17.85579	20.77553	43.63636	148.91859
50	15.65769	18.04629	21.07717	45.45455	164.62383
52	15.76476	18.21986	21.35728	47.27273	181.78927
55	15.90444	18.45174	21.74040	50.00000	210.57570
60	16.09085	18.77305	22.29149	54.54545	267.96474
72	16.37292	19.29792	23.26344	65.45455	470.90920
75	16.41841	19.38937	23.44608	68.18182	540.94029
80	16.47912	19.51610	23.70880	72.72727	680.55528
84	16.51681	19.59826	23.88661	76.36364	816.87970
90	16.55964	19.69610	24.10849	81.81818	1072.68244
96	16.59022	19.77012	24.28615	87.27273	1406.67449
100	16.60558	19.80915	24.38446	90.90909	1684.29792
108	16.62767	19.86846	24.54232	98.18182	2412.12984
120	16.64677	19.92473	24.70656	109.09091	4126.18446
132	16.65652	19.95693	24.81186	120.00000	7048.22688
144	16.66149	19.97535	24.87937	130.90909	1.2030E+04
180	16.66598	19.99538	24.96821	163.63636	5.9678E+04
240	16.66664	19.99972	24.99656	218.18182	8.5952E+05
360	16.66667	20.00000	24.99996	327.27273	1.7819E+08
480	16.66667	20.00000	25.00000	436.36364	3.6941E+10
600	16.66667	20.00000	25.00000	545.45455	7.6581E+12

15.00%   Time Value of Money Factors Geometric Series - Present Worth   15.00%

TABLE A-b-5

j	4%	5%	6%	10%	15%
	To Find P Given A_1	To Find P Given A_1	To Find P Given A_1	To Find P Given A_1	To Find P Given A_1
n	$(P\|A_1\ i\%,j\%,n)$	$(P\|A_1\ i\%,j\%,n)$	$(P\|A_1\ i\%,j\%,n)$	$(P\|A_1\ i\%,j\%,n)$	$(P\|A_1\ i\%,j\%,n)$
1	0.86957	0.86957	0.86957	0.86957	0.86957
2	1.65595	1.66352	1.67108	1.70132	1.73913
3	2.36712	2.38843	2.40986	2.49692	2.60870
4	3.01027	3.05030	3.09083	3.25792	3.47826
5	3.59190	3.65462	3.71850	3.98584	4.34783
6	4.11789	4.20640	4.29706	4.68211	5.21739
7	4.59357	4.71019	4.83033	5.34810	6.08696
8	5.02375	5.17017	5.32187	5.98514	6.95652
9	5.41278	5.59016	5.77494	6.59448	7.82609
10	5.76460	5.97362	6.19255	7.17733	8.69565
11	6.08277	6.32374	6.57748	7.73484	9.56522
12	6.37051	6.64342	6.93229	8.26811	10.43478
13	6.63072	6.93529	7.25933	8.77819	11.30435
14	6.86604	7.20179	7.56077	9.26609	12.17391
15	7.07885	7.44511	7.83862	9.73278	13.04348
16	7.27131	7.66728	8.09473	10.17919	13.91304
17	7.44536	7.87012	8.33080	10.60618	14.78261
18	7.60276	8.05533	8.54839	11.01460	15.65217
19	7.74511	8.22443	8.74895	11.40527	16.52174
20	7.87383	8.37883	8.93381	11.77896	17.39130
21	7.99025	8.51980	9.10421	12.13639	18.26087
22	8.09553	8.64851	9.26127	12.47829	19.13043
23	8.19074	8.76603	9.40604	12.80532	20.00000
24	8.27684	8.87333	9.53948	13.11813	20.86957
25	8.35471	8.97131	9.66248	13.41734	21.73913
26	8.42513	9.06076	9.77585	13.70355	22.60870
27	8.48881	9.14243	9.88035	13.97731	23.47826
28	8.54640	9.21700	9.97667	14.23916	24.34783
29	8.59849	9.28509	10.06545	14.48963	25.21739
30	8.64559	9.34725	10.14729	14.72921	26.08696
36	8.84730	9.62183	10.52003	15.96313	31.30435
40	8.92797	9.73718	10.68445	16.62072	34.78261
48	9.01801	9.87306	10.88881	17.63200	41.73913
50	9.03129	9.89418	10.92224	17.83343	43.47826
52	9.04215	9.91178	10.95065	18.01773	45.21739
55	9.05485	9.93285	10.98545	18.26521	47.82609
60	9.06909	9.95739	11.02750	18.61094	52.17391
72	9.08438	9.98570	11.07967	19.18519	62.60870
75	9.08608	9.98911	11.08649	19.28691	65.21739
80	9.08799	9.99309	11.09473	19.42902	69.56522
84	9.08896	9.99520	11.09929	19.52203	73.04348
90	9.08984	9.99722	11.10386	19.63393	78.26087
96	9.09032	9.99839	11.10666	19.71963	83.47826
100	9.09052	9.99888	11.10790	19.76530	86.95652
108	9.09073	9.99946	11.10944	19.83554	93.91304
120	9.09086	9.99982	11.11048	19.90353	104.34783
132	9.09089	9.99994	11.11087	19.94341	114.78261
144	9.09090	9.99998	11.11102	19.96680	125.21739
180	9.09091	10.00000	11.11111	19.99330	156.52174
240	9.09091	10.00000	11.11111	19.99953	208.69565
360	9.09091	10.00000	11.11111	20.00000	313.04348
480	9.09091	10.00000	11.11111	20.00000	417.39130
600	9.09091	10.00000	11.11111	20.00000	521.73913

TABLE A-c-1

j	4%	5%	6%	10%	15%
	To Find F Given A_1 $(F|A_1\ i\%,j\%,n)$	To Find F Given A_1 $(F|A_1\ i\%,j\%,n)$	To Find F Given A_1 $(F|A_1\ i\%,j\%,n)$	To Find F Given A_1 $(F|A_1\ i\%,j\%,n)$	To Find F Given A_1 $(F|A_1\ i\%,j\%,n)$
n					
1	1.00000	1.00000	1.00000	1.00000	1.00000
2	2.08000	2.09000	2.10000	2.14000	2.19000
3	3.24480	3.27610	3.30760	3.43560	3.60010
4	4.49946	4.56477	4.63092	4.90402	5.26498
5	5.84929	5.96287	6.07863	6.56428	7.22458
6	7.29992	7.47766	7.66000	8.43737	9.52492
7	8.85723	9.11686	9.38492	10.54642	12.21898
8	10.52745	10.88864	11.26395	12.91700	15.36776
9	12.31712	12.80164	13.30836	15.57726	19.04150
10	14.23312	14.86503	15.53017	18.55830	23.32103
11	16.28269	17.08853	17.94223	21.89438	28.29943
12	18.47345	19.48241	20.55821	25.62327	34.08380
13	20.81342	22.05756	23.39274	29.78663	40.79740
14	23.31103	24.82552	26.46138	34.43036	48.58208
15	25.97515	27.79847	29.78073	39.60508	57.60107
16	28.81510	30.98933	33.36852	45.36653	68.04218
17	31.84068	34.41178	37.24361	51.77616	80.12149
18	35.06221	38.08027	41.42613	58.90168	94.08761
19	38.49051	42.01010	45.93752	66.81766	110.22657
20	42.13698	46.21746	50.80062	75.60628	128.86740
21	46.01359	50.71945	56.03978	85.35803	150.38864
22	50.13290	55.53419	61.68093	96.17260	175.22570
23	54.50813	60.68082	67.75171	108.15978	203.87947
24	59.15317	66.17958	74.28152	121.44048	236.92611
25	64.08260	72.05186	81.30172	136.14783	275.02833
26	69.31174	78.32029	88.84566	152.42845	318.94842
27	74.85668	85.00877	96.94887	170.44376	369.56315
28	80.73432	92.14258	105.64917	190.37150	427.88099
29	86.96240	99.74841	114.98682	212.40736	495.06184
30	93.55954	107.85449	125.00468	236.76675	572.43977
36	142.05920	168.78836	202.16597	446.81247	1354.98109
40	184.65464	223.89681	274.23487	674.30392	2391.47751
48	303.25515	383.07414	491.16717	1507.44509	7389.36531
50	341.66747	436.07164	565.67355	1838.06949	9786.82507
52	384.32944	495.62196	650.51483	2239.27239	1.2959E+04
55	457.25979	598.92640	800.19773	3006.87959	1.9736E+04
60	606.90158	815.95585	1123.40317	4899.36687	3.9759E+04
72	1166.00278	1670.28717	2476.77264	1.5646E+04	2.1308E+05
75	1366.24433	1988.74313	3005.58331	2.0883E+04	3.2413E+05
80	1773.06147	2651.16420	4137.30972	3.3756E+04	6.5207E+05
84	2177.94269	3327.72366	5329.99997	4.9535E+04	1.1406E+06
90	2952.63462	4661.10317	7767.25889	8.7982E+04	2.6385E+06
96	3985.09305	6501.45689	1.1279E+04	1.5615E+05	6.1034E+06
100	4856.24502	8099.63097	1.4440E+04	2.2884E+05	1.0675E+07
108	7177.79516	1.2517E+04	2.3584E+04	4.9118E+05	3.2656E+07
120	1.2769E+04	2.3825E+04	4.8876E+04	1.5433E+06	1.7472E+08
132	2.2488E+04	4.4942E+04	1.0062E+05	4.8464E+06	9.3481E+08
144	3.9276E+04	8.4161E+04	2.0612E+05	1.5215E+07	5.0015E+09
180	2.0148E+05	5.3533E+05	1.7366E+06	4.7045E+08	7.6598E+11
240	2.8260E+06	1.0949E+07	5.8595E+07	1.4325E+11	3.3581E+15
360	4.6911E+08	4.1121E+09	6.4361E+10	1.3281E+16	6.4540E+22
480	6.9217E+10	1.4671E+12	7.0103E+13	1.2312E+21	1.2404E+30
600	9.5746E+12	5.1545E+14	7.6293E+16	1.1415E+26	2.3840E+37

TABLE A-c-2

j	4%	5%	6%	10%	15%
n	To Find F Given A_1 $(F\|A_1\ i\%,j\%,n)$	To Find F Given A_1 $(F\|A_1\ i\%,j\%,n)$	To Find F Given A_1 $(F\|A_1\ i\%,j\%,n)$	To Find F Given A_1 $(F\|A_1\ i\%,j\%,n)$	To Find F Given A_1 $(F\|A_1\ i\%,j\%,n)$
1	1.00000	1.00000	1.00000	1.00000	1.00000
2	2.09000	2.10000	2.11000	2.15000	2.20000
3	3.27610	3.30750	3.33910	3.46750	3.63250
4	4.56477	4.63050	4.69707	4.97188	5.33500
5	5.96287	6.07753	6.19440	6.68457	7.35076
6	7.47766	7.65769	7.84235	8.62931	9.72965
7	9.11686	9.38067	9.65298	10.83233	12.52919
8	10.88864	11.25680	11.63926	13.32267	15.81567
9	12.80164	13.29710	13.81507	16.13239	19.66548
10	14.86503	15.51328	16.19531	19.29696	24.16663
11	17.08853	17.91784	18.79592	22.85555	29.42052
12	19.48241	20.52407	21.63401	26.85144	35.54394
13	22.05756	23.34613	24.72791	31.33244	42.67138
14	24.82552	26.39909	28.09724	36.35133	50.95774
15	27.79847	29.69897	31.76300	41.96640	60.58133
16	30.98933	33.26285	35.74771	48.24197	71.74746
17	34.41178	37.10887	40.07545	55.24904	84.69246
18	38.08027	41.25633	44.77199	63.06596	99.68834
19	42.01010	45.72577	49.86493	71.77918	117.04821
20	46.21746	50.53900	55.38378	81.48404	137.13240
21	50.71945	55.71925	61.36010	92.28575	160.35555
22	55.53419	61.29118	67.82767	104.30028	187.19485
23	60.68082	67.28100	74.82259	117.65557	218.19934
24	66.17958	73.71657	82.38347	132.49265	254.00076
25	72.05186	80.62750	90.55158	148.96702	295.32598
26	78.32029	88.04523	99.37103	167.25008	343.01123
27	85.00877	96.00316	108.88896	187.53076	398.01859
28	92.14258	104.53678	119.15576	210.01729	461.45483
29	99.74841	113.68375	130.22523	234.93915	534.59318
30	107.85449	123.48407	142.15488	262.54920	618.89830
36	168.78836	198.57655	235.54359	502.41729	1473.60036
40	223.89681	268.19005	324.57292	764.38534	2608.23558
48	383.07414	475.48661	599.26021	1732.31928	8089.99442
50	436.07164	546.06666	695.27545	2118.46906	1.0722E+04
52	495.62196	626.12003	805.40771	2588.00247	1.4205E+04
55	598.92640	766.62829	1001.46907	3488.47023	2.1650E+04
60	815.95585	1067.38205	1430.85050	5716.04907	4.3653E+04
72	1670.28717	2300.23777	3283.25810	1.8441E+04	2.3422E+05
75	1988.74313	2773.76328	4022.42349	2.4661E+04	3.5634E+05
80	2651.16420	3776.10980	5623.45524	3.9977E+04	7.1701E+05
84	3327.72366	4819.37931	7332.27629	5.8776E+04	1.2543E+06
90	4661.10317	6919.74558	1.0873E+04	1.0465E+05	2.9019E+06
96	6501.45689	9891.32894	1.6057E+04	1.8608E+05	6.7131E+06
100	8099.63097	1.2524E+04	2.0780E+04	2.7298E+05	1.1742E+07
108	1.2517E+04	1.9984E+04	3.4651E+04	5.8691E+05	3.5921E+07
120	2.3825E+04	3.9876E+04	7.3928E+04	1.8472E+06	1.9219E+08
132	4.4942E+04	7.8772E+04	1.5631E+05	5.8067E+06	1.0283E+09
144	8.4161E+04	1.5432E+05	3.2807E+05	1.8241E+07	5.5016E+09
180	5.3533E+05	1.1173E+06	2.9379E+06	5.6443E+08	8.4258E+11
240	1.0949E+07	2.7826E+07	1.0624E+08	1.7190E+11	3.6939E+15
360	4.1121E+09	1.4563E+10	1.2461E+11	1.5937E+16	7.0994E+22
480	1.4671E+12	6.7751E+12	1.3874E+14	1.4775E+21	1.3645E+30
600	5.1545E+14	2.9549E+15	1.5207E+17	1.3697E+26	2.6224E+37

TABLE A-c-3

j	4%	5%	6%	10%	15%
n	To Find F Given A_1 $(F|A_1\ i\%,j\%,n)$	To Find F Given A_1 $(F|A_1\ i\%,j\%,n)$	To Find F Given A_1 $(F|A_1\ i\%,j\%,n)$	To Find F Given A_1 $(F|A_1\ i\%,j\%,n)$	To Find F Given A_1 $(F|A_1\ i\%,j\%,n)$
1	1.00000	1.00000	1.00000	1.00000	1.00000
2	2.10000	2.11000	2.12000	2.16000	2.21000
3	3.30760	3.33910	3.37080	3.49960	3.66510
4	4.63092	4.69707	4.76406	5.04058	5.40588
5	6.07863	6.19440	6.31238	6.80711	7.47924
6	7.66000	7.84235	8.02935	8.82605	9.93935
7	9.38492	9.65298	9.92963	11.12717	12.84877
8	11.26395	11.63926	12.02904	13.74352	16.27972
9	13.30836	13.81507	14.34463	16.71172	20.31553
10	15.53017	16.19531	16.89479	20.07237	25.05233
11	17.94223	18.79592	19.69932	23.87045	30.60103
12	20.55821	21.63401	22.77958	28.15580	37.08948
13	23.39274	24.72791	26.15855	32.98357	44.66510
14	26.46138	28.09724	29.86100	38.41486	53.49780
15	29.78073	31.76300	33.91356	44.51725	63.78337
16	33.36852	35.74771	38.34493	51.36553	75.74744
17	37.24361	40.07545	43.18598	59.04244	89.64990
18	41.42613	44.77199	48.46991	67.63945	105.79016
19	45.93752	49.86493	54.23244	77.25774	124.51302
20	50.80062	55.38378	60.51199	88.00911	146.21558
21	56.03978	61.36010	67.34984	100.01716	171.35505
22	61.68093	67.82767	74.79040	113.41844	200.45787
23	67.75171	74.82259	82.88136	128.36382	234.13009
24	74.28152	82.38347	91.67399	145.01995	273.06935
25	81.30172	90.55158	101.22337	163.57088	318.07869
26	88.84566	99.37103	111.58864	184.21984	370.08236
27	96.94887	108.88896	122.83334	207.19121	430.14410
28	105.64917	119.15576	135.02569	232.73267	499.48806
29	114.98682	130.22523	148.23891	261.11763	579.52296
30	125.00468	142.15488	162.55164	292.64778	671.86979
36	202.16597	235.54359	276.69912	569.13571	1611.16222
40	274.23487	324.57292	388.14030	874.33844	2861.97587
48	491.16717	599.26021	742.36400	2015.58405	8922.29822
50	565.67355	695.27545	868.87520	2474.26747	1.1836E+04
52	650.51483	805.40771	1015.31890	3033.65117	1.5694E+04
55	800.19773	1001.46907	1279.02612	4110.22052	2.3944E+04
60	1123.40317	1430.85050	1867.22778	6787.34872	4.8345E+04
72	2476.77264	3283.25810	4508.67499	2.2230E+04	2.5988E+05
75	3005.58331	4022.52349	5593.65006	2.9821E+04	3.9549E+05
80	4137.30972	5623.45524	7984.60328	4.8565E+04	7.9606E+05
84	5329.99997	7332.27629	1.0584E+04	7.1637E+04	1.3929E+06
90	7767.25889	1.0873E+04	1.6087E+04	1.2809E+05	3.2231E+06
96	1.1279E+04	1.6057E+04	2.4340E+04	2.2859E+05	7.4572E+06
100	1.4440E+04	2.0780E+04	3.2010E+04	3.3603E+05	1.3044E+07
108	2.3584E+04	3.4651E+04	5.5100E+04	7.2498E+05	3.9908E+07
120	4.8876E+04	7.3928E+04	1.2319E+05	2.2905E+06	2.1354E+08
132	1.0062E+05	1.5631E+05	2.7267E+05	7.2193E+06	1.1425E+09
144	2.0612E+05	3.2807E+05	5.9855E+05	2.2719E+07	6.1128E+09
180	1.7366E+06	2.9379E+06	6.0957E+06	7.0481E+08	9.3620E+11
240	5.8595E+07	1.0624E+08	2.6811E+08	2.1484E+11	4.1043E+15
360	6.4361E+10	1.2461E+11	4.3763E+11	1.9921E+16	7.8882E+22
480	7.0103E+13	1.3874E+14	6.3497E+14	1.8468E+21	1.5161E+30
600	7.6293E+16	1.5207E+17	8.6370E+17	1.7122E+26	2.9138E+37

TABLE A-c-4

j	4%	5%	6%	10%	15%
n	To Find F Given A_1 $(F|A_1\ i\%,j\%,n)$	To Find F Given A_1 $(F|A_1\ i\%,j\%,n)$	To Find F Given A_1 $(F|A_1\ i\%,j\%,n)$	To Find F Given A_1 $(F|A_1\ i\%,j\%,n)$	To Find F Given A_1 $(F|A_1\ i\%,j\%,n)$
1	1.00000	1.00000	1.00000	1.00000	1.00000
2	2.14000	2.15000	2.16000	2.20000	2.25000
3	3.43560	3.46750	3.49960	3.63000	3.79750
4	4.90402	4.97188	5.04058	5.32400	5.69812
5	6.56428	6.68457	6.80711	7.32050	8.01694
6	8.43737	8.62931	8.82605	9.66306	10.83000
7	10.54642	10.83233	11.12717	12.40093	14.22606
8	12.91700	13.32267	13.74352	15.58974	18.30868
9	15.57726	16.13239	16.71172	19.29230	23.19857
10	18.55830	19.29696	20.07237	23.57948	29.03631
11	21.89438	22.85555	23.87045	28.53117	35.98549
12	25.62327	26.85144	28.15580	34.23740	44.23643
13	29.78663	31.33244	32.98357	40.79957	54.01033
14	34.43036	36.35133	38.41486	48.33180	65.56415
15	39.60508	41.96640	44.51725	56.96248	79.19627
16	45.36653	48.24197	51.36553	66.83597	95.25296
17	51.77616	55.24904	59.04244	78.11454	114.13587
18	58.90168	63.06596	67.63945	90.98047	136.31073
19	66.81766	71.77918	77.25774	105.63843	162.31725
20	75.60628	81.48404	88.00911	122.31818	192.78075
21	85.35803	92.28575	100.01716	141.27750	228.42536
22	96.17260	104.30028	113.41844	162.80550	270.08942
23	108.15978	117.65557	128.36382	187.22632	318.74310
24	121.44048	132.49265	145.01995	214.90326	375.50887
25	136.14783	148.96702	163.57088	246.24332	441.68493
26	152.42845	167.25008	184.21984	281.70235	518.77238
27	170.44376	187.53076	207.19121	321.79077	608.50641
28	190.37150	210.01729	232.73267	367.07984	712.89237
29	212.40736	234.93915	261.11763	418.20881	834.24722
30	236.76675	262.54920	292.64778	475.89279	975.24739
36	446.81247	502.41729	569.13571	1011.68773	2444.78343
40	674.30392	764.38534	874.33844	1645.79111	4452.08581
48	1507.44509	1732.31928	2015.58405	4233.47929	1.4448E+04
50	1838.06949	2118.46906	2474.26747	5335.94786	1.9325E+04
52	2239.27239	2588.00247	3033.65117	6714.75678	2.5822E+04
55	3006.87959	3488.47023	4110.22052	9452.95712	3.9811E+04
60	4899.36687	5716.04907	6787.34872	1.6608E+04	8.1590E+04
72	1.5646E+04	1.8441E+04	2.2230E+04	6.2548E+04	4.5000E+05
75	2.0883E+04	2.4661E+04	2.9821E+04	8.6720E+04	6.8802E+05
80	3.3756E+04	3.9977E+04	4.8565E+04	1.4897E+05	1.3940E+06
84	4.9535E+04	5.8776E+04	7.1637E+04	2.2902E+05	2.4499E+06
90	8.7982E+04	1.0465E+05	1.2809E+05	4.3470E+05	5.6992E+06
96	1.5615E+05	1.8608E+05	2.2859E+05	8.2144E+05	1.3240E+07
100	2.2884E+05	2.7298E+05	3.3603E+05	1.2528E+06	2.3211E+07
108	4.9118E+05	5.8691E+05	7.2498E+05	2.9003E+06	7.1254E+07
120	1.5433E+06	1.8472E+06	2.2905E+06	1.0114E+07	3.8253E+08
132	4.8464E+06	5.8067E+06	7.2193E+06	3.4915E+07	2.0508E+09
144	1.5215E+07	1.8241E+07	2.2719E+07	1.1954E+08	1.0985E+10
180	4.7045E+08	5.6443E+08	7.0481E+08	4.6192E+09	1.6846E+12
240	1.4325E+11	1.7190E+11	2.1484E+11	1.8753E+12	7.3876E+15
360	1.3281E+16	1.5937E+16	1.9921E+16	2.6078E+17	1.4199E+23
480	1.2312E+21	1.4775E+21	1.8468E+21	3.2236E+22	2.7289E+30
600	1.1415E+26	1.3697E+26	1.7122E+26	3.7357E+27	5.2449E+37

TABLE A-c-5

j	4%	5%	6%	10%	15%
n	To Find F Given A_1 $(F|A_1\ i\%,j\%,n)$	To Find F Given A_1 $(F|A_1\ i\%,j\%,n)$	To Find F Given A_1 $(F|A_1\ i\%,j\%,n)$	To Find F Given A_1 $(F|A_1\ i\%,j\%,n)$	To Find F Given A_1 $(F|A_1\ i\%,j\%,n)$
1	1.00000	1.00000	1.00000	1.00000	1.00000
2	2.19000	2.20000	2.21000	2.25000	2.30000
3	3.60010	3.63250	3.66510	3.79750	3.96750
4	5.26498	5.33500	5.40588	5.69812	6.08350
5	7.22458	7.35076	7.47924	8.01694	8.74503
6	9.52492	9.72965	9.93935	10.83000	12.06814
7	12.21898	12.52919	12.84877	14.22606	16.19143
8	15.36776	15.81567	16.27972	18.30868	21.28016
9	19.04150	19.66548	20.31553	23.19857	27.53121
10	23.32103	24.16663	25.05233	29.03631	35.17876
11	28.29943	29.42052	30.60103	35.98549	44.50114
12	34.08380	35.54394	37.08948	44.23643	55.82870
13	40.79740	42.67138	44.66510	54.01033	69.55325
14	48.58208	50.95774	53.49780	65.56415	86.13903
15	57.60107	60.58133	63.78337	79.19627	106.13559
16	68.04218	71.74746	75.74744	95.25296	130.19299
17	80.12149	84.69246	89.64990	114.13587	159.07955
18	94.08761	99.68834	105.79016	136.31073	193.70275
19	110.22657	117.04821	124.51302	162.31725	235.13362
20	128.86740	137.13240	146.21558	192.78075	284.63543
21	150.38864	160.35555	171.35505	228.42536	343.69729
22	175.22570	187.19485	200.45787	270.08942	414.07340
23	203.87947	218.19934	234.13009	318.74310	497.82915
24	236.92611	254.00076	273.06935	375.50887	597.39498
25	275.02833	295.32598	318.07869	441.68493	715.62940
26	318.94842	343.01123	370.08236	518.77238	855.89277
27	369.56315	398.01859	430.14410	608.50641	1022.13348
28	427.88099	461.45483	499.48806	712.89237	1218.98882
29	495.06184	534.59318	579.52296	834.24722	1451.90275
30	572.43977	618.89830	671.86979	975.24739	1727.26362
36	1354.98109	1473.60036	1611.16222	2444.78343	4794.31884
40	2391.47751	2608.23558	2861.97587	4452.08581	9316.99291
48	7389.36531	8089.99442	8922.29822	1.4448E+04	3.4201E+04
50	9786.82507	1.0722E+04	1.1836E+04	1.9325E+04	4.7116E+04
52	1.2959E+04	1.4205E+04	1.5694E+04	2.5822E+04	6.4803E+04
55	1.9736E+04	2.1650E+04	2.3944E+04	3.9811E+04	1.0424E+05
60	3.9759E+04	4.3653E+04	4.8345E+04	8.1590E+04	2.2873E+05
72	2.1308E+05	2.3422E+05	2.5988E+05	4.5000E+05	1.4685E+06
75	3.2413E+05	3.5634E+05	3.9549E+05	6.8802E+05	2.3265E+06
80	6.5207E+05	7.1701E+05	7.9606E+05	1.3940E+06	4.9914E+06
84	1.1406E+06	1.2543E+06	1.3929E+06	2.4499E+06	9.1664E+06
90	2.6385E+06	2.9019E+06	3.2231E+06	5.6992E+06	2.2717E+07
96	6.1034E+06	6.7131E+06	7.4572E+06	1.3240E+07	5.6049E+07
100	1.0675E+07	1.1742E+07	1.3044E+07	2.3211E+07	1.0211E+08
108	3.2656E+07	3.5921E+07	3.9908E+07	7.1254E+07	3.3736E+08
120	1.7472E+08	1.9219E+08	2.1354E+08	3.8253E+08	2.0055E+09
132	9.3481E+08	1.0283E+09	1.1425E+09	2.0508E+09	1.1803E+10
144	5.0015E+09	5.5016E+09	6.1128E+09	1.0985E+10	6.8890E+10
180	7.6598E+11	8.4258E+11	9.3620E+11	1.6846E+12	1.3188E+13
240	3.3581E+15	3.6939E+15	4.1043E+15	7.3876E+15	7.7089E+16
360	6.4540E+22	7.0994E+22	7.8882E+22	1.4199E+23	2.2224E+24
480	1.2404E+30	1.3645E+30	1.5161E+30	2.7289E+30	5.6952E+31
600	2.3840E+37	2.6224E+37	2.9138E+37	5.2449E+37	1.3682E+39

TABLE B-a-1

	Single Sums		Uniform Series				Gradient Series	
n	To Find F Given P $(F\|P\ r\%,n)_\infty$	To Find P Given F $(P\|F\ r\%,n)_\infty$	To Find F Given A $(F\|A\ r\%,n)_\infty$	To Find A Given F $(A\|F\ r\%,n)_\infty$	To Find P Given A $(P\|A\ r\%,n)_\infty$	To Find A Given P $(A\|P\ r\%,n)_\infty$	To Find P Given G $(P\|G\ r\%,n)_\infty$	To Find A Given G $(A\|G\ r\%,n)_\infty$
1	1.05127	0.95123	1.00000	1.00000	0.95123	1.05127	0.00000	0.00000
2	1.10517	0.90484	2.05127	0.48750	1.85607	0.53877	0.90484	0.48750
3	1.16183	0.86071	3.15644	0.31681	2.71677	0.36808	2.62625	0.96668
4	1.22140	0.81873	4.31828	0.23157	3.53551	0.28284	5.08245	1.43754
5	1.28403	0.77880	5.53968	0.18052	4.31431	0.23179	8.19765	1.90011
6	1.34986	0.74082	6.82370	0.14655	5.05512	0.19782	11.90174	2.35439
7	1.41907	0.70469	8.17356	0.12235	5.75981	0.17362	16.12987	2.80042
8	1.49182	0.67032	9.59263	0.10425	6.43013	0.15552	20.82211	3.23821
9	1.56831	0.63763	11.08446	0.09022	7.06776	0.14149	25.92313	3.66780
10	1.64872	0.60653	12.65277	0.07903	7.67429	0.13031	31.38191	4.08923
11	1.73325	0.57695	14.30149	0.06992	8.25124	0.12119	37.15141	4.50252
12	1.82212	0.54881	16.03474	0.06236	8.80005	0.11364	43.18834	4.90774
13	1.91554	0.52205	17.85686	0.05600	9.32210	0.10727	49.45289	5.30491
14	2.01375	0.49659	19.77240	0.05058	9.81868	0.10185	55.90849	5.69409
15	2.11700	0.47237	21.78615	0.04590	10.29105	0.09717	62.52163	6.07534
16	2.22554	0.44933	23.90315	0.04184	10.74038	0.09311	69.26156	6.44871
17	2.33965	0.42741	26.12870	0.03827	11.16779	0.08954	76.10020	6.81425
18	2.45960	0.40657	28.46834	0.03513	11.57436	0.08640	83.01188	7.17205
19	2.58571	0.38674	30.92795	0.03233	11.96111	0.08360	89.97322	7.52215
20	2.71828	0.36788	33.51365	0.02984	12.32898	0.08111	96.96293	7.86463
21	2.85765	0.34994	36.23194	0.02760	12.67892	0.07887	103.96169	8.19957
22	3.00417	0.33287	39.08959	0.02558	13.01179	0.07685	110.95198	8.52703
23	3.15819	0.31664	42.09375	0.02376	13.32843	0.07503	117.91799	8.84710
24	3.32012	0.30119	45.25195	0.02210	13.62962	0.07337	124.84545	9.15986
25	3.49034	0.28650	48.57206	0.02059	13.91613	0.07186	131.72157	9.46539
26	3.66930	0.27253	52.06241	0.01921	14.18866	0.07048	138.53486	9.76377
27	3.85743	0.25924	55.73170	0.01794	14.44790	0.06921	145.27511	10.05510
28	4.05520	0.24660	59.58913	0.01678	14.69450	0.06805	151.93323	10.33946
29	4.26311	0.23457	63.64433	0.01571	14.92907	0.06698	158.50120	10.61695
30	4.48169	0.22313	67.90744	0.01473	15.15220	0.06600	164.97197	10.88766
35	5.75460	0.17377	92.73456	0.01078	16.11485	0.06205	195.68067	12.14288
40	7.38906	0.13534	124.61321	8.0248E−03	16.86456	0.05930	223.34520	13.24346
45	9.48774	0.10540	165.54621	6.0406E−03	17.44844	0.05731	247.80975	14.20240
50	12.18249	0.08208	218.10522	4.5849E−03	17.90317	0.05586	269.13638	15.03289
55	15.64263	0.06393	285.59233	3.5015E−03	18.25731	0.05477	287.51627	15.74801
60	20.08554	0.04979	372.24749	2.6864E−03	18.53311	0.05396	303.20957	16.36042
65	25.79034	0.03877	483.51492	2.0682E−03	18.74791	0.05334	316.50551	16.88218
70	33.11545	0.03020	626.38512	1.5965E−03	18.91519	0.05287	327.69681	17.32453
75	42.52108	0.02352	809.83410	1.2348E−03	19.04547	0.05251	337.06401	17.69786
80	54.59815	0.01832	1045.38724	9.5658E−04	19.14694	0.05223	344.86651	18.01158
85	70.10541	0.01426	1347.84347	7.4193E−04	19.22595	0.05201	351.33820	18.27416
90	90.01713	0.01111	1736.20495	5.7597E−04	19.28749	0.05185	356.68605	18.49313
95	115.58428	8.6517E−03	2234.87096	4.4745E−04	19.33542	0.05172	361.09061	18.67508
100	148.41316	6.7379E−03	2875.17080	3.4781E−04	19.37275	0.05162	364.70751	18.82580

TABLE B-a-2

	Single Sums		Uniform Series				Gradient Series	
	To Find F Given P	To Find P Given F	To Find F Given A	To Find A Given F	To Find P Given A	To Find A Given P	To Find P Given G	To Find A Given G
n	$(F\|P\ r\%,n)_\infty$	$(P\|F\ r\%,n)_\infty$	$(F\|A\ r\%,n)_\infty$	$(A\|F\ r\%,n)_\infty$	$(P\|A\ r\%,n)_\infty$	$(A\|P\ r\%,n)_\infty$	$(P\|G\ r\%,n)_\infty$	$(A\|G\ r\%,n)_\infty$
1	1.10517	0.90484	1.00000	1.00000	0.90484	1.10517	0.00000	0.00000
2	1.22140	0.81873	2.10517	0.47502	1.72357	0.58019	0.81873	0.47502
3	1.34986	0.74082	3.32657	0.30061	2.46439	0.40578	2.30037	0.93344
4	1.49182	0.67032	4.67643	0.21384	3.13471	0.31901	4.31133	1.37535
5	1.64872	0.60653	6.16826	0.16212	3.74124	0.26729	6.73745	1.80086
6	1.82212	0.54881	7.81698	0.12793	4.29005	0.23310	9.48151	2.21012
7	2.01375	0.49659	9.63910	0.10374	4.78663	0.20892	12.46102	2.60329
8	2.22554	0.44933	11.65285	0.08582	5.23596	0.19099	15.60632	2.98060
9	2.45960	0.40657	13.87839	0.07205	5.64253	0.17723	18.85888	3.34227
10	2.71828	0.36788	16.33799	0.06121	6.01041	0.16638	22.16979	3.68856
11	3.00417	0.33287	19.05628	0.05248	6.34328	0.15765	25.49851	4.01976
12	3.32012	0.30119	22.06044	0.04533	6.64448	0.15050	28.81164	4.33618
13	3.66930	0.27253	25.38056	0.03940	6.91701	0.14457	32.08202	4.63814
14	4.05520	0.24660	29.04986	0.03442	7.16361	0.13959	35.28778	4.92598
15	4.48169	0.22313	33.10506	0.03021	7.38674	0.13538	38.41161	5.20008
16	4.95303	0.20190	37.58674	0.02661	7.58863	0.13178	41.44005	5.46081
17	5.47395	0.18268	42.53978	0.02351	7.77132	0.12868	44.36299	5.70856
18	6.04965	0.16530	48.01372	0.02083	7.93662	0.12600	47.17307	5.94373
19	6.68589	0.14957	54.06337	0.01850	8.08618	0.12367	49.86531	6.16673
20	7.38906	0.13534	60.74927	0.01646	8.22152	0.12163	52.43668	6.37798
21	8.16617	0.12246	68.13832	0.01468	8.34398	0.11985	54.88581	6.57790
22	9.02501	0.11080	76.30449	0.01311	8.45478	0.11828	57.21267	6.76690
23	9.97418	0.10026	85.32951	0.01172	8.55504	0.11689	59.41837	6.94542
24	11.02318	0.09072	95.30369	0.01049	8.64576	0.11566	61.50488	7.11388
25	12.18249	0.08208	106.32686	9.4050E−03	8.72784	0.11458	63.47492	7.27269
26	13.46374	0.07427	118.50936	8.4382E−03	8.80211	0.11361	65.33176	7.42228
27	14.87973	0.06721	131.97310	7.5773E−03	8.86932	0.11275	67.07910	7.56305
28	16.44465	0.06081	146.85283	6.8095E−03	8.93013	0.11198	68.72097	7.69541
29	18.17415	0.05502	163.29748	6.1238E−03	8.98515	0.11129	70.26162	7.81975
30	20.08554	0.04979	181.47162	5.5105E−03	9.03494	0.11068	71.70545	7.93646
35	33.11545	0.03020	305.36438	3.2748E−03	9.22121	0.10845	77.62884	8.41851
40	54.59815	0.01832	509.62900	1.9622E−03	9.33418	0.10713	81.78644	8.76204
45	90.01713	0.01111	846.40443	1.1815E−03	9.40270	0.10635	84.65077	9.00281
50	148.41316	6.7379E−03	1401.65325	7.1344E−04	9.44427	0.10588	86.59588	9.16915
55	244.69193	4.0868E−03	2317.10378	4.3157E−04	9.46947	0.10560	87.90169	9.28264
60	403.42879	2.4788E−03	3826.42655	2.6134E−04	9.48476	0.10543	88.77015	9.35924
65	665.14163	1.5034E−03	6314.87911	1.5836E−04	9.49404	0.10533	89.34326	9.41046
70	1096.63316	9.1188E−04	1.0418E+04	9.5991E−05	9.49966	0.10527	89.71900	9.44444
75	1808.04241	5.5308E−04	1.7182E+04	5.8201E−05	9.50307	0.10523	89.96395	9.46683
80	2980.95799	3.3546E−04	2.8334E+04	3.5293E−05	9.50514	0.10521	90.12287	9.48149
85	4914.76884	2.0347E−04	4.6722E+04	2.1403E−05	9.50640	0.10519	90.22554	9.49103
90	8103.08393	1.2341E−04	7.7037E+04	1.2981E−05	9.50716	0.10518	90.29161	9.49722
95	1.3360E+04	7.4852E−05	1.2702E+05	7.8728E−06	9.50762	0.10518	90.33400	9.50122
100	2.2026E+04	4.5400E−05	2.0943E+05	4.7750E−06	9.50790	0.10518	90.36110	9.50379

TABLE B-a-3

	Single Sums		Uniform Series				Gradient Series	
n	To Find F Given P $(F/P\ r\%,n)_\infty$	To Find P Given F $(P/F\ r\%,n)_\infty$	To Find F Given A $(F/A\ r\%,n)_\infty$	To Find A Given F $(A/F\ r\%,n)_\infty$	To Find P Given A $(P/A\ r\%,n)_\infty$	To Find A Given P $(A/P\ r\%,n)_\infty$	To Find P Given G $(P/G\ r\%,n)_\infty$	To Find A Given G $(A/G\ r\%,n)_\infty$
1	1.16183	0.86071	1.00000	1.00000	0.86071	1.16183	0.00000	0.00000
2	1.34986	0.74082	2.16183	0.46257	1.60153	0.62440	0.74082	0.46257
3	1.56831	0.63763	3.51169	0.28476	2.23915	0.44660	2.01607	0.90037
4	1.82212	0.54881	5.08001	0.19685	2.78797	0.35868	3.66251	1.31369
5	2.11700	0.47237	6.90212	0.14488	3.26033	0.30672	5.55198	1.70289
6	2.45960	0.40657	9.01912	0.11088	3.66690	0.27271	7.58482	2.06846
7	2.85765	0.34994	11.47873	0.08712	4.01684	0.24895	9.68445	2.41096
8	3.32012	0.30119	14.33638	0.06975	4.31803	0.23159	11.79281	2.73106
9	3.85743	0.25924	17.65650	0.05664	4.57727	0.21847	13.86673	3.02947
10	4.48169	0.22313	21.51392	0.04648	4.80040	0.20832	15.87490	3.30699
11	5.20698	0.19205	25.99561	0.03847	4.99245	0.20030	17.79540	3.56446
12	6.04965	0.16530	31.20259	0.03205	5.15775	0.19388	19.61369	3.80276
13	7.02869	0.14227	37.25224	0.02684	5.30003	0.18868	21.32098	4.02281
14	8.16617	0.12246	44.28092	0.02258	5.42248	0.18442	22.91291	4.22554
15	9.48774	0.10540	52.44709	0.01907	5.52788	0.18090	24.38850	4.41191
16	11.02318	0.09072	61.93483	0.01615	5.61860	0.17798	25.74927	4.58286
17	12.80710	0.07808	72.95801	0.01371	5.69668	0.17554	26.99858	4.73935
18	14.87973	0.06721	85.76511	0.01166	5.76389	0.17349	28.14107	4.88231
19	17.28778	0.05784	100.64484	9.9359E−03	5.82173	0.17177	29.18227	5.01264
20	20.08554	0.04979	117.93262	8.4794E−03	5.87152	0.17031	30.12822	5.13125
21	23.33606	0.04285	138.01816	7.2454E−03	5.91437	0.16908	30.98527	5.23898
22	27.11264	0.03688	161.35423	6.1975E−03	5.95125	0.16803	31.75981	5.33666
23	31.50039	0.03175	188.46686	5.3060E−03	5.98300	0.16714	32.45822	5.42507
24	36.59823	0.02732	219.96726	4.5461E−03	6.01032	0.16638	33.08666	5.50497
25	42.52108	0.02352	256.56549	3.8976E−03	6.03384	0.16573	33.65109	5.57706
26	49.40245	0.02024	299.08657	3.3435E−03	6.05408	0.16518	34.15714	5.64200
27	57.39746	0.01742	348.48902	2.8695E−03	6.07151	0.16470	34.61012	5.70042
28	66.68633	0.01500	405.88648	2.4637E−03	6.08650	0.16430	35.01500	5.75289
29	77.47846	0.01291	472.57281	2.1161E−03	6.09941	0.16395	35.37639	5.79997
30	90.01713	0.01111	550.05127	1.8180E−03	6.11052	0.16365	35.69855	5.84215
35	190.56627	5.2475E−03	1171.36068	8.5371E−04	6.14674	0.16269	36.84680	5.99453
40	403.42879	2.4788E−03	2486.67270	4.0214E−04	6.16385	0.16224	37.47473	6.07977
45	854.05876	1.1709E−03	5271.18827	1.8971E−04	6.17193	0.16202	37.81176	6.12641
50	1808.04241	5.5308E−04	1.1166E+04	8.9558E−05	6.17574	0.16192	37.99005	6.15149
55	3827.62582	2.6126E−04	2.3645E+04	4.2292E−05	6.17755	0.16188	38.08328	6.16479
60	8103.08393	1.2341E−04	5.0064E+04	1.9974E−05	6.17840	0.16185	38.13158	6.17176
65	1.7154E+04	5.8295E−05	1.0599E+05	9.4346E−06	6.17880	0.16184	38.15640	6.17537
70	3.6316E+04	2.7536E−05	2.2439E+05	4.4565E−06	6.17899	0.16184	38.16908	6.17723
75	7.6880E+04	1.3007E−05	4.7505E+05	2.1051E−06	6.17908	0.16184	38.17552	6.17819
80	1.6275E+05	6.1442E−06	1.0057E+06	9.9435E−07	6.17912	0.16184	38.17877	6.17867
85	3.4455E+05	2.9023E−06	2.1290E+06	4.6970E−07	6.17914	0.16183	38.18041	6.17892
90	7.2942E+05	1.3710E−06	4.5072E+06	2.2187E−07	6.17915	0.16183	38.18123	6.17904
95	1.5442E+06	6.4760E−07	9.5417E+06	1.0480E−07	6.17916	0.16183	38.18164	6.17910
100	3.2690E+06	3.0590E−07	2.0200E+07	4.9505E−08	6.17916	0.16183	38.18184	6.17913

	TABLE B-b-1			
n	To Find P Given $\overline{A}$ $(P\|\overline{A}\ r\%,n)$	To Find $\overline{A}$ Given P $(\overline{A}\|P\ r\%,n)$	To Find F Given $\overline{A}$ $(F\|\overline{A}\ r\%,n)$	To Find $\overline{A}$ Given F $(\overline{A}\|F\ r\%,n)$
1	0.97541	1.02521	1.02542	0.97521
2	1.90325	0.52542	2.10342	0.47542
3	2.78584	0.35896	3.23668	0.30896
4	3.62538	0.27583	4.42806	0.22583
5	4.42398	0.22604	5.68051	0.17604
6	5.18364	0.19291	6.99718	0.14291
7	5.90624	0.16931	8.38135	0.11931
8	6.59360	0.15166	9.83649	0.10166
9	7.24744	0.13798	11.36624	0.08798
10	7.86939	0.12707	12.97443	0.07707
11	8.46100	0.11819	14.66506	0.06819
12	9.02377	0.11082	16.44238	0.06082
13	9.55908	0.10461	18.31082	0.05461
14	10.06829	0.09932	20.27505	0.04932
15	10.55267	0.09476	22.34000	0.04476
16	11.01342	0.09080	24.51082	0.04080
17	11.45170	0.08732	26.79294	0.03732
18	11.86861	0.08426	29.19206	0.03426
19	12.26518	0.08153	31.71419	0.03153
20	12.64241	0.07910	34.36564	0.02910
21	13.00125	0.07692	37.15302	0.02692
22	13.34258	0.07495	40.08332	0.02495
23	13.66726	0.07317	43.16386	0.02317
24	13.97612	0.07155	46.40234	0.02155
25	14.26990	0.07008	49.80686	0.02008
26	14.54936	0.06873	53.38593	0.01873
27	14.81519	0.06750	57.14851	0.01750
28	15.06806	0.06637	61.10400	0.01637
29	15.30859	0.06532	65.26229	0.01532
30	15.53740	0.06436	69.63378	0.01436
35	16.52452	0.06052	95.09205	0.01052
40	17.29329	0.05783	127.78112	7.8259E−03
45	17.89202	0.05589	169.75472	5.8909E−03
50	18.35830	0.05447	223.64988	4.4713E−03
55	18.72144	0.05341	292.85264	3.4147E−03
60	19.00426	0.05262	381.71074	2.6198E−03
65	19.22452	0.05202	495.80680	2.0169E−03
70	19.39605	0.05156	642.30904	1.5569E−03
75	19.52965	0.05120	830.42164	1.2042E−03
80	19.63369	0.05093	1071.96300	9.3287E−04
85	19.71472	0.05072	1382.10825	7.2353E−04
90	19.77782	0.05056	1780.34263	5.6169E−04
95	19.82697	0.05044	2291.68569	4.3636E−04
100	19.86524	0.05034	2948.26318	3.3918E−04

TABLE B-b-2

n	To Find P Given $\overline{A}$ $(P\|\overline{A}\ r\%,n)$	To Find $\overline{A}$ Given P $(\overline{A}\|P\ r\%,n)$	To Find F Given $\overline{A}$ $(F\|\overline{A}\ r\%,n)$	To Find $\overline{A}$ Given F $(\overline{A}\|F\ r\%,n)$
1	0.95163	1.05083	1.05171	0.95083
2	1.81269	0.55167	2.21403	0.45167
3	2.59182	0.38583	3.49859	0.28583
4	3.29680	0.30332	4.91825	0.20332
5	3.93469	0.25415	6.48721	0.15415
6	4.51188	0.22164	8.22119	0.12164
7	5.03415	0.19864	10.13753	0.09864
8	5.50671	0.18160	12.25541	0.08160
9	5.93430	0.16851	14.59603	0.06851
10	6.32121	0.15820	17.18282	0.05820
11	6.67129	0.14990	20.04166	0.04990
12	6.98806	0.14310	23.20117	0.04310
13	7.27468	0.13746	26.69297	0.03746
14	7.53403	0.13273	30.55200	0.03273
15	7.76870	0.12872	34.81689	0.02872
16	7.98103	0.12530	39.53032	0.02530
17	8.17316	0.12235	44.73947	0.02235
18	8.34701	0.11980	50.49647	0.01980
19	8.50431	0.11759	56.85894	0.01759
20	8.64665	0.11565	63.89056	0.01565
21	8.77544	0.11395	71.66170	0.01395
22	8.89197	0.11246	80.25013	0.01246
23	8.99741	0.11114	89.74182	0.01114
24	9.09282	0.10998	100.23176	9.9769E−03
25	9.17915	0.10894	111.82494	8.9425E−03
26	9.25726	0.10802	124.63738	8.0233E−03
27	9.32794	0.10720	138.79732	7.2048E−03
28	9.39190	0.10647	154.44647	6.4747E−03
29	9.44977	0.10582	171.74145	5.8227E−03
30	9.50213	0.10524	190.85537	5.2396E−03
35	9.69803	0.10311	321.15452	3.1138E−03
40	9.81684	0.10187	535.98150	1.8657E−03
45	9.88891	0.10112	890.17131	1.1234E−03
50	9.93262	0.10068	1474.13159	6.7837E−04
55	9.95913	0.10041	2436.91932	4.1035E−04
60	9.97521	0.10025	4024.28793	2.4849E−04
65	9.98497	0.10015	6641.41633	1.5057E−04
70	9.99088	0.10009	1.0956E+04	9.1271E−05
75	9.99447	0.10006	1.8070E+04	5.5339E−05
80	9.99665	0.10003	2.9800E+04	3.3558E−05
85	9.99797	0.10002	4.9138E+04	2.0351E−05
90	9.99877	0.10001	8.1021E+04	1.2343E−05
95	9.99925	0.10001	1.3359E+05	7.4857E−06
100	9.99955	0.10000	2.2025E+05	4.5402E−06

TABLE B-b-3

n	To Find P Given $\overline{A}$ $(P|\overline{A}\ r\%,\ n)$	To Find $\overline{A}$ Given P $(\overline{A}|P\ r\%,\ n)$	To Find F Given $\overline{A}$ $(F|\overline{A}\ r\%,\ n)$	To Find $\overline{A}$ Given F $(\overline{A}|F\ r\%,\ n)$
1	0.92861	1.07687	1.07889	0.92687
2	1.72788	0.57874	2.33239	0.42874
3	2.41581	0.41394	3.78875	0.26394
4	3.00792	0.33246	5.48079	0.18246
5	3.51756	0.28429	7.44667	0.13429
6	3.95620	0.25277	9.73069	0.10277
7	4.33375	0.23075	12.38434	0.08075
8	4.65871	0.21465	15.46745	0.06465
9	4.93840	0.20249	19.04950	0.05249
10	5.17913	0.19308	23.21126	0.04308
11	5.38633	0.18566	28.04653	0.03566
12	5.56467	0.17971	33.66432	0.02971
13	5.71817	0.17488	40.19125	0.02488
14	5.85029	0.17093	47.77447	0.02093
15	5.96401	0.16767	56.58491	0.01767
16	6.06188	0.16497	66.82118	0.01497
17	6.14612	0.16270	78.71403	0.01270
18	6.21863	0.16081	92.53154	0.01081
19	6.28104	0.15921	108.58521	9.2094E−03
20	6.33475	0.15786	127.23691	7.8594E−03
21	6.38099	0.15672	148.90710	6.7156E−03
22	6.42078	0.15574	174.08426	5.7443E−03
23	6.45503	0.15492	203.33595	4.9180E−03
24	6.48451	0.15421	237.32156	4.2137E−03
25	6.50988	0.15361	276.80721	3.6126E−03
26	6.53172	0.15310	322.68299	3.0990E−03
27	6.55052	0.15266	375.98305	2.6597E−03
28	6.56670	0.15228	437.90887	2.2836E−03
29	6.58062	0.15196	509.85642	1.9613E−03
30	6.59261	0.15169	593.44754	1.6851E−03
35	6.63168	0.15079	1263.77512	7.9128E−04
40	6.65014	0.15037	2682.85862	3.7274E−04
45	6.65886	0.15018	5687.05842	1.7584E−04
50	6.66298	0.15008	1.2047E+04	8.3009E−05
55	6.66492	0.15004	2.5511E+04	3.9199E−05
60	6.66584	0.15002	5.4014E+04	1.8514E−05
65	6.66628	0.15001	1.1435E+05	8.7447E−06
70	6.66648	0.15000	2.4210E+05	4.1306E−06
75	6.66658	0.15000	5.1253E+05	1.9511E−06
80	6.66663	0.15000	1.0850E+06	9.2164E−07
85	6.66665	0.15000	2.2970E+06	4.3535E−07
90	6.66666	0.15000	4.8628E+06	2.0564E−07
95	6.66666	0.15000	1.0294E+07	9.7139E−08
100	6.66666	0.15000	2.1793E+07	4.5885E−08

ANSWERS TO EVEN NUMBERED PROBLEMS

Chapter 1

FE2. b   **FE4.** a   **FE6.** b   **FE8.** d   **FE10.** d   **FE12.** c

2. (a) Yes   (b) $1,600 to $2,400

4. You are lender

$450-$600 interest

6. (a) $1,900   (b) $6,400   (c) WSI-Future spending is less   (d) 2, 10   (e) 1, 4, 5, 7

8. (a) None; C; D; CD; BC; BD; BCD; AD; ABD   (b) None   (c) 1

10. Q; P; PR

12. (c) 2, 3, 4, 5, 9   (d) 1, 4, 5, 6, 7

14. (a) 10 years   (b) 2, 3, 8   (c) 1, 2, 5, 7

16. (a) BC: 879; CI: 750   (b) At least $6,000   (c) 2   (d) 1, 5, 7

18. (a) 36.36%   (b) $11.32

20. (a) 60% A; 40% B   (b) $1.60

22. (a) 150 units/day   (b) 100 units/day

24. (a) 10th floor: $4,800,000; $88,888.89   (b) 10   (c) $dTC/dX = (80 + 4X)\ (400,000/X) + (200 + 80X + 2X^2)(-400,000/X^2) = 0\ X = 10$

26. (a) Loss of $25,000   (b) 220,000   (c) $125,000   (d) 132,000

28. (a) C   (b) $0.45/mile

30. (a) A   (b) B   (c) 280

Chapter 2

FE2. d   **FE4.** c   **FE6.** b   **FE8.** b   **FE10.** a   **FE12.** b   **FE14.** a

2. 1) Money has a time value   2) Money cannot be added or subtracted unless it occurs at the same point(s) in time   3) To move money forward one time unit, multiply times one plus the discount or interest rate   4) To move money backward one time unit, divide by one plus the discount or interest rate

4. (a) $971.70   (b) $1,030.00

6.

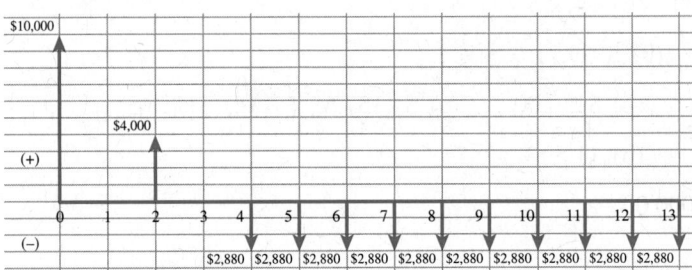

8.

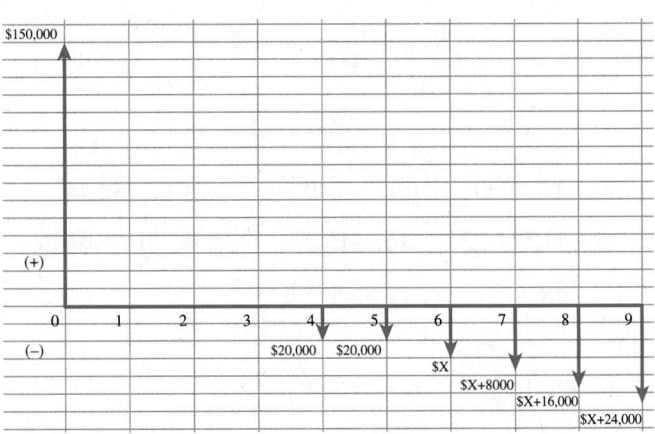

10.

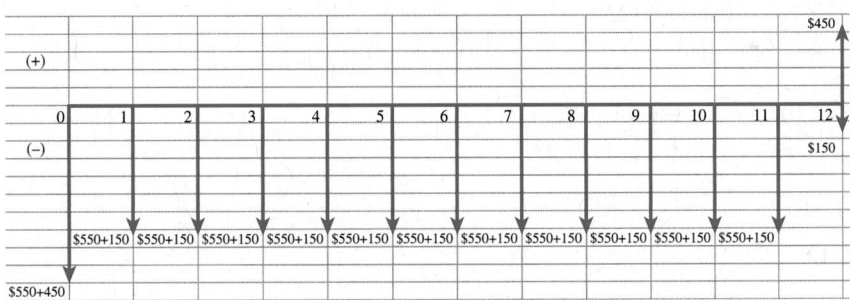

12.

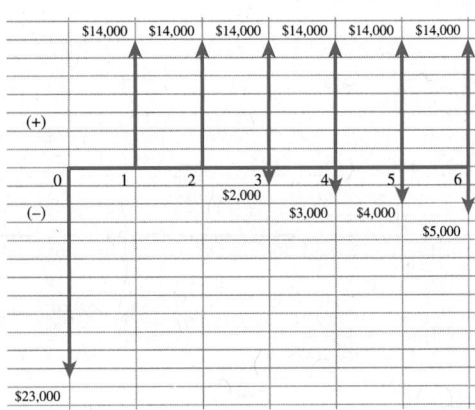

14. (a) $5,000.00   (b) $4,454.70

16. (a) $240.00   (b) $259.71

18. (a) $1,150.00   (b) $150.00   (c) $1,157.63   (d) $157.63

20. (a) $3,705.55   (b) 11.59%

22. Principal $11,000.00
Interest $4,428.07
Total $15,428.07

24. Account 2

26. $36,733.20

28. $49,178.78

30. 4.8641%

32. (a) $7,462.15   (b) $4,777.69   (c) $1,689.70   (d) $8,382.44

34. (a) $12,348.70   (b) $1,551.33   (c) $15.27   (d) $550.77   (e) $2,315.97

36. (a) $5,863.80   (b) $5,863.87   (c) $5,863.87

38. $12,000.00

40. (a) $2,714.10   (b) $2,714.10   (c) $2,714.10

42. 18.5631%

44. (a) 7.1773%   (b) 11.6123%   (c) 14.8698%

46. 19

48. (a) 12   (b) 19   (c) 24

50. 12.9116%

52. $161,201.97

54. $19,949.14

56. (a) $150.76   (b) 97.02   (c) $97.02

58. (a)

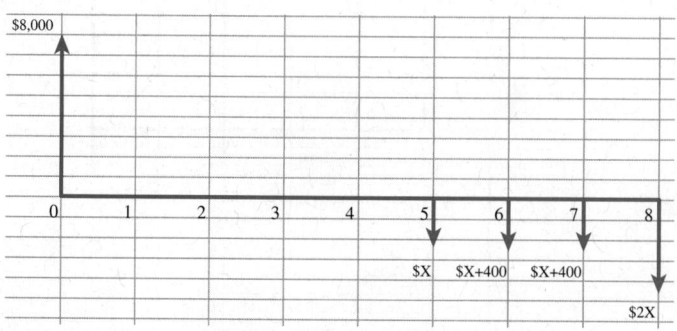

(b) $2,272.61   (c) $2,272.61, $2,372.61, $2,672.61, $4,545.22

60. (a) $1,711.50   (b) $3,167.86   (c) $1,996.29

62. Payment method 2

64. $7,947.62

66. $46,573.45

68. $6,097.27

70. (a) $12,194.53   (b) $14,938.83

72. Prefer to receive $10K/year for 5 years; prefer to pay $5K/year for 10 years

74. (a) $17,908.48   (b) $25,937.42

76. (a) $5,746.64   (b) $10,363.63   (c) $13,999.09

78. $25,180.40

80. (a) $43,157.13   (b) $63,856.54   (c) $95,010.55

82. (a) 6.367   (b) 9.196%

84. (a) $402,532.54   (b) $39,181.05   (c) $36,227.93

86. $11,194.61

88. $7,169.72

90. $929.42

92. $(F|G\,12\%,25) = 902.78225$ (Not tabulated in Appendix A)

94. $65,199.82

96. (a) $8,528.79   (b) $2,690.58

98. (a) $3,154.12   (b) −$719.29

100. $15,173.55

102. $107.87

104. $12,771.80

106. $13,725.51

108. $314.13

110. (a) $313,890.35   (b) $2,354.17

112. (a) $8,471.54   (b) $53,357.69   (c) $47,356.75

114. $41,322.31

116. (a) INR 143,956.88   (b) INR 12,961,004.83

118. $4,622.18

120. $800, $950, $500, $50, − $400, − $600, − $600, − $600

122. (a) $(F|Gi\%, n) = (P|Gi\%, n) * (F|Pi\%, n)$
(b) $(F|Gi\%, n) = ((1+i)^\wedge n - (1 + n*i))/(i^\wedge 2)$ (c) $11,051.00

124. $926,130.51

126. $2,317,332.23

128. $25,656.82

130. −4.04%

132. $286,447.62

134. $8,933.81

136. $50,116.78

138. (a) $7,783.79   (b) $2,455.56

140. $168,206.35

142. (a) For year 5: $1,629,012.50; $3,509,575.68; $2,176,782.34; $7,315,370.52
(b) $8,295,499.60; $15,693,016.73; $9,307,846.73; $33,296,363.05   (c) $7,065,996.66

144. (a) $12,544.41   (b) $18,366.27

146. TO GO FROM NOMINAL ANNUAL TO EFFECTIVE ANNUAL
NOMINAL ANNUAL INTEREST RATE $r = 10.000\%$
NUMBER OF COMPOUNDING PERIODS PER YEAR $m = 4$
EFFECTIVE ANNUAL INTEREST RATE $i_{eff} = 10.381\%$

TO GO FROM EFFECTIVE ANNUAL TO NOMINAL ANNUAL
EFFECTIVE ANNUAL INTEREST RATE $i_{eff} = 10.381\%$
NUMBER OF COMPOUNDING PERIODS PER YEAR $m = 4$
NOMINAL ANNUAL INTEREST RATE $r = 10.000\%$

148. 34.113 so go with 35 months

150. (a) 5.0625%   (b) 5.0838%   (c) 5.0945%   (d) 5.1053%   (e) 5.1162%

152. (a) $17.99   (b) $19.10

154. $8,197.46

156. (a) $12,548.25   (b) $12,463.34   (c) $12,419.86   (d) $12,390.48
(e) $12,379.09   (f) $12,376.16   (g) $12,375.69   (h) $12,375.67   (i) $12,375.67

158. (a) $447,107.83   (b) $549,886.24   (c) $19,869.02

160. (a) 0.911%   (b) 10.932%   (c) 11.497%

162. (a) $970.00   (b) 3.093%   (c) 160.825%   (d) 387.382%

164. $965.95

166. 36.18 quarters

168. 19.338 quarters

170. (a) $(P|F\,i\%, n+m) = (1+i)^{\wedge} - (n+m) = ((1+i)^{\wedge} - n) * ((1+i)^{\wedge} - m) = (P|F\,i\%, n) * (P|F\,i\%, m)$

(b) $(P|F\,i\%, n-m) = (1+i)^{\wedge} - (n-m) = ((1+i)^{\wedge} - n) * ((1+i)^{\wedge}m) = (P|F\,i\%, n) * (F|P\,i\%, m)$

(c) $(P|F\,i\%, nm) = (1+i)^{\wedge} - (nm) = ((1+i)^{\wedge} - n)^{\wedge}m = (P|F\,i\%, n)^{\wedge}m$

(d) $(P|F\,i\%, nm) = (1+i)^{\wedge} - (nm) = ((1+i)^{\wedge} - m)^{\wedge}n = (P|F\,i\%, m)^{\wedge}n$

172. (a) 5.000%   (b) 5.127%   (c) 5.127%

174. $16,487.21

176. (a) $9,886.20   (b) $4,909.34   (c) $4,909.34

178. (a) $42,410.96   (b) $21,060.66   (c) $2,145.15

180. $3,972.80

Chapter 3

FE2. b   **FE4.** a   **FE6.** a   **FE8.** d   **FE10.** a   **FE12.** d   **FE14.** b

2. (a. - Method 1) – Year 2: $1,020.00; Year 4: $1,020.00

(b. - Method 2) – Year 1: $3,420.00; Year 3: $3,012.00; Year 5: $2,604.00

(c. - Method 3) – Year 2: $3,045.19; Year 4: $3,045.19

(d. - Method 4) – Year 1: $0.00; Year 3: $0.00; Year 5: $18,043.88

(e. - Different) – Year 2: $2,818.00; Year 4: $3,307.57

4. (a. - Method 1) – Year 1: $87.50; Year 6: $87.50; Year 12: $5,087.50

(b. - Method 2) – Year 1: $504.17; Year 6: $467.71; Year 12: $423.96

(c. - Method 3) – Year 1: $465.57; Year 6: $465.57; Year 12: $465.57

(d. - Method 4) – Year 1 $0.00; Year 6: $0.00; Year 12: $6,157.20

(e. - Different) – Year 1 $254.17; Year 6: $400.42; Year 12: $678.33

6. (a. - Method 1) – PW(4%) = $14,403.98

(b. - Method 2) – PW(4%) = $13,480.08

(c. - Method 3) – PW(4%) = $13,556.64

(d. - Method 4) – PW(4%) = $14,830.75

(e. - Different) – PW(4%) = $13,649.02

8. (a. - Method 1) – PW(36%) = $4,377.87

(b. - Method 2) – PW(36%) = $4,644.79

(c. - Method 3) – PW(36%) = $4,634.27

(d. - Method 4) – PW(36%) = $4,318.53

(e. - Different) – PW(36%) = $4,568.34

10. (a) $689.86   (b) $688.23

12. Use of Google

14. (a) $1,241.57   (b) $178,507.54   (c) 7.0405%   (d) 6.8230%

16. (a) $1,194.63   (b) $1,214.04   (c) $180,645.74   (d) 6.80832%   (e) 6.60468%

18. (a) $1,123.92   (b) $1,193.69   (c) $187,486.61   (d) 6.6357%   (e) 6.44202%

20. (a) $1,552.46   (b) $1,647.25   (c) $151,783.50   (d) 6.6173%   (e) 6.42471%

22. $12,336.70

24. (a) $3,354.16; $3052.77; $3,052.77, $3,297.10, $3,543.87, $3,792.40, $4,042.06, $4,292.22; $2,492.70
(b) −$484,135.81; − $462,540.33; − $501,614.37; − $479,239.93

26. (a) $658.35   (b) $150.07   (c) $6,825.49   (d) $4,473.77

28. (a) $2,921.71   (b) $151,127.13   (c) From $0.00 to $8,719.49

30. (a) $1,178.08   (b) $1,178.08; $0.00   (c) $437.14; $740.94   (d) $183.34; $994.74   (e) $14,437.43

32. (a) $40,015.30   (b) $940,550.79   (c) $500,000.00   (d) $423,175.45

34. $3,103,408.41

36. $619,962.84 at the end of year 20

38. Went to www.wachovia.com

40. (a) Pay $6,500 instead of PW = $6,872.76   (b) $i_{\text{eff}} = 17.27\%$

42. Q = $656.97; R = $1,511.34

44. X = $798.12; Y = $849.73

46. 8.82% Do not invest

48. $6,056.31 or less

50. 10.00%

52. (a)

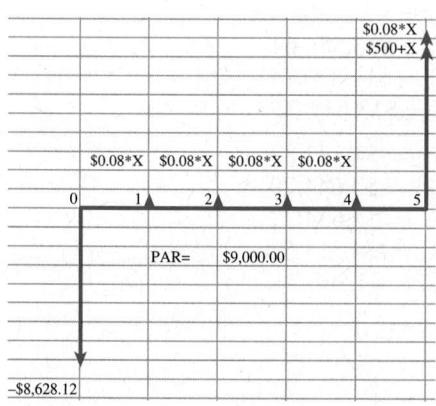

     (b) $9000.00

54. Buy bond since the effective yield is 8.6768%

56. (a) $3,692.51   (b) 3.97721%

58. The 2nd alternative at $11,818.72

60. (a) FW = $3,059.20   (b) PW = $2,299.18   (c) A = $918.79

Chapter 4

FE2. a   **FE4.** a   **FE6.** c   **FE8.** b   **FE10.** d   **FE12.** d

2. (a) prior projects, equipment vendors, trade publications
(b) prior projects, company guidelines, federal guidelines, cost of capital
(c) prior projects, equipment guidelines, company needs, planning horizon methodology

4. (a) Least Common Multiple = 15 years

EOY	Alt 1	Alt 2
0	−$50,000.00	−$80,000.00
1	$25,000.00	$35,000.00
2	$30,000.00	$45,000.00
3	−$15,000.00	$50,000.00
4	$25,000.00	$55,000.00
5	$30,000.00	−$20,000.00
6	−$15,000.00	$35,000.00
7	$25,000.00	$45,000.00

EOY	Alt 1	Alt 2
8	$30,000.00	$50,000.00
9	−$15,000.00	$55,000.00
10	$25,000.00	−$20,000.00
11	$30,000.00	$35,000.00
12	−$15,000.00	$45,000.00
13	$25,000.00	$50,000.00
14	$30,000.00	$55,000.00
15	$35,000.00	$60,000.00

(b) Shortest Life = 3 years

EOY	Alt 1	Alt 2
0	−$50,000.00	−$80,000.00
1	$25,000.00	$35,000.00
2	$30,000.00	$45,000.00
3	$35,000.00	$60,000.00

(c) Fixed Life = 2 years

EOY	Alt 1	Alt 2
0	−$50,000.00	−$80,000.00
1	$25,000.00	$35,000.00
2	$40,000.00	$65,000.00

6. (a) Least Common Multiple = 12 years

EOY	Alt 1	Alt 2
0	−$100.00	−$70.00
1	$20.00	$30.00
2	$20.00	$40.00
3	$40.00	−$20.00
4	−$40.00	$30.00
5	$20.00	$40.00
6	$20.00	−$20.00

EOY	Alt 1	Alt 2
7	$40.00	$30.00
8	−$40.00	$40.00
9	$20.00	−$20.00
10	$20.00	$30.00
11	$40.00	$40.00
12	$60.00	$50.00

(b) Shortest Life = 3 years

EOY	Alt 1	Alt 2
0	−$100.00	−$70.00
1	$20.00	$30.00
2	$20.00	$40.00
3	$40.00	$50.00

(c) Longest Life = 4 years

EOY	Alt 1	Alt 2
0	−$100.00	−$70.00
1	$20.00	$30.00
2	$20.00	$40.00
3	$40.00	−$20.00
4	$60.00	$80.00

8. (a) 7 years;   (b) SV(A) = $3,000, SV(B) = $12,000, SV(C) = $25,000

10. (a) 7 years;   (b) FW,   (c) AW;
(d) FW(W) = $186.85K, FW(X) = $220.01K, prefer X

12. graph required

14. 15.6%

16. (a) 13.33%,   (b) 17.33%

18. 6.87%

20. 10.93%

22. 25% loan, 75% stock

24. 19.12%

26. 11.12%

28. 3.84%

30. 5.61%

32. 10.4%

34. 14.90%

36. (a) less volatile than market;   (b) risk free;   (c) market risk;
(d) more volatile than market

38. (a) 9.75%;   (b) 11.50%;   (c) 12.00%;   (d) 6.00%;   (e) 11.00%

Chapter 5

FE2. d   **FE4.** c   **FE6.** c   **FE8.** b   **FE10.** d

2. (a) the term "present value" is used in multiple places   (b) the term "present value" is used rather than "present worth"

4. (a) BTCC = 10.00%;ATCC = 10.00%   (b) BTCC = 10.50%;ATCC = 9.30%
(c) BTCC = 11.00%;ATCC = 8.60%   (d) BTCC = 11.50%;ATCC = 7.90%
(e) BTCC = 12.00%;ATCC = 7.20%

6. (a) prefer project, PW > 0   (b) prefer do nothing, IRR < MARR
(c) prefer do nothing, AW < 0   (d) prefer project, B/C > 1
(e) prefer project, FW > 0   (f) prefer project, ERR > MARR
(g) prefer do nothing, PW < 0   (h) prefer project, IRR > MARR
(i) prefer project, AW > 0   (j) prefer do nothing, B/C < 1
(k) prefer do nothing, FW < 0   (l) prefer do nothing, ERR < MARR
(m) the assumption being made is that the un-invested funds can be invested elsewhere to earn at least MARR   (n) no, it is not possible; PW and IRR are consistent measures of worth; when correctly calculated they will lead to the same accept/reject decision   (o) yes, it is possible; AW and B/C are consistent measures of worth and they lead to the same accept/reject conclusion   (p) the PW must be less than zero for project (j)
(q) the IRR must be less than MARR for project (j)

8. (a) (1);   (b) (2),   (c) (3),   (d) (1),   (e) (3),   (f) (1)

10. (a) PW = −$31,203   (b) if PW >= 0, accept; otherwise, reject   (c) do not buy the gang punch

12. (a) PW = −$4,870   (b) if PW >= 0, accept; otherwise, reject   (c) the filter is not economically justified   (d) environmental issue

14. (a) PW = $838   (b) if PW >= 0, accept; otherwise, reject   (c) implement the process improvement

16. $79,427

18. (a) PW = $89   (b) if PW >= 0, accept; otherwise, reject   (c) investment is attractive

20. (a) PW = $3.87   (b) if PW >= 0, accept; otherwise, reject   (c) investment is attractive

22. (a) PW = $342.76   (b) if PW >= 0, accept; otherwise, reject   (c) pursue the new product

24. (a) PW = $1,480   (b) if PW >= 0, accept; otherwise, reject   (c) buy the truck

26. PW(A − B) = −$4,904; therefore, Vendor B is preferred

28. (a) PW(127B) = $17,707; PW(334A) = −$245   (b) highest PW is preferred
(c) prefer Model 127B

30. PW(none) = −$2,304, 213; PW(1 inch) == −$353,463; PW(2 inch) = −$396,837;
1 − inch insulation is preferred

32. (a) PW(Lagrange) = $1,341,897; PW(Auburn) = $1,222,454; PW(Anniston) = $1,198,722
(b) highest PW is preferred   (c) locate in Lagrange

34. (a) PW(7745) = −$11,650; PW(A37Y) = −$10,208   (b) highest PW is preferred
(c) purchase A37Y

36. (a) PW(Y) = −$20,804; PW(Z) = −$19,377   (b) highest PW is preferred
(c) use structure Z

38. (a) PW(I) = $2,409; PW(II) = −$1,117; PW(III) = $2,967   (b) purchase Polisher III

40. savings account establishes MARR at 12%, therefore,
PW(savings certificate) = −$349
PW(racehorse) = −$991
PW(savings account) = $0
Prefer savings account

42. service costs are treated as revenue is equipment is purchased, leading to
    (a) PW(equipment) = −$66,099; therefore, the service contract is preferred
    (b) PW(equipment) = $44,081; therefore, the equipment purchase is preferred
    (c) approximately 380 units

44. (a) PW(T1) = $371,552; PW(T2) = $392,225; PW(T3) = $215,375; PW(T4) = $195,575; prefer T2
    (b) PW(T1) = $25,672; PW(T2) = −$33,957; PW(T3) = −$29,240; PW(T4) = −$72,095; prefer T1

46. PW = −$1,859; van is not economically attractive

58. PW(M1) = −$926, PW(M2) = −$903; PW(M3) = −$876; prefer M3

50. PW = $999; sprinkler system is economically attractive

52. PW(D1) = −$21.22M, PW(D2) = −$23.73M; prefer Design 1

54. PW = $38,577; filter is economically attractive

56. PW = $5,652; investment is attractive; if PW >= 0, then attractive; otherwise not attractive

58. PW(purchase) = $4,711; PW(lease) = −$249; prefer purchase

60. PW(A) = −$58,327; PW(B) = −$61,979; prefer pump B

62. PW(I) = $2,207; PW(II) = $1,194, prefer Option I

64. PW(1) = $72,765; PW(2) = $76,987; PW(3) = $100,000; prefer Alternative 3

66. (a) PBP = 10   (b) if PBP <= 3 yrs, accept; otherwise, reject   (c) do not buy the gang punch   (d) PW results in buy decision, DPBP and PBP result in not to buy decisions; PW is a superior measure of worth, therefore the recommendation should be to buy

68. (a) PBP = 3
    (b) if PBP <= 3 yrs, accept; otherwise, reject
    (c) pursue the new product
    (d) PW and PBP results in pursue decision, DPBP results in do not pursue decision; PW is a superior measure of worth, therefore the recommendation should be to pursue the new product

70. DPBP(127B) = 7.202 yrs; DPBP(334A) = not achieved; prefer 127B; consistent with PW analysis

72. CC = $40,334,518

74. CC = $2,909,500

76. Scholarships(20yr) = $36,790; Scholarships(30yr) = $28,915
    Scholarships(50yr) = $23,275; Scholarship(forever) = $20,000

78. CC = $210

80. CC(Pay-Me-Now) = $5,000;   CC(Pay-Me-Later) = $3,957;   CC(Pay-Me-Forever) = $4,167;
    Pay-Me-Later is preferred

Chapter 6

FE2. a   **FE4.** b   **FE6.** c   **FE8.** a   **FE10.** d   **FE12.** b

2. (a) true;   (b) true,   (c) true,   (d) true,   (e) false,   (f) false

4. (a) $4,060;   (b) $3,678;   (c) first = $2,285, last = $10,085;
    (d) first = $2,385, last = $15,319

6. (a) $15,985;   (b) $1,450;   (c) $568

8. $14,401

10. (a) $1,075,274;   (b) $141,366;   (c) $126,302;   (d) $118,463

12. (a) $3,449;   (b) $2,785;   (c) $2,507;   (d) $2,405

14. (a) $17,392;   (b) no need to switch, identical balance

16.
25	$2,049.80
30	$3,343.06
35	$5,496.21
40	$9,159.04
45	$15,624.39
50	$27,816.62
55	$53,963.14
60	$129,607.38
65	$1,000,000.00

18. (a) FW = $7,893   (b) if FW >= 0, then accept; otherwise, reject   (c) buy the gang punch

20. (a) FW = $1,121.34   (b) if FW >= 0, then accept; otherwise, reject   (c) implement the process improvement

22. $79,427

24. (a) $597   (b) if FW >= 0, then accept; otherwise, reject   (c) invest

26. (a) $12.01   (b) if FW >= 0, then accept; otherwise, reject   (c) invest

28. (a) $552   (b) if FW >= 0, then accept; otherwise, reject   (c) pursue the new product

30. (a) $2,822   (b) if FW >= 0, then accept; otherwise, reject   (c) buy truck

32. (a) average for each = $9,500/yr
(b) I = varies from the average using a positive gradient
   II = varies from the average using a negative gradient
   III = uses the average
(c) yes, deposit sooner (negative gradient) to accumulate a larger balance

34. (a) FW(A) = $23,767; FW(B) = $30,947   (b) prefer highest FW   (c) purchase from Vendor B

36. approximately 7,765 units/yr

38. FW(none) = −$5,976,534; FW(1 inch) = −$916,793; FW(2 inch) = −$1,029,293; prefer 1 inch

40. order: null, Auburn, Lagrange, Anniston
FW(Auburn-null) = $6,540434
FW(Lagrange − Auburn) = $639,052
FW(Anniston − Lagrange) = −$766.023
Prefer Lagrange

42. order: A37Y, 7745
FW(7745 − A37Y) = −$2,582; prefer A37Y

44. FW(I) = $9,745; FW(II) = −$4,518; FW(III) = $12,003; prefer III

46. FW(savings account) = 0; FW(savings certificate) = −$633; FW(race horse) = −$1,800; prefer savings account

48. (a) FW(equipment)=−$205,292.41; prefer service contract   (b) FW(equipment) = $136,908; prefer equipment purchase   (c) approximately 380 units

50. (a) FW(T1) = $3,460,348;   FW(T2) = $3,652,877;   FW(T3) = $2,005,835;   FW(T4) = $1,821,439;   prefer   T2   (b) FW(T1) = $855,730;   FW(T2) = −$1,131,910;   FW(T3) = −$974,689; FW(T4) = −$2,403,198; prefer T1

52. FW = −$2,637; do not purchase delivery van

54. FW(M1) = −$1,458; FW(M2) = −$1,420; FW(M3) = −$1,378; prefer M3

56. FW = $3,515; sprinkler system is economically attractive

58. FW(D1) = −$28.24M; FW(D2) = −$31.59M; prefer Design 1

60. FW = $119.8K; filter is economically justified

62. (a) FW = $216,688;   (b) investment is attractive   (c) if FW >= 0, accept; otherwise, reject

64. FW(purchase) = $6,270; FW(lease) = −$331; prefer purchase

66. (a) Total Portfolio Value(light bar) = $40,233; Total Portfolio Value(sliding spots) = $37,634; Total Portfolio Value(light bar) = $39,459   (b) FW analysis and Total Portfolio Value analysis produce a consistent decision

68. FW(334A − 127B) = −$124,368; prefer 127B

Chapter 7

FE2. c   **FE4.** a   **FE6.** c   **FE8.** d   **FE10.** d

2. (a) true;   (b) true,   (c) true,   (d) true,   (e) false,   (f) false

4. (a) AW = $14,187   (b) if AW >= 0, then accept; otherwise, reject   (c) project is economically justified

6. (a) AW = $1,161;   (b) investment is attractive   (c) if AW >= 0, accept; otherwise, reject

8. $7,448

10. (a) AW = $4,366   (b) if AW >= 0, accept; otherwise, reject   (c) buy the gang punch

12. (a) AW = $1,107   (b) if AW >= 0, accept; otherwise, reject   (c) buy the gang punch

14. $79,428

16. (a) AW = $14.18   (b) if AW >= 0, accept; otherwise, reject   (c) invest

18. (a) AW = $0.68   (b) if AW >= 0, accept; otherwise, reject   (c) invest

20. (a) AW = $90.42   (b) if AW >= 0, accept; otherwise, reject   (c) pursue new product

22. (a) AW = $747   (b) if AW >= 0, accept; otherwise, reject   (c) buy truck

24. AW(A − B) = −$1,547; therefore, Vendor B is preferred

26. AW(none) = −$375,000; PW(1 inch) == −$57,525; PW(2 inch) = −$64,583; 1-inch insulation is preferred

28. (a) AW(Lagrange) = $247,554; AW(Auburn) = $225,519; AW(Anniston) = $221,141   (b) highest AW is preferred   (c) locate in Lagrange

30. (a) AW(7745) = −$1,583; AW(A37Y) = −$1,387   (b) highest AW is preferred   (c) purchase A37Y

32. (a) AW(A) = $806; AW(B) = −$41   (b) pursue Project A

34. (a) AW(A001) = $27.56; AW(B002) = $27.45; AW(C003) = $29.52 (b) recommend C003

36. (a) AW(T) = −$16,941; AW(M) = −$14,443 (b) purchase Drill M

38. (a) null, X1 only, X2 only, X1&Y1, X2&Y2 (b) AW(null) = $0; AW(X1) = −$274; AW(X2) = −$212; AW(X1Y1) = $1,101; AW(X2Y2) = $1,601; prefer X2&Y2

40. AW = −$378; van is not economically attractive

42. AW(M1) = −$305, AW(M2) = −$297; AW(M3) = −$288; prefer M3

44. AW = $209; sprinkler system is economically attractive

46. AW(D1) = −$8.53M, AW(D2) = −$9.54M; prefer Design 1

48. AW = $6,828; filter is economically attractive

50. PW(purchase) = $1,894; PW(lease) = −$100; prefer purchase

52. (a) 15 years (b) AW(1) = $9,577; AW(2) = $26,748
(c) AW(1) = $9,577; AW(2) = $26,748

54. AW(Pipe A) = −$11,733; AW(Pipe B) = −$11,556; prefer Pipe B

56. (a) PW(127B) = $2,639; PW(334A) = −$37 (b) highest AW is preferred
(c) prefer Model 127B

58. (a) PW(Y) = −$1,508; PW(Z) = −$1,404 (b) highest AW is preferred
(c) use structure Z

60. CR(1) = $25,600; CR(2) = $24,831; CR(3) = $21,002; CR(4) = $18,915; CR(5) = $16,680; CR(6) = $14,869

62. $6,761.20

64. $14,869.76

66. selected values of n and CR

1	$20,600.00
5	$4,838.67
10	$2,911.56
15	$2,299.76
20	$2,015.19
25	$1,859.90

Chapter 8

FE2. a **FE4.** d **FE6.** c **FE8.** c **FE10.** c **FE12.** d

2. (a) true; (b) true, (c) true, (d) true, (e) false, (f) false

4. (a) one positive real root; (b) unique positive real root; (c) 12.98%; (d) attractive

6. (a) 4, 2, or 0 real positive roots; (b) no conclusion; (c) 8.08% and 37.43%; attractive

8. (a) 9.82%, 25.67%, 57.45%; (b) not attractive

10. (a) IRR > MARR; (b) IRR = MARR; (c) IRR < MARR;
(d) IRR > MARR; (e) IRR = MARR; (f) IRR < MARR;
(g) IRR > MARR; (h) IRR = MARR; (i) IRR < MARR

12. (a) 36.35%; (b) if IRR >= MARR, accept; otherwise, reject; (c) justified

14. (a) $7,413; (b) $10,414; (c) $20,344; (d) $3,718; (e) −$3,000

16. (a) 7.42%; (b) if IRR >= MARR, accept; otherwise, reject; (c) not justified

18. (a) 17.91%; (b) if IRR >= MARR, accept; otherwise, reject; (c) buy sprinkler system

20. (a) 16.52%; (b) if IRR $>=$ MARR, accept; otherwise, reject; (c) do not buy computer system

22. (a) 15.70%; (b) if IRR $>=$ MARR, accept; otherwise, reject; (c) do not invest

24. (a) 25.16%; (b) if IRR $>=$ MARR, accept; otherwise, reject; (c) buy water filtration system

26. (a) 7.45%; (b) if IRR $>=$ MARR, accept; otherwise, reject; (c) do not implement design change

28. IRR $= -0.35\%$; do not purchase van

30. IRR $= 26.83\%$; filter is justified

32. (a) null; (b) A; (c) D; (d) F; (e) G

34. (a) in K$ by year, $-\$130$, \$80, \$80, \$80, \$80, \$80, \$80, \$80, \$80, \$80, \$85;
(b) 61%, (c) A; (d) C < 0, D < 0, A > 0, B $= 0$

36. IRR$(A - B) = 7.71\%$, purchase from Vendor B

38. order: null, Auburn, Lagrange, Anniston
IRR(Auburn-null) $= 40.29\%$
IRR(Lagrange $-$ Auburn) $= 25.09\%$
IRR(Anniston $-$ Lagrange) $= 4.73\%$
Prefer Lagrange

40. order: null, A, B
IRR(A-null) $= 13.89\%$
IRR(B $-$ A) $= 7.75\%$
Prefer A

42. order: null, B002, C003, A001
IRR(B002-null) $= 42.11\%$
IRR(C003-B002) $= 16.48\%$
IRR(A001-C003) $= 5.65\%$
Prefer C003

44. (a) null, X1 only, X2 only, X1&Y1, X2&Y2 (b) order: null, B002, C003, A001;
IRR(X1-null) $= 5.84\%$
IRR(X2-null) $= 7.90\%$
IRR(X1&Y1-null) $= 19.44\%$
IRR(X2&Y2-X1Y1) $= 18.62\%$
Prefer X2Y2

46. IRR(onetime-extended) $= 7.36\%$; prefer onetime

48. order: null, bar, spots, beam
IRR(bar-null) $= 24.29\%$
IRR(spots-bar) $= 3.47\%$
IRR(beam-bar) $= 9.35\%$
Prefer light bar

50. IRR(purchase-lease) $= 17.94\%$; prefer purchase

52. ERR $= 11.57\%$; attractive

54. ERR $= 10.35\%$; attractive

56. ERR $= 9.9997\%$; not attractive

58. (a) ERR $= 8.97\%$ (b) if ERR $>=$ MARR, accept; otherwise, reject   (c) implement the process improvement

60. (a) ERR $= 14.07\%$ (b) if ERR $>=$ MARR, accept; otherwise, reject   (c) invest

62. (a) ERR $= 14.68\%$ (b) if ERR $>=$ MARR, accept; otherwise, reject   (c) pursue new product

64. order: null, A, B
ERR(A-null) $= 12.30\%$
ERR(B-A) $= 11.28\%$
Prefer A

66. order: Gate 1, Gate 2, Gate 3
ERR(2-1) $= 16.81\%$
ERR(3-1) $= 21.27\%$
Prefer Gate 3

68. IRR(II-I) $= 21.86$; prefer II

70. (a) IRR(equip-serv) $= -8.35\%$;   prefer   service   (b) IRR(equip-serv) $= 22.01\%$;   prefer equipment

72. IRR(D2-D1) $= -21.76\%$; prefer Design 1

74. IRR(Z-Y) $= 7.11\%$; prefer Structure Z

76. 11.98%

78. 6.45%

80. (a) 10.01%   (b) if MIRR $>=$ MARR, accept; otherwise, reject   (c) do not invest

82. order: First, Second, Both
MIRR(Second-First) $= 12.87\%$
MIRR(Both-Second) $= 10.69\%$
Prefer Both

Chapter 9

FE2. c   **FE4.** b   **FE6.** d   **FE8.** a   **FE10.** d   **FE12.** b

2. (a) One reason is that U.S. Tax Law prohibits simply subtracting the investment all at one time (with certain exceptions covered in Chapter 10).   (b) Depreciation charges, while not cash flows, can be treated as expenses for the purpose of figuring taxable income.

4. (b) Tangible, Personal, Nondepreciable (d) Tangible, Personal, Depreciable (f) Tangible, Personal, Depreciable (h) Tangible, Real, Depreciable

6. (a) $9,974.18   (b) $15,346.51   (c) Sinking fund depreciation   (d) $110,000.00

8. (a) Year 1: $10,574.02; Year 2: $11,631.42; Year 3: $12,794.56   (b) Less depreciation occurs in the early years and more in the back years.   (c) Because it is band end loaded.

10. (a) Year 2: $300,000.00   (b) Year 2: $391,238.40   (c) Year 2: $384,000.00
(d) Year 2: $384,000.00   (e) Year 2: $400,000.00

12. (a) $38,000.00   (b) $1,500.00   (c) (i) $14,300.00; (ii) $2,781.79; (iii) $6,708.00;
(iv) $6,708.00; (v) $6,900.00

14. (a) Year 4: $24,000.00   (b) Year 4: $0.00   (c) Year 4: $10,368.00   (d) Year 4: $12,960.00   (e) Year 4: $16,000.00

16. Year 1: 1.7708% and $1,558.33
Year 5: 2.5000% and $2,200.00
Year 41: 0.7292% and $641.67

18. Year 1: 20.00%; Year 2: 32.00%; Year 3: 19.20%; Year 4: 11.52%; Year 5: 11.52%; Year 6: 5.76%

20. Year 1: 25.00%; Year 2: 37.50%; Year 3: 18.75%; Year 4: 12.50%; Year 5: 6.25%

22. (b) MACRS-GDS(3); 200% DBSLH   (d) NA; NA   (f) MACRS-GDS(5); 200% DBSLH
(h) MACRS-GDS(27.5); SLM

24. (a) $800,000.00   (b) $449,820.00 using MACRS-GDS(7)

26. (a) MACRS-GDS(5)   (b) Depreciation deduction in years 1, 3, 5, 7: $70,000.00; $67,200.00; $40,320.00; $0.00   (c) Unrecovered investment in years 1, 3, 5, 7: $280,000.00; $100,800.00; $20,160.00; $0.00

28. (a) MACRS-GDS(3)   (b) Depreciation and unrecovered investment in year 4: $6,669.00; $0.00   (c) Depreciation and unrecovered investment in year 4: $3,334.50; $3,334.50   (d) Depreciation and unrecovered investment in year 3: $6,664.50; $13,333.50

30. (a) MACRS-GDS(5)   (b) Depreciation and unrecovered investment in year 3: $307,200.00; $460,800.00   (c) Depreciation and unrecovered investment in year 3: $153,600.00; $614,400.00

32. (a) $4,400.00; $4,224.00; $1,267.20   (b) $4,400.00; $4,224.00; $1,267.20

34. (a) MACRS-GDS(10)   (b) Depreciation in years 5 and 6: $23,050.00; $9,212.50
(c) Depreciation in years 6 and 7: $18,425.00; $8,187.50

36. (a) MACRS-GDS(10)   (b) Depreciation and unrecovered investment in year 5: $248,940.00; $995,220.00

38. (a) MACRS-GDS(39)   (b) $15,996.50; $16,666.00; $16,666.00   (c) $15,996.50; $16,666.00; $9,027.42

40. (a) MACRS-GDS(27.5)   (b) Years 1–7: $16,864.60; $19,270.80; $19,270.80; $19,270.80; $19,270.80; $19,270.80; $4,014.75   (c) Years 0–7: $530,000.00; $513,135.40; $493,864.60; $474,593.80; $455,323.00; $436,052.20; $416,781.40; $412,766.65

42. (a) MACRS-GDS(27.5)   (b) Years 1–5: $1,932.05; $3,090.60; $3,090.60; $3,090.60; $2,189.18   (c) Years 0–5: $85,000.00; $83,067.95; $79,977.35; $76,886.75; $73,796.15; $71,606.98

44.

	Depreciation in year 3	PW of Depreciation	Unrecovered Investment end year 3
(a)	$125,885.00	$695,417.17	$62,985.00
(b)	$125,925.93	$674,681.95	$62,962.96
(c)	$62,962.96	$709,854.95	$31,481.48
(d)	$94,444.44	$732,873.93	$0.00
(e)	$283,333.33	$692,385.84	$0.00
(f)	$283,333.33	$658,078.43	$141,666.67
(g)	$141,666.67	$0.00	$716,428.02

46. (a) 1,600; 9,350; 7,600; 1,190　　(b) 4,260

48. (a) $380,000.00　　(b) $60,000.00　　(c) 4　　(d) $32,000.00;　$64,000.00;　$96,000.00; $128,000.00

50. (a) $200,000.00　　(b) $148,500.00

52. (a) $255,555.56　　(b) $202,500.00

Chapter 10

FE2. b　　**FE4.** b　　**FE6.** b　　**FE8.** b　　**FE10.** b

2. One is: Perform after-tax analyses, not before-tax analyses, except in unusual situations

4. (a) Gross income – a company's income before taking deductions or taxes into account
(c) Depreciation – method of attributing cost of assets across its useful life

6. (a) $1,800.00; 15%; 15%　　(b) $11,250.00; 17.31%; 25.00%　　(c) $69,050.00 31.39%; 39.00%　　(d) $340,000.00; 34.00%; 34.00%　　(e) $6,754,999.99; 35.00%; 35.00%

8. (a) $100,001.00　　(b) $335,000.00　　(c) $18,333,333.33

10. (a) 15.00%　　(b) 31.25%　　(c) 35.05%　　(d) 39.00%

12. (a) 35.00%　　(b) 35.00%　　(c) 35.00%　　(d) 35.00%

14. (a) $7,325,000.00　　(b) $4,210,000.00

16. (a) $70,000.00　　(b) $18,850.00

18.

		ATCF(2)	ATCF(7)	PW	AW	IRR	ERR
(a)		$300,000.00	$300,000.00	$293,779.34	$55,067.18	15.24%	12.65%
(b)	M(5)	$419,200.00	$240,000.00	$369,389.01	$69,239.76	17.34%	13.27%
(c)		$345,000.00	$259,667.97	$343,590.85	$64,404.05	16.61%	13.06%

20.

		ATCF(2)	ATCF(4)	PW	AW	IRR	ERR
(a)		$225,000.00	$1,125,000.00	$16,519.66	$5,099.10	9.42%	9.33%
(b)	M(7)	$312,246.00	$956,142.00	$38,021.09	$11,735.92	10.03%	9.76%
(c)		$255,000.00	$1,032,500.00	$31,038.34	$9,580.56	9.83%	9.62%

22.

	ATCF(2)	ATCF(8)	PW	AW	IRR	ERR
(a)	$57,000.00	$75,000.00	$50,425.36	$10,150.77	17.63%	14.70%

(b) PW here is $50,425.36 versus only $8,520.80 where MACRS-GDS(5) is used. Expensing the entire marketing study in year 0 is far more attractive than depreciating an asset over years 1–6.

24.

	ATCF(2)	ATCF(4)	PW	AW	IRR	ERR
(a)	$22,200.00	$25,800.00	$18,829.86	$5,940.27	24.90%	18.54%

(b) PW here is $18,829.86 versus only $12,790.37 where MACRS-GDS(3) is used. Expensing the entire 100-day project in year 0 is far more attractive than depreciating an asset over years 1–4.

26.

	ATCF(2)	ATCF(12)	PW	AW	IRR	ERR
(a)	$27,000.00	$30,000.00	$70,925.57	$13,294.57	21.44%	14.53%

(b) PW here is $70,925.57 versus only $49,755.75 where MACRS-GDS(7) is used. Expensing the entire design portfolio in year 0 is far more attractive than depreciating an asset over years 1–8.

28. (a) Select virtual mold apparatus costing $87,500.00 since its AW is −$85,494.12 versus the higher cost AW of −$97,016.07.   (b) Select virtual mold apparatus costing $87,500.00 since its AW is −$86,304.66 versus the higher cost AW of −$97,557.97.

30. Investment A is (slightly) less costly at −$9,181.26 versus −$9,249.26.

32. (a) Select investment A with AW = −$16,878.62 versus −$17,368.53.   (b) $104,039.51

34. (a) −$109,854.04 (MACRS_GDS(39))   (b) −$90,480.00   (c) −$97,221.43
(d) −$90,480.00

36. BTCF means we have not deducted income taxes; BTLCF means we have not deducted interest payment, principal payment, or income taxes from cash flow.

38. (a) $148,020.00   (b) $59,208.00   (c) $260,292.00

40. (a) $183,408.00   (b) $6,000.00   (c) $77,592.00

42.

	PW	FW	AW	IRR	ERR
(a)	$470,030.09	$936,564.39	$84,922.39	29.39%	16.11%
(b)	$451,256.92	$899,157.68	$81,530.56	24.04%	16.43%
(c)	$453,286.63	$903,202.00	$81,897.28	24.54%	16.45%
(d)	$464,294.97	$925,136.80	$83,886.20	31.54%	15.73%

44. (a) $220,209.06   (b) $215,428.05   (c) $216,512.27   (d) $216,872.68

46.

	PW	AW	IRR	ERR
(a)	$37,475.30	$5,839.40	9.50%	9.25%
(b)	−$38,519.14	−$6,002.06	8.64%	8.72%
(c)	−$25,820.80	−$4,023.40	8.74%	8.81%
(d)	$105,148.18	$16,384.20	10.52%	9.69%
(e)	$29,153.73	$4,542.74	9.29%	9.21%
(f)	$41,852.08	$6,521.40	9.44%	9.30%

48. (a) MACRS(7)   (b) 12.00%   (c) $5,000.00   (d) 15.00%
   (e) Interest payment (3) = $-$1,713.82; TI(3) = $-$16,811.82; ATCF(3) = $33,921.66 plus more

50. (a) LTD/TSE = $1,157,000/$15,935,000 or 7.26% on 29 March 2007 Plus more. These will vary over time.

52. (a) $460,332.97   (b) $450,597.36

Chapter 11

FE2. d   **FE4.** c   **FE6.** a   **FE8.** a   **FE10.** b

2. (i) A dishwasher that lasted 22 years; (ii) A 10 year old desktop computer; (iii) incandescent lighting, plus more.

4. (a) Replace – EUAC of replacement is $297,425.02   (b) Replace – EUAC of replacement is $306,965.93

6. (a) $17,000.00   (b) Invest in new DL technology; its EUAC is $28,729.62
   (c) $17,000.00   (d) Invest in new DL technology; its EUAC is $33,214.18

8. (a) Trade in existing and purchase new MH system; EUAC = $40,099.51

10. (a) CF for years 0 to 8 for new turret lathe:-
     $-$47,000.00; $-$ $10,000.00; $-$ $10,000.00; $-$ $10,000.00; $-$ $10,000.00; $-$$10,000.00;
     $-$10,000.00; $-$ $10,000.00; $-$ $6,252.88

   EUAC = $20,200.98

   (b) Replace with new turret lathe
   (c) CF for years 0 to 8 for new turret lathe:
     $-$65,000.00; $-$ $10,000.00; $-$ $10,000.00; $-$ $10,000.00; $-$ $10,000.00;
     $-$10,000.00; $-$ $10,000.00; $-$ $10,000.00; $-$ $6,252.88

   EUAC = $24,212.28

   (d) Replace with new turret lathe

12. (a) CF for years 0 to 10 for existing plus buy additional:
     $-$18,000.00; $-$ $5,050.00; $-$ $5,400.00; $-$ $5,750.00; $-$ $6,100.00; $-$ $6,450.00;
     $-$6,800.00; $-$$7,150.00; $-$ $7,500.00; $-$ $7,850.00; $-$ $5,200.00.

   EUAC = $10,303.69

   (b) Keep existing HVAC unit and buy additional unit
   (c) CF for years 0 to 10 for existing plus buy additional:
     $-$25,000.00; $-$ $5,050.00; $-$ $5,400.00; $-$ $5,750.00; $-$ $6,100.00;
     $-$6,450.00; $-$ $6,800.00; $-$ $7,150.00; $-$ $7,500.00; $-$ $7,850.00; $-$ $5,200.00.

   EUAC = $11,973.35

   (d) Keep existing HVAC unit and buy additional unit

14. (a) Replace with new painting machine at EUAC = $167,051.17   (b) Replace with new painting machine at EUAC = $171,602.20   (c) Replace with new painting machine at EUAC = $164,522.83

16. (a) Keep existing shredder at EUAC = $58,687.99
   (b) Keep existing shredder since EUAC of no shredder is $72,966.89

18. (a) Keep existing crane at EUAC = $21,000.00   (b) Keep existing crane at EUAC = $28,133.39   (c) Keep existing crane; EUAC of new = $17,776.95

20. (a) ATCF of Keep and Buy S for years 0–5: −$210,000.00; − $39,712.00; − $39,698.00; −$45,956.00; − $52,200.00; $11,578.68

  EUAC = $93,325.82

(b) Keep existing multi-axis machine and buy machine S   (c) Keep existing multi-axis machine and buy machine S at EUAC = $93,325.82

22. (a) ATCF of Trade in Existing Auger and Buy Treated Auger for years 0–7: −$51,000.00; $1,896.00; $6,264.00; $3,038.40; $1,103.04; $1,103.04; −$348.48; $8,308.80

  EUAC = $7,114.38

(b) Trade in existing auger and buy treated auger

24. 8 years at EUAC = $8,229.90

26. 17 years at EUAC = $30,454.67

28. 7 years at EUAC = $4,882.01

30. 16 years at EUAC = $17,913.30

Chapter 12

FE2. c   **FE4.** d   **FE6.** c   **FE8.** d   **FE10.** d

2. Gasoline, copper, mechanic labor, tuition

4. Homes and land

6. CPI measures price changes from the perspective of the purchaser, while...

8. Not irrelevant. CPI does not describe any individual's purchasing habits. Also, the economy is very "connected."

10. (a) 284.571; (b) 318.341; (c) 342.627   (b) 7.16394%

12. (a) $15.13; (b) $17.55; (c) $19.42; (d) $16.27; (e) $14.20   (b) 2.20969%

14. 2.1155%

16. 18.5396%

18. $262,268.73

20. (a) 3.18%   (b) $19,005.50   (c) $666.01

22. (a) $35,236.17   (b) $242,628.93

24. (a) $944,160.00; $1,273,483.01; $1,717,673.88; $2,316,798.53; $3,124,897.86
(b) $840,000.00; $1,008,000.00; $1,209,600.00; $1,451,520.00; $1,741,824.00
(c) $3,879,152.31   (d) $3,879,152.31

26. (a) $17,599,971.78   (b) $67,938.73

28. (a) Defer payments. It is worth $1,085,748.75.   (b) 5.24%   (c) Take it now and run.

30. (a) $111,292.23   (b) $111,292.23

32.

	Paid(2)	Paid(5)	PW(then current)	PW(constant $)
(a)	$13,600.00	$173,600.00	$156,888.28	$156,888.28
(b)	$42,880.00	$34,720.00	$158,026.05	$158,026.05
(c)	$40,602.52	$40,602.52	$157,929.64	$157,929.64
(d)	$0.00	$240,585.07	$156,363.79	$156,363.79

34.

	Paid(2)	Paid(4)	PW(then current)	PW(constant $)
(a)	$50,000.00	$550,000.00	$403,986.77	$403,986.77
(b)	$162,500.00	$137,500.00	$435,313,57	$435,313.57
(c)	$157,735.40	$157,735.40	$432,705.28	$432,705.28
(d)	$0.00	$732,050.00	$390,658.52	$390,658.52

36. $1,316.60

38. (a) −$9,000,000.00; $4,292,307.69; $4,065,088.76; $3,014,474.28; $2,154,504.39;
$1,540,869.61; $1,183,879.62   (b) $1,615,078.51   (c) $461,767.31
(d) $4,359,991.90   (e) 26.68%   (f) 21.29%   (g) 31.74%   (h) 26.14%

40. (a) −$190,000.00; $37,452.74; $44,241.35; $38,851.05; $35,145.43; $32,605.15; $32,388.71;
$32,192.26; $29,495.88; $27,000.00; $27,000.00; $27,000.00; $30,000.00
(b) $43,495.36   (c) $6,383.52   (d) $136,507.08
(e) 14.92%   (f) 11.91%   (g) 19.40%   (h) 16.27%

42. (a) −$1,400,000.00; $347,485.60; $405,045.07; $335,035.55; $294,722.97; $292,517.24;
$265,200.21; $240,000.00; $360,000.00   (b) $326,090.32   (c) $61,123.68
(d) $699,003.57   (e) 16.49%   (f) 12.92%   (g) 21.38%   (h) 17.66%

44. (a) −$9,000,000.00; $4,320,000.00; $4,152,000.00; $3,091,200.00; $2,214,720.00;
$1,614,720.00; $1,227,360.00   (b) $865,610.93   (c) $278,075.46
(d) $2,956,751.41   (e) 27.73%   (f) 24.61%   (g) 22.82%   (h) 19.82%

46. (a) −$190,000.00; $37,860.40; $45,612.40; $40,292.40; $36,492.40; $33,786.80; $33,779.20;
$33,786.80; $30,389.60; $27,000.00; $27,000.00; $27,000.00;
$30,000.00   (b) $7,483.92   (c) $1,358.31   (d) $38,481.69
(e) 15.61%   (f) 14.99%   (g) 10.95%   (h) 10.35%

48. (a) −$5,000,000.00; $4,015,384.62; $3,798,816.57; $2,758,443.33; $1,908,320.79;
$1,304,154.60; −$2,204,989.07   (b) $3,547,544.14   (c) $1,014,278.80
(d) $9,576,787.51   (e) 59.09%   (f) 29.03%   (g) 65.45%   (h) 34.19%

50. (a) −$90,000.00; $29,945.52; $37,015.92; $31,896.84; $28,452.25; $26,163.21; −; 53,300.36;
$32,192.26; $29,495.88; $27,000.00; $27,000.00; $27,000.00; $30,000.00
(b) $68,533.67   (c) $10,058.23   (d) $215,088.00
(e) 26.13%   (f) 14.77%   (g) 31.05%   (h) 19.25%

52.

	ATCF(2)	ATCF(6)	PW	FW
(a)	$4,108,800.00	−$2,790,014.60	$3,547,544.14	$12,117,691.37
(b)	$3,490,133.33	$783,318.73	$2,929,877.79	$10,007,868.38
(c)	$3,592,237.79	$566,778.36	$3,021,558.55	$10,321,031.27
(d)	$4,396,800.00	−$4,839,189.05	$3,759,823.63	$12,842,795.08

	AW	IRRc	ERRc	IRRr	ERRr
(a)	$1,139,640.14	65.45%	34.19%	59.09%	29.03%
(b)	$941,216.29	52.96%	32.53%	47.08%	27.43%
(c)	$970,668.52	54.95%	32.78%	48.99%	27.67%
(d)	$1,207,834.43	71.45%	34.74%	64.86%	29.56%

(e) Method 4

Chapter 13

FE2. a   **FE4.** c   **FE6.** b   **FE8.** c   **FE10.** b

2. (a) (3)   (b) (1)   (c) (2)

4. (a) false   (b) true   (c) false

6. (a) 6,137 (rounded)   (b) Plan I

8. (a) $67,584 profit   (b) 307,692 (rounded) units   (c) $132,480 profit

10. (a) 0.1636 inches   (b) steel

12. $5,170.21/yr

14. 426 (rounded) holes/day

16. (a) $500,000 loss   (b) 58.33%

18. (a) $25,000 loss   (b) 220,000 units   (c) $125,000 profit   (d) 132,000 units

20. (a) $7,120   (b) −$3,280, −$680, $1,920, $4,520, $9,720, $12,320   (c) −54.8%

22. graph required

24. graph required; most sensitive is annual revenues, least sensitive is salvage value

26. graph required; favorable/unfavorable line is $y = 9.2 - 60.5x$

28. (a) PW(pessimistic) = −$5.12M, not attractive   (b) PW(most likely) = $2.00M, attractive
(c) PW(optimistic) = $9.66M, attractive   (d) PW(expected) = $2.09M, attractive

30. (a) E[PW] = $91,565, SD[PW] = $10,067   (b) E[PW] = $91,565, SD[PW] = $30,723

32. (a) E[PW] = −$1,031,532, SD[PW] = $835,870
(b) P[PW > 0] = 0.109   (c) E[PW] = −$1,031,539, SD[PW] = $828,138
P[PW > 0] = 0.107   (d) E[PW] = −$1,032,209, SD[PW] = $827,269 P[PW > 0] = 0.107

34. (a) P[PW(A)−PW(B) > 0] = 0.229   (b) 0.234   (c) 0.232

36. (a) P[PW < 0] = 0.437   (b) 0.440   (c) 0.437

38. (a) E[PW] = $825,709, SD[PW] = $649.192   (b) P[PW < 0] = 0.102
(c) P[PW > 1,000,000] = 0.394   (d) 0.101   (e) 0.104

40. (a) P[PW < 0] = 0.289   (b) P[PW > 10000] = 0.142   (c) 0.284, 0.141   (d) 0.288, 0.141

42. (a) E[PW] = −$1,209   (b) PW = −$1,274, P[PW < 0] = 0.560   (c) E[PW] = −$1,209,
P[PW < 0] = 0.631   (d) E[PW] = −$1,304, P[PW < 0] = 0.640   (e) E[PW] = −$1,211,
P[PW < 0] = 0.632

44. (a) decision tree required   (b) purchase new compressor

46. (a) decision tree required   (b) purchase automatic

48. (a) decision tree required   (b) select option A

Chapter 14

FE2. c   **FE4.** d   **FE6.** c   **FE8.** d   **FE10.** b

2. Visited "The World Bank" about International Development Association (IDA)

4. (d) Benefit – Kids of all ages go for fun. Disbenefit – Requires upkeep and maintenance.

6. (a) #3   (b) #3 at $540.00

8. Yes, support at 1.43

10. (a) Do not approve at −$57,712.56   (b) $3.94

12. (a) 1.09   (b) $2800.00

14. Construct B

16. (a) SA   (b) SA at −$9,258,747.13   (c) SB at −$12,860,000.00

18. $2,082, 210.98

20. (a) Steel bridge – it is a sunk cost; also, there is no TVM in the analysis, plus more Concrete bridge –
the bridge is being prorated over 60 years, well beyond the planning horizon; only one resurfacing is
planned during the horizon, plus more   (b) AW of steel bridge is $27,126.51

22. (a) B or C   (b) A   (c) A

24. (a) 7%   (b) $5,677,027.20

26. (a) Project 3 at $395,341.57   (b) Project 1 at $245,918.42

28. (a) Acceptable at 1.16   (b) Not acceptable at 0.53

30. (a) −$139,076.30   (b) −$139,076.30   (c) −$289,076.30   (d) −$364,076.30

32. (a) There is the assumption that the number of visitors will not be impacted.   (b) $B/C = 0.28$

34. (a) $7.00   (b) $0.00   (c) No feasible solution

36. (a) No, at PW net cost of $12,030,872.91   (b) 4.22   (c) $38,762,555.32

38. (a) $5,600,000   (b) $12,686,300   (c) $37,713,700   (d) $13,500,000
    (e) $78,500,000

40. (a) $7,000,000   (b) $8,000,000   (c) $10,570,000
    (d) $22,000,000   (e) $10,820,000   (f) $53,320,000

42. (a) $4,280,000.00   (b) $1,712,000.00   (c) $2,568,000.00
    (d) $28,000,000.00   (e) 9.17%   (f) $11,300,000.00   (g) $6,368,000.00

44. (a) $90,000   (b) 20 years   (c) 6.00%   (d) $31,965

46. Year 1: $329,394.00; Year 3: $356,343.00

Chapter 15

FE2. a   **FE4.** c   **FE6.** d   **FE8.** c   **FE10.** c

2. (a) 2, 4, 5   (b) $43,617.79   (c) 16.94%
    (d) 2, 4, 5   (e) $43,617.79   (f) 16.94%
    (g) (1)   2, 4, 5 $43,617.79
          (2)   2, 3, 4, 5 $49,000.00
          (3)   2, 3, 4 $33,507.05
    (h) (1)   2, 4, 5 $43,617.79
          (2)   2, 4, 5 $21,150.07
          (3)   2, 4, 5 $68,860.59

4. (a) 1, 2, 3, 4   (b) $113,550.45   (c) 24.60%
    (d) 1, 2, 4, 5   (e) $111,387.62   (f) 25.43%
    (g) (1)   1, 2, 3, 4 $113,550.45
          (2)   2, 3, 4, 5 $130,492.90
          (3)   2, 3, 5 $94,445.14
    (h) (1)   1, 2, 3, 4 $113,550.45
          (2)   1, 2, 3, 5 $86,844.50
          (3)   1, 2, 3, 4 $143,619.14

6. (a) 1, 3, 4   (b) $90,978.88   (c) 12.00%
    (d) 1, 2, 3   (e) $79,606.52   (f) 12.33%
    (g) (1)   1, 3, 4 $90,978.88
          (2)   1, 2, 3, 4 $113,723.60
          (3)   1, 2, 3 $79,606.52
    (h) (1)   1, 3, 4 $90,978.88
          (2)   1, 3 $10,814.33
          (3)   1, 3, 4 $191,650.08

8. (a) 2, 4   (b) $530,720.51   (c) 21.99%
    (d) 2, 5   (e) $522,889.02   (f) 20.75%

(g)   (1) 2, 4 $530,720.51

(2) 1, 2, 4 $741,563.04

(3) 1, 4 $507,829.17

(1) 2, 4 $530,720.51

(2) 2, 4 $411,546.84

(3) 2, 5 $668,318.72

10. (a) 2, 4, 5, 6   (b) $9,950.82   (c) 11.42%   (d) 1, 2, 3, 4, 6 $7,676.34
(e) 2, 4, 5, 6 $9,950.82   (f) 2, 4, 5, 6 $9,950.82   (g) 1, 2, 4, 6 $7,486.80

12. (a) 4   13.55%   (b) 4 $3,722.84   13.55%

14. (a) 6   11.70%   (b) 6 $3,222.17   11.70%

16. (a) H11   (b) B9:G9   (c) B9:G9 binary H10 $<=$ H12   (d) Set up any cell for $x_4 + x_5$.
Then, constrain it to be $<= 1$ (e) Set a constraint to have $x_6 <= x_5$ (f) Set up any cell to
be the sum of the x's. Then, constrain this cell to be equal to 3.

18. True

20. (a) 3, 5, 2, 4(60%)

(b) (1) 3, 5, 2, 4(60%) $626,331.89

(2) 3, 5, 2, 4, 1(14.29%) $729,864.52

(3) 3, 5, 2, 4(10%) $522,258.61

(c) (1) 3, 5, 2, 4(60%) $626,331.89

(2) 3, 5, 2, 4(60%) $447,693.13

(3) 3, 5, 2, 4(60%) $834,615.69

(d) 3, 5, 2, 4(60%) $626,331.89

22. (a) 2, 1, 4(43.75%)

(b) (1)   2, 1, 4(43.75%) $68,171.11

(2)   2, 1, 4(87.5%) $79,751.65

(3)   2, 1 $56,590.68

(c) (1)   2, 1, 4(43.75%) $68,171.11

(2)   2, 1, 4(43.75%) $27,695.48

(3)   2, 1, 4(43.75%) $115,128.65

(d) 2, 4, 1(40%) $66,630.85

24. (a) 5, 4, 2, 3(17.65%)

(b) (1)   5, 4, 2, 3(17.65%) $20,883.82

(2)   5, 4, 2, 3(76.47%) $21,816.13

(3)   5, 4, 2(41.67%) $18,775.04

(c) (1)   5, 4, 2, 3(17.65%) $20,883.82

(2)   5 $6,074.70

(3)   5, 4, 2, 3(17.65%) $31,588.24

(d) 5, 4, 2, 3(17.65%) $20,883.82

26. (a) 6, 1, 7, 9, 4, 5, 10(50%)

(b) (1)   6, 1, 7, 9, 4, 5, 10(50%) $1,058,608.60

(2) 6, 1, 7, 9, 4, 5, 10, 3(88.89%) $1,210,595.46

(3) 6, 1, 7, 9, 4, 5(42.86%) $884,659.61

(c) (1) 6, 1, 7, 9, 4, 5, 10(50%) $1,058,608.60

(2) 6, 1, 7, 9, 4, 5, 10(50%) $761,080.10

(3) 6, 1, 7, 9, 4, 5, 10(50%) $1,400,672.13

(d) 6, 1, 7, 9, 4, 10, 5(14.29%) $1,043,918.42

(e) 6, 1, 7, 9, 4, 5, 10(50%) $1,058,608.60

(f) 6, 1, 7, 9, 4, 2, 10(75%) $1,028,578.56

28. (a) 4, 1, 2, 3(75%)

(b) (1) 4, 1, 2, 3(37.5%) $623,633.06

(2) 4, 1, 2, 3(87.5%) $714,431.01

(3) 1, 2, 4(90%) $531,518.25

(c) (1) 4, 1, 2, 3(37.5%) $623,633.06

(2) 4, 1, 2, 3(37.5%) $511,830.60

(3) 4, 1, 2, 3(37.5%) $752,584.83

(d) 2, 4, 1(50%), 3(50%) $581,080.90

Chapter 16

FE2. c   **FE4.** d   **FE6.** c   **FE8.** b   **FE10.** a

2. (a) 2   (b) 3   (c) 11   (d) 13   (e) 6   (f) 12   (g) 4   (h) 7   (i) 9   (j) 10   (k) 8   (l) 1   (m) 5

4. for $X <= 7.5$, prefer Method II; otherwise, prefer Method I

6. (a) 100 units   (b) $30,000   (c) $50,000

8. (a) −$500,000 (loss)   (b) approximately 583,333 tools   (c) $15/tool

10. (a) graph required; for Order $<= 50$, use M1, $50 <$ order $<= 125$, use M3, order > 125 use M2
(b) use M3 for $875
(c) M2 is preferred, penalty for using M3 is $70, penalty for using M1 is $510

12. (a) $180,000   (b) $600/ton

14. (a) 63.63   (b) 0.279   (c) weight   (d) cost   (e) $231.03
(f) 98.24% of the changes in cost can be explained by changes in weight

16. (a) graphs required, regression results for labor hours $y = 5.96x + 9466.9$, $r^2 = 0.0059$; for boards completed $y = 13.95x + 21811.0$, $r^2 = 0.222$; for average cycle time $y = 330.5x + 6572.8$, $r^2 = 85.41$ (b) average cycle time   (c) 85.41%

18. (a) Assets: cash, accounts receivable, raw materials inventory, work-in-process inventory, finished goods inventory, land, net buildings, net equipment; Liabilities: notes payable, accounts payable, declared dividends payable; Net Worth: common stock, retained earnings
(b) $318,000

20. Net Income = $85,000

22. Balance Sheet balancing total = $74,700; Net Income = $1,500

24. (a) $2.43B   (b) $60.75B   (c) $12.79   (d) 69.43B

26. (a) many sites provide valuable information; among them are www.investopedia.com, www.fool.-com, www.business.com   (b) investopedia.com   (c) investopedia.com has a well organized and easy to navigate tutorial on financial ratios,   (d) there are many including cash conversion cycle, return on capital employed, interest coverage ratio, cash flow to debt ratio, fixed asset turn-over, price to sales ratio.

28. $4,062.50

30. (a) made   (b) units should be made unless overhead rate exceeds $10.8333 per hour

32. (a) $189,374   (b) $7,430.40

34. Net Income = $160,000

36. (a) 42.86%   (b) 33.80%   (c) $1.7143/hr   (d) $214

38. (a) many sites provide valuable information, among them are www.investopedia.com, www.valuebasedmanagement.net, www.valuationresources.com
(b) investopedia.com
(c) investopedia.com has a well organized and easy to navigate tutorial on economic value added

40. (a) Lower = $201.04/unit, Upper = $367.92/unit   (b) Lower = $166.08/unit, Upper = $437.85/unit

42. (a) PS = $300/unit, VI = $325/unit   (b) PS = $217/unit, VI = $450/unit

INDEX

USEFUL EXCEL®FINANCIAL FUNCTIONS

Present Worth (Solve for P)

1. To compute the present worth of a single future sum or a uniform series of cash flows or both, use the PV function: **=PV(rate,nper,pmt,**fv,type).

2. To compute the present worth of multiple cash flows, use the NPV function: **=NPV(rate, value1,value2, …)** or **=NPV(rate,value1:valueN)**, noting that the value obtained occurs one time period before value1.

Annual Worth (Solve for A)

To compute the uniform series equivalent of a single sum occurring at the present or n periods in the future or both, use the PMT function: **=PMT(rate,nper,pv,**fv,type).

Future Worth (Solve for F)

To compute the future worth equivalent of a uniform series of cash flows or a present worth amount or both, use the FV function: **=FV(rate,nper,pmt,**pv,type)

Rate of Return (Solve for i)

1. To compute the interest rate that yields a present worth of zero for a given combination of (P & F), (P & A), (A & F) or (P,A & F) for a given value of n, use the RATE function: **=RATE(nper,pmt,pv,fv,**type,guess)

2. To compute the interest rate that makes the present worth of a series of cash flows equal zero, use the IRR function: **=IRR(value1:valueN,**guess)

3. To compute the interest rate that makes the future worth of an investment of capital at time zero equal to the future worth of reinvested returns, when the returns are reinvested at a rate called the minimum attractive rate of return (*MARR*), use the MIRR function: **=MIRR(values,finance_rate,*MARR*)**

Effective Interest Rate (Solve for i_{eff})

To compute the effective interest rate of a nominal rate (r) compounded m times per year, use the EFFECT function: **=EFFECT(r,m)**

Determining the Number of Payments (Solve for n)

To solve for the number of interest periods, given an interest rate, that yields a present worth of zero for a given combination of (P & F), (P & A), (A & F) or (P, A & F), use the NPER function: **=NPER(rate,pmt,pv,**fv,type)

rate:	compound interest rate	guess:	best estimate of IRR, if needed
nper:	number of compound interest periods	finance_rate:	interest rate paid on borrowed investment capital (for our purposes, this is generally zero or left blank)
pv:	net present value		
fv:	net future value	r:	nominal interest rate, usually per year
pmt:	magnitude of uniform series of cash flows	m:	number of compounding periods, usually in a year
type:	0 or omitted denotes end-of-period cash flow 1 denotes beginning-of-period cash flow		

The Perfect Job Seeker:
2012 Edition

Stuart Mease

Printed in the United States of America.

ISBN 978-1-118-37642-3

The Perfect Job Seeker:

A step-by-step guide from selecting your major to accpeting your offer

Objectives

- ❖ Articulate a clear job search mission to share with others
- ❖ Create a diversifed approach to managing a career
- ❖ Uniquely implement an individual job search strategy to achieve a personal mission
- ❖ Close the job-search process by handling the final stages with professionalism
- ❖ Put the plan into action

OVERVIEW

This job search guide will provide a step-by-step, detailed job search plan starting with selecting a major and ending with accepting a job offer. The guide has four parts, which are as follows:

- ✓ Mission Phase—Selecting and Articulating Your Major LIC (Major, Location, Industry, and Companies) and Developing Your Branding Materials
- ✓ Strategy Phase—Designing a Perfect Job Seeker Strategy
- ✓ Implementation Phase—Creative Company Interaction
- ✓ Closing Phase—Ask for the Job

This document is based on industry data, research, personal experiences, job seeker testimonies, interviews, and over a decade of experience in connecting job seekers and employers in the higher education, government, and private sectors.

Other distribution outlets for this document can be found on blog posts at www.stuartmease.com, classroom presentations, guest speaking engagements, webinars, and social media outlets, such as YouTube, Twitter, Facebook, LinkedIn, SlideShare, Wikipedia, and Google Docs. For more information, contact Stuart Mease at stuartmease@gmail.com.

DISCLAIMER

By reading this guide, we cannot guarantee or "get" you a job; however, you can create opportunities if you follow this guide. We share tips and techniques to enhance your ability to convert these opportunities into jobs. It's hard to help someone who does not want help. You must come at least half way in this partnership.

Perfect Job Seeker

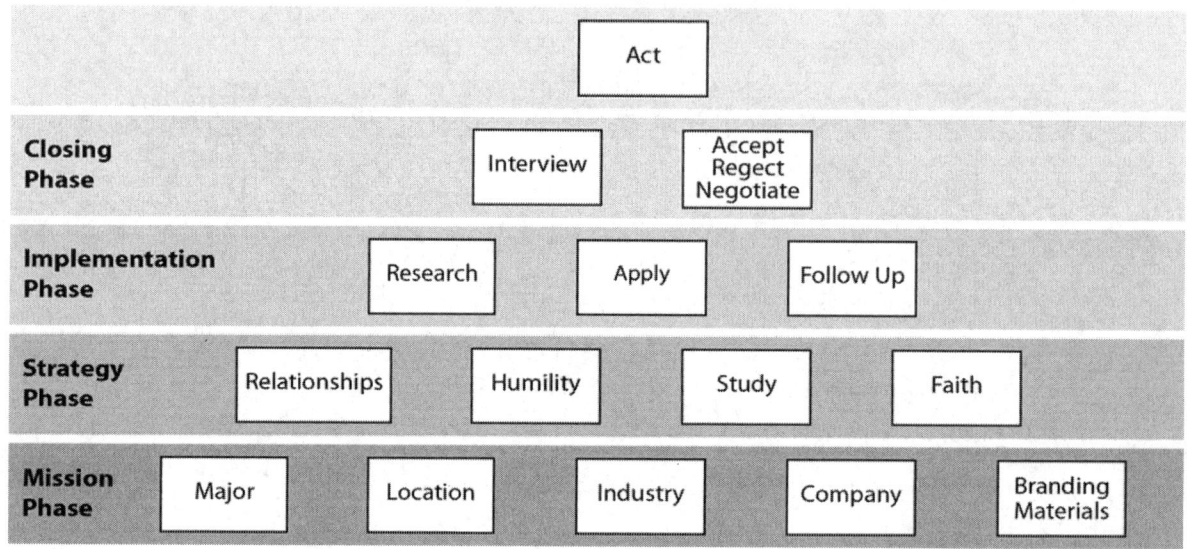

STEP 1: DETERMINE YOUR MAJOR LIC
(MAJOR, LOCATION, INDUSTRY, AND COMPANIES)

BEFORE YOU SELECT A MAJOR:

- ✓ Identify which companies are hiring for that major;
- ✓ Know what the placement rate is for that major;
- ✓ Know the average salary for that major; and
- ✓ Know what titles or functions those majors have.

WHERE DO YOU WANT TO LIVE?

What regions have the highest concentration of people in your background or major? For instance, if you want to live in Omaha, Nebraska, and you want to be an ocean engineer that may not be a good fit. Resources like Chmura Economics (www.chmuraecon.com) and the Creative Class Group (www.creativeclass.com) provide an insight into the region-wise opportunities that are available. There are 360+ Metropolitan Statistical Areas (MSAs) in the United States. Many people refer to these regions and employment data is based off of these regional designations.

WHAT INDUSTRY INTERESTS YOU?

The North American Industry Classification System (NAICS) codes (www.naics.com) are used by many economists to determine jobs, companies, and functions. Although the average person will not be able to recite the names, it will be useful to know yours when doing research.

WHAT SPECIFIC COMPANIES DO YOU WANT TO WORK FOR?

Name brands are important to people, especially college students. The business-to-consumer model of marketing has contributed to this fact. Unfortunately, the majority of the companies with brand names do not come to campus to recruit, and there are also fewer jobs at these firms. Everybody wants to work for the name brand. As a result, competition is greater. Therefore, you must employ tactics to differentiate yourself. Upwards of 75 percent of all new job creation is being done by small businesses (under 100 employees). These firms do not have brand names, but they do have growth potential. Identifying these small companies can be difficult, but CareerShift helps you identify some of these emerging firms. It is important to use Career-Shift because the small firms will not come to campus to recruit. They do not have the time or resources to dedicate a day to recruit on campus to hire one or two students who may not be available for another 6 months.

If you cannot determine your Major LIC, then you cannot create a career roadmap. You must have a destination or goal and being able to answer these three questions is a must and is your first step.

STEP 2: DEVELOP YOUR BRANDING MATERIALS

Now that you have discovered your Major LIC, the next step is to create your branding materials. First, you should create a "30-second commercial" as your branding material. Communicate who you are and what you want to do. Be sure to use your Major LIC in this commercial.

The 30-second commercial should be used for information interviews, writing cover letters, and talking to people at job fairs.

Second, creating an effective resume is essential. There are many different types and no one particular type is the best format. Keeping it to one page is helpful for recruiters because it forces you to condense your information and highlight the most important parts. There are many samples, just find one you are comfortable with and model it.

Third, writing cover letters to complement your resume is a standard marketing tool. The best advice is making your cover letter stand out. Take a risk and show the reader you are not like any other candidate. Do not write the same boring information everyone else writes. Quote a famous person, highlight people you know, write a poem. Whatever it is, be unique.

Fourth, create a personal business card. This is a necessity in the business world. It will demonstrate your knowledge of the unwritten and unspoken aspects of business. By distributing your card you may receive one from the recruiter, but you may have to ask for it. Vista Print is a firm where you can print business cards for free. Also, if you are using Outlook, you can create a card as an attachment or add a signature.

Finally, create a portfolio (both online and offline) highlighting all of your important accomplishments. Items to include are not limited to: academic transcripts, letters of recommendations, resume, listing of relevant personal contacts, projects/white papers, and so on. It would also be wise to keep a paper version in a folder and an electronic version on www.yourname.com for easy reference and distribution.

STEP 3: BECOME A PERFECT JOB SEEKER

Once you have declared a major, clearly articulated your location, industry and company preference and created your branding materials, the next step is to design a diversified career strategy called the Perfect Job Seeker.

A Perfect Job Seeker (www.perfectjobseeker.com) invests time in four areas to maximize opportunities and to spread career risk. Specifically, the steps include Relationships, Humility, Study, and Faith.

Relationships are king. Establishing and nurturing relationships are essential to the job search process as upwards of 80 percent of all jobs are never advertised and are uncovered through networking.

Humility is a disciplined and learned trait. If you do not humble yourself someone will do it for you. This may mean taking a job that is "beneath" you or taking on multiple jobs simultaneously for a period of time. Eliminate actions of entitlement and practice humility. Employers want humble job seekers.

Study is essential to keeping your skills current. You have to invest in formal or informal continuing education in this ever-changing and dynamic world. New job titles and tasks that we do not have a vocabulary for are being invented daily. We must stay relevant and ongoing study is the answer.

Faith is crucial. You need a personal Board of Directors to help you on this journey. There will be times when you must take a leap a faith in making a decision or starting a business. Surround yourself with people you can learn from.

Ultimately, this approach helps you to diversify your workable hours—the time you can devote to a career. It is baffling how people invest all of their workable hours into one revenue stream for life (parents at jobs for 30+ years) and then some unforeseen, uncontrollable event occurs and the sole income stream ceases. This job seeker has not been actively networking, the job loss humbles them, there is no thought given to continuing education or alternative revenue streams through business creation. Diversify your workable hours NOW to minimize the risk of an employer laying you off without any backup plan like so many people have experienced (perhaps someone you know) during the Great Recession. Plan ahead. Be proactive. Create a long-term approach to your career by becoming a Perfect Job Seeker.

STEP 4: DEVELOP YOUR PERSONAL NETWORK

Once you have your Major LIC identified and branding materials created, you will want to engage your network through proven techniques. Nearly 80 percent of all jobs are never advertised, and they are uncovered through personal relationships. You cannot ignore this tactic in your job search. Often, people do not know how to reach out or do not feel comfortable asking for help.

GETTING STARTED

You get started by conducting information interviews. The purpose of an information interview is to expand your network by identifying people you want in it. The information interview is designed to obtain information about a person, his/her company and industry. Follow this 10-step process:

- ✓ Write a handwritten note to the person. Why? When was the last time you got one? It breaks through the communication clutter we receive on a daily basis and it stands out.
- ✓ Tell the recipient who you are and why you are writing.
- ✓ Request a 10-miunte timeframe to ask about their company, industry, and interests.
- ✓ Ask for a convenient day and time for the interview.
- ✓ Say when you will follow up and do it.
- ✓ Prepare for the information interview by researching the person, firm, and industry.
- ✓ Be prepared to conduct the interview at any time.
- ✓ Keep notes during the interview and do not go over 10 minutes.
- ✓ Ask for referrals at the end of the conversation.
- ✓ Write a handwritten thank-you note.

Once you conduct your information interview, you will need to create an electronic database of contact information. You will want to add everyone you know to this list. You have the information—it is more than likely scattered in smart phones, email inboxes, business cards, social media sites, Google search, and so on. It would be wise to take some time to compile it for future easy retrieval.

As you meet more people, it will be critical to create a systematic approach to keeping in touch. Keeping in touch may mean electronically on social networking sites, formal face-to-face visits, or anything in between. The important thing is that you do it and oftentimes this step in the networking process is the most difficult to complete. Selecting a dedicated time and schedule will make it easier.

EXPAND YOUR NETWORK

In addition to information interviews, attend offline events, join offline groups, and volunteer for public speaking opportunities, as well as find a publisher of your written thoughts and ideas about a topic of interest. Online activities such as blogging, LinkedIn, Twitter and Facebook are also useful but these popular social networking techniques are just one avenue to building your network.

Networking is the first step to becoming a Perfect Job Seeker. The next will require you to remain humble in your interaction with your network.

STEP 5: PRACTICE HUMILITY

The UNemployment rate for recent college graduates in 2009 was 9 percent (1 out of 11 graduates). The UNDERemployment rate is often measured as two times the UNemployment rate. Using this figure, 18 percent are UNDERemployed, meaning they are working in jobs they had not anticipated with a college degree and quite likely could have obtained that job without a degree.

We lose sight of this known, hard-to swallow fact—the only reason a company hires people is to make money off their time and talents. You are not entitled to a job with a degree. Companies are not in the business of creating jobs, but profits. Many jobs were lost in the Great Recession, and they will never come back. Automation, cheaper overseas labor, and the fact that someone with more experience is always willing to do your job for less than you are all reasons why certain positions will not return. Creativity, uniqueness, attitude, and relationships are keys to becoming an indispensable employee. The Great Recession taught us that even the most secure jobs—government, teachers, and so on—are not recession proof. Practicing humility is not based on your education attainment, geographic location, industry trends, or market conditions. You control it. Separate yourself from others by simply being humble. If you do not humble yourself, someone else will do it for you.

You may have to hold down more than one job for a short-term period, or you may have to take a platform job. A platform job is defined as a job that pays the bills yet offers time and flexibility to go back to school, continue a job search, or start a business. Food service and retail have been the common platform jobs of choice for recent college graduates for years. The goal is to keep that platform job temporary and not long-term. This requires a lot of discipline and commitment by the individual to not make the platform job permanent.

FOLLOW THE PROACTIVE STEPS OF THESE HUMBLE JOB SEEKERS:

- ✓ After being laid off a second time in 12 months, a lady decided to start a business helping other job seekers and started taking courses in health care administration while also seeking other employment.
- ✓ A banker in Charlotte lost her job and used the severance to put herself through nursing school.
- ✓ After relocating for a statewide marketing position for a major soft drink company, nearly one year later, a man was driven home in his company car with his items boxed up, with no job. The man vowed to never work for someone else again and started three successful businesses in the area he was planning to retire.

Events like these will more than likely humble you during your career whether it is a demotion or layoff. You will realize that you will have to engage your network for help and also determine how you will update your skill sets for your next job through an ongoing commitment to lifelong learning and continuing education.

STEP 6: STUDY (CONTINUING EDUCATION FOR LIFETIME LEARNING)

The third step of becoming a Perfect Job Seeker, after networking and humility, is study or continuing education. A person attending any form of college, seminar, company-sponsored training program or simply reading a book, magazine, newspaper, or website is committed to continuing education. It does not matter if it is formal education (degree) or informal education (on your own), the important point is that you are committed to it over your lifetime. Many think their college degree is all the education they will need in their careers. Sadly, that is not the case. Most graduates will now switch jobs/careers 11 times in their lifetimes.

Typically, the most in-demand jobs are ones we do not have a vocabulary for 10 years prior to the demand. Think back to the early 1990s - if someone said they needed a webmaster, more than likely a person would not have thought about the Internet but rather some type of pest elimination specialist. Also, think back to 2000 and if someone said they were a social media manager, you may have thought they hosted parties for newspaper journalists instead of managing a company's Twitter and Facebook accounts.

When thinking about graduate schools, ask yourself if a particular degree is in demand in the region I want to live. By having this degree, will I have more employment options? Will my compensation be significantly more than if I did not have this degree? Also, if the graduate degree is pursued full-time you must account for the lost salary during the time period of obtaining the degree. Oftentimes we see far too many people seeking refuge in graduate schools rather than facing the reality of the job market and their ability to become employable.

No one is going to argue that more education is better, but what you are being educated in and at what time you receive this education, along with how much you pay for it are certainly factors to consider. The following chart indicates in dollars how remaining constant in your education attainment does not provide a lifestyle that it used to, in the past.

	Avg. U.S. Salary	Life Wages in 1979 ($)	Life Wages in 2004 ($)	$ Change
Less than HS Grad	$18,641	$1,577,466	$960,365	-39.1
High School Grad	$26,123	$1,814,595	$1,380,636	-23.9
Some College/2-year Degree	$31,936	$2,007,712	$1,738,411	-13.4
Bachelor's Degree	$45,221	$2,736,270	$2,702,793	-1.2
Graduate/Prof. Degree	$59,804	$3,039, 355	$3,506,939	15.2

The last thing you want to do is to borrow money to acquire a degree that does not give you the return on your investment and ends up putting you in a bigger hole. When getting the formal degree, make certain that the degree is in demand in the region you are living in, and that you can easily recoup the personal investment you are making. Not all degrees are created equal.

STEP 7: TAKE A LEAP OF FAITH

The last step of diversifying your job search process en route to becoming a Perfect Job Seeker requires relinquishing control of your situation, taking risks, and trusting and relying on others for guidance.

No one will ask you whether you want to work for someone else or for yourself—and then show you how to work for yourself. But that is exactly what colleges and universities must do—promote student entrepreneurship. The U.S. economy needs you to think about how you can create a business and become a member of the Free Agent Nation (read "Free Agent Nation" by Dan Pink.) Approximately 70 percent of all new job creation is started by small businesses. A little over 1.2 percent of all working U.S. adults are entrepreneurs. Are you one of them?

No one says your small business has to be your primary income stream. Start small and online as serial entrepreneur Cameron Johnson advises in his book "You Call the Shots".

Online businesses in particular are easier to start than ever before. First, the Virginia Tech Pamplin Business Information Technology Department has created a class and enterprise called the Online Business Guidebook that gives step-by-step directions for taking your idea online. Second, Inc. magazine's annual list of the 5,000 fastest-growing private companies in the United States indicated that 87 percent of the companies were self-funded with a median investment of $25,000. Third, there are organizations in Blacksburg, Virginia (Day One Ventures, RBTC, VT KnowledgeWorks, etc.) willing to invest and help you start now!

So what are you waiting for? Perhaps validation of your idea from a mentor or trusted advisor. It's a good idea to get that feedback. As relationship guru Keith Ferrazzi states in his book

"Who's Got Your Back", creating a personal Board of Directors will help you take a leap of faith in launching a business and help you make important life and career decisions. Find these people in your network (Step 4—Conducting Information Interviews).

Of course, owning your own business is not as easy or glamorous as you may think. And, it is not for 99 percent of the population. It takes sacrifice, long hours, uncertain revenue streams, high levels of risk tolerance, persistence, passion, commitment, vision, determination, luck, and the execution of an idea. Many new businesses die in the first year and most do not make it after year three. But the ride and the reward could be the best of your life. It's worth taking the risk now, as a young adult, before other life commitments (i.e., spouse, mortgage, children, poor health, etc.) make that leap of faith much more difficult.

However, self-employment is a viable and real option that cannot be overlooked or dismissed. It is another avenue on your career path and deserves careful consideration.

STEP 8: RESEARCH AND PREPARE FOR COMPANY INTERACTION

You can now articulate your Major LIC, you have developed your unique branding materials, and you understand the perfect job seeker strategy. You are now ready to contact companies. But before you send that email, pick up the phone or apply online, you need to know relevant information about the firm you are contacting and use that knowledge in your correspondence.

The easiest and most common way to research companies is to visit their websites. However, this information is company selected. It's filtered. It's positive information they want you to know about their firm. Another common approach is Google search. But there is too much information with this format, and it is extremely difficult to filter and find exactly what you need. Most people will do these two activities and be done with it. But if you want to get noticed and be coveted, you will do more.

- ✓ Ask your network of contacts. Remember Step 4? When conducting information interviews ask people for information you cannot find online, from people who currently work at your desired firm.

- ✓ CareerShift is a database that offers a plethora of pertinent information about companies. You must register to use.

- ✓ Social Media sites such as LinkedIn and Twitter provide current information about people in the organization, products, services, and other detailed data points.

- ✓ Attaain Inc. is providing a real-time mash up of Web information from various sources to give job seekers a more comprehensive and organized review of companies.

- ✓ The best opportunity for successful job prospecting is job fairs. To maximize the opportunities presented at job fairs, you must learn how to prepare for a job fair. View this video for a step-by-step approach (www.stuartmease.com/uncategorized/how-to-prepare-for-a-job-fair/).

Now that you have used a myriad of data sources to assimilate a good and thorough understanding of your target company, you are now ready to apply that knowledge in your initial interaction with companies.

STEP 9: BE UNIQUE IN APPLYING FOR JOBS

Now that you have researched your companies, you need to respond by contacting recruiters. The common practice is to apply online, and many recruiters will tell you that's the only way, but it is not. The reason you are given this information is that the online application provides an easy way for them to monitor, search, and report on their recruiting activity. Find another way to apply, such as:

✓ A student walks into a job fair wanting to impress his top employer, Philip Morris. He has nothing to lose. When he walks into the room, he is not dressed in a suit like everyone else, but he is wearing a cowboy outfit identical to the Marlboro Man—white t-shirt, jeans, boots, belt buckle, and hat—and is smoking a cigarette. He clearly articulates his desire to work for Philip Morris, submits a resume and walks out. It stopped the fair. It was the best unique first impression ever.

✓ As a lifetime UNC basketball fan, I wanted to use a similar technique to apply for the current Director of Basketball Operations job that became available with my favorite sports team. I sent a Carolina blue and white basketball overnight FedEx with pieces of my resume pasted on each leather strip and a cover letter outlining everyone in my personal network who would be a reference and had ties to the university and the key decision maker.

These stories illustrate how you should make your first impression with your number one employer. You cannot and should not do it for every application, but reserve for jobs you really, really want. Here are some more suggestions:

ESSENTIAL BASICS

✓ Conduct Informational Interviews—See Step 4 on Networking. It is better than applying online.

✓ Contact Staffing Agencies and Headhunters—These people work with dozens of recruiters.

✓ Volunteer—Many influential people serve on nonprofit boards. Show them your skills as a volunteer.

✓ Coffee Shop Job Searching—Set up your office there, schedule appointments, and meet others.

✓ Be a Voracious Reader—Through local/industry publications you can be educated on the current trends.

BOLD BASICS

- ✓ Overnight FedEx—Anyone can apply online. People open these immediately and must sign for it.

- ✓ Write Your Own Job Description—If the job is not advertised, then tell them what you can do for them.

- ✓ Offer to Work Part-Time, Short-Term—Solution to company budget constraints and it's a differentiator.

- ✓ Stop and Drop—Drop your application in person, and perhaps you meet the recruiter face-to-face.

- ✓ Auction You—Design a PR stunt with a local media outlet to benefit a charity.

SOCIAL MEDIA BASICS

- ✓ Blog about an Expertise You Have—Show your skills and talents about a topic online for others to view.

- ✓ Social Media Bounty Fee—Motivate your Facebook friends with a cash bounty for help in landing a job.

- ✓ Tweet Deck Monitor Mentions—Use this platform to connect with and follow recruiters.

- ✓ Google Job Experiment—Watch this at http://www.youtube.com/watch?v=7FRwCs99DWg.

Not all of these tactics will result in an immediate response. You must follow up, again and again.

STEP 10: FOLLOWING UP

You have just created the most unique initial interaction with a company recruiter ever. You are feeling pretty confident. Time passes and you have not received an immediate response. Do not be discouraged, this is normal.

RECRUITERS' WORK LOAD

Recruiters are not online every minute of the day like you are. Recruiters are in meetings, interviews, handling employee complaints, on the phone, traveling, dealing with personal business, on vacation, and are hiring for more positions than the one you are applying for. Bottom line - they are busy and interact with many people on a daily basis. It is easy for a recruiter not to follow up in a timely, personal fashion. It's okay, it does not mean they have rejected you. Sometimes it takes persistence on your part.

My unique application for the UNC basketball job never received a response, but I realized that I never followed up. I thought the idea was good enough to get a call back, but it did not. Therefore, what should I have done?

Ideally, you want to give enough time for a person to respond, and without knowing their schedule, a week to 10 days would be ideal. When you do follow up, make certain that you use a different communication vehicle than the one used initially. So, if you wrote a letter, then you may want to call this time. If you did a stop and drop, then maybe an email will suffice.

WHAT IF I DO NOT RECEIVE A RESPONSE AFTER THE FOLLOW-UP?

You must decide how badly you want the position you have applied for. This is where determination and persistence can differentiate you from everyone else. If you really want the position, then wait another seven to 10 days and respond differently. If not, let it go and move on to the next opportunity. You cannot fixate on one job. You must have multiple options available at all times. Do not stop prospecting. Do not put all of your eggs in one basket.

TIP TO GET A RESPONSE OR TO SCHEDULE A MEETING

Earlier you were given a step-by-step process of conducting an information interview. Five of that process is "Say when you will follow up and do it." This step is where you can almost guarantee a follow-up from the receiver. When you write your information interview handwritten note, cover letter, email, phone call, and so on, state that "if I do not hear from you by `x date (i.e., January 3), then I will call you on y' date (i.e., January 5 at 11 a.m. EST)." If they respond before January 3, then it is a moot point. If they do not respond by January 3, then perhaps they may be testing you to see whether you will call. Maybe they have put the "meeting" on their calendar and are expecting you to call them. When you do call asking for the person, reference the letter. If they are not prepared or their assistant did not put the "meeting" on their calendar, then they will feel like they made a mistake and more than likely will want to try to make up for the mistake by taking your call. It works. Try it and find out.

Ultimately, you are trying to get a response. You want that response to be positive based on your follow-up techniques. You are hoping that a positive impression of your style and technique has been formed by the recruiter and it will be just enough for them to ask you for a formal interview.

STEP 11: INTERVIEWING

After successfully contacting and following up with companies to secure an interview, you must repeat Step 8 by researching the company before your interview. During your research, list some questions you may have about the position, the company, and its culture—anything showing that you are prepared to seriously consider this firm as your future employer.

Interview Stream is a wonderful interactive tool to help you prepare for your interview in front of your own computer.

Also, watch this video to see a sample interview (http://www.blueridgepbs.org/videos/local-productions/jobquest/jobquest-video-archives/223-job-interview-pointers). You may even get a friend to ask these or other questions in preparation for the real thing.

Dress in professional attire or one level above what you would wear every day to work. If you do not know the dress culture of the company, then play it safe and wear a business suit.

Arrive early for the interview. If you are able and willing, go to the site before the interview to know exactly where you need to be.

If possible, ask before arriving what your itinerary will be on the day of the interview. This information will show whether you will have a one-to-one individual and/or a group/panel interview.

If names of the interviewers are listed, then Google your interviewers. Try and find a nugget of information that you can casually bring up and that will build instant rapport with the interviewer.

You will more than likely receive some questions that start out "tell me about a time when . . .." These are behavioral interview questions. Recruiters know that past performance is the best indicator of future behavior. That is why these questions are asked. If you respond to one of these questions with a story exposing a weakness, then be certain to share what you learned from the experience and, if possible, tell a short second story about how you applied the lesson learned in a similar situation.

If you are asked a question you do not have an answer for, use one of the following three stall techniques:

- ✓ Ask them to repeat the question—perhaps you now better understand it.
- ✓ Drink some water—it will give you a couple extra seconds to think of a response.
- ✓ Ask them if they want a personal, academic, or work example—this is risky, but can give you some more time and it shows them that you have many experiences and you can think on your feet.

Never bring up compensation until the company mentions it first.

Ask for the job. If at the end of the interview you know that you really want the job, then ask for it.

At the end of the interview, be certain to send handwritten thank-you notes or emails to those who interviewed you. This simple follow-up technique is done by fewer than 10 percent of job seekers.

After your interview, your patience will be tested. So be prepared.

STEP 12: ACCEPTING, REJECTING, AND NEGOTIATING

Your point of contact with the company you interviewed with may not be the final decision maker. Typically, it is the hiring manager. Uncontrollable market circumstances can derail hiring plans in an instant. There is nothing you can do about it. Things change within the economic market of your potential future employer. So you must be patient.

Realize that you are not the only one being interviewed for the position. It takes a lot of time and coordination to get calendars, travel plans, and changing schedules to come together perfectly. Most recruiters are not working on filling only one role but many roles simultaneously, so the process can be very tedious. Again, hiring managers and recruiters have many different tasks that may be more important than filling an open position or filling a newly created position. Using the techniques in Step 10 on following up is essential. There will most likely be unexpected and awkward twists and turns from this point forward. Just know that this is part of the process. Not every recruiting department is as organized as you may think. So you must be patient.

HANDLING REJECTION

If you are contacted and the message conveyed is that you did not get the job, then politely ask why and gather that feedback for future interviews. Additionally, a classy move would be to send another thank-you note to the company recruiter showing your appreciation in making it that far through the process. Also, 3 to 6 months from the time of the rejection, follow up with that same contact and ask them how the new person is doing. You may be surprised that their first choice was a mistake and by simply following up you may get another chance at the position. So you must be patient.

ACCEPTING

You get the call or email, and there is the formal offer. Do not accept the position on the spot. The offer is usually valid for about a week. Use this time wisely by carefully reading the employment contract (perhaps seek a legal review), consult with your personal Board of Directors (see Step 7), and use the offer as leverage with other companies that have interviewed you but who have not extended an offer (tell them you have an offer with another company that ends by "x" date). You must be patient.

NEGOTIATION

Typically, the first financial offer extended to you is their base, low amount. They probably have a high amount and another amount in between. Most people take it and do not ask for more by building a logical case. During the week provided to you for considering your offer, it would be very wise to construct data for why you should receive more money, vacation, or other benefit. The website www.salary.com, cost of living websites, your network of contacts, and existing employees can provide bits of data to provide a range of pay for your services. It would be wise for you to create similar low, high, and in-between amounts. Some larger organizations who hire many, many college graduates will not budge. It is what it is. You do not want to push them too much or they will push you away. This tactic works better with smaller firms, so you must be patient.

Once you accept the offer, the proper ethical job search etiquette is to cease all other interviewing by notifying any other companies you are actively pursuing. Those students not compliant with this etiquette damage their own reputation, their school's reputation, and can adversely affect future students' chances of working for that company.

STEP 13: ACTION: GAIN EXPERIENCE THROUGH INTERNSHIPS, EXTERNSHIPS, AND VOLUNTEERING

What is the next step? If you are currently in the job market put this information into action. If you are a college student, read this final step. The methods and techniques to get full-time jobs are the same for internships. Experience is the number one factor employers look for when seeking out college students—not just GPA.

Paid internships are the desired outcomes, but only 50 percent of all internships are paid. You must ask yourself, what skills can I possess that a company can make money off of me by paying me an hourly rate. This is why only one in two internships is paid.

Therefore, volunteering or unpaid internships will be done by the other half. It is important to have some experience on your resume before your senior year in college. If possible, try and get academic credit, but do not pay summer tuition for it. Academic departments may have an internship program during the semester to help with credit and obtaining an unpaid internship. If volunteering is the only way, then do it. No one is asking or expecting you to work full-time for free during the summer.

As a result, I often recommend hybrid internships. These are work situations where you volunteer half time for the company in your field of study and the other time you are making money working in retail, food services, or on the golf course. A future employer will not care if that summer experience is 20 or 40 hours a week. The main goal is that you had that experience.

An emerging trend for underclassmen, especially for accounting majors who want to work for the Big 4, are externships. These are one day-to-one week sessions with employers for you to learn about their profession and company and for them to learn more about you. It is a great resume builder.

Cooperatives are internships that last for a summer and a fall or spring semester. They are almost always paid, but it does usually delay your graduation date. Schedule wisely.

One of the biggest deciding factors in determining your summer internship plans revolves around housing for the summer. Typically, a student will want to work at home where they can live with parents or in their college town where they have a lease. Those students who are willing to go elsewhere during the summer, and are willing to secure their own short-term housing, may have more opportunities and also differentiate themselves from other students. Some companies also provide housing assistance and it would be appropriate to ask that question to an employer.

At the end of the internship, a company may ask your plans for next summer or post-graduation. If the firm is interested in you, then they will extend a full-time offer after the internship. Upwards of 50 percent of interns will receive such an offer. Many students accept full-time jobs with companies before they start their senior year.

Finally, remember that there is no such thing as a bad internship. Each experience is short-term and helps you determine a career path you do not want or validate a desire that you do have. Again, the main goal is getting experience in preparation for graduation and the full-time job search process.

DISCUSSION QUESTIONS

1. Which step of the Perfect Job Seeker is the most challenging? How are you going to overcome this challenge? Do you believe this step is preventing you from obtaining an offer?

2. Which step of the Perfect Job Seeker is the most critical to master? Why?

3. Is Location, Industry or the Company most important in setting your mission? Why or why not?

4. Do you want to work to for someone else or for yourself? Why?

5. Who do you know in your network of contacts that could help you achieve your job mission by presenting your 30-second commercial?

6. How are you going to invest in lifelong learning in the short-term and the long-term?

7. What is your first action step to becoming a Perfect Job Seeker?

ABOUT STUART MEASE

Stuart Mease's primary focus is "connecting people" to create mutually beneficial relationships. This mission is currently being filled as the Director of Undergraduate Career Services in the Pamplin College of Business at Virginia Tech. Prior to his current role, Mease served as the Recruiting Leader for the publicly traded Blacksburg division of Rackspace Email and Apps.

Mease previously worked for the City of Roanoke, Virginia, to create programs and events aimed at attracting and retaining the creative class workforce for the RNR (Roanoke and New River Valleys) region. These activities and programs have been uniquely recognized by many local, state and national media outlets and organizational groups, including the International Economic Development Council annual conference in 2008. His strategy was to implement new Web technologies in the traditional industry of economic development to highlight people and place, generating thousands of contacts, friends, connections, followers, and subscribers. This style and strategy was recognized by the Creative Class Group as it selected Roanoke as one of only three cities globally to partner in their Creative Community Leadership Project in 2008.

Mease's work in "connecting people" has been recognized over 100 times in various news outlets. Nationally, he has appeared in Tech Crunch, Staffing Management Magazine, Florida Times Union, Providence Journal, St. Petersburg Times, Strengthening Brand America, Innovators Traction, and www.CreativeClass.org. Blue Ridge PBS also recognized Mease's work and invited him to be a content contributor to the Emmy Award-winning "JobQuest," a live monthly television show assisting job seekers in the RNR.

Mease is married, has one child and enjoys spending time with his family, studying Christianity, playing golf, watching sports, following politics, and engaging in the community.

SPEAKING AND CONSULTING:

Stuart Mease's expertise with "connecting people" is evidenced by the number of organizations that have asked him to serve as a speaker. He has presented keynote speeches on areas related to his core expertise (e.g., career development, personal networking, generational differences, and workforce development) to over 150 diverse audiences in the private, educational, and government sectors. To request Stuart Mease to be a guest speaker in your organization, email stuartmease@gmail.com.